UNITY OF PHYSICS is reflected in th drawing on the opposite page, which shows how the branches of the subject have converged during a four-century period to form the physics of the twentieth century. The pioneers whose portraits appear here are:

Galileo Galilei **1**
Isaac Newton **2**
Count Rumford **3**
James Prescott Joule **4**
Lord Kelvin **5**
Joseph Black **6**
René Descartes **7**
Christian Huygens **8**
Thomas Young **9**
Augustin Jean Fresnel **10**
Benjamin Franklin **11**
André Marie Ampère **12**
William Gilbert **13**
Hans Christian Oersted **14**
Michael Faraday **15**
James Clerk Maxwell **16**
Hendrik A. Lorentz **17**
Max Planck **18**
Albert Einstein **19**

FOUNDATIONS OF PHYSICS

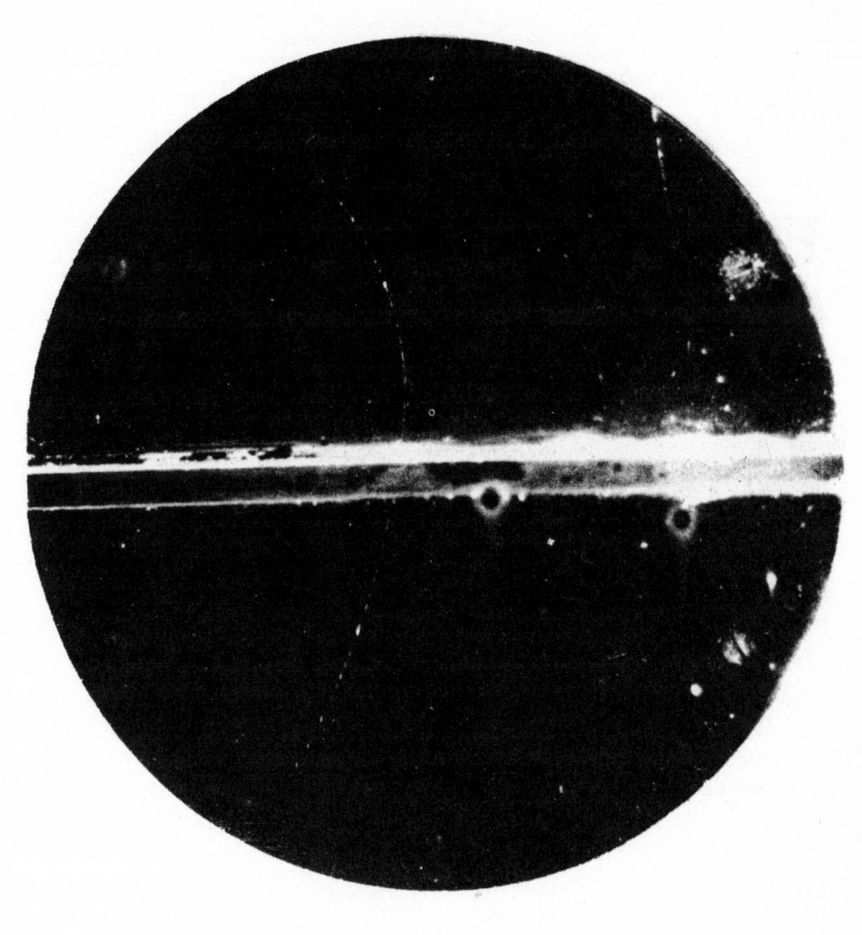

D. VAN NOSTRAND COMPANY, INC.

FOUNDATIONS OF PHYSICS

WALTER C. MICHELS
Marion Reilly Professor of Physics • Bryn Mawr College

MALCOLM CORRELL
Professor of Physics • University of Colorado

A. L. PATTERSON
Late Head, Department of Molecular Structure
Institute of Cancer Research
and Lankenau Hospital Research Institute

Princeton, New Jersey • Toronto • London • Melbourne

Van Nostrand Regional Offices: *New York, Chicago, San Francisco*

D. Van Nostrand Company, Ltd., *London*

D. Van Nostrand Company (Canada), Ltd., *Toronto*

D. Van Nostrand Australia Pty., Ltd., *Melbourne*

Published simultaneously in Canada by
D. Van Nostrand Company (Canada), Ltd.

Library of Congress Catalog Card No. 68-23172

PRINTED IN THE UNITED STATES OF AMERICA

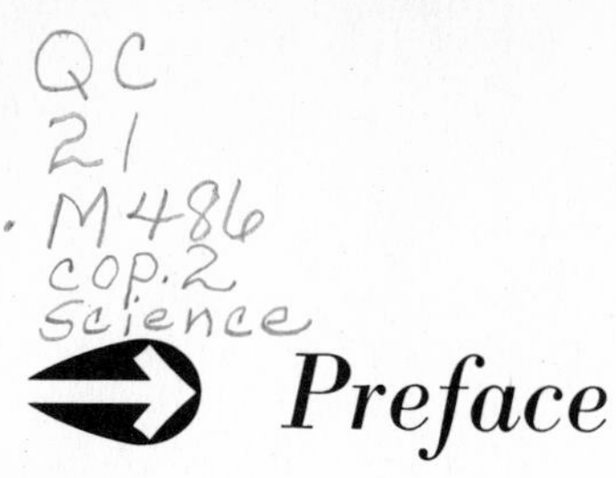

Preface

Foundations of Physics is based on the conviction of the authors that every college or university freshman or sophomore who takes an introductory physics course deserves something more than exposure to a body of facts, a package of techniques, and that collection of propositions which constitutes currently accepted theory. It attempts to present physics as a human activity—or even, perhaps as an attitude of mind—which constantly seeks to reinterpret, to refine, and to extend our knowledge of the physical world. We believe that the early cultivation of this attitude is as important to the student who plans to be a physicist as it is to the one who is studying the subject because of its bearing on engineering, biology, chemistry, or geology, or because of intellectual curiosity alone. Even if he is to take physics courses for four or more years, he will benefit if he is encouraged to develop physical intuition at an early stage.

In keeping with this purpose, we fully recognize the important role that mathematics plays, but we try to indicate that physics is something more than a series of applications of mathematical analysis. A course that has calculus as a prerequisite can be based on this text, but such a prerequisite is not essential. The necessary mathematical concepts and techniques are introduced as they are needed, with physical motivation and without any attempt at mathematical rigor. It has been our experience that many students capture the ideas more easily in this context than in the usual, more formal approach and that they soon develop sufficient skill to use derivatives and integrals in a meaningful way, if they are expected to do so in problems, as well as in understanding the text. This is especially true of—but not only of—students who are studying calculus concurrently.

Because we wish to present physics as it is practiced by physicists, we use nonmathematical as well as mathematical reasoning. Symmetry, induction, guessing at results, and heuristic arguments are employed extensively. The second-order differential equation is not accepted as the source of all knowledge. For example, Newton's laws of motion are introduced as consequences of experimentally established conservation laws; the dynamics of oscillations and of waves are derived directly from the conservation of energy and of momentum; Kepler's laws of planetary motion are indicated to demand an inverse square law of force, rather than to be consequences of it.

Because we believe that courses for students with different backgrounds and different goals should differ in breadth and depth rather than in kind, we have tried to produce a book that offers flexibility. One way of accomplishing this involves the use of both "exercises" and "problems." The former are generally limited to the application of ideas and methods that have been developed rather completely in the text. The problems, on the other hand, often require the integration of several different ideas or introduce concepts that go beyond the material that has been covered. They are generally more difficult than are the exercises. By judicious balance in his assignments the instructor can adapt his course to a variety of classes, or even of individual students. Depending on whether or not some chapters are omitted and on how many problems are assigned, the text should be suitable either to courses of two semesters or to those that extend over three or four semesters.

The death of A. L. Patterson, while the book was in preparation, deprived us of his guidance and wisdom at a time when these would have been extremely helpful. We can only hope that we have succeeded in producing something that is compatible with the high standards that he set for any work with which he was connected. Since the present volume draws some of its organization and content from its predecessor, *Elements of Modern Physics*, it does bear the stamp of his scholarship.

We are indebted to so many colleagues, with whom we have discussed this material, that individual recognition is impractical. Special gratitude, however, is due to Rosalie C. Hoyt, John R. Pruett, and Francis Worrell, with whom we have shared the teaching of courses based on the earlier volume. We also wish to thank Professor Richard E. Garrett, who read the entire manuscript and made many valuable suggestions for its improvement before publication, and Professors Thurston Manning and Raymond Emrich, who gave us extensive and useful advice.

WALTER C. MICHELS
MALCOLM CORRELL

January 1968

Contents

1 ⇨ *Introduction*

1.1 The Problem of Description

In his novel *Storm*, George Stewart discusses the growth and progress of a storm from its birth as a small low-pressure area southeast of Japan to its death over the United States twelve days later. To each of the characters in that novel the storm had a different meaning. To the farmers it meant relief from a serious drought; to the superintendent of a hydro-electric plant it gave a close encounter with death; to the road maintenance crew on Route 40 it meant hard extra work removing snow from the road over Donner Pass; to the passengers on an airliner over Nevada it gave an hour of unpleasant air sickness and the subsequent thrill of a safe landing.

Just as different people encountered different experiences in the storm, so did they later describe it differently. The newspaper editors spoke in human interest terms of its effect on crops and of lives lost. The pious, in their descriptions, quoted the Psalmist, "Fire and hail, snow and vapours; stormy wind fulfilling his word." In an interview with reporters, the Mayor of New York discussed it in terms of the cost of snow clearance. In the records of the Weather Bureau, its story was represented by daily figures showing air pressures, temperatures, cloud coverages, and precipitation in its path. Whether one of these descriptions is to be preferred to others will depend upon the taste of the reader, but all are necessary to complete the picture of the storm and of its effects. And, to the same extent, each represents a simplification, a singling out of particular elements by conscious or unconscious choice.

Just as the descriptions of the storm in Stewart's book varied with the interests, experiences, and backgrounds of the people concerned, so have man's efforts to describe the world in which he finds himself. The artist, the poet, the theologian, the philosopher, and the scientist—all have attempted parts of this description and the work of each makes some contribution to the whole. It is with one of these attempts, that of the natural scientist, that we are immediately concerned. We shall see that the scientist limits himself professionally to certain aspects of the problem and therefore cannot pretend that his description is complete. On the other hand, the very limitations that he imposes enable him to give his description a coherence which would otherwise be lacking and account for the progress of science.

1.2 The Realm of the Natural Sciences

Just as the Weather Bureau meteorologists in *Storm* limited their record to the "dry figures" indicated by their instruments, the natural scientist confines himself, in his description of the world, to the objective confirmable data that he can obtain by observation of nature. He does this, not because he is uninterested in the subjective effects of the phenomena taking place, but rather because experience has shown that the objective data are simpler and are more amenable to correlation. It is possible, though not probable, that we shall know enough at some time in the future to predict the aesthetic effect of a rose of a given variety on a particular person, but we must be content at present to limit the scientific description of the rose to prosaic data such as its size, color, and structure.

How can we judge whether a given piece of information is objective or subjective? The only test that has been found is that objective data are those which can be agreed upon by all normal observers under similar circumstances. This requirement of agreement has had a tremendously important influence on the history of science, since it has continually furnished a test as to what data constitute the core of scientific knowledge. This core consists of the body of information on which all competent scientists agree. The growth of science is by the gradual extension of this central body of data. As a rough analogy, this core of knowledge has sometimes been compared to a clearing in a forest. The great majority of scientists spend their time extending the edges of the clearing, rather than dashing out into the forest and cutting down individual trees at a distance. The occasional genius, it is true, may spot at some distance a tree whose felling will make easier the extension of the clearing, but this type of activity demands a very thorough acquaintance with the clearing itself and with the methods by which it is enlarged. The justification for the gradual extension of science, the progression from the known to the unknown, is the purely common sense one that it has been found to be more efficient than the more adventurous and individualistic method of dashing wildly into the forest with an axe.

Agreement among various observers can be achieved, of course, only if there is sufficient orderliness in the universe so that the events we study do not depend on the whims of a capricious nature. This, in turn, implies that definite effects follow definite causes. We shall see later (Chapter 24) that nature is so constituted that we are unable to verify completely a law of causality, because the very process of observing the causes and effects creates a disturbance which results in an uncertainty in their description. These disturbances become important, however, only when we are dealing with the smallest particles of which the universe is built. Even with these particles, it is found that there are general laws which describe adequately all the phenomena that have been observed. Because laws of this sort seem to represent the simplest and most general description of natural phenomena, most of the effort of science has been directed toward their discovery, and it is in terms of them that the greater part of the body of scientific knowledge is stated.

If the orderliness which we assume does exist, it is only reasonable to suppose that it will hold in the future, as well as in the past and present. This in turn implies that, once we have discovered the natural laws that govern the behavior of the world, we should be able to predict events which will follow upon given circumstances. Prediction then becomes the test both of the orderliness of nature and of our scientific knowledge, and the degree of success of a science must be judged by its ability to state in advance what will happen under specified conditions. The prediction may involve either natural events, as in weather forecasting, or experimental results, which follow upon man-made conditions. Because we may have to wait a long time before the proper conditions to produce a given effect occur naturally, and because natural events are usually complicated by a variety of influences which may be very difficult to observe and allow for, the scientist uses experiments, rather than purely natural observations, whenever he can.

1.3 The Divisions of Science

For reasons of convenience, an individual scientist ordinarily devotes the major part of his effort to a study of some limited aspect of the universe, rather than to the problem as a whole. Thus chemistry deals with the various combinations of those substances known as elements, biology is concerned with those bodies characterized by life, geology has as its province the structure of the planet on which we live, and astronomy treats the behavior of extraterrestrial bodies. Physics, with which we are principally concerned here, has traditionally dealt with matter and energy.

Although each of the natural sciences is characterized by a special body of knowledge and by special methods of working—those that have been found particularly applicable to its field of activities—the various sciences are far from independent. For example, living organisms depend upon chemical processes that change the constituents of food into parts of the organisms. Hence biologists lean heavily upon the experience of chemists. In general, the further any science advances the more does it overlap with other sciences. This has been particularly true of physics, since matter and energy are the raw materials with which any natural science works. Because of this broad extent of physics, all scientific theories must be consistent with basic physical laws. On the other hand, the physicist must be continually on the watch for results in the other sciences which may indicate necessary changes in his description of the universe and of its parts.

1.4 Observation and Experiment

As we saw above, the first problem of physics is to describe those characteristics of natural or experimental phenomena which may be objectively observed (Sec. 1.2). Having selected some particular phenomenon, the physicist tries by careful observation to give as complete a description of it as possible. He may start with a qualitative observation, but eventually his description usually makes use of measurements and numbers, since it is only in this way that exact description is possible. He then tries to correlate his observations among themselves or with other data, in order that he may reduce the description to workable proportions.

An example of the process just outlined is furnished by the work of Robert Boyle in the 17th century. The qualitative fact that the volume of a gas decreases when the pressure on it increases had been known for a long time, but it remained for Boyle to make a careful experimental study of the quantitative relations between volume and pressure. He arranged a sample of gas in such a way that he could both change the pressure upon it and measure the pressure and the volume at each stage. Having collected a very considerable number of readings, he examined his data to see if they could be stated in a simpler form than in two long columns of associated readings. Eventually he noted that the product of the volume of the gas and of the pressure gave the same result for any pressure, provided that the temperature remained constant and that the volume and pressure were measured at the same time. He was thus able to state the law which has since been associated with his name, "At a given temperature, the product obtained by multiplying the pressure acting upon a gas by the volume of the gas is a constant." This simple statement summarized all of his data in a form which could be remembered easily and which could be applied to gaseous samples other than those with which Boyle worked. In stating his results, the physicist may use words, numbers, graphs, sketches, or any other means of description, but he always attempts to express his summary in some form which will combine brevity, accuracy, and completeness.

Generally, a series of experiments, such as those performed by Boyle, are repeated by others, under somewhat different circumstances, before the conclusions drawn from them are accepted as fact. Thus Boyle's law has been experimentally tested thousands of times. In this case, as in many others, it was later shown that the result originally found is obtained only under certain limiting conditions, and that some modification of the original conclusions is needed. The modifications of Boyle's law will be discussed in the chapter on the properties of gases (Chapter 20).

1.5 The Role of Physical Theory

Although generalizations such as Boyle's law simplify the statement of observational results, they do not furnish, by themselves, a workable description of the physical world. It has usually been found possible to show that such generalizations follow from more basic laws, or that they may be deduced as consequences of the constitution of the material bodies which they describe. Thus it was found, in the 19th century, that a gas made up of a very large number of very small molecules, in continual motion, would necessarily obey not only Boyle's law, but also a number of other laws which had been experimentally determined. At the time that this theory was developed, the existence of the individual molecules could not be demonstrated directly, but the molecular theory of gases was accepted because it could account for nearly all of the known physical properties of gases while no other picture of their structure which could do so had been proposed.

The invention of physical theories requires a thorough understanding of known experimental facts and a disciplined, as well as a vivid, imagination. It is only occasionally that a fundamental and significant theoretical development follows on the long and hard spadework involved in the accumulation and correlation of data. But these occasional developments are usually the great forward steps in science, and they lead to the satisfaction that comes when masses of past observations are found to follow from a single basic assumption or law and when new and unexpected results are predicted.

Just as it is the problem of experimental physics to obtain the simplest possible complete description of individual phenomena, it is the problem of theoretical physics to reduce the multitude of descriptions thus obtained to a minimum number of basic laws, which are of universal validity. In the coming chapters, we shall trace the development of our present approximations to some of these laws and see how they may be used both to describe the world around us and to predict natural and experimental phenomena.

1.6 The Interplay of Experiment and Theory

The last few paragraphs above might be read to indicate that the progress of physics always follows the fixed pattern: observation, correlation, theoretical statement. Actually, this is practically never true, but there is a constant interplay between experiment and theory. An attempt at theoretical interpretation is usually made long before the data regarding some phenomenon or group of phenomena are nearly complete. If the theory is successful, it will usually not only explain the known facts, but will predict new phenomena, and so suggest new experiments for which it anticipates particular results. When these experiments have been performed, they may either support the theory or may yield results other than those expected. In the latter case the theory must be discarded or modified. This process of exchange between experiment and theory accounts in part for the gradual growth of scientific knowledge which was discussed in Sec. 1.2.

1.7 The Validity of Physical Theory

It should be clear from the above discussion that there is a real difference between the "truth" of physical data and that of physical theory. Although, as we shall see in the following chapters, sources of error often creep into observations and experiments, every effort is made to keep the reports of such experiments completely factual. If two carefully performed experiments yield different results, every effort is made to find the factors which account for the differences. Consequently the basic data resulting from careful scientific observation may generally be accepted as true in the broadest sense. On the other hand, the theoretical explanation of such data seldom follows by a rigorous deductive process from them. The most that we can say of a theory is that it is "satisfactory," in the sense that it accounts for all known phenomena on which it has any bearing. Few physical theories that have been satisfactory in this sense have later so failed that they have been abandoned completely, but most of them have required modification as further data were obtained. It has usually been found that the theories which failed in some respects were close approximations to their successors. It is probable that the later theories, in turn, are only approximations to the complete description for which we are searching. The scientist continually strives toward this complete description, but he has thus far found no way of recognizing it when he meets it. In the meantime, he tries to describe the world which he finds about him, to reduce his description to as simple terms as he can find, and, finally, to bend every effort to testing his description by experiment and observation, in the hope that, if he cannot prove it to be true, he may be able to prove it false and so may force himself to search for a more adequate answer.

In this book we shall examine in an elementary way the present state of the science of physics. We shall see how some of the basic laws and some of our ideas of the constitution of matter and energy have grown from experiment and how they have led to further developments. We shall see that our description of the world about us is not complete and that there are many unsolved problems now in sight, to say nothing of those which can be expected to arise as new phenomena are discovered and studied. If past experience has any validity, the solution of these problems can be expected to result from an extension of our present knowledge and methods into the field of the unknown. It will therefore be profitable to review the past before speculating too widely on the future.

In the course of our study, we shall not be using any mysterious methods, but shall, instead, be relying on careful observation and on common sense. We shall apply to our material any tools that may come to our hands, whether they come from formal logic, from algebra, from geometry, or from any other source.

REFERENCES

1A James B. Conant, *On Understanding Science* (Mentor M68), New American Library, New York, 1951. An authoritative effort to help the layman understand science as enterprise.

1B A. Einstein and L. Infeld, *The Evolution of Physics*, Simon and Schuster, New York, 1938. Pages 3–12 deal with an introduction to the nature of physics.

1C Richard P. Feynman, "The Value of Science," in *Science and Ideas—Selected Readings*, edited by A. B. Arons and A. M. Bork, Prentice-Hall, Englewood Cliffs, N.J., 1964, pp. 3–9. This essay discusses several reasons why some men are scientists.

1D P. A. M. Dirac, "The Evolution of the Physicist's Picture of Nature," *Scientific American*, May 1963, pp. 45–53. Interesting ideas on the nature of physics.

1E Ernst Mach, *The Science of Mechanics*, Open Court, La Salle, Ill., 6th edition, 1960. Mach was a foremost analyst of the processes of science. See particularly pp. 1–9 and 596–615.

1F William Francis Magie, *A Source Book in Physics*, Harvard, Cambridge, Mass., 1935. Consult particularly the work of Robert Boyle, pp. 84–87.

1G Morris H. Shamos, ed., *Great Experiments in Physics*, Holt, New York 1959. Further reference will be made to this collection. At this point the editor's introduction, pp. 1–11, is appropriate.

1H George Stewart, *Storm*, Random House, New York, 1941.

2 ⮕ *Length and Time*

2.1 Change

In any attempt at a description of the world in which we live, we have to recognize the importance of the changes that are continually taking place in it, and it is one of the chief purposes of science to study the nature of these changes and to relate them among themselves. The motion of the earth around the sun and the rotation of the earth on its axis are of interest, and attempts may be made to connect these motions with the growth of plants and animals on the earth. One may also wonder, as did Newton, about the relationship between the motion of the earth and the motion of the planets. He found that these motions follow the same laws and that these laws are connected quite closely with the fact that a heavy body released above the ground inevitably falls toward the center of the earth. This connection between two phenomena, which at first sight are unconnected, is only one of the many which form the body of science.

Some of the happenings on the earth and in the more remote parts of the universe are obviously of great complexity and some are much simpler. It seems reasonable for us at first to try to understand the simplest phenomena in the hope that we can later arrive at an explanation of the more complicated in terms of the simpler.

Before we can study changes we must be certain that we can recognize those situations in which nothing is changing, i.e., *static* situations. We may then proceed to a consideration of things which are changing continuously but uniformly. Thus we might start with a study of the sticks and stones which seem immutable and then advance to the study of the sun and the planets and the clocks and spinning tops, which are in continuous motion but which exhibit a certain monotony or uniformity of change. We may then go on to the more complicated phenomena in which the nature of the changes taking place is itself changing.

2.2 Comparison

One of the simplest ways of testing two objects for similarity is the ***method of superposition.*** If we take two sheets of typewriter paper from the same box, we can superimpose one on the other and find that they are identical in shape and size. We may find slight differences in their colors, textures, etc., but we shall interest ourselves for the moment only in the fact that all their edges can be made to coincide. We then make a water color painting on one of them and type a letter on the other. If after this differential treatment we find that the two sheets do not superpose, we can conclude that one or the other or both of the sheets have changed. If they do superpose, then we must conclude either that both sheets have changed by the same amount or that neither of them has changed at all.

One way of testing whether or not a given object has undergone any change in shape is to make a pattern which just fits the object. If the pattern continues to fit the object after the latter has been maltreated, then we can be sure either that the object is unchanged in shape or that both the object and the pattern have changed in the same manner.

It is obviously a very cumbersome procedure to make patterns for each object which we wish to study. Fortunately we need not do this. We can make a series of measurements of the object and then at a later stage repeat these measurements. If each of the repeated measurements agrees with the corresponding original measurement, we can be sure either that the object and the measuring devices are unchanged or that both the object and the measuring devices have changed in the same way.

We now see that the problem of observing a change in shape of an object, or a lack of change, depends on our ability to construct measuring devices which, to the best of our knowledge, do not change in shape.

2.3 *Rigid Rods*

In order to find materials suitable for measuring devices we perform a series of experiments on a wide variety of rods. For example, we may construct many rods of the shape shown in Fig. 2.1 of various types of wood, various metals, and of

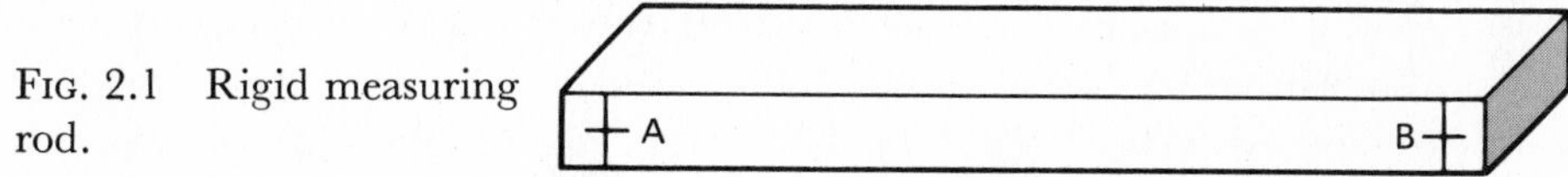

FIG. 2.1 Rigid measuring rod.

other miscellaneous materials: rubber, any one of a number of plastics, putty, soap, salt, sugar, clay, etc. On each of the rods we shall make two cross-marks, one at either end, as shown at A and B (Fig. 2.1) in such a way that when any two of the rods are placed side by side, the two cross-marks (A and B Fig. 2.2) of one rod may be made to correspond to the two cross-marks (A′ and B′) of the other rod. Each rod is compared with all of the other rods in this manner and at the beginning of the experiment the crosses are moved about on the rods until this condition of similarity is satisfied.

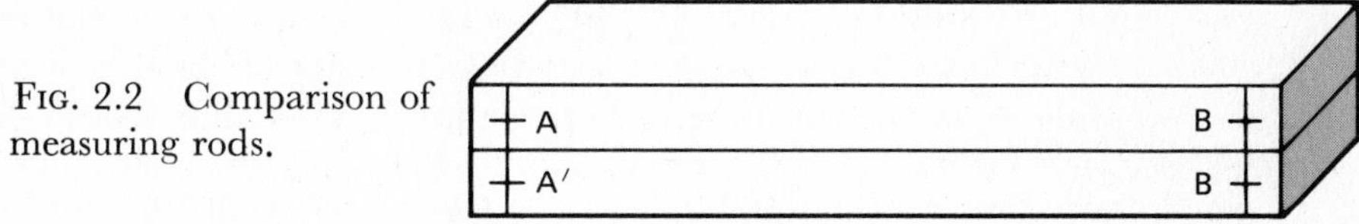

FIG. 2.2 Comparison of measuring rods.

We now proceed to mistreat these rods in a rather gentle way. Perhaps we might bend them in our hands, heat them gently, soak them in water, or freeze them. We then compare the crosses of all the rods one with another, and we find that some of the rods no longer agree, whereas others still agree if our maltreatment has not been too violent. The soap, salt, and clay rods have probably collapsed completely under the maltreatment, the plastic rods may have warped after heating, and the soft wood rods may have warped or shrunk or swollen under the influence of moisture. The metal rods (except perhaps the lead rod) and some of the hardwood rods may still agree with one another quite precisely after all this manipulation.

By this process we have divided our rods into two classes. In the first class (the metals, hardwoods, etc.), several rods remain in agreement with one another. In the second class, none of the rods remains in agreement with any of the first class nor with any of its classmates. If now we repeat our maltreatment many times, we may retain in one class those rods in which agreement is maintained and in the other class those in which agreement is lost. We can then say that the rods of the first class are ***rigid*** with respect to one another under the specified types of maltreatment, whereas the other rods are ***nonrigid***.

There is no way of knowing whether or not all our rigid rods have changed in precisely the same way. In our discussion of rigid rods we have implied that we can find a large number of different materials that will remain rigid with respect to one another under the specified maltreatment. It is *extremely improbable* that a given type of maltreatment would affect several quite different materials in exactly the same way. However it is *possible* that this could happen. We must therefore retain our reservation. If all the rigid rods that we possess should change at the same time and in the same way, we would have no means of telling, from measurements made on the rods alone, that they had changed. It is possible however that we might detect such a change indirectly.

We may also note that in discussing rods it has been necessary to compare them while they are at rest with respect to one another. Later, Chapter 8, we shall discuss the method to adopt if we are to compare two rods that are moving with respect to one another.

2.4 The Comparison of Lengths

One of the most important measurements is that used to find whether two lengths are alike or whether one is greater or less than the other. The rigid rod is a simple tool for this purpose, since it enables us to compare two lengths in different locations. If we want to know whether a safe will go through a door, we need only make two marks on a rod corresponding to the width of the safe and then compare the two marks with the width of the door. This is frequently far easier than carrying the safe to the door.

The compasses and dividers commonly used in geometric drawing are merely rigid rods of adjustable length. We can bring the two points of the dividers into coincidence with any two points on the object being studied and, when once adjusted, the distance between the divider points remains fixed and can be used to make a comparison with the distance between any other two points.

As an example of the use of measuring rods for comparison, consider the physical meaning of the definition given in elementary geometry texts, "A straight line is the shortest line that can be drawn between two points." In Fig. 2.3 there are three paths joining points P and Q. We adjust a pair of dividers to some small length PA and step off along each path a number of intervals equal to the separation between the points of the dividers. The number of steps along one of the curves may be equal to, less than, or greater than, the number

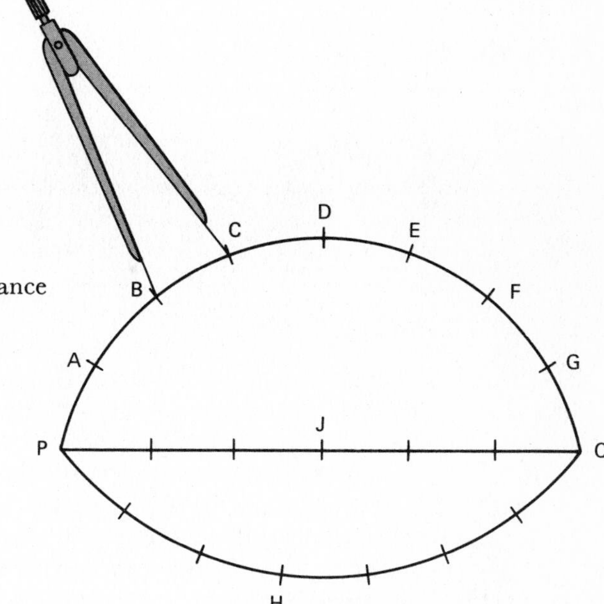

FIG. 2.3 Determination of the distance between two points.

along some other curve. If a fraction of a step is involved, its size may be remembered by setting it on an extra pair of dividers. If we repeat this stepping process for all possible paths between P and Q, we find that there is one path PJQ which requires fewer steps than all others and that this is a straight line.

This process of successively applying a rigid measuring rod along the straight line joining two points is the basic process for measuring the distance between the two points. Such a ***distance*** is defined as the number of times that a specified measuring rod must be applied. Notice that both the rod and the number of applications must be specified in stating the distance. In many cases, of course, the distance between two points will not contain an integral number of measuring rods exactly. In such cases fractions of the length of the rod may be included in the statement of the distance.

The distance between two points is identical with the ***length*** of the straight line joining the points. The length of a curved line, such as PHQ in Fig. 2.3, is measured by a flexible chain of measuring rods (Fig. 2.4) which can be bent to fit the curve. Thus a flexible steel tape with appropriate markings on it can be looked upon as a measuring chain with very short links and can be used to measure lengths along a curved line.

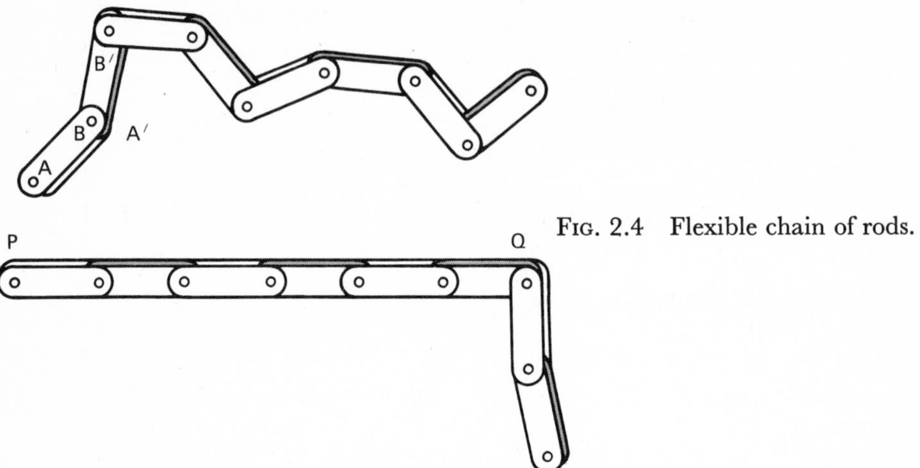

FIG. 2.4 Flexible chain of rods.

2.5 *Standards of Length*

In the preceding sections we have seen how the distance between two points can be measured in terms of an arbitrarily chosen measuring rod, and in Sec. 2.3 we have seen how it is possible to prepare a number of duplicates of a given rod. If a single worker wishes to make measurements of his surroundings, it really does not matter very much what he uses as measuring rods as long as they are rigid and he makes careful notes as to the rods used. If, however, he wishes to compare his results with those of another worker, some relationship must be established between the measuring rods that they use. It is of course a great advantage if they both use rods which are exact duplicates of one another and if they both have agreed on standard rods of various lengths which are known fractions and multiplies of these standards.

The facts discussed above were recognized very early in history, and various units of length were established in the various countries of the world. The English system of units which uses the inch, foot, yard, and mile is one well-known system, but it is only one of many systems developed by various nations. Since the latter half of the 17th century, an international metric system has been developed, and this is now used in almost all scientific work.

The ***metric system*** for the measurement of length is based on a single standard rigid rod preserved in the archives of the International Bureau of Weights and Measures at Sèvres near Paris, France. This rod is made of an alloy of platinum and iridium, and near each end it bears a fine mark scratched into its surface, the two scratches being parallel to each other. The distance between these two scratches measured along the midsection of the rod is by definition one ***international meter*** (abbreviated m) and the rod itself is known as the ***International***

Prototype Meter. Many exact copies of this rod were made and distributed among the nations of the world, and these copies are known as the ***National Prototype Meters*** of the nations possessing them. The meter sticks, rulers, steel tapes, etc., that are used for the everyday measurement of lengths have been compared by their manufacturers with ***working standard rods*** which, in turn, have been compared with the National Prototype Meters. Thus all measurements of length are made in terms of the same standard. By the use of such standards we may be reasonably sure that two parts of a machine, made in different factories at different times, will fit each other.

In the metric system there are a number of units smaller than the meter. Those in most general use are the ***centimeter*** (cm), defined by the equation

$$100 \text{ cm} = 1 \text{ m}, \tag{2.5-1}$$

the ***millimeter*** (mm), defined by the equation

$$1000 \text{ mm} = 1 \text{ m}, \tag{2.5-2}$$

and the ***micron**** (abbreviated by the Greek letter mu, μ), defined by the equation

$$1{,}000{,}000\ \mu = 1 \text{ m}. \tag{2.5-3}$$

The unit larger than the meter in most common use is the ***kilometer*** (km), defined by the equation

$$1000 \text{ m} = 1 \text{ km}. \tag{2.5-4}$$

The United States system of units of length is based on the metric system, the inch being defined by the equation

$$1 \text{ inch} = 2.540\,000 \text{ cm}. \tag{2.5-5}$$

Since July 1, 1959, the standards laboratories of Australia, Canada, New Zealand, South Africa, the United Kingdom, and the United States have defined a new unit, the ***international yard***, in terms of the meter. Thus

$$1 \text{ international yard} = 0.9144 \text{ m}. \tag{2.5-5A}$$

The agreement to base measurements on the international yard, when the metric system is not being used, avoids difficulties arising out of slight differences in the various national standards. For example, the traditional British yard was shorter than the traditional U.S. yard by about three parts per million. Note that with 36 inches per yard Eqs. (2.5-5) and (2.5-5A) are equivalent.

2.6 *The Power of Ten Notation*

In the course of our study of physics, we shall often be concerned with quantities that are very large or very small compared with the units in which they

*To be consistent with the rest of the metric system this unit should be called "micrometer" and abbreviated μm (cf. Sec. 2.6). Custom, however, has adopted the usage given in the text to avoid confusion with the term micrometer meaning an instrument for measuring small lengths.

are measured. The expression of such numbers by the ordinary Arabic system sometimes becomes cumbersome. As an example, consider recent budgets of the United States Federal Government, which are very large compared with the unit, the dollar, in which they are measured. Rather than stating that a budget is \$91,000,000,000, a newspaper reporter is likely to say that it is 91 billions of dollars or \$91 billion, which is easier to read and understand. Physicists might write this quantity as \$$91 \times 10^9$, which is read as "ninety-one times ten to the ninth dollars." In doing this we make use of the fact that ten raised to the ninth power is 1,000,000,000. The reason for using powers of ten, rather than of some other number, is that calculations are made easy by the fact that multiplying a number by ten merely shifts the decimal point one place to the right. Thus, we could equally well state the above amount as \$$9.1 \times 10^{10}$, or as \$$0.91 \times 10^{11}$. As another example of this notation, we may note that Eqs. (2.5-3) and (2.5-4) could be written as

$$10^6\ \mu = 1\ \text{m}, \tag{2.6-1}$$

and

$$10^3\ \text{m} = 1\ \text{km}, \tag{2.6-2}$$

where the multiplying number 1 has been omitted in accordance with ordinary algebraic practice.

One advantage of the power of ten notation is that it can be used equally well for very small numbers and very large ones. Thus we could again rewrite Eq. (2.6-1) as

$$1\ \mu = 10^{-6}\ \text{m}, \tag{2.6-3}$$

which is read "one micron equals ten to the minus sixth meters." In doing this, we have made use of the algebraic relation

$$10^{-6} = 1/10^6 = 1/1{,}000{,}000.$$

Another great advantage of this system is that it eases calculations. If we remember that

$$(a^b)(a^c) = a^{b+c},$$

where a, b, and c are any numbers, we notice that large or small numbers may be manipulated quite easily. Thus, suppose that we want to multiply 33,000,000,000,000 by 0.000 000 23. We may write this as

$$(3.3 \times 10^{13}) \times (2.3 \times 10^{-7}) = 7.59 \times 10^6,$$

where the 7.59 in the result is 3.3×2.3 and the sixth power of ten is obtained by taking $13 - 7$. We have here followed a common practice of expressing the coefficients as numbers between one and ten.

In the metric system, there is another convenient method for expressing some powers of ten by a prefix in front of the name of the unit. The most commonly used prefixes are listed in Table 2.1. Thus the kilometer defined by Eq. (2.5-4) is 1000 meters, and the centimeter and millimeter of Eqs. (2.5-1) and (2.5-2) are, respectively, one one-hundredth and one one-thousandth of a meter. Correspondingly, the budget figure given at the beginning of this section could be expressed as ninety-one kilomegabucks or ninety-one gigabucks.

Table 2.1 *Prefixes in the Metric System for Powers of Ten*

Prefix	Abbreviation	Number	Power of Ten
tera-	T	1,000,000,000,000	10^{12}
giga-	G	1,000,000,000	10^{9}
mega-	M	1,000,000	10^{6}
kilo-	k	1000	10^{3}
centi-	c	1/100	10^{-2}
milli-	m	1/1000	10^{-3}
micro-	μ	1/1,000,000	10^{-6}
nano-	n	1/1,000,000,000	10^{-9}
pico-	p	1/1,000,000,000,000	10^{-12}

2.7 Units and Their Relations

In discussing measured physical quantities such as length it is necessary always to mention two things: (a) the unit and (b) the number which indicates how many times the unit appears in the measurement. Thus the statement that a certain person has walked a distance of 10.36 has no meaning whatever. It might mean 10.36 miles, kilometers, yards, feet, parasangs, or any arbitrary unit we might happen to think up.

Notice that Eq. (2.5-1) makes sense as written above. It means in words that "one hundred one-centimeter measuring rods will measure the distance between the marks on the International Standard Meter." The same equation without the units, i.e.,

$$100 = 1,$$

is of course quite incorrect.

We note that in all the equations of Sec. 2.5 the smaller number is always associated with the larger unit and vice versa. Thus in Eq. (2.5-1) the larger number 100 is associated with the smaller unit, the centimeter, while the smaller number 1 is associated with the larger unit, the meter. The equations are identities expressing the fact that two lengths are identical, e.g., a length of 100 cm is identical with a length of 1 m.

All the quantities in the equations of Sec. 2.5 can be manipulated algebraically; for example, we can divide both sides of Eq. (2.5-1) by 100 and obtain the equation

$$1 \text{ cm} = 0.01 \text{ m}. \tag{2.7-1}$$

We can divide both sides of Eq. (2.5-1) by 1 cm and obtain the equation

$$1 \text{ m}/1 \text{ cm} = 100 \tag{2.7-2}$$

which of course means that the ratio of the size of the meter to the size of the centimeter is 100 to 1. In accordance with usual algebraic practice, we may omit the number 1 when it appears and write Eq. (2.7-2) in the form

$$\mathrm{m/cm} = 100 \tag{2.7-3}$$

with the same meaning as before.

We can combine two equations from Sec. 2.5 by algebraic methods; we thus eliminate the quantity 1 m from Eqs. (2.5-1) and (2.5-2) and write

$$1000\ \mathrm{mm} = 100\ \mathrm{cm}.$$

Dividing both sides of this equation by 100, we obtain the equation

$$10\ \mathrm{mm} = 1\ \mathrm{cm}. \tag{2.7-4}$$

The following exercises illustrate the many manipulations of this kind that are useful in obtaining expressions for a length in terms of any one of the many units of length in use at the present time. Some exercises involve units of area and volume. These can be solved by simple extensions that the reader can make to the methods of this section.

EXERCISES

2.7-1 Calculate to four digits the length of 1 m in inches, in feet, and in yards.

2.7-2 Starting with the definition 1 mile = 1760 yards, calculate to four digits the length of 1 mile in kilometers.

2.7-3 Calculate to three digits the length of 5 miles in kilometers.

2.7-4 Starting from the definition 1 yard = 3 feet, and using the methods of Sec. 2.6, prove that 1 square yard = 9 square feet and that 1 cubic yard = 27 cubic feet.

2.7-5 Obtain equations connecting the square centimeter with the square meter and the square micron with the square meter. Use the power of ten notation throughout.

2.7-6 Obtain equations connecting the cubic meter with the cubic centimeter and with the cubic micron. Use the power of ten notation throughout.

2.7-7 In track meets both 100 yards and 100 m are used as distances for dashes. Which is the longer? By how many meters is it longer? By how many feet?

2.8 The Process of Measurement

We have seen how it is possible to establish standards of length so that all people throughout the civilized world can refer their measurements to the same system of units. It is now necessary to consider briefly how measurements of length are made and how a scientific statement of the result of a measurement is presented so that there can be no ambiguity in the mind of the readers as to exactly what the writer means by any statement he makes about a physical measurement.

The reader is familiar with the construction of a ruler such as that illustrated in Fig. 2.5, in which the straight edge is first divided according to some unit of length and then subdivided into tenths or some other fraction of that length.

Let us consider how such a ruler or ***scale*** is used to measure the length of a small rectangular steel block, and let us suppose for simplicity that Fig. 2.5 is an enlargement of a ruler in which the large divisions are each 1 cm long. The method of using the ruler is shown in Fig. 2.6. The zero mark of the scale is brought into coincidence with one end of the block, and the other end of the

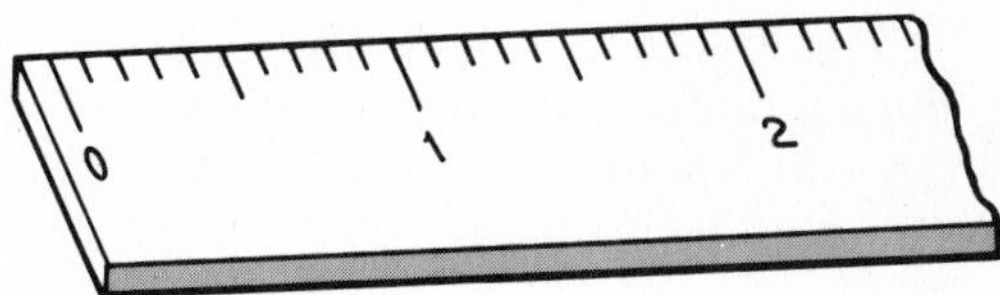

FIG. 2.5 Divided scale.

block is found to be somewhere between 2.5 cm and 2.6 cm. Actually it is somewhat nearer to 2.5 than it is to 2.6 cm. If we are content with a rough estimate of the length of the block, we could say simply that its length is 2.5 cm. The reader should note that in this case we write only the two figures 2.5 and not 2.50 or 2.517. In this manner we indicate that we have made no attempt to carry our measurement beyond the second figure, and we write only the ***significant figures***—those figures which have physical meaning—in stating the result of our measurement.

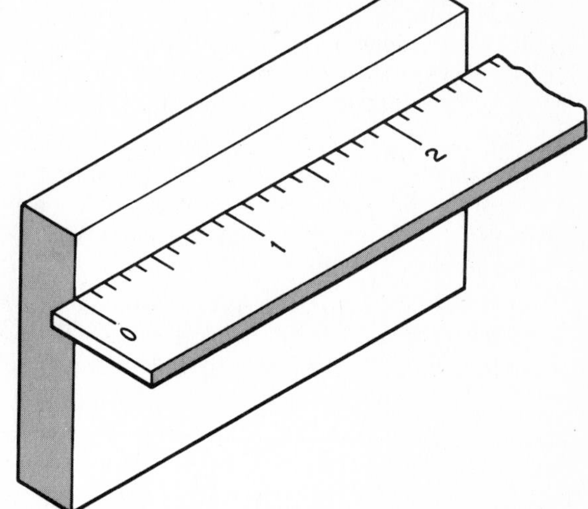

FIG. 2.6 Measurement of length.

If we now examine our scale and block more closely, we find that the end of the block is just short of halfway between the 2.5 cm and the 2.6 cm marks and we can ***estimate*** that it is about 4/10 of this distance. If we have confidence in our ability to make this estimate within one or two tenths of a division, we can write 2.54 cm as the result of our measurement of the length of the block. In this statement there are three significant figures, and by this we mean that we are quite sure of the 2 and the 5 and are pretty sure of the 4. We can be *quite* *certain* that what we have written as 4 is not 2, and that it is not 6. We can be *reasonably sure* that it is not 3 and that it is not 5.

It is an important convention of exact science that in expressing any final result we write only those figures that are significant. We write all those figures that certainly have physical meaning, and include in addition one and only one figure that may possibly be doubtful.

It is also necessary in stating the result of physical investigations to include as a part of the result an estimate of the degree of ***uncertainty*** of the observer in making the observation, i.e., of the amount by which he is likely to be in error. Thus in making the measurement described above the observer might be sure that he had placed the zero of the scale within 0.01 cm of the left edge of the block, and he also might be sure that the right-hand end lay between 2.53 and 2.55. He could then be sure that the length of the block was between 2.52 and 2.56 cm. This conclusion he would write as (2.54 ± 0.02) cm.

Another observer making the same observation with greater care might be sure that the left end of the block and the zero of the scale coincided within 0.002 cm and that the right end lay between 2.535 and 2.545. He would then write his result as (2.540 ± 0.007) cm.

The statement of the result of a physical observation thus includes the observer's estimate of the value which most nearly represents his observation, together with his estimate of how uncertain he is of this value. It must be emphasized that both these quantities depend on the observation, the instrument with which the observation was made, and the way in which the observer made the observation. Thus a very careful observer might be justified in writing (2.540 ± 0.007) cm for the length of the block discussed above, while a very rough measurement of the same block by the same observer using the same ruler might be written (2.5 ± 0.1) cm. If one tried to measure visually the height of bounce of a tennis ball in a tennis match, one might be very lucky to be able to write (25 ± 5) cm. A more precise statement of the height would be justified only if some very special means were adopted to enable one to follow more accurately the flight of the moving ball.

If we follow the rule given above for significant figures, the statement that the distance from the earth to the sun is 93,000,000 miles is ridiculous unless we know this to be true within a few miles. If we only know it to be true to the nearest million miles we would have to write $(93{,}000{,}000 \pm 1{,}000{,}000)$ miles. To save writing zeros it is usual to use the power of ten notation, and to write $(9.3 \pm 0.1) \times 10^7$ miles. The 9 and the 3 are the only significant figures. The six zeros after the three are not significant. In the statement that the diameter of a certain blood cell is 0.000 25 cm, only the 2 and the 5 are significant as is clearly indicated by the fact that the same result can be written as 2.5×10^{-4} cm or 2.5×10^{-6} m $= 2.5\ \mu$. It follows that zeros which serve only to locate the decimal point ahead of the first nonzero digit are not significant.

All physical measurements have some uncertainty since no conceivable physical quantity can be measured exactly. Definitions and mathematical calculations are of course exact. Thus the statement that two blocks of steel have been measured and found to have "the same" length has meaning only if an uncertainty is stated. On the other hand, all the equations (2.5-1)–(2.7-4) are definitions and are therefore taken to be exact. This means that no added uncertainty is introduced in converting from one of these units to another.

2.9 The Use of Significant Figures in Calculations

As indicated in the preceding section, the complete statement of a physical quantity demands an estimate of the uncertainty involved as well as the magnitude of the quantity. This applies not only to a measurement, but also to any quantity which is calculated from measurements. Thus, if the measurement of two sides of a rectangle yields the values (5.62 ± 0.02) cm and (10.4 ± 0.1) cm, there will be obviously be an uncertainty in the area calculated by multiplying these two figures together. We therefore need to find some way in which the uncertainty of a calculated result may be obtained. In Appendix B, sample calculations are carried out and rules for finding the uncertainty in various calculations are derived.

In order to minimize the amount of arithmetic involved in solving the exercises and problems given in this book, the reader is not expected to compute uncertainties for the results obtained, except where specifically indicated. However, some idea of the uncertainty can be obtained by estimating the number of significant figures in the answer. This can be done by observing the following rough rules:

(a) The number of significant figures in the result of multiplication or division is equal to the number of significant figures in the least accurate of the numbers entering into the product or quotient. The least accurate of these numbers is of course the one with the fewest significant figures.

(b) The number of decimal places which are significant in any sum or difference is the same as the smallest number of significant decimal places in any term of the sum of difference.

These rules, which are justified in Appendix B, are satisfactory if the uncertainty is not more than ± 1 or ± 2 in the last significant figure.

The uncertainties of most of the data given in the exercises and the text have been omitted. The reader may assume that the uncertainty is ± 1 in the last digit unless some other uncertainty is stated.

It is necessary, in the course of a calculation, to carry one more digit than is significant at any stage. This prevents the accumulation of errors which might otherwise affect the significant figures in the result. It is usually a waste of time to carry more digits than this rule requires.

2.10 Positive and Negative

In everyday life we use a large number of different pairs of words to represent two things which are exactly opposites to one another. We speak of motions forward or back, up and down, left and right, north and south; we speak of things speeding up and slowing down, heating and cooling, and of music growing louder or softer. In physics we are usually more economical of our terms and pick one term from each pair of antonyms and call this ***positive***; the opposite we then call ***negative***. Thus if we call a motion upward positive, then a motion downward is called negative. If we call an increase in loudness positive, then a decrease in loudness—a softening—is called a negative increase in loudness. The direction we choose to call positive is initially quite arbitrary—we could call upness negative downness or loudness negative softness if we wished—but once the choice has been made it is necessary to adhere to it strictly throughout any single discussion, or difficulties will arise.

The reason for this convention as to sign is illustrated by a simple example. Suppose in an experiment we wish to discuss the motion of a ball with respect to the top of a table. At one stage in the experiment we locate the ball at position A (Fig. 2.7), which is 6 cm above the table top. At another time the ball is at

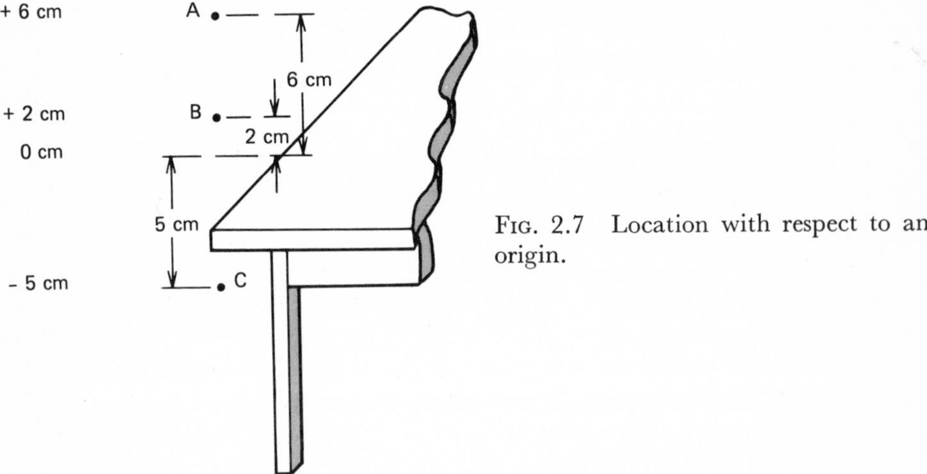

FIG. 2.7 Location with respect to an origin.

position B, which is 2 cm above. At yet another time the location is at C, which is 5 cm below the table. If now we wish to know the distance from B to A, we take the difference between 6 cm and 2 cm and get 4 cm, i.e.,

$$6 \text{ cm} - 2 \text{ cm} = 4 \text{ cm}.$$

If, on the other hand, we want to know the distance from C to B, we add 2 cm and 5 cm and get 7 cm, i.e.,

$$2 \text{ cm} + 5 \text{ cm} = 7 \text{ cm}.$$

In other words, we have to use two different rules to find the distance between two points when we are given the distances above and below the table. This is extremely unsatisfactory and can obviously lead to grave errors. To avoid this possibility we may say that A, B, C are respectively 6 cm, 2 cm, and −5 cm *above* the table. Then, the distance from B to A is given by

$$6 \text{ cm} - 2 \text{ cm} = 4 \text{ cm},$$

and that from C to B by

$$2 \text{ cm} - (-5 \text{ cm}) = 2 \text{ cm} + 5 \text{ cm} = 7 \text{ cm},$$

whereas the distance from B to C is given by

$$-5 \text{ cm} - 2 \text{ cm} = -7 \text{ cm}.$$

This last result is quite in accord with our convention since the distance from B to C is a distance measured downward and is, according to our convention, the negative of a distance measured upward.

We can now write a very general rule which enables us to calculate the distance between any two points on a straight line when the distances of the two points from some other point are known. Let x_1 be the distance from one point to an arbitrary point O, which we call the ***origin***, and let x_2 be the distance from the second point to the origin. Then the distance D_{12} between point 1 and point 2 measured in the direction from point 1 to point 2 is given by

$$D_{12} = x_2 - x_1, \qquad (2.10\text{-}1)$$

in which all distances are given algebraic signs according to the same arbitrarily chosen convention. Conversely, the distance D_{21} between point 2 and point 1 is expressed by

$$D_{21} = x_1 - x_2. \qquad (2.10\text{-}1A)$$

The rule just given is of the greatest simplicity and is typical of many of the rules of physics in that it is a concise expression of a very simple fact. It is also typical of the rules of physics in that errors of calculation are easily avoided if the rule is followed but are very likely to arise if the rule is disobeyed. It may also be pointed out that the only reason for the establishment of the rule is the convenience of the user and his colleagues. Anyone who can think of a better one is at liberty to use it himself, and if it is a great improvement he may prevail upon others to use it too.

EXERCISES

2.10-1 A builder determines the height from ground level of three points A, B, and C, which are on a vertical line in a building, to be $x_A = 1098.5$ ft, $x_B = 29.2$ ft, and $x_C = -108$ ft. Calculate the distances from B to A, from C to A, and from B to C.

2.10-2 A state trooper patrols a road which runs straight north and south through the town in which his patrol station is located. During the course of an evening, which he starts at his patrol station, he reports a series of accidents—in the order in which he visited them—at the following locations: 8.3 miles north of the station, 10.2 miles north of the station, 1.1 mile south of the station, 2.8 miles north of the station, 3.9 miles south of the station. He finally ends his tour at the station. What is his total mileage, if we assume that he goes directly from one location to the next?

2.11 *Recapitulation*

It is now easy to see that we have found a solution to the problem of studying the change in shape of material objects, which we set ourselves in the first section of this chapter. By using measuring rods such as we have described and with the aid of the methods of geometry, we can record completely the shape of an object at the beginning of an experiment and again at the end of the experiment. If the set of measurements made at the end of the experiment agrees (within the uncertainty of the measurements) with that made at the beginning, we can say that the object has not changed (within the uncertainty of the measurements) during the course of the experiment. If the two sets do not agree, our measurements will enable us to state as completely as we please how the shape of the object has changed. If we make our measurements in terms of one of the well-known standards of length, we can communicate our results to others in a way they will be able to understand. Furthermore, if we record our uncertainty, these others will know how closely our measurements were made and how far these measurements are to be trusted.

It is a tradition of science that an observer be highly critical of his own measurements and results and that he make an entirely objective statement of the results of his self-criticism. He should make his measurements with all the accuracy necessary to decide the point in question, but there is no virtue in going unnecessarily beyond this accuracy. In building an airplane engine it is sometimes necessary to machine parts which are accurate in size to a few one hundred thousandths of an inch, but a builder who tried for this accuracy in building houses would be idiotic and for that matter would be bankrupt, since no one would buy the houses at the price he would have to charge for them.

2.12 *Before and After*

We often speak of one event occurring before or after the other, or of two events occurring simultaneously. We say that an event A occurs ***before*** the event B—as far as an individual observer is concerned—if the knowledge of the event B appears on a record which already contains A. The record may be in the mind of the observer or in a camera or other device that he is using to aid his observation. If the two events appear on the record in such a manner that it is impossible to tell whether A was before B or B before A, the two events are said to be ***simultaneous*** within the accuracy of the observation.

If the events A and B occur at some distance from one another and from the observer, then there is some difficulty in establishing their simultaneity, since the occurrence of these events can then be observed only with the aid of a ***signal*** such as light or radio or sound. Since all these signals take time to travel any given distance, we must postpone discussion of this problem until we have studied light and sound in some detail. If the events occur close to the observer, this problem does not arise, since the time taken by light to travel a short distance can be neglected or allowed for very easily. The problem of making such an allowance for longer distances needs careful discussion.

2.13 The Ordering of Events

If an observer wishes, he can make a list of all the events which he observes in order of their occurrence. He does this by writing a given event lower in the list than all events which occur before it and higher in the list than all events which occur after it. An event occupies the same place in the list with all other events which occur at the same time.

If two observers each make lists of this sort, they will not be able to compare them and merge them into one list unless the two lists have many events in common. It is to provide such common events that standard time signals are established in every community and in the world at large. Such signals may consist of a series of short "beeps" sent out by a radio station, or of bells rung at regular intervals, or they may simply be the successive passages of the second hand of a watch or clock past the markings on its dial. If an observer notices that an event A occurs after the time signal called 12:00:00 (12 hours, 0 minutes, 0 seconds) and before that called 12:00:01, and a second observer locates an event B between the signals 12:00:02 and 12:00:03, then it is easy to see that A occurred before B.

It is obvious that such a system of signals can be quite arbitrary as long as the two observers both know the names for all the signals and that the signals occur often enough to separate to a sufficient degree of accuracy all events which cannot be said to occur simultaneously.

2.14 Duration

Suppose now that we observe that a certain event B occurs six time signals later than A and that an event C occurs six time signals later than B. If now we wish to decide whether or not the duration or elapsed time between the events A and B is greater than, equal to, or less than, that between B and C, we must know whether the duration between any pair of time signals is always the same. We define a ***clock system*** or a ***clock*** as any mechanism which gives us a set of signals such that the duration between any two adjacent signals is always the same. The problem of defining a clock system is then very similar to that involved in defining a rigid rod. We shall be able to define a class of clocks by a process of comparison just as we were able to define a class of rigid rods by comparison. The chief difference between the two problems is that in defining rigid rods we made use of objects which remained unchanged with respect to one another for all time, while in defining clocks we must use objects which are changing constantly.

Before we can proceed with the definition of a clock, we must decide what we mean by ***time*** or ***duration.*** To do this we must return to the idea of the orderliness of nature which we discussed in Sec. 1.2. Suppose that a certain mechanism when started in a given manner goes through a sequence of operations. It is then not unreasonable to assume that the same mechanism when started again later in exactly the same manner will go through the same sequence of events in exactly the same way. For example, a mouse trap is to be expected to behave in the same way every time it is set and released, provided that the setting and releasing are done in the same way each time. In particular, the time which elapses between the beginning and the end of the operation of the mechanism is to be expected to be the same provided that the mechanism repeats its circumstances of operation exactly.

Historically a great many different mechanisms have been used as clocks. Many of them were of the mousetrap variety and required resetting by human agency. Examples of this variety are the water clock, the sand glass, and the candle. Most modern clocks reset automatically and consequently repeat some simple process again and again. It is with this type of clock that we are most concerned here.

2.15 Periodic Processes

There are many processes in nature in which the same phenomenon repeats again and again and, in accordance with the assumption of the preceding section, we can expect that the time taken in each repetition will be the same. Such processes are called ***periodic processes.*** Obvious examples are the rotation of the earth on its axis, which causes the apparent rising and setting of the sun, and the motion of the earth around the sun, which produces the changes of the seasons. The motion of the moon around the earth is another example of a periodic process.

Other examples of periodic motions are provided by various sorts of rotating machinery. Electric motors, gasoline motors, steam engines, all go round and round quite regularly provided we feed them with the fuel they need. There are also many things that oscillate or vibrate. A heavy weight hung on a string will oscillate to and fro with seeming regularity, as does a tuning fork, a piano string, or a flag in a steady wind.

All these rotating and oscillating systems constitute possible clocks, and our concern is with the accuracy with which they continuously repeat precisely the same set of circumstances.

2.16 The Test for Good Clocks

If we wish to find out whether one of the periodic processes described in the preceding section is "a good clock," we shall soon see that we cannot test it by comparison with itself. For example, if we keep an automobile engine well-oiled and give it a constant supply of gasoline, it will seem to run quite steadily. This judgment that the motor is running steadily depends, however, on two things. It depends first on our memory of the previous running of the motor and second on our feeling that, since all the conditions of running remain the same, the orderliness of nature requires that the running will be steady. It is obvious that our judgment—based on memory and a preconceived notion—may well be untrustworthy. It would be difficult for us to judge whether or not a motor had changed its speed slightly during the course of an hour or a day. Also, while it is easy to recognize that speed changes during the early stages of warmup, it is difficult to judge when the warmup is complete and the speed is constant.

The problem can be solved, though, if we compare two different periodic processes that take place at the same time. We can compare the running of an automobile motor with that of an electric motor. When both are warmed up and running steadily, we count the number of revolutions of the gasoline engine, and during the same time interval we count the number of revolutions of the electric motor. Suppose we count exactly 2000 revolutions of the automobile engine in a given interval and find that during the same interval the electric motor has done exactly 1800 revolutions. Later we count 1000 revolutions of the gasoline engine and find that the electric motor has made 900 revolutions. At still another time 90 revolutions of the automobile engine correspond to 81 of the electric motor. In other words we find—whenever we experiment—that every time the engine does 10 revolutions the electric motor does 9. The conclusion that both of them are running steadily is now based on much surer grounds than could be obtained by the observation of one of them alone. The gasoline engine and the electric motor are machines of quite different nature; they run quite independently from quite different sources of power. It would be a remarkable coincidence if both machines changed their speeds in precisely the same manner.

We may now further find that in each rotation of the earth on its axis the automobile engine does 3,000,000 revolutions while the electric motor does 2,700,000 revolutions, and that this observation can be repeated day after day. Our conclusion must then be that the rotation of the earth, the rotation of the automobile engine, and the rotation of the electric motor, which we believe to be quite independent of each other, are all occurring quite steadily. The only other possibility would be that, by a very curious coincidence, all of these rotations are changing together.

In setting up a system for measuring time, physicists have assumed that coincidences such as that mentioned above very seldom occur. Until quite recently it was assumed that they never did occur; now we know—and we shall discuss this point in Chapter 8—that there are well defined conditions under which all good clocks must be expected to change their rates together. However, such changes never occur under circumstances affecting our use of ordinary clocks.

If we consider an automobile engine and an electric motor other than those discussed above, we might find that for every thousand revolutions of the engine a series of experiments gave 896, 700, 950, 942, etc. revolutions of the electric motor. We can conclude that one or the other is running unsteadily or that both are running unsteadily. We cannot decide which.

It is possible to recognize a steady repetition only by comparison with another steady repetition, or better, by comparison with several such repetitions. If we have a group of steady repetitions, we can recognize that some other repeating motion is not repeating isochronously when it does not match with the members of the group. This process is exactly analogous to the way in which we were able to recognize a nonrigid rod by its failure to match after maltreatment with the class of rigid rods (Sec. 2.3).

We can now define the class of ***good clocks*** as the class of physical phenomena which repeat themselves over and over again in such a way that the number of repetitions of any one of the members of the class has always a constant ratio to the number of repetitions of any other member of the class. Thus the earth, the automobile engine, and the electric motor discussed above can be considered as belonging to the class of good clocks. In this particular set of clocks there are always 3,000,000 engine revolutions to one earth revolution, 2,700,000 motor revolutions to one earth revolution, and 10 engine revolutions to 9 electric motor revolutions.

We shall see later that the definition given above is not complete until we state the accuracy with which the comparison is made. For everyday use, clocks which do not vary with respect to one another by more than one or two seconds a day are excellent, but for astronomical purposes we require clocks whose rates are known to a fraction of a second in a year.

The measurement of the ***time interval*** between two events then involves the counting of the number of repetitions of a good clock which occur between the two events. This measurement is thus quite closely analogous to the measurement of the distance between two points. Just as it was necessary to establish a standard of length for scientific purposes, it is also necessary to establish a standard of time.

EXERCISES

2.16-1 Four machines A, B, C, and D, which exhibit repeating phenomena, are provided with counters. While these machines are operating, a number of photographs P_1, P_2, etc., are made of the readings of these counters as shown in the following table:

	P_1	P_2	P_3	P_4	P_5	P_6	P_7	P_8
A	000,923	001,409	001,652	003,353	005,783	006,755	009,914	010,643
B	078,416	078,902	079,550	080,198	081,332	084,410	088,460	091,052
C	002,125	002,625	003,981	005,136	008,625	014,284	019,419	022,125
D	728,009	728,684	729,584	730,484	732,059	736,334	741,959	745,559

On the evidence available, which machines would be most satisfactory as clocks? Justify this choice.

2.16-2 A ship carries five chronometers. Exactly at noon (obtained from a standard time signal) on the successive days of one week, the clocks read as follows:

	Sun.	Mon.	Tues.	Wed.	Thurs.	Fri.	Sat.
A	12:37:45	12:38:01	12:38:17	12:38:32	12:38:49	12:39:04	12:39:19
B	11:59:57	12:00:00	11:59:55	12:00:05	12:00:00	11:59:54	12:00:01
C	16:55:50	16:56:48	16:57:46	16:58:44	16:59:42	17:00:40	17:01:38
D	12:04:44	12:03:37	12:02:30	12:01:23	12:00:16	11:59:09	11:58:02
E	12:02:52	12:01:42	12:00:47	12:00:45	12:00:25	12:00:15	12:00:05

On the basis of such data, arrange the five chronometers in order of their relative value as clocks and give your reasons.

2.17 The Earth as a Clock

There are two motions of the earth that repeat themselves again and again and can therefore be used as clocks. The earth rotates on its axis, and as it rotates it moves in its (very nearly circular) orbit around the sun. In order to make use of these two motions as clocks, we have to decide on what we shall use as "hands."

The most obvious indicator to use is the sun, since it is so important to us in our life. If we erect a vertical stick on any flat horizontal plane and mark on the plane a straight line passing through the lower end of the vertical stick—the line is usually drawn north and south, i.e., along the ***meridian***, but it need not be—then the shadow of this stick will coincide with the line on the plane once every day. The time interval between successive passages of the shadow across the line is called an ***apparent solar day***. A comparison of this time interval with good mechanical clocks indicates that it is not constant but that it varies during the year by as much as half a minute between its shortest and its longest day. The average length of the apparent solar day is called the ***mean solar day*** and is the day used in keeping standard time. The mean solar day is divided into twenty four (mean solar) hours, each hour is divided into sixty (mean solar) minutes and each minute into sixty (mean solar) seconds. The ***second*** (abbreviated sec), the scientific unit of time, is therefore defined as 1/86,400 of a mean solar day.*

If instead of using the sun as an indicator we use a star, we get a different length for the day, equal to the time between successive passages of a star across the meridian. This is called the ***sidereal day*** (Latin: *sidus*, *sideris*—a star) and its length is 23 hours, 56 minutes, and 4.091 seconds of mean solar time. The difference between the mean solar day and the sidereal day is due to the fact that the earth goes around the sun and that consequently the sun as seen from the earth seems to move among the stars.

This motion of the earth around the sun provides us with a second astronomical clock motion. The earth, the sun, and the stars return to their same relative position once every ***sidereal year***. As we shall see later, the motion of the earth around the sun and the rotation of the earth on its axis are quite independent of one another so that we can compare these two motions with one another (Sec. 2.16) to check on their value as clocks. It is found that there are always very close to 365 days, 6 hours, 9 minutes, and 9.5 seconds of mean solar time in one sidereal year, and this indicates that the motion of the earth around the sun and the motion of the earth on its axis are both good clocks.

Our calendar is based on the ***tropical year***, which is slightly different from the sidereal year. The length of the tropical year is 365 days, 5 hours, 48 minutes, and 45.5 seconds of mean solar time; this length of time is the interval between one vernal equinox and the next. The ***calendar year*** of 365 days in ordinary years and 366 in leap years is of course a compromise to allow for the fact that the year is not exactly a whole number of days.

* This is not quite the most recent definition of the second, but it is very close to it. Because the rate of rotation of the earth is decreasing slowly, the present definition of the second is based on the length of the mean solar day during the year 1900.

A disadvantage of the earth as a clock lies in the fact that the day is too large a unit of time for convenient study of any but slowly changing processes. We have to use some sort of mechanical or electric clock to subdivide the day into hours, minutes, or seconds, units that are of more convenient size.

In order to have a convenient time unit available for the discussion of the next few sections, we shall assume that we have a mechanical clock that always gives 86,400 signals in one mean solar day, i.e., it gives one signal every second. We shall not bother at the moment to consider how this clock is made, but shall merely assume that it is so made that we can use it as a timekeeper to aid us in the study of other possible clock motions.

EXERCISE

2.17-1 Our calendar was introduced by Pope Gregory XIII in 1582. It provides for 366 days in those years whose number is divisible evenly by 4; these are called *leap years*, and all other years have 365 days. The Gregorian calendar further specifies that years whose number is divisible evenly by 100 be nonleap years unless the year number is also divisible by 400. State the length of the tropical year in mean solar days to seven significant figures. Then determine how much error the Gregorian calendar will have in 10^4 years.

2.18 Rotational Motions—Angle

We have seen that the rotation of the earth about its axis and the revolution of the earth as a whole around the sun are both good clock motions. There are many other uniform rotational motions which are also available for clock motions in addition to their many other uses, and in Sec. 2.16 we have used the rotational motions of an electric motor and a gasoline engine as examples of clocks.

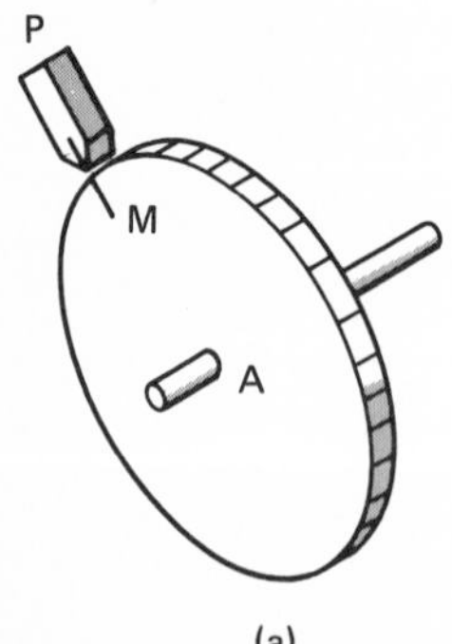

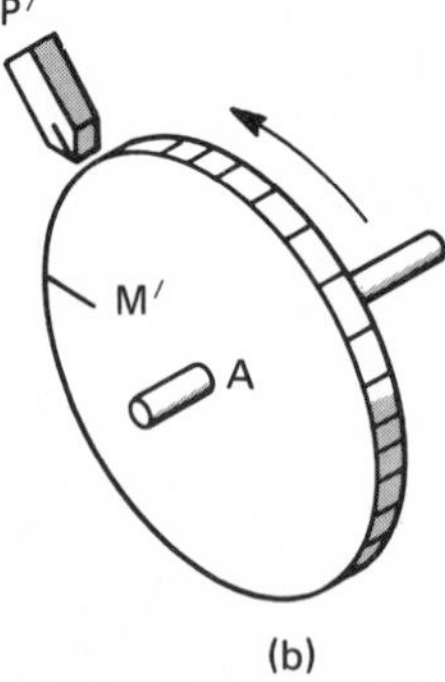

FIG. 2.8 Rotation of a wheel.

In considering rotational motions we must have some measure of the amount of rotation or ***angle*** of rotation. Let us consider a wheel (Fig. 2.8a) which rotates about a fixed axis A. A pointer P is mounted near the rim of the wheel and is fixed with respect to the earth, and a mark M is made on the rim of the wheel at a point which is initially opposite the pointer P. As the wheel rotates, the mark M moves to M′ away from P as shown in Fig. 2.8b. If the rotation continues, the mark M will ultimately return to the pointer P, and we shall say that the wheel has completed one ***revolution*** (rev). If the rotation continues, the mark will again depart from P and will ultimately return to P for the second time. We then say that the wheel has completed two revolutions. The revolution is thus a simple measure of the amount of rotation.

It is of course quite unnecessary that the object whose rotation is measured be circular, as long as the axis of rotation is fixed with respect to it. We can make the mark M on an object of any shape (Fig. 2.9) and observe its departure from and return to the pointer P.

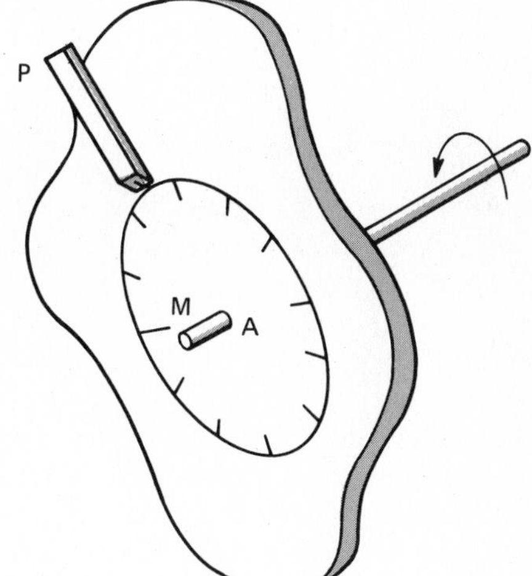

FIG. 2.9 Rotation of an irregular object about an axis.

We can also make use of fractions of revolutions in measuring the amount of rotation or angle. Suppose we draw a circle about A on the rotating object (Fig. 2.9) so that the end of the pointer P always touches the circumference of the circle as the object rotates. If we divide the circumference into a number of equal parts and place a mark at each division, then as each mark passes the pointer we can say that the object has rotated through a certain fraction of a revolution.

There are two fractions of a revolution which are in common use as measures of angles. The ***degree*** (°) is defined in terms of one revolution by the equation

$$360° = 1 \text{ rev.} \tag{2.18-1}$$

The ***radian*** (rad) is defined in terms of one revolution by the equation

$$2\pi \text{ rad} = 1 \text{ rev.} \tag{2.18-2}$$

These equations, being defining equations for the degree and the radian, are to be taken as exact (Sec. 2.8).

Although common speech probably makes greater use of degrees and right angles, we shall find that the radian is frequently a more useful measure of angle for scientific work. This greater utility stems from a different (but equivalent) way of defining a radian. This definition may be understood by reference to Fig. 2.10, where line segments AO and BO meet at O to form the angle AOB, which we shall designate by the symbol θ, the Greek letter *theta*.

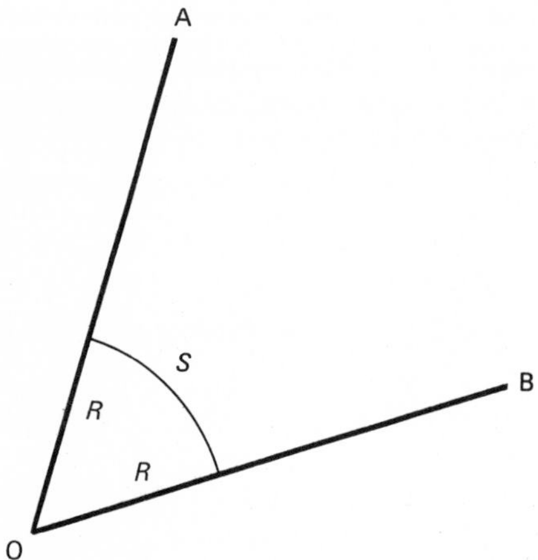

FIG. 2.10 Angular measure. If $S = R$, $\theta = 1$ radian.

Choosing any radius R, draw the circular arc S. We can then express the size of the angle as

$$\theta = S/R, \tag{2.18-3}$$

where S is the distance *measured along the arc* in the same length units as those used to measure R. Now an angle for which $S/R = 1$ is an angle of one radian.

We should recall that the circumference of a circle is $C = 2\pi R$. This relation compares with Eq. (2.18-3), written in the form $S = \theta R$; for the circle, the arc is the entire circumference and θ is 2π radians.

We can also note that, since π is an irrational number, the number of degrees per radian is an irrational number. Thus,

$$360° \div 2\pi \approx 57.2957\ldots°$$

and the relation can be carried to as many significant figures as we wish but it can never be made exact.

In discussing clock systems we have been concerned with rotations in which the angle turned through is a constant multiple of the time elapsed from the start of the measurement. In fact if θ represents the angle and t represents the time, then we may represent a rotational clock motion by the equation

$$\theta = \omega t \tag{2.18-4}$$

in which ω (Greek *omega*) is a constant. The quantity ω can be determined for any motion by determining the time t taken by the rotator to turn through a measured angle θ. This quantity ω, which is called the ***angular velocity*** of the rotator, is then defined by the equation*

$$\omega = \theta / t.$$

Typical units in which angular velocities are expressed are thus rpm (or rev/min), rps (or rev/sec), °/min, rad/sec, etc.

EXERCISES

2.18-1 The synodic month has a mean length of 29 days, 12 hours, 44 minutes, 2.8 seconds, all of the time units being based on the mean solar day. The synodic month can be defined as the average period from the new moon to new moon. Find the total angle through which the earth rotates during one synodic month and express your result in revolutions, radians, and degrees to four significant figures.

2.18-2 Through what angle in revolutions, radians, and degrees does the hour hand of a clock move in one hour?

2.19 Oscillations

In addition to the periodic motions presented to us directly by rotating machinery and by other things that rotate, there is another large class of periodic motions called ***oscillations.*** Typical of these phenomena are the swinging motion of a weight on the end of a string or chain, the vibration of a weight on the end of a spring, and the pulse beat of the human and of other organisms. The reader will think of other such motions and will meet many of them later in this text.

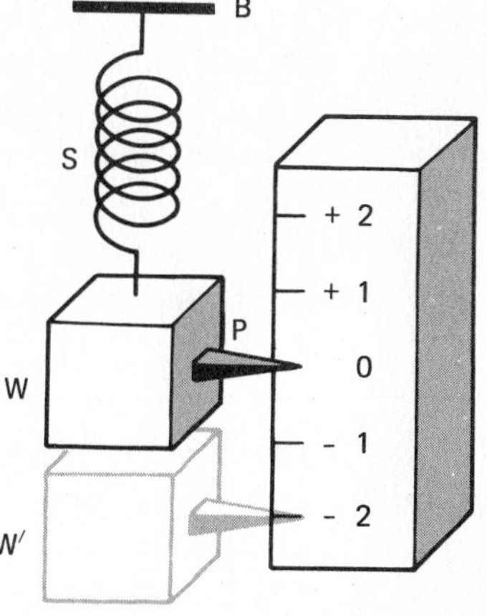

FIG. 2.11 Oscillation of a weight on a spring.

As a first example for detailed study let us consider a weight W (Fig. 2.11) suspended by a spring S which is fastened to a rigid support B. The position of the weight is indicated by a pointer P which moves up and down a scale. When

* This definition applies only to constant angular velocities. We shall see in Chapter 7 how it must be modified if the velocity is changing.

the weight is allowed to hang on the spring, it will come to rest at the position marked W in the figure, and in this location the scale is adjusted so that the pointer points to the mark 0 on the scale. This position is taken as the origin, and distances measured up from this point are said to be positive, those down negative (cf. Sec. 2.10).

We now pull the weight down to the position marked W′ in Fig. 2.11 and release it. The weight will bob up and down and if we start to take pictures at the time of release, and at equal time intervals thereafter, we shall obtain a

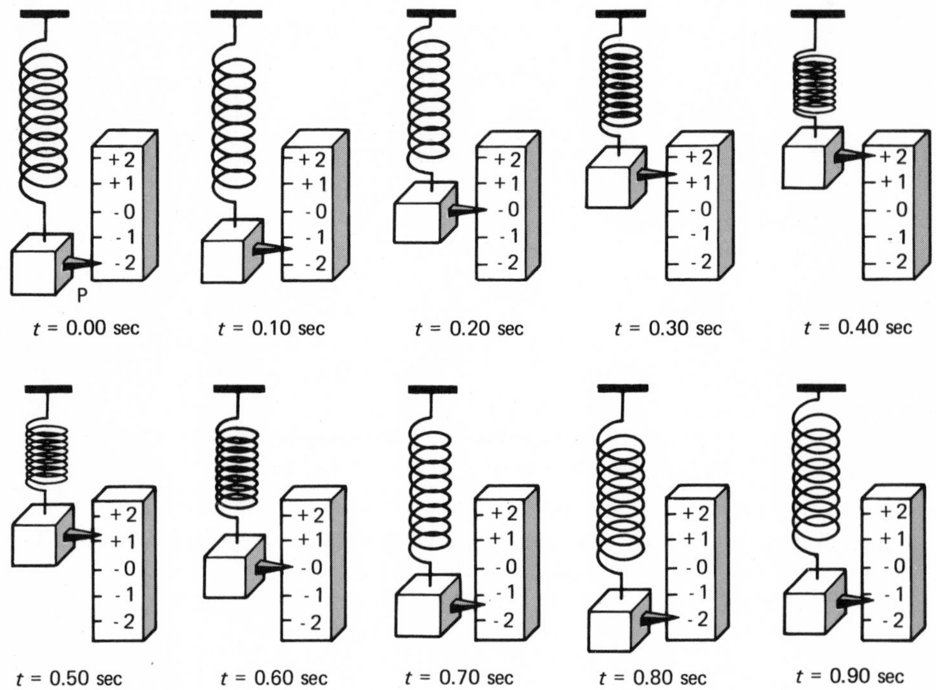

FIG. 2.12 Series of pictures of an oscillating weight.

series such as that shown in Fig. 2.12. The weight moves upward from its initial position at −2 cm until at the end of 0.40 sec it has reached +2 cm. It then starts a return journey, reaching its starting point at −2 cm at the end of 0.80 sec. At times later than 0.80 sec it repeats* the same cycle over again as indicated in Fig. 2.12, in which the situation at 0.90 sec is the same as that at 0.10 sec. If we take pictures somewhat more frequently, we can use the data obtained from them to plot a graph as shown in Fig. 2.13, in which the ordinate

*In actual practice, the motion of the weight will die down after a number of oscillations, due to the effect of air resistance and other friction, so that the repetition cannot be exact. However, if the weight W is a heavy one, the oscillations will repeat a large number of times to a high degree of accuracy (Chapter 22).

is the height x (in cm) of the weight above the zero point and the abscissa is the time t (in sec) after the start of the oscillation. From such a curve we can determine the position of the weight at any stage of its oscillation.

The motion just described occurs frequently in nature and is known as ***simple harmonic motion*** (SHM). In common with all periodic phenomena, SHM possesses the property that the time interval between any two repetitions of the same situation is a constant. This time interval is called the ***period***, or ***periodic time***. Thus the periodic time of the oscillating weight is 0.80 sec, and

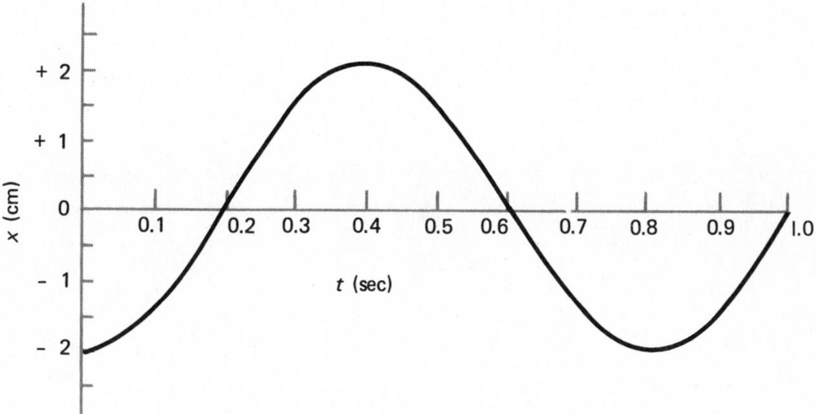

FIG. 2.13 Graph of an oscillatory motion.

that of the earth in its motion around the sun is one year. The number of repetitions of any periodic phenomenon occurring in one unit of time is called the ***frequency***, and it follows from these two definitions that the period τ (Greek *tau*) and the frequency ν (Greek *nu*) are connected by the equation

$$\nu = 1/\tau. \qquad (2.19\text{-}1)$$

Thus the frequency of the oscillating weight is $(1/0.80 \text{ sec}) = 1.25 \text{ sec}^{-1}$.

The term ***amplitude*** is often applied to oscillations. It refers to the maximum excursion of the oscillation on either side of the rest position. In the example of vibration of the weight on the spring, the amplitude is 2.0 cm. It is a remarkable property of the motion of a weight on a spring that the period is independent of the amplitude. Thus, if the weight had been pulled down to -1.0 cm initially, it would have oscillated with an amplitude of 1.0 cm, but the period would have been the same as before, i.e., 0.80 sec.

Another example of a periodic motion is that of the ***pendulum*** (Fig. 2.14). If a weight is hung from a rigid support A by a wire or a rod, it will rest in a vertical position. If it is pulled to one side and then released, it will swing to and fro between the positions M and M′. The Italian physicist Galileo Galilei (1564–1642) discovered that the time of swing of such an arrangement was approximately independent of the amplitude, and he first suggested its use as a timekeeper in clocks. It is interesting to note that he made this observation in the cathedral at Pisa, where he observed that the number of swings of the lamps hung by chains from the roof and the number of beats of his pulse were always in the same proportion to one another. He thus used the method of comparison discussed in Sec. 2.16.

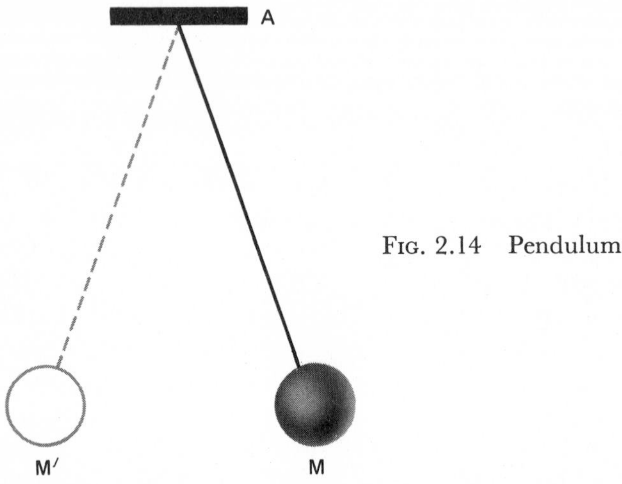

FIG. 2.14 Pendulum.

The balance wheel of a watch also executes periodic motion. It consists of a small wheel heavily weighted on the rim (Fig. 2.15). This wheel is provided with a spiral spring so arranged that it opposes any motion from a zero position. If the wheel is forcibly displaced from the zero position and then released, it flies back

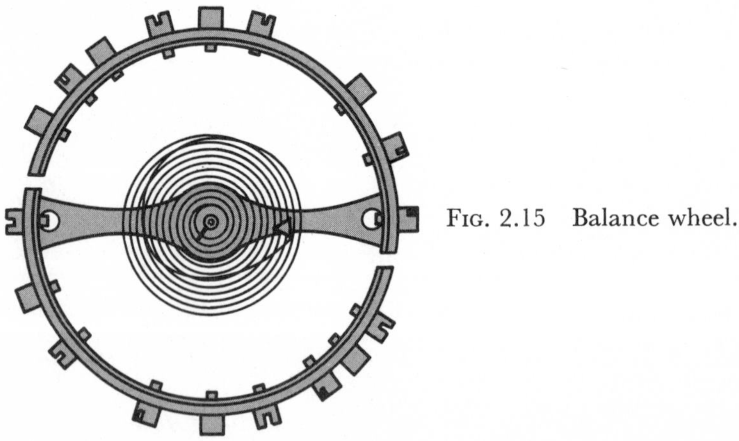

FIG. 2.15 Balance wheel.

toward the zero and starts to oscillate to and fro as did the pendulum and the weight on the spring.

A bar of solid elastic material (Sec. 9.2), such as most metals or wood, clamped at one end to a rigid support but otherwise free, will vibrate in oscillatory motion if it is first bent out of its normal position and then released.

EXERCISE

2.19-1 While the amplitudes and the periods may be different, the general shape of Fig. 2.13 applies to all simple harmonic motions. Suppose that an oscillator executing SHM has an amplitude of seven centimeters and a period of 2.00 minutes, and further suppose that at time = 0.50 minutes its displacement is −7.0 cm. What will its displacement be at time = 4.00 minutes?

2.20 Practical Clocks

Many periodic motions have at one time or another been used as clocks, but only a few of them have had general application. Most of the clocks now in use belong to one of two classes; those which depend on the maintenance of a rotation at a constant angular velocity and those which depend on the maintenance of an oscillation.

All clocks possess some mechanism that counts the number of oscillations or rotations and translates this number into the hours, minutes, and seconds that we use to measure time, and all man-made clocks must be supplied with energy to keep them in operation.

In addition to the motions of the earth, the only important clocks now in use which depend on a rotation at constant angular velocity are the electric clocks. The "electric clocks" used in our homes are not really clocks. They are merely indicators which tell us of the rotation of the electric generator supplying the power used to light our lights and run our machinery. In Sec. 2.16 we discussed the use of motors and engines as clocks, but small motors and engines are not suitable for this purpose. However, it is quite easy to keep a large machine running at a speed which is very nearly constant. As we shall see later, the modern electric generator supplies an alternating electric current that varies periodically in the manner indicated by the curve of Fig. 2.13, and a fixed whole number of oscillations of the current occur in one revolution of the generator. Thus the oscillations of the current are tied to the rotation of the generator.* This oscillating current is made to drive a motor in the clock in the home in such a manner that a whole number of revolutions of the motor correspond to a whole number of oscillations of the current. Thus the clock in the home is connected to the generators in the power house, and if the power companies keep the generators running at a constant rate—and they are required to by law—our clocks will also run at a constant rate.

Large clocks with fixed locations usually depend on pendulums for the constancy of their motion. Portable clocks and watches, on the other hand, use balance wheels or tuning forks. Such instruments, if well built, are sufficiently accurate for ordinary timing needs. For the greater precision required by modern scientific work, however, pendulums and balance wheels will not suffice. A better clock employs the mechanical vibrations of a small wafer of quartz. These oscillations are picked up electrically and used to control the oscillations in an electronic circuit which produces an alternating current. This

* In most parts of the U.S. the period of this current is 1/60 sec.

alternating current must have its frequency reduced electronically, but it can ultimately be used to run what is essentially an ordinary electric clock. As stated above, this clock will tell us of the constancy of the electric generator; the quartz crystal can control this constancy more accurately than can the devices used by the power companies.

Even quartz clocks are subject to temperature changes and to drifting brought about by ageing of the crystal. The best clocks are molecular or atomic clocks. The ammonia clock can be understood qualitatively by referring to Fig. 2.16. In the ammonia molecule, three hydrogen atoms are arranged at the corners of the base of an equilateral triangular prism with the nitrogen atom at the vertex. The distance of the nitrogen from the plane of the hydrogens is about one-fifth of the distance between the hydrogens. It is possible to set this molecule into oscillation so that the nitrogen vibrates in a direction perpendicular to the plane of the hydrogens, and simultaneously the three hydrogens move together in the opposite direction, maintaining their planar configuration. At one extreme of the oscillation the nitrogen will be above the plane of the hydrogens as indicated in Fig. 2.16. At the other extreme the nitrogen will be an equal

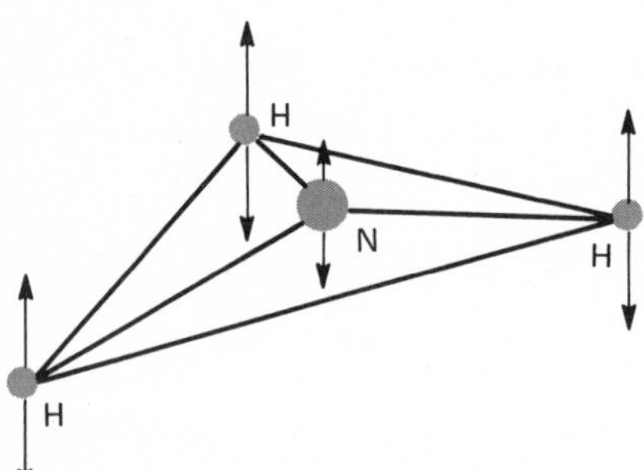

FIG. 2.16 The ammonia molecule.

distance below the plane of the hydrogens. Effectively, the nitrogen passes through the plane of the hydrogens, but as we shall see in Chapter 7, the plane of the hydrogens moves almost five times as far as does the nitrogen atom. The frequency with which this oscillation occurs is 2.3870×10^{10} sec^{-1}. This frequency is used to control that of an electronic oscillator whose alternating current, after suitable frequency reduction, can be used to drive an electric clock. Of course the effect of any one ammonia molecule is very small, but the combined influence of many vibrating molecules can provide reliable control for a clock.

Other molecules have vibrations that occur at fixed frequencies, and even atoms possess internal motions that may be used as clocks. One of the best of these motions occurs in the cesium atom, at a frequency of 9.192×10^9 sec^{-1}. It is the basis of the cesium clock, which is probably the most precise timing device yet developed.

As stated earlier, all man-made clocks must be supplied with energy to replace that which is lost to the surroundings. The gearing and the pendulum or the balance wheel are all subject to frictional losses. In a mechanical clock this energy is restored from a wound spring or from a suspended weight by means of an ***escapement mechanism.*** Such mechanisms vary widely with the different types of clocks and are more easily studied directly than described. In all cases, however, the escapement provides that the rate of the clock depend almost entirely on the nature of the vibrator and that it be independent of variations in the power supply which would occur, for example, as the spring of a watch runs down. Escapement mechanisms are made at the same time to serve as counters to record the number of oscillations of the vibrator, and the motion of some part of the escapement mechanism is made to control the hands of the clock.

Quartz crystals, atoms, and molecules will also lose their vibrational energy to their surroundings. Moreover, when they are used as oscillating elements to control clocks, the rest of the clock must somehow be able to count the oscillations. Special electronic circuits are provided to restore energy to the vibrator and to count the number of vibrations. These circuits may be regarded as analogous to mechanical escapement mechanisms. We shall return to such circuits in Chapter 22.

2.21 The Stroboscope

In most clocks, the positions of hands or the indications of counting devices are used to furnish a reading of time intervals. One very ingenious variation on such schemes, which is of great value in studying motion, uses a flashing light as an indicator. Such a device, which flashes a light for very short times at regular and known intervals, is known as a ***stroboscope.*** If the times during which the light is on are short enough, a moving object illuminated by a stroboscope will not move appreciably during each flash, so it will be seen (by the eye or by a camera) as stationary. Succeeding flashes will capture the object in new positions, so a series of "snapshots" of the object are obtained showing its position at known time intervals. Therefore the stroboscope allows detailed study of motions which are too fast to appear as more than blurs under ordinary light.

It is necessary in most physical studies of motion to know the intervals between successive flashes of the stroboscope. Therefore the light is usually controlled by a clock of some sort. When intervals of 1/60 or 1/120 of a second are sufficiently short, the light flashes are usually timed by the alternating current from an electrical generator as mentioned in Sec. 2.20 above. For slower stroboscopic action, mechanical oscillators are used to trigger the flashes; for faster flashing rates, electronic circuits sometimes regulated by quartz oscillators are most convenient.

EXERCISE

2.21-1 An electric fan has three identical blades located 120° apart, and the motor drives the fan through 1800 rpm (rev/min). What is the highest flashing rate of a stroboscope which will make the fan appear to stand still? What is the next highest flashing rate that will make the fan appear to stand still? If one of the blades bears a chalk mark so that it can be distinguished from the other two, what are the highest three flash rates that will make the fan appear to stand still?

2.22 *Summary*

In this chapter a number of basic steps have been made to set up the methods of physical measurement. We have considered the fundamental quantities length, time, and angle, and have discussed the units in terms of which these quantities are measured. The properties of measuring rods and clocks have been considered in some detail. We have also considered a number of the problems of measurement and established some of the conventions which are important for a clear understanding among scientists.

PROBLEMS

2.1 The International Prototype Meter was originally intended to have a length equal to exactly $1/10^7$ of the distance from the north pole to the equator on the meridian passing through Paris. The earth is now known to be very closely approximated by a sphere of radius 6.3676×10^6 m. By what fraction of its length does the meter fall short of its intended length?

2.2 The four corners of a quadrilateral figure are labeled A, B, C, D, in consecutive order. The following distances have been measured: AB = CD = 1.05 m, AD=2.00 m, AC = 2.00 m, BD = 1.70 m. Is the figure a rectangle, a parallelogram, or some other figure?

2.3 The measurement of distance by the successive application of measuring rods, as was described in Sec. 2.4, is often impractical. In such cases, distance may be measured indirectly by the assumption of the validity of Euclidean geometry. As an example, suppose that one wishes to measure the width of a river. He might establish a ***base line*** A-B, both ends of which are on one bank of the river. He measures this base line directly and finds its length to be (105.3 ± 0.1) m. He then observes a point P on the other bank and finds that the line of sight to it from point A is at an angle of $90°00' \pm 01'$ to A-B. Observation of point P from point B shows that the line of sight makes an angle of $65°00' \pm 01'$ with the line B-A. (a) Find the distance from A to P by making a scale drawing. Estimate the uncertainty in this distance. (b) Using the trigonometric definitions of Appendix F, compute the distance A-P. What is the uncertainty in the distance thus computed?

2.4 Both Kisangani (formerly Stanleyville) in the Congo and Quito in Ecuador are very close to the earth's equator. Their respective longitudes are 25°15′ east and 78°31′ west of the meridian through Greenwich. At a prearranged time, when the moon is directly above the equator, astronomers in the two cities observe the same spot on the moon. In Kisangani it is found that the angle between the line of sight to this spot and the vertical is 54°32′; the corresponding angle at Quito is 50°44′. Assuming the equator to be a circle of radius 6378 km, find the distance from the center of the earth to the surface of the moon, as given by these data. Include an estimate of the uncertainty in this distance.

2.5 A rotating disk is observed with stroboscopic light. When the frequency of the stroboscope is either 15.0/sec or 30.0/sec, a stationary spot is observed on the disk. At a frequency of 60.0/sec two stationary spots are seen, at the opposite ends of a diameter. What is the angular velocity of the disk in revolutions per second?

2.6 The disk described in Prob. 2.5 is observed with a stroboscope while it is rotating at a different angular velocity. The frequency of the flashes is 60.0/sec. Two spots are seen, and the line joining them is found to rotate clockwise at an angular velocity of 1.0 rev/sec. When the frequency of the flashes is changed to 62.0/sec, the same spots are seen and the line joining them rotates counterclockwise at 1.0 rev/sec. (a) Is the disk rotating clockwise or counterclockwise? (b) What is its angular velocity in revolutions per second?

REFERENCES

2A Percy W. Bridgman, "Suggestions from Physics," in *Science and Ideas—Selected Readings*, edited by A. B. Arons and A. M. Bork, Prentice-Hall, Englewood Cliffs, N.J., 1964. Pages 10–36 discuss operationalism.

2B Harold Lyons, "Atomic Clocks," *Scientific American*, February 1957. (Reprint No. 225, W. H. Freeman Co., San Francisco.)

2C Akira Harashima, Hachirō Nakagome, Masakuni Hotta, and Takeshi Takahashi, *Stroboscope*, Kōdansha, Tokyo, 1966. An excellent collection of stroboscopic photographs, showing details of many motions.

2D *Encyclopaedia Britannica*, 11th Edition, 1911, "Weights and Measures" (by H. J. Chaney and W. M. F. Petrie), vol. 28, pp. 477–494. "Clocks" (by J. G. J. Penderel-Brodhurst), vol. 6, pp. 536–553.

3 ⇨ *Linear Motions*

3.1 Motion

When the motion of a body changes, we can be sure that some agency, internal or external, has produced the change. It is such changes of motion that make us aware of the physical agencies that act in our environment. If we ourselves were purely static beings and nothing in the world could move, there would be very little to be learned from nature; and life, if it existed at all, would be very dull.

As soon as motion and change of motion can be observed, we can immediately learn something about the region in which that motion is taking place. If we watch a car ahead of us on the road, we can learn about the bumps on the road long before we can see them. Similar uses of a moving body to investigate physical phenomena are so important in science that we shall find that there is very little we can say about nature without some reference to a moving object.

The study of moving objects without concern for the causes of the motion forms the science of ***kinematics***. The study of the causes of motion is called ***mechanics***, and we include within that science those cases in which no motion takes place. This branch of mechanics is called ***statics*** and is concerned largely with structures, such as bridges and the frames of buildings and houses, which are designed to remain stationary.

The science of mechanics has played such an important part in physics that it may be said that every great advance in the understanding of physics has come from an advance in our knowledge of mechanics. For this reason we base our study of physics on a number of mechanical problems. In Chapter 2 we laid the foundations for kinematical discussions by our definitions of measures for the lengths and angles which enable us to describe the relative arrangements of moving bodies at any given time. The notion of a system of time signals enables us to discuss a sequence of positions of a moving body and thus to investigate the nature of its motion.

Some of the motions which we have mentioned in Chapter 2 are quite complex and may seem at first very difficult to discuss. In this chapter and in Chapter 4 we shall treat only the simplest cases, those motions that take place in a straight line. In Chapters 5 and 6 and in later parts of the text we shall find that the ideas which we develop for straight-line motion can readily be generalized to deal with the more complicated motions that occur in a plane and in space.

3.2 *Change of Position and Speed*

The fundamental question to be answered in connection with a body moving in a straight line is, "How rapidly does it change its position?" Everyone is familiar in a general way with the manner in which an answer to this question can be obtained. If two cities are a hundred miles apart and a driver travels from one to the other in two and a half hours he "averages" forty miles an hour. Someone has measured the distance between the two cities with measuring rods, and the motorist has determined the time interval which elapses between his arrival and his departure. Division then enables him to decide how far "on the average" he travels in each hour, i.e., forty miles. It now remains to formalize this process, and to do it in a way which will enable us to give a detailed description of the whole trip.

Rather than list the distances between a large number of pairs of points on a line, it is most convenient to list the distance between each point in which we have interest and some reference point or origin (Fig. 3.1). Then if two points

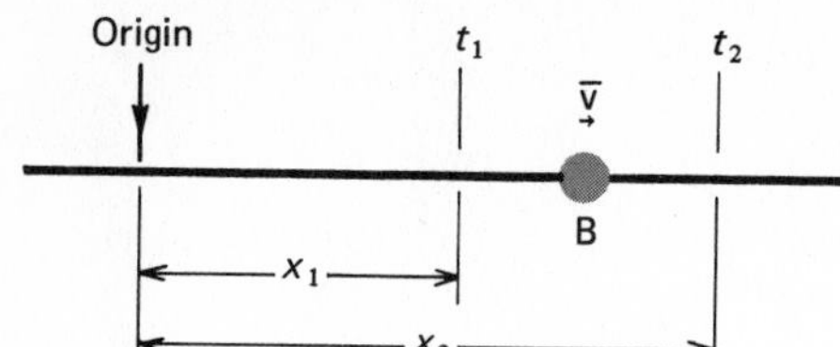

FIG. 3.1 The measurement of average velocity.

are respectively at distances x_1 and x_2 from a reference point, the distance from the first point to the second (cf. Eq. 2.10) is $(x_2 - x_1)$. If the times at which a body B passes these two points are t_1 and t_2, respectively, then the ***average speed*** of the body over this line segment is defined as the ratio of the distance covered to the time taken to cover it, or

$$\bar{v} = (x_2 - x_1)/(t_2 - t_1) \tag{3.2-1}$$

The bar over v (i.e., $\bar{v}$) is used, in accordance with a notation that we shall continue to employ, to indicate that the value obtained from this equation is an average value. We shall see later that this average value of the speed does not necessarily agree with the instantaneous speed at any particular instant.

Since Eq. (3.2-1) tells both what an average speed is and how to measure it, it is known as a ***defining equation***. From the defining equation of a quantity, we can always deduce certain properties of the quantity itself. For example, since the calculation of a speed always involves a length in the numerator and a time in the denominator, the units in which speed are measured must always be those of length divided by time. Thus speeds may be measured in m/sec, mi/sec, ft/hr, etc. The first of these is the basic unit of speed in the set of units which we shall customarily use. We can indicate the ***dimensions*** of speed by writing

$$[v] = [\ell/t] \quad \text{or} \quad [v] = [\ell t^{-1}], \tag{3.2-2}$$

where ℓ indicates a length and t indicates a time. Equations of the type of Eq. (3.2-2), which give only the dimensions of a quantity, i.e., the connection between the units of the quantity and those of more fundamental quantities, such as length and time, are known as ***dimensional equations.*** A dimensional equation such as Eq. (3.2-2) may be read "a measurement of speed is always equivalent to the quotient of a measurement of some length divided by a measurement of some time." We shall find that dimensional equations are of considerable value in showing the relations between various physical quantities and in checking our physical reasoning. To distinguish between them and the more complete equations which include magnitudes of the quantities as well as dimensions, we shall enclose the terms of dimensional equations in square brackets, as in Eq. (3.2-2).

Applications of Eq. (3.2-1) will ordinarily be simple. If we know the positions of a body at two different times, we can find its average speed, or, conversely, if we know the average speed and the elapsed time, we can find the distance by solving the equation for $x_2 - x_1$. Equation (3.2-1) may be simplified considerably if we locate the origin at the point occupied by the particle at the time $t = 0$. Then x_1 and t_1 are both zero, and letting $x_2 = s$ and $t_2 = t$, we have

$$\bar{v} = s/t \qquad \text{or} \qquad s = \bar{v}t. \tag{3.2-3}$$

Since there are many units in which speed may be measured, conversions from one set of units to another are frequently necessary. These conversions can be carried out without much chance of error if the methods of Sec. 2.7 are used. Thus, suppose that a car is known to be traveling at a speed of 50 mi/hr and we wish to find its speed in m/sec. We start with the basic conversion equations:

$$1 \text{ mi} = 5280 \text{ ft}; \;\; 1 \text{ ft} = 12 \text{ in}; \;\; 1 \text{ in.} = 0.0254 \text{ m}; \;\; 1 \text{ hr} = 3600 \text{ sec};$$

and write:

$$\frac{50 \cancel{\text{mi}}}{\cancel{\text{hr}}} \times \frac{5280 \cancel{\text{ft}}}{\cancel{\text{mi}}} \times \frac{12 \cancel{\text{in}}}{\cancel{\text{ft}}} \times \frac{0.0254 \text{ m}}{\cancel{\text{in}}} \times \frac{\cancel{\text{hr}}}{3600 \text{ sec}} = \frac{22 \text{ m}}{\text{sec}}.$$

Notice here that every factor on the left-hand side of the equation except the first one has the value of unity or is an identity—i.e., there are 5280 feet per mile by definition—and that the units as well as the numbers on the right side of the equation result from algebraic processes; these features in calculations minimize chances for mistakes.

3.3 Speed and Velocity; Distance and Displacement

In one sense, the quantity defined in Sec. 3.2 is not speed but *velocity*. In common speech the terms speed and velocity are frequently used interchangeably and indistinguishably. In kinematics and mechanics, however, we define ***velocity*** as being speed in a specified direction. Thus, in the previous section, since we discussed change of position along a certain line, we might have spoken in each instance of the velocity along the line. As we proceed we shall see that, in some situations, the direction of motion will be of no real concern, so it will be convenient to use the term speed. In other instances, the direction and the change of direction will be highly significant; then it will be more appropriate to speak of velocity.

In a similar fashion, we distinguish between *distance* and *displacement*. Thus, ***displacement*** is distance in a specified direction. Therefore, in Sec. 2.10 we were speaking of positive and negative displacements in a vertical direction. Which term is appropriate in a given situation depends, of course, upon the details.

Just as the displacement between two points may be positive or negative, so the velocities calculated by the methods of Sec. 3.2 may be positive or negative. Thus, if we measure positive displacements to the right in Fig. 3.1, the quantity $x_2 - x_1$, will be positive, and the average velocity of the body will be positive if the body is traveling from left to right. Had the body been traveling to the left, the velocity would have been found to be negative. If we use Eq. (3.2-1) or Eq. (3.2-3) to connect velocities, times, and displacements, *positive velocities will always be in the same direction as positive displacements.*

The units used to express speed and the magnitude of velocity are, of course, the same as are those used to express distance and the magnitude of displacement.

EXERCISES

3.3-1 An airplane travels from San Francisco to Honolulu, a distance of 2410 mi, in 4 hr 36 min. What is its average speed in mi/hr? In ft/sec? In m/sec?

3.3-2 A rifle bullet leaves the gun with a speed of 425 m/sec. How long will it take it to travel 10 m? How long will it take to travel 30 ft?

3.3-3 In a recent laboratory experiment, a neutron (one of the constituents of an atom) was found to pass two points, 7.00 m apart, at an interval of 0.00021 sec. What was the average speed of the neutron over this path? What is the ratio of this speed to that of the airplane in Ex. 3.3-1?

3.3-4 An automobile engine is turning over at 3600 revolutions per minute. Find its angular velocity (Sec. 2.18) in °/sec, and in rad/sec, in rt angles/hr.

3.3-5 When a body moves from one point to another during a given time interval, it is possible for the magnitude of the average velocity to be quite different from

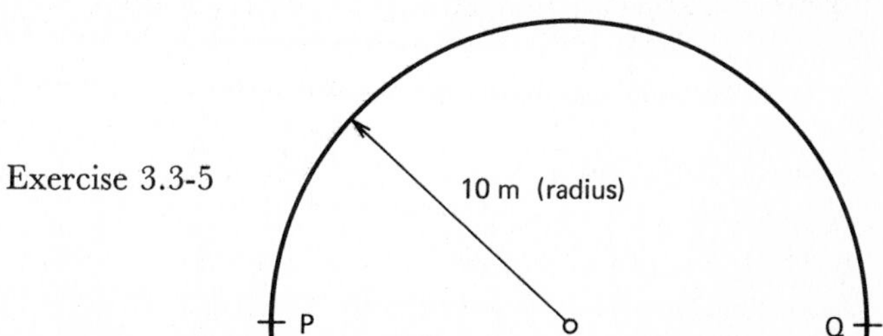

Exercise 3.3-5

the average speed. In order to see this, suppose that a body moves from point P along a semicircular path to point Q, which is directly to the right of P. Let the body be at P at 0.0 sec and at Q at 10.0 sec. The radius of the path is 10.0 m. Show that the average speed is 3.14 m/sec while the average velocity is 2.00 m/sec to the right.

3.4 *Variable and Instantaneous Velocities*

In Secs. 3.2 and 3.3 we saw how we can measure the average velocity of a moving body during a given interval. The fact that the average velocity over a long period of time has little relation to the velocity during an included shorter period is familiar to everyone. A motorist who "averaged" forty miles per hour for two and a half hours probably traveled at speeds near sixty miles per hour for several long periods and spent many minutes with a velocity zero, facing red lights.

If we wish to determine the velocity of a moving body at a given instant, we may measure the distance traveled during a very short period of time which includes the instant in which we are interested. During such a short period, the velocity will not have changed greatly and will therefore approximate closely the velocity desired at the instant. However, if the distance is very short and the time taken to cover the distance is very small, we shall have difficulty in making the measurement, since small quantities are hard to measure with any accuracy. There are, fortunately, several ways to avoid this difficulty.

In order to establish an operational process for defining and determining instantaneous velocity, consider Fig. 3.2 and its related Table 3.1. The figure

Fig. 3.2 Stroboscopic photograph of cart on a horizontal track.

is a stroboscopic photograph of a cart that runs on a smooth horizontal track. So that friction may be minimized, the wheels of the cart turn on ball bearings. A white rod is mounted vertically on the cart to provide an index by which the position of the cart may be established. The white vertical and horizontal lines immediately behind the track provide a grid with reference to which position may be established. The spacing of the grid lines is 10 cm.

In Fig. 3.2 the cart moves from right to left. Let us number the various photographed positions of the cart beginning at the extreme right. The flash interval of the stroboscopic light was 0.10 sec. Suppose now that for each position we

Table 3.1 *Motion of Cart on a Horizontal Track*

Position Number	Time t (sec)	Displacement s (m)
1	0.00	0.000
2	0.10	0.070
3	0.20	0.140
4	0.30	0.207
5	0.40	0.273
6	0.50	0.338
7	0.60	0.400
8	0.70	0.463
9	0.80	0.524

measure its displacement along the track from position 1. These data are presented in the third column of Table 3.1. If the cart was at position 1 at the time $t = 0.00$ sec, the second column gives the time at which the cart was at each position. The fact that we have written two decimal places in the time column and three in the displacement column indicates that these measurements have an accuracy of ± 0.01 sec and ± 0.001 m,* respectively.

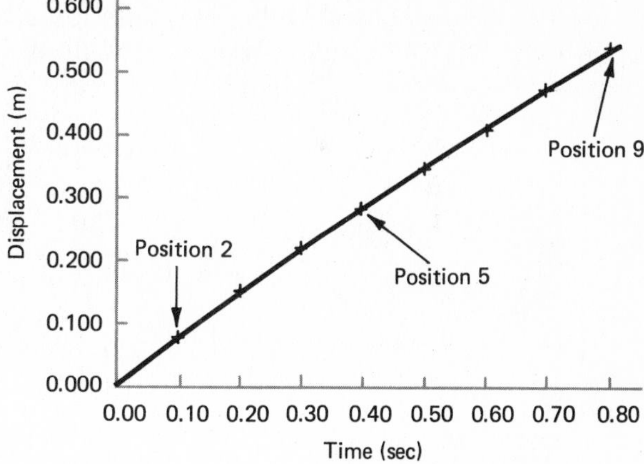

FIG. 3.3 Graph of the data of Table 3.1.

Figure 3.3 shows a graph of the data concerning the motion of the cart. The small crosses mark the actual measurements as plotted on the graph. If the apparatus is good and if the measurements have been taken carefully, we can draw a smooth curve through the plotted points. In any event, we draw the best smooth curve that we can, fitting as many of the points as possible and having as many aberrant points above as below wherever a smooth curve must miss some of the points.

* Measurements may be taken on the photograph by use of a travelling microscope. By way of criticism of this experiment, the student should recall our discussion of rigid rods (Sec. 2.3) and the fact that photographic paper becomes damp in the development process.

The average speed during the first time interval, according to Eq. (3.2-1) is

$$\bar{v} = (s_2 - s_1)/(t_2 - t_1) = (0.070 - 0.000)\ \text{m}/(0.10 - 0.00)\ \text{sec}$$

$$= \frac{0.070\ \text{m}}{0.10\ \text{sec}} = 0.70\ \text{m/sec}.$$

Similarly, the average speed during the first four time intervals is

$$\bar{v} = (0.273 - 0.000)\ \text{m}/(0.40 - 0.00)\ \text{sec} = \frac{0.273\ \text{m}}{0.40\ \text{sec}} = 0.68\ \text{m/sec}.$$

Over all eight time intervals, the average speed is found to be 0.65 m/sec. During the eighth time interval alone—i.e., from $t = 0.70$ sec to $t = 0.80$ sec—the average speed is 0.61 m/sec. Clearly, the car is slowing down, and the average speed shows great dependence upon the particular time interval which is used.

In order to define ***instantaneous speed***, let us first establish a convenient notation. In determining average speed we needed to use the distance between two positions. Thus, in the preceding paragraph, we took the differences between several pairs of displacements: $s_2 - s_1$, $s_5 - s_1$, $s_9 - s_1$, and $s_9 - s_8$. It will be convenient to represent such differences by the symbol Δs (read "delta ess"): the symbol indicates that we are to take the difference between two displacements, and it *does not* mean delta times s. Likewise, Δt will mean the difference between two times—e.g., in the preceding paragraph $\Delta t = t_5 - t_1 = 0.40$ sec. Using this notation we can write Eq. (3.2-1) as

$$\bar{v} = \frac{\Delta s}{\Delta t}. \tag{3.4-1}$$

Now let us establish Table 3.2, with a view to determining the instantaneous speed at position 5, or at $t_5 = 0.40$ sec. In the first three columns we specify several time intervals, each of which has $t_5 = 0.40$ sec at its middle. Thus, the

Table 3.2 *Determination of Speed at 0.40 sec.*

Time Interval Δt (sec)			Displacement Δs (m)	Average Speed $\bar{v}$ During Interval (m/sec)
From	To	Duration		
0.30	0.50	0.20	0.131	0.655
0.20	0.60	0.40	0.260	0.650
0.10	0.70	0.60	0.393	0.655
0.00	0.80	0.80	0.524	0.655

first interval goes from $t_4 = 0.30$ sec to $t_6 = 0.50$ sec, the second from $t_3 = 0.20$ sec to $t_7 = 0.60$ sec, etc. The duration Δt is given in the third column, and the corresponding magnitude of the displacement Δs is recorded in the fourth. In the fifth column of the table, which records the average speed as calculated by

Eq. (3.2-1) or (3.4-1), we have retained one more than the number of significant figures in our time measurement. We now drop the third decimal place to find that the average speed to two significant figures over each of the intervals is 0.65 m/sec. This suggests that even were we to take our measurements from $t = 0.3999$ sec to $t = 0.4001$ sec, using instruments of sufficient precision, of course, we should still get an average speed of 0.65 m/sec over the interval. Or, if we plot $\bar{v} = \Delta s/\Delta t$ as ordinates against Δt as abscissas, as in Fig. 3.4, the curve we obtain is a horizontal line which is shown solid in the figure. We can then *extrapolate* to $\Delta t = 0$ sec and read from the graph the speed that the cart had at $t = 0.40$ sec. This extrapolation is shown in the figure by the dashed curve.

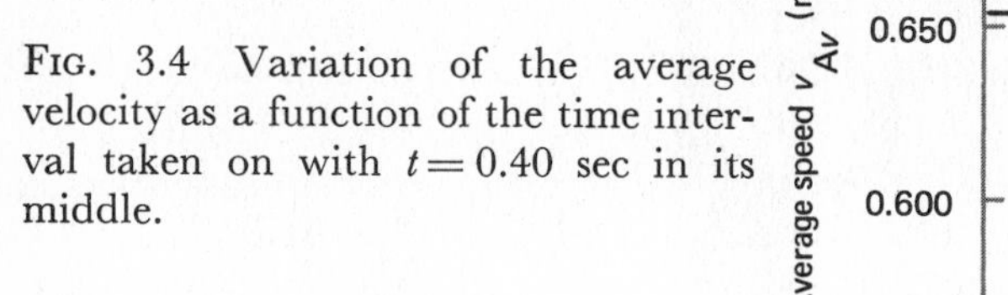

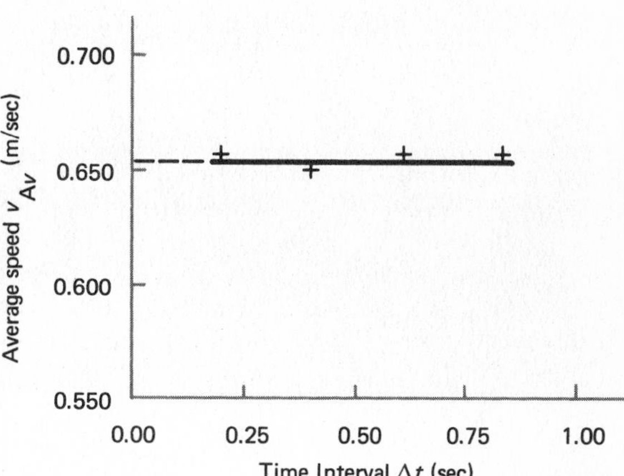

FIG. 3.4 Variation of the average velocity as a function of the time interval taken on with $t = 0.40$ sec in its middle.

What we have done above is to study the trend of $\bar{v} = \Delta s/\Delta t$ as $\Delta t \to 0$ (delta t approaches zero). We assume that the trend is smooth or regular and that it does not make any abrupt changes as the time interval becomes smaller and smaller. The whole procedure may be summarized by an equation that defines operationally what we mean by instantaneous speed:

$$v = \lim_{\Delta t \to 0} \frac{\Delta s}{\Delta t}. \tag{3.4-2}$$

An alternative way of writing Eq. (3.4-2) is

$$v = \frac{ds}{dt}, \tag{3.4-2A}$$

where the dt and the ds* remind us that we take shorter and shorter Δt and their corresponding shorter and shorter Δs, always studying the trend of the ratio $\Delta s/\Delta t$ as $\Delta t \to 0$. The right sides of Eqs. (3.4-2A) and (3.4-2) are entirely equivalent to each other. Note that the bar over v has been dropped in Eqs. (3.4-2) and (3.4-2A) because in vanishingly small intervals the average speed is indistinguishable from the instantaneous speed.

* The reader is cautioned again that dt (read "dee tee") is *not* d times t but rather indicates an operation which is to be carried out on the time measurements.

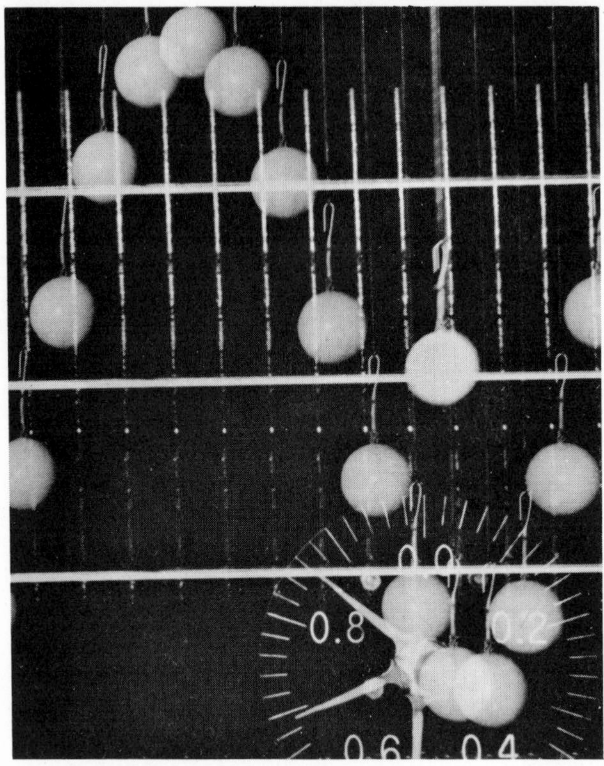

FIG. 3.5 Stroboscopic photo of an oscillating mass.

We have not yet mentioned that the instant t at which v is to be determined should *always* be in a constant relation, relative to the ends of the intervals, within the time intervals Δt as the limit process $\Delta t \rightarrow 0$ is being carried out. Thus, for Table 3.2, t was always at the center of the interval. The intervals could just as well have been chosen so that t was always at the low end of the interval or always at the high end. We shall illustrate this point as we discuss instantaneous speed in simple harmonic motion.

3.5 Instantaneous Speed in SHM

The stroboscopic photograph in Fig. 3.5 shows several positions of a heavy ball suspended by a spring (cf. Sec. 2.19). In order to provide a time axis for the photograph, the camera was moved at constant velocity in a horizontal direction while the ball oscillated along a vertical line. The graph in Fig. 3.6 shows the displacement, as measured on the photograph, plotted against time (analogous to Fig. 3.3). The amplitude is 17.2 cm and the period is 2.24 sec. The flash period was 0.170 sec. Let us determine v at $t = 2.00$ sec.* By way of illustration of the point made at the end of the preceding section we shall apply our operational definition three ways: with $t = 2.00$ sec always at the beginning of the time interval, with $t = 2.00$ sec always at the end of the time interval, and with $t = 2.00$ sec always at the middle of the time interval.

* This particular choice of instant will also exemplify the use of negative displacements and negative velocities.

Table 3.3 shows the data and the various calculated average speeds. The displacements at the various times have been read from the original plot of Fig. 3.6. Note that the rows of the table are divided into three groups; those

Table 3.3 *Determination of Speed at $T = 2.00$ sec in the Simple Harmonic Motion of Fig. 3.6*

	Time Interval Δt (sec)			Displacement Δs (m)	Average Speed $\bar{v}$ During Interval (m/sec)
	From	To	Duration		
E	1.70	2.00	0.30	$0.125 - 0.172 = -0.047$	-0.157
	1.80	2.00	0.20	$0.125 - 0.167 = -0.042$	-0.210
	1.90	2.00	0.10	$0.125 - 0.150 = -0.025$	-0.250
M	1.70	2.30	0.60	$-0.019 - 0.172 = -0.191$	-0.318
	1.80	2.20	0.40	$0.043 - 0.167 = -0.124$	-0.310
	1.90	2.10	0.20	$0.090 - 0.150 = -0.060$	-0.300
B	2.00	2.30	0.30	$-0.019 - 0.125 = -0.144$	-0.480
	2.00	2.20	0.20	$0.043 - 0.125 = -0.082$	-0.410
	2.00	2.10	0.10	$0.090 - 0.125 = -0.035$	-0.350

rows bracketed by "E" have the instant $t = 2.00$ sec at the end of the time interval, and those bracketed by "M" and "B" have $t = 2.00$ sec at the middle and at the beginning of the interval, respectively.

The instantaneous speeds to be derived from Table 3.3 are obtained by the use of the graphs in Fig. 3.7. The average speeds $\bar{v} = \Delta s/\Delta t$ are plotted against the duration of the time interval Δt. The three curves E, M, and B correspond to the similarly designated sections of Table 3.3. Note that as $\Delta t \to 0$ the

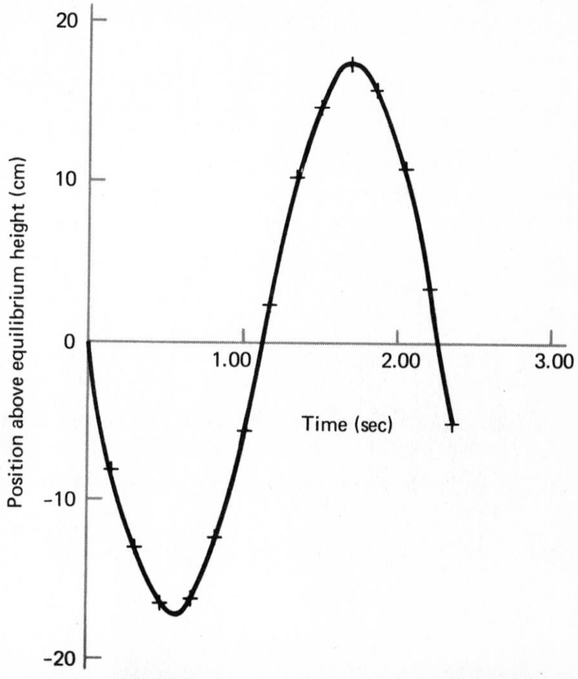

FIG. 3.6 Graph of a single complete oscillation of a mass suspended by a spring.

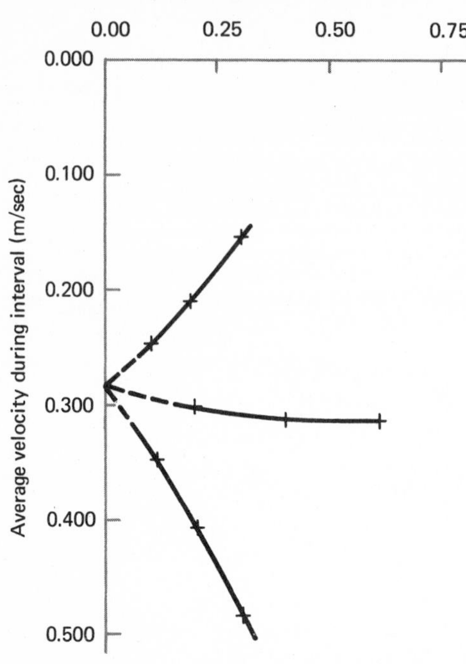

FIG. 3.7 Variation of average speed as a function of time interval, taken three different ways.

extrapolations of all three curves give the same instantaneous speed; thus,

$$v=\frac{ds}{dt}=\lim_{\Delta t\to 0}\frac{\Delta s}{\Delta t}=-0.284 \text{ m/sec}$$

at $t=2.00$ sec for the motion graphed in Fig. 3.6. It is quite generally true that the instantaneous motion at a specified instant will be independent of the particular systematic way in which the time interval closes in on that instant. However, a particular graphical treatment may be more easily carried out if the time interval is chosen in one way rather than in another.

3.6 Instantaneous Speed as a Slope

By reference to Fig. 3.8, we can take a somewhat different point of view of the operations that define what we mean by *instantaneous speed*. The figure is in two parts and shows identical sections of the displacement vs. time curve for a SHM. We can define a ***chord*** as a straight line joining any two points on a curve. In Fig. 3.8a are shown four chords, all of which terminate at a point on the curve corresponding to $t=T$. (Note that the shortest of these four chords has been extended each way beyond its end points so that it can be more easily seen.) Each of these chords can be regarded as the hypotenuse of a right triangle whose base is a time interval Δt and whose altitude is a change of displacement Δs. Thus, each chord corresponds to a particular $\Delta s/\Delta t$, and therefore each chord corresponds to the average speed over a particular time interval. As the chords become shorter—always ending at $t=T$—they correspond to shorter and shorter Δt. The *limit* of the chords as they become shorter is the ***tangent*** to the curve at $t=T$.

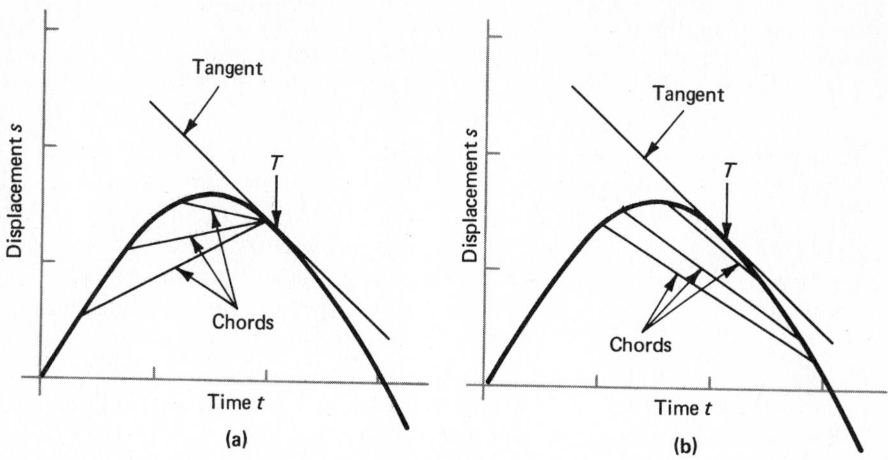

FIG. 3.8 Defining the slope of a curve at t.

The ***slope*** of each chord is defined as the ratio $\Delta s/\Delta t$ where, of course, the Δs and the Δt are defined by the end points of the chord. Hence, the slope of each chord is identical to the average speed represented by that chord. In a similar manner, we define the slope of the tangent at point $t = T$ as ds/dt. We cannot, to be sure, measure the slope of the tangent in quite the same way as we measure the slope of a chord, since we have made Δt approach zero ($\Delta t \to 0$); this is equivalent to saying that the end points of our chord have moved together. Now, as we have done for the shortest chord in Fig. 3.8a, any straight line segment may be extended indefinitely. It is only when this is done that a tangent can be seen at all. Furthermore, we may choose any two points on the tangent for measuring its slope. This is illustrated by Fig. 3.9, where $\Delta s_1/\Delta t_1 = \Delta s_2/\Delta t_2$.

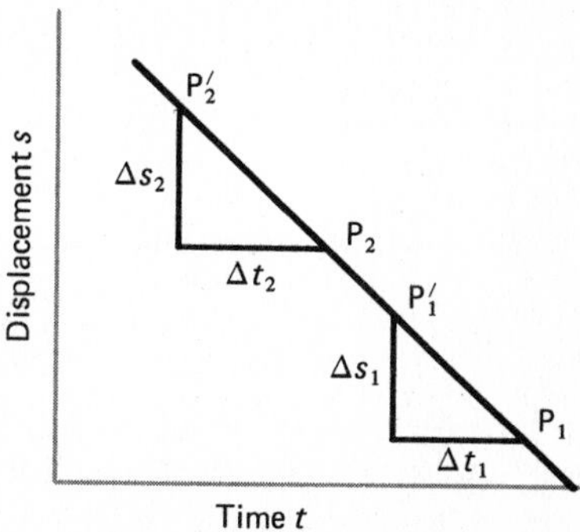

FIG. 3.9 The slope of a straight line may be measured by using arbitrarily chosen points.

The slope of the tangent to a curve at a point such as $t = T$ is said to be the *slope of the curve* at that point. We have defined instantaneous speed as ds/dt. Therefore, the instantaneous speed of a body at a given instant is the slope of its s vs. t curve at the point corresponding to that instant.

Let us note two other things in passing. Figure 3.8b shows that the chords may be drawn so that $t = T$ is always at the midpoint of the time interval Δt. This is consistent with our use of Table 3.3 and Fig. 3.7. Moreover, we can now reinterpret Figs. 3.4 and 3.7 as graphs of the slopes of chords plotted against the durations of the interval; the intercept of graph with the $\Delta s/\Delta t$ axis is then the slope of the tangent which is the limit of the slopes of the set of chords.

Now consider the two graphs that relate displacement to time, Figs. 3.3 and 3.6. Each of these graphs plots s against t, and for each we have shown how to find the instantaneous speed at a specific time. In Fig. 3.3 (Sec. 3.4) we found that the instantaneous speed at $t = 0.40$ sec is

$$\frac{ds}{dt} = \lim_{\Delta t \to 0} \frac{\Delta s}{\Delta t} = v = 0.65 \text{ m/sec.} \tag{3.6-1}$$

The point which we are presently making is that Eq. (3.6-1) expresses the slope of the s vs. t curve for $t = 0.40$ sec. This idea that the slope of an s vs. t curve at a particular time t is identical to the instantaneous speed at that time is extremely useful for drawing qualitative conclusions about the nature of the motion. Thus, in Fig. 3.3 the slope of the graph is nearly the same throughout the length of the curve. Therefore one can readily conclude that the instantaneous speed of the car does not change very much during the 0.90 sec for which the data are plotted.

Similarly in Fig. 3.6, using the fact that the slope of the curve at a point corresponding to a particular time t is identical to the instantaneous speed at that time, we can make some general statements about the nature of the motion. For example, for $t = 1.20$ sec the slope of the curve is zero (the tangent is horizontal) *even though the displacement is a maximum*! Therefore, at that instant the instantaneous speed is zero. This does not mean, of course, that the speed is not changing. Also, we can note that the instantaneous speed is positive at $t = 0.60$ sec and that it is negative at $t = 1.80$ sec, since for the latter Δs represents a decrease in s while Δt is an increase in t; therefore, $\Delta s/\Delta t$ is negative at $t = 1.80$ sec. Furthermore, we can assert that the instantaneous speeds are the greatest (disregarding sign) at $t = 0.60$ sec and at $t = 1.80$ sec, since at these times the slopes are the greatest. Thus, we can observe that for SHM the speeds are zero instantaneously when the displacements are maximum and the speeds are maximum when the displacements are zero.

EXERCISES

3.6-1 The graph shows the displacement as a function of time of a heavy ball suspended by a spring. The displacement is zero at $t = 0$ and moves positively to a maximum of 0.10 m at $t = 0.40$ sec, etc. (a) During what time intervals is the velocity positive? Negative? (b) When is the velocity zero? What displacements correspond to zero speeds? (c) When does the velocity have the greatest value? Qualitatively,* how does the speed at $t = 0.20$ sec compare with the speeds at $t = 0.00$ sec and $t = 0.40$ sec? Is the speed at $t = 0.20$ sec more nearly equal to that at $t = 0.0$ sec or that at $t = 0.40$ sec?

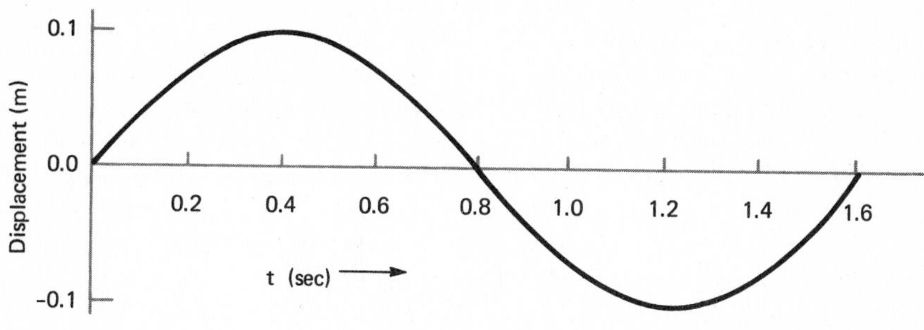

Exercise 3.6-1

3.6-2 On a piece of graph paper lay off a time axis similar to that in the figure of Ex. 3.6-1 and label the vertical axis "velocity" so that positive velocities can be plotted above the time axis and negative velocities below. Now qualitatively plot the velocities you thought about in Ex. 3.6-1. Extend your velocity-time plot by suitable points to $t = 1.60$ sec.

3.7 *Motions at Constant Velocity—The Speed of Photons*

We discussed at some length the way to determine the instantaneous velocity of a body whose velocity is varying before discussing the simpler case of a body whose velocity is constant. For bodies moving with such a ***constant velocity***, the average velocity $\bar{v}$ determined from Eq. (3.2-3) or Eq. (3.4-2) for any time interval is always the same and is equal to the velocity at any instant during these time intervals. Any driver knows that it is very difficult to maintain a constant speed in a car and that it is almost impossible to do so unless the highway is straight and smooth and level. Most moving objects in nature are subject to disturbances which change their velocities, and we seldom have the opportunity of observing such a body in uniform motion in a straight line. What we frequently do observe to move with constant velocities, however, are certain disturbances or signals, which bring to us impressions from the outside world. Chief among these are light and radio signals. We shall see later that light signals may be described in terms of the motion of particles that we call ***photons***, which are given off by the source and which travel through intervening space to the observer. It is found that these photons always travel with a constant speed in a vacuum, and with very nearly the same constant speed in air.

* By *qualitatively* we suggest that you simply sketch or imagine the tangents to the displacement-time curve at the various instants. You can then say which velocities are greatest, zero, negative, nearly equal, etc.

The speed of a light signal is so great that early attempts to measure it were doomed to failure. If we attempt to measure the speed of light by a method in which we send out a signal and time its passage between two points with an ordinary clock, we find that the time taken for the travel over any reasonable distance is zero within the accuracy of the measurement. This fact indicates to us that the speed of light signals is extremely high compared with the speeds we are accustomed to measure for material objects.

The method used to measure the speed of high-speed particles such as photons is very simple and is one that can be applied to the measurement of the speed of anything that moves in a straight line at a constant speed. A gate G_1 (Fig. 3.10a) is open for a very short time and, during this time, one or more particles, all traveling at the same speed c, pass through it. These particles will reach G_2, the second gate of the figure, at a time t later than the opening of the first gate. This time is calculated from Eq. (3.2-3) to be $t = d/c$, if d is the distance between the two gates. If the second gate is opened at exactly this time later than the opening of the first gate, the particles passed by the first gate G_1 will also pass the second gate (Fig. 3.10c). Otherwise they will not (Fig. 3.10b, d).* When we are dealing with particles such as the photons of light or with sound signals, either of which can be reflected by a mirror, we can simplify the situation and use only one gate. The particles which leave the gate G when it is open (Fig. 3.11a) travel a distance $d/2$ and are reflected by the mirror M (Fig. 3.11b). They reach the gate G again at a time $t = d/c$ after the first opening and, if G is open at this time, the particles will pass through (Fig. 3.11c). If not, they will be stopped.

* This is the principle on which "progressive" traffic lights are timed.

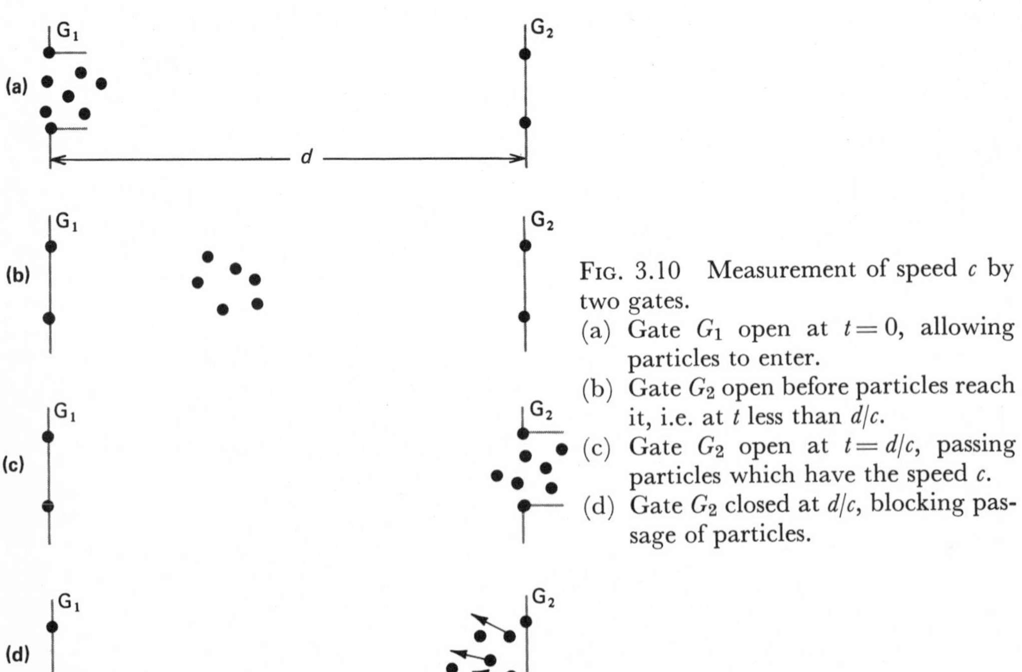

FIG. 3.10 Measurement of speed c by two gates.
(a) Gate G_1 open at $t = 0$, allowing particles to enter.
(b) Gate G_2 open before particles reach it, i.e. at t less than d/c.
(c) Gate G_2 open at $t = d/c$, passing particles which have the speed c.
(d) Gate G_2 closed at d/c, blocking passage of particles.

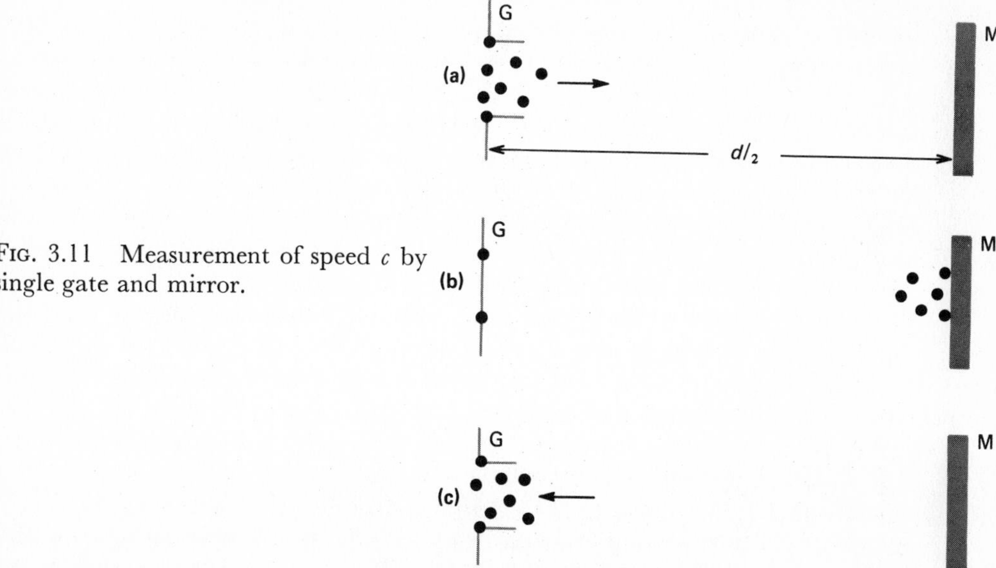

FIG. 3.11 Measurement of speed c by single gate and mirror.

The French physicist Armand Fizeau (1819–1896) in 1848 realized that anything like an ordinary gate could not be moved fast enough and be timed accurately enough to measure the speed of photons. He therefore simplified the problem by substituting a rotating toothed wheel both for the gate and for the clock needed to time the interval between its two openings. His apparatus is shown schematically in Fig. 3.12. Light from the source S passes through a lens L_1* and falls on a plate of glass, P. This glass reflects some of the light and sends it through a space in the slotted wheel W, which is revolving rapidly.

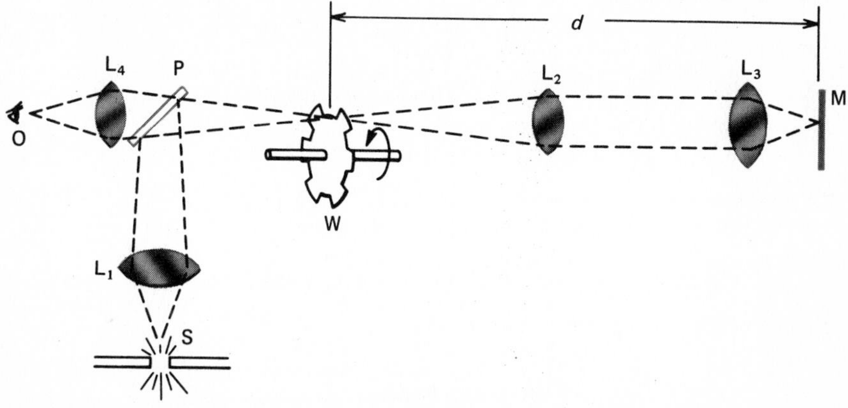

FIG. 3.12 Fizeau's method for the speed of light.

* The lenses used here converge light. For a description and explanation of their action see Chapter 13.

This wheel thus takes the place of the gate G which we have discussed. The light then passes through two more lenses, L_2 and L_3, the first of which serves to keep the beam of light from spreading out too much and the second of which converges the light onto a mirror M. This mirror reflects the beam, which returns through L_3 and L_2. If the wheel happens to be in a position such that a slot is exposed to the light when it returns, the beam will pass through the slot to fall once more on P. Part of it is again reflected toward the source, while the rest is transmitted through the glass. The latter part of the light then falls on the lens L_4, which converges it so that it may be seen by an observer at O. Now, if the wheel is stationary or is rotating very slowly, the light can travel the distance d to the mirror and back and still return through the same slot through which it first passed. If the wheel is speeded up, light passing through a slot will return in time to meet the solid tooth which has rotated into the position previously occupied by a slot. Still more rapid rotation will result in the succeeding slot coming into position just in time to receive the returning light beam. Hence, if the experimenter at O watches as the rotational speed of the wheel is increased, he will observe first light, then darkness, then light again, etc. If the wheel contains N equally spaced slots and is rotating with a frequency ν (revolutions per unit time), the round trip time for light which leaves through one slot and returns through the next must be $1/\nu N$. Consequently, the speed of light is given as $c = d\nu N$.

In Fizeau's original experiments he used a distance of over 6,000 m between the lenses L_2 and L_3. Jean Foucault (1819–1868) later improved the method by replacing the toothed wheel with a rapidly rotating set of mirrors, and so made it possible to use shorter distances. Albert Abraham Michelson (1852–1931), in turn, refined Foucault's method and spent much of his life on a series of determinations of the speed of light. Since the speed of light is affected by the medium through which it travels, his final determinations were made in a vacuum. As a result of this work we know that the ***speed of light*** in a vacuum is

$$c = 2.998 \times 10^8 \text{ m/sec} \tag{3.7-1}$$

The speed of light in air is so little different from this that we usually need to make no correction for the fact that we work in an atmosphere. For many purposes we can round off the speed to the convenient value of 3.00×10^8 m/sec.

While the quantity given by Eq. (3.7-1) is known, for historical reasons, as the speed of light, it is the speed of all photons traveling in a vacuum. Actually all electromagnetic radiations, such as those sent out by radio, may also be described as photons, and it has been found that all of these radiations travel with the speed given by Eq. (3.7-1).

EXERCISES

3.7-1 Table 3.4 shows the history of an automobile that starts from rest at $t = 0.00$ sec and that then accelerates until it reaches a steady speed of 5.82 m/sec. Make a table similar to Table 3.2 and use a plot similar to that of Fig. 3.7 to determine the speed of the car at $t = 2.00$ sec, taking all intervals on the positive side of this time.

Table 3.4 *Motion of an Automobile Starting from Rest*

Time t (sec)	Displacement s (m)	Average Velocity in Each Interval of One Second (m/sec)
0.00	0.00	
		1.40
1.00	1.40	
		3.65
2.00	5.05	
		4.91
3.00	9.96	
		5.46
4.00	15.42	
		5.69
5.00	21.11	
		5.77
6.00	26.88	
		5.80
7.00	32.68	
		5.81
8.00	38.49	
		5.82
9.00	44.31	
		5.82
10.00	50.13	

3.7-2 Verify the result of Ex. 3.7-1 by taking intervals which have $t = 2.00$ sec as midpoint.

3.7-3 Verify the statement made in Ex. 3.7-1 that the speed of the car of Table 3.4 at $t = 0$ is zero. How closely can you be sure of this verification?

3.7-4 Make a table similar to Table 3.2 and use a curve similar to Fig. 3.7 to determine the speed of the car of Table 3.4 at $t = 6.00$ sec, taking all intervals on the negative side of this time.

3.7-5 How far from its rest position will the automobile of Table 3.4 have moved in the first 3.50 sec? How far will it have moved in the first 9.50 sec? Comment on the relative accuracy which you can ascribe to each of your answers.

3.7-6 Suppose that the distant mirror in Fig. 3.12 is 5000 m from the toothed wheel, which has 48 equally spaced teeth on it. What is the lowest frequency of rotation which will allow no light to return? What will be the lowest frequency above this which will allow light to return?

3.7-7 In the use of radar for navigation, a short signal of electromagnetic waves is sent out from the ship or airplane, and the time taken for it to travel to and return from a distant obstacle, which reflects it, is measured. If an airplane in flight sends such a signal directly downward and the reflection returns 1.95×10^{-5} sec later, what is the height of the plane?

3.7-8 We shall see later that sound travels in air at a speed of about 340 m/sec. Two men are listening to the same radio program, which is broadcast from New York. One is in the studio at a distance of 16.0 m from the speaker. The other is in San Francisco, seated 1.00 m from his radio. The distance from the speaker to the microphone is 0.50 m. Which of the two listeners will hear the speaker first, and how much sooner will he hear each word? The distance from New York to San Francisco is 4220 km.

3.8 Acceleration

Because the motions of most material bodies take place with variable velocities, it is important to have a means of discussing the rate at which these velocities are changing. It is clear that, if the velocity of a particle along a straight line changes from v to $v + \Delta v$ in a time Δt, then the average rate of change of velocity, i.e., the ***average acceleration***, during this time interval will be given by

$$\bar{a} = \Delta v/\Delta t. \tag{3.8-1}$$

Equation (3.8-1) will serve to find the average acceleration for any time interval if the velocities at the beginning and at the end of the interval are known.

For example, in Sec. 3.4 we found that the cart in Fig. 3.2 had an average speed of 0.70 m/sec between $t = 0.00$ sec and $t = 0.10$ sec. Also, between $t = 0.70$ sec and $t = 0.80$ sec the average speed was found to be 0.61 m/sec. Thus, in *about* 0.70 sec the speed had decreased 0.09 m/sec. The average acceleration is therefore

$$\bar{a} = \frac{\Delta v}{\Delta t} = \frac{0.61 \text{ m/sec} - 0.70 \text{ m/sec}}{0.70 \text{ sec}} = \frac{-0.09}{0.70} \frac{\text{m/sec}}{\text{sec}} = -0.13 \text{ m/sec}^2.$$

Actually, the example just considered is a little forced, since we have used average speeds instead of instantaneous ones. Undoubtedly, the instantaneous speed was 0.70 m/sec sometime during the first 0.10 sec, and also v must have been 0.61 m/sec sometime between $t = 0.70$ sec and $t = 0.80$ sec. But we are not able to say, on the basis of the data at hand, whether these two instantaneous velocities occurred exactly 0.70 sec apart.

Using Fig. 3.6 and the appropriate slopes, we can find an example of a positive average acceleration. At $t = 0.58$ sec the tangent to the curve has zero slope, so the instantaneous speed is zero. At $t = 1.14$ sec the slope of the curve indicates that the displacement changes from -0.010 m to $+0.010$ m or $\Delta s = 0.020$ m during a time interval that lasted from $t = 1.10$ sec to $t = 1.18$ sec or $\Delta t = 0.08$ sec. Thus, within the limits of our measurements, the instantaneous speed at $t = 1.14$ sec is $v = 0.25$ m/sec. Now we can employ Eq. (3.8-1) to find the average acceleration between $t_1 = 0.58$ sec and $t_2 = 1.14$ sec. We get

$$\bar{a} = \frac{v_2 - v_1}{t_2 - t_1} = \frac{0.25 \text{ m/sec} - 0.00 \text{ m/sec}}{1.14 \text{ sec} - 0.58 \text{ sec}},$$
$$= 0.45 \text{ m/sec}^2.$$

If we wish to determine the acceleration at any instant t, we proceed, as we did in the case of velocity, by taking a succession of time intervals Δt which include the instant t. The ***acceleration*** is then defined by the limit

$$a = \lim_{\Delta t \to 0} (\Delta v/\Delta t) = dv/dt, \tag{3.8-2}$$

where Δv is the change in velocity during the time interval Δt and dv/dt, by definition, indicates that the limiting process has been carried out [cf. Sec. 3.4, Eqs. (3.4-2) and (3.4-2A)].

The dimensions of acceleration may be obtained from Eq. (3.8-1) or (3.8-2):

$$[a] = [v/t] = [\ell/t^2] = [\ell t^{-2}]. \tag{3.8-3}$$

In the system of units commonly used in this text, the unit of acceleration is the meter per second squared (m/sec^2). Other units, such as ft/sec^2, cm/hr^2, or even mi/hr^2, may be encountered, but all will be characterized by a length in the numerator and the product of two time intervals in the denominator, as indicated by the dimensional equation, Eq. (3.8-3).

Since Eq. (3.8-2) is so similar to the defining equation for velocity, Eq. (3.6-1), accelerations may be determined from known changing velocities. However, we shall be mainly interested in motions in which the accelerations are constant, in which there is no necessity for the determination of a limiting value. For ***constant accelerations***, it is clear that the instantaneous and average values of the acceleration are the same, so Eqs. (3.8-1) and (3.8-2) become equivalent and may be replaced by

$$a = \Delta v/\Delta t. \qquad (3.8\text{-}4)$$

We must remember that accelerations given by Eqs. (3.8-1), (3.8-2), and (3.8-4) can be either positive or negative and that the sign of the acceleration depends only on the sign of the change in v, i.e., on the sign of Δv. Thus if a body is moving with a positive velocity and the speed is increasing, the acceleration is positive, but the acceleration is negative if the speed is decreasing. For a body moving with a negative velocity, an increase in speed corresponds to a negative acceleration, and a decrease in speed to a positive acceleration.

Everything that we have said in this section is rigorously true for the change of speed of a body as it moves along a straight line. But speeds in a straight line path define velocities—that is, both magnitudes and directions are specified—and these are vector quantities.* Equation (3.8-2) employs Δv, which is the difference between two vectors, so the acceleration a must itself be a vector quantity that requires both magnitude and direction for its complete expression. In this section the direction of a is sufficiently expressed by the fact that all motion occurs along the straight line. We shall see later, however, that in less simple motions we will need in general to express direction as well as magnitude. The reason for mentioning this point here is that unlike the situation with *speed* and *distance*, which express magnitude without regard for direction, there is no term for acceleration that considers magnitude without direction.

EXERCISES

3.8-1 From the data of Table 3.4, determine the average acceleration of the automobile during the first 9.0 sec of its travel.

3.8-2 From the calculations of Exs. 3.7-1 and 3.7-2, determine the average acceleration of the automobile between $t = 4.00$ sec and $t = 6.00$ sec.

3.8-3 Using the results of Ex. 3.7-1 or 3.7-2, determine the average acceleration of the automobile (a) during the second second of its travel, and (b) during the first two seconds of its travel.

3.8-4 A car traveling 50 mi/hr is to be stopped in 5.0 sec. What will be the average acceleration during the braking? (Call the direction of motion positive, and express your result in units of ft/sec^2.)

* The meaning of the term "vector" will be discussed in Chapter 5.

3.9 Motions of Constant Acceleration—Free Fall

The motions of bodies which fall freely to the surface of the earth were the subject of considerable speculation by the ancient and medieval philosophers. The riddle was first solved by Galileo Galilei, who showed that all *freely falling* bodies move with a uniformly accelerated motion. We shall now recapitulate the experiments and arguments by which he arrived at this conclusion.

We recognize first, as did Galileo, that the presence of our atmosphere prevents true "free fall," since air offers some resistance to motion through it. This fact is illustrated by Fig. 3.13, which shows the stroboscopic technique adapted to the study of falling bodies. When the photographs were made, the white horizontal lines were 0.100 m apart and the period of the flashes was 0.0714 ± 0.0026 sec, as may be seen from the successive positions of the hand on the one rev/sec clock. Figures 3.13a and 3.13b show the distance fallen from rest as related to time for a steel ball and a ping-pong ball, respectively.

Notice that the steel ball and the ping-pong ball fall through nearly equal distances during the first three intervals but that the ping-pong ball falls through distances that are less than those covered by the steel ball during later intervals. Not only does air friction affect the fall of the lighter ball, but the effect of air friction seems to become greater as the speed increases.

If we wish to experiment on freely falling bodies, therefore, we must either perform the experiments in a vacuum or confine our studies to heavy bodies where the effects of air resistance are less noticeable. In practice, both of these expedients are used. Heavy bodies, such as stones or metal balls, are dropped through large distances to study their motion. The motion of a light body, such as a feather or pith ball, is compared with that of a heavy body by dropping the two simultaneously in a vacuum through shorter distances. Under these circumstances, it can be found that all *freely falling bodies that start from rest* fall through equal distances in equal times.

Once all bodies falling freely from rest have been shown to have the same motion, it will be sufficient to study the fall of one of them in detail. With this in mind we shall carefully analyze the free fall of the steel ball as recorded by the stroboscopic photograph in Fig. 3.13a. Table 3.5 in its first column presents the time as read from the multiply exposed clock face. Column 2 gives the distance fallen, or the displacement downward from the rest position at the instant of each flash. These data suffice, as before, for us to calculate the average speed, or velocity downward, during each time interval except the first; the results are tabulated in column 3. The first interval is an exception because the release of the ball was not synchronized with the flashes. The fall may have started nearly simultaneously with a flash, about half-way between two flashes, or at any other time. For each time interval, we may subtract the average speed in that interval from that of the following time interval, to obtain the values in column 4; these are the changes in average speed from one time interval to the next. The entries in column 4 show no progressive change. On the other hand, the values are *not* constant, or nearly so, despite the fact that the time intervals between flashes are very nearly constant. The spread of the values in column 4

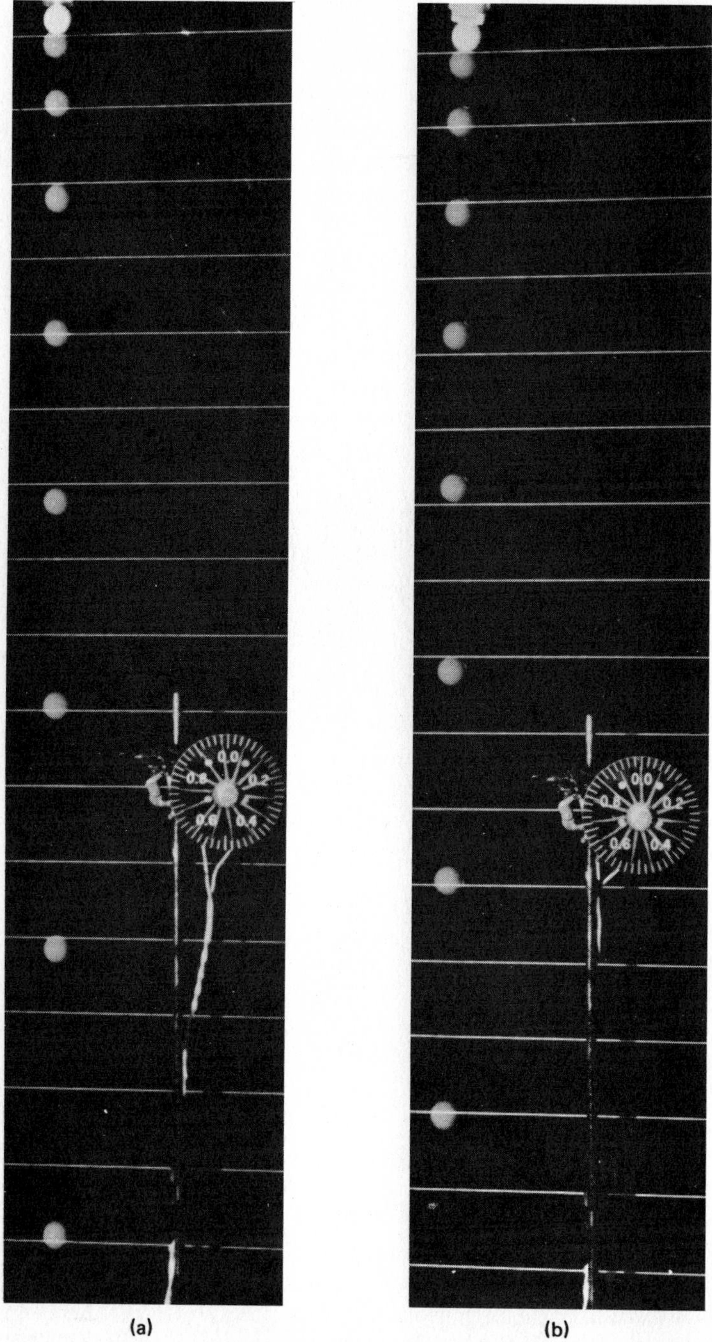

FIG. 3.13 Stroboscopic photo of falling balls. (a) Steel ball, (b) ping-pong ball.

Table 3.5 *Motion of a Falling Steel Ball*

Time (sec)	Distance (m)	Average Speed (m/sec)	Change of Average Speed (m/sec)
—	0.000		
		—	
0.071	0.027		—
		1.22	
0.143	0.115		0.58
		1.80	
0.214	0.243		0.67
		2.47	
0.286	0.421		0.63
		3.10	
0.358	0.644		0.69
		3.79	
0.429	0.913		0.77
		4.56	
0.500	1.237		0.75
		5.31	
0.572	1.619		

is fairly large, ranging from 0.58 to 0.77 m/sec, and their average is 0.68 m/sec. This is not surprising, since the reading of each displacement from the photograph may be in error by as much as 0.5 cm. Hence the velocities in column 3 are uncertain by about $(\pm 0.7 \text{ cm})/(0.0714 \text{ sec})$ or by 0.10 m/sec (see Appendix B.2). Hence the changes of velocity in column 4 may be uncertain by as much as 0.14 m/sec. All of the values in column 4 agree with the mean within this uncertainty. Let us *assume* that better measurements would show the values in column 4 to be more nearly constant and that this constant value would be close to the average of the values in column 4. This is done as a kind of guess to see whether in this way we can get a result which will stand further tests.

Thus, we note that *on the average* the change of average speed from one interval to the next was 0.68 m/sec. Also, *on the average*, the time from an instant in one interval to the corresponding instant in the next interval was 0.0714 sec. Thus, the rate of change of speed is 0.68 m/sec every 0.0714 sec. There are 14 of these time intervals in one second—i.e., $1/0.0714 = 14$. Thus, there should be 14 times as much change of speed in one second or 14×0.68 m/sec $= 9.5$ m/sec. Since this is a rate of change of speed, or an acceleration, we express it in terms of the units introduced in the preceding section; thus, the acceleration of this falling body is

$$g \approx 9.5 \text{ m/sec}^2,$$

where g is a special symbol used to represent the ***acceleration due to gravity.***

EXERCISES

3.9-1 Using the graphical method of Fig. 3.7, find the instantaneous speed of the falling steel ball of Fig. 3.13a when it has fallen through a distance of 0.243 m. Use the data of Table 3.1.

3.9-2 The following displacements of the ping-pong ball at the positions shown in Fig. 3.13b have been obtained by measurement of the photograph: 0.000 m, 0.027 m, 0.114 m, 0.231 m, 0.396 m, 0.596 m, 0.836 m, 1.109 m, 1.422 m, all ± 0.005 m. Construct a table similar to Table 3.5 for the falling ping-pong ball. What is the average acceleration? Is this acceleration constant within the accuracy of the observations?

3.9-3 A car is coasting along a straight level road. At some instant, which is taken as $t = 0.00$ sec, the front of the car passes a marked point. The position of the car is observed at regular intervals thereafter and the distances through which it has moved from the original marked point are given below.

Time (sec)	2.0	4.0	6.0	8.0	10.0	12.0
Displacement (ft)	80	146	199	242	278	308

Find the average acceleration during each interval of two seconds. Also find the speed of the car at $t = 0$.

3.10 An Alternative Treatment of Falling Body Data

If we examine the data of columns 1 and 2 in Table 3.5, we see that in the first two time intervals the steel ball fell about four times as far as it fell in the first time interval. Also, in the first three time intervals, the ball fell about nine times as far as in the first time interval. These observations are summarized in Table 3.6, which relates total time to total distance. We note that the multipliers

Table 3.6 *Distance Fallen Related to Time of Falling*

Time Interval	Lapsed Time (sec)	Total Distance (m)
1st time interval	$1 \times 0.071 = 0.071$	$1 \times 0.027 = 0.027$
1st two time intervals	$2 \times 0.071 \approx 0.143$	$4 \times 0.027 = 0.108 \approx 0.115$
1st three time intervals	$3 \times 0.071 \approx 0.214$	$9 \times 0.027 = 0.243$

1, 4, and 9 in the third column are the squares of the corresponding multipliers 1, 2, and 3 in the second column. We may then guess that the accumulated distance fallen is proportional to the square of the lapsed time since the fall began; thus, we may write

$$s = Kt^2, \tag{3.10-1}$$

where s is the distance through which the body has fallen in a time t, both being measured from rest position, and K is a constant. To test whether Eq. (3.10-1) is a good or a bad guess, we may try a graphical check.

When it is suspected that two variables are related by a simple mathematical equation, one can often plot the observed values of one as a function of the observed values of the other and then see how closely a calculated curve based on the equation can be made to pass through or near all of the plotted points. This can be done most easily if the predicted relationship is linear, i.e., if the expected curve is a straight line. The relation between s and t in Eq. (3.10-1) is parabolic, but we can arrive at a linear relation if we take the square root of each side:

$$s^{1/2} = K^{1/2}t. \tag{3.10-1A}$$

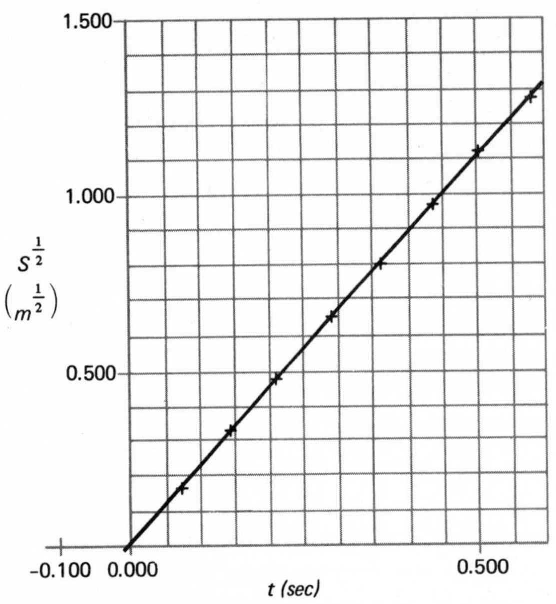

FIG. 3.14 Displacement vs. time curve for the falling steel ball.

Figure 3.14 shows the points representing pairs of the variables $s^{1/2}$ and t as shown in Table 3.7, which is based on Table 3.5. The straight line in the figure clearly

Table 3.7 *Experimental Test of Eq. (3.10-1)*

t (sec)	s (m) Observed	$s^{1/2}$ ($m^{1/2}$) Observed	s (m) Calculated
0.000	—	—	0.00030
0.071	0.027	0.164	0.030
0.143	0.115	0.339	0.110
0.214	0.243	0.493	0.238
0.286	0.421	0.649	0.417
0.358	0.644	0.802	0.644
0.429	0.913	0.956	0.922
0.500	1.237	1.111	1.245
0.572	1.619	1.273	1.624

misses none of the plotted points by appreciably more than the estimated uncertainty determined by the accuracy with which the position of the ball was found. Having found this line, we can establish two things:

1. Equation (3.10-1A), and therefore Eq. (3.10-1), represents the fall of the ball *if* the ball started falling before the time chosen as zero. In other words, we have established the time at which the ball was released—something that we could not do by our earlier analysis. This conclusion is certainly consistent with the photograph, on which the first image of the falling ball would very nearly coincide with the white image of the stationary ball.
2. The value of K in Eq. (3.10-1) is the square of the slope of the line, so that

$$K = \left[\frac{1.273 \text{ m}^{1/2}}{(0.527 + 0.008) \text{ sec}}\right]^2 = 4.82 \text{ m/sec}^2.$$

The last column of Table 3.7 shows the values of s calculated from Eq. (3.10-1) using $K = 4.82$ m/sec^2 and the time of fall as $t + 0.008$ sec. No calculated position departs from the observed position by as much as 1.0 cm; the average departure for the eight positions is 0.5 cm—the estimated uncertainty with which the positions were determined.

In the preceding section, we found that the acceleration experienced by the steel ball (g) was about 9.5 m/sec^2. This suggests that $K = \frac{1}{2}g$, so that Eq. (3.10-1) might be rewritten as

$$s = \tfrac{1}{2}gt^2. \tag{3.10-1B}$$

We shall arrive at this same conclusion later by a different reasoning process.

It appears that our value of $2K = 9.64$ m/sec^2 for g is better than the earlier value of 9.5 m/sec^2. Can we accept it as correct? In the long run, the accepted value of the factor or constant in question—in this case the acceleration experienced by a body in free fall—will depend on many more measurements than we can study here. Repeated measurements with the same apparatus, measurements with improved apparatus, and measurements by additional competent experimenters are all used in order to reduce the arbitrariness and to increase the confidence in the accepted value of the constant in question. A repetition of many experiments analogous to that of Fig. 3.13a indicates that, while g is constant for all bodies at a given spot on the earth's surface, it is found to vary slightly as we move over the earth, being greater near the poles than it is near the equator, and greater at sea level than on mountain tops. The reasons for these variations will be discussed in Chapter 14.

Since the value of g enters into many engineering calculations (Sec. 4.12 and Appendix D), a "standard" value of $g = 9.80665$ m/sec^2 has been agreed on for such purposes. In this text we shall, unless otherwise stated, make use of the simpler figure $g = 9.80$ m/sec^2 as more appropriate for use in the continental United States, where g at sea level varies from 9.78 m/sec^2 in Florida to 9.81 m/sec^2 in the Northern States and in Southern Canada.

3.11 Three Graphs for the Same Motion

Our analysis of Fig. 3.13 and the data of Table 3.5, for a body falling freely from rest, has indicated

(a) that the acceleration is constant in time,
(b) that the speed increases in direct proportion to time, and
(c) that the distance fallen is proportional to the square of the time required for that fall.

Let us now examine the curves of Fig. 3.15. Figure 3.15a shows an acceleration of 10 m/sec^2, which is constant for the graphed interval from $t = 0.00$ to $t = 1.00$ sec. Figure 3.15b graphs a motion in which the speed is directly proportional to the time, being 5.0 m/sec when $t = 0.50$ sec and 10.0 m/sec when $t = 1.00$ sec. Figure 3.15c plots distances that are proportional to the square of the time.

These three curves, then, express properties similar to those labelled (a), (b), and (c) above, similar to those of a falling body. We may emphasize this point by applying the techniques of the preceding sections to the three curves.

We begin by recalling that we defined the instantaneous speed in a particular motion at a given time t as $v = ds/dt$. Also, we found that ds/dt represents the slope of the s vs. t curve for that motion at time t. Drawing the tangent, then, to the curve in Fig. 3.15c at $t = 0.50$ sec, we get $ds/dt = 5.0$ m/sec. Similarly, if we draw the tangents at $t = 1.00$ sec and $t = 0.00$ sec, we get slopes of 10.0 m/sec and 0.00 m/sec, respectively. In Fig. 3.15c the speeds at $t = 0.00$, $t = 0.50$,

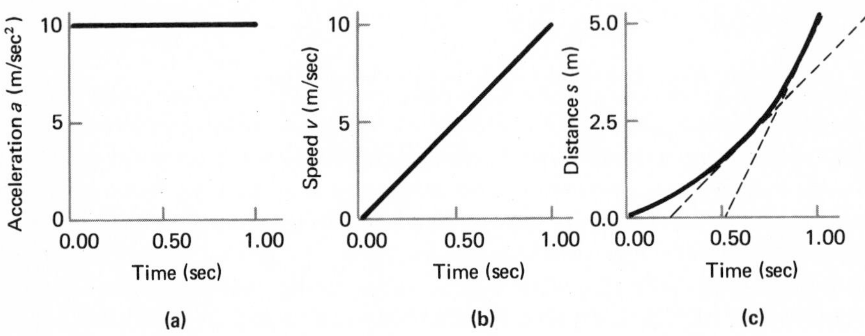

FIG. 3.15 Three representations of the same motion.

and $t = 1.00$ sec are 0.0, 5.0, and 10.0 m/sec, respectively—that is, the three speeds found by taking slopes on the s vs. t curve of Fig. 3.15c are represented by corresponding points on the v vs. t curve of Fig. 3.15b. By further analysis of Figs. 3.15b and c, we can see that the slope at any point of the latter curve is represented by a corresponding point on the former curve. Thus, Figs. 3.15b and c graph different representations of the same motion.

We have also defined acceleration as $a = dv/dt$; thus, the acceleration at a given time is the slope of the v vs. t curve corresponding to that time. In Fig. 3.15b the v vs. t curve has a constant slope of 10.0 m/sec^2. At every instant between $t = 0.00$ and $t = 1.00$ sec the motion graphed in Fig. 3.15b has an acceleration of 10.0 m/sec^2. This is shown in Fig. 3.15a. All three graphs, then, plot different aspects of the same motion.

The reader should note that Figs. 3.15a, 3.15b, and 3.15c, respectively, show $a = 10.0$ m/sec^2, $v = at = (10.0 \text{ m/sec}^2)t$, and $s = \frac{1}{2}at^2 = (5.0 \text{ m/sec}^2)t^2$. More accurately, for a body freely falling from rest, we have

$$a = g = 9.80 \text{ m/sec}^2, \tag{3.11-1A}$$

$$v = gt, \tag{3.11-1B}$$

and

$$s = \tfrac{1}{2}gt^2. \tag{3.11-1C}$$

EXERCISES

3.11-1 From Eqs. (3.2-3) and (3.11-1), show that the average velocity of a body that has fallen from rest for a time t is one-half of its final velocity.

3.11-2 A stone is dropped from a high bridge and strikes the water 4.2 sec later. What is the height of the bridge?

3.11-3 A car starts from rest into motion with a constant acceleration of 2.5 m/sec². What is its speed at the end of 10 sec? How far has it traveled from its starting point?

3.11-4 A rocket is accelerated vertically upward as it is fired. What must be the average value of its acceleration if it is to achieve a speed of 1.00×10^4 m/sec in 1.00 minute?

3.12 Algebraic Determination of Instantaneous Speed

So far our determinations of instantaneous speed at a time t' have been made graphically, or geometrically, by finding the slope of the s vs. t curve at that time t'. When the equation of the curve relating s to t is known, we can also find v by algebraic methods. Let us illustrate this by finding v at $t' = 0.50$ sec for the curve of Fig. 3.15c. The equation of the curve is $s = (5.0 \text{ m/sec}^2)t^2$. We shall evaluate the equation at t' and at $t' + \Delta t$ to find s' and $s' + \Delta s$. To simplify the equations, we can represent the quantity 5.0 m/sec² as K, (cf. Sec. 3.10) to write

$$s' + \Delta s = K(t' + \Delta t)^2 = Kt'^2 + 2Kt' \, \Delta t + (\Delta t)^2 \qquad (3.12\text{-}1A)$$

and

$$s' = Kt'^2. \qquad (3.12\text{-}1B)$$

If we now subtract Eq. (3.12-1B) from Eq. (3.12-1A), we get

$$\Delta s = 2Kt' \, \Delta t + K \, \Delta t^2. \qquad (3.12\text{-}2)$$

and, upon dividing both sides of Eq. (3.12-2) by Δt, we obtain

$$\frac{\Delta s}{\Delta t} = 2Kt' + K \, \Delta t. \qquad (3.12\text{-}3)$$

We can now employ our definition of instantaneous speed [Eq. (3.4-2)] by taking the limit in Eq. (3.12-3) of $\Delta s/\Delta t$ as $\Delta t \to 0$. Thus,

$$v' = \frac{ds}{dt} = \lim_{\Delta t \to 0} \frac{\Delta s}{\Delta t} = 2Kt'. \qquad (3.12\text{-}4)$$

Note that as $\Delta t \to 0$—that is, as Δt is taken smaller and smaller or as Δt approaches zero—the term $K \, \Delta t$ also approaches zero. Thus in the limit $v' = 2Kt'$. At $t' = 0.50$ sec, then, $v' = 2Kt' = 2(5.0 \text{ m/sec}^2)(0.50 \text{ sec}) = 5.0$ m/sec. This is the same value found graphically in the preceding section.

In Sec. 3.5 we went to considerable length to stress that, although Δt could be taken various ways around a particular $t = t'$, the limiting process would nonetheless yield the same instantaneous speed v'. We can show this algebraically.

We write

$$s' = Kt'^2 = Kt'^2$$

and

$$s' - \Delta s = K(t' - \Delta t)^2 = Kt'^2 - 2Kt' \Delta t + K(\Delta t)^2.$$

When the latter equation is subtracted from the former, we get

$$\Delta s = 2Kt' \Delta t - K(\Delta t)^2,$$

$$\frac{\Delta s}{\Delta t} = 2Kt' - K \Delta t,$$

and

$$v' = \lim_{\Delta t \to 0} \frac{\Delta s}{\Delta t} = 2Kt',$$

the same result as before.

We can also write

$$s' + \Delta s_{(+)} = K(t' + \Delta t)^2 = Kt'^2 + 2Kt' \Delta t + K(\Delta t)^2 \qquad (3.12\text{-}5A)$$

and

$$s' - \Delta s_{(-)} = K(t' - \Delta t)^2 = Kt'^2 - 2Kt' \Delta t + K(\Delta t)^2. \qquad (3.12\text{-}5B)$$

The subscripts on $\Delta s_{(+)}$ and $\Delta s_{(-)}$ are necessary because, as we shall see in Ex. 3.12-2, when Δt is added to t' in the equation $s = Kt^2$, one gets a larger Δs than when Δt is substracted from t'. However, Ex. 3.12-3 will show that as $\Delta t \to 0$, $\Delta s_{(+)}$ and $\Delta s_{(-)}$ become more and more nearly equal. Therefore, if we subtract $s' - \Delta s_{(-)}$ from $s' + \Delta s_{(+)}$ in Eqs. (3.12-5), we can write $\Delta s_{(+)} + \Delta s_{(-)} \approx 2\Delta s$, with an error that becomes negligible as $\Delta t \to 0$. Therefore, as a result of the subtraction, we get

$$2 \Delta s = 4Kt' \Delta t,$$

$$\frac{\Delta s}{\Delta t} = 2Kt'$$

and

$$v' = \frac{ds}{dt} = 2Kt',$$

again the same result as before.

EXERCISES

3.12-1 If a body starts from rest at $t = 0$ with an acceleration of 10.00 m/sec^2, the distance it covers in a time t is given by the equation $s = (5.00 \text{ m/sec}^2)t^2$. Express the distance s' covered in $t' = 1.0000$ sec.

3.12-2 Using your result from the preceding exercise, compute $s' + \Delta s_{(+)}$ for $t = t' + \Delta t$ where $\Delta t = 0.1000$ sec—that is, $t = 1.1000$ sec. Also, compute $s' - \Delta s_{(-)}$ for $t = t' - \Delta t$ where $\Delta t = 0.1000$ sec. Compare $\Delta s_{(+)}$ with $\Delta s_{(-)}$.

3.12-3 Repeat Ex. 3.12-2 for $\Delta t = 0.0100$ sec and again compare $\Delta s_{(+)}$ with $\Delta s_{(-)}$. On the basis of these two exercises, is it true that $\Delta s_{(+)}$ and $\Delta s_{(-)}$ become more and more nearly equal as $\Delta t \to 0$?

3.12-4 Make a plot similar to Fig. 3.14 for the falling ping-pong ball of Fig. 3.13b, using the data given in Ex. 3.9-2. On the basis of this plot, is the acceleration constant within the accuracy of the observations?

3.13 Algebraic Determination of Instantaneous Acceleration

The equation relating speed to time in Fig. 3.15b is $v = at$. We can apply the limiting process to this equation algebraically just as we did in Sec. 3.12 for determining instantaneous speed.

$$v + \Delta v = a(t + \Delta t),$$

$$v = at,$$

$$\Delta v = a\,\Delta t,$$

$$\frac{dv}{dt} = \lim_{\Delta t \to 0} \frac{\Delta v}{\Delta t} = a. \tag{3.13-1}$$

The process above is that of computing the derivative, and dv/dt is called the *derivative* of v with respect to t, or the time derivative of the speed. Similarly, we may say that the speed, $v = ds/dt$, is the time derivative of the distance.

3.14 Constant Acceleration and Area Under the Curve

Let us consider some other information inherent in the graphs of Figs. 3.15a, b, and c. Recall that in Sec 3.11 we showed that the point-by-point slopes of Fig. 3.15c are represented by the graph of Fig. 3.15b. Also, the point-by-point slopes of Fig. 3.15b graph into Fig. 3.15a. In other words, we have derived Fig. 3.15b from 3.15c and Fig. 3.15a from 3.15b. We can now ask whether we might reverse the procedure, obtaining Fig. 3.15b from 3.15a and Fig. 3.15c from 3.15b. The answer, of course, is that we can.

The process of obtaining Fig. 3.15b from Fig. 3.15a is almost trivial, but not quite so. First, notice our definition of average acceleration, $\bar{a} = \Delta v/\Delta t$. We observe again that Fig. 3.15 shows a case of constant acceleration (and this is what makes the case almost trivial), so that the instantaneous acceleration is equal to the average acceleration: $a = \bar{a} = \Delta v/\Delta t$ [Eq. (3.8-4)]. If we multiply both sides of the Eq. (3.8-4) by Δt, we get

$$\Delta v = a\,\Delta t. \tag{3.14-1}$$

If $a = 10.0\ \text{m/sec}^2$ as in Fig. 3.15a, then Eq. (3.14-1) says that in *any* 0.10 sec the change of speed will be $10.0\ \text{m/sec}^2 \times 0.10\ \text{sec} = 1.0$ m/sec. Any other Δt could be chosen for this purpose; thus, if $\Delta t = 0.5$ sec, Eq. (3.14-1) says that in *any* 0.5 sec, Δv will be 5 m/sec.

In terms of the graph of Fig. 3.16, the meaning of $a\,\Delta t$ is seen to be the area of a rectangle whose width is expressed in seconds and whose height is given in meters per second squared; the area, thus, is measured in meters per second—that is, in units of speed. Moreover, since the height of each rectangle in Fig. 3.16 is $a = 10.0$ m/sec^2 and the widths are each $\Delta t = 0.050$ sec, it follows that each of the rectangles shown represents the same speed change, $\Delta v = 0.50$ m/sec.

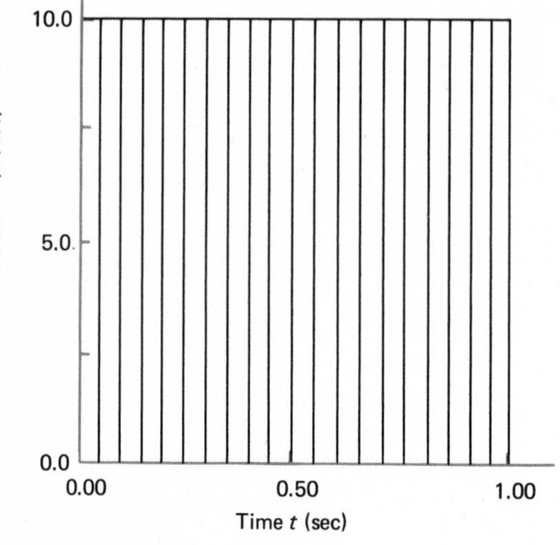

FIG. 3.16 The simplest case of finding the area under a curve.

But these changes of speed are cumulative. The change of speed from $t = 0.000$ sec to $t = 0.150$ sec is the sum of the speed changes for each of three separate 0.050 sec intervals that make up the 0.150 sec interval. *Since the acceleration is constant*, the speed change in each 0.050 sec interval is 0.50 m/sec, and the total speed change in three such intervals will be 1.50 m/sec.

Figure 3.15b does indeed show that in the first 0.050 sec the speed changes by 0.50 m/sec, in the first 0.150 sec the speed changes by 1.50 m/sec, and, in the interval between $t = 0.50$ sec and $t = 0.55$ sec, $\Delta v = 0.50$ m/sec. Thus, *except for one detail*, Fig. 3.15b is derivable from Fig. 3.15a. Figure 3.15a deals only with changes in speed, and it does not tell us how fast the body was moving at $t = 0.000$ sec. If we know from other information that $v = 0$ at $t = 0.000$ sec, then the v vs. t curve is that of Fig. 3.15b. Lacking such information concerning the speed at a certain time, we can determine from Fig. 3.15a only the fact that the v vs. t curve is an unknown one of an infinite family of such curves, all of which have the same slope, the slope corresponding to $a = 10.0$ m/sec^2. Some members of such a family of curves are shown in Fig. 3.17. In the figure the more heavily drawn curve has a v_0 (the v at $t = 0.00$ sec) of 3.5 m/sec. It is customary to call a given v_0 an *initial condition* of the motion.

We should note in passing that any other appropriate speed-time specification will do equally well for selecting the unique curve in Fig. 3.17. For example, if we know that the speed at $t = 0.50$ sec is 5.0 m/sec, then we know that only the curve passing through this point of the graph will do. We can then deduce that this curve passes through the origin and that $v_0 = 0$ at $t = 0$.

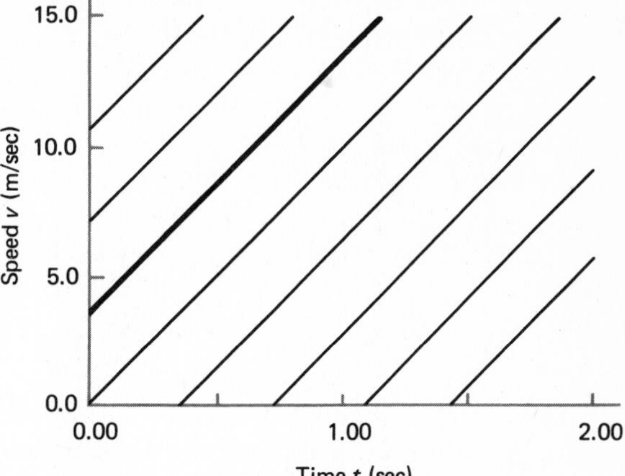

FIG. 3.17 Various speed vs. time curves for the same constant acceleration but for different initial speeds.

3.15 Summing Speed Increments Algebraically

In Eq. (3.14-1) Δv is the increment of speed that occurs in the increment of time Δt if the acceleration is a. In order to find the total speed change between $t=0$ and $t=t'$, it is necessary simply to add the increments of speed from each time increment in the interval. Figure 3.18 shows the time interval between $t=0$ and the specified time $t=t'$ divided into ten equal time increments Δt. The

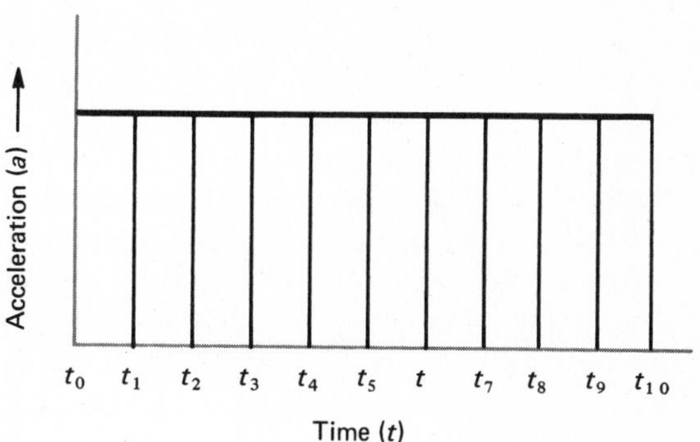

FIG. 3.18 The integral is the area under the curve

instants that divide one time increment from the other are $t_0, t_1, t_2, \ldots, t_{10}$, and t_{10} is, of course, identical to t'. We can designate the speed increments as follows:

$$\Delta v_{0,1} = \text{speed acquired between } t_0 \text{ and } t_1,$$

$$\Delta v_{1,2} = \text{speed acquired between } t_1 \text{ and } t_2, \text{ etc.}$$

Thus, we would have for $\Delta v_{5,6}$

$$\Delta v_{5,6} = a(t_6 - t_5). \tag{3.15-1}$$

We can write the sum of these speed increments as

$$\Delta v_{0,1} + \Delta v_{1,2} + \cdots + \Delta v_{9,10} = v' - v_0 \tag{3.15-2}$$

where the ellipsis (the series of dots) is used to save space but is supposed to suggest what the missing terms are; thus, the first omitted term is $\Delta v_{2,3}$ and the last is $\Delta v_{8,9}$. The right-hand side of Eq. (3.15-2) expresses the total speed change in terms of the speed v_0 which the body has at $t = t_0 = 0.00$ sec and the speed v' which the body has at $t = t_{10} = t'$, the end of the total interval. Thus, $v' - v_0$ is the change of speed occurring in t' seconds.

The right-hand sides of the equations for speed increments, the set of equations like Eq. (3.15-1), can be added in a similar way, Thus, we have

$$a[(t_1 - t_0) + (t_2 - t_1) + \cdots + (t_{10} - t_9)] = a[t_{10} - t_0]. \qquad (3.15\text{-}3)$$

In this sum we note that each instant except the first and the last—i.e., except t_0 and t_{10}—occurs twice, once with a plus sign and once with a minus; hence, only t_0 and t_{10} appear in the resulting expression.

From Eqs. (3.15-2) and (3.15-3) we get

$$v' - v_0 = a(t_{10} - t_0) = at',$$

since $t_0 = 0$ and $t_{10} = t'$. There is nothing particular about t'; it can be *any* value of the variable t, so we may drop the primes to get

$$v - v_0 = at. \qquad (3.15\text{-}4)$$

Equation (3.15-4) is exactly the equation which fits Fig. 3.15b, if v_0 is set equal to zero. Actually, one should recall our discussion in Sec. 3.14 and realize that the v_0 here, too, determines the proper curve of the family represented in Fig. 3.17.

Before leaving this section we should introduce some notation that will be valuable to us in the remainder of this chapter. In Eq. (3.15-1) we have $\Delta v = a\,\Delta t$. It is common practice to indicate the addition of several terms whose natures are known and similar, such as those in Eq. (3.15-2), by the use of the operator symbol Σ (the Greek letter *sigma*). This is done by writing

$$v - v_0 = \Sigma\,\Delta v = \Sigma\,a\,\Delta t, \qquad (3.15\text{-}5)$$

where this simply means to add all of the Δv as in Eq. (3.15-2) and to add all of the $a\,\Delta t$ as in Eq. (3.15-3) ($\Sigma\,\Delta v$ is read "sigma delta vee" or "summation delta vee" and *not* "sigma times delta vee"). Since a is constant in Eq. (3.15-5) we may write

$$\Sigma\,\Delta v = a\,\Sigma\,\Delta t. \qquad (3.15\text{-}6)$$

We shall see in the next sections that it is sometimes necessary—indeed, it is usually desirable—to divide a time interval not into ten time increments but into a very large number of them. Previously, as $\Delta t \to 0$, we symbolized it by the infinitesimal dt, and similarly we changed from Δv to dv as $\Delta t \to 0$. We may recognize that each Δt is t/N, where N is the number of intervals; hence N increases without limit as $\Delta t \to 0$. To obtain a simple notation, we use the elongated "S", known as an integral sign, to replace Σ as we approach the limit and, in analogy with our notation for derivatives, replace Δt by dt. We then have

$$\int dv = \lim_{\Delta t \to 0} \Sigma \Delta v = \lim_{\Delta t \to 0} \Sigma\, a\, \Delta t = \int a\, dt = a \int dt. \qquad (3.15\text{-}7)$$

The meaning in Eq. (3.15-7) is the same as that in Eq. (3.15-6) except that we are now adding infinitesimal increments.

Adding all of the infinitesimal changes of speed on the left of Eq. (3.15-7), we get the total change of speed, $v - v_0$; adding all of the infinitesimal increments of time, we obtain the total lapsed time from $t = 0.00$ sec. Thus, we have as before,

$$v - v_0 = at. \qquad (3.15\text{-}4)$$

In Sec. 3.13 we started with $v = at$ and computed the derivative $dv/dt = a$. In this section we started with the derivative $dv/dt = a$, rewritten as $dv = a\, dt$, and we summed, or integrated, both sides to get $v = at$ again. Thus, our summing or integrating operation may be thought of as *the inverse of that by which we found the derivative.*

3.16 Areas Under a Speed vs. Time Curve

We can extend the method of Sec. 3.14 to obtain a geometrical interpretation of the area under Fig. 3.15b and by analogy to the earlier treatment we shall see that we can obtain Fig. 3.15c from Fig. 3.15b. First, we refer to Eq. (3.4-1) and rewrite it as

$$\Delta s = \bar{v}\, \Delta t. \qquad (3.16\text{-}1)$$

This is analogous to Eq. (3.14-1). This equation says that the distance increment—i.e., the *increase* in the total distance—which is added during time increment Δt is equal to the average speed $\bar{v}$ times the duration Δt. Let us apply this equation for each 0.10 sec in Fig. 3.15b.

In order to do this we use Fig. 3.19, which is drawn to a larger scale and has areas of width $\Delta t = 0.10$ sec drawn under the curve. The question now arises concerning what values to use for the *height* of the rectangles; that is, what is $\bar{v}$ for each one? In a strictly linear case such as this, we might make a shrewd guess that $\bar{v}$ is the average of the two instantaneous speeds which occur at the beginning and at the end of the interval. Thus, if v_2 is the instantaneous speed at $t_2 = 0.20$ sec and v_3 is that at $t_3 = 0.30$ sec, we would guess that $\bar{v}_{2,3}$, the average speed between instants t_2 and t_3, is $\frac{1}{2}(v_2 + v_3)$. From Fig. 3.19 we see that $v_2 = 2.0$ m/sec while $v_3 = 3.0$ m/sec. Their average is $\bar{v}_{2,3} = 2.5$ m/sec. Inspection of the figure confirms that this is the right value to use for $\bar{v}$. Throughout the *first half* of the time interval $(t_3 - t_2)$, the average speed is greater than any of the instantaneous speeds. This means that to use the average speed for calculating the distance covered during the *first half* of the time interval would give a distance greater than that traversed by the body using the actual instantaneous speeds. The excess distance is represented by the area of the small shaded right triangle.

Conversely, in the second half of the time interval, the use of the average speed for calculation of the distance traveled gives a result that is smaller than that traversed by the body moving with the actual instantaneous values. The amount of the deficiency is represented by the area of the small white right triangle.

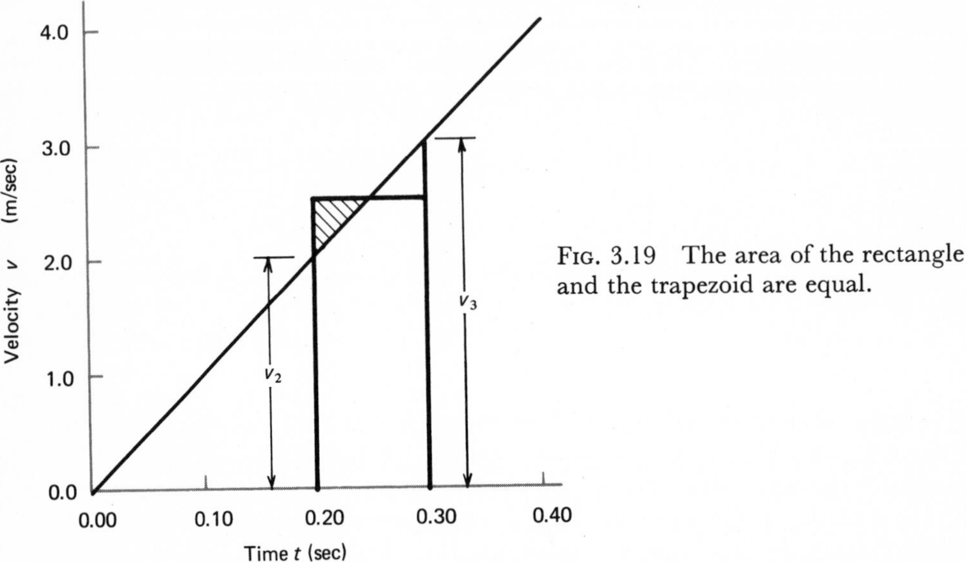

FIG. 3.19 The area of the rectangle and the trapezoid are equal.

Since the surplus represented by the shaded triangle is exactly the same as the deficiency represented by the white triangle, $\bar{v}_{2,3} = \frac{1}{2}(v_2 + v_3)$ is the correct expression for an average speed for the time interval $(t_3 - t_2)$ The criterion by which the proper average speed is chosen is that the average speed must yield the same total distance of travel during the time interval as that which occurs when the body moves with its varying instantaneous speed.

A case in which the "average" speed as the numerical average of the initial (v_i) and the final (v_f) speeds does not work is shown in Fig. 3.20. Note that the shaded "triangle" is larger than the white one, indicating that the total distance as calculated by the numerical average will be too large.

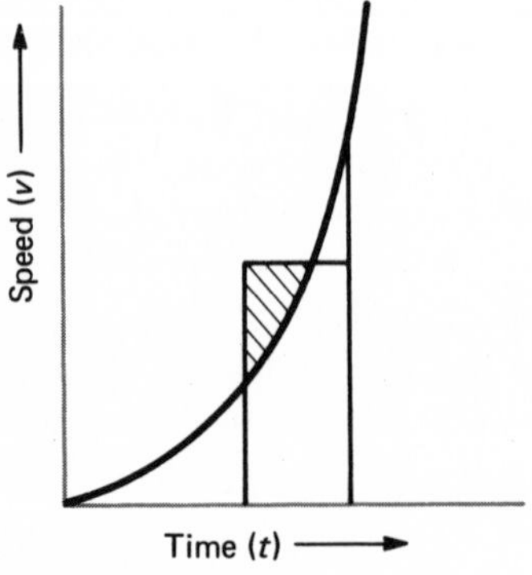

FIG. 3.20 The average speed may not be equal to the average of the initial and final speeds.

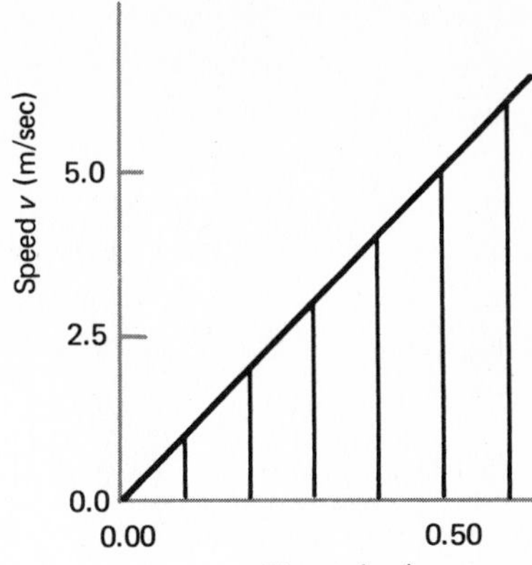

FIG. 3.21 Speed vs. time curve.

It remains now to see whether we can obtain Fig. 3.15c from Fig. 3.15b by graphical means. Figure 3.21 redraws a portion of Fig. 3.15b and shows the areas under the curve for each 0.10 sec of travel. The average speed during the first 0.10 sec is $v_{0,1} = 0.5$ m/sec, and this average pertains over the time interval $(t_1 - t_0) = 0.10$ sec. The distance traversed then will be (0.50 m/sec) × (0.1 sec) or 0.050 m. We enter this point (x) on the graph, Fig. 3.22—that is, at

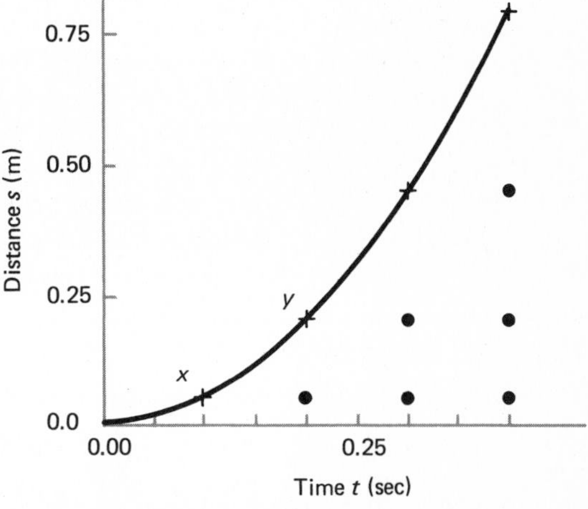

FIG. 3.22 The distance vs. time curve corresponding to Fig. 3.21.

$t = 0.10$ sec we place a point indicating a distance $s = 0.050$ m. But this distance will also be a part of the total distance covered by any later time; hence, we place a row of horizontal dots—one at each tenth of a second, all at $s = 0.050$ m.

During $(t_2 - t_1) = (0.20 \text{ sec} - 0.10 \text{ sec}) = 0.10$ sec, $\bar{v}_{1,2} = 1.50$ m/sec; the distance traversed is then 1.50 m/sec × 0.10 sec = 0.15 m. Now this distance is *in addition to* that covered in the first time interval $(t_1 - t_0)$. Therefore, on Fig. 3.22, we place point y 1.5 m above the point x at $t = 0.20$ sec. Point y then shows that the total distance traveled in the first 0.20 sec is 0.20 m. We proceed by calculating the additional travel during $(t_3 - t_2)$ and enter this distance on Fig. 3.22 by placing point z above points y and x at $t = 0.30$ sec. Figure 3.22 shows this construction carried out through $t = 0.40$ sec.

The reader should convince himself that Fig. 3.22 is indeed the same graph as Fig. 3.15c and that the derived graph is $s = \frac{1}{2}at^2$, where $a = 10.0$ m/sec^2.

3.17 *Analytic Determination of Distance Traveled from the Speed vs. Time Curve*

We have seen that the distance traveled during any time interval (say, $t = 0.20$ sec to $t = 0.30$ sec in Fig. 3.19) is the area under the velocity vs. time curve between those two times. Hence the distance covered during the time interval from 0 to T is the total area under the speed vs. time curve between $t = 0$ and $t = T$. Returning to the notation of Sec. 3.15, we can state that

$$s = \lim_{\Delta t \to 0} \sum v \, \Delta t = \int_0^T v \, dt.$$

where the subscript "zero" and the superscript T indicate that the integral extends between a ***lower limit*** (0) and an ***upper limit*** (T). Using Eq. (3.15-4) and setting $v_0 = 0$, we have $v = at$, so

$$s = \int_0^T at \, dt = a \int_0^T t \, dt, \tag{3.17-1}$$

where the final expression is valid if a is a constant. This equation is somewhat more complicated than was Eq. (3.15-7), because the little areas that must be added together are trapezoidal instead of rectangular (compare Figs. 3.18 and 3.19).

To evaluate the integral, let us first consider the sum

$$\sum v_j \, \Delta t_j.$$

If we divide the time interval from 0 to T into N identical smaller intervals of Δt each, we will have

$$\Delta t = T/N.$$

At the beginning of the first interval, $v_1 = 0$; at the beginning of the second interval,

$$v_2 = a \, \Delta t = aT/N;$$

at the beginning of the third,

$$v_3 = 2aT/N,$$

etc. Since we have taken the lowest value of v_j for each interval, the area

$$s_1 = \sum v_j \, \Delta t_j = (aT/N)[0 + 1 + 2 + 3 + \cdots (N - 1)](T/N)$$

computed in this way will certainly be less than the actual area under the curve. We can therefore say that the actual distance (s) covered in the time interval from 0 to T is greater than s_1.

We have found a lower limit for s. To find an upper limit, we can take the values of v at the end of each interval, instead of the beginning. For the first, second, and third intervals, the velocities are then, respectively,

$$aT/N,\ 2aT/N,\ 3aT/N.$$

Because we have used the greatest velocity for each interval, the sum

$$s_2 = (aT/N)[1 + 2 + 3 + \cdots + N](T/N)$$

is certainly greater than s.

By these two processes, we have determined that

$$s_2 > s > s_1.$$

By direct subtraction of s_1 from s_2, we see that

$$s_2 - s_1 = (aT/N)(N)(T/N) = aT^2/N.$$

As N becomes very large, the difference between s_1 and s_2 becomes very small, being inversely proportional to N. Hence, as N gets larger, s is determined more and more precisely. As we allow N to increase without limit, which corresponds to allowing Δt to approach zero, the difference between s_1 and s_2 becomes less than any quantity that we can name, so we can take

$$s = \lim_{\Delta t \to 0} s_1 = \lim_{\Delta t \to 0} s_2.$$

Let us now try to compute the limiting values of s_1 and s_2. We have

$$s_1 = (aT^2/N^2)[0 + 1 + 2 + 3 + \cdots + (N - 1)].$$

The quantity in brackets is the sum of all the integers from 1 to $(N - 1)$ inclusive. It is easily shown (Exs. 3.17-1 and 3.17-2) that

$$\sum_{j=1}^{j=n} j = \tfrac{1}{2}n(n + 1). \qquad (3.17\text{-}2)$$

Letting $n = (N - 1)$ in this expression, we find that

$$s_1 = (aT^2/N^2)(N - 1)(N)/2 = \tfrac{1}{2}aT^2(N - 1)/N.$$

Similarly, we can let $n = N$ in Eq. (3.17-2) to find that

$$s_2 = (aT^2/N^2)(N)(N + 1)/2 = \tfrac{1}{2}aT^2(N + 1)/N.$$

As Δt becomes very small, or N becomes very large, both of the ratios, $(N - 1)/N$ and $(N + 1)/N$, approach unity to any accuracy that we may wish.

Hence we can say that

$$\lim_{\Delta t \to 0} s_1 = \lim_{\Delta t \to 0} s_2 = \tfrac{1}{2} a T^2.$$

We have thus shown that

$$s = \int_0^T v\, dt = a \int_0^T t\, dt = \tfrac{1}{2} a T^2.$$

We have used the symbol T for the upper limit only to avoid confusion between the general time t and the specific time T. Having obtained this result, we can replace T by t and find, for the distance s covered by a body that undergoes uniform acceleration a for any time t, having started from rest,

$$s = \tfrac{1}{2} a t^2. \qquad (3.17\text{-}3)$$

EXERCISES

3.17-1 By trial of the special choices $n = 1, 2, 3, 4, 5$, show that Eq. (3.17-2) is valid for each of these choices.

3.17-2 (a) Assume that Eq. (3.17-2) is valid for some value of n, say $n = N$. By direct addition, show that

$$\sum_1^{N+1} j = \frac{N^2 + 3N + 2}{2} = \frac{(N+1)(N+2)}{2}.$$

(b) By combining the result just obtained with the result of Ex. 3.17-1, show that Eq. (3.17-2) is valid for every integer N. (The process used here is known as ***proof by induction***.)

3.17-3 Repeat the argument of this section for a body that experiences a uniform acceleration a, but that starts with an initial velocity v_0. Show that the distance covered during the time interval for $t = 0$ to $t = T$ is greater than

$$s_1 = v_0 T + \tfrac{1}{2} a T^2 \left(\frac{T}{\Delta t} - 1 \right) \Big/ \left(\frac{T}{\Delta t} \right)$$

and less than

$$s_2 = v_0 T + \tfrac{1}{2} a T^2 \left(\frac{T}{\Delta t} + 1 \right) \Big/ \left(\frac{T}{\Delta t} \right).$$

Hence show that

$$s = v_0 T + \tfrac{1}{2} a T^2 = \tfrac{1}{2}(2v_0 + aT)T.$$

3.18 The General Equations of Uniformly Accelerated Motion

We might suspect that a body started with an initial speed v_0 and continuously subjected to a constant acceleration a would combine these two motions. If so, the distance traveled in any time t would be the sum of the distances $v_0 t$, due to the uniform speed, and $\frac{1}{2} a t^2$, due to the uniformly accelerated motion. The total distance covered in time t would then be

$$s = v_0 t + \tfrac{1}{2} a t^2. \qquad (3.18\text{-}1)$$

If this equation is correct, we should be able to derive the corresponding equations for v and a by taking derivatives of Eq. (3.18-1). If we write $s + \Delta s$ for the displacement at time $t + \Delta t$, taking the limit as $\Delta t \to 0$, etc., we get

$$v = \frac{ds}{dt} = v_0 + at. \qquad (3.18\text{-}2)$$

If then we proceed by taking the derivative of Eq. (3.18-2), we get

$$a = \frac{dv}{dt} = a. \qquad (3.18\text{-}3)$$

We may solve Eq. (3.18-2) for a and substitute in Eq. (3.18-1) to obtain an equation connecting the distance covered with the initial and final velocities:

$$s = \tfrac{1}{2}(v_0 + v)t. \qquad (3.18\text{-}4)$$

Similarly, we can eliminate t from Eqs. (3.18-1) and (3.18-2) to find that

$$s = (v^2 - v_0{}^2)/2a \qquad (3.18\text{-}5)$$

or that

$$v^2 = v_0{}^2 + 2as. \qquad (3.18\text{-}6)$$

Whether our guess that the two motions are superimposed is correct can be told only by the comparison of Eqs. (3.18-1) to (3.18-3) with the results of observation. Such comparison has been carried out many times and has completely justified the assumption of ***superposition***, which was first made by Galileo.

3.19 An Illustrative Example

The equations which we have derived are equally valid for positive or negative values of the displacements, velocities, and accelerations. To be consistent with the notation of Sec. 3.18, it will be convenient to choose the vertical downward direction as positive. Then downward displacements, velocities, and accelerations will be positive, while these quantities, if directed upward, will be negative.

In order to see how negative quantities may enter into our considerations, let us investigate the motion of a ball thrown vertically upward with a speed of 4.0 m/sec. Under these conditions, $v_0 = -4.0$ m/sec, while $g = +9.80$ m/sec^2. From Eq. (3.18-2), we see that the velocity, starting as negative, will at first gradually decrease in magnitude as the term gt becomes larger with increasing time. Eventually the velocity will become zero, after which it will be positive, i.e., the ball will be falling. Since the ball must have been moving upward just before the time when $v = 0$ and downward later, it is obviously at the top of its flight when $v = 0$. We can therefore find out how long the ball takes to rise by letting the time of rise be t_1, and putting

$$v = v_0 + gt_1 = 0,$$

whence

$$t_1 = -v_0/g.$$

Substituting the values of v_0 and g into this equation, we find that the ball rises for a time

$$t_1 = 4.0 \text{ m sec}^{-1}/9.80 \text{ m sec}^{-2} = 0.41 \text{ sec}.$$

If we wish to know how high the ball rises, we may substitute this value for t_1 into Eq. (3.18-1). Denoting the extreme height by s_1, we have

$$s_1 = v_0(-v_0/g) + \tfrac{1}{2}g(-v_0/g)^2$$
$$= -v_0^2/g + v_0^2/2g = -v_0^2/2g.$$

Notice that, since both v_0^2 and g are positive, s_1 is necessarily negative, which is consistent with our assumption that upward displacements are negative. Substitution of numerical values shows that

$$s_1 = -(4.0 \text{ m/sec})^2/2(9.80 \text{ m/sec}^2)$$
$$= -16.0 \text{ m}^2 \text{ sec}^{-2}/19.6 \text{ m sec}^{-2} = -0.82 \text{ m}.$$

After the ball has reached the top of its flight, it will fall faster and faster, until it strikes the ground. If we are interested in how long it takes to return to its starting height, we notice that $s = 0$ when the ball has returned. Therefore, letting the total time in the air be t_2, we can use Eq. (3.18-1), putting

$$s = v_0 t_2 + \tfrac{1}{2}gt_2^2 = 0,$$

to find that

$$t_2 = -2v_0/g.$$

Comparing this result with that obtained for the time of rise, we find that the total time for the round trip of the ball is twice the time of rise, or that the ball takes just as long to fall as it does to rise.

Finally, using the value of t_2 in Eq. (3.18-2), we can find the velocity with which the ball returns to be

$$v_2 = v_0 + g(-2v_0/g) = -v_0,$$

showing that the *speed* of the returning ball is exactly that with which it was projected upward, the *velocity* having reversed.

EXERCISES

3.19-1 The results obtained in Sec. 3.19 could have been obtained equally well by first calculating the height to which the ball rises and the time of rise and subsequently treating the ball as a freely falling body starting from rest. Use these ideas to find the time that the ball is in the air and the speed with which the ball returns.

3.19-2 A ball is thrown vertically downward from the top of a building 120 m high. It strikes the ground 4.0 sec later. With what speed was it thrown? With what speed does it strike the ground?

3.20 Summary

In this chapter we have found methods for describing the motions of bodies. Ways of finding the velocity of a moving body, or the time rate of its change of position, have been worked out, both for bodies in uniform motion and for those with changing velocities. In the latter case, the term acceleration is used to describe the time rate at which the velocity is changing. While few material bodies move with constant speed, light and radio waves do so at a speed of about 3.00×10^8 m/sec. On the other hand, motions of constant acceleration are frequently observed, since all falling bodies which are massive enough so that air friction does not appreciably affect their motion are characterized by constant accelèration. Everywhere on the surface of the earth this acceleration has a magnitude close to 9.80 m/sec^2. We have studied the motion of uniformly accelerated bodies in some detail, finding relations between the acceleration, velocity, time of fall, and distance covered.

PROBLEMS

3.1 A train starts from rest and is accelerated uniformly at 1.40 m/sec^2 for 10.0 sec. What is its speed at the end of the 10 sec, and how far does the train move in this time?

3.2 How far will the car of Ex. 3.8-4 move, after the brakes are applied, before it comes to rest?

3.3 A car is started at the beginning of a measured kilometer and travels over this distance with a constant acceleration. At the end of the 1.00 km distance the speed of the car is 108 km/hr. Calculate the acceleration of the car and the time taken to cover the kilometer distance.

3.4 A tennis ball is dropped onto the floor from a height of 1.5 m. It rebounds to a height of 1.2 m. Find the speed with which it struck the floor and the speed with which it rebounded from the floor. If it was in contact with the floor for 0.010 sec, what was the average acceleration of the ball during this contact?

3.5 A body starts moving along a line with an initial velocity v_0 and experiences a uniform acceleration a. When its velocity has become v, it has traveled a distance s. Derive an expression for the acceleration in terms of v_0, v, and s.

3.6 In the illustrative example in Sec. 3.19 we chose to express the initial upward velocity as negative, $v_0 = -4.0$ m/sec, and $g = +9.80$ m/sec^2. But there are strong customs in graphing, thermometer scales, and the like to call upward directions positive and downward negative. Starting with Eqs. (3.18-1) and (3.18-2), rework the example, considering displacements, speeds, and accelerations in the upward direction as positive and those in the downward direction as negative. Are your answers, properly interpreted, consistent with those of Sec. 3.19?

3.7 In Eq. (3.18-1) suppose $v_0 = 0$ and $a = g = 9.80$ m/sec. Calculate the position s for $t = 3.0$ sec and for $t = -3.0$ sec. How would you interpret the fact that you get the same s at two different times?

3.8 The driver of an automobile which is initially travelling at 20 m/sec puts on his brake at $t = 0.0$ sec, providing an acceleration of 4.0 m/sec^2. How long does it take for the automobile to stop? How far will it travel while stopping? What do the motion equations imply (!) about the state of affairs at $t = 8.0$ sec?

3.9 If $z = a/y^n$, where a is a constant, show that

$$dz/dy = -na/y^{n+1}$$

Hint: Use Eq. H.1 of Appendix H to approximate $(1/y^n)(1 + \Delta y/y)^{-n}$.

3.10 Using an integration process similar to that of Sec. 3.16, derive Eq. (3.18-1) for a body moving for a time t with constant acceleration a, having started with a velocity v_0 at $t = 0$.

3.11 A body moves in such a way that its displacement is

$$s = Kt^2/(k + t),$$

where K and k are constants. (a) Show that the displacement is zero when $t = 0$ and is approximately Kt when $t \gg k$. (b) Show that the displacement is approximately Kt^2/k when $t \ll k$ and hence that the initial velocity of the body is zero. (c) Find the acceleration of the body for $t \ll k$. For $t \gg k$. (d) Show that the instantaneous velocity at time t is

$$v = \frac{ds}{dt} = \frac{2Kt}{k + t} - \frac{Kt^2}{(k + t)^2}.$$

Hint: Write $(k + t + \Delta t)$ as $(k + t)[1 + \Delta t/(k + t)]$ and then use Eq. H.1 of Appendix H to approximate $[1 + \Delta t/(k + t)]^{-1}$. (e) Check the result obtained in (d) by showing that it agrees with the results obtained in (a), (b), and (c).

3.12 Using the conclusion reached at the end of Sec. 3.15 and the results of Probs. 3.9 and 3.11, show that

(a) $\int \frac{dy}{y^n} = -\frac{1}{(n-1)y^{n-1}} + C$, where C is a constant, if $n \neq 1$,

(b) $\int \left[\frac{2at}{b + t} - \frac{at^2}{(b + t)^2}\right] dt = \frac{at^2}{b + t} + C$, where a, b, and C are constants.

(c) Why can the result found in (a) not be valid for $n = 1$?

REFERENCES

3A F. Friedman, *Velocity and Acceleration in Free Fall*, produced by Educational Services, Inc. A 2¼-min film loop. (No. 80-256, the Ealing Corp., Cambridge, Mass.) Velocity and acceleration vectors are displayed on an oscilloscope face to describe the motion of a spot, which is also displayed.

3B Bernard Jaffe, *Michelson and the Speed of Light*, Doubleday, Garden City, N.Y., 1960 (No. S 13). An attractively written biography of A. A. Michelson, with several chapters devoted to measurements of the speed of light.

3C A. A. Michelson, *Studies in Optics*, University of Chicago Press, Chicago, 1927. Pages 120–138 deal with the speed of light.

3D Morris Shamos, editor, *Great Experiments in Physics*, Holt, New York, 1960. Chapter 2 concerns accelerated motion, and pp. 18–35 are an excerpt from Galileo's *Two New Sciences*, recounting his researches on uniform and accelerated motion.

3E William Francis Magie, *A Source Bookin Physics*, Harvard, Cambridge, Mass., 1935. Pages 1–22 present Galileo's arguments about the motion of material bodies.

3F D. Kleppner and N. Ramsey, *Quick Calculus*, Wiley, New York, 1965. A good and simple treatment of calculus, suitable either for those who are first meeting the subject or for review purposes.

3G AAPT College Physics Series, *Measurement of the Speed of Light*, McGraw-Hill, New York. An animated film illustrating the Fizeau and Michelson experiments.

4 ⮕ *Mass, Momentum, Force and Energy*

4.1 The Inertia of Matter

It is a matter of common experience that some difficulty is encountered in starting a material body into motion or in stopping one that is moving. Any driver faced with a situation in which he needs to accelerate his car rapidly, or to stop it within a short distance, appreciates this. In a qualitative way, we sum up the tendency of undisturbed bodies to stay at rest or to keep moving by saying that matter possesses ***inertia.***

It is also easily recognized that different bodies are characterized by different degrees of inertia. The common expressions, "One could have knocked me down with a feather" and "I felt as if I had been hit by a truck" illustrate extreme cases of the difference. Without further discussion, we can probably agree that the difference between the truck and the feather is that the first is more massive than the second.

The fact that the massiveness of a body depends on something besides its size and shape may be seen if we consider a simple experiment performed with two balls, one made of lead and the other of cork, but otherwise identical. Suppose that the balls are dropped through the same distance and that an observer catches each of them at the end of its fall. It will be found that the lead ball strikes the hand with a greater impact than the cork. Since both, having fallen through the same distance, have the same velocity (cf. Eq. 3.18-4), the difference in the impacts must be due to the difference in the masses of the two balls. A similar effect to that observed in stopping the balls is noticed in starting them into motion. A considerably greater effort is required to throw the lead ball than the one of cork.

4.2 Collisions of Equal Masses

Tests of the type just described serve to distinguish between bodies of widely different masses but are not sufficiently precise to show the difference between two nearly equal masses or to compare two masses quantitatively. However, it is fortunately possible to devise exact experiments by substituting, for the hand of the observer, a standard body which receives the impact of the moving mass that we desire to measure. One of the simplest arrangements for such an experiment uses two small cars, mounted on a smooth horizontal track, as shown in Fig. 4.1. One car (A) is initially at rest near the center of the track, while the other (B) is started from the end of the track and allowed, while

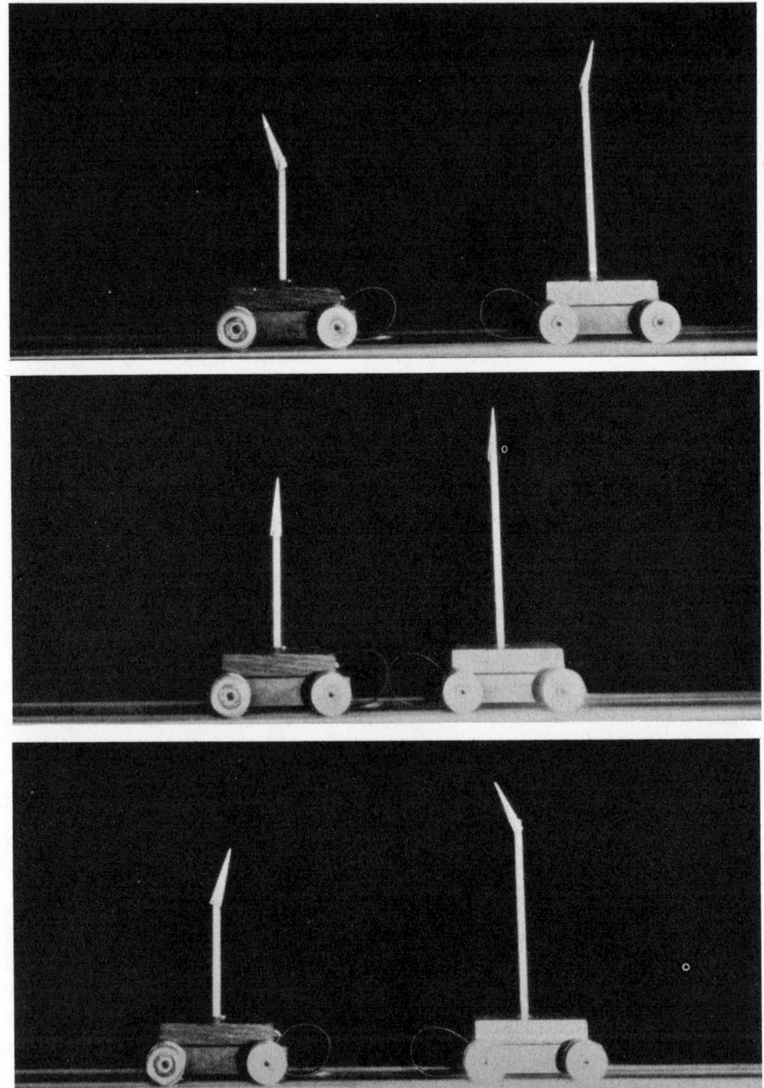

Fig. 4.1 Carts and track used in collision experiments.

moving freely, to collide with A. In our first experiment, we make sure that the two cars are as nearly *identical* as possible. Moreover, the "bumpers" of the cars are made of good springs, which suffer no permanent change in shape due to the collision. For convenience, we shall speak of a collision satisfying this condition as a ***perfectly elastic collision.***

We may take stroboscopic pictures of the cars before, during, and after collision so that the velocity of B just before collision can be measured (cf. Sec. 2.21). Stroboscopic photographs are, of course, multiple exposures in which the stationary background has a number of images of a moving object superposed upon it. Under some circumstances, images, say of car A after collision, may occur in the same general region as images of car A before collision. We need some way to distinguish the *before* images from the *after* images. In order to do this we equip each car with an ***impact flag***, shown in Fig. 4.2. The impact flag consists of a small triangular piece of metal loosely hinged in a slot at the top of its flagpole. Before collision the flag is tilted *away*

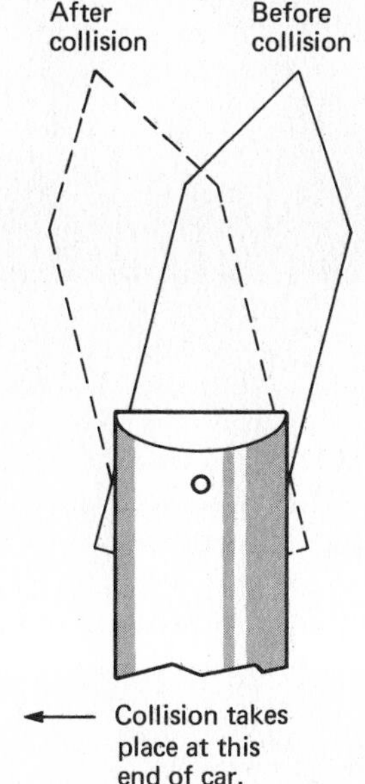

FIG. 4.2 The impact flag.

from the end of the car which is to collide. The collision jars the flag toward the point of impact. The altered position of the flag makes it possible to distinguish the after-collision images from the before-collision images.

Figure 4.3 shows a stroboscopic photograph of our first experiment. Car A, with the shorter flagpole, may be distinguished in its rest position before the collision by its brighter image near the center of the picture. Note that the impact flag leans to the left. After collision car A moves to the left, making a series of images whose impact flags tilt to the right. Car B, on the other hand, has approached from the right before the collision with its impact flag leaning toward the right. It comes to rest as a result of the collision, as is evidenced by its bright image, flag tilted to the left. The white lines in the background of the photograph are 10.0 cm apart. If the first one at the right of the photograph is labeled 0.0 cm, then a displacement scale may be laid out to the left. The experiment can then be analyzed graphically as in Fig. 4.4. The period of the flashes was 0.133 sec, as can be seen from a careful study of the 15 positions of

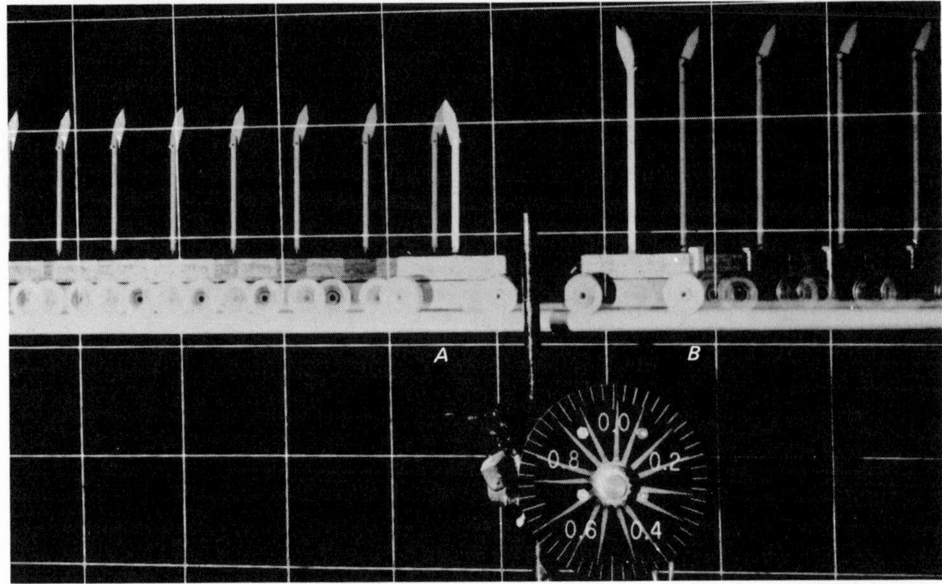

FIG. 4.3 Elastic collision of a moving car with an identical car that was initially stationary.

the hand on the 1.00 rev/sec clock. One can easily see from the graph that the speed of car A just after the collision is the same, within experimental error, as that of car B before the collision.

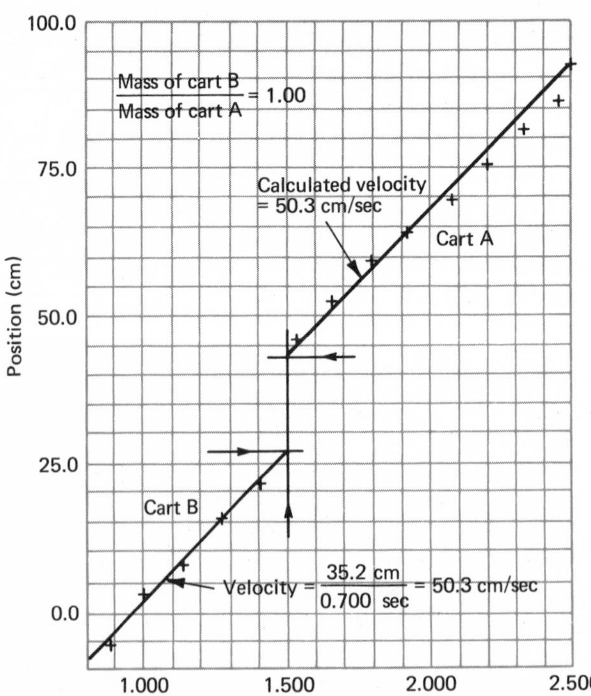

FIG. 4.4 Analysis of the collision of Fig. 4.3.

The experiment can be performed in another way. In this case, a coupling is arranged so that the two cars, after the collision, are fastened together and must move as a unit. Such a collision is known as a ***perfectly inelastic collision.*** When the experiment is performed in this way with two identical cars, it is found that the velocity of the two cars after the collision is half that of car B before the collision (Fig. 4.5). With dividers the reader can easily verify, at least qualitatively, that the images just before collision are spaced twice as far apart as are the images just after collision.

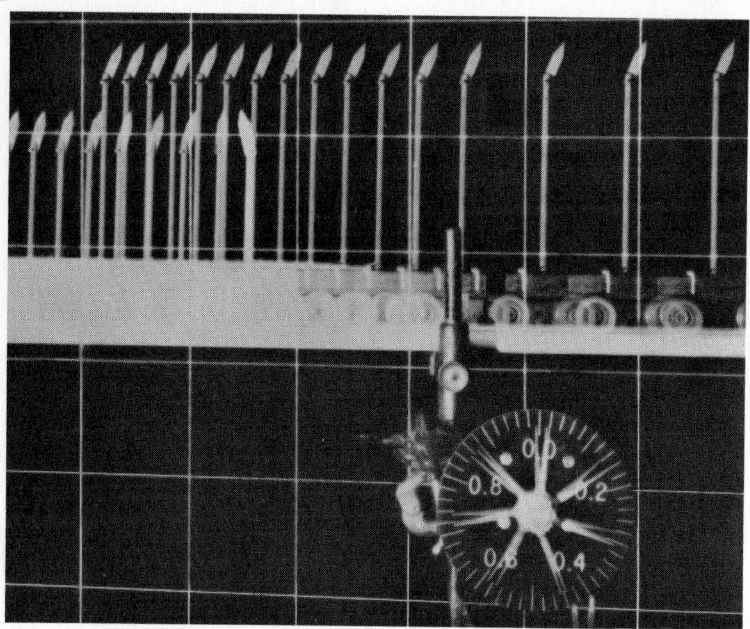

FIG. 4.5 Inelastic collision of cars of equal masses, one of which was initially at rest.

In each of these observations of collisions between cars of equal masses, it has been found that one car gained just as much velocity as a result of the collision as the other lost. We may express this fact algebraically in a simple way. Let v_A and v_B be the velocities of the two cars before the collision and let v_A' and v_B' be their velocities afterward. Then

$$v_A' - v_A = -(v_B' - v_B). \tag{4.2-1}$$

For the perfectly elastic collision, we have the experimental results

$$v_A = 0, \quad v_A' = v_B, \quad \text{and} \quad v_B' = 0.$$

Substitution in Eq. (4.2-1) then gives us the identity

$$v_B - 0 = -(0 - v_B) = v_B.$$

For the inelastic collision, we have $v_A' = v_B' = v_B/2$, which is again an identity. Thus Eq. (4.2-1) is indeed satisfied by the experimental data of the two experiments which we have described.

This result is so simple that it is worth while to see if it holds under more complicated conditions, say with both cars moving before the impact. If we produce such conditions experimentally, we find that Eq. (4.2-1) holds in every case in which the two cars are identical (and therefore of equal mass). For example, if the two cars are moving with the same speed but in opposite directions before the collision and collide perfectly elastically, it is found that each car reverses its motion as a result of the impact. We thus have $v_B = -v_A$, $v_B' = v_A$, and $v_A' = -v_A$, and Eq. (4.2-1) again takes the identical form

$$-v_A - v_A = -(v_A + v_A).$$

If the same velocities are used and the cars collide perfectly inelastically, the two cars come to rest as a result of the collision, again satisfying Eq. (4.2-1).

EXERCISE

4.2-1 Figure 4.6 is a stroboscopic photograph of an elastic collision of cars A and B where the cars have equal masses and each is moving toward the other before the collision. Make a graph similar to Fig. 4.4 in order to analyze this collision and check to see how well Eq. (4.2-1) applies.

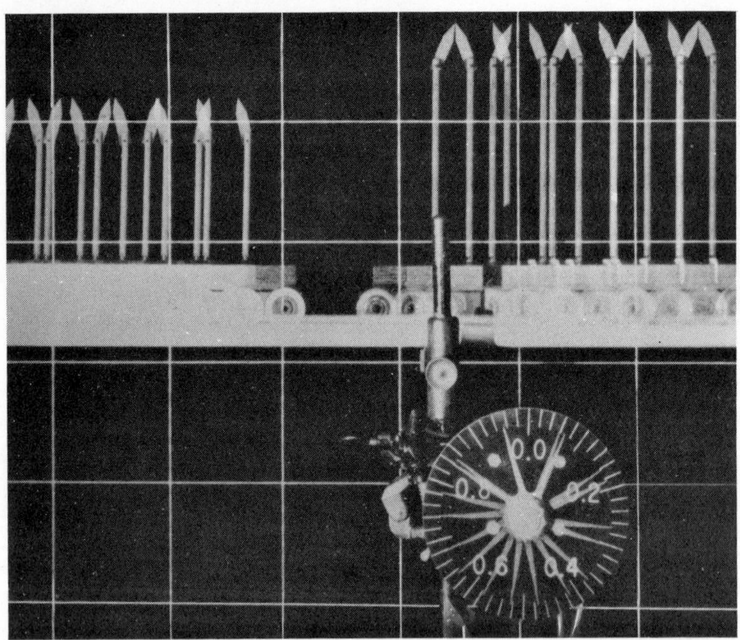

FIG. 4.6 Elastic collision of two cars of equal mass, both of which are moving before the collision.

4.3 The Comparison of Masses by Collision

It might be suspected that, if car A instead of being identical with car B were somewhat more massive, it would be less affected by the collision and would therefore gain less velocity than was lost by car B. This can be tested easily by loading some masses on to A. If any one of the previous experiments is repeated under these circumstances, it is found that this intuitive guess is true. For example, if A is initially at rest and the cars collide perfectly elastically, it is found that the heavier car A moves to the left after the collision with a smaller speed than B had before the collision, while the lighter car B rebounds from A and retreats with a speed which is also less than it had before the collision.

This is illustrated in the stroboscopic photograph of Fig. 4.7, where car B comes from the right and rebounds toward the right, while A, initially at rest,

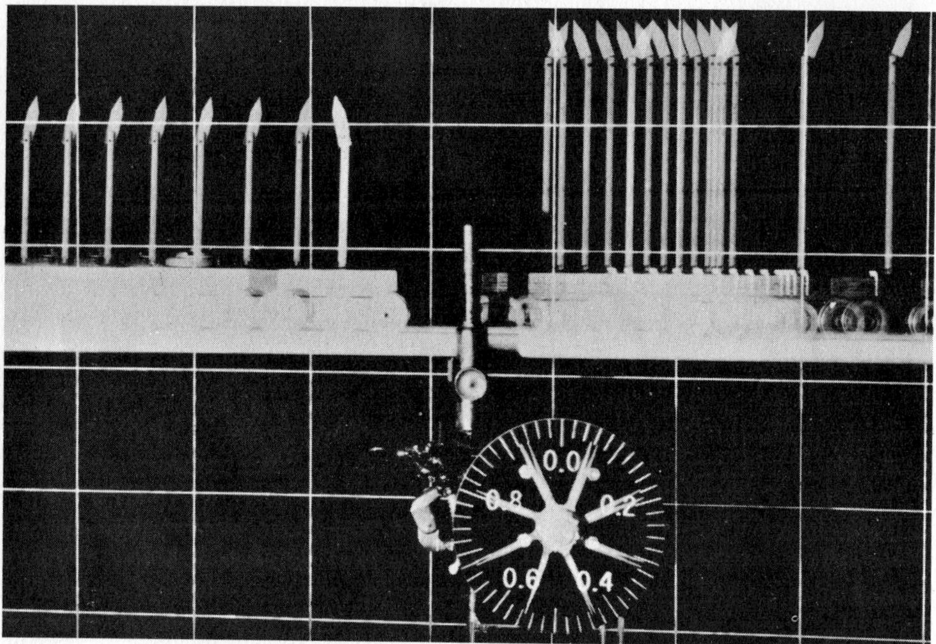

FIG. 4.7 Elastic collision between two cars of unequal masses, the heavier of which was initially at rest.

moves to the left after the collision. Because the velocity of B becomes negative as the result of the impact, this car is found to lose more velocity than it had initially, while A gains less than B had initially. Hence for this experiment, in which A was more massive than B, Eq. (4.2-1) must be replaced by

$$v_A' - v_A = -k(v_B' - v_B), \tag{4.3-1}$$

where k is a quantity less than one.

Figure 4.8 shows a graphical analysis of the collision of Fig. 4.7. From the graph it is seen that $v_A = 0$, $v_A' = 35.6$ cm/sec, $v_B = 55.0$ cm/sec, and $v_B' = -15.2$ cm/sec. If these values are substituted into Eq. (4.3-1), we get

$$35.6 - 0 = -k(-15.2 - 55.0)$$

or $k = 35.6/70.2 = 0.507$.

If a number of other collision experiments are now done with the same pair of unequal cars, a remarkable result is found, for it is discovered that the quantity

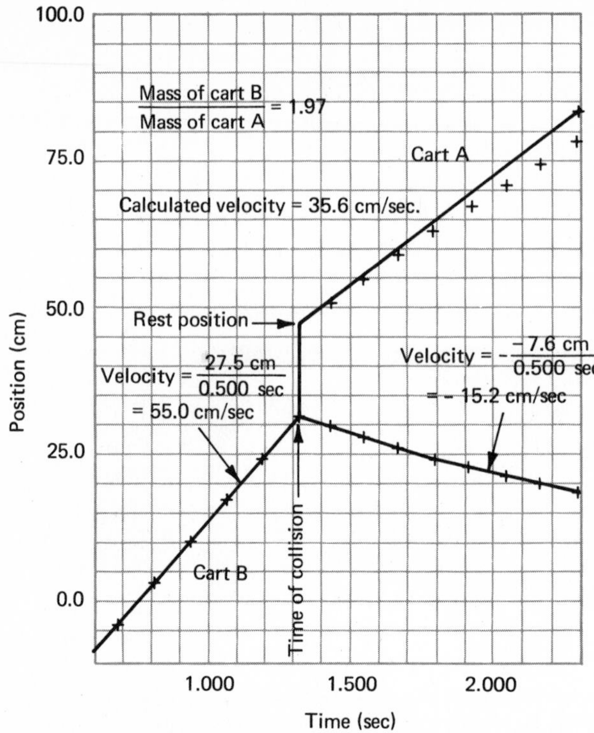

FIG. 4.8 Analysis of the collision of Fig. 4.7.

k which enters into Eq. (4.3-1) has the same value for all of the experiments, within experimental error, regardless of what combinations of initial velocities are used* or whether the collisions were elastic or inelastic. This result could not have been anticipated; it must be accepted as an experimental fact which expresses a fundamental characteristic of masses (cf. Sec. 4.7).

Since the ratio of the velocity gained by one of the bodies in a two-body collision to that lost by the second body is found to be constant, and since this constant has the particular value unity when the two bodies are identical, collision experiments of this type would appear to be a satisfactory way of comparing masses. Let us now suppose that each of the cars in our experiment has a definite mass, which is a measure of its resistance to a change of motion. We may denote these masses by m_A and m_B. Then we say that the ratio of the masses,

$$m_B/m_A = k, \tag{4.3-2}$$

where k is determined by the insertion of experimentally determined velocities into Eq. (4.3-1). Equations (4.3-1) and (4.3-2) therefore give us a satisfactory way of obtaining the ratio of any two masses, provided only that we can bring

* While this statement is true for all conditions which can ordinarily be obtained in the laboratory, Eq. (4.3-1) fails when any of the velocities concerned becomes so large that it is comparable to the speed of light. We shall see, in Chapter 8, that this exception to the rule that we have stated is accounted for by the theory of special relativity, and that it need not bother us for our present purposes.

the two into a collision in which no other bodies are involved. As we shall see later, there are other and less direct ways of comparing the masses when this cannot be done.

Some readers may challenge the determination of k as outlined above by asking whether the mass ratio determined in this way is unique. For example, if three masses, m_A, m_B, and m_C are compared in pairs, the ratios $m_B/m_A = k_1$, $m_C/m_B = k_2$, and $m_C/m_A = k_3$ might be found. Unless these satisfy the relation $k_1 k_2 = k_3$, our method of comparing masses is not satisfactory. Repeated measurements of this sort have shown that this relation is always satisfied.

4.4 Standards of Mass

The experiments we have described cannot determine both constants m_A and m_B, but merely their ratio. We thus can choose one of the two quite arbitrarily if we wish, and then determine the other in terms of it. If we choose some one body as a standard of ***mass***, then we can perform collision experiments with this body as one of the masses and determine the masses of all other bodies in terms of this one. This, then, operationally defines mass and the operation whereby it can be measured. The procedure is quite similar to that which we have used in measuring lengths in terms of an arbitrary standard.

In the system of units used in this book, the unit of mass chosen as standard is called the ***kilogram.*** The ***International Standard of Mass*** is defined as the mass of a block of platinum-iridium alloy called the ***International Prototype Kilogram.*** This standard is kept at Sèvres in France, and precise copies of it have been distributed to all the nations that have agreed to adopt it as standard. In writing dimensional equations we shall represent the dimensions of mass by $[m]$, and we shall abbreviate the unit itself as kg. We have so far defined three arbitrary standards, the meter, the kilogram, and the second. These three units form the basis of the ***meter-kilogram-second system*** of units (***mks system***).

For the measurement of small masses, the gram (1 gm $= 10^{-3}$ kg), the milligram (1 mgm $= 10^{-6}$ kg), and the microgram (1 μgm $= 10^{-9}$ kg) are in common use.

In English-speaking countries another unit of mass, called the ***avoirdupois pound***, is in common use. In the United States this pound is defined as 0.453 592 427 7 kg. In the British Commonwealth a slightly different pound is used. It is the mass of a standard kept in London, and comparison has shown it to be equivalent to 0.453 592 43 kg. The U.S. and the British pound thus agree very closely. The system of units based on the foot, the pound, and the second is called the ***fps system.***

We have set up a method of making comparison between a standard mass and an unknown mass by allowing them to collide with one another. Such a treatment of the International Prototype Kilogram or even of one of its copies would not be permitted for one moment by those entrusted with the care of such standards. Fortunately, there are other gentler methods of comparison based on the gravitational attraction of one body for another. These will be discussed later, particularly in Sec. 4.16.

EXERCISES

4.4-1 Suppose that two cars are used on a collision track. Car A has a mass of 2.00 kg and is at rest before the collision. Car B strikes it with a velocity of +30.0 cm/sec. After the collision car B has a velocity of −10.0 cm/sec and car A has a velocity of +20.0 cm/sec. What is the mass of car B?

4.4-2 If the cars of Ex. 4.4-1 are in contact for a time of 0.0010 sec, what is the average acceleration of each during impact?

4.4-3 A body whose mass is 0.230 kg is moving with a speed of 10 m/sec in a given direction. A second body moving in the same direction along the straight line with a speed of 15 m/sec collides with the first. The two stick together and move on with a speed of 12 m/sec. What is the mass of the second body?

4.5 The Conservation of Momentum

As valuable as collision experiments are for the comparison of masses, they have an even more important role in the development of physics, since they are the basis of one of the most fundamental of all physical laws. To see this, we may substitute the value of k from Eq. (4.3-1) into Eq. (4.3-2) to obtain

$$v_{\mathrm{A}}' - v_{\mathrm{A}} = -(m_{\mathrm{B}}/m_{\mathrm{A}})(v_{\mathrm{B}}' - v_{\mathrm{B}}).$$

On removing the parentheses and rearranging terms, we find that

$$m_{\mathrm{A}} v_{\mathrm{A}} + m_{\mathrm{B}} v_{\mathrm{B}} = m_{\mathrm{A}} v_{\mathrm{A}}' + m_{\mathrm{B}} v_{\mathrm{B}}', \tag{4.5-1}$$

a result which we have seen to be valid for all two-body collisions. The left-hand side of Eq. (4.5-1) contains only quantities which describe the two bodies before the collision and the right-hand side contains only quantities which describe them after the collision. Since every term in the equation involves the product of the mass and velocity of a body, we may simplify the equation by attaching a special significance to such a product. We shall define the ***momentum*** (plural ***momenta***) of a body as the product of the mass of the body by its velocity. Denoting momentum by p, we therefore have the defining equation

$$p = mv. \tag{4.5-2}$$

If we let p_{A} and p_{B} be the momenta of two bodies before the collision and p_{A}' and p_{B}' their respective momenta afterward, Eq. (4.5-1) becomes

$$p_{\mathrm{A}} + p_{\mathrm{B}} = p_{\mathrm{A}}' + p_{\mathrm{B}}'. \tag{4.5-3}$$

We can therefore say, as a result of our experiments, that *the sum of the momenta of the two bodies before collision is equal to the sum of their momenta after the collision.* Stated in another way, this says that the *total momentum of the two bodies is unchanged by the collision.*

This remarkable experimental fact is the basis of one of the most firmly established laws of physics. No observation ever made has indicated an exception to it, either in a collision or in any other process. For example, if a stationary body, due to internal forces such as those of an explosion, breaks into two pieces, it is always found that these two pieces fly off in exactly opposite directions and that their speeds are inversely proportional to their masses, so that the algebraic sum of the two momenta after the disruption is zero.

Because the total momentum of any ***isolated system*** of bodies (i.e., a set of bodies which do not react in any way with other bodies outside of the set) remains constant through any processes that may take place, we say that momentum is a conserved quantity. ***The law of the conservation of momentum*** states that *the total momentum of any isolated system of bodies remains constant regardless of any processes which may take place among them.* It will be seen readily that Eq. (4.5-3) is merely a statement of a special case of this law. We shall see in Chapter 6 that the more general form in which it has just been stated has experimental confirmation.

While mass, like length and time, has been set up in our system of units as a fundamental quantity, it will be seen that momentum, like velocity or acceleration, is a derived quantity. The dimensions of momentum are found from Eq. (4.5-2) to be

$$[p] = [m][v] = [ml t^{-1}]. \tag{4.5-4}$$

Hence the unit of momentum in the "mks" system is the ***kilogram meter per second.***

Illustrative Example

As practical application of the conservation of momentum, consider two automobiles that collide head on. The first car has a mass of 3000 lb and is moving at 60 mi/hr, and the second has a mass of 2000 lb and is moving at 40 mi/hr. When they collide, their broken frames lock into each other sufficiently tightly so that the collision may be approximated closely as being perfectly inelastic.

We shall take the original direction of motion of the more massive car as positive. Then the total momentum before collision is

$$\begin{aligned} p &= (3000 \text{ lb})(60 \text{ mi/hr}) - (2000 \text{ lb})(40 \text{ mi/hr}) \\ &= (1.80 \times 10^5 - 0.80 \times 10^5) \text{ lb mi/hr} = 1.00 \times 10^5 \text{ lb mi/hr}. \end{aligned}$$

After the collision, the two bodies have a combined mass of 5000 lb and are moving with a velocity V. (We neglect any small pieces that fly off in various directions.) The conservation of momentum demands that

$$\begin{aligned} (5000 \text{ lb})\ V &= 1.00 \times 10^5 \text{ lb mi/hr} \\ V &= \frac{1.00 \times 10^5}{5.00 \times 10^3} \text{ mi/hr} = 20 \text{ mi/hr} \end{aligned}$$

as the velocity *immediately* after the collision. This velocity will, of course, rapidly decrease to zero, as the cars do not form an isolated system—friction exists between them and the earth. Notice that the direction of motion immediately after collision is given by the positive sign of V. We may also realize that the velocity of the less massive car changes from -40 mi/hr to $+20$ mi/hr during the short time of collision. If we estimate that time as one second, the acceleration of the car during collision is

$$a = \frac{(20 \text{ mi/hr}) - (-40 \text{ mi/hr})}{1.0 \text{ sec}}$$

$$= \frac{60 \text{ mi}}{\text{sec hr}} \times \frac{5280 \text{ ft}}{\text{mi}} \times \frac{\text{hr}}{3600 \text{ sec}} = 88 \text{ ft/sec}^2.$$

Hence the acceleration is nearly three times that of a freely falling body.

4.6 Conservation Laws

The law of the conservation of momentum is the first of a number of similar laws that we shall find as we progress in our study. It has been fortunate, in the development of physics, that a number of quantities have been found to possess the property that they can be exchanged among bodies, but can be neither created nor destroyed. Such quantities are known as ***conserved quantities.*** The existence of a conservation law has generally not been deduced,* but such a law has been arrived at by generalizing from large numbers of observations or experiments. It is interesting to note that a single reliable observation which contradicted the law of the conservation of momentum would ruin our confidence in the law, yet no such observation has been recorded in the period of nearly three centuries since the law was formulated. Conservation laws can never be proved, since they are only generalizations from experience, yet the balance of evidence in favor of such laws as that of the conservation of momentum is so great that they can be taken as the soundest part of all physical theory.

4.7 The Conservation of Mass

Mass, which was defined in Secs. 4.3–4.4, is also found to be a conserved quantity. The discussion of those sections was based on the observed fact that the ratio of the masses of two bodies remained constant throughout any set of collision experiments in which the identities of the two bodies were not lost. This fact is suggestive of a conservation law and may tempt us to inquire what happens when the bodies do not retain their individualities. For example, suppose that two water drops collide and merge into a single drop. Measurement of the individual masses before the collision and of the combined mass afterward shows that the total mass of the system of two drops has not changed. Similarly, when a disruption such as that discussed in Sec. 4.5 takes place, the sum of the masses of the resulting particles is found to be equal to that of the original body.

The best evidence for the conservation of mass comes from chemical processes. The bodies that enter such processes frequently change their natures radically

* The exceptions are conservation laws that have been derived from basic symmetry relations that have been assumed to be valid. The connections between symmetry and conservation laws need not concern us at this stage. These connections have been recognized clearly only in the last forty years, since the development of the quantum mechanics (cf. Chapter 24).

as a result. For example, if solid carbon is burned in the presence of gaseous oxygen, no solid is left behind, all products of the reaction being gaseous. But, if the process is carried out in a closed chamber, it is found that the mass of the system does not change as a result of the burning. In no chemical process ever observed has the mass of the products been shown to be different from the mass of the reagents.

As a result of all of these experiments, we may conclude that mass is a conserved quantity and state ***the law of the conservation of mass***: *the total mass of any isolated system of bodies remains constant regardless of any processes which may take place among them.*

We shall see in Chapter 8 that certain of the masses involved in a collision may change if the speeds of the particles involved are so large that they are comparable with the speed of light. However, the statements made above have been verified for all reasonable velocities, and the conservation law which we have enunciated is adequate for all processes except those in which the very highest speeds are involved. We shall later reconcile the law with the exceptions to it, when we see that it is a special case of a more general conservation law (Sec. 8.13). In the meantime, the law of the conservation of mass may be considered valid for all terrestrial bodies large enough to be seen with the naked eye or even the best microscope, and for all chemical and biological processes.

EXERCISES

4.7-1 A bullet with a mass of 0.0050 kg and traveling horizontally at a speed of 400 m/sec strikes a block of wood with a mass of 2.0 kg. The bullet is embedded in the wood. At what speed will the block be moving just after the bullet strikes it?

4.7-2 Two bodies, of masses 100 gm and 200 gm, moving in the same line and direction with speeds of 200 cm/sec and 100 cm/sec, respectively, collide. After the collision, the first is moving at a speed of 167 cm/sec. What is the speed of the second body?

4.7-3 Two bodies, each of mass 1.3586 kg, are moving in the same straight line in opposite directions. If the speed of each of them is 3.1416 m/sec before the collision, and if they stick together, what is their speed after collision?

4.7-4 A rifle, whose mass is 8.0 pounds, fires a bullet, whose mass is 0.265 oz, at an initial speed of 1225 ft/sec. Calculate the initial recoil speed of the rifle.

4.7-5 The earth is known to have a mass of about 6.0×10^{24} kg. If a raindrop with a mass of 0.020 g is moving with a speed of 10 m/sec just before it strikes the earth, what speed will it impart to the earth?

4.7-6 When a ball is thrown upward, it acquires momentum. How do you reconcile this with the law of conservation of momentum?

4.7-7 What experiments might you make to demonstrate that a growing plant draws most of its nutriment from the air rather than from the soil?

4.7-8 When hydrogen is burned completely to form water, the amount of oxygen consumed always has a mass 8 times as great as that of the hydrogen. If the result of the burning of a small quantity of hydrogen was the formation of 1.00 g of water, how much oxygen was required to burn it?

4.8 The Notion of Force

In Sec. 4.1, we noted that an effort is required to put a stationary body into motion or to stop a moving one. We ordinarily experience this as a muscular effort, and say that we must push or pull on a mass to accelerate it. The concept of force is directly based on this muscular push or pull. Our problem at the moment is to make the idea of force more definite and quantitative than is possible by one's estimation of the physiological processes involved in changing the motion of a mass.

Holding to our muscular reactions for the moment, we know that a greater force is required to get a massive body into motion than is needed for a light one, provided that they are given the same speeds and that equal times are used to accelerate them. The lead and cork balls considered in Sec. 4.1 give a good example of this. Similarly, if the same body is to be accelerated to different speeds in two equal times, we know that a greater force is needed to give the greater speed. In other words, the force required to change the motion of a body increases when either the mass or the change of velocity increases. Since these two quantities determine the momentum of the body, it is entirely consistent with our crude concept of force to suppose that force is the agent which produces change of momentum.

It requires very little consideration to convince ourselves that the time during which we exert a force, as well as the magnitude of the force, determines the change of momentum. One or two persons can usually start an automobile into motion by pushing it along a level road. If an attempt is made to give the car a speed of two miles per hour by a sudden push it will seldom be successful, but a continued push over a few minutes results in the gradual acceleration of the car to this speed. Similarly, in catching a baseball, one's hand receives less of a blow if it is allowed to travel a short distance in the direction of motion of the ball during the catch than it does if an attempt is made to hold the hand absolutely steady. We may therefore conclude that the force necessary to change the momentum of a body depends on the rate at which that momentum is changed.

Guided by the common experiences quoted thus far, we may define ***force*** as the time rate of the change of momentum. It will then remain for us to see whether this definition is satisfactory in a more quantitative sense.

4.9 Force and the Conservation of Momentum

In our discussion of the conservation of momentum, we dealt with an isolated system of bodies as a set of bodies that did not react with any bodies outside the set. In line with our definition of force, we can see that this may be restated thus: An ***isolated system of bodies*** is set of bodies among which internal forces may act but which are subject to no outside forces. For, if the momentum of the set of bodies is to be constant and if a force produces a change of momentum, no net internal force can be acting on the set as a whole.

The simplest isolated system of bodies consists of a single body. If we apply the conservation law to such a body, we reach the conclusion that as long as no forces act upon it its momentum will remain unchanged. This, in turn, implies that it will continue at rest or in uniform motion in a straight line. Everyday experience verifies the maintenance of a state of rest in the absence of forces, but the maintenance of steady motion under similar circumstances is not so easily recognized. If a billiard ball is started in motion, it is found that its speed is gradually reduced until it comes to rest. To account for this, we must either abandon the law of the conservation of momentum or seek for evidence that the billiard ball is not an isolated system, i.e., that outside forces act upon it. We shall see in Chapters 6 and 11 that the latter explanation is the correct one, and that a ***frictional force*** exerted on the ball by the surface of the table accounts for the decrease of the ball's momentum. This may be shown in a qualitative way if we start the same ball moving, at the same speed, over smoother and smoother surfaces. It will be found that the smoother the surface, the more slowly the ball loses its momentum. It is therefore not a far step to suppose that a body moving over a perfectly smooth frictionless surface would continue in steady motion idefinitely. A more quantitative discussion of this problem will be given in Chapter 11.

We may therefore conclude, from the experimentally demonstrated conservation law for momentum and from our definition of force, that a *body that is acted upon by no net force continues in its state of rest or of uniform motion in a straight line.* This statement was originally enunciated by Sir Isaac Newton (1642–1727), the founder of the science of mechanics, as the first of his three laws of motion. We must recognize, of course, that the term *no force* includes the case of two forces of equal magnitude which are exerted on the body in opposite directions, and so add to zero. A book resting on a table furnishes an example, since its weight acts downward, while the table pushes up on the book with an equal and opposite force. We shall see later that more than two forces may balance to produce a zero net effect, i.e., no force.

If we desire to change the momentum of a mass, i.e., to give the mass a positive or negative acceleration, it is necessary to exert a force. This force must always be exerted by some other body. For example, when an automobile or train is being speeded up, the force is exerted between the driving wheels and the ground; when a billiard ball is started in motion, the force is exerted by the cue; when a baseball is thrown, the force is exerted by the hand. Suppose that the force is constant and has a magnitude F. During any short time interval Δt the momentum of the body will change by some amount Δp. Since we have defined force as the time rate of change of momentum, we have the relation

$$F = \Delta p / \Delta t. \tag{4.9-1}$$

Had the force F not been constant, we should have needed to define it in terms of the instantaneous time rate of change of momentum, instead of the average rate $\Delta p/\Delta t$. This can be done in the same manner that we defined instantaneous speeds or accelerations by finding the time derivative of the momentum—i.e., by using the idea of a limit. The defining equation for ***force*** is, therefore,

$$F = \frac{dp}{dt} = \lim_{\Delta t \to 0} \frac{\Delta p}{\Delta t}. \tag{4.9-2}$$

If we now replace the momentum in Eq. (4.9-2) by the product of mass and velocity [cf. Eq. (4.5-2)] and remember that for *speeds small compared to the speed of light* the mass of the body being accelerated remains constant, so that any change in momentum must be due to a change in velocity, we find that

$$F = \lim_{\Delta t \to 0} \Delta(mv)/\Delta t = \lim_{\Delta t \to 0} (m\, \Delta v/\Delta t)$$
$$= m \lim_{\Delta t \to 0} (\Delta v/\Delta t) = ma. \quad (4.9\text{-}3)$$

Or, alternatively, the operations and the results indicated in Eq. (4.9-3) may be written as

$$F = d(mv)/dt = m(dv/dt) = ma. \quad (4.9\text{-}4)$$

Equation (4.9-4) is Newton's second law of motion, which states that *the force required to accelerate a body is directly proportional to the mass of the body and to the acceleration produced.* This law of motion is equivalent to our definition of force.

4.10 Units of Force

We can easily see from the defining equation of force, Eq. (4.9-2), that the dimensions of force are given by

$$[\mathscr{F}] = [p]/[t] = [\ell m t^{-1}][t^{-1}] = [\ell m t^{-2}]. \quad (4.10\text{-}1)$$

Thus, the unit in which force is measured in the mks system is the meter kilogram per second squared. In order to save constant repetition of this cumbersome name, this unit is called the newton (N) after Sir Isaac Newton. One ***newton*** is the force which produces a change of momentum at the rate of one kilogram meter per second per second. Notice here that we can, if we wish, use the ***newton-second*** as a unit for momentum instead of the more awkward kilogram meter per second. The reader should justify this usage by a dimensional argument.

A second metric system of units is also common in physics. In this system, the centimeter, gram, and second are taken as fundamental units, and the system is called the ***cgs system.*** The cgs unit of force is the gram centimeter per second squared, and it is specially called a ***dyne***. It is left as an exercise for the reader to show that

$$1 \text{ N} = 10^5 \text{ dynes}. \quad (4.10\text{-}2)$$

In the fps system, the unit of force is called the ***poundal*** and it is equivalent to the pound foot per second squared. The reader can also verify that

$$1 \text{ N} = 7.2330 \text{ poundals}. \quad (4.10\text{-}3)$$

EXERCISES

4.10-1 An automobile has a mass of 1200 kg and has four-wheel brakes. What must be the average force between each wheel and the road if the car is to be stopped with a negative acceleration of 2.20 m/sec^2?

4.10-2 A car is started at the beginning of a measured kilometer and travels over the distance with a constant acceleration. At the end of the 1.000 km distance the speed of the car is 108 km/hr. If the car has a mass of 2500 kg and drives by its two rear wheels, what force is necessary between each driving wheel and the road during the run?

4.10-3 A hammer of 0.500 kg mass, moving at 30.0 m/sec, strikes a nail and is brought to rest by it in 0.0150 sec. What is the average force of the nail on the hammer?

4.11 Impulse and Work

When a force acts on a body and accelerates it, it is obvious that the force acts both through a time and through a distance. We might ask whether there are any useful relationships to be developed from either the time during which the force acts or the distance through which the body travels while the force is acting.

We have already encountered an equation involving the time during which the force acts. If we write Eq. (4.9-1) as $F\,\Delta t = \Delta p = m\,\Delta v$, we see that the terms on the right, either Δp or $m\,\Delta v$, express the *change of momentum* produced by the force F acting for the interval Δt. It is useful to give the term $F\,\Delta t$ a special name, so it is called an increment of ***impulse.*** If a constant force F_c acts during the time interval $(t_1 - t_0)$, the total impulse during the interval is $F_c(t_1 - t_0)$. If the force producing the change of momentum is not constant, then in order to find the total impulse we must somehow sum up all of the infinitesimal incremental impulses, $F\,dt$, i.e., we find $\int F\,dt$. In this book, however, we shall be concerned with constant forces, or at least with forces that vary in a very simple way, so that our calculations of impulse will not be difficult.

If the force is constant and if the body is at rest when the force begins to act, the force can act for a time t producing a speed v; thus,

$$F\int_0^t dt = m\int_0^v dv,$$

$$Ft = mv. \tag{4.11-1}$$

This equation says that the total impulse Ft produced the momentum mv. More generally a body at time $t = 0$ may have a momentum mv_0; if an impulse Ft is then exerted upon the body, a change of momentum is produced so that

$$Ft = mv - mv_0. \tag{4.11-2}$$

Now let us ask whether the quantity $F\,\Delta s$ has a useful meaning, where F is the average force acting on a body as it accelerates through a distance Δs. We start with Eq. (4.9-4) and multiply both sides of the equation by Δs; thus,

$$\begin{aligned} F &= ma, \\ F\,\Delta s &= ma\,\Delta s = m(\Delta v/\Delta t)\,\Delta s \\ &= m(\Delta s/\Delta t)\,\Delta v = mv\,\Delta v, \end{aligned} \tag{4.11-3}$$

where first we made use of the definition of average acceleration that $a = (\Delta v/\Delta t)$ and then we regrouped the Δv, Δs, and Δt to recognize that $\Delta s/\Delta t = v$.

Now if F and m are both constants, we may write Eq. (4.11-3) in terms of integrals as

$$F\int_0^s ds = m\int_0^v v\,dv, \tag{4.11-4}$$

where for convenience we have assumed that the body was at rest at the origin when the force started to act. In analogy with the discussion of Sec. 3.17, the integral on the right must sum to $\frac{1}{2}v^2$, and that on the left sums to s. Thus, we have

$$Fs = \tfrac{1}{2}mv^2. \tag{4.11-5}$$

The quantity on the right of Eq. (4.11-5) is called the ***kinetic energy*** of the body. We shall abbreviate this as KE; thus,

$$KE = \tfrac{1}{2}mv^2. \tag{4.11-6}$$

The force F accelerating the body from rest through a distance s produces an amount of kinetic energy of the body given by $\frac{1}{2}mv^2$. The term Fs is defined as ***work***. The infinitesimal increment of work is $F\,ds$.

More generally, we can have a body whose kinetic energy initially is $KE_0 = \frac{1}{2}mv_0^2$. If a constant force F then acts on the body as it travels a distance s, the force does an amount of work $w = Fs$. This work shows up as a change in the kinetic energy. Therefore,

$$w = Fs = KE - KE_0 = \tfrac{1}{2}mv^2 - \tfrac{1}{2}mv_0^2. \tag{4.11-7}$$

The notions of work and kinetic energy, as we shall see, are very important. First, work can be done in order to produce kinetic energy. Also, a body having kinetic energy can be made to do work *at the expense of the kinetic energy*. We shall see later that such conversions of work to kinetic energy and of kinetic energy to work will supply us with the groundwork on which a conservation law can be based. The expression of Eq. (4.11-7) is known as the ***work-energy theorem.***

4.12 Units and Dimensions of Impulse, Work, and Energy

As already noted, the dimensions of momentum are

$$[p] = [m][v] = [m\ell t^{-1}], \tag{4.5-4}$$

and the unit in the mks system is kilogram meter per second. The dimensions of impulse are, of course,

$$[f][t] = [\ell m t^{-2}][t] = [\ell m t^{-1}], \tag{4.12-1}$$

and the unit is the newton-second. Note that Eqs. (4.5-4) and (4.12-1) are of the same dimensions, as they must be.

Work has the dimensions

$$[f][\ell] = [\ell m t^{-2}][\ell] = [\ell^2 m t^{-2}]. \tag{4.12-2}$$

A unit of work would be the ***newton-meter***; however, a special name is provided for this unit of work so that

$$1 \text{ newton-meter} = 1 \textit{ joule}. \tag{4.12-3}$$

As indicated earlier, the abbreviation for newton is N, so the newton-meter would be abbreviated Nm. The abbreviation for joule is J.

The dimensions of kinetic energy are

$$[m][\ell^2 t^{-2}] = [m\ell^2 t^{-2}]. \tag{4.12-4}$$

A suitable unit would be kilogram-meter squared per second squared; however, since this unit is equivalent to the joule, kinetic energy is usually expressed in joules. Note that Eqs. (4.12-2) and (4.12-4) necessarily express the same dimensions.

EXERCISES

4.12-1 An automobile having a mass of 1500 kg and an initial speed of 20 m/sec is slowed to a speed of 5 m/sec in 5 sec. What is the average acceleration? What is the change of momentum? What impulse is required? What average decelerating force is required?

4.12-2 In Ex. 4.12-1, how far does the automobile travel during the deceleration interval? How much work does the decelerating force do? What is the kinetic energy at the start of the deceleration? At the end? What is the total change in kinetic energy?

4.12-3 A baseball with a mass of 0.40 kg is attracted by the earth with a force of 3.92 N. If the ball falls from rest through a height of 20.0 m, according to Eqs. (3.11-1B) and (3.11-1C), what speed does it have at the end of the fall? What is its kinetic energy? How much work does the attraction of the earth do in producing the kinetic energy?

4.12-4 For Ex. 4.12-3 show that the total impulse is equal to the total change of momentum during the fall.

4.13 Forces During Collisions

In a collision between two bodies, such as those discussed in Secs. 4.2–4.3, both bodies are accelerated, the accelerations being in opposite directions. Suppose that the two bodies have masses m_A and m_B, and that their velocities change by Δv_A and Δv_B, respectively, during any short time interval Δt. In order that momentum may be conserved during this time interval, it must be true that

$$m_A \, \Delta v_A = -m_B \, \Delta v_B.$$

Dividing both sides of this equation by Δt, we find that

$$m_A \, a_A = - m_B \, a_B,$$

where a_A and a_B are the respective accelerations of the two bodies. Finally, by the use of Eq. (4.9-4), we see that the forces on the two bodies, during any time interval whatever, are equal in magnitude and opposite in direction.

It is an intrinsic property of forces that they always act between two bodies rather than upon a single body. Newton summed up the property in the third of his laws of motion: *To every action there is an equal and opposite reaction.* When a runner starts into motion, the ground pushes forward on his feet just as hard as he pushes backward on the ground. It is this forward push of the earth that accelerates him. The necessity of the force can be demonstrated if one attempts to start running on smooth ice, on which the friction is so low that an appreciable horizontal force cannot be exerted.

The action and reaction in the case of a runner can be demonstrated quite easily by the experiment sketched in Fig. 4.9. The four-wheeled truck sits on a

FIG. 4.9 Demonstration of action and reaction.

smooth horizontal floor. If the man starts running toward the left, the truck itself will move toward the right, due to the force exerted on it by his feet. The more massive the truck, the more slowly it will move, in accordance with the conservation law for momentum.

Many of the forces that we encounter are *elastic forces*, which are exerted by a body when it is deformed. For example, a helical spring that is stretched beyond its natural (or normal) length pulls on any bodies attached to its ends. The same spring, when compressed to less than its normal length, exerts pushes on bodies attached to its ends. Elastic forces of this sort allow the nice adjustment of the forces exerted by inanimate bodies. When you sit on a chair your weight causes the seat and legs of the chair to be compressed. During the compression the upward elastic force exerted on you by the chair increases until its magnitude is just equal to your weight; equilibrium of the system is then attained.

In the collisions illustrated in Figs. 4.1, 4.3, and 4.5–4.7, it is an elastic force exerted by the spring bumpers that transfers momentum from one car to another. A careful examination of Fig. 4.1 shows that these bumpers have a different shape during the collision than they have before or after. It is this compression of the bumpers that supplies the push needed to accelerate the cars to their final velocities. The magnitude of the force during the collision varies somewhat as shown in Fig. 4.10. It is zero until the springs make contact,

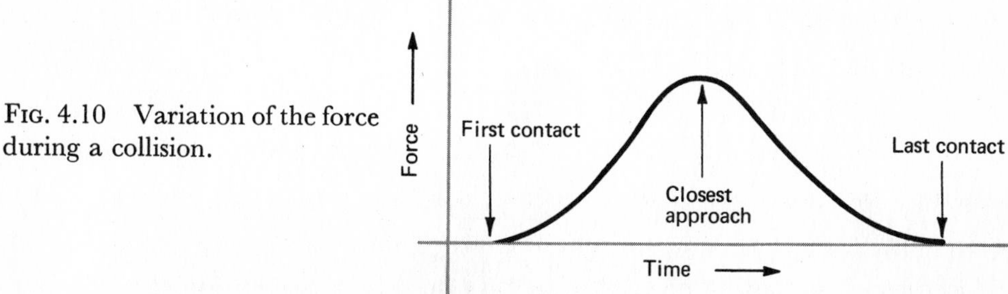

FIG. 4.10 Variation of the force during a collision.

then increases as the deformation becomes greater, reaches a maximum when the two cars are closest to each other, and finally decreases to zero as the cars separate to the point at which the springs are no longer in contact. The area under the force vs. time curve is the impulse delivered from one car to the other during the collision.

4.14 Kinetic Energy Exchange in Collisions

We have seen that momentum is transferred from one body to another in any two body collision in such a way that the sum of the momenta of the bodies remains constant. From the considerations of Sec. 4.11 it is clear that kinetic energy is also exchanged among interacting bodies. It seems reasonable to ask whether kinetic energy is also conserved—whether the kinetic energy lost by one body is equal to that gained by a second body, with which it collides.

To answer this question, we re-examine those collisions already studied. Table 4.1 shows the values of the masses involved in the various collisions, the velocities before and after collision as obtained from analyses of the photographs, and the total kinetic energies before and after the collisions, calculated as the sum of the $\frac{1}{2}mv^2$ of the two bodies. A glance at the last two columns of the table is sufficient to show that kinetic energy is not, in general, conserved. It is equally apparent, however, that the kinetic energy after impact is never greater than before impact. It appears that kinetic energy can be lost in collisions of this sort, but not gained. Hence we can write an inequality:

$$\tfrac{1}{2}m_A v_A{}^2 + \tfrac{1}{2}m_B v_B{}^2 \geq \tfrac{1}{2}m_A v_A{}'^2 + \tfrac{1}{2}m_B v_B{}'^2, \qquad (4.14\text{-}1)$$

where the unprimed velocities are those before impact and the primed are those after impact.

The study of many interactions among "passive" bodies, such as these used in our collisions, supports completely the inequality (4.14-1). By "passive" we indicate that the bodies can do work only by decreasing their speeds, i.e., that they do not include such devices as percussion caps that explode on impact or previously compressed springs that are released during the collision (e.g., mousetraps), or riders who push with poles at approaching objects.

Table 4.1 *Kinetic Energies in Collisions*

Collision Shown in	Mass		Velocity (cm/sec)				Kinetic Energy	
	Body A	Body B	A before impact	B before impact	A after impact	B after impact	Before Impact	After Impact
Fig. 4.3	m	m	0.0	50.3	50.3	0.0	$m(1.27 \times 10^3\ \text{cm}^2/\text{sec}^2)$	$m(1.27 \times 10^3)\ \text{cm}^2/\text{sec}^2$
Fig. 4.5	m	m	0.0	50.3	25.2	25.2	$m(1.27 \times 10^3\ \text{cm}^2/\text{sec}^2)$	$m(0.64 \times 10^3)\ \text{cm}^2/\text{sec}^2$
Fig. 4.6	m	m	47.8	−35.0	−29.8	40.4	$m(1.70 \times 10^3\ \text{cm}^2/\text{sec}^2)$	$m(1.26 \times 10^3)\ \text{cm}^2/\text{sec}^2$
Fig. 4.7	$2m$	m	0.0	55.0	35.6	−15.2	$m(1.51 \times 10^3\ \text{cm}^2/\text{sec}^2)$	$m(1.38 \times 10^3)\ \text{cm}^2/\text{sec}^2$

Returning now to Table 4.1, we see that the two collisions in which the total kinetic energy remained most nearly constant were those in which good spring bumpers were employed. These were the ones in which we approximated perfectly elastic collisions. It is easy to imagine that imperfections in the elastic behavior of the springs account for the decreases in kinetic energy in the collisions of Figs. 4.6 and 4.7. We can therefore sharpen our concept of a ***perfectly elastic collision*** and define such a collision as one in which the total kinetic energy remains unchanged. The collisions of Figs. 4.6 and 4.7 are not perfectly elastic under this definition, that of Fig. 4.3 is.

The collision shown in Fig. 4.5 was one in which the cars stuck together after impact. In perfectly inelastic collisions of this sort it is easy to show that the kinetic energy after the collision is (see Prob. 4.6)

$$(KE)' = \frac{1}{2}\frac{(m_A v_A + m_B v_B)^2}{m_A + m_B}, \tag{4.14-2}$$

It is also easy to show that the kinetic energy given by Eq. (4.14-2) is less than that for any collision in which the conditions are other than perfectly inelastic ones (see Prob. 4.7). Hence we may rewrite the inequality (4.14-1) as

$$\tfrac{1}{2}m_A v_A^2 + \tfrac{1}{2}m_B v_B^2 \geq \tfrac{1}{2}m_A v_A'^2 + \tfrac{1}{2}m_B v_B'^2 \geq \frac{1}{2}\frac{(m_A v_A + m_B v_B)^2}{m_A + m_B}. \tag{4.14-3}$$

This expression is a quite general one for all interactions among passive bodies.

We saw in Sec. 4.11 that the impulse delivered by one body during any interval Δt is equal and opposite to that delivered to the body with which it is interacting during the same interval. Thus, if F_{BA} is the force with which body B acts on body A, and F_{AB} that with which A acts on B,

$$F_{BA}\,\Delta t = -F_{AB}\,\Delta t.$$

During the same interval, the work done by body A is $F_{AB} v_B \Delta t$. This, in general, is not equal to $-F_{BA} v_A \Delta t$, the work done by body B. Hence we cannot expect the kinetic energy to be conserved *during* the collision process, even when the collisions are perfectly elastic. An illustrative example can be found in the perfectly elastic collision of two equal masses moving with velocities of equal magnitude and opposite directions before collision. The bodies are approaching each other before the collision and are separating after; there must be some instant during the collision when they are at rest with respect to each other. At this instant, the requirement of the conservation of momentum, that the two velocities be equal in magnitude, requires that each body have zero velocity. It follows that the total kinetic energy of the system at this instant is zero. What has happened is that the work done by the bodies has been done on the spring bumpers. We shall see later that energy can be stored by elastically deformed bodies. This is one form of potential energy, and we shall return to it in Sec. 4.18.

In any collision, the kinetic energy of the bodies decreases as they approach each other. At the same time the elastic deformation, and hence the potential energy, increases. As the bodies separate, some or all of the potential energy is converted to kinetic energy. In a perfectly elastic interaction all of the potential energy is returned and the kinetic energy after the impact is the same as before. In all other collisions some of the potential energy is not returned as kinetic energy. A permanent change takes place in the colliding bodies, some of which are left in a deformed state (e.g., balls of putty or soft wax) and some become warmer. We shall find later that we can set up a kind of balance sheet in which the energy of the system is entirely accounted for. At the moment, however, we do not have the evidence before us to justify a law of conservation of energy. We have only an approach to it in the form of the work-energy theorem of Eq. (4.11-7), which connects the change in kinetic energy of a single body with the work done by or on that body.

4.15 Weight

In Chapter 3 we saw that any freely falling body, at a given spot on the earth's surface, experiences an acceleration g. The concepts which we have now developed show us that this acceleration must be due to a downward force acting on the body. This force, which is due to the gravitational attraction between the earth (or other very massive body, such as a planet) and the body, is the ***weight*** of the body. The constancy of the acceleration due to gravity indicates that the weight of any body, at a given location on the earth, is proportional to the mass of the body. Since the acceleration produced in a body is given by the quotient obtained by dividing the force by the mass [cf. Eq. (4.9-3)], we have

$$g = w/m, \qquad (4.15\text{-}1)$$

where w is the weight of the body whose mass is m. Since Eq. (4.15-1) is valid for all bodies and since g depends only on location, the proportionality of weight and mass follows.

The proportionality between weight and mass leads to a confusion of these two terms in common parlance. One often speaks of the weight of a body as so many kilograms or so many pounds, although kilograms and pounds are units of *mass* rather than weight. In physics we dare not slip into this error, as may be simply shown by two facts:

(a) As shown by Eq. (4.15-1), weight is a force and therefore has the dimensions $[m\ell t^{-2}]$, quite different from those of mass.
(b) The weight of a body depends on the location of the body, whereas its mass is an intrinsic property. Even when a body is kept on the surface of the earth but moves from the equator toward one of the poles, its weight changes. If we consider a more radical move, which removes the body from the earth, the weight does not stay even approximately constant. Thus a body transported to the moon, where gravitational attraction is less than on the earth, would weigh only about one sixth as much as it does here, although its mass would remain unchanged.

In order to avoid the error of confusing mass and weight, we shall customarily measure weights in newtons or poundals. If we desire, for simplicity, to compromise with the less exact common speech, we may refer to the weight of a kilogram as one ***kilogram weight***, but in doing so we must remember that this is only an abbreviation for the weight of one kilogram at a particular location. Similarly, the weight of a one pound mass may be referred to as one ***pound weight*** if it is sufficiently clear in the particular context involved that we are dealing with the weight of the mass on the surface of the earth, so that no confusion can arise. Since the variation of g over the earth's surface is a few tenths of a percent, the kilogram weight and the pound weight are not fixed units of force, but vary from point to point. In the ordinary applications of commerce and engineering, in which inaccuracies of the order of one percent are not serious, there is no harm in this inconstancy of the unit. It is left as an exercise for the reader to show that, on the average (see Sec. 3.9),

$$1 \text{ K wt} = 9.80 \text{ N} \tag{4.15-2}$$

and that

$$1 \text{ lb wt} = 32.2 \text{ poundals.} \tag{4.15-3}$$

A discussion of the engineering systems of units which make use of these units of force is given in Appendix D.

EXERCISES

4.15-1 Find the average force with which each of the cars of Ex. 4.2-1 acts on the other during the collision. Assume that the cars are in contact for 5×10^{-4} sec.

4.15-2 The weight of a body on the planet Jupiter is 2.68 times its weight on the earth. What would be the speed of a freely falling body which had fallen one second from rest on Jupiter? How far would it have fallen during the second?

4.15-3 Two masses, 100.0 g and 105.0 g, are connected by a light string which passes over a pulley. The pulley may be considered to turn perfectly freely and the masses of the string and of the pulley are negligible. What will be the acceleration of the masses?

4.15-4 A rocket is fired by exerting an average upward force of 1.1×10^5 N on it for 1.00 min. If the mass of the rocket is 1.0×10^4 kg, what is its speed at the end of the minute?

4.16 The Equal Arm Balance

Although mass and weight are distinctly different quantities, the proportionality of the two at a given location gives us a simple way of comparing masses. This method of measurement is based on the fact that two equal masses, in the same location, have equal weights. In the ***equal arm balance***, which is sketched in Fig. 4.11, two pans are supported by a beam which is free to rotate about a

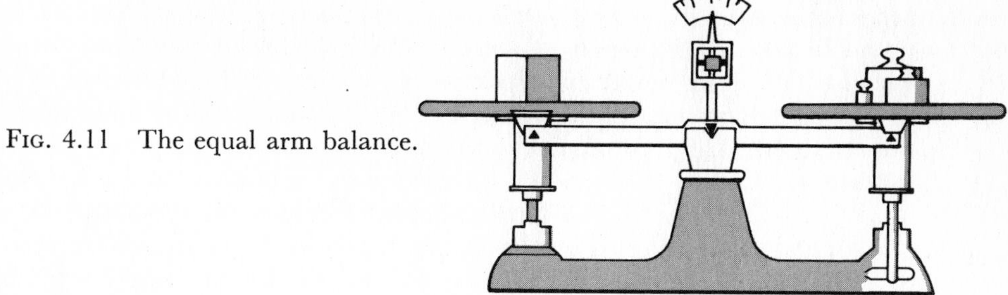

FIG. 4.11 The equal arm balance.

point exactly halfway between the two pans. If unequal masses are loaded on the pans, it is found that the pan containing the larger mass is depressed. On the other hand, if the two masses are equal, equal forces press down on the two pans. Since the two halves of the balance are then exactly alike, there is no reason for one side to behave differently from the other, and the balance arm will come to rest in a horizontal position. The type of reasoning used here is called a ***symmetry argument***. All symmetry arguments make use of the fact that, when two parts of a system are exactly alike, there is no reason to expect that one of the parts will behave differently from the other. Another simple case of such reasoning is that which we can use to decide that a perfectly symmetrical spherical ball will rest on a horizontal table in any position, since there is nothing about the ball to determine what point shall be "up" or "down." Symmetry arguments are powerful tools in reasoning, and we shall use them repeatedly. A different method of discussing the equal arm balance will appear in Chapter 7 and will verify that used here.

In the practical use of the equal arm balance, an unknown mass is placed on one pan and a number of standard masses are placed on the other until the instrument ust balances. The unknown mass in one pan is then equal to the sum of the masses in the other pan. In order that a variety of masses may be determined, the standard set of masses (sometimes referred to, rather carelessly, as a set of weights) contains a number of pieces of metal whose masses are whole-number multiples or fractional multiples of the unit of mass. Thus, a set to be used with a sensitive balance might contain the following standards, all given in grams: 50, 20, 20, 10, 5, 2, 2, 1, 0.5, 0.2, 0.2, 0.1, 0.05, 0.02, 0.02, 0.01.

The equal arm balance provides one of the gentler methods referred to in Sec. 4.4 for the comparison of the International Prototype Kilogram with its copies, and in fact such methods are almost universally used for the comparison of large masses in the laboratory. However, for very small masses, such as those involved in atomic systems, or very large ones, such as those of the heavenly bodies, the balance is hardly suitable, and in the measurement of such masses we shall be forced to return to the basic definition of Sec. 4.3.

4.17 Inertial Mass and Gravitational Mass

In Sec. 4.3 we devised a method by which the mass of a given body could be compared with that of a standard body. Our method involved a collision experiment and depended on the inertia of the masses for its operation. We call the mass determined by this measurement the ***inertial mass***.

We can also determine the mass of the given body by comparing its weight with that of the standard body. The gist of the weighing method was described in Secs. 4.15 and 4.16. We call the mass determined in this manner the ***gravitational mass***.

Since the determination of inertial mass uses resistance by the body to acceleration whereas the measurement of gravitational mass prevents acceleration by a balancing force that prevents fall, one may reasonably ask whether the two kinds of measurements measure the same property of matter. Sir Isaac Newton first considered the question and devised experiments intended to show the difference, if any, between inertial mass and gravitational mass. His experiments all failed to show any difference. Since then, several other experiments of extreme sensitivity have been employed in attempts to discover a difference, and none were successful. We conclude, therefore, that inertial mass and gravitational mass are the same thing. We shall return to the equivalence of gravitational and inertial masses in Chapter 14, where we shall find it to form the basis of the theory of general relativity.

4.18 Gravitational Potential Energy

We have seen that some or all of the kinetic energy of bodies that undergo collisions is converted to potential energy during the collisions, this potential energy being stored in the springs or other devices through which the bodies interact. Elastic potential energy is stored whenever a compressed, stretched, or otherwise deformed body can exert forces on other bodies as it returns to its normal configuration.

There is another simple and important way in which potential energy may be stored. Suppose that we lift a mass m to a height h and then allow it to fall freely. In returning to its original level (Fig. 4.12), it acquires a speed

$v = (2gh)^{1/2}$ in accordance with Eq. (3.18-6). It therefore has a kinetic energy

$$KE = \tfrac{1}{2}mv^2 = mgh \tag{4.18-1}$$

on its return. While the body is at a height h, it is said to possess a ***gravitational potential energy*** mgh, equal to the work that it can do in falling.

There is one property of gravitational potential energy which is worthy of considerable notice. Suppose that the mass m was originally sitting on a table whose height above the floor is H, and that h is measured from the table top, as in Fig. 4.12. The energy of the mass is now mgh. If we remove the table, the mass can fall through a distance $h + H$ and the work that it can do in falling to the floor is $mg(h + H)$. Which of these two results is correct? Since the body itself has not been affected, either of the two expressions for the energy seems equally valid. This conclusion is indeed correct, and it is a property of potential energy that the position of the body at which the potential energy is zero is entirely a matter of choice. If two observers disagree regarding the zero of potential energy for a body in the earth's field, their expressions for this energy will differ by mgz, where z is the vertical component of the distance between their zeros. For any two observers this quantity will be a constant. Consequently, if we are to be quite rigorous, we should write the potential energy as

$$PE = mgh + A, \tag{4.18-2}$$

where A can take on any value, depending on the level chosen for zero potential energy. Such an expression might seem to be worthless, since it never enables

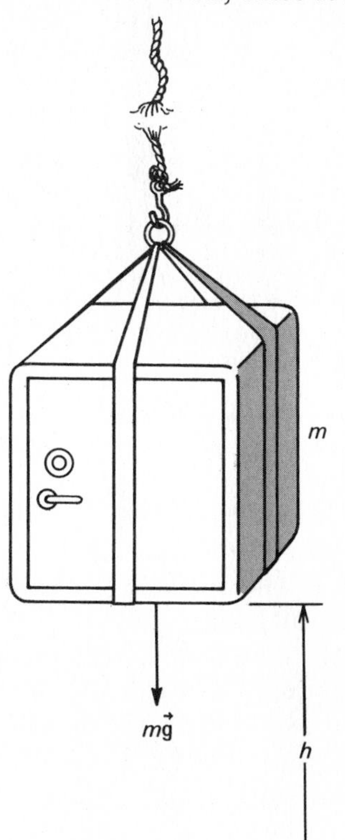

FIG. 4.12 Gravitational potential energy.

us to determine the potential energy. We shall find, however, that every physical problem in which potential energy occurs involves a change in the energy, rather than its absolute value. Suppose that an observer wishes to know how much the potential energy of the mass m changes when the mass drops from a height h_1 to a new height h_2. He finds for the two energies

$$PE_1 = mgh_1 + A$$

and

$$PE_2 = mgh_2 + A,$$

so that the difference is given by

$$PE = mgh(h_1 - h_2).$$

In this expression the unknown constant has disappeared. Consequently, since we are interested only in differences of potential energy, we need not worry about the constant A.

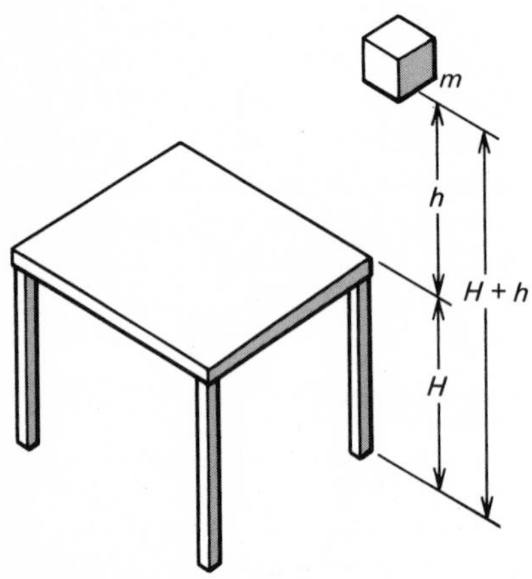

FIG. 4.13 The indefiniteness of the zero of potential energy.

4.19 *Summary*

In this chapter we have arrived at definitions of several quantities which have involved physical description and which are particularly important in the consideration of changes of motion of material bodies. Two of these, mass and momentum, have been found to have the important property that they are conserved in all processes, i.e., that they can neither be created nor destroyed. The third important quantity, force, is the agent which acts between bodies to transfer momentum from one to the other. One type of force in which we have particular interest is weight, which is due to the gravitational attraction between the earth (or other massive body) and any mass on or near its surface. We have also met work and kinetic energy and have encountered partial evidence that kinetic energy is only one form of energy, a quantity that we shall later find to be conserved.

PROBLEMS

4.1 (a) Three bodies, A, B, and C, are used in a collision experiment on a straight, frictionless track. Body A is initially moving with a velocity v_A, body C with a velocity v_C, and body B initially at rest. After the collision all three bodies stick together and move with a common velocity u. Show that

$$m_B = \frac{m_A(v_A - u) + m_C(v_C - u)}{u}$$

where m_A, m_B, and m_C are the respective masses of the three bodies.

(b) In a second experiment the conditions of the first are repeated, except that the initial velocity of body A is $2v_A$. The final velocity is then V. Find the ratio m_A/m_C in terms of v_A, v_C, u, and V.

4.2 A truck with a total mass of 6000 lb passes under a bridge, from which a 200-lb mass drops onto the truck, falling vertically. Just before the mass strikes, the truck is moving at 35.0 mi/hr. (a) What is the speed of the truck immediately after the mass strikes? (b) Does the kinetic energy of the truck increase or decrease? By what fraction of its original kinetic energy does it change?

4.3 A jet plane with a mass of 2.1×10^4 kg accelerates on the runway from rest to a speed of 67 m/sec in 17 sec. Assume the acceleration to be uniform and neglect frictional effects. (a) What is the average thrust of the engines during this time? (b) How much work must the engines do during the acceleration?

4.4 Two bodies, of mass m and M, are moving with respective velocities v and V just before they collide head-on, perfectly elastically. After the collision they are found to be moving with respective velocities u and U. (a) Show that $(v + u) = (V + U)$. (b) Show that the kinetic energy transferred from m to M during the collision is

$$\Delta E = \frac{2mM(MV + mv)(v - V)}{(m + M)^2}$$

4.5 Suppose that V in Prob. 4.4 is zero. (a) Find u as a function of v and the ratio m/M. (b) Find the amount of kinetic energy transferred as a function of the ratio m/M and v. (c) Plot a curve of the fraction of the initial kinetic energy of m that is transferred to M for ratios m/M between zero and ten. (d) What fraction of the initial kinetic energy of m is transferred if $M \gg m$?

4.6 Derive Eq. (4.14-2) for a perfectly inelastic collision.

4.7 Two bodies, of mass m_A and m_B, collide head-on. The respective velocities before the collision are v_A and v_B. After the collision the respective velocities are

$$v_A' = v' + u \quad \text{and} \quad v_B' = v' + w,$$

where v' is the velocity that they would have if the collision were perfectly inelastic, i.e.,

$$v' = \frac{m_A v_A + m_B v_B}{m_A + m_B}.$$

(a) Show from the conservation of momentum that

$$u/w = -m_B/m_A.$$

(b) Compute the total kinetic energy of the two bodies after the collision in terms of m_A, m_B, v', u, and w. (c) Using the result obtained in (a), show that the kinetic energy after the collision is greater than $\frac{1}{2}(m_A + m_B)v'^2$, regardless of whether u or w is positive or negative. Hence, justify the inequality (4.14-3).

4.8 Two bodies with equal masses collide head-on. Before the collision one is moving with a velocity v_A and the other with a velocity v_B. After the collision the velocity of the first is $v_A' = 2v_A$. (a) What is the velocity of the second body after the collision? (b) Prove that v_B must have been equal to or less than $2v_A$ if the bodies are passive.

4.9 The standard masses used with the equal arm balance are usually calibrated against a single standard mass. Suppose that a set of five masses marked 1 g, 2 g, 2*g, 5 g, and 10 g are to be calibrated against a single standard, which is known to have a mass of (10.0000 ± 0.0001) g. An analytical balance, with which the uncertainty in the weighing is 0.0001 g, is used. The 10-g mass is first compared with the standard and found to have a mass of (10.0023 ± 0.0001) g. The four other masses are then placed on one side of the balance and the standard on the other. The sum of the four is found to be (9.9982 ± 0.0001) g. Finally, the 1, 2, and 2* masses together are found to have a mass that is (0.0032 ± 0.0001) g less than that of the 5-g mass.

(a) What is mass of the 5-g mass? What is its uncertainty? (b) Devise a scheme for calibrating the other three masses.

REFERENCES

4A Ernst Mach, *The Science of Mechanics*, Open Court, La Salle, Ill., 6th edition 1960. The following selections discuss basic principles: pp. 235–242, 247–252, 264–271.

4B William Francis Magie, *A Source Book in Physics*, Harvard, Cambridge, Mass., 1935. Selections from d'Alembert, Leibnitz, and Young relate to the development of the concepts of momentum and energy.

4C Franklin Miller, *Inertial Forces—Translational Acceleration*, a 2-min film loop. (No. 80-213, The Ealing Corp., Cambridge, Mass.)

5 ⇨ *Motions in Space*

5.1 Coordinates

The discussions in Chapters 3 and 4, which considered only motions along straight lines, were sufficient to establish the fundamental principles of mechanics, but they are not general enough to allow the description of most real motions. It is therefore necessary to extend our study of the motions of material bodies to include those cases in which the bodies move about in the three dimensions of space.

Before discussing the motion of bodies in space, we must have methods by which the bodies can be located. When it is known that a body always remains on a given straight line, we can specify its position completely by stating its displacement, or its distance, with due regard to sign, from some fixed point, as we did in Fig. 3.1. On the other hand, if we say that an automobile is at a position 70 mi from a certain flagpole in Philadelphia, we have merely indicated that it is located somewhere on a circle of 70 mi radius and with its center in Philadelphia. If we wish to locate the car more precisely, we must give two pieces of data. Thus, we might say that the car is 70 miles from the flagpole in a direction 63° west of south. One piece of data is the distance, 70 miles; the other piece of data is the direction, 63° west of south. Alternatively, we might say that the car is 70 miles from the flagpole and on Route 1 between Philadelphia and Baltimore. Or in yet another way, we could say that the car is 32 miles south of the flagpole and 62 miles west of it.

Any one of the three statements above will be sufficient to locate the car. The important thing is that each statement requires, in addition to a specified reference point or origin (the flagpole in Philadelphia, in this case), two pieces of information. Other examples in which two pieces of data are used to locate a point on a surface are the latitude and longitude used in navigation for locating a point on the earth's surface, or the street and avenue numbers used in many cities. Thus, the statement that New York City has a longitude of 74°W and a latitude of 41°N locates that city with respect to the north-south line running through Greenwich, England, and with respect to the equator. Similarly, the statement that the New York Public Library is on the southwest corner of 42nd Street and Fifth Avenue locates it with respect to any other corner.

Although two pieces of data are sufficient to locate a point on the surface of the earth with respect to the origin, three are needed if we wish to locate a point which is not subject to the restriction that it is on a given surface. Thus, if we are giving the position of an airplane with respect to San Francisco, it is not sufficient to say that it is 100 mi east and 50 mi north of the city, but we must also specify its altitude. For example, the additional datum might be that the airplane is at an elevation of 12,500 ft above sea level. A little consideration should convince the reader that three pieces of properly chosen information can locate any point in space, with respect to a specified origin, and that two are adequate for a body which remains on a surface such as a sphere or a plane.

These pieces of information that locate a point with respect to an origin are called the ***coordinates*** of the point. On a line, one coordinate is required; on a surface such as a plane, two; in space, three. For simplicity, we shall limit the discussion of the next few sections to those situations in which two coordinates are sufficient. Since there are a number of equivalent ways of choosing these coordinates, we shall now consider some of the most useful.

5.2 *Coordinate Systems*

If we wish to locate a point on a plane surface, such as a table top, we can do so rapidly and easily by the construction of a coordinate system, such as that shown in Fig. 5.1. In the case shown, the system is constructed by drawing two

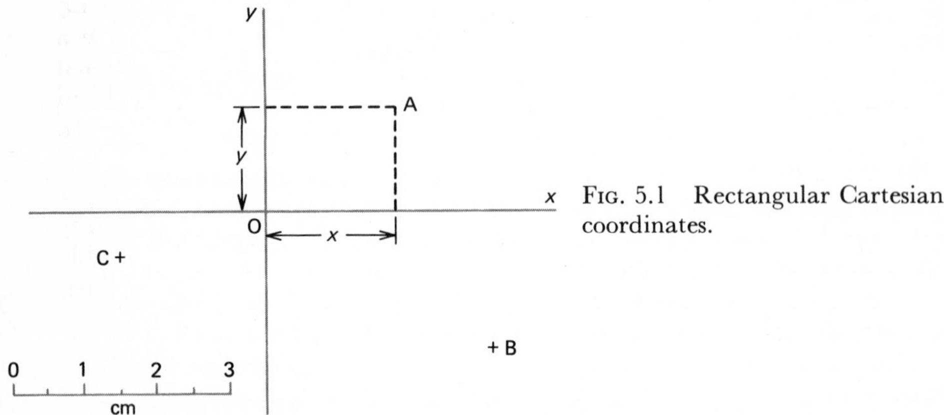

FIG. 5.1 Rectangular Cartesian coordinates.

lines, at right angles to each other, through the origin O, which is chosen at any convenient point. These lines are known as the ***axes*** (singular, ***axis***) of the coordinate system. For convenience, we shall label one line x and other y. To locate any point, such as A in Fig. 5.1, we draw two lines from A parallel to the two axes. We then say that the x-coordinate of A is the distance from the origin to the point where one of these lines intersects the x-axis. The y-coordinate of A is defined similarly. Since only one point corresponds to any pair of coordinates, the two coordinates are sufficient data to locate the point. Thus, if we say that A has the coordinates

$$x = 18 \text{ mm} \qquad \text{and} \qquad y = 14 \text{ mm},$$

we have located point A. If, as in the usual notation, we call distances to the right of or above the origin as positive, the signs of the coordinates will indicate in which of the four quadrants any point lies. Thus, in Fig. 5.1, B has the coordinates $x = 31$ mm, $y = -18$ mm, and C has the coordintaes $x = -20$ mm, $y = -6$ mm.

The type of ***coordinate system*** here illustrated is known as a ***rectangular Cartesian system.*** The term rectangular indicates that the two axes are at right angles to each other; the term Cartesian is in honor of René Descartes (1596–1650), who made wide use of this type of system. It will be recognized that the third way of stating the position of the car in Sec. 5.1 made use of a rectangular Cartesian system in which the axes were chosen as the east-west and north-south lines through the location of a flagpole in Philadelphia.

Another coordinate system for which we shall find occasional use is the ***polar coordinate system*** shown in Fig. 5.2. In this system a single line OP is drawn

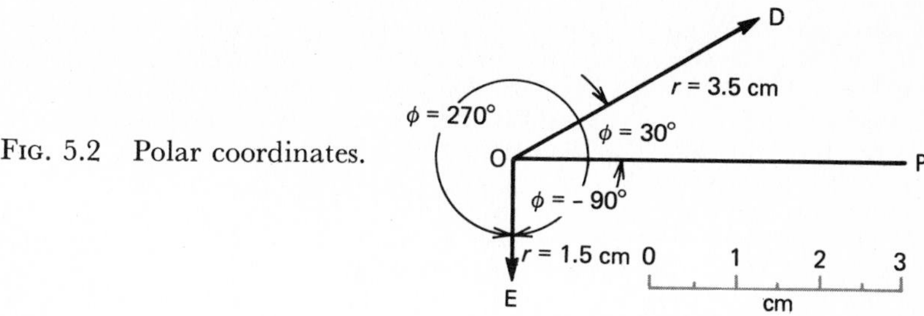

FIG. 5.2 Polar coordinates.

from the origin O in any convenient direction. To specify the position of any point with respect to the origin, a line is drawn from the origin to the point. The length of this line (usually denoted by r) and the angle that it makes with the initially chosen line, often indicated by the Greek letter ϕ (*phi*), are taken as the two coordinates of the point. It is conventional to call the angle positive when a counterclockwise rotation is needed in going from the axis OP to the point. Thus D in Fig. 5.2 has the coordinates $r = 3.5$ cm, $\phi = 30°$, and the coordinates of E are $r = 1.5$ cm, $\phi = 270°$. The latter may be equally well expressed as $r = 1.5$ cm and $\phi = -90°$. Thus the first method of stating the position of the car in Sec. 5.1 made use of a polar coordinate system.

As an example of the use of these two coordinate systems, Fig. 5.3 shows a stroboscopic photograph of four positions of a ball thrown or projected into the field of the camera. Figure 5.3a is marked with an origin and a set of rectangular Cartesian coordinate axes. Figure 5.3b uses the same origin, and the axis OP is the same as the axis Ox in Fig. 5.3a. Table 5.1 records the positions of the ball as expressed in each of the two coordinate systems.

There are many possible coordinate systems in addition to the two that we have just seen, but these two will serve most of our purposes. It must be remembered, whenever a coordinate system is established, that the origin may be chosen in any convenient location, and that the direction of one axis may also

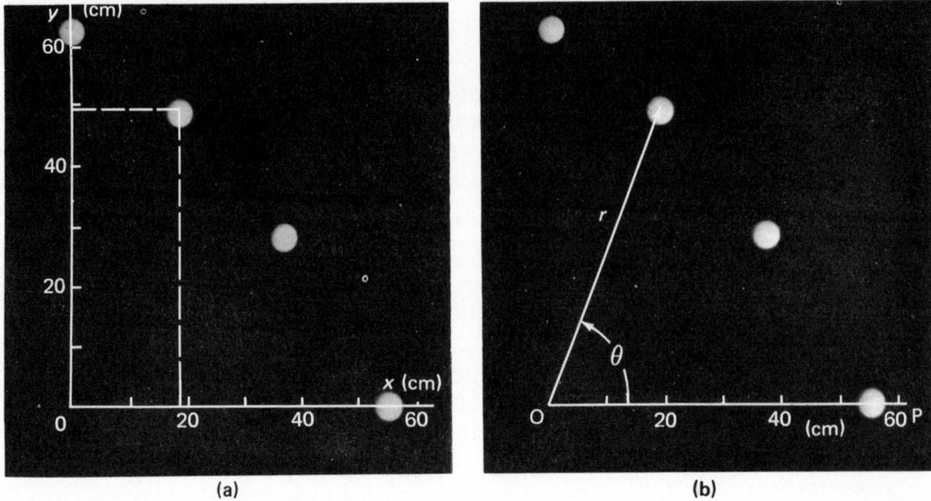

FIG. 5.3 Cartesian and polar coordinates applied to the same stroboscopic photograph of the trajectory of a thrown ball.

be chosen for convenience. Thus, in maps the convenient directions of the axes are commonly east-west and north-south, while in studies of the motion of a ball the most convenient choice of the x-axis is usually the horizontal direction of the ball's travel and that of the y-axis is the vertical.

Table 5.1 *Positions in Fig. 5.3 as Expressed in Cartesian and Polar Coordinates*

Position Number	x(cm)	y(cm)	r(cm)	θ
(1)	0.0	61.8	61.8	90.0°
(2)	18.9	48.4	51.9	75.6°
(3)	37.3	27.8	47.1	36.7°
(4)	55.6	0.0	55.6	0.0°

EXERCISES

Note: In many of the exercises of this book, either a rough sketch or an accurate scale drawing is essential to the solution. It is convenient to make such drawings on paper which is cross-ruled at intervals of about 4 to 6 lines per inch.

5.2-1 A room has the horizontal dimensions 20.0 ft by 32.0 ft. An experimenter establishes a rectangular Cartesian coordinate system with its origin in the exact center of the floor, and with the x-axis parallel to the longer dimension of the room. A second experimenter establishes the origin of another set of similar coordinates in the corner of the room which has a positive y-coordinate and a negative x-coordinate in the first experimenter's system. The positive x-axis of this second system is along the shorter wall through the new origin and the positive y-axis along the other wall. If a point is located at $x = 6.6$ ft and $y = 4.5$ ft in the first system, what will be its coordinates in the second system?

5.2-2 A point is located in a polar coordinate system at the position $r = 3.50$ in. and $\phi = 60°$. By construction of the coordinate system and subsequent measurement, find its coordinates in a rectangular Cartesian system which has the same origin as the polar system, has its x-axis along the line $\phi = 0°$, and has its y-axis along the line $\phi = 90°$.

5.3 *Displacement*

In Sec. 3.3 we made a distinction between displacement and distance. We stated that displacement is a notion requiring both a distance and a direction for its complete specification. Distance on the other hand is a term to be used when the particular direction is either irrelevant or ignorable. In both Chapters 3 and 4, since all motions and positions lay along straight lines, the directions were always constant and were therefore generally ignorable. What we were concerned with was the magnitude of the displacement or a distance.

We saw in Sec. 5.1, however, that in two dimensions the specification of the location of one point relative to another demanded not only the distance between the two points, but also some other piece of information. This latter datum was necessary to determine the direction of the second point from the first. The separation of any point B from any other point A, when specified in this complete fashion, is called the ***displacement*** of B from A. We must notice that the statement of *a displacement requires both a magnitude* (such as 50 mi) *and a direction* (such as north), whereas the specification of *a length requires only a magnitude.*

Displacements can always be represented by straight lines drawn on a map or scale drawing. Thus, the line OA in Fig. 5.4a indicates graphically the displacement of an automobile that has traveled 32 mi in a northeasterly direction

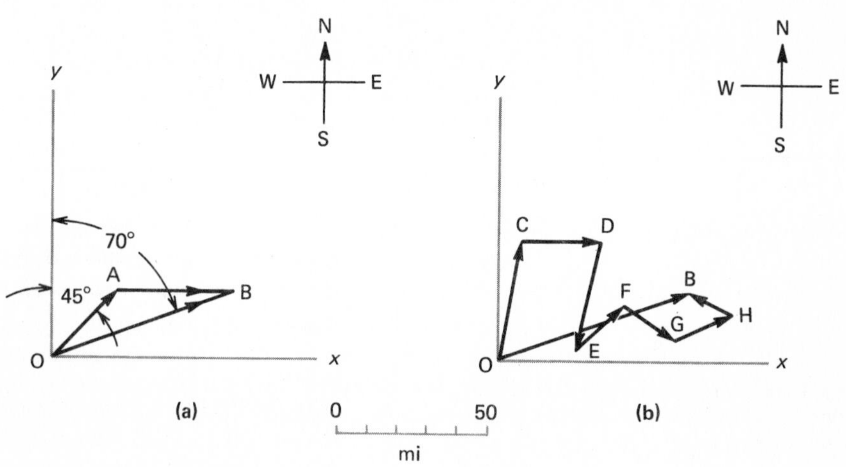

FIG. 5.4 Displacements and their addition.

from its starting point at O. If the car then continues its motion in an easterly direction for a distance of 40 mi, the displacement of its final position B from A is denoted by the line AB. If we wish to know the displacement of B from O, we need merely draw the line OB. Measurement of this displacement shows that it has a length of 67 mi and is directed 70° east of north.

The process just carried out shows that displacements add in a somewhat different way than do numbers or simple magnitudes, such as length. Since the displacement of B from O is 67 mi, 70° east of north, and the two individual displacements which carried the car from O to B had the combined lengths of 72 mi, we see that we cannot add displacements by ordinary algebraic methods. In fact, had the car traveled from O to B by the very indirect route OCDEFGHB (Fig. 5.4b) it would have traveled a total of 181 mi, but its final displacement would still be 67 mi, 70° east of north. To add displacements, then, we must draw them to scale, as we did in Fig. 5.4, starting each displacement at the end of the previous one, and determine the sum by the help of the line connecting the initial point of the first displacement with the final point of the last. We shall later find analytical ways of adding displacements, but they will merely be refinements of the graphical process outlined here (cf. Sec. 5.8).

5.4 Newtonian Relativity

When we discussed motion in a straight line, in Chapter 3, we arrived at a definition of velocity as the time rate of change of position, i.e.,

$$v = ds/dt = \lim_{\Delta t \to 0} (\Delta s/\Delta t). \tag{5.4-1}$$

We shall now have to ask whether this definition can be extended to motions that are not limited to one dimension. To do so, we will consider a very simple motion and see how this motion appears to two different observers.

Suppose that a train is moving eastward at 60 mi/hr and a man is running from the back to the front of the train at 10 mi/hr. In terms of basic measurements, the first of these statements means that the train covers a distance of 1 mile, as determined by measuring rods laid in a west-east line *along the ground*, during every minute as measured by a clock located *on the ground* somewhere along the track. Similarly, the second statement means that the man covers a distance of $\frac{1}{6}$ mile, as determined by measuring rods laid *along the floor of the train*, during every minute, as measured by a clock located *on the train.* Letting u be the speed of the train relative to the ground and v' be the speed of the man relative to the train, we get the state of affairs shown in Fig. 5.5. During a 5.0 min interval, the train has moved 5.0 mi to the east, *relative to the ground.* During the same interval, the man has moved 0.83 mi in the same direction, *relative to the train,* so that his displacement *relative to the ground* during this interval is

$$5.0 \text{ mi} + 0.83 \text{ mi} = 5.83 \text{ mi eastward.}$$

Applying the definition of velocity, we find the man's velocity v, relative to the ground, is

$$v = \frac{5.83 \text{ mi}}{5.0 \text{ min}} = \frac{5.83 \text{ mi}}{0.083 \text{ hr}} = 70 \text{ mi/hr eastward.}$$

This is exactly the algebraic sum of the velocity v' of the man relative to the train, and the velocity u of the train, relative to the ground. A consideration of time intervals other than 5.0 min convinces one that, for any interval,

$$v = u + v' \tag{5.4-2}$$

or that

$$v' = v - u.$$

Although our consideration of this case seems to be simple and straightforward, it does involve some assumptions that need experimental test. When we spoke of the displacements of the train relative to the ground and of the man relative to the ground during the "same interval," we assumed that two clocks, one on the ground and one on the train, were running at the same rate.

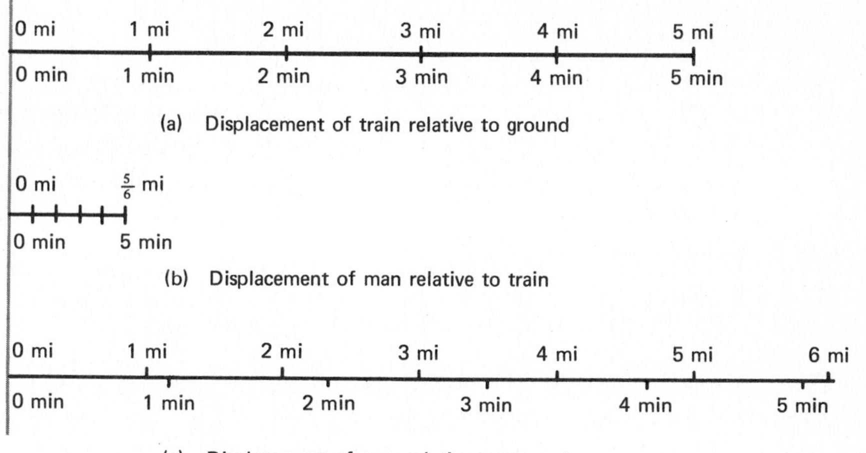

FIG. 5.5 Linear motion as seen in two reference frames.

Similarly, when we added 0.83 mi to 5.0 mi, we assumed that the measuring rods used on the ground and in the train were of identical length. We can suppose that the two people doing the measurement realize the importance of these considerations and that they have compared their clocks and measuring rods before and after the observations. These comparisons, however, would most easily be made with the rods or clocks sitting side by side, one rod or one clock not moving relative to the other. Do we have any guarantee that such a comparison still holds when one of the rods and one of the clocks have been put aboard the moving train? In the terms used in Chapter 2, is the clock on the train a "good" clock for an observer on the ground, and is the measuring rod used on the train a "rigid" rod during its transfer from the ground to the train?

It is certainly true that our assumptions are in accord with common experience and common sense—we do not notice that meter sticks shrink or stretch as they are put aboard a moving vehicle and we do not find that our watches lose or gain time as a result of a trip on a jet plane. We shall therefore continue to use the assumptions unless we find evidence that they are in error.

We now consider a case in which the motions as observed in the two systems are not parallel to each other. Suppose that a boat is traveling across a stream flowing southward at $u = 8$ mi/hr, and that the boat is operating with its throttle so set that it would be traveling at $v' = 20$ mi/hr if it were in *still water*. Because the propeller of the boat pushes against the water, whether the latter is still or in motion, the speed of the boat will be 20 mi/hr *relative to the water* in the stream. Its direction of motion, again relative to the water, will be along the line joining the center of the stern to the bow, i.e., along the direction in which the boat is pointed, or headed. We shall assume that this direction is due east.

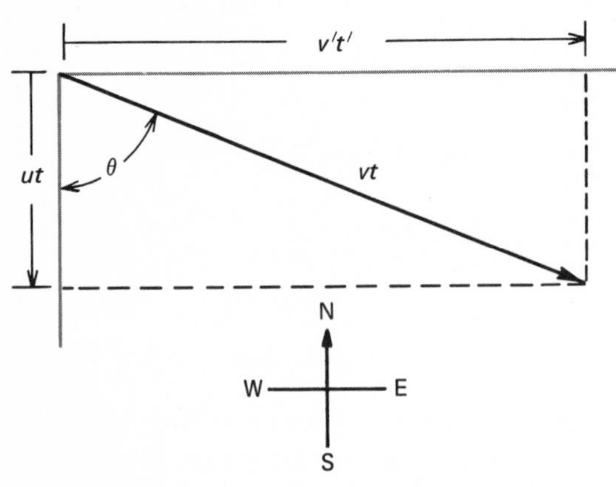

FIG. 5.6 Addition of two velocities that are not in the same direction.

Following the same reasoning used in constructing Fig. 5.6, we arrive at the diagram of Fig. 5.7a. We have there used t' to indicate a time interval as measured by a clock on the boat and t to indicate an interval as measured by a clock on the shore, but we have supposed that t always equals t'. We find that the boat has moved a distance $v't' = (20 \text{ mi/hr})(1/60) \text{ hr} = 0.33$ mi eastward in one minute and that the water has moved $ut = (8 \text{ mi/hr})(1/60) \text{ hr} = 0.13$ mi southward during the same interval. Hence, the *speed* of the boat *relative to the ground* is

$$v = \frac{\sqrt{(0.33 \text{ mi})^2 + (0.13 \text{ mi})^2}}{(1/60) \text{ hr}} = 21 \text{ mi/hr}.$$

Without restricting ourselves to a particular time, we can write

$$v = \frac{\sqrt{(ut)^2 + (v't')^2}}{t} = \sqrt{u^2 + v'^2}.$$

Similarly, we notice that the boat is traveling, relative to the ground, in a direction making angle θ with the bank, such that

$$\tan\theta = \frac{v't'}{ut} = \frac{v'}{u} = \frac{20\text{ mi/hr}}{8\text{ mi/hr}} = 2.5,$$

which gives $\theta = 68°$. Both this direction and the speed computed above are identical with those obtained if we add the velocities $\vec{u}$ and $\vec{v}'$ graphically, as we added displacements. In Fig. 5.7a we have shown such an addition and have put small arrows over the symbols for velocity to indicate that these are quantities having a direction associated with them, so that they add in a way different

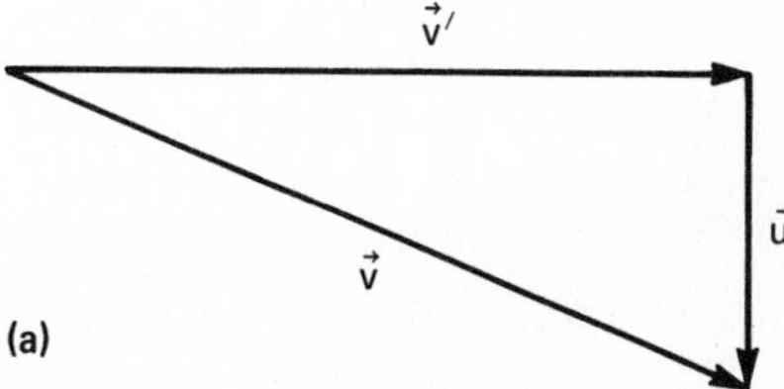

FIG. 5.7 Addition of velocities.

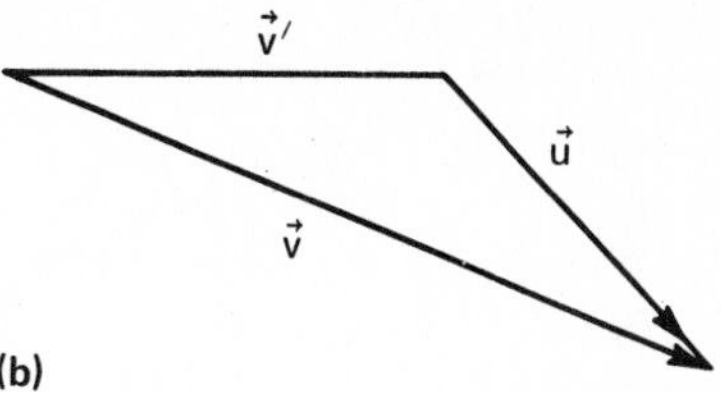

from numbers. If $\vec{v}'$ and $\vec{u}$ were neither parallel nor perpendicular to each other, we would arrive at the construction of a diagram similar to that of Fig. 5.7b. We may therefore write a general expression for the velocity $\vec{v}$ of a body, relative to some coordinate frame (or reference frame), whenever the velocity of the same body is $\vec{v}'$ in a reference frame moving with a velocity $\vec{u}$ relative to the first frame:

$$\vec{v} = \vec{u} + \vec{v}'. \tag{5.4-3}$$

In drawing diagrams such as Fig. 5.7, we must use scales in which any line segment representing a velocity has a length proportional to the magnitude of the velocity. Thus, the scale in Fig. 5.7 is such that

1 inch represents 10 mi/hr.

This may seem strange at first sight, but is actually no more trouble than it is to let one centimeter represent 30 mi, as we did in Fig. 5.3.

We shall see later that there is much good, although indirect, evidence that the Newtonian velocity transformation, expressed by Eq. (5.4-3), gives results that agree with experience. Under most, but not all circumstances, this is a valid way of computing the velocity of a body in one reference frame when the velocity in some other frame is known. Equation (5.4-2) is, of course, just a special case, valid when $\overrightarrow{\mathrm{u}}$ and $\overrightarrow{\mathrm{v}}'$ happen to be velocities directed along the same straight line.

5.5 *Vectors*

Displacement and velocity are the first two of many quantities that have certain common characteristics:

1. Each requires the statement of both a magnitude (e.g., 2 m or 40 m/sec) and a direction (e.g., northward or vertically downward).
2. The quantities can be added in the graphical manner illustrated in Figs. 5.3 and 5.7.

Quantities that satisfy these two conditions are called ***vectors.*** Those quantities which do not involve direction (such as length, mass, or speed) are called *scalars.* To distinguish the two, we shall denote vectors in this book by using roman letters as symbols for them, instead of italics, and by placing a small arrow over them. Thus, in reference to Fig. 5.3, the symbol $\overrightarrow{\mathrm{OB}}$ means the displacement of B from O, which has the magnitude 67 mi and the direction 70° east of north. The symbol OB merely means the length from O to B, which is a scalar quantity that is specified completely by its magnitude, 67 mi.

The ordinary algebra learned in school is only one of many algebras—it is applicable to scalars. It will now be necessary that we consider some of the ideas of ***vector algebra***, by which computations may be done with quantities such as displacements or velocities. The start on this algebra may be made by establishing a rule for the addition of vectors. We shall require that the only quantities to be called vectors, in addition to needing a magnitude and a direction to specify them, shall add in the same manner as do displacements. We therefore return to a consideration of Fig. 5.4. Since $\overrightarrow{\mathrm{OA}}$ and $\overrightarrow{\mathrm{AB}}$ in that figure together lead to the same result as the vector $\overrightarrow{\mathrm{OB}}$, we may say that the sum of the first two vectors is identical with the third. We indicate this symbolically as

$$\overrightarrow{\mathrm{OA}} + \overrightarrow{\mathrm{AB}} = \overrightarrow{\mathrm{OB}}.$$

Similarly, we may write for the more complicated situation of Fig. 5.4b,

$$\overrightarrow{\mathrm{OC}} + \overrightarrow{\mathrm{CD}} + \overrightarrow{\mathrm{DE}} + \overrightarrow{\mathrm{EF}} + \overrightarrow{\mathrm{FG}} + \overrightarrow{\mathrm{GH}} + \overrightarrow{\mathrm{HB}} = \overrightarrow{\mathrm{OB}}.$$

The sum of two or more vectors is sometimes called the ***resultant*** of the other vectors.

The following graphical process will always serve for the addition of vectors, although the diagram may be difficult to construct if the vectors do not all lie in one plane:

1. Draw a line representing the first vector to scale ($\overrightarrow{\mathrm{OC}}$ in Fig. 5.3). Call the starting point O the ***initial point*** of this vector and the end point C the ***terminal point.***

2. Draw a line representing the second vector to scale ($\overrightarrow{CD}$), making its initial point coincide with the terminal point of the first.
3. Continue in the same way, making the initial point of each vector coincide with the terminal point of the previous vector, until all vectors involved in the sum have been represented.
4. The resultant of the vectors is represented to scale by the line ($\overrightarrow{OB}$) which, as its initial point, has the initial point of the first vector and, as its terminal point, has the terminal point of the last vector.

It is important to investigate a few other simple processes in vector algebra. For example, if we wish to multiply a vector by a scalar, we remember that the multiplication of any quantity by a number n gives the same result as if we added n of the original quantities. Thus

$$3 \times 4\text{ ft} = 4\text{ ft} + 4\text{ ft} + 4\text{ ft} = 12\text{ ft}.$$

Applying the same definition to the ***multiplication of a vector by a scalar***, we see that $n\overrightarrow{V}$ is obtained by successive additions of the vector $\overrightarrow{V}$ to itself. Since any particular vector always points in the same direction, the result of the multiplication of the vector by a scalar n will be a vector in the same direction as the original vector but with a magnitude n times as great. Thus Fig. 5.8 shows the result of multiplying by 3 a displacement of 1.5 cm at an angle of 30° with the x-axis.

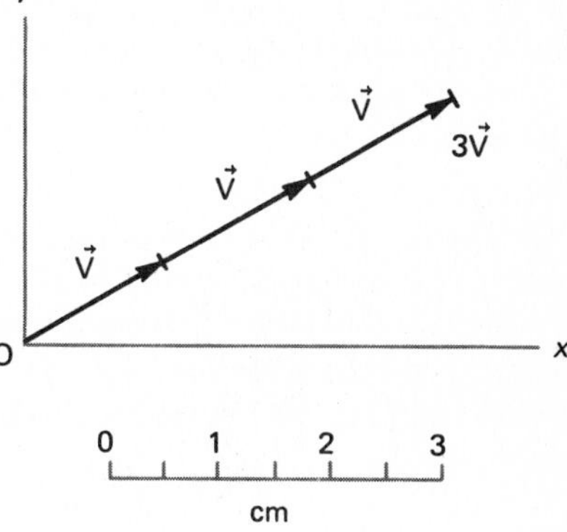

FIG. 5.8 Multiplication of a vector by a scalar.

If we multiply a vector by a negative number, we reverse the direction of the vector, as well as change its magnitude. The reason for this becomes apparent if we consider the multiplication of a vector by -1. Thus $(-1)\overrightarrow{V} = -\overrightarrow{V}$, and

$$\overrightarrow{V} + (-\overrightarrow{V}) = \overrightarrow{V} - \overrightarrow{V} = 0.$$

We see therefore that, in order that the sum of $\overrightarrow{V}$ and $-\overrightarrow{V}$ shall be zero, the vector $-\overrightarrow{V}$ must be equal and opposite to the vector $\overrightarrow{V}$. Applied to displacements, this rule merely says that, if we walk a mile and then retrace our steps, we are right back where we started. It is clear from this example that the ***subtraction*** process indicated by $\overrightarrow{A} - \overrightarrow{B}$ may be carried out if a vector $-\overrightarrow{B}$ is added to $\vec{A}$, i.e., if there is added to $\vec{A}$ a vector having the same magnitude as $\vec{B}$ but having the opposite direction. Figure 5.9 illustrates both such a subtraction and the addition of two vectors $\vec{A}$ and $\vec{B}$.

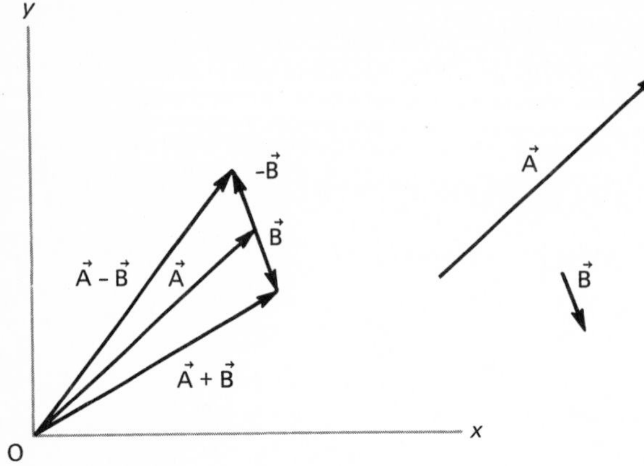

FIG. 5.9 Addition and subtraction of vectors.

EXERCISES

(See note on page 116)

5.5-1 A car is driven westward for 50 mi, then northward for 30 mi, and, finally, in a direction 30° west of north for 25 mi. By drawing a vector diagram similar to Fig. 5.3, find its final displacement from the starting point.

5.5-2 A starts from a particular point and walks a distance of 3.60 km in a direction 20° east of north. B later starts from the same point, walks eastward for 1.23 km, and remains at this point. By construction of a vector diagram, find how far and in what direction A must walk to reach B.

5.5-3 V is a vector defined by a magnitude of 1.50 m and direction 30.0° from a given line. What are the magnitudes and directions of the vectors:

$$\text{(a) } 3.50\,\vec{V}, \qquad \text{(b) } -\vec{V}, \qquad \text{(c) } -6.20\,\vec{V}?$$

5.5-4 An airplane leaves a city at 1:00 P.M. and flies eastward at a speed of 320 km/hr. A second plane leaves another city, 500 km northeast of the first city, at 1:30 P.M. and flies southward at 400 km/hr. By a graphical construction, find the displacement of the intersection of the courses of the two planes from each city. At what time will each plane pass this intersection?

5.6 *Velocity as a Vector*

We recognize that velocities are vectors, so the distinction that was made in Sec. 3.3 between velocity and speed becomes more meaningful. The ***speed*** of a body is just the magnitude of its velocity and is therefore a scalar. It tells how fast the body is moving but does not indicate in what direction it is going. To determine a velocity, we must generalize the definition expressed by Eq. (3.6-1) to the vector form:

$$\vec{v} = d\vec{s}/dt = \lim_{\Delta t \to 0} (\Delta\vec{s}/\Delta t). \tag{5.6-1}$$

Division of the vector $\vec{\Delta s}$ by Δt is equivalent to multiplication by the scalar $1/\Delta t$; hence the average velocity $\langle\vec{v}\rangle_{av}$ during any time interval Δt is a vector having the same direction as the displacement $\vec{\Delta s}$ which took place during that interval. As an example, suppose that Fig. 5.10 is a map showing the path of a particle that moves from A to B in five seconds. Suppose that we

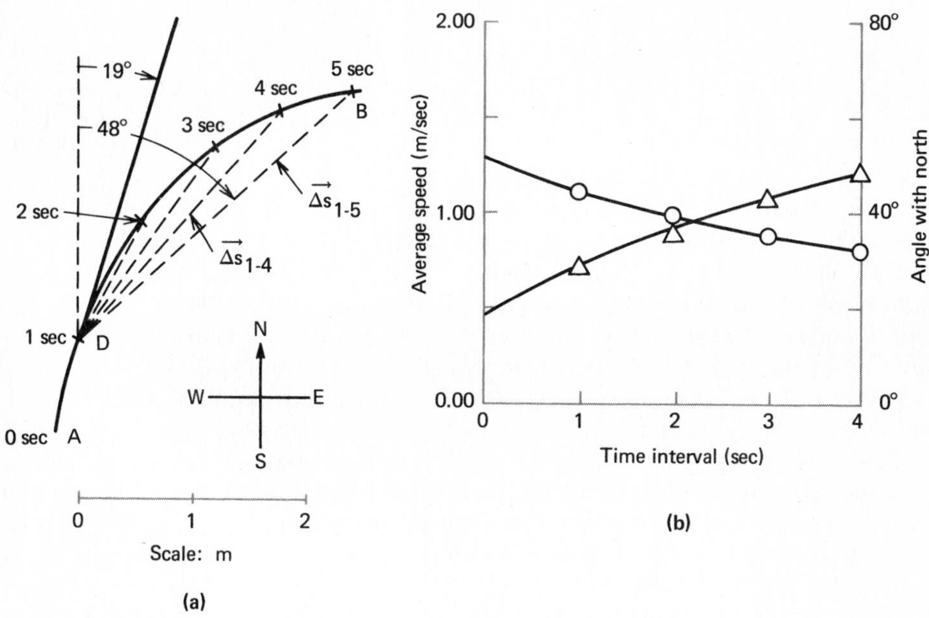

FIG. 5.10 The instantaneous velocity has the direction of the tangent to the path.

wish to determine the instantaneous velocity at the time when the body passes point D. During the time interval from 1.0 sec to 5.0 sec, the displacement is given by the vector $\vec{\Delta s}_{1-5} = \vec{DB}$, a vector of magnitude 3.2 m/sec and having a direction 48° east of north. Hence the average velocity during this interval is directed 48° east of north and has a magnitude of 0.80 m/sec. We then take the displacement $\vec{\Delta s}_{1-4}$ for the shorter time interval from 1.0 sec to 4.0 sec to find an average velocity of 0.87 m/sec in a direction 43° east of north. To find the instantaneous velocity at D, we must find two limiting values as Δt approaches zero—both the speed and the direction of motion are needed. The solid line of Fig. 5.10b, which is analogous to the plot of Fig. 3.7, shows the speed at D to be 1.3 m/sec. In regard to the direction of motion, it is clear by inspection of the vector displacements $\vec{\Delta s}_{1-5}$, $\vec{\Delta s}_{1-4}$, etc., that the limiting direction of these, as the time interval gets very short, is that of the tangent to the path DE. By constructing this tangent and measuring the angle between it and the northward direction, we find that the velocity at D is 1.3 m/sec, 19° east of north. A second way of determining the direction is illustrated by the dashed plot of Fig. 5.10b, where the angle between the displacement (during any time interval) and north is plotted as a function of the time interval. By extrapolating this plot to $\Delta t = 0$, we again find that the tangent to the path at D, and therefore the velocity, is directed 19° east of north.

EXERCISES

Note: All the exercises in this set except Ex. 5.6-3 should be solved graphically by the construction and measurement of vector diagrams similar to Figs. 5.6, 5.7, and 5.9.

5.6-1 A car moving eastward at 58 km/hr turns onto a road which runs northward. As the car turns, its speed is increased to 75 km/hr. What is the change in its velocity?

5.6-2 A train moving at a constant speed of 60 mi/hr moves eastward for 30 min, then in a direction 45° east of north for 20 min, and finally, westward for 45 min. What is its average velocity during the run? (Hint: Find the total displacement.)

5.6-3 The speed of an airplane relative to the air is 300 mi/hr. The speed of the wind is roughly constant and it blows from west to east. One airport is 1800 mi due east of another. Calculate times of flight for this plane for an eastward and for a westward flight if the average wind speed is 30 mi/hr.

5.6-4 A plane flies in a straight line from one point to a point 500 km directly to the north in 1.95 hr. During the flight, a wind was blowing from the west with a speed 35 km/hr. What was the average speed of the plane relative to the air?

5.6-5 A stream is flowing due south with a velocity 1.6 m/sec. A boat that can travel at 4.0 m/sec in still water is to go from a point on one bank to a point directly opposite. In what direction must the boat be steered? If the stream is 300 m across, what is the time of crossing?

5.6-6 A stone is dropped from a bridge over a railroad track. If the point from which it is dropped is 14.5 m above the track, what is the velocity of the stone relative to the earth as it strikes the ground? What is its velocity relative to a train which is passing at a speed of 72 km/hr?

5.7 *Some Problems in Aerial Navigation*

Some of the more interesting problems connected with the transformation of velocity vectors from one reference frame to another are those that arise in connection with the navigation of a jet plane. Such a plane is propelled in the same manner as a rocket, i.e., by ejecting the products of combustion backward. With the ejection taking place at a constant rate there is a net forward force on the plane, and the speed of the latter becomes constant when the propelling force is equal to the ***drag***, i.e., the frictional force exerted on the plane by the air through which it moves. The velocity of the plane will therefore be constant relative to the body of air surrounding it, under given operating conditions of fuel consumption and altitude. This airspeed is that which would be determined by an observer who attaches his reference frame to a free balloon that moves with the wind. The same observer would, of course, find the direction of the plane's velocity to be along the line in which the plane is pointed, or headed—the pilot can control both the magnitude and the direction of his velocity relative to the air.

The reference frame in which the pilot must navigate to reach a given destination is that to which the landing fields are attached—the earth. In the absence of any wind, the plane's velocity relative to the ground is identical with that relative to the air, and no problem arises. In the presence of wind, however, the navigator must determine what heading of the plane is necessary to establish a given track of the plane relative to the ground.

Suppose that a plane with an airspeed of 560 mi/hr is flying at an altitude of 30,000 ft on a flight from Spokane to Los Angeles. When the plane is over Walla Walla, Washington, the navigator is informed that the wind at his altitude is blowing from a direction 60° west of south at a speed of 70 mi/hr. He knows that Los Angeles is directly south of Walla Walla at a distance of 815 miles. To determine the course of the plane, he may apply Eq. (5.4-3), letting $\vec{v}'$ be the velocity relative to the air and $\vec{u}$ be the velocity of the air relative to the ground. The vector sum of these, $\vec{v}$, must be directed exactly southward if the plane is to reach its destination. The graphical solution is shown in Fig. 5.11a, in which the north-south line NS is first drawn, then the line FT is drawn in the direction of the wind. On any convenient scale, the wind speed of 70 mi/hr is measured off along FT to determine the point P. Finally, Q is located as the point on NS that is separated from P by a speed of 560 mi/hr, to the same scale that was used for the wind. The vector $\vec{v}'$ is clearly the velocity of the plane relative to the air. A measurement of the angle between this vector and south shows that the plane must fly a course 6° west of south to achieve the desired track.

We may also determine the ground speed v by measurement of the vector $\vec{v}$. It scales to 520 mi/hr; hence the time of flight can be expected to be 815 mi/(520 mi/hr) = 1.57 hr.

Another way of obtaining the same results, in which displacements are plotted instead of velocities, is shown in Fig. 5.11b. Here W and L are the locations of Walla Walla and Los Angeles, respectively, on a map of which the scale is given. While the plane is in flight, it will be carried eastward and northward by the wind, in a reference frame attached to the ground. An exactly equivalent statement is that Los Angeles has "drifted against the wind" in a frame of reference attached to the air. Thus, in this frame of reference, Los Angeles changes its position from L, where it was at the start of the flight, to some new position L′ at the end of the flight. In order that it shall arrive at Los Angeles, the plane must follow the course WL′; it is along this course that the speed is 560 mi/hr. Hence, in the triangle WL′L, we must have the proportion: WL′/L′L = 560/70. The navigator measures off on his chart any convenient distance LA. He then determines the point B, eight times as far from A as is A from L. The line BA is in the direction in which the plane must fly, relative to the air; direct measurement shows that the heading should be 6° west of south, as was found before. The actual course of the plane relative to the air is along the line WL′, which is drawn through W and parallel to BA. Measurement of this course shows the distance through the air to be 878 miles, so the expected time of flight is 878 mi/(560 mi/hr) = 1.57 hr, in agreement with the result obtained from Fig. 5.11a.

The facts that jet planes, and even higher speed rockets, reach their destinations and that they do so at predetermined times supply good evidence that Newtonian relativity works, at least for speeds up to about 2×10^4 mi/hr (8×10^3 m/sec). The exact computations necessary to check the assumptions of Newtonian relativity are slightly more involved than those we have used,

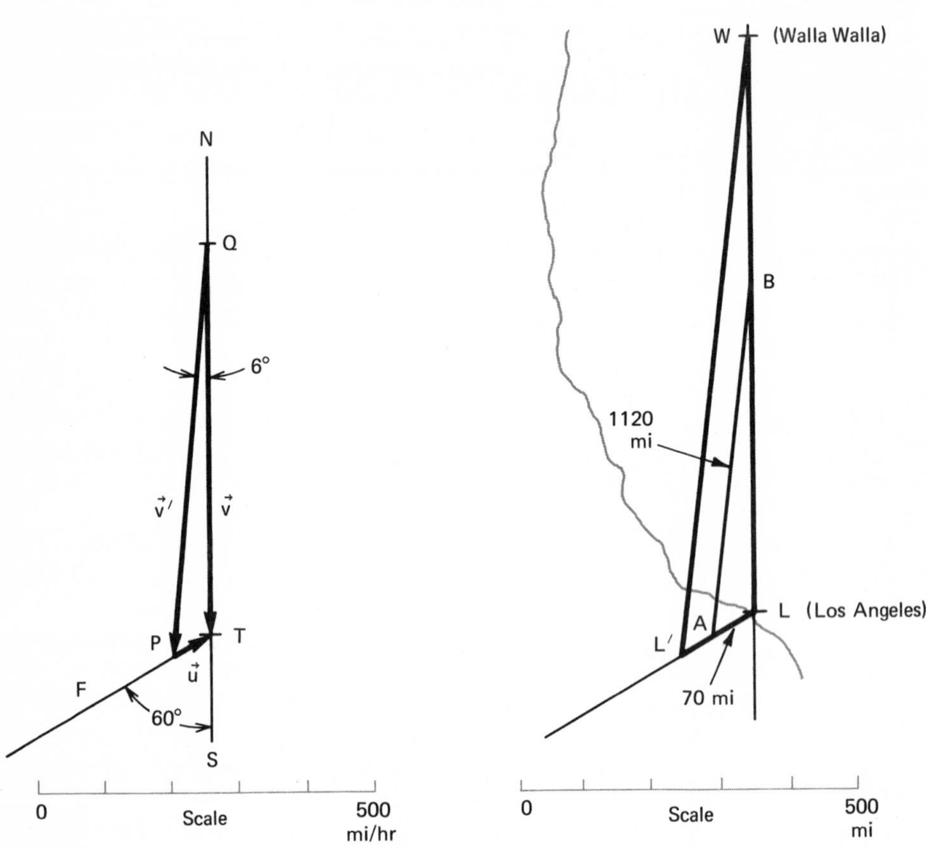

FIG. 5.11 Equivalent ways of solving a navigation problem. (a) Velocity plot, (b) displacement plot.

because they must take into account the curvature of the earth, which we have treated as flat. If a plot similar to Fig. 5.11b is made on a Mercator projection, however, the course found needs essentially no correction—it is an interesting property of the Mercator projection that angles measured on it are identical with those measured on the surface of a sphere. For long flights, however, the predictions of time would be in error, because distances on a Mercator projection do not scale correctly.

Before leaving aerial navigation, we shall consider the slightly more involved problem of a round trip flight. Suppose that a plane is to fly at an airspeed v

from over a point A, as shown in Fig. 5.12a, to a point B, at a distance L from A, and is then to return at once to A. In the absence of any wind, the time for the round trip is clearly $2L/v$. If a wind is blowing with a speed u, relative to the ground, directly along the line AB, the plane will have a ground speed $v + u$ in one direction and $v - u$ in the other. We now ask whether the time taken will be greater, less than, or equal to that needed in the absence of wind.

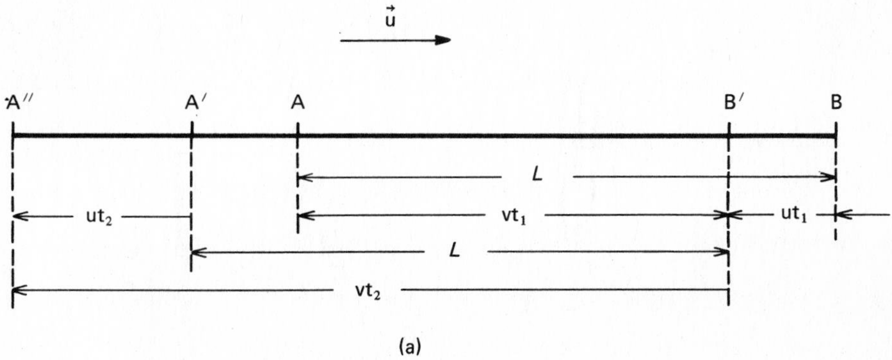

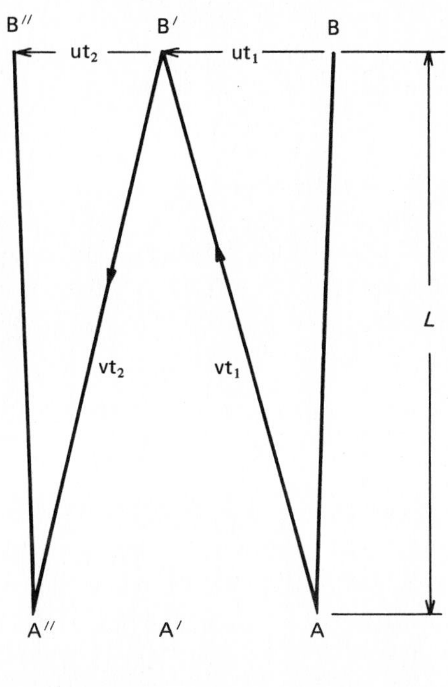

FIG. 5.12 The time taken for a round trip is always increased by a steady wind in any direction.

Considering a displacement plot of the type of Fig. 5.12a, we may consider that B has drifted (relative to the air) against the wind to some point B′ during the time t_1 taken by the plane on its outward trip. The amount of this drift is ut_1; hence we have, from examination of Fig. 5.12a,

$$vt_1 + ut_1 = L,$$

$$t_1 = \frac{L}{v+u}.$$

During this outward trip, A has also drifted a distance ut_1 relative to the air, to the position A′. Similarly, during the time t_2 required for the return trip, A will have experienced a further drift (relative to the air) through a distance ut_2 to the new position A″. A glance at the figure shows that

$$vt_2 - ut_2 = L,$$

$$t_2 = \frac{L}{v-u}.$$

Hence, the time for the round trip is

$$t_{\parallel} = t_1 + t_2 = \frac{L}{v+u} + \frac{L}{v-u} = \frac{2Lv}{v^2 - u^2} = \frac{2L}{v} \cdot \frac{1}{1 - u^2/v^2}, \tag{5.7-1}$$

where the symbol $t_{\parallel}$ is used to indicate that plane and the wind move in parallel directions.

We note at once that u^2/v^2 is always positive and that quantity $1 - u^2/v^2$ in the final expression is therefore always less than unity. Hence, $t_{\parallel}$ is always greater than $2L/v$, the time without any wind. The plane always loses more time in its flight against the wind than it gains while it has a tailwind. If $u = \frac{1}{4}v$, as was chosen for Fig. 5.12a, the time is increased by a factor of 16/15.

Figure 5.12b shows the plot for a round trip in which the wind is perpendicular to the desired track of the plane. On the outward flight the plane must be headed along the direction AB′ to reach the location B′ to which B has drifted during this flight. Again inspection of the figures shows that

$$(vt_1)^2 = L^2 + (ut_1)^2,$$

where t_1 is the time of the outward flight. Hence,

$$t_1 = \frac{L}{(v^2 - u^2)^{1/2}} = \frac{L}{v} \cdot \frac{1}{(1 - u^2/v^2)^{1/2}}. \tag{5.7-2}$$

The time t_2 taken for the return flight is obviously equal to t_1; hence the time t_1 for a roundtrip perpendicular to the wind is

$$t_{\perp} = \frac{2L}{v} \cdot \frac{1}{(1 - u^2/v^2)^{1/2}}. \tag{5.7-3}$$

Once more we find that the roundtrip takes longer because of the wind. Because $(1 - u^2/v^2)^{1/2}$ is always greater than $(1 - u^2/v^2)$, $t_{\perp}$ is always less than $t_{\parallel}$. For the case of $u = \frac{1}{4}v$, t is greater than $2L/v$ by the factor $(16/15)^{1/2} = 1.03$.

We return to the consideration of roundtrip flights in Chapter 8, where further tests of Newtonian relativity will be considered.

EXERCISES

5.7-1 In Eq. (5.7-1) recall the interpretation of the factor $2L/v$. Note that the other factor $(1 - u^2/v^2)^{-1}$ becomes division by zero if $u = v$. Does this represent a failure of the mathematics or can you give a useful physical interpretation of the result of division by zero in this case?

5.7-2 Extend the line of thought of the preceding exercise to the case where $u > v$. The result given by Eq. (5.7-1) is now negative. Can you give a physical interpretation for this perfectly valid mathematical result?

5.7-3 Make a rough graph of $t_{\parallel}$ as given by Eq. (5.7-1) to show how $t_{\parallel}$ changes as u is varied while L and v are constant. This would correspond to an airplane with a fixed airspeed v, always traveling between the same two cities where the wind speed, always blowing from one city to the other, varies on different days. (For convenience, let $2L/v = 10^4$ sec and let $u = 0v$, $\frac{1}{4}v$, $\frac{1}{2}v$, $\frac{3}{4}v$, and $\frac{7}{8}v$.)

5.7-4 Notice that Eq. (5.7-2) can also have zero in the denominator for $u = v$. Refer to Fig. 5.12b and discuss the shape of this figure as $u \to v$.

5.7-5 Repeat the content of Ex. 5.7-3 for Eq. (5.7-2). Plot your results on the same graph as those of Ex. 5.7-3.

5.8 Vector Components

Before leaving our discussion of relative velocities, we shall describe an analytic method for adding vectors. The analytic method is far more accurate than the graphical ones used heretofore, and it is much more convenient to use.

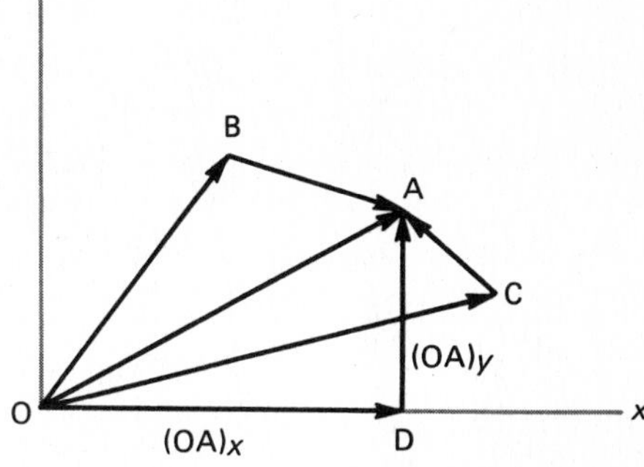

Fig. 5.13 Vector components.

We saw in Sec. 5.4 that any vector is equivalent to the sum of two or more other vectors. Thus the vector shown as $\overrightarrow{OA}$ in Fig. 5.13 is equal to any one of the vector sums

$$\overrightarrow{OB} + \overrightarrow{BA},$$
$$\overrightarrow{OC} + \overrightarrow{CA},$$
$$\overrightarrow{OD} + \overrightarrow{DA}.$$

In each of these pairs of vectors, we may choose at will two distinct directions for the two vectors whose sum is to equal $\overrightarrow{OA}$, and their magnitudes will then be determined. To do so, we merely draw two lines, in the desired directions, from the ends of the line representing the vector. We then measure, to the scale of the drawing, the lengths of the line segments (such as OC and CA) determined by the intersection of the lines.

We shall be particularly interested in the pair of vectors $\overrightarrow{OD}$ and $\overrightarrow{DA}$, which were obtained by choosing directions parallel to the rectangular coordinate axes. The magnitudes of these vectors, together with signs (+ or −) indicating whether they are directed along the positive or negative axes, are known as the ***components*** of the vector $\overrightarrow{OA}$. Because these vectors are directed along the axes, it is convenient to label them with the names of the axes. This is usually done by attaching a subscript to the symbol denoting them. Thus, the ***x-component*** of $\overrightarrow{OA}$, which has the magnitude OD, is usually written $(OA)_x$, and the ***y-component***, which has the magnitude DA, is usually written $(OA)_y$.

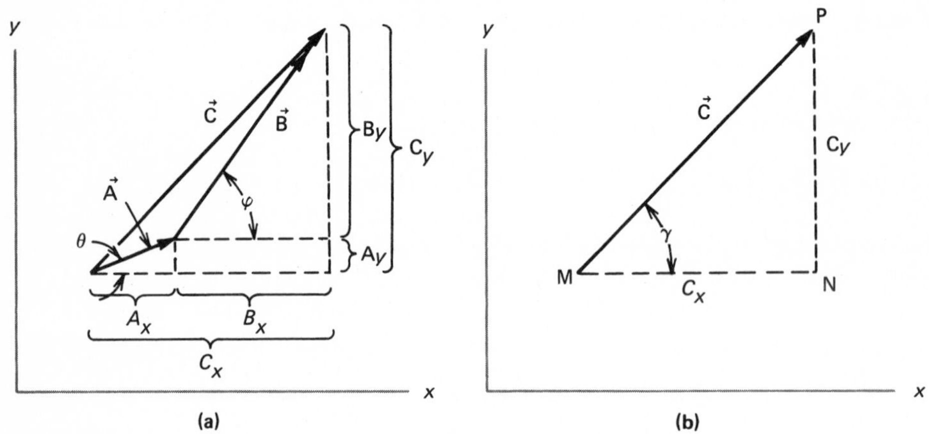

FIG. 5.14 Vector addition using components.

To find the components of any vector in a two-dimensional rectangular coordinate system, we can construct a vector diagram such as that shown in Fig. 5.14, where A_x and A_y are the components of $\vec{A}$. It is obvious from the figure that if

$$\vec{C} = \vec{A} + \vec{B},$$

then

$$C_x = A_x + B_x$$

and

$$C_y = A_y + B_y. \tag{5.8-1}$$

We have therefore arrived at a new rule for ***vector addition***: *The components of the sum of two vectors are obtained by taking the sums of the corresponding components of the two vectors.*

This new procedure for vector addition would be of little value to us if we were to continue to solve vector problems by the graphical methods that we have used thus far. The reader who has done the exercises of this chapter has probably discovered objections to the graphical method, since it is both slow and inaccurate. For these reasons and because a number of general problems cannot be solved graphically, we shall find it worth while to search for an analytical method of handling vectors instead of the graphical one. Such a method is available with the help of ***trigonometry***, the study of the properties of triangles. The amount of trigonometry needed is small, and the reader who has not met this subject previously should have no trouble in learning enough of the subject from Appendix E. Anyone without a knowledge of elementary trigonometry is advised to study that appendix before going further with his reading.

With the aid of trigonometry we can obtain simple expressions for the components C_x and C_y of the vector $\vec{C}$ (Fig. 5.14b). Since the *x*-axis and the *y*-axis are at right angles to one another, it is easy to see that the triangle MNP is right-angled at N. Therefore, letting γ (*gamma*) be the angle between $\vec{C}$ and the *x*-axis and denoting the magnitude of $\vec{C}$ by C, we see at once that

$$C_x = C \cos \gamma \tag{5.8-2A}$$

and

$$C_y = C \sin \gamma. \tag{5.8-2B}$$

We therefore have a way of computing the components of a vector if we know the magnitude of the vector and the angles that it makes with the coordinate axes. Similarly, if we know the components of a vector, we can find its magnitude and direction, since by the Pythagorean theorem

$$C = \sqrt{C_x^2 + C_y^2} \tag{5.8-2C}$$

and the angle between the vector and the *x*-axis can be determined by the relation:

$$\tan \gamma = C_y/C_x. \tag{5.8-2D}$$

We can immediately apply these methods to avoid the necessity of accurate scale drawing in the determination of the sum of the two vectors $\vec{A}$ and $\vec{B}$ (Fig. 5.14a) which make respectively the angles θ and ϕ with the *x*-axis. We first compute the components of these two vectors:

$$A_x = A \cos \theta, \qquad B_x = B \cos \phi,$$
$$A_y = A \sin \theta, \qquad B_y = B \sin \phi.$$

Notice that the quantities A and B are the *magnitudes* of the vectors $\vec{A}$ and $\vec{B}$ and are therefore necessarily *positive*. The signs of the components are determined by the signs of the trigonometric functions (cf. Appendix G). The components of the vector sum can then be obtained from Eq. (5.8-1) as:

$$C_x = A_x + B_x = A \cos \theta + B \cos \phi,$$
$$C_y = A_y + B_y = A \sin \theta + B \sin \phi.$$

Finally, substitution of these components into Eqs. (5.8-2C and D) gives us all the other information that we need about the vector $\vec{C}$, which is the sum of $\vec{A}$ and $\vec{B}$.

5.9 *Illustrative Examples*

Suppose that a ship wishes to go from the port A, shown in Fig. 5.15, to the port B, which lies 200 mi from A in a direction 25.0° north of west. In order to avoid the island, the ship sails due west for 125 mi to the point C. We wish to know in what direction it should sail to reach B, and how far it must travel.

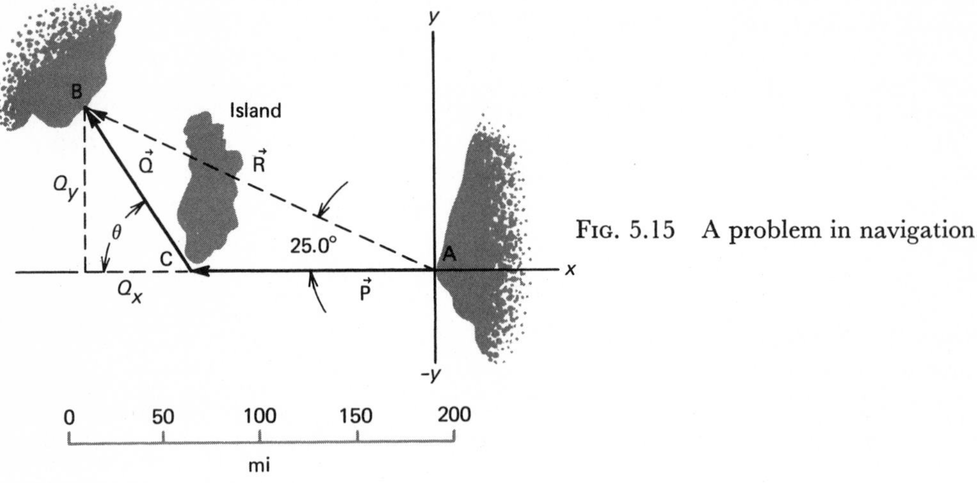

FIG. 5.15 A problem in navigation.

We shall choose a coordinate system with the origin at A, with the *x*-axis directed toward the east, and with the *y*-axis toward the north, as shown. If the displacement of B from A is called $\vec{R}$ and that of C from A is called $\vec{P}$, the required further displacement of the ship is

$$\vec{Q} = \vec{R} - \vec{P}.$$

The components of the two known vectors are found to be

$$R_x = -(200 \text{ mi})(\cos 25.0°) = -(200 \text{ mi})(0.9063) = -181.3 \text{ mi},$$
$$R_y = (200 \text{ mi})(\sin 25.0°) = (200 \text{ mi})(0.4226) = 84.5 \text{ mi},$$
$$P_x = -125 \text{ mi}, \quad \text{and}$$
$$P_y = 0.$$

Notice here that the *x*-components of both vectors are negative, since the vectors are directed toward negative values of *x*. Applying the rule for vector addition [Eq. (5.8-1)], we find that

$$Q_x = -181.3 \text{ mi} - (-125 \text{ mi}) = -56.3 \text{ mi},$$
$$Q_y = 84.5 \text{ mi}.$$

Hence the distance to be covered, or the magnitude of $\vec{Q}$, is

$$Q = \sqrt{(56.3 \text{ mi})^2 + (84.5 \text{ mi})^2} = 101 \text{ mi}.$$

The direction in which the ship must sail is given by

$$\tan \theta = 84.5 \text{ mi}/56.3 \text{ mi} = 1.50.$$

When we look in the trigonometric tables of Appendix F for the angle corresponding to this tangent, we find that $\tan 56° = 1.483$ and $\tan 57° = 1.540$. Interpolating between these two values, we see that

$$\theta = 56.3°.$$

As a second example, consider a ball thrown outward and downward from the top of a vertical cliff 50 m high (Fig. 5.16). The initial velocity $\vec{v}_0$ of the ball is 30 m/sec in a direction 45° below the horizontal. How far from the base of the cliff will the ball strike the ground?

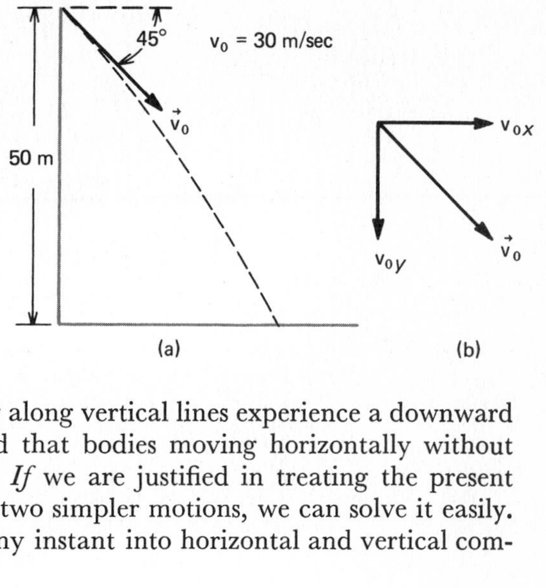

FIG. 5.16 The trajectory of a stone thrown from a cliff.

We have seen that bodies moving along vertical lines experience a downward acceleration $\vec{g}$ [Eq. (3.11-1C)] and that bodies moving horizontally without friction move at constant velocity. *If* we are justified in treating the present problem as a combination of these two simpler motions, we can solve it easily. We can resolve the velocity $\vec{v}$ at any instant into horizontal and vertical components, v_x and v_y. Then

$$v_x = v_{0x} \tag{5.9-1}$$

and

$$v_y = v_{0y} + gt, \tag{5.9-2}$$

where v_{0x} and v_{0y} are the magnitudes of the two components at $t = 0$.

Notice that we have assumed that the vertical and horizontal components are independent of each other, that the vertical acceleration does not change because the ball is also moving horizontally, and vice versa. Whether this assumption is justified can only be answered by an appeal to experiment. One such experiment is already available to us, in data obtainable from the photograph of Fig. 5.3. Measurement of the horizontal components of the displacement between any two successive pictures of the ball shows that they are equal—the horizontal component of velocity is constant. Similarly, the vertical components of displacement increase from one pair of pictures to the next in exactly the way demanded by Eq. (5.9-2). This observation and many others that have been made confirm the idea that the two components of motion are independent.

We now substitute values of v_{0x} and v_{0y} into Eqs. (5.9-1) and (5.9-2) to obtain

$$v_{0x} = v_0 \cos 45° = (30 \text{ m/sec})(0.707) = 21.2 \text{ m/sec}$$

and

$$v_{0y} = v_0 \sin 45° = (30 \text{ m/sec})(0.707) = 21.2 \text{ m/sec}.$$

We first determine how long it takes the ball to reach the ground. From Chapter 3 we have

$$s_y = v_{0y}\,t + \tfrac{1}{2}gt^2,$$

$$50 \text{ m} = (21.2 \text{ m/sec})t + \tfrac{1}{2}(9.8 \text{ m/sec}^2)t^2,$$

or

$$(4.9 \text{ m/sec}^2)t^2 + (21.2 \text{ m/sec})t - 50 \text{ m} = 0.$$

This equation has the form $at^2 + bt + c = 0$ which, by the quadratic formula, has the solutions

$$t = \frac{-21.2 \pm \sqrt{451 + 980}}{9.8} \text{ sec}$$

$$= \frac{-21.2 \pm \sqrt{1431}}{9.8} \text{ sec} = \frac{-21.2 \pm 37.8}{9.8} \text{ sec}$$

or $t = 1.69$ sec and $t = -6.1$ sec. For the moment let us forget our negative answer to concentrate on $t = 1.7$ sec.

During this time of fall the ball will have a horizontal velocity component of $v_{0x} = 21.2$ m/sec. The displacement in the x-direction then will be

$$s_x = v_{0x}\,t = (21.2 \text{ m/sec})(1.69 \text{ sec}) = 37 \text{ m}.$$

The ball will therefore strike the ground 37 m from the base of the cliff.

Now either $t = 1.69$ sec or $t = -6.1$ sec will satisfy our expression for s_y. What can $t = -6.1$ sec mean? Our equations *do not state that the ball* was not traveling in negative time. All we have been able to assert is that at the time $t = 0$, *which we set arbitrarily*, the ball was leaving the top of the cliff with the specified v_0. As far as the equations are concerned, the cliff could be the side of a butte as in Fig. 5.17. We know that the ball had velocity v_0 at point P at $t = 0$ and that at $t = 1.69$ sec it was 50 m down at the ground on the right. But at $t = -6.1$ sec the ball might also have been 50 m down at the ground on the left.

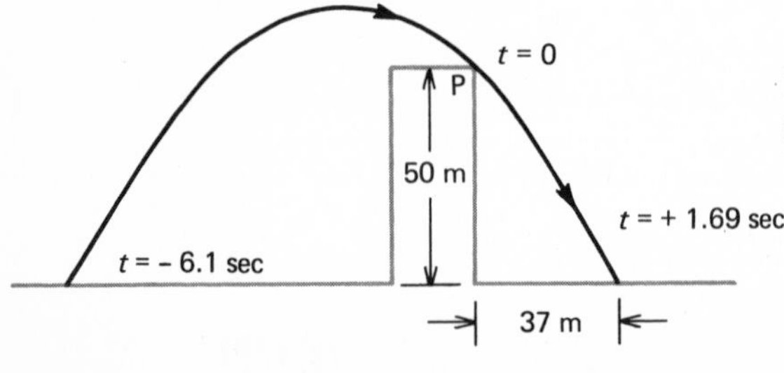

FIG. 5.17 Meaning of the negative solution for the time of flight.

EXERCISES

5.9-1 Solve Ex. 5.2-1 by the use of trigonometric methods.

5.9-2 Solve Ex. 5.5-2 analytically.

5.9-3 Solve Ex. 5.6-4 analytically.

5.9-4 Solve Ex. 5.6-5 analytically.

5.9-5 Solve Ex. 5.6-6 analytically.

5.9-6 Two cars start from the same point at the same time. One moves eastward at a speed v, while the other moves along a road at an angle θ north of east. Show that the second car must move at speed $(v/\cos\theta)$ in order that the line connecting the two cars shall always be in the north-south direction. (Hint: Consider the positions of the cars at any time t after they start. Notice that this exercise would present difficulties if an attempt were made to solve it graphically.]

5.10 Summary

The present chapter has extended our study of the motions of particles to three-dimensional space. We have found that such motions can be described quite well with the help of coordinate systems and by the use of vectors, which are directed physical magnitudes that obey a particular addition rule. We have developed some of the algebra of vectors and have applied them to physical problems, sometimes graphically and sometimes with the help of trigonometric methods. In particular, we have found relations among velocities measured in different coordinate frames, on the basis of the assumptions of Newtonian relativity and have seen evidence that components of motion that are mutually at right angles to each other are independent.

PROBLEMS

5.1 Suppose that city B lies a distance L east of city A and that an airplane is to make the round trip travelling at an airspeed v. The wind blows with a constant velocity $\vec{u}$ toward the northeast at an angle θ with the line joining the two cities. Develop an equation giving the time for the roundtrip.

5.2 If, in the notation of Sec. 5.7, $2L/v = 1.0 \times 10^4$ sec and if $u = fv$, where $0 < f < 1$, find f for $t_{\parallel} = 4 \times 10^4$ sec. Find f for $t_{\perp} = 4 \times 10^4$ sec.

5.3 A small hoop is mounted in a vertical plane which is perpendicular to the front of a barn. Boy A stands 5 m to the left and boy B, 5 m to the right. If the bottom of the hoop is 4 m from the ground and boy A launches a ball from 2 m above the ground, determine the velocity with which the ball must have passed through the hoop to be caught by boy B 2 m above the ground.

5.4 A projectile is fired from a gun with a speed v_0, which is independent of the direction in which the gun is pointed. Its velocity as it leaves the muzzle is at an angle θ above the horizontal. In the following calculations, neglect any frictional effects.

(a) Find expressions for x, the horizontal component of the displacement of the projectile from the gun muzzle at any time t after it is fired, and y, the vertical component of the displacement at time t.

(b) By eliminating t from the two equations, show that the range of the projectile, i.e., the horizontal distance from the muzzle to the point at which the projectile returns to the height of the muzzle, is

$$r = 2v_0^2 \sin\theta \cos\theta/g.$$

(c) Plot a curve of $\sin\theta \cos\theta$ vs. θ, for $0° < \theta < 90°$. Using this curve, show that the greatest possible range of the projectile is achieved when $\theta = 45°$.

5.5 Suppose that v_0 in Prob. 5.4 is 500 m/sec and that the gun is mounted on a railway car moving at 15 m/sec. The gun is at an angle θ with the horizontal and points toward the rear of the car, i.e., opposite to the direction of motion.

(a) What must be the value of θ if the projectile is to move vertically upward, relative to the ground? (b) What is the greatest height to which the projectile will rise?

5.6 Suppose that the gun of Prob. 5.4 is mounted on a hill, so that its muzzle is at a height h above a surrounding horizontal plane. How far from the gun will the projectile strike the ground?

5.7 When mud is thrown from the tire of a car it leaves the tire in a tangential direction, as shown in the figure, at a speed V equal to the speed of the car. (This speed is measured relative to a coordinate system attached to the moving car.)

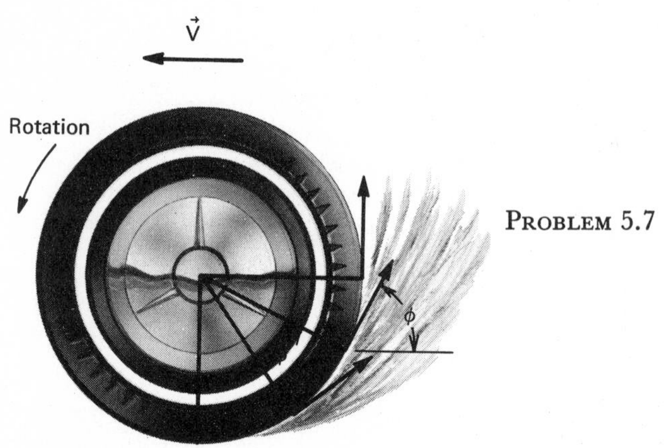

PROBLEM 5.7

(a) Show that the speed of the mud as it leaves the tire has a horizontal component of velocity, relative to the earth, equal to

$$v_x = V(1 - \cos\phi),$$

where the $+x$-direction is taken as the direction of motion of the car and ϕ is the angle between the tangent and the horizontal. Show that the vertical component, again relative to the earth, is

$$v_y = V \sin\phi.$$

(b) Using the results given in (a), prove that the greatest height to which any piece of mud can be thrown by the tire is $V^2/2g$. Also show that none of the mud can have a negative horizontal component of velocity.

(c) In view of the results found in (b) comment on the fact that your windshield can be splattered with mud thrown off by the tires of a car ahead of you.

(d) Suppose that both cars are travelling at 15 m/sec. How far should the windshield of the second car be behind the rear wheels of the first car if none of the mud is to reach the windshield? Suppose that the height of the bottom of the windshield above the road is 1.0 m more than the height of the axle of the first car.

REFERENCES

5A A. Einstein and L. Infeld, *The Evolution of Physics*, Simon and Schuster, New York, 1938. Motion and vectors are discussed in pp. 3–27.

5B F. Friedman, *The Velocity Vector* and *The Acceleration Vector* produced by Educational Services, Inc. Film loops. (Nos. 80-251 and 80-253. The Ealing Corp., Cambridge, Mass.)

5C J. N. Patterson Hume and Donald G. Ivey, *Frames of Reference*, produced by Educational Services, Inc. (No. 0307, Modern Learning Aids.) A filmed demonstration lecture giving excellent visual examples of motion as observed in different coordinate frames.

6 Momentum, Force, and Energy in Space

6.1 A More General Interpretation of the Conservation of Momentum

In Sec. 4.5 we found that when two bodies moving in a straight line underwent a collision, the sum of the momenta (mv) of the bodies after the collision remained the same as the sum of the momenta before the collision. We found, furthermore, that this result remained true whatever the nature of the interactions taking place between the two bodies. This led us to state the law of conservation of momentum. In the initial discussions of momentum we confined ourselves to motions in a straight line but, now that we have begun to study motions in space, it is important for us to find out whether the law of conservation of momentum holds for the more complicated processes in which a large number of bodies, moving in various directions in space, interact with one another. Does this law hold, for example, when a bowling ball hits the pins at the end of a bowling alley?

Before we can answer this question, we must return to our definition of momentum (Eq. 4.5-2) and decide on a method for the computation of the total momentum of a large number of bodies moving in a variety of directions in space. Since momentum, according to Eq. (4.5-2), is obtained by multiplying a vector v by a scalar m, we might expect it to be a vector (cf. Sec. 5.5). We can therefore add the momenta in accordance with the laws of vector addition. Figure 6.1b shows how the individual momenta $\vec{p}_1 = m_1\vec{v}_1$, $\vec{p}_2 = m_2\vec{v}_2$, etc., may be added to find the total momentum $\vec{p}$ of the system of bodies of Fig. 6.1a.

In order for "the total momentum of a system of bodies" to have a useful meaning, we must require that the system of bodies be free of all outside influences; that is, no body in the system can be interacting with any body outside the system. Strictly speaking, however, we may hedge a little against this requirement. For example, in Sec. 4.5, where we studied a collision between the two cars which constituted a two-body system, the frictional interaction between these cars and a body outside the system (the track) was made small enough to be ignored. Moreover, the interactions of the cars with the earth—that is to say, the weights of the cars—were just balanced by the supportive interactions with the track. Under these circumstances, then, we could treat the cars as a two-body system.

On the other hand, once the system of bodies has been so established, the interactions between the bodies of the system can be of any sort: collisions; magnetic, electric, or gravitational attractions; or none at all.

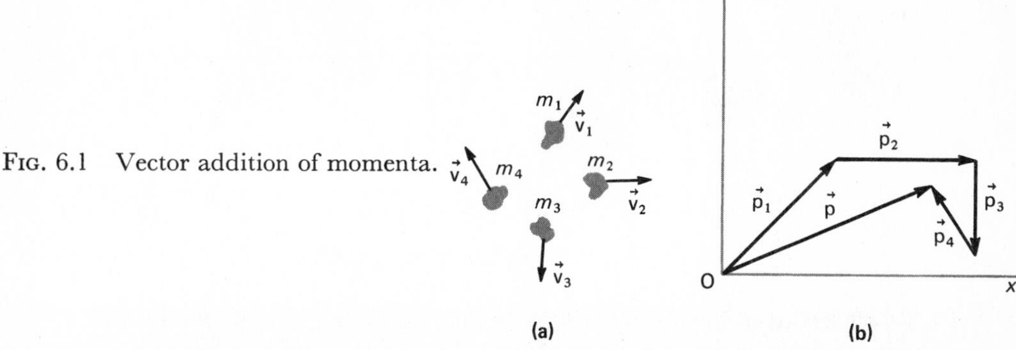

FIG. 6.1 Vector addition of momenta.

In practice, of course, the momenta are usually added analytically, rather than graphically (cf. Sec. 5.8). Since interactions of more than two bodies generally involve motions not restricted to a plane, all three components of the momenta must be considered, and a graphical solution presents difficulties. If we consider a coordinate system of three axes, mutually at right angles, and denote the vector components along these axes by the subscripts x, y, and z, we have

$$\begin{aligned} p_x &= p_{1x} + p_{2x} + p_{3x} + \cdots, \\ p_y &= p_{1y} + p_{2y} + p_{3y} + \cdots, \\ p_z &= p_{1z} + p_{2z} + p_{3z} + \cdots, \end{aligned} \tag{6.1-1}$$

where there are as many terms on the right-hand side of each equation as there are bodies concerned.

In other words, the components of the total momentum of a system are the sums of the components of the momenta of the individual bodies that make up that system.

As a simple case of a collision in which the motion is not confined to a straight line, we may consider a collision of two bodies such as that illustrated in Fig. 6.2. In Fig. 6.2a, two balls, of masses m_1 and m_2, are shown just before they collide. The heavier ball m_1 is moving with a velocity $\vec{v}_1$ and the lighter ball m_2 is at rest. If the collision were head on, i.e., if the straight line joining the centers of the two balls is parallel to and collinear with $\vec{v}_1$, both balls would continue to move along the direction of $\vec{v}_1$. With the glancing collision shown here, however, the heavy ball will be slowed down slightly and deflected away from its original direction of motion, while the light ball will be set in motion with a velocity $\vec{v}_2'$, as shown in Fig. 6.2b. From the known masses and the measured velocities, the momenta of the balls before and after the impact may be calculated. In every experiment of this sort, it is found that the vector sum of the momenta after the collision is equal to the momentum of the moving ball before the collision. The relations of the various momenta in this particular collision are shown in the vector diagram of Fig. 6.2c. It should be noted that each momentum is in the same direction as the velocity associated with it.

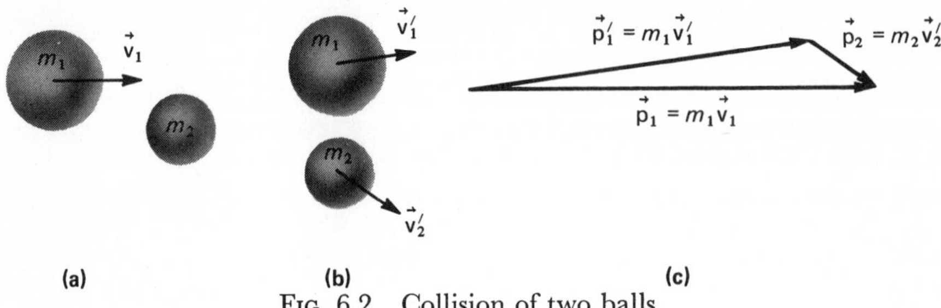

FIG. 6.2 Collision of two balls.

More involved experiments may be performed by having both balls moving before the collision, or by having more than two bodies involved. In all of these cases, it is found that the conservation law is obeyed within the experimental uncertainty. We can therefore conclude that the law of the conservation of momentum, as stated in Sec. 4.5, can be applied to any physical process. The law does not even need restatement, since we readily recognize that the adding of the momenta must be done vectorially. In order to indicate this, we rewrite Eq. (4.5-3) as

$$\overrightarrow{p_A} + \overrightarrow{p_B} = \overrightarrow{p_A}' + \overrightarrow{p_B}', \tag{6.1-2}$$

where $\overrightarrow{p_A}$ and $\overrightarrow{p_B}$ are the momenta of two bodies just before a collision in which no other bodies are involved, and $\overrightarrow{p_A}'$ and $\overrightarrow{p_B}'$ are their momenta after the collision.

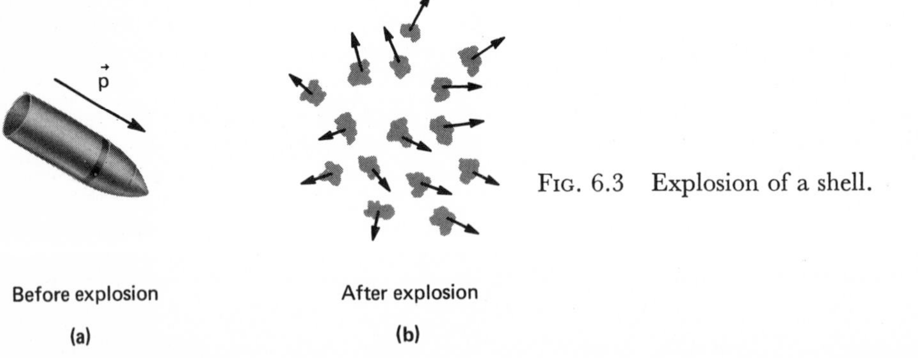

FIG. 6.3 Explosion of a shell.

An interesting consequence of the law of the conservation of momentum occurs when a shell bursts in midair. If the shell possesses a momentum $\vec{p}$ before it bursts, as shown in Fig. 6.3, and it explodes into a large number of parts, the vector sum of the momenta of all the parts must be equal to $\vec{p}$. An individual fragment may be moving in any direction, but the average motion will be forward with the velocity of the shell. Anyone who has played pool will recollect a similar example, which occurs when the cue ball strikes the racked set of fifteen balls and the balls scatter over the table.

EXERCISES

6.1-1 A billiard ball moving at a speed of 2.0 m/sec strikes a glancing blow on an identical ball, which is stationary. After the collision, one ball is observed to be moving at a speed of 1.0 m/sec in a direction at an angle of 60° from the original line of motion. Calculate the velocity of the other ball.

6.2-2 Two balls, of different and unknown masses, collide. Before the collision, ball A is at rest, while ball B is moving with a speed v. After the collision, ball B is found to be moving with a speed $v/2$ in a direction at right angles to its original motion. In what direction is ball A moving after the collision? Can the speed of ball A be found from the data given? Why?

6.2 *Force and Acceleration*

The reader should have no difficulty, after he has dealt with velocity and momentum, in convincing himself that acceleration and force are vectors, having the same direction as the change of velocity or the change of momentum that they bring about. We can therefore rewrite the defining equations for ***acceleration*** and ***force***, Eqs. (3.8-2) and (4.9-2), respectively, using vector notation. They become

$$\vec{a} = d\vec{v}/dt = \lim_{\Delta t \to 0} (\Delta\vec{v}/\Delta t), \tag{6.2-1}$$

and

$$\vec{f} = d\vec{p}/dt = \lim_{\Delta t \to 0} (\Delta\vec{p}/\Delta t). \tag{6.2-2}$$

In Chapter 8 we shall see that the mass of a body depends upon its speed. The effect is negligible even up to speeds many times greater than those of jet airplanes, rockets, and satellites, but as the speed of a body approaches that of light, the mass of the body increases without limit.

In all those processes in which the observed mass of a body does not change, Eq. (6.2-2) may be derived from Eq. (6.2-1) by multiplying both sides of the latter by the mass m of the body being accelerated. Hence, unless the speeds involved are so high that relativistic corrections are necessary, the force acting on a body is equal to the product of the mass of the body m by the acceleration $\vec{a}$ produced, so the force is

$$\vec{f} = m\vec{a}. \tag{6.2-3}$$

As an illustration of the action of forces in two dimensions, consider a billiard ball that bounces from the cushion, along the path shown in Fig. 6.4. In this case a force acts on the ball only during the very short time it is in contact with the cushion, and the entire change of velocity takes place during that time. If the ball and cushion are perfectly elastic (cf. Sec. 4.14), it can be shown experimentally that the speed of the ball after the impact is identical with the speed before. Direct measurement also shows that, unless the ball spins, its path is such that the ***angle of reflection*** (i.e., the angle between the line of motion and the perpendicular to the surface of the cushion, labeled ϕ in Fig. 6.4a) is equal to the ***angle of incidence*** θ. Figure 6.4b shows a vector diagram for the velocities, in which the initial and final velocities are redrawn to exhibit the relation between them and the average acceleration of the ball. The change in velocity

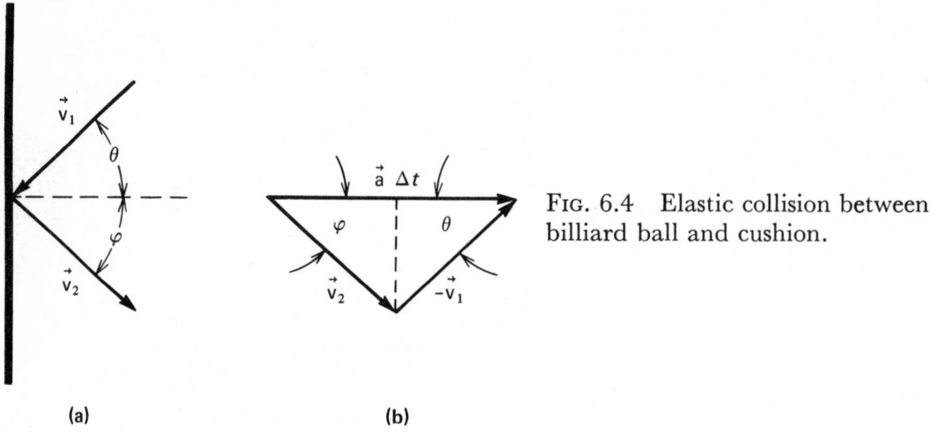

FIG. 6.4 Elastic collision between billiard ball and cushion.

of the ball during its contact with the cushion is the difference between the final velocity v_2 and the initial velocity $\vec{v}_1$, i.e., $\vec{v}_2 - \vec{v}_1$, as shown in the figure. If a is the average acceleration of the ball during the time Δt it is in contact with the cushion, the change in velocity is $a\Delta t$. Therefore,

$$\vec{v}_2 - \vec{v}_1 = \vec{a}\Delta t$$

as shown in the diagram. Because of the equality of θ and ϕ, the vector triangle is isosceles. The acceleration of the ball is directed to the right, at an angle θ to $\vec{v}_1$. The acceleration of the ball is hence at right angles to the surface of the cushion.

In order to find the magnitude of the average acceleration, we drop a perpendicular from the vertex of the vector triangle to the base. We can compute the length (that is to say, *the velocity*) of each piece of the base thus formed, to find that

$$\bar{a} = v_1 \cos\theta + v_2 \cos\theta = 2v_1 \cos\theta.$$

The average acceleration therefore has a magnitude

$$\bar{a} = (2v_1 \cos\theta)/\Delta t.$$

The force acting on the ball must have the same direction as the acceleration, i.e., perpendicular to the cushion, and its average magnitude is given by Eq. (6.2-3) as

$$\bar{f} = m\bar{a} = (2mv_1 \cos\theta)/\Delta t,$$

where m is the mass of the ball.

If the time during which the ball is in contact with the cushion is small, as it usually is, the acceleration and force may be very large. Thus, if

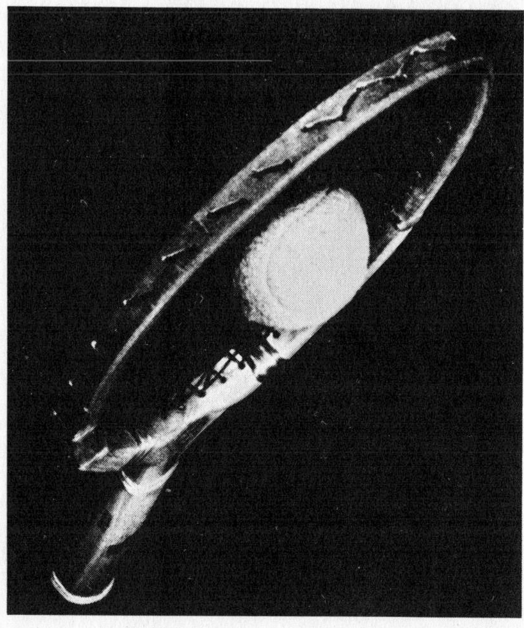

FIG. 6.5 Impact. (By permission of Harold E. Edgerton.)

$m = 0.20$ kg, $v_1 = 3.0$ m/sec, $\theta = 30°$, and $t = 0.010$ sec,

$$\bar{a} = 2(3.0 \text{ m/sec})(0.866)/(0.010 \text{ sec}) = 5.2 \times 10^2 \text{ m/sec}^2,$$
$$\bar{f} = (5.2 \times 10^2 \text{ m/sec}^2)(0.20 \text{ kg}) = 1.0 \times 10^2 \text{ N}.$$

Notice that the average acceleration of the ball during the impact is more than 50 times the acceleration due to gravity, and that the force on the ball is therefore more than 50 times the weight of the ball. The maximal acceleration may be even greater. Such large accelerations as this cause little permanent injury to hard, rigid bodies, like billiard balls, or even tennis balls, but their effects on less rigid bodies, such as a ball of putty or a human body, would be disastrous. An illustration of a violent collision, such as we have been discussing, is given by Fig. 6.5, which is a high-speed photograph of a tennis ball in contact with a racket. The very considerable distortions of the racket and of the ball give an idea of the magnitude of the forces involved in the rapid accelerations of the ball.

In order to discuss in some detail the type of collision shown in Fig. 6.5, let us consider a tennis ball, which at the top of its bounce is traveling horizontally at a speed of 4.00 m/sec. At this point the ball is hit by the player and is returned at a speed of 16.0 m/sec at an angle of 30° up from the horizontal. The velocities before and after the collision are related as shown in Fig. 6.6, and the average

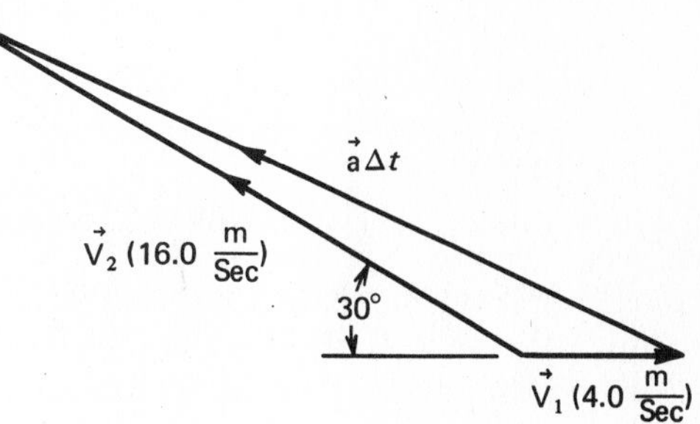

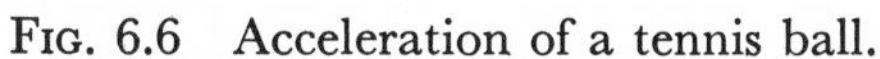

FIG. 6.6 Acceleration of a tennis ball.

acceleration during the time Δt in which the collision is taking place is given by

$$\vec{a}_{av}\,\Delta t = \vec{v}_2 - \vec{v}_1;\ \vec{v}_2 - \vec{a}_{av}\,\Delta t = \vec{v}_1;\ \vec{v}_1 + \vec{a}_{av}\,\Delta t = \vec{v}_2.$$

We can calculate $\vec{a}_{av}\,\Delta t$ by the methods of Sec. 5.8. The horizontal component of $\vec{a}_{av}\,\Delta t$ (measured positive to the right) is clearly

$$(a_{av}\Delta t)_x = (-16.0 \text{ m/sec}) \cos 30° - 4.00 \text{ m/sec}$$
$$= -(16.0 \times 0.866) \text{ m/sec} - 4.00 \text{ m/sec} = -17.86 \text{ m/sec},$$

and the vertical component (positive upward) is

$$(\vec{a}_{av}\,\Delta t)_y = (16.0 \text{ m/sec}) \sin 30° = 16.0 \times 0.500 \text{ m/sec} = 8.00 \text{ m/sec}.$$

The magnitude of $\vec{a}_{av}\,\Delta t$ is therefore given by

$$\vec{a}_{av}\,\Delta t = \sqrt{(17.86)^2 \times (8.00)^2} \text{ m/sec} = 19.6 \text{ m/sec}.$$

If this collision takes place in less than 0.05 sec the average acceleration is more than 390 m/sec^2 and, since the ball has a regulation mass of 2 ounces (57 gm), the average force acting on the ball is of the order of magnitude of 20 N.

EXERCISES

6.2-1 A car moving eastward at 58 km/hr turns onto a road running northward. As the car turns, its speed is increased to 75 km/hr. If it requires 3.0 sec to make the turn and increase its speed, what are the magnitude and direction of the average force on the car during this time? Assume that the mass of the car is 1500 kg.

6.2-2 An airplane flying at 400 km/hr changes its course by flying exactly one quarter of the way around a circle of 100 m radius. If the plane has a mass of 2000 kg, what is the average horizontal force on the plane during the turn? What is the ratio of this force to the weight of the plane?

6.2-3 A ball is thrown in a horizontal direction with a speed of 4.00 m/sec and is then acted upon by no forces except its own weight. What will be the direction and magnitude of its velocity at the end of 1.00 sec? At the end of 5.00 sec?

6.3 *Resolution and Composition of Forces*

When a number of forces are acting on a body simultaneously, the resultant force can be found by their vector addition. For example, we saw in Sec. 4.15 that the force on a freely falling body is $m\vec{g}$, where m is the mass of the body and $\vec{g}$ is the acceleration due to gravity. If the same body falls in air, it will also be subject to an upward frictional force due to its motion through the air. If a wind is blowing, it will also be subject to a horizontal force from this cause. If the force due to a sudden gust of wind is $\vec{f}_w$, and that due to air resistance is $\vec{f}_r$, both at some particular moment of the fall, the total force acting on the body at that instant is

$$\vec{f} = m\vec{g} + \vec{f}_w + \vec{f}_r,$$

and has a magnitude and direction such as that shown in Fig. 6.7. Consequently, the acceleration of the body, during this particular instant of its fall, will be in the direction denoted by $\vec{f}$.

In order that the total force acting on a body at any instant may be calculated, the forces are resolved into components along two mutually perpendicular axes (cf. Sec. 5.8). Thus, in Fig. 6.7, the x-axis might be chosen horizontally to the right and the y-axis vertically upward. Then the components of f with respect to these axes would be

$$f_x = f_w,$$
$$f_y = -mg + f_r.$$

From these expressions for the components, it follows that

$$f^2 = f_w^2 + (f_r - mg)^2,$$
$$\tan \theta = f_w/(mg - f_r).$$

This process of finding the resultant force on a body when the individual forces are known is called the ***composition of forces.*** It should be clear to the reader that the effect of all of the forces acting is exactly equivalent to that which would be produced by a single force of magnitude f acting in the direction shown.

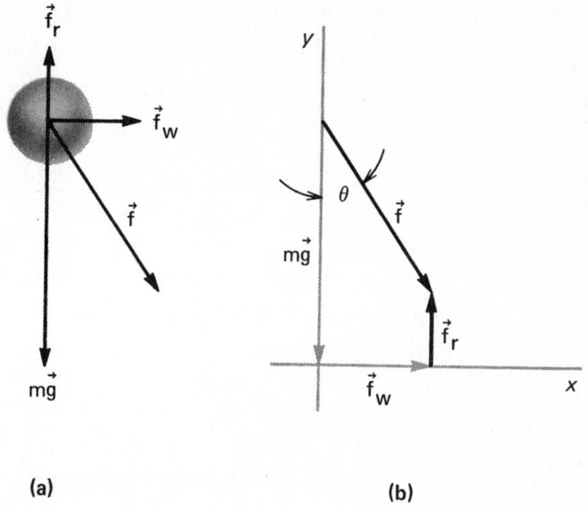

FIG. 6.7 Forces on a body falling in air.

It is sometimes necessary to resolve a force $\vec{f}$, which acts on a body, into components along the coordinate axes. For example, in order to determine the force required to move a hand-operated lawn mower through the grass, we can choose the x-axis along the ground with the y-axis perpendicular to it as in Fig. 6.8. As can be seen readily from the figure, the components of force along the two axes are

$$f_x = f_A \cos \theta,$$

and

$$f_y = -f_A \sin \theta.$$

The component f_x is effective in propelling the lawn mower through the grass. The other component, f_y, acts only to push the mower against the ground. Except for the fact that it would be inconvient for the operator, the lawn mower handle could be redesigned so that $f_A = f_x$.

The process just illustrated is called ***resolution of forces.*** The reader who has mastered the technique of finding the components of a vector will have no difficulty in resolving forces into their components along any convenient axes.

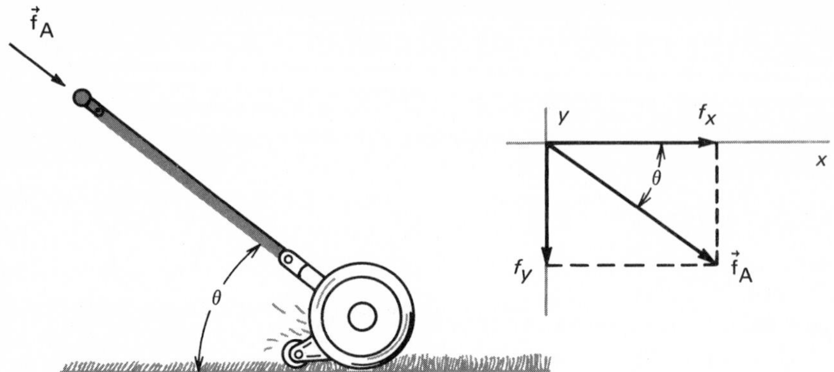

FIG. 6.8 Forces on a lawn mower.

6.4 *The Condition for Translational Equilibrium*

A body at rest or moving with constant velocity is said to be in ***translational equilibrium.*** Until Chapter 7 we disregard the fact that the body might be rotating. Instead we shall treat bodies of even considerable size as if they were mass points or particles.

The reader will recognize that to say a body is in translational equilibrium is simply to say it is not accelerating. But the change in term shifts the emphasis from the motion to the forces that might change that motion. We saw in Sec. 4.9 that the only condition under which a body is not accelerated is that no force is acting upon it. Since we now know that force is a vector, this condition requires only that *the vector sum of all the forces acting upon any body which is to remain in equilibrium be equal to zero.*

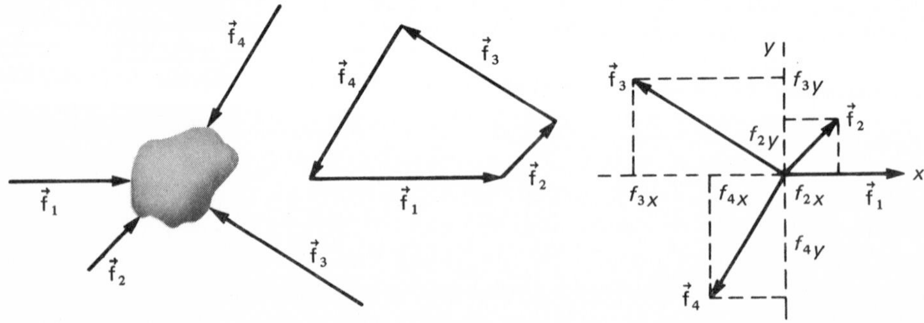

FIG. 6.9 Equilibrium of a body under the action of a number of forces that act through a single point.

The condition for equilibrium can be represented either graphically or analytically. Let us suppose that a small body, such as that shown in Fig. 6.9a, is acted upon by the forces $\vec{f}_1$, $\vec{f}_2$, $\vec{f}_3$, and $\vec{f}_4$. The four forces may be added on a vector diagram such as that shown in Fig. 6.9b. In order that the resultant force on the body shall be zero, in accordance with the law of vector addition, the length of the line joining the start of the first vector $\vec{f}_1$ with the end of the last vector $\vec{f}_4$ must be zero. Therefore, the polygon formed by adding the vectors successively to one another must be a closed figure, as shown.

If we wish to express the balancing of the forces analytically, we remember that a vector of zero magnitude has all of its components of zero magnitude. Therefore the sum of the corresponding components of the individual forces must vanish. If the forces are all in a single plane, there are then two conditions to be satisfied if the particle is to be in equilibrium:

$$f_x = f_{1x} + f_{2x} + f_{3x} + f_{4x} = 0 \quad (6.4\text{-}1A)$$

and

$$f_y = f_{1y} + f_{2y} + f_{3y} + f_{4y} = 0. \quad (6.4\text{-}1B)$$

If the angles that the forces make with the axes are known, the components can be calculated by trigonometry, as will be seen readily by reference to Fig. 6.9c.

Both ways of combining the forces to obtain a zero resultant are merely expressions of the fact that a set of forces which push and pull equally on a body will be equivalent to no force at all. Put in another way, they are expressions of Newton's third law of motion, that to every action there is an equal and opposite reaction. In Sec. 4.13 we discussed this law in terms of dynamic reactions, i.e., of equal and opposite changes of momentum. When no momentum change takes place, a body is in equilibrium, and the action and reaction are forces of equal magnitudes in opposite directions. Thus, in Fig. 6.10, the suitcase the man is carrying is in equilibrium under the combined action of its weight $\vec{mg}$ acting downward and the upward pull $\vec{f} = -\vec{mg}$ exerted on the suitcase by the man's hand. On the other hand, the meter stick shown in Fig. 6.11 is also subject to two equal and opposite forces, $\vec{f}_1$ and $\vec{f}_2$, but it is clear that it will not remain at rest but will rotate about its center O in the direction shown by the arrow, since the two forces do not directly oppose one another. As we said before, we shall not consider the cases of extended bodies

FIG. 6.10 Equilibrium under equal and opposed forces.

until we come to Chapter 7, in which rotational motion is discussed, but at present we must bear in mind that the vanishing of the resultant force on a body insures equilibrium only if all the forces acting are directed through a single point in the body.

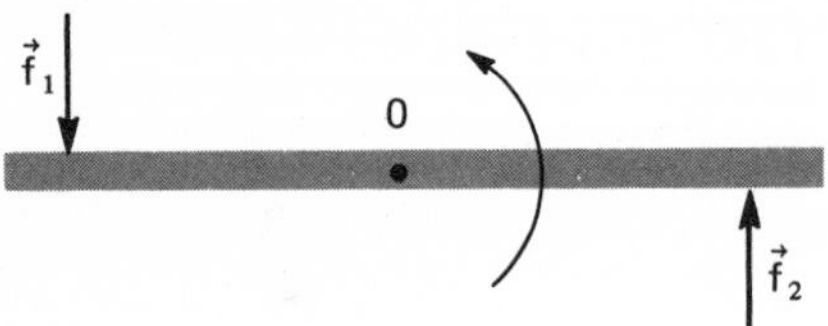

Fig. 6.11 Rotation under the action of equal and opposite forces that are not directly opposed.

6.5 Some Illustrative Examples

The simplest case of a body in equilibrium is that which occurs when only two forces act. For example, when a mass m is placed on a table top, it is subject to a downward force $\overrightarrow{mg}$. Since the body stays in place, the sum of the forces acting on it must be zero, and we therefore find that the table top pushes up on the body with a force $-\overrightarrow{mg}$. If the table top is not strong enough to exert this force, equilibrium cannot be maintained, and the body will be accelerated downward, with unfortunate results to the table. A slightly more involved case arises when three forces act on a particle. Suppose that a mass m is hung between points at

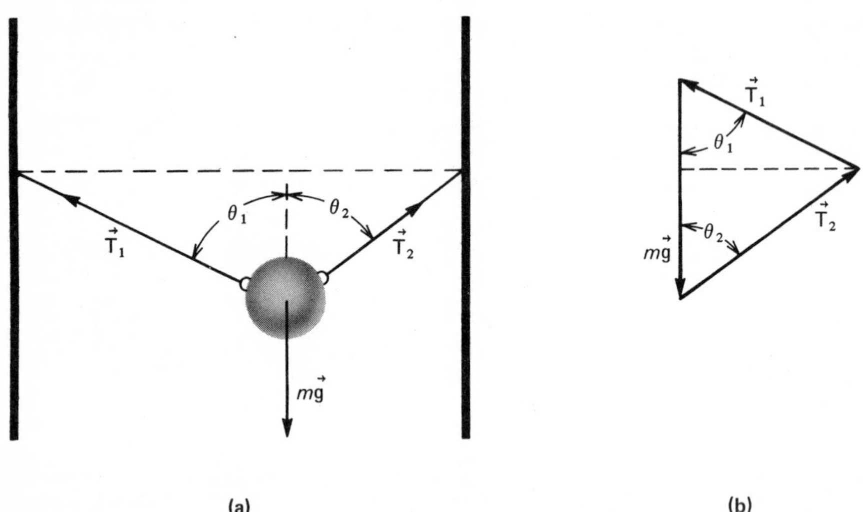

Fig. 6.12 Heavy body supported by two cables.

the same height on two buildings by two ropes of unequal lengths, as shown in Fig. 6.12a. We can see immediately that three forces are acting on m. The weight $\overrightarrow{mg}$ pulls it downward, while the tension in each rope pulls along the direction of the rope. We wish to find the magnitude of the tension in each rope. Since we know the direction of all three forces, and the magnitude of the weight as well, we can draw the vector diagram of Fig. 6.12b in the following way. A line is drawn, to a chosen scale, in a vertical downward direction to represent the known force $\vec{mg}$. From its ends the lines are drawn in the known directions of the other two forces, which we shall call $\vec{T}_1$ and $\vec{T}_2$. Since the sum of the three forces must be zero, the forces $\vec{T}_1$ and $\vec{T}_2$ will be represented both in magnitude (to the scale of the figure) and in direction by the sides of the triangle thus drawn. Having drawn the vector diagram, either to scale or schematically, we can calculate the magnitudes of the tensions. Thus, either from Eqs. (6.4-1) or by inspection of Fig. 6.12b, we see that

$$T_1 \cos \theta_1 + T_2 \cos \theta_2 - mg = 0$$

and

$$T_2 \sin \theta_2 - T_1 \sin \theta = 0.$$

Since we have two equations here and they contain two unknowns, the magnitudes T_1 and T_2, they can be solved for these unknowns. It is not worth while to carry the algebra further unless the values of m, θ_1, and θ_2 are known numerically.

In the example just considered, we know the lengths of the two ropes, or, what amounts to the same thing, their directions. As a variation on the problem, suppose that the weight is hung by a pulley from a continuous rope, which is stretched between the two points on the buildings so that it can slide freely along the rope (Fig. 6.13). It will then move along the rope until it comes to some equilibrium position. We wish to know the directions of the two parts of the rope, as well as the tension in the rope. We first notice that, since the rope can slide freely through the pulley, the tension in the two parts must be the same. Were it not, the part with the greater tension would pull the other

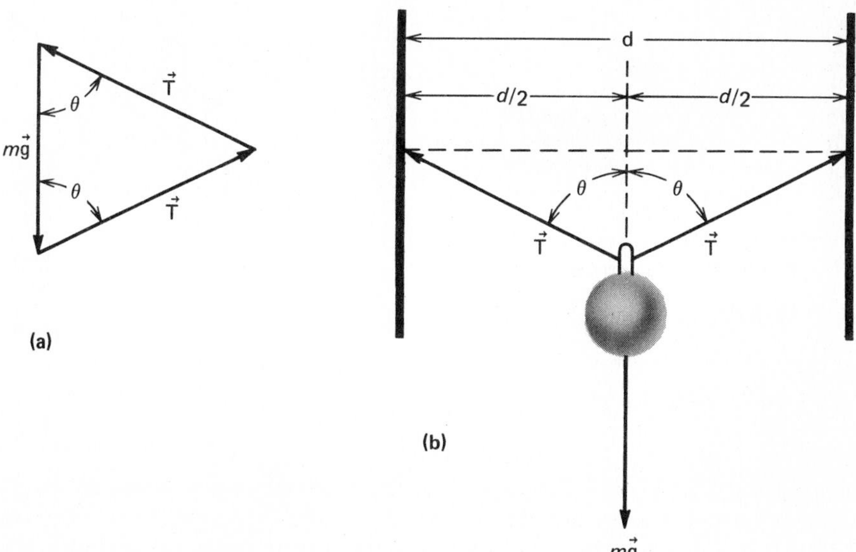

Fig. 6.13 Heavy body hung on a running pulley.

part through the pulley. It therefore follows at once that the vector triangle, similar to that of Fig. 6.12b, will be isosceles, as shown in Fig. 6.13a. The two base angles therefore are equal and the two parts of the rope must make equal angles with the vertical, as shown in Fig. 6.13b. From this figure it is clear that, if l is the length of the rope and d the distance between the buildings,

$$d/2 = (l/2)\sin\theta,$$

where θ is the angle of either rope with the vertical. We find from this relation that

$$\sin\theta = d/l,$$

and the value of θ thus found enables us to complete the vector diagram of Fig. 6.13a. From the diagram, we see that the tension in the rope is

$$T = mg/2\cos\theta.$$

In Figs. 6.12 and 6.13, it has not been necessary to take into account the fact that ropes stretch under tension. In each figure, for example, if the weight of the heavy body were doubled, the ropes would lengthen slightly and the designated angles would become slightly smaller; the heavy body would thus hang slightly lower. The table top mentioned in the first paragraph of this section will also be slightly distorted under load. In fact, any body that supports a load, or is otherwise reacting to a force, will be more or less distorted. If the force is too great, the body may be permanently deformed or it may break. We shall not pursue this matter further at this point, but see Prob. 6.4 at the end of this chapter.

Each of the examples above is a case in which the velocity of the body, or the system, is zero. Figure 6.14 illustrates the forces that act on an automobile when it travels at constant velocity $\vec{v}$. The weight $m\vec{g}$ of the automobile is balanced by the supportive reaction $\vec{f}_R$ of the road. The propelling force $\vec{f}_P$ of the road

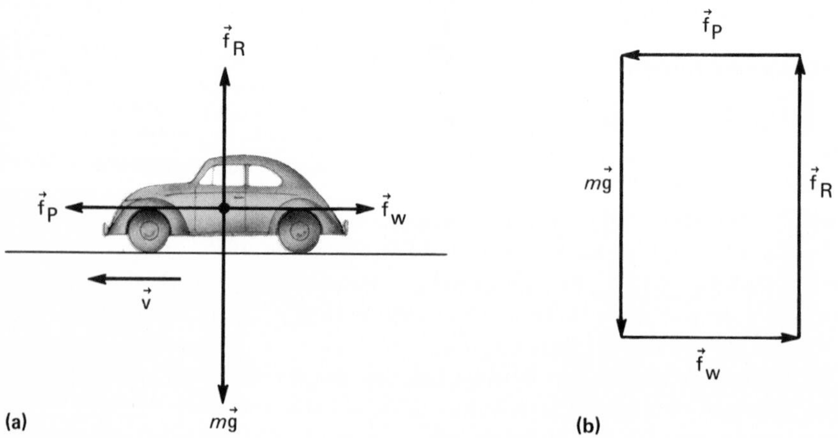

FIG. 6.14 Forces on an automobile moving with constant velocity.

against the wheels is balanced by the wind resistance $\vec{f}_W$. Figure 6.14b shows the resulting closed polygon. Analytically, the horizontal and vertical components each sum to zero:

$$f_R - mg = 0$$

and

$$f_P - f_W = 0.$$

EXERCISES

6.5-1 In Fig. 6.12, suppose that m equals 500 kg, $\theta_1 = 35°$, and $\theta_2 = 42°$. Find the tension in each rope.

6.5-2 A picture which with its frame has a mass of 3.0 kg is hung from a single hook by a wire attached to the sides of the frame and passing over the hook. If the wire is at an angle of 15° with the horizontal on each side of the hook, what is the tension in the wire? What force acts on the hook?

6.5-3 A safe of mass 450 kg is being hoisted into a building by means of a rope over a pulley. The length of the rope from the pulley to the top of the safe is 40 ft. In order to keep the safe from striking the building, a second rope is attached to its top and is stretched horizontally to a building across the street, pulling the safe 2.0 ft out of line from the vertical through the pulley. What is the tension in each rope?

6.5-4 By consideration of arguments similar to those used in discussing Fig. 6.13, show that the mass m cannot be supported by a rope of a length which is exactly the distance between the two buildings.

6.5-5 A block of mass M is resting on a plane smooth surface inclined at an angle θ to the horizontal. By resolving the weight of the block into forces perpendicular and parallel to the plane, show that the block will slide down the plane with an acceleration of magnitude $g \sin \theta$.

6.5-6 The pulley of Ex. 4.15-3 is fastened to the ceiling by a hook. With what force does the hook pull down on the ceiling? (Hint: Find the tension in the string.)

6.6 Work and Energy

We saw in Sec. 4.11 that the kinetic energy of a body moving with a speed v along a straight line is $\frac{1}{2}mv^2$ [Eq. (4.11-5)]. We also obtained in that section the work-energy theorem, which stated that the work necessary to produce a given change of speed of the body is equal to the change of kinetic energy [Eq. (4.11-7)]. Now that we have developed the tools to study motion in two or three dimensions, we are in a position to make the concepts of work and energy more meaningful and to give them a closer connection with reality than they had in our earlier rather formal treatment.

The definition of kinetic energy in the general case is very simple. Suppose that a particle of mass m is moving at some instant with measured velocity components v_x, v_y, and v_z along the three axes of a Cartesian coordinate system. At that instant the body is moving in a particular direction with a velocity

$\vec{v}$, equal to the vector sum of the components. It is in every way equivalent (at the instant) to a body of the same mass moving along a line, so kinetic energy is $\frac{1}{2}mv^2$ and the Pythagorean theorem tells us that

$$KE = \tfrac{1}{2}mv^2 = \tfrac{1}{2}mv_x^2 + \tfrac{1}{2}mv_y^2 + \tfrac{1}{2}mv_z^2. \tag{6.6-1}$$

Before developing the meaning of the work-energy theorem, let us recall the example of Fig. 6.8, where we noted that only the *horizontal component* of the force exerted on the handle of the lawn mower was useful in propelling the machine through the grass. A similar example arises if we think of the problem of pushing an automobile. Suppose that a person pushes the automobile along a road by exerting a force $\vec{F}$, directed horizontally against the back of the car (Fig. 6.15a). As the force is applied to the automobile during the process of pushing it, the point of application of the force undergoes a displacement $\vec{s}$. In this case the entire force is effective during the displacement, so we can write $w = Fs$. Note that this product does indeed make the work dependent on both the magnitude of the force and the magnitude of the displacement.

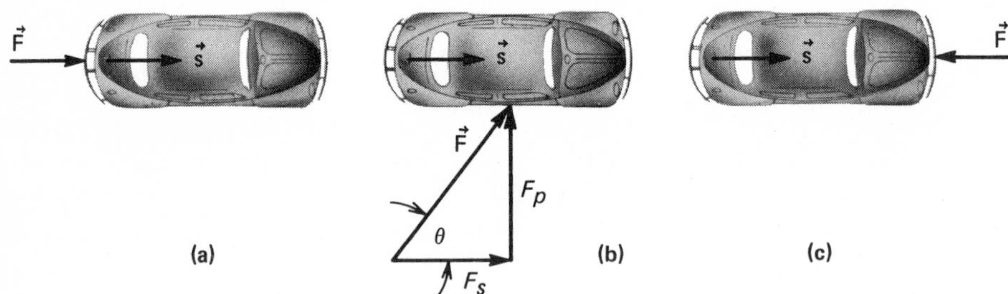

FIG. 6.15 Work done in pushing a car.

Moreover, since the work is the same whether the car happens to be pointed north, south, east, or west, it is clear that *work is a scalar, not a vector quantity*. Now suppose that the car is again pushed, but that the force is exerted against the side of the car, at an angle θ to the direction of motion. We represent this by a vector diagram, Fig. 6.15b. If we resolve the force vector into two components, F_s along the direction of the motion and F_p perpendicular to this direction, the former is the only part of the force that can act through a displacement $\vec{s}$. The other component acts through no displacement and therefore does not contribute to the work. Since $F_s = F\cos\theta$, the work done in this case is

$$W = Fs\cos\theta. \tag{6.6-2}$$

Before we definitely decide to accept Eq. (6.6-2) as an amplification of $w = Fs$, it may be well to consider a few special cases. If $\theta = 0$, the push is in the direction of motion of the car. Since $\cos\theta = 1$, the work done in this case turns out to be Fs in agreement with our earlier conclusion. Again, if $\theta = 90°$, $\cos\theta = 0$, and the equation tells us that no work is done. The force in this case is not accompanied by a displacement, for a car cannot normally be moved sideways by pushing on it sideways.

Finally, if θ is greater than 90°, cos θ becomes negative (see Appendix G) and Eq. (6.6-2) tells us that the work done is negative. We can see that this result is in agreement with our ordinary idea of negative quantities, if we realize that in this case the role of the car and the person are interchanged and that the car is pushing the person. Hence we interpret the statement that a body does negative work to mean that work is done *on* the body. It appears, then, that Eq. (6.6-2) leads to results in agreement with experience.

It has just been said that the component F_p of the force perpendicular to the direction of motion of the car does no work in pushing hard against an obstacle without moving it. We can resolve the difficulty by considering the exactly analogous case in which one holds a heavy weight stationary over his head. Here again, a force is exerted without producing a displacement and yet physiological work is done. But the weight could be held indefinitely in the same position by having a platform built under it, and we would not say that the platform did work. The fact is that the physiological work done in such processes as these is work done within the body in keeping muscles extended or contracted. Therefore, physiological work does not necessarily imply external physical work.

We may summarize the result of this important section by restating the result of Eq. (6.6-2) in words. *The work done by a force acting on a body is the product of the magnitude of the displacement* (s) *of the point of application of the force times the component of the force* (F cos θ) *in the direction of the displacement.* If the component is in the same direction as the displacement, the work done is positive. The man does work on the car. If the force component is in the opposite direction to the displacement, the work done is negative. The car does work on the man in pushing him. If there is no force component in the direction of motion, there is no work done. The car stays still or continues to move oblivious of the fact that the man is pushing—foolishly—at right angles to the direction in which the car can move.

EXERCISES

6.6-1 A man draws a sled, on a horizontal sheet of ice, by pulling on a rope inclined at 35° to the horizontal. He exerts a force of 240 N. How much work does he do in pulling the sled 500 m?

6.6-2 A piano with a mass of 400 kg is raised 5.2 m from the ground to a second-floor window. How much work is done?

6.6-3 The engine of a small automobile is inoperative. A man who pushes the automobile for 30 sec at a constant speed of 1.0 m/sec must exert a force of 80 N to do so. Is he doing work? If so, how much?

6.6-4 The automobile in Ex. 6.6-3 has a mass of 400 kg. If the man exerts 80 N while bringing the car from rest up to a speed of 1.0 m/sec, what is the *minimum* amount of work he must have done? Why is the actual work more than this? In view of the minimum amount of work that you calculated, what would be the minimum displacement?

6.7 *Products of Vectors*

In Sec. 5.5 we discussed the addition and subtraction of vectors. These are elementary steps in the algebra of vectors. We found that velocity vectors could be added in order to obtain a resultant velocity. Similarly, we found that we could add vectorially forces or displacements. Moreover, given a single vector, we can resolve it into two or more components; thus, we could regard the single vector *as if* it were the resultant of the vector sum of its components.

In general, vectors which are added or subtracted are always of a single kind —that is, they are all forces or they are all displacements or they are all some other kind of vector. It is no more analytically possible to add or subtract vectors of different kinds than it is to try to simplify the expression "two pigs plus two cows."

In Sec. 5.5 we also noted the multiplication of a vector by a scalar. Thus, mass is the scalar m which is the factor by which the acceleration vector $\vec{a}$ must be multiplied in order to get the force vector $\vec{f}$ which produces that acceleration of m:

$$\vec{f} = m\vec{a}. \tag{6.7-1}$$

In Sec. 6.6, however, we encountered the *product of two vectors*, and *these two vectors are of different kinds*. In defining work we have stipulated that a force must always be multiplied by a displacement, and as an additional factor, we must multiply by the cosine of the angle between the two vectors: $Fs \cos \theta$. The resulting work is a scalar; no spatial orientation is relevant to the quantitative expression of the work.

We may now adopt a conventional notation to represent this kind of product of two vectors. We shall write the symbols of the two vectors with a multiplicative dot between them; thus,

$$Fs \cos \theta = \vec{F} \cdot \vec{s}. \tag{6.7-2}$$

The symbols $\vec{F} \cdot \vec{s}$ are said to constitute the ***scalar product*** or the ***dot product*** of the two vectors. The symbolism may be read as "eff dot ess." By this we understand that the magnitude of the two vectors and the cosine of the angle between them are to be taken as a three-factor product.

We defined in Sec. 4.12 the joule (J) as the unit of work in the mks system, equal to one newton-meter. In the cgs system, where force is expressed in dynes and displacement in centimeters, an acceptable unit of work would be the dyne-centimeter. Again, however, this unit is given a special name, so that one dyne-centimeter equals one ***erg***. One erg is calculated to be 10^{-7} J. The corresponding unit in the fps system is a *foot-poundal*, which, of course, is equivalent to a force of one poundal acting through a displacement of one foot. There is no special name for the foot-poundal. In the engineering system of units (Sec. 4.15 and Appendix D), the unit of work is the *foot-pound* (*wt*).

EXERCISES

6.7-1 In any equation involving vectors, what must be true dimensionally on the two sides of the equality sign? What must be true dimensionally term-by-term in a vector addition or subtraction?

6.7-2 In Eqs. (6.7-1) and (6.7-2), analyze the factors and terms for their dimensional constitution.

6.7-3 In the spirit of this section, consider the equation $\Delta w = (\vec{F} \cdot \vec{v})\Delta t$, in which $\vec{F}$ is a force whose point of application moves with velocity $\vec{v}$ and Δt is an increment of time, a scalar. Does the equation appear to be one that might apply to a physical situation? Explain.

6.7-4 Calculate the amount of work, in foot-poundals, done when a man of 160-lb mass climbs a flight of 50 steps, each rising 8.0 in.

6.7-5 Convert the work in the preceding problem into joules.

6.7-6 Using approximations—e.g., 1 ft $\approx$ 1/3 m, g $\approx$ 10 m/sec² $\approx$ 30 ft/sec²—show that one foot-poundal $\approx$ 1/20 J.

6.7-7 Using approximations, show that one foot-pound (wt) $\approx$ 1.6 J.

6.8 Power

We are frequently more interested in the rate at which work is done than we are in the total amount of work, so we shall define ***power*** as the time rate of doing work. Thus, we have as the defining equation for power

$$P = dw/dt, \tag{6.8-1}$$

which reduces to

$$P = w/t \tag{6.8-2}$$

in the special case when an amount of work w is done at a uniform rate during a time t. The dimensional equation is

$$[\mathscr{P}] = [w]/[t] = [m\ell^2 t^{-3}] \tag{6.8-3}$$

The unit of power, like that of work, is given a special name in the mks system. This is the ***watt*** (abbreviated W), which is defined as one joule per second. The unit is named for James Watt (1736–1819), the inventor of the modern steam engine. Watt himself developed a commonly used unit of power, the horsepower. He found that a strong horse could do work, over extended periods of time, as a rate corresponding to the lifting of a 550-lb mass with a speed of one foot per second. Since he was an engineer, he used the pound weight (Sec. 4.15) as a unit of force and thus defined the ***horsepower*** as

$$1 \text{ hp} = 550 \text{ ft-lb(wt)/sec.} \tag{6.8-4}$$

The reader can easily verify that

$$1 \text{ hp} = 746 \text{ watts.*} \tag{6.8-5}$$

The latter definition, taken as exact in modern engineering, is approximately equivalent to that developed by Watt. There is a unit of work called the ***kilowatt-hour*** (kW-hr), which is very commonly used in the electrical industry. The reader should verify that

$$1 \text{ kW-hr} = 3.6 \times 10^6 \text{ J.} \tag{6.8-6}$$

* Note that g, in the fps system, has the magnitude 32.2 ft/sec².

EXERCISES

6.8-1 Show that the definitions of Eqs. (6.8-4) and (6.8-5) are approximately equivalent.

6.8-2 Suppose that the man in Ex. 6.7-4 climbs the stairs in 1.0 min. How many horsepower does he develop?

6.8-3 Suppose that the man of Ex. 6.6-1 pulls the sled at a speed of 4.5 km/hr. At what rate is he doing work?

6.8-4 Verify that the kilowatt-hour is a unit of work and that Eq. (6.8-6) is correct.

6.9 Energy

We define the ability of a body to do work as the ***energy*** of the body, and we measure a body's energy by the amount of work that the body can do. Hence, *energy is measured in the same units as work*. We recall that this was true in Sec. 4.11 where we first introduced the concept of kinetic energy.

A body may possess energy for one or more of a number of reasons. Thus, a mass lifted against the gravitational pull of the earth can exert a force, and hence do work, as it falls again. A spring that has been extended or compressed can do work in returning to its normal length. A moving body requires a force to stop it, so it can do work on any obstacle in its path. We say, therefore, that all of these bodies possess energy.

6.10 The Conservation of Mechanical Energy

We saw in Sec. 4.14 that the total kinetic energy of a system of bodies among which only perfectly elastic collisions take place is the same after the collisions as it was before. We also recognized that it is quite possible that at least some of the kinetic energy that the bodies possessed before collision was stored as potential energy in the bumpers during the time when they were in contact, so that the sum of the kinetic and potential energies might remain constant at all times.

Such idealizations as "perfectly elastic impact" seldom fit exactly the real world of people, automobiles, baseballs, and other objects of ordinary scale. On the other hand, the ideal situation in which mechanical energy—kinetic plus potential—is conserved is sometimes approximated closely.

To illustrate, let us return to the problem of the falling body. We found in Sec. 4.18 that the potential energy of a mass m, when it is at a height h above some arbitrary reference plane, is mgh, where g is the acceleration due to gravity. It is true that we were then considering that the body fell along a vertical line, rather than that it slid along a slope such as that shown in Fig. 6.16 or was forced to move in a circular arc, as is the pendulum bob of Fig. 6.17. The work-energy theorem of Sec. 4.11 still applies to these motions *if the motion is frictionless*. To see this, we need merely to consider the forces acting on the moving body at any arbitrary point. In Fig. 6.18a the sled of Fig. 6.16 is shown at a point at which the slope makes an angle θ with the horizontal. The only

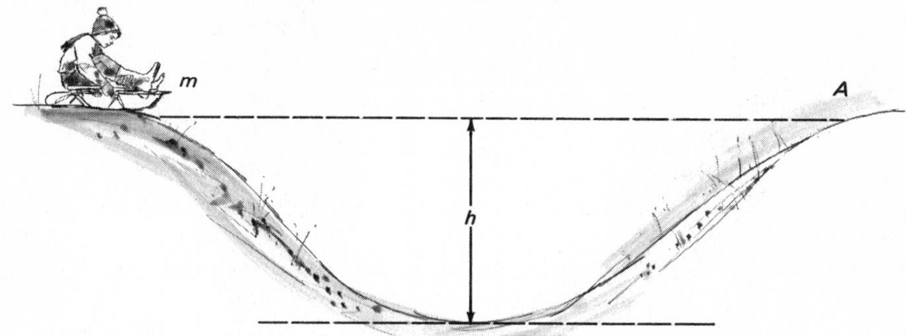

FIG. 6.16 Energy conservation law for a sliding body.

forces acting on the sled are its weight $\overrightarrow{mg}$ and the push $\vec{F}$ of the surface which, if the surface is smooth (frictionless), is perpendicular to the surface. The latter force, being perpendicular to the motion of the sled, does no work. On the other hand, the gravitational force is doing work at the rate

$$-\frac{d(PE)}{dt} = \overrightarrow{mg} \cdot \vec{v} = mgv \cos (90° - \theta) = mgv \sin \theta.$$

We may now note that $v \sin \theta$ is just the vertical component of velocity; i.e., it is the rate at which the height of the sled is changing. Hence the rate of change

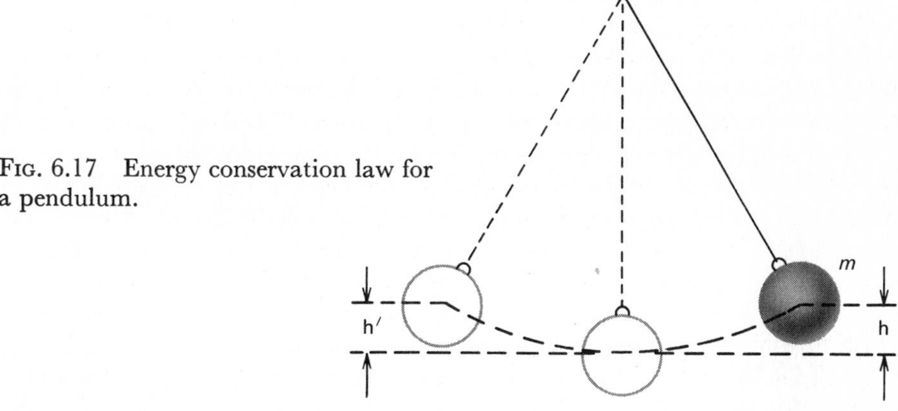

FIG. 6.17 Energy conservation law for a pendulum.

of potential energy depends only on the vertical component of motion; the amount of work that the sled can do going down the slope, and hence the gain in its kinetic energy between the top of its path and the bottom is mgh, as it would be in vertical fall. On the up-grade, of course, the kinetic energy decreases as potential energy is gained.

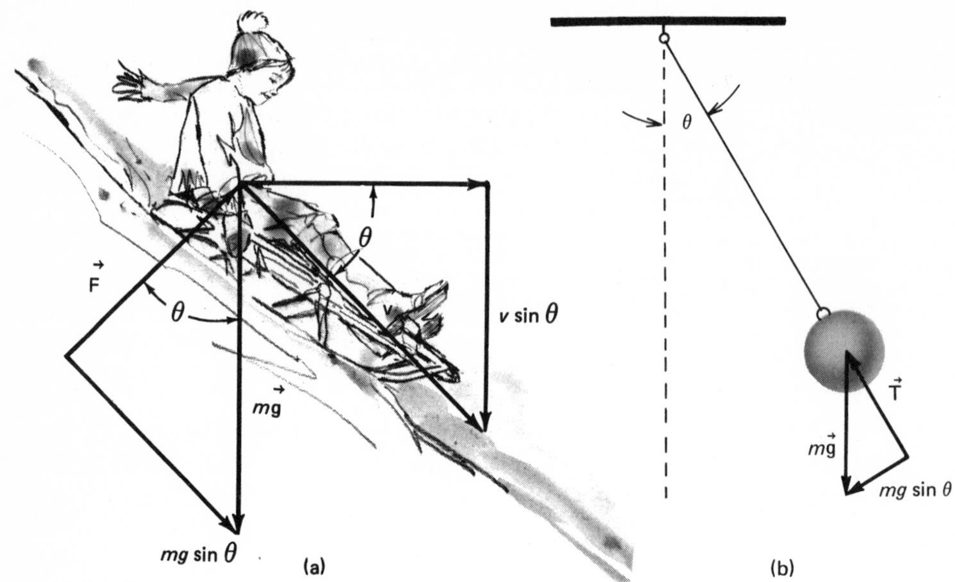

FIG. 6.18 The work-energy theorem.

Consideration of the forces on the pendulum bob of Fig. 6.18b, in which the tension $\overrightarrow{T}$ in the string plays the same roll as did the force $\overrightarrow{F}$ on the sled, will again show the work-energy theorem to be valid in this case.

We know that a pendulum bob rises to a height h' that is very nearly equal to the height h from which it started its swing (Fig. 6.17). We also know that the sled of Fig. 6.16 will climb to a point A that is very nearly at the same height as the point from which it started, provided that the surface is smooth and hard. We ascribe the small decrease in the total energy of either body to frictional forces and imagine ideal systems from which such forces are absent.

As a result of many observations similar to those discussed here, we are able to make a generalization known as the ***law of the conservation of mechanical energy***: *In any isolated system of bodies in which there is no friction and in which no inelastic collisions take place, the sum of the potential energy and the kinetic energy remains constant.* The quantitative application of this law is made somewhat difficult by the fact that isolated systems without friction can never be obtained in the laboratory or in the experiences of ordinary life. We shall find later, however, that such systems do exist, or are approximated very closely, when we deal with the motions of large astronomical bodies or when we go to the other extreme and deal with the motions of the atoms and molecules of which matter is composed.

Systems in which mechanical energy is conserved are often called ***conservative systems.***

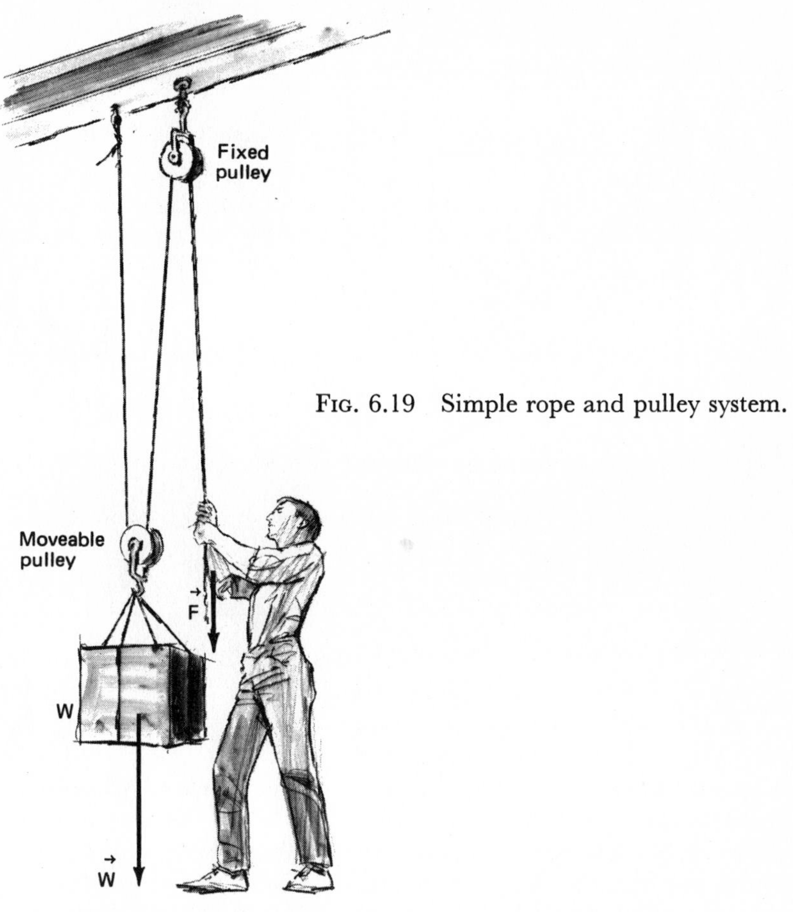

FIG. 6.19 Simple rope and pulley system.

Illustrative Example

Suppose that a body of 100-kg mass is being lifted by a system of ropes and pulleys shown in Fig. 6.19. What is the magnitude of the force $\vec{F}$ with which a man must pull on the rope?

First we shall assume that the weight is being raised slowly, without acceleration. When the mass rises by an amount Δh, its potential energy changes by an amount

$$\Delta(PE) = mg\,\Delta h.$$

Since the kinetic energy does not change, the man must do exactly this amount of work (neglecting any frictional forces) during the time that the mass rises through Δh. We notice, however, that the weight is supported by two ropes and that the man must therefore pull his portion of the rope through a distance $2\Delta h$ to cause a Δh change in height. Hence the work that he does to produce this change is

$$W = 2F\,\Delta h.$$

Equating this work to the change in potential energy, we find that

$$2F\,\Delta h = mg\,\Delta h$$

or that

$$F = \tfrac{1}{2}mg = \tfrac{1}{2}(100\text{ kg})(9.80\text{ m/sec}^2) = 490\text{ kg m/sec}^2 = 490\text{ N}.$$

Suppose next that the body is being accelerated as it lifts. Suppose that the acceleration is $a = 1.00$ m/sec^2. Then the kinetic energy, as well as the potential energy, changes. To relate the two, we use Eq. (3.18-4) to show that the time taken to raise the body through Δh is

$$\Delta t = 2\Delta h/(v_2 + v_1),$$

where v_1 is the initial speed and v_2 is the final speed. We then use Eq. (3.18-2) to find the change in velocity,

$$v_2 - v_1 = a\,\Delta t = 2a\,\Delta h/(v_2 + v_1).$$

Clearing fractions, we have

$$v_2^2 - v_1^2 = 2a\,\Delta h.$$

Hence the change in kinetic energy as the body rises through Δh is

$$\Delta(KE) = \tfrac{1}{2}mv_2^2 - \tfrac{1}{2}mv_1^2 = ma\,\Delta h.$$

We now equate the work done to the *total* change in energy of the body:

$$2F\,\Delta h = m(g + a)\Delta h.$$

$$F = \tfrac{1}{2}m(g + a) = \tfrac{1}{2}(100\text{ kg})(10.80\text{ m/sec}^2) = 540\text{ kg m/sec}^2 = 540\text{ N}.$$

Had we taken frictional forces into account, we would have found somewhat greater forces. It is left as an exercise for the reader to show that the man who raises the weight with an acceleration must himself have a mass of at least 119 lb.

6.11 Summary

The ideas of momentum, acceleration, and force, which proved so useful in discussing motion in a straight line, have been extended to apply to motion in space. All of these quantities have been found to be vectors. The law of the conservation of momentum, originally stated in Chapter 4, has been found to hold for the more general motions when the momenta are added vectorially. Similarly, the relations between accelerations and forces which were found earlier can be applied without difficulty in two or three dimensions. We have used these relations to study the conditions under which a particle will be in equilibrium and have found that this requires that the vector sum of the forces acting on the particle be zero. This condition has been applied to several practical problems.

The concepts of potential energy, kinetic energy, and work, which we met in Chapter 4, turn out to be of as great value in real, three-dimensional motions as they were in the one-dimensional motions considered earlier. Energy and work are scalar quantities, and it is found that mechanical energy, the sum of the kinetic and potential energies, is conserved in idealized, conservative systems, which some real systems approximate very closely.

PROBLEMS

6.1 A child whose mass is 15 kg sits in a swing and asks a boy to give the swing a push. The boy does so by displacing the swing and child so that the ropes make an angle of 30° with the vertical. Under these circumstances the boy's arms are thrusting upward at a 45° angle with the horizontal. Find the tension in the ropes and the thrust by his arms when the swing and child are so held.

6.2 Three hooks, a, b, and c, are attached to the ceiling at the vertices of an equilateral triangle, so that hooks b and c lie on a north-south line and hook a is to the west of this line, as shown in the figure. Equal lengths of rope A, B, and C are attached to their respective hooks and their other ends are tied into a single ring which is attached to a 40 kg mass. Each rope A, B, and C makes an angle of 60° with the plane of the ceiling. What is the tension in each rope? What force component parallel to the ceiling must be provided by each hook?

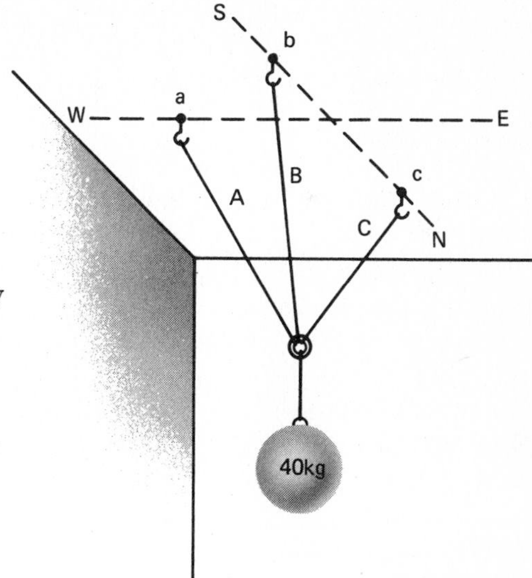

Problem 6.2 Weight supported by three ropes.

6.3 Referring to Fig. 6.8, suppose that $f_A = 50$ N at $\theta = 30°$. When the machine is operated at uniform velocity, what resistance is offered by the grass if it is assumed that the gears, bearings, and blades are virtually frictionless? Now suppose that the machine is operated under identical conditions except that the grass lies on a 20° upward incline. Place the x-axis parallel to this slope with the y-axis perpendicular to it and use these coordinates to find what force the operator must provide for equilibrium operation.

6.4 A sample of rope is known to stretch 0.01 m per meter of length for each newton of tension applied to it. A piece of this rope which is 5.00 m long when under no tension is used to support 2.0 kg from a ceiling 10.0 m high. How far from the floor is the point where the rope attaches to the load?

6.5 A rocket of mass M is moving at some instant with a velocity $\vec{V}$. During a short time Δt it burns a small amount of fuel and ejects the products of the combustion, which have a mass Δm, directly backward with a velocity $-\vec{v}$, relative to the rocket. Suppose that no external forces, such as gravity, act on the rocket.

(a) Show that the change of the rocket's velocity during the time Δt is

$$\Delta V = V\Delta m/(M - \Delta m).$$

(b) By letting Δt approach zero and by recognizing that the rate of change of the mass of the rocket is $-dm/dt$, show that the acceleration of the rocket is

$$\frac{dV}{dt} = -V\frac{dM}{dt}\bigg/M.$$

(c) Show that the thrust of the rocket, that is, the force accelerating it forward, is $-v\, dM/dt$ at the instant when the fuel is first ignited and the rocket is still at rest.

(d) Show that the rocket, having started from rest, can attain a velocity greater than v if it is still burning fuel at the time when $V = v$.

6.6 (a) Suppose that the rocket of Prob. 6.5 starts from rest and is accelerated vertically upward at a place where the acceleration due to gravity has the magnitude g. Show that the thrust must be greater than $M_0 g$, where M_0 is the initial mass of the rocket (including its fuel).

(b) Find the initial acceleration of the rocket in terms of dM/dt, v, and M_0.

(c) Suppose that $v = 300$ m/sec. What fraction of its mass must the rocket discharge per unit time if it is to move upward with an initial acceleration of 4.00 g?

6.7 For the rocket of Prob. 6.5, on which all external forces are neglected, show that the combusion of the fuel must supply an amount of energy, per unit mass of material ejected, that is equal to

$$\tfrac{1}{2}v^2.$$

(Hint: Find the rate of change of kinetic energy per unit time and remember that the calculation must be made in an unaccelerated reference frame.)

6.8 An airplane of mass 3.0×10^4 lb is in steady horizontal flight at 500 mi/hr. Its engines develop 4000 horsepower. (a) What is the magnitude of the "drag", i.e., of the frictional force on the plane that results from its motion through the air? (b) What is the ratio of the "lift," i.e., the vertical component of force on the airplane, to the drag?

REFERENCES

6A O. W. Gail, *Romping through Physics*, Knopf, New York, 1934. Pages 27–37 present interesting examples of force and weight.

6B Ernst Mach, *The Science of Mechanics*, 6th edition, Open Court, La Salle, Ill., 1960. A history of the understanding of composition of forces is presented on pp. 32–59.

6C Akira Harashima, Hachirō Nakagome, Masakuni Hotta, and Takeshi Takahashi, *Stroboscope*, Kōdansha, Tokyo, 1966. Many of these excellent stroboscopic photographs, particularly those involving bodies moving on tracks, offer good illustrations of the conservation laws.

7 ⇨ *Rotation*

7.1 Angular Displacement of a Rigid Body

In Chapter 2, after discussing periodic motions, clocks, and time units, we devoted Sec. 2.18 to an operational definition of angular measure. We observed that the notion of angle was necessary in order to treat rotation, but we have deferred a more detailed discussion of rotation until we could first consider the dynamics of particles. In the treatment thus far, a ball, a hanging sign, or even the earth itself could be regarded as a particle *if* rotation was absent or somehow irrelevant to the situation. We now need to focus our attention on rotational motion because, in the more general case of motion, a body moving in a straight line, a parabola, or any other path may also be spinning as it goes.

Let us first accept the fact that bodies rotate and define terms for describing this rotation or its changes, leaving till later the question of *how* rotation is produced or changed. This procedure is the same one used with particle motion, by which we first defined displacement, velocity, and acceleration. For rotational motion, similarly, we shall define angular displacement, angular velocity, and angular acceleration.

In Sec. 2.18, we defined angle by means of Fig. 2.8a. In Fig. 2.8a, the mark M is drawn opposite to pointer P. In Fig. 2.8b the wheel has been rotated 30°

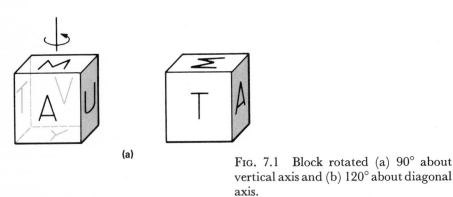

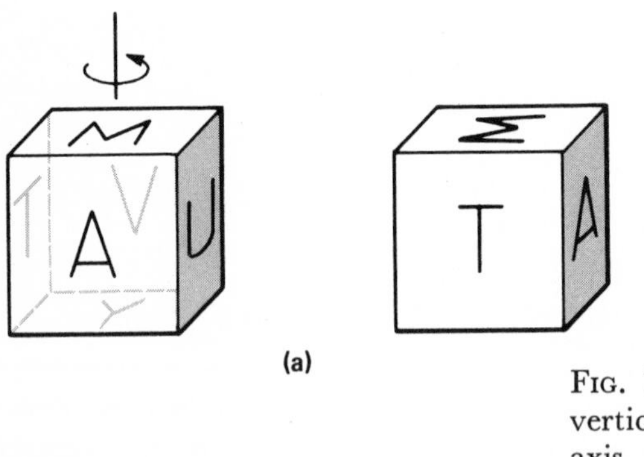

Fig. 7.1 Block rotated (a) 90° about vertical axis and (b) 120° about diagonal axis.

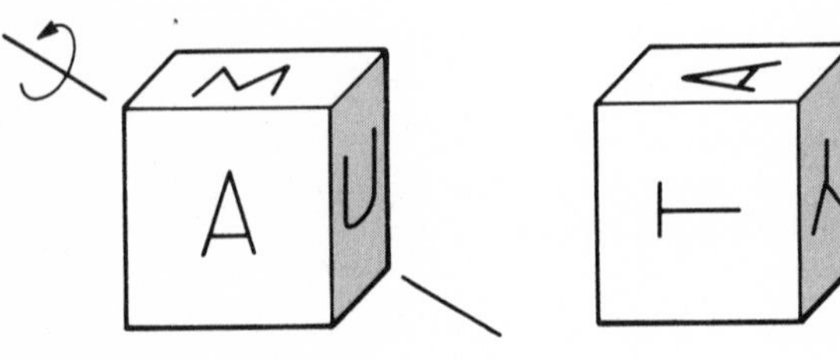

Fig. 7.2 Vectors add commutatively.

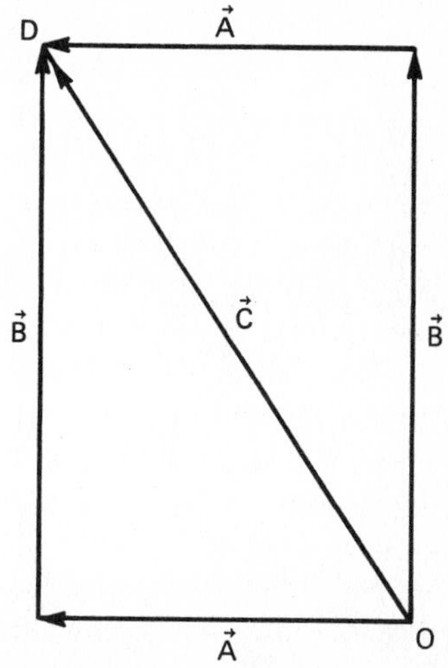

($\pi/6$ rad) counterclockwise. This change of position is described as an ***angular displacement*** of $\pi/6$ rad counterclockwise about the axle of the wheel. Notice in Fig. 7.1 that in three dimensions we must express (1) the *angular magnitude* of the displacement, (2) the *plane* in which the angle is measured (or better, the direction in space of the *axis* around which the angle is measured), and (3) the *sense* in which the displacement exists (a 45° displacement in one sense is 315° displacement in the opposite sense). In the figure a cube with opposite faces lettered A and V, U and T, and M and Y is positioned so that face A is outward as shown. In Fig. 7.1a, the block is rotated 90° about an axis passing through the centers of faces M and Y; this angular displacement brings T into the outward position while A is brought to face the right. On the other hand, from the same starting position, an angular displacement of 120° about a diagonal axis which runs from the upper left front corner to the lower right rear corner brings T *on its side* to the front face, while A appears on the top face and Y on the right, inverted, as shown in Fig. 7.1b. In either of these cases, if the magnitude had been 360°, the cube would have come back to its original position—that is, A would have returned to face outward. Clearly, then, the amount of turning, the direction of the axis, and the direction of turning, must all be specified in order to express the angular displacement.

This is reminiscent of the requirements for linear displacement. There we had to express a distance and a direction, for example, 3.5 km northwest. ("Northwest" establishes not only the path orientation in space along a northwest-southeast line, but it also gives the sense as northwest rather than southeast.) We saw in Sec. 5.4 that linear displacements are vectors. Is angular displacement also a vector quantity? One extremely useful property of vectors is that of commutative addition. In Fig. 7.2 the linear displacement $\vec{C}$ can be achieved either by going west first, then north, or by going north first, then west. That is, $\overrightarrow{A}+\overrightarrow{B}=\overrightarrow{B}+\overrightarrow{A}=\overrightarrow{C}$; in either case, we get from the origin O to the destination D. This is a general property of vectors of all kinds.

Let us test angular displacements to see whether they can be added commutatively. In Fig. 7.3a the same cube as in Fig. 7.1 is subjected first to rotation through an angle of $\pi/2$ rad about an axis coming out of the page (through faces A and V in the first drawing). Next, the block is turned $\pi/2$ rad about a horizontal axis lying in the plane of the page. The result of these two angular displacements puts U on the front face and the letter is turned on its side. Now let us reverse the order of the rotations, turning first about the horizontal axis in the plane of the paper and then about that perpendicular to the page. Figure 7.3b illustrates the procedure. This order of rotations places Y on its side on the front face of the block. If the rotations are numbered (I) and (II) as shown in the diagrams, then $\text{Rot(I)} + \text{Rot(II)} \neq \text{Rot(II)} + \text{Rot(I)}$, and angular displacements are not commutative. Therefore, we can not class angular displacements as vectors.

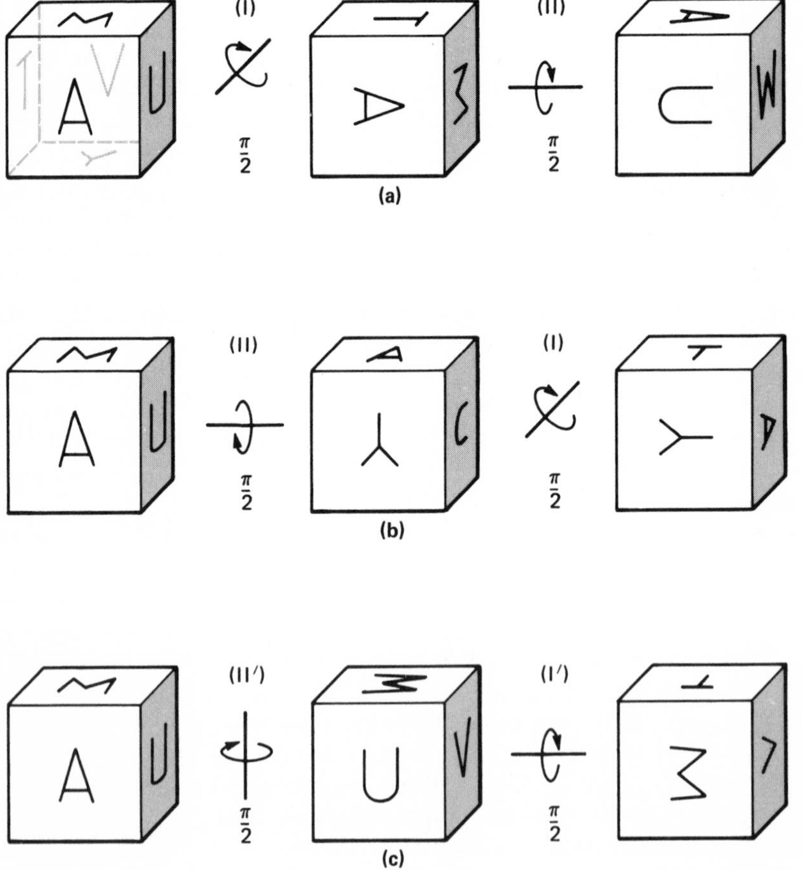

FIG. 7.3 Unlike vectors, angular displacements do not add cumulatively.

Referring to Fig. 7.3a, one might say that Rot(I) was taken about an axis through faces A and V and Rot(II) was taken about an axis through faces M and Y; therefore, one might argue, Fig. 7.3b is incorrect in taking axes fixed in space and should have considered axial positions attached to the block itself. Figure 7.3c takes the first angular displacement about an axis through faces M and Y; this is called Rot(II′). Next, the block is given Rot(I′) about an axis through faces A and V. The result of these two operations is to place M on its side on the front face. Again the result is different from that illustrated in Fig. 7.3a and we see that

$$\text{Rot(I)} + \text{Rot(II)} \neq \text{Rot(II}') + \text{Rot(I}').$$

It does not matter whether the axes of rotation are fixed in space or fixed in the cube—in neither case is the addition commutative. Hence angular displacements are not vectors.

EXERCISE

7.1-1 As in Fig. 7.3, *but using angular displacements of π radians in each operation*, show that the processes represented by Fig. 7.3a and b give the same result. Then show that the process represented by Fig. 7.3c, again using π rad each time, disagrees with that result.

7.2 *Angular Velocity*

In spite of the difference between angular and linear displacements, we shall find it useful to define angular velocity in the same manner we defined velocity. If a body rotates about a fixed axis, moving through an angle $\Delta\theta$ in a time Δt, we can define its average angular speed $\langle\omega\rangle_{\text{av}}$ by an equation analogous to Eq. (3.4-1):

$$\langle\omega\rangle_{\text{av}} = \Delta\theta/\Delta t.$$

Passing to the limit, we can then define the instantaneous angular velocity [cf. Eqs. (3.4-2)] as

$$\omega = \lim_{\Delta t \to 0} (\Delta\theta/\Delta t) = d\theta/dt.$$

It is not difficult to see that the dimensions of angular velocity are those of angle divided by those of time. The unit in which they are measured depends on the unit in which angles are measured; hence angular velocities may be expressed in radians per second, degrees per minute, revolutions per hour, etc.

Because of the simple relation between angle and arc length when the radian is used as a unit of angle (cf. Sec. 2.18), it has become common usage to employ the radian much more often than any other unit of angle. It has also become customary to consider angles to be dimensionless, i.e., to define a central angle measured in radians as the dimensionless ratio of arc length to radius [cf. Eq. (2.18-3)]. Although this practice may occasionally cause confusion, we shall follow it here, trusting that the context in which angular velocities are used will eliminate any difficulties that may arise.

It is interesting that angular velocity can be shown to be a vector, even though angular displacement is not. To see that this is so, consider a line such as OP of length r, as shown in Fig. 7.4a. Suppose that one end of this line is fixed at O but that the line is rotated about an axis perpendicular to the paper

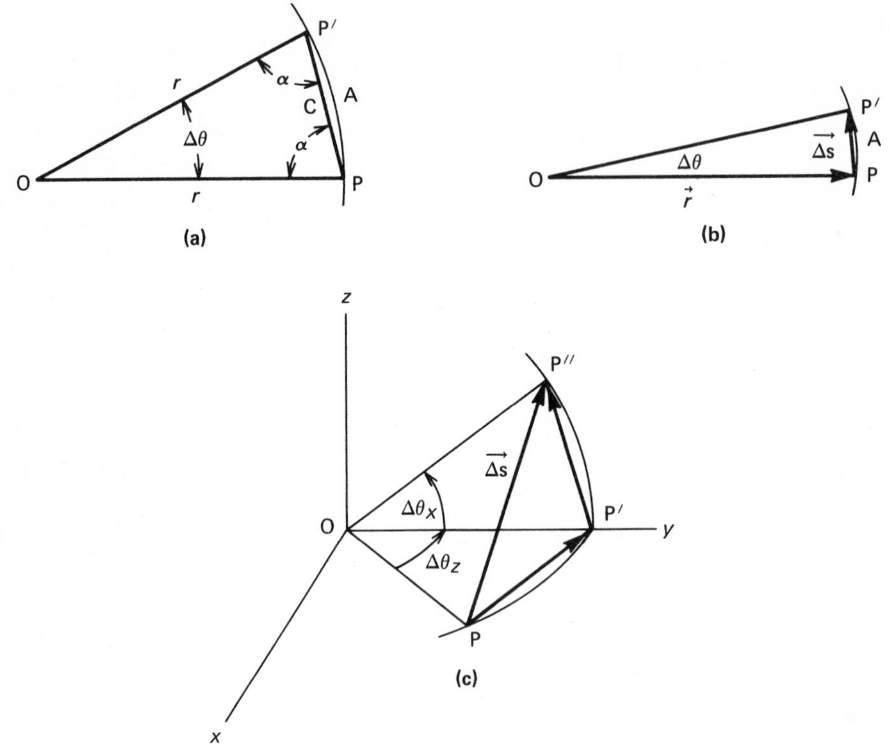

FIG. 7.4 Addition of angular velocities.

at O. If the line moves through an angle $\Delta\theta$, the point P moves along the arc PAP′. Its displacement is measured by the chord PCP′. Letting this chord be denoted by the vector $\overrightarrow{\Delta s}$, we see that the velocity of P is

$$\mathrm{v} = \lim_{\Delta t \to 0} \left(\frac{\overrightarrow{\Delta s}}{\Delta t} \right) = \frac{\overrightarrow{ds}}{dt}.$$

We may now let Δt approach the limit zero. As we do so, $\Delta\theta$ becomes small and the difference between $\overrightarrow{\Delta s}$ and the length of the arc becomes less and less, as one can see by comparison of Fig. 7.4b and Fig. 7.4a. In the limit, then, the arc length and the chord length become equal, so we see that

$$v = ds/dt = \lim_{\Delta t \to 0} (r\,\Delta\theta/\Delta t) = r(d\theta/dt) = r\omega. \tag{7.2-1}$$

We may now notice that the angle between the $\overrightarrow{\Delta s}$ and OP approaches $\frac{1}{2}\pi$ radians, or 90°, as may be seen if we notice that the triangle OPP′ is isosceles, so that

$$\alpha + \alpha + \Delta\theta = \pi \text{ rad} = 180°.$$

Hence the velocity $\vec{v}$ of P is a vector perpendicular to the radius $\vec{r}$ and of magnitude given by Eq. (7.2-1).

Let us now consider a three-dimensional situation, such as that shown in Fig. 7.4c. The line OP is first rotated through an angle $\Delta\theta_z$ about the z-axis, bringing it to a point P′. The line OP′ is then taken as the y-axis of a rectangular Cartesian coordinate system and the x-axis is drawn perpendicular to the z-axis and the y-axis. The line OP′ is then rotated through an angle $\Delta\theta_x$ about the x-axis, bringing P to P″. We have supposed the two rotations to take place successively, but we could equally well let them take place simultaneously. Under these circumstances, the total displacement of P in a time Δt would be the vector $\overrightarrow{ds}$. This vector is the sum of the two displacements PP′ and P′P″ and the velocity has a magnitude

$$v = (v_z^2 + v_x^2)^{1/2},$$

where v_z is the component of velocity corresponding to rotation about the z-axis and v_x is the component corresponding to rotation about the x-axis. Writing each of these two components in accordance with Eq. (7.2-1), we find that

$$v = r(\omega_z^2 + \omega_x^2)^{1/2}. \tag{7.2-2}$$

Consider now a rotation about an axis OA, perpendicular to the plane OPP″ of Fig. 7.4c. If the angular velocity of this rotation is ω, Eq. (7.2-1) tells us that the speed of the point P is

$$v = \omega r,$$

where ω is the angular velocity of rotation about OA. Substitution of this value into Eq. (7.2-2) shows that

$$\omega = (\omega_z^2 + \omega_x^2)^{1/2}, \tag{7.2-3}$$

which is exactly the relation of the magnitude of a vector to its components. Moreover, the direction of motion of P is clearly that of the line PP″, so it appears that ω may be expressed as a vector. We therefore conclude that angular velocity is a vector.

The line of argument that we have followed not only shows angular velocity to be a vector; it also indicates why angular displacement is *not* a vector. Our procedure depended on the fact that the two components of velocity, v_x and v_y, are perpendicular to each other. This, in turn, is true only because the two displacements are perpendicular as $\Delta t \to 0$. The two finite displacements $\overrightarrow{\Delta s_1}$ and $\overrightarrow{\Delta s_2}$, shown in Fig. 7.5, are not perpendicular, hence $\overrightarrow{\Delta s}$, their vector sum, is not equal to the square root of the sum of their squares, and no relation similar to Eq. (7.2-3) can be derived.

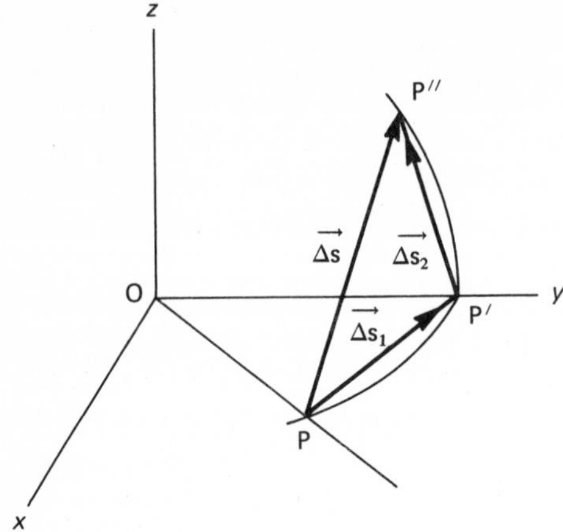

FIG. 7.5 Addition of angular displacements.

7.3 Rotation of a Rigid Body About a Fixed Axis

We can now discuss the simple and very important case shown in Fig. 7.6. The disk shown there is rotating about an axis that is fixed in space, being held in place by bearings that are not shown. Under these circumstances we do not need to worry about the fact that the angular displacement θ through which the body has turned is not a vector—the motion is quite analogous to that of a particle moving along a straight line, which we studied in Chapter 3. We shall also simplify our problem by supposing the body to be rigid, in the sense that its

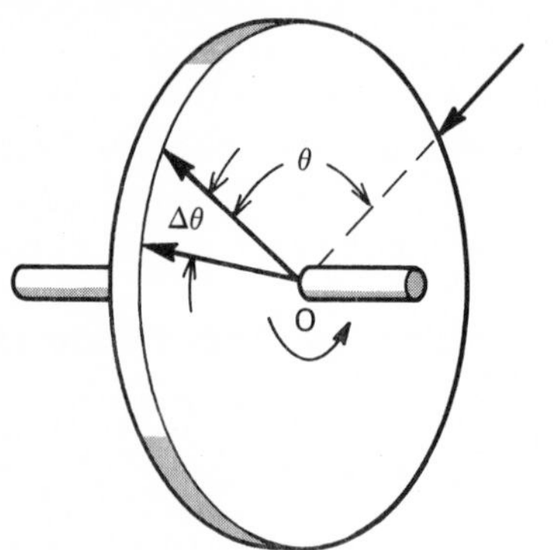

FIG. 7.6 Rotating body.

shape and size are not changed by any forces that may act upon it. (Such bodies, of course, are only approximations to real bodies which experience elastic deformation.)

We have already seen how the angular velocity ω of the body can be determined. If ω changes with time, we can define the angular acceleration α in strict parallelism to Eq. (3.8-2):

$$\alpha = \lim_{\Delta t \to 0} (\Delta\omega/\Delta t) = d\omega/dt. \tag{7.3-1}$$

Angular accelerations are then measured in units such as rad/sec^2, rev/sec^2, etc.

The definitions of angular speed and acceleration correspond exactly to those of Eqs. (3.4-2A) and (3.8-2) for linear speed and acceleration, the linear distances of the latter being replaced by the angles of the former. We can therefore employ analogy to translate all of the results of Chapter 3 into forms useful for the discussion of rotational motion and thereby avoid the necessity of a number of new derivations. The complete kinematic analogy is shown in Table 7.1, in which the symbol ω_0 is used for the initial value of the angular speed in a uniformly accelerated angular motion; this is analogous with v_0 as used in Chapter 3.

Table 7.1 *Kinetic Analogies Between Linear and Rotational Motions*

	Linear Motion		Rotational Motion	
Displacement	s	—	θ	—
Speed	$v = ds/dt$	Eq. (3.4-2A)	$\omega = d\theta/dt$	Eq. (7.3-3)
Acceleration	$a = dv/dt$	Eq. (3.8-2)	$\alpha = d\omega/dt$	Eq. (7.3-4)
Displacement (const. accel.)	$s = v_0 t + \frac{1}{2}at^2$	Eq. (3.18-1)	$\theta = \omega_0 + \frac{1}{2}\alpha t^2$	Eq. (7.3-5)
Speed (const. accel.)	$v = v_0 + at$	Eq. (3.18-2)	$\omega = \omega_0 + \alpha t$	Eq. (7.3-6)

We should emphasize that the equations for s and v in lines 3 and 4 of the table are both scalar equations although generally speaking s and v are each vector quantities. The importance of this observation is that, in the equations, the linear speed v_0 and the linear acceleration a must each lie on the same straight line path. Similarly, Eqs. (7.3-5) and (7.3-6) require that ω_0 and α be around the same axis of rotation. Of the two quantities, θ and ω, only ω behaves as a vector. We shall say more of this later.

The two new Eqs. (7.3-5) and (7.3-6) that result from the analogy can be used at once in the study of rotations. Thus, a wheel which starts from rest ($\omega_0 = 0$) with a constant angular acceleration α of 10 rev/sec² will, at the end of 5.0 sec, according to Eq. (7.3-6), have reached an angular speed

$$\omega = \alpha t = 10 \text{ rev/sec}^2 \times 5.0 \text{ sec} = 50 \text{ rev/sec}.$$

In this time it will have rotated through an angle

$$\theta = \tfrac{1}{2}\alpha t^2 = \tfrac{1}{2} \times 10 \text{ rev/sec}^2 \times (5.0 \text{ sec})^2 = 125 \text{ rev}.$$

Further examples of rotational motions under constant acceleration are given in Exs. 7.3-2 through 7.3-4.

We shall find as we proceed with the study of rotational motion that the analogy with linear motion, whose beginning we have indicated here, is maintained completely. We must therefore try to find the angular quantities which correspond to mass, momentum, force, etc.

EXERCISES

7.3-1 Find the angular velocity of the rotation of the earth on its axis in degrees per second and degrees per hour.

7.3-2 The wheels of the car of Prob. 3.3 are 0.70 m in diameter. What is the angular velocity of one of these wheels about its axis at the end of the measured kilometer?

7.3-3 What is the angular acceleration of any wheel of the car of Ex. 7.3-2 during the time the car is being accelerated?

7.3-4 A wheel is spinning at a rate of 30 rev/min. It is brought to rest in 10 sec. What is the average angular acceleration in revolutions per second squared? In degrees per second squared?

7.3-5 If a particle is moving in a circle of radius r with a speed v, prove that the periodic time τ is given by

$$\tau = 2\pi r/v = 2\pi/\omega. \tag{7.3-7}$$

7.4 *Axial Vectors*

We learned in Sec. 7.2 that angular velocity is a vector, and we know that all vector quantities require the specification of a direction in space. What is the direction of this vector for the disk of Fig. 7.6, which is shown again in Fig. 7.7a? It certainly cannot be the direction of motion of any point in the disk, for different points are moving in different directions as a result of the rotation. There is only one unambiguous direction associated with the rotation—that of the axis. Thus we can indicate the direction of $\vec{\omega}$ by laying an arrow along the direction of AA′; and by employing a suitable scale the magnitude ω can be represented by the length of the arrow. It remains for us to state which way the arrow shall point. The convention usually employed is adopted from our common practice of manufacturing most screws with a right-hand thread. In Fig. 7.7b a right-hand screw is shown. As one drives the screw into a piece of wood, he faces the head of the screw with the point of the screw away from

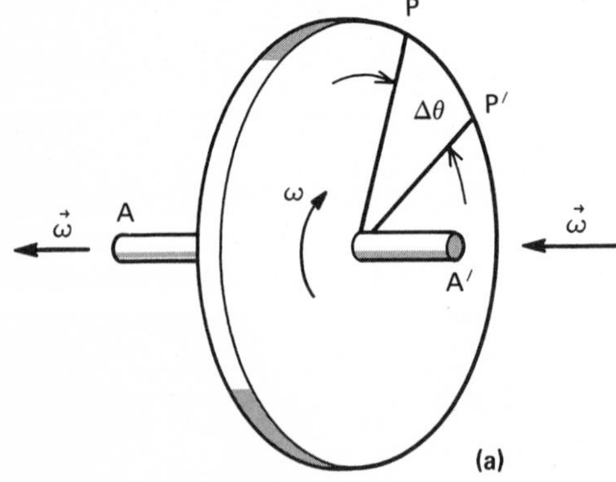

FIG. 7.7 Right-hand screw convention for axial vectors.

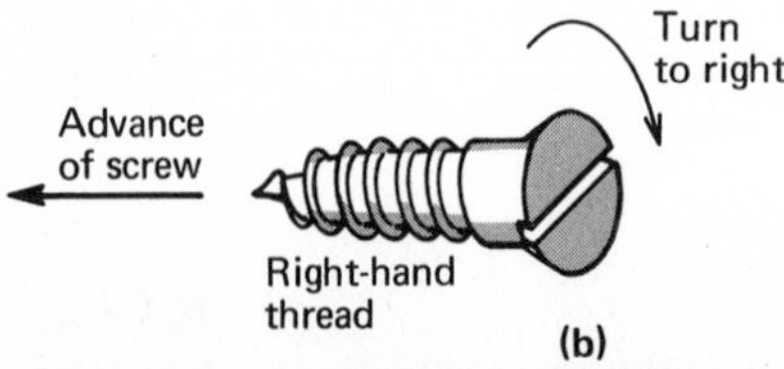

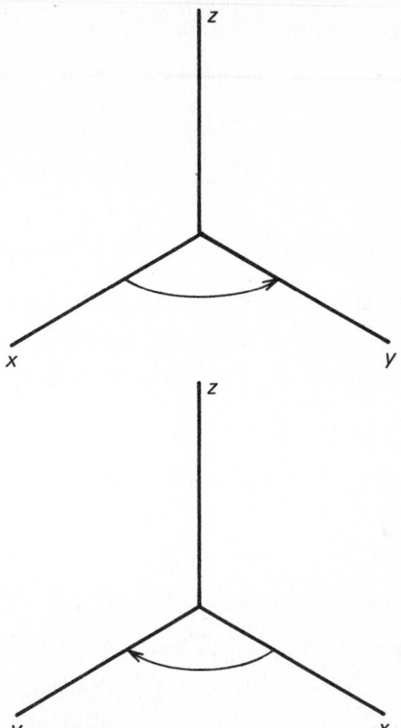

FIG. 7.8 Right- and left-hand coordinate systems.

him. When the head is turned top-to-the-right, or clockwise, the threads advance the screw into the wood or away from the person who wields the screwdriver.

Using this convention, then, we represent $\vec{\omega}$ by an arrow of suitable length placed in the direction A′A as shown in Fig. 7.7.

Vectors we met earlier—$\vec{s}$, $\vec{v}$, $\vec{a}$, $\vec{f}$, $\vec{p}$—are known as ***polar vectors***. The vectors which are the subject of this section, vectors concerned with rotational motion, are ***axial vectors***. In this text, we shall not spend a great deal of effort on understanding the formal mathematical differences between axial vectors and polar vectors. Instead we shall caution that more care must be used in dealing with the senses, the directions, of axial vectors. It was an arbitrary choice to derive the sense of axial vectors from a *right-hand screw* rather than from a *left-hand* one. But having made such a choice, we must be *implicity consistent* so that all of our axial vectors are *right-hand ones*.

Some awareness of the difference between right-hand and left-hand systems may be gained by looking at Fig. 7.8. In Fig. 7.8a, if the system is twisted so that the positive x-axis moves into the position of the positive y-axis, a right-hand thread would cause advance along the positive z-axis. In Fig. 7.8b, however, a right-hand thread, when positive x is turned toward positive y, would advance along negative z. The system in Fig. 7.8b, then, is defined as a ***left-hand system,*** while that in Fig. 7.8a is a ***right-hand system.***

EXERCISES

7.4-1 Suppose an axial vector 1.0 cm long is used to represent the angular velocity of the hour hand of a clock. Which way should the vector point? On the same scale describe the vector that represents the angular velocity of the minute hand.

7.4-2 On the same scale as in Ex. 7.4-1 give the magnitude, orientation, and sense of the angular velocity vector for the rotation of the earth. (If you want to be sophisticated about this, you will differentiate between solar and sidereal days.)

7.5 *Motion in a Circle*

Consider a small particle of mass m moving in a circle of radius r with an angular velocity $\vec{\omega}$ (Fig. 7.9). During a time Δt, the line Om joining the center O of the circle and the mass m will have rotated through an angle $\Delta\theta = \omega\,\Delta t$, and m will

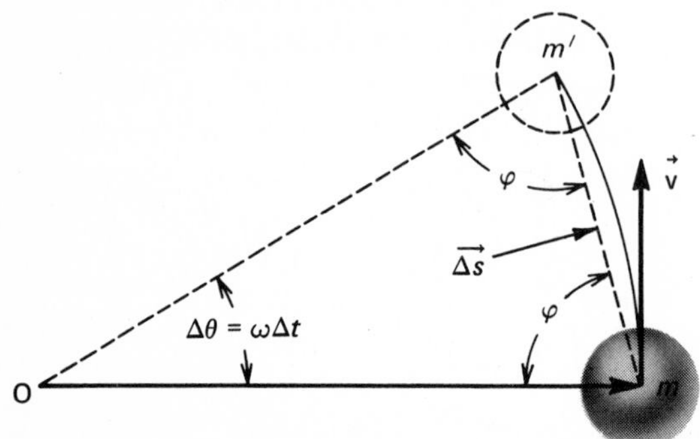

FIG. 7.9 Motion in a circle.

have been displaced through a distance $\vec{\Delta s}$ from m to m'. According to Eq. (5.6-1), the average velocity during the time interval Δt will be given by

$$\vec{v}_{av} = \vec{\Delta s}/\Delta t$$

and the instantaneous velocity $\vec{v}$ will be

$$\vec{v} = \lim_{\Delta t \to 0} (\vec{\Delta s}/\Delta t) = \vec{ds}/dt. \tag{7.5-1}$$

In order to evaluate this instantaneous velocity, consider what happens for very short intervals Δt. As Δt decreases, $\Delta\theta$ also decreases, and it is clear that for small $\Delta\theta$ the length of the circular arc mm' approaches that of the chord Δs. However, by Eq. (G.12) of Appendix G,

$$\Delta\theta = (mm')/r \approx \Delta s/r.$$

Multiplying this equation by r, we get $\Delta s = r\,\Delta\theta$ and, with the aid of Eq. (7.2-1),

$$\Delta s = r\,\Delta\theta = \omega r\,\Delta t. \tag{7.5-2}$$

Finally we substitute Eq. (7.5-2) into Eq. (7.5-1) to get

$$v = \frac{ds}{dt} = \lim_{\Delta t \to 0} \frac{\omega r\,\Delta t}{\Delta t} = (\omega r). \tag{7.5-3}$$

In order to calculate the direction of $\vec{v}$ with respect to the radius $\vec{Om}$, notice that the triangle mOm' is isosceles, since the distance of m from O is constant in circular motion. Representing the value of either of its base angles by ϕ, and remembering that the sum of the angles of a triangle is 180°, we see that

$$2\phi + \Delta\theta = 180^\circ$$

or that

$$\phi = 90^\circ - \Delta\theta/2.$$

As $\Delta\theta$ tends to zero, i.e., as $\Delta t \to 0$, ϕ approaches a right angle. Thus in the limit $\Delta t \to 0$, $\vec{\Delta s}$ (and consequently $\vec{v}$) is at right angles to $\vec{Om}$. We can summarize this result in words by saying that when a particle is moving in a circle of constant radius r with an angular velocity ω, the instantaneous linear velocity of the particle has a magnitude $r\omega$ in a direction at *right angles* to the line joining the particle and the center of the circle. The *velocity* of the particle is thus continuously changing (in direction) while the magnitude of the velocity, i.e., its *speed*, is constant.

Let us look again at Eq. (7.5-3) and Fig. 7.9. In the figure we see that $\vec{r}$ is the position vector of m with respect to the origin O. Moreover, $\vec{v}$ is the instantaneous velocity (linear velocity) of m, and $\vec{\omega}$, coming straight out of the paper from O, is the angular velocity vector. The vector $\vec{\omega}$ twisted toward $\vec{r}$ constitutes a right-hand system that advances along $\vec{v}$. Thus, in Eq. (7.5-3) we can see that the vector $\vec{v}$ is, in a peculiar sense, a result of the product of the two vectors $\vec{\omega}$ and $\vec{r}$.

Earlier we dealt with the product of two vectors when we expressed work in terms of force and displacement (Sec. 6.7). There we wrote $w = \vec{f} \cdot \vec{s}$. The work w is a *scalar* resulting from the product $fs \cos \beta$, where f is the magnitude of $\vec{f}$, s is the magnitude of $\vec{s}$, and β is the angle between $\vec{f}$ and $\vec{s}$. The "·" (raised dot) is taken to mean "cosine of the angle between the directions of the two vectors." Thus,

$$\vec{f} \cdot \vec{s} = fs \cos \beta = sf \cos \beta$$

are all equivalent statements.

We now adopt a new notation for the multiplication of two vectors *where the product is a vector.* We write Eq. (7.5-3) as

$$\vec{v} = \vec{\omega} \times \vec{r},$$

where the $\times$ indicates that the right-hand sense of $\vec{\omega}$ twisted toward $\vec{r}$ must be taken. We shall see shortly that we shall also want the cross that shows multiplication to indicate an additional factor $\sin \beta$, where β is the angle between $\vec{\omega}$ and $\vec{r}$; however, in Fig. 7.9, $\beta = \pi/2$, so $\sin \beta = 1$. Note that $\vec{v}$ is normal to the plane containing $\vec{\omega}$ and $\vec{r}$.

It should be clear from our definitions of the right-hand system that

$$\vec{\omega} \times \vec{r} \neq \vec{r} \times \vec{\omega},$$

and, in fact, that

$$\vec{\omega} \times \vec{r} = -(\mathrm{r} \times \omega).$$

Just as the dot product $\vec{f} \cdot \vec{s}$ is read "eff dot ess," the cross product $\vec{\omega} \times \vec{r}$ is read "omega cross are."

EXERCISE

7.5-1 By repeating the reasoning of Sec. 3.12, i.e., by finding the angular displacement $\Delta\theta$ which a rotating body obeying Eq. (7.3-5) undergoes in a short time interval between t and $t + \Delta t$, show that Eq. (7.3-6) also applies to this body. Then show that this body is subjected to a constant angular acceleration α.

7.6 *Rotational Kinetic Energy and Moment of Inertia*

It is now easy for us to calculate the kinetic energy of the particle in the preceding section. We have found that its linear velocity has a magnitude $v = \omega r$, and it follows from Eq. (4.11-6) that its kinetic energy must be

$$KE = \tfrac{1}{2}mv^2 = \tfrac{1}{2}mr^2\omega^2.$$

The factor here that pertains to angular motion is ω^2. If we define the ***moment of inertia*** I for a single particle of mass m moving in a circle of radius r as

$$I = mr^2, \tag{7.6-1}$$

the expression for rotational kinetic energy takes the form [cf. Eq. (4.11-6]

$$KE = \tfrac{1}{2}I\omega^2. \tag{7.6-2}$$

Thus the analogue of mass in rotational mechanics is the moment of inertia. The dimensions of moment of inertia are shown by Eq. (7.6-1) to be $[m\ell^2]$.

The moment of inertia as we have defined it can be calculated only for a mass so small that all points on it can be considered to be at the same distance r from the center of rotation. This condition is approximately satisfied for a body like the earth revolving about the sun, but it is obviously far from true for a solid wheel rotating about its own axis. In order to generalize the definition to include extended bodies, we may first consider a number of small heavy bodies of masses m_1, m_2, m_3, m_4 (Fig. 7.10), all rigidly connected together (by light rods whose masses are negligible) and rotating at the same angular velocity $\vec{\omega}$ about the axis O. If the distances of the masses from the center of rotation are, respectively, r_1, r_2, r_3, r_4, then the magnitudes of their velocities are $v_1 = r_1\omega$, $v_2 = r_2\omega$, $v_3 = r_3\omega$, $v_4 = r_4\omega$, and it is easy to see that the kinetic energy of all the masses taken together is

$$\begin{aligned} KE &= \tfrac{1}{2}(m_1 v_1^2 + m_2 v_2^2 + m_3 v_3^2 + m_4 v_4^2) \\ &= \tfrac{1}{2}(m_1 r_1^2 + m_2 r_2^2 + m_3 r_3^2 + m_4 r_4^2)\omega^2. \end{aligned} \tag{7.6-3}$$

If there are a large number of masses, it is inconvenient for us to repeat the same expression for each of them, and we abbreviate the result of Eq. (7.6-3) in the form (cf. Appendix C.5)

$$KE = \tfrac{1}{2}\omega^2 \sum_{j=1}^{n} m_j r_j^2, \tag{7.6-4}$$

where the Greek capital letter Σ indicates a summation. The factor

$$\sum_{=1}^{n} m_j r_j^2$$

is an abbreviation for "the summation of the quantities $m_j r_j^2$ calculated for each of the n particles of the system, each particle being indicated by a particular value of j." Thus Eq. (7.6-4) is entirely equivalent to Eq. (7.6-3) if $n=4$. Comparing Eq. (7.6-4) with Eq. (7.6-2), we can now calculate the moment of inertia for a rigidly connected system of n particles by forming the summation

$$I=\sum_{j=1}^{n} m_j r_j^2 \qquad (7.6\text{-}5)$$

and can see that Eq. (7.6-2) will then hold for all such systems.

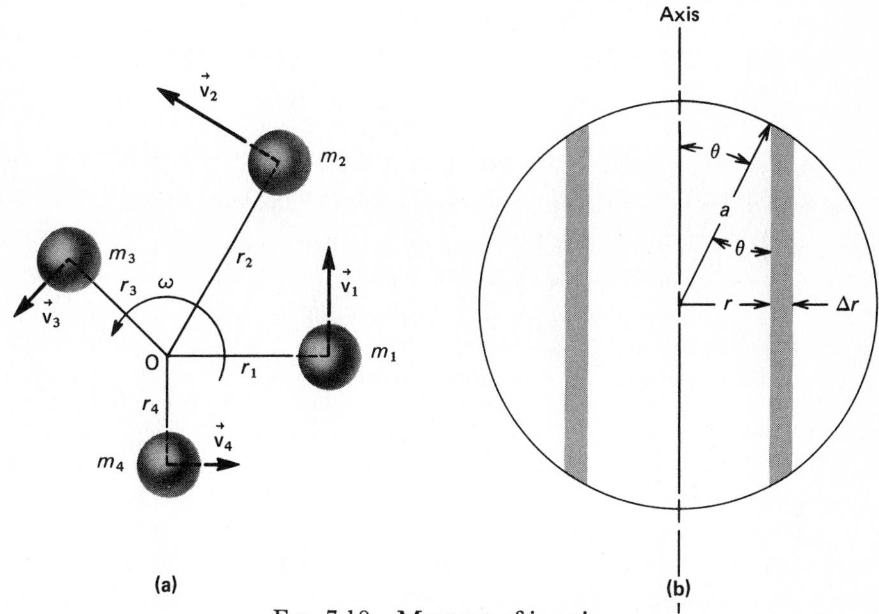

FIG. 7.10 Moment of inertia.

Thus far we have considered only those systems (Figs. 7.9 and 7.10a) which consist of a rather small number of small mass particles. But most rotating bodies are not as simple as these. The calculation of the moment of inertia of a body whose mass is distributed continuously requires that the masses m_j of Eq. (7.6-5) be taken as the masses of such very small volumes that each point in the volume is at essentially the same distance from the center of rotation. This, of course, means that we must increase n without limit. Hence the summation is replaced by an integral:

$$I=\int r^2\,dm=\int r^2\rho\,dV, \qquad (7.6\text{-}6)$$

where dV is an element of volume at a distance r from the center and ρ is the density of that volume element. The limits of integration must be taken in such a way that all of the body is included. The integration may be easy or hard to carry out, depending on the shape of the body, whether its density is uniform, etc. (See Ex. 7.6-2 for an easy case.)

Illustrative Example

Suppose that we wish to determine the moment of inertia of a sphere of radius a in rotation about an axis through its poles, as shown in Fig. 7.10b. We divide the sphere into a number of thin shells, one of which is shown cross-hatched. This shell extends from radius r to radius $r + \Delta r$. If Δr is small enough, the height of the shell can be closely approximated as $2a \cos \theta$. The cross-sectional area of the shell is $\pi[(r + \Delta r)^2 - r^2] \approx 2\pi r \,\Delta r$. Hence the volume is approximately equal to $4\pi ra \cos \theta \,\Delta r$. Multiplying this volume by the density ρ, we obtain the mass of the shell. Because the distance of any point in the shell from the axis is very close to r, the moment of inertia of the shell is

$$\Delta I \approx (4\pi ra \cos \theta \,\Delta r)(\rho)(r^2) = 4\pi a\rho r^3 \cos \theta \,\Delta r.$$

To obtain the moment of inertia of the sphere, it is necessary to add the contributions of all the shells:

$$I = \lim_{\Delta r \to 0} \sum \Delta I_j = 4\pi a\rho \lim_{\Delta r \to 0} \sum_{j=0}^{j=a/\Delta r} r_j^3 \cos \theta_j \,\Delta r. \tag{7.6-7}$$

Note that we have divided the sphere into $(a/\Delta r)$ shells and have denoted the radius of any particular shell by r_j, and that

$$\sin \theta_j = r_j/a. \tag{7.6-8}$$

We rewrite Eq. (7.6-7) in a more convenient notation, substituting for r_j from Eq. (7.6-8) at the same time:

$$I = 4\pi a^4\rho \int_0^{\pi/2} \sin^3 \theta \cos \theta \, dr.$$

Noting [cf. Eq. (I.1) of Appendix I] that $d(\sin \theta) = \cos \theta \, d\theta$ and again using Eq. (7.6-8), we get

$$I = 4\pi a^5\rho \int_0^{\pi/2} \sin^3 \theta \cos^2 \theta \, d\theta.$$

To evaluate the integral, we use the fact that $\sin^2 \theta + \cos^2 \theta = 1$, to get

$$\begin{aligned} I &= 4\pi a^5\rho \int_0^{\pi/2} (\cos^2 \theta - \cos^4 \theta) \sin \theta \, d\theta \\ &= 4\pi a^5\rho \left[-\frac{\cos^3 \theta}{3} + \frac{\cos^5 \theta}{5} \right]_0^{\pi/2} = 4\pi a^5\rho \left(\frac{1}{3} - \frac{1}{5} \right) \\ &= 8\pi a^5\rho/15. \end{aligned} \tag{7.6-9A}$$

A more convenient expression for the moment of inertia is obtained by replacing ρ by $3m/4\pi a^3$, where m is the mass of the sphere. This gives

$$I = 2a^2m/5. \tag{7.6-9B}$$

If the shape of a body is such that an exact integral is impossible to evaluate, one may often use a summation, without going to the limit, to obtain a good approximation to the moment of inertia. Thus, if we use the summation of Eq. (7.6-7) with $\Delta r = a/8$, corresponding to Fig. 7.10b, we can take $r_1 = 0$, $r_2 = a/8$, $r_3 = a/4$, etc. The resulting computation leads to $I = 0.49\pi a^5\rho$, which is within ten percent of the value given by Eq. (7.6-9A).

EXERCISES

7.6-1 Prove that the units in which the moment of inertia I is measured may be expressed as J sec^2.

7.6-2 Calculate the moment of inertia of a thin metal ring of mass 0.50 kg and diameter 0.24 m.

7.6-3 A car has a total mass 1125 kg. Each of its wheels has a moment of inertia of 2.0 kg m^2 and a circumference of 2.20 m. If the car is traveling at a speed of 10.0 m/sec, what is the translational kinetic energy of the car? What is the total rotational kinetic energy of the four wheels?

7.7 *Centripetal Acceleration*

In earlier sections of this chapter we discussed the analogies which exist between the displacements, velocities, and accelerations of linear motion and those of rotational motion about a fixed axis. We saw also that the moment of inertia plays the same role as did mass in rotational motion. Before we enter into any consideration of the ways in which angular accelerations may be brought about, it is necessary for us to consider one important difference between linear motion and rotational motion. We know, from Newton's first law of motion (Sec. 4.9), that a body moves with a constant velocity only if no net force is acting on it. On the other hand, a particle moving *uniformly in a circle*, and therefore *at constant angular velocity*, must be continually acted upon by a force. To demonstrate this, we need merely to remember the discussion of Sec. 7.5, in which we saw that, although the *speed* of such a body is constant, its *velocity* is continually changing in direction. Such a change in direction is a change of the velocity, and therefore means that a force must be acting to produce a continual acceleration of the body.

We can demonstrate the presence of the force needed to maintain uniform motion of constant angular velocity if we tie a mass to the end of a string and whirl it around in a circle. As long as the mass moves in a circle, the tension in the string is easily felt, and the string must therefore be pulling the mass inward toward the hand. If the string breaks, the inward pull stops and the mass no longer moves in a circle about the hand. It is apparent that the string before it broke must have accelerated the mass toward the center of the circle. We shall now calculate the magnitude of this acceleration.

We have seen that, when a mass m (Fig. 7.11a) moves in a circle of radius r at a constant angular velocity $\vec{\omega}$, its speed remains constant but its velocity $\vec{v}$ is continually changing. In a time Δt, the particle moves through an angle $\Delta\theta = \omega\,\Delta t$ in traveling from m to m' (cf. Sec. 7.5). Let the velocity of the particle at the position m be $\vec{v_1}$, and let its velocity at the position m' be $\vec{v_2}$. These two velocities have the same magnitude v, but they differ in direction, and the change of velocity $\vec{\Delta v}$ is

$$\vec{\Delta v} = \vec{v_2} - \vec{v_1}.$$

In order to find the magnitude and direction of $\vec{\Delta v}$, we construct the vector diagram of Fig. 7.11b. If we now draw the circular arc BC, centered at A, we

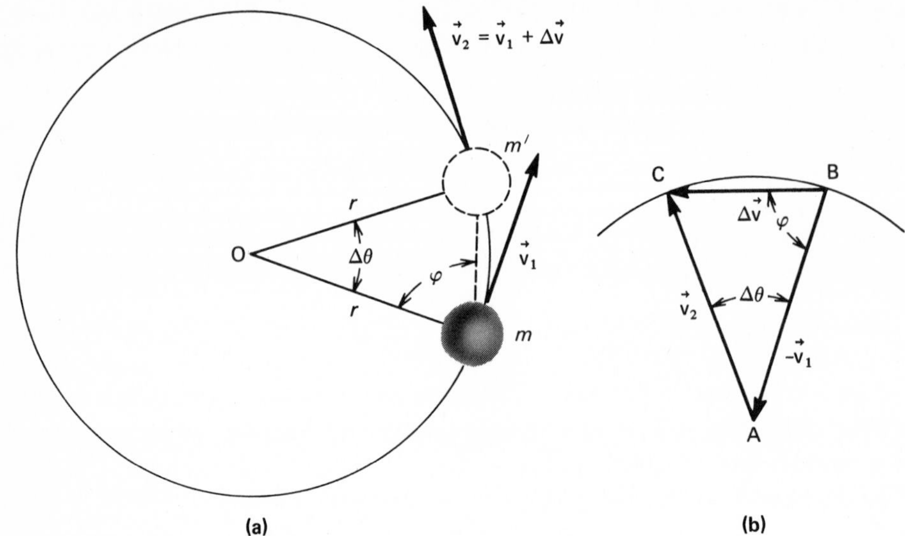

FIG. 7.11 Centripetal acceleration.

see that the arc is equal to the angle $\Delta\theta$ times the radius $v_1 = v_2 = v$. If $\Delta\theta$ is small, the chord Δv is very closely equal to the arc BC, so we have

$$\Delta v \approx v\,\Delta\theta = \omega v\,\Delta t.$$

However, we know from Eq. (3.8-2) that

$$a = \lim_{\Delta t \to 0} \Delta v/\Delta t = dv/dt$$

and it follows that

$$a = \omega v. \tag{7.7-1}$$

We also note that, in the limit $\Delta t \to 0$, the angle ϕ in Fig. 7.11a tends to a right angle (cf. Fig. 7.9) so that $\overrightarrow{\Delta v}$ (in the limit as $\Delta\theta \to 0$) is at right angles to $\overrightarrow{v}$ and is thus directed inward along the radius from m toward O. We can thus write for the radial acceleration

$$a_r = -\omega v, \tag{7.7-2}$$

where the subscript r denotes that the acceleration is in the direction of the radius and the negative sign (according to the usual convention) indicates that the acceleration is in the direction of decreasing r. We can use Eq. (7.5-4A) to eliminate either v or ω from Eq. (7.7-2) and to obtain the two equivalent formulae

$$a_r = -\omega^2 r = -v^2/r. \tag{7.7-3}$$

The radial acceleration whose existence we predicted from experiment and whose magnitude and direction we have just calculated is known as the ***centripetal acceleration*** (Latin: *centrum*, center; *petere*, to move toward). The force that provides this acceleration is known as the ***centripetal force.*** Thus, a mass m moving at constant angular velocity in a circle must experience a radial force

$$F_r = -m\omega^2 r = -mv^2/r. \tag{7.7-4}$$

Whenever any massive body is rotating in a circle, some agency must be present to provide a force directed toward the center of rotation. This force depends on the mass m of each portion of the body, on its distance r from the axis of rotation, and on the angular velocity ω of the mass m about the axis of rotation.

EXERCISES

7.7-1 Write Eqs. (7.7-1) and (7.7-2) as vector equations involving cross products.

7.7-2 Write Eq. (7.7-2) as a vector equation in which one of the vectors is the instantaneous linear momentum $\vec{p}$.

7.7-3 Show that an appropriate way to write Eq. (7.7-4) is

$$\vec{F}_r = -m\vec{\omega} \times (\vec{\omega} \times \vec{r}).$$

7.8 Centrifugal Accelerations and Forces

Thus far we have discussed the forces on a rotating body from the point of view of an observer fixed with respect to the axis of rotation. From the point of view of an observer moving in a circle, the phenomenon just described takes on a slightly different appearance. Consider an observer on a merry-go-round who is holding onto a weight that can slide freely on the floor of the merry-go-round. As long as he holds on to the weight he must exert a force toward the center of rotation of the merry-go-round. To an observer on the ground, the force exerted in holding the weight is simply the centripetal force. However, the observer on the merry-go-round finds that he must pull inward to keep the weight fixed *with respect to the merry-go-round.* Thus, as far as he is concerned, the weight is apparently being pulled outward with a radial force

$$F_r' = mr\omega^2 = mv^2/r. \tag{7.8-1}$$

This force is known as the ***centrifugal force*** (Latin: *fugare*, to flee), and the corresponding acceleration is called the ***centrifugal acceleration.***

We can clarify these two points of view by the consideration of a passenger in a car rounding a curve. The passenger experiences a force that tends to fling him outward with respect to the car. From his point of view, he needs to hold tight to counteract this centrifugal force. From the point of view of a man beside the road, the passenger is kept moving in a circle with the car by the centripetal acceleration provided by the reaction of the car on the passenger, i.e., by the centripetal force.

In dealing with centrifugal forces, we must remember that they are experienced only because the observer on the merry-go-round or in the car considers that a body is fixed when its coordinates stay constant in the polar coordinate system attached to the rotating vehicle. In other words, he describes such a body as experiencing no acceleration without recognizing that the coordinate system itself is accelerated. Because of this acceleration of the system, Newton's laws of motion do not hold. We often speak of a coordinate system in which these laws do hold as an ***inertial system.*** Coordinate frames that are accelerated with respect to inertial frames are then described as ***noninertial systems.*** It is sometimes said that centripetal forces are "real" and that centrifugal forces are "fictitious." This is true for an observer in an inertial system, but one must be careful in making the distinction. To the person who is thrown out of a car on a curve, or to the astronaut who experiences "weightlessness" (cf. Chapter 14) the centrifugal forces are as real as is the gravitational attraction of the earth.

EXERCISES

7.8-1 A body of mass m is located on a smooth horizontal table on a merry-go-round and is attached to the axis of rotation by a string of length r. If the angular velocity of the merry-go-round is ω, what is the tension in the string? What will be the outward acceleration of the body with respect to the table if the string is cut?

7.8-2 A boy is spinning a bucket full of water in a vertical plane. The handle of the bucket is attached to a rope of such length that the distance from the center of rotation to the surface of the water is 1.0 m. What is the minimum speed of the bucket at the top of the swing if no water is to be spilled?

7.8-3 An airplane pilot traveling 300 km/hr desires to loop in a vertical circle. What is the greatest radius in which he can do this if he is not strapped to the seat?

7.9 Torque and Moment of a Force

In the preceding sections we were concerned with the forces necessary to maintain a rotating body in motion at constant angular velocity. We now consider the forces which must be applied to change the angular velocity of a rigid body rotating about a fixed axis. If we consider the problem of accelerating the rotation of a wheel (Fig. 7.12), it is easy to see that a force directed along the radius of the wheel will be quite useless in increasing the angular velocity, since it can do no work as the wheel rotates (Sec. 6.6). If a force $\overrightarrow{F}$ acting on the rim of a wheel of radius r makes an angle ϕ with the radius, then only the tangential component $F_t = F \sin \phi$ will do work as the wheel rotates. If the force $\overrightarrow{F}$ remains constant in magnitude while the wheel rotates, and if it continues to be directed at an angle ϕ with the radius, the tangential component F_t will remain constant. The displacement of P as the wheel rotates through an angle $\Delta\theta$ (radians) is $r\,\Delta\theta$, and the work done by the force $\overrightarrow{F}$ as the wheel rotates through this angle is

$$\Delta w = r\,\Delta\theta\, F_t = r\,\Delta\theta(F \sin \phi). \tag{7.9-1}$$

We define the ***torque*** τ (Latin: *torquere*, to twist) due to the force as the work done by the force per unit angle of rotation, and we have

$$\tau = \lim_{\Delta t = 0} (\Delta w/\Delta\theta) = rF \sin \phi. \tag{7.9-2}$$

This definition is quite in accord with our physical feeling for the problem of speeding up a rotating wheel. The farther away from the center the force is exerted, the easier it is to speed the rotation, and it is better to push tangentially

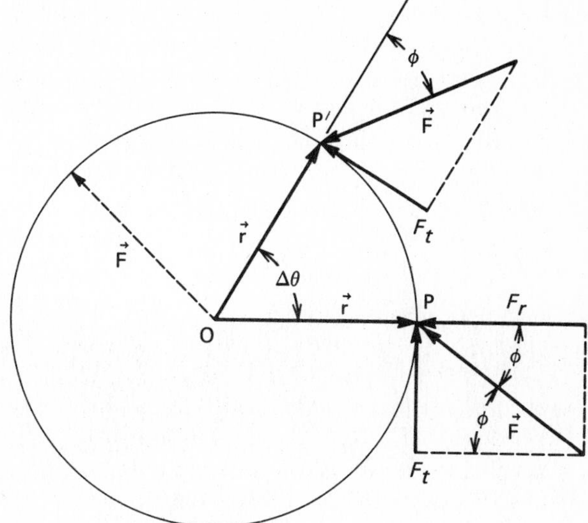

FIG. 7.12 Work done in angular acceleration.

rather than radially. It is clear that an identical argument applies to the angular acceleration of an irregular body, such as that shown in Fig. 7.13.

From Eq. (7.9-2) it is apparent that there is an alternative definition of torque as the product of the radius r by the force component $F_t = F \sin \phi$ perpendicular to the radius. But this just fits our definition of the cross product.

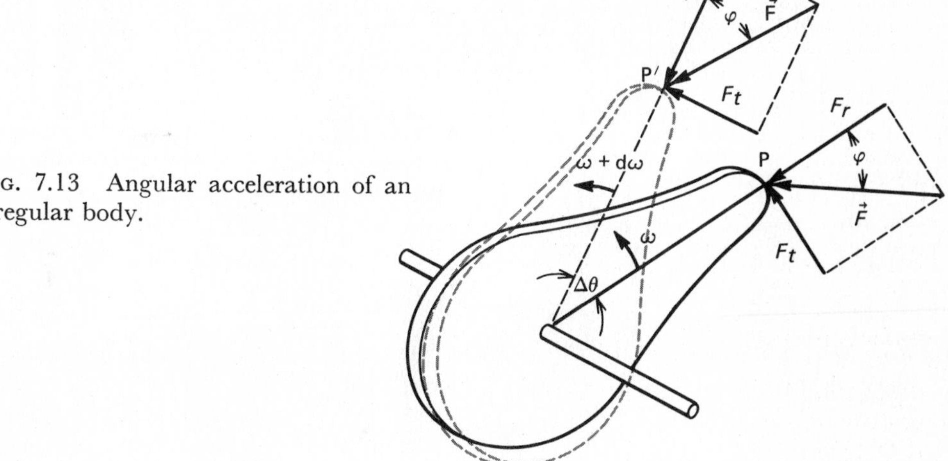

FIG. 7.13 Angular acceleration of an irregular body.

Thus,

$$\vec{\tau} = \vec{r} \times \vec{F}; \tag{7.9.3}$$

this is possibly somewhat more easily seen if the vector $\vec{F}$ is drawn from the origin as the dashed vector in Fig. 7.12. Note that the sense of $\vec{r} \times \vec{F}$ is correct. If the wheel rotates P to P', then $\vec{\omega}$ comes out of the page. If the applied torque $\vec{\tau}$ is to increase the angular velocity then the angular acceleration $\vec{\alpha}$ must also come out of the page as must the torque $\vec{\tau}$. That this is so in this simple case follows from the figure.

We have just defined torque as the work per unit angle of rotation: $\tau = dw/d\theta$. This is analogous to defining force as the work per unit displacement: $f = dw/ds$. From neither of these definitions does it follow that the left member of the equation is a vector. That each left member is a vector, though, follows from other considerations.

According to Eq. (7.9-2), the dimensions of torque are

$$[\tau] = [\mathscr{F} r] = [m\ell t^{-2}][\ell] = [m\ell^2 t^{-2}],$$

so that torque has the same dimensions as energy. But energy and torque are two very different physical quantities. Usually, if some caution is used, no confusion results. Had we assigned dimensions to angles (cf. Sec. 7.2), the two quantities would have been found to have different dimensions.

The term ***moment of a force*** is sometimes used instead of torque to denote the cross product $\vec{r} \times \vec{F}$.

Suppose that we apply a torque to a rotating body, such as that of Fig. 7.12 or that of Fig. 7.13, which is initially moving with an angular velocity ω and a kinetic energy $\frac{1}{2}I\omega^2$ [Eq. 7.6-2A)]. As a result of the application of the torque, the angular velocity increases at a rate $d\omega/dt$. The kinetic energy increases at a rate

$$\frac{d(KE)}{dt} = \frac{d(\frac{1}{2}I\omega^2)}{dt} = \frac{1}{2}I\frac{d(\omega)^2}{dt} = I\omega\frac{d\omega}{dt},$$

if I is a constant. This rate of increase of kinetic energy must be equal to the rate at which work is being done on the wheel. If the average torque during a time interval Δt is $\langle\tau\rangle_{av}$, the work done is $\tau\,\Delta\theta$, where $\Delta\theta$ is the angle through which the wheel rotates. Since $\Delta\theta = \langle\omega\rangle_{av}\,\Delta t$, the rate at which work is done is

$$\langle\tau\rangle_{av}\langle\omega\rangle_{av}\,\Delta t/\Delta t = \langle\tau\rangle_{av}\langle\omega\rangle_{av}.$$

As we pass to the limit, $\Delta t \to 0$, the average values may be replaced by the instantaneous ones, so we have

$$\frac{dw}{dt} = \tau\omega = \frac{d(KE)}{dt} = I\omega\frac{d\omega}{dt},$$

and

$$\tau = I\frac{d\omega}{dt}. \tag{7.9-4}$$

It must be remembered that Eq. (7.9-4) was derived on the assumption that I is a constant.

If the moment of inertia of the rotating body remains constant, as it does if the body is rigid, and if the speeds involved are not too great, we may rewrite Eq. (7.9-4) as

$$\tau = I \lim_{\Delta t \to 0} (\Delta\omega/\Delta t) = I\frac{d\omega}{dt} = I\alpha, \tag{7.9-5}$$

where the last equality follows from Eq. (7.2-4). Notice that Eqs. (7.9-4) and (7.9-5) are analogous to $F = dp/dt = ma$ from linear mechanics.

Equations (7.9-4) and (7.9-5) are both written in scalar form. We shall consider them further in Sec. 7.12.

7.10 Angular Momentum

The analogy between Eq. (7.9-5) and Eq. (4.9-3), the definition of force, immediately suggests that the quantity $I\omega$ that occurs in the former has a special significance and is the analogue of momentum in linear mechanics. If we define the ***angular momentum*** L as the product of the moment of inertia of a body by its angular velocity, i.e.,

$$L = I\omega, \tag{7.10-1}$$

Eq. (7.9-4) takes the form:

$$\tau = \lim_{\Delta t \to 0} (\Delta L/\Delta t) = \frac{dL}{dt}. \tag{7.10-2}$$

This equation shows that there is a third definition of torque, equivalent to those that we have already given, as the time rate of change of angular momentum, and completes the analogy with Eqs. (4.9-2) and (4.9-3).

We can now predict the effect of a torque on the angular acceleration of a rotating body. For example, suppose that a wheel of radius r and moment of inertia I, free to rotate about its own axis, which is fixed in space, has a rope wrapped around its rim (Fig. 7.14) and that this rope is pulled with a force $\vec{F}$. Since in this case $\sin\phi = 1$, the torque is $\vec{\tau} = \vec{r} \times \vec{F}$, $\tau = rF$, and the angular acceleration is

$$\alpha = \tau/I = rF/I.$$

If the wheel starts from rest, the angular velocity ω_t at the end of time t will be given by Eq. (7.3-6) as

$$\omega_t = Frt/I$$

and the angle θ_t through which the wheel has rotated will be (Eq. 7.3-5)

$$\theta_t = Frt^2/2I.$$

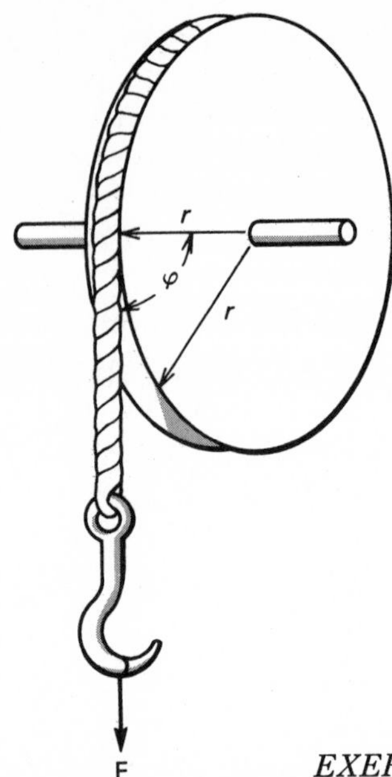

FIG. 7.14 Torque on a wheel.

EXERCISES

7.10-1 A wheel of moment of inertia 2.20 kg m^2 and of outside radius 12.5 cm is mounted on an axle passing through its center and is initially at rest. A string is wrapped around the wheel and is pulled by a constant force through a distance of 1.00 m in 0.50 sec. What is the magnitude of the force acting on the string?

7.10-2 The wheel of Ex. 7.10-1 is started into rotation by a string wrapped around the axle, whose radius is 1.00 cm. This string is pulled with a force of 14.0 N. Through what angle will the wheel turn while it is being accelerated to an angular velocity of 2.0 rad/sec?

7.10-3 A wheel, similar to that of Ex. 7.10-1 but of outside radius 15.0 cm, is accelerated by a force of 20.0 N acting through a string wrapped around the wheel. The wheel starts from rest and rotates through 2.50 rev in 1.10 sec. Calculate the moment of inertia of the wheel.

7.11 The Law of Conservation of Angular Momentum

In Sec. 7.10 we found that, for a body rotating on an axis fixed in space, the time rate of change of angular momentum is proportional to the torque applied to the rotating body [Eq. (7.10-2)]. It then follows that if the torque applied to a body is zero, the angular momentum of that body will remain constant. We are thus led to state ***the law of the conservation of angular momentum***: *The angular momentum of an isolated system is a constant.* This very important law is a consequence of the laws of particle mechanics and makes its appearance in many interesting natural phenomena.

An example of the law of conservation of angular momentum is provided by the rotation of the earth on its axis. Since the earth is a rigid body (or very nearly so) its moment of inertia about its axis is constant. The usefulness of the rotating earth as a clock is evidence that its angular velocity is a constant and hence that its angular momentum is also constant. We shall see in the next section that the motions of the planets around the sun provide examples of applications of the law to cases in which the moment of inertia varies.

An example of the conservation law for rotation, quite analogous to that of Fig. 4.9 for linear motion, would be provided by a man running around the edge of a horizontal turntable which is free to rotate about a vertical axis through its center (Fig. 7.15). If the man and the turntable are initially at rest and the man starts to run in one direction around the axis, the turntable will

FIG. 7.15 Action and reaction in rotation.

start to rotate in the opposite direction. A similar example is provided by a wheel, with its axis vertical, spun by the hand of an experimenter who sits on the turntable (Fig. 7.16). As he starts the wheel spinning in one direction the turntable rotates in the opposite direction.

A number of examples of the law of conservation of momentum can be obtained from athletics. A diver off the high board wishing to do a number of forward somersaults rolls himself up into a ball and rotates at a high speed. His moment of inertia is small and his angular velocity (about a horizontal axis) is large for a given angular momentum. Just before he enters the water, he straightens himself out, thus increasing his moment of inertia and decreasing his angular velocity. A similar effect can be demonstrated by a man standing on a turntable with two heavy weights in his hands. If initially he is rotating slowly with his arms outstretched, his speed of rotation will increase markedly

Fig. 7.16 Conservation of angular momentum.

(a) (b)

Fig. 7.17 Variable moment of inertia.

as he lowers his arms or otherwise brings the weights closer to his axis or rotation. The identical principle is used by the figure skater who starts a spin in a crouch with arms and one leg stretched out as far as possible (Fig. 7.17a). As he rises on the points of his skates with arms folded or raised above the head (Fig. 7.17b), his moment of inertia decreases and his angular velocity increases. All these phenomena in which no outside torque acts on the system can be summed up in the equation

$$I\omega = I'\omega', \tag{7.11-1A}$$

in which I and ω are the initial values of the moment of inertia and of the angular velocity and I' and ω' are the final values. This result may be rewritten

$$I/I' = \omega'/\omega, \tag{7.11-1B}$$

which indicates that in an isolated system the angular velocity is inversely proportional to the moment of inertia.

EXERCISES

7.11-1 Two 0.1 kg masses slip onto a meter stick and are positioned at the 25 cm and 75 cm marks, where they are held by a string. The meter stick is arranged to rotate about a vertical axis perpendicular to the meter stick and passing through the 50 cm mark. As the system is rotating one can apply a match to the midpoint of the string so that it separates, letting the two masses move to the 0 cm and 100 cm marks, respectively, where the masses lodge against stops. What is the moment of inertia I_B before the string is burned, if the mass of the meter stick itself can be neglected?

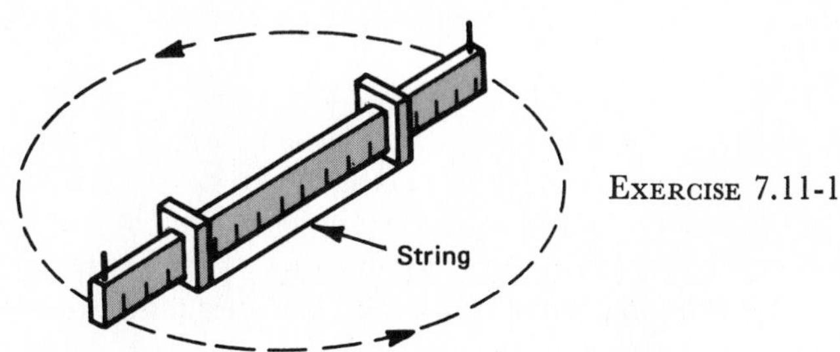

EXERCISE 7.11-1

What is the moment of inertia I_A after the string has been burned?

7.11-2 If the angular velocity at the start ω_B is 2π rad/sec, what will ω_A be after the string is burned?

7.11-3 Is rotational kinetic energy conserved in the experiment performed in Exs. 7.11-1 and 7.11-2? Again neglect the mass of the meter stick.

7.12 The Analogy between Linear and Rotational Dynamics

In Table 7.1 we saw a number of analogies between the kinematics of motion in a straight line and that of rotation about an axis fixed in space. As our study of rotation has progressed, we have found that other quantities, such as mass and force, also have their analogies. Table 7.2 completes the analogy that was partly displayed in Table 7.1 and may help the reader remember the basic equations of the mechanics of rotation about a fixed axis.

Table 7.2 *Analogies Between Linear and Rotational Motions*

Linear Motion		Rotational Motion	
Displacement	s	Angle	θ
Velocity	$v = \lim\limits_{\Delta t \to 0} \Delta s/\Delta t$	Angular velocity	$\omega = \lim\limits_{\Delta t \to 0} \Delta\theta/\Delta t$
Acceleration	$a = \lim\limits_{\Delta t \to 0} \Delta v/\Delta t$	Angular acceleration	$\alpha = \lim\limits_{\Delta t \to 0} \Delta\omega/\Delta t$
Mass	m	Moment of inertia	$I = \sum m_j r_j^2$
Momentum	$p = mv$	Angular momentum	$L = I\omega$
Force	$F = \lim\limits_{\Delta t \to 0} \Delta p/\Delta t$	Torque	$\tau = \lim\limits_{\Delta t \to 0} \Delta L/\Delta t$
Kinetic energy	$KE = \frac{1}{2}mv^2$	Kinetic energy	$KE = \frac{1}{2}I\omega^2$

One must remember the limitation of a fixed axis. This is important because the very first step in establishing both Table 7.1 and 7.2 is valid only if the angular displacement is in a fixed direction, in which case it is analogous to displacement along a straight line. In other words, we must remember that angular displacement is not a vector. We shall discuss the more general case briefly in Sec. 7.17. Before doing so, however, we can find some interesting applications of the results that we have obtained in the special case.

7.13 The Motion of the Planets

In many places in this book we have referred to Newton as being responsible for the establishment of a systematic mechanics, and we can recognize in him one of the greatest of all scientists in these achievements. If we wish to select from all his work his most brilliant effort, we can perhaps choose his deduction of the law of gravitation from the mechanics which he had first established and from the experimental observations of his predecessors. Before we enter into Newton's treatment of gravitation, with which we shall be concerned later in this section and in Chapter 14, it is worth while to digress briefly and to consider a little of the historical background for this important advance. Beginning in the time of the Greeks, there raged a continual controversy between the ***geocentric theory*** and the ***heliocentric theory*** of the universe. The geocentric theory claimed that the sun, the planets, and the stars revolved around the earth as the center. The heliocentric notion held that the earth and the planets moved around the sun and that the apparent motion of the sun and stars was due to rotation of the earth on its axis. The geocentric theory was known as the ***Ptolemaic theory*** after the Greek astronomer Ptolemy (2nd century A.D.) who, following Hipparchus (about 130 B.C.), was an exponent of this notion. The heliocentric theory originated with Aristarchus of Samos (about 380 B.C.)

but became known as the ***Copernican theory*** after the great Polish astronomer Nikolaus Copernicus (1493–1543), who revived the theory in 1530. The controversy came to a head in the sixteenth century and, so the story relates, Galileo was forced to recant his Copernican ideas by the Inquisition, which held that the Ptolemaic theory was in accord with Holy Writ. He is reported to have negated his recantation in the famous phrase "*E pur si muove* (But still it does move)," as he left the hall of the Inquisition. The Danish astronomer, Tycho Brahe (1546–1601), although a believer in the Ptolemaic theory, saw, as did Galileo, that measurement provided the only possible clue to the decision between the two theories. He devoted his life to observations of the planetary motions and, with the aid of the many instruments which he perfected, prepared a detailed catalogue of these motions. He was unable to find an interpretation of his results by the application of the Ptolemaic theory, but the German astronomer Johannes Kepler (1571–1630), having access to Tycho's records, was able to find their correct interpretation in the Copernican theory. He reduced the great mass of observations to the three laws of planetary motion that we know as ***Kepler's laws.*** They are:

1. The orbits of the planets are ellipses, having the sun at one focus.
2. The area swept out per unit time by the radius vector from the sun to a given planet is a constant.
3. The squares of the periodic times of the planets are proportional to the cubes of their mean distances from the sun.*

These three laws were in precisely the form needed by Newton to deduce the nature of the force of attraction between the sun and the earth. We shall follow Newton in our discussion in this section and in Chapter 14, although the details of our approach will differ quite considerably from his.

We start by a consideration of Kepler's second law. Suppose a planet moves in the orbit of Fig. 7.18, which is an ellipse with the sun at S. Kepler's second

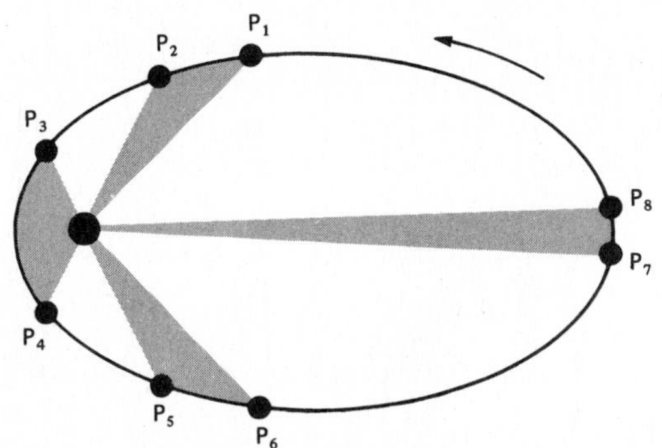

FIG. 7.18 The law of equal areas.

* The third law is stated here in the form in which it is ordinarily quoted. It is clear from the context of Kepler's publication, however, that the word that is translated as "mean" did not carry the modern meaning of "average." A better statement would replace "the cubes of their mean distances from the sun" by "the cubes of the semimajor axes of their elliptical orbits."

law then states that, if the time taken by the planet in traveling from P_1 to P_2 is the same as that taken from P_3 to P_4, then the shaded area SP_1P_2 is equal to the shaded area SP_3P_4. Similar equal areas are indicated in SP_5P_6 and SP_7P_8, in which the times between P_5 and P_6 and between P_7 and P_8 are the same as those for P_1P_2 and P_3P_4. Kepler's statement implies that this is true whatever the time between successive planetary positions.

We notice that the distance traveled by the planet in a given time is much greater when the planet is close to the sun than when it is far away. This suggests a correlation of Kepler's second law with the law of conservation of angular momentum, and this we can undertake quite simply.

Suppose that in a small time Δt the planet moves from P to P′ (Fig. 7.19). In this time the radius changes from r (= SP) to $(r+\Delta r)$ (= SP′) and sweeps out the area SPP′. The angle (measured in radians) through which the radius has rotated is $\Delta\theta = \omega\,\Delta t$, where ω is the angular velocity of the planet. Since Δr is small compared with r when Δt is small, we can replace the orbit PP′ by the circular arc PQ in the limit as Δt tends to zero, and we can take the area of the sector SPQ as equal to the area SPP′. Since the number of radians in a

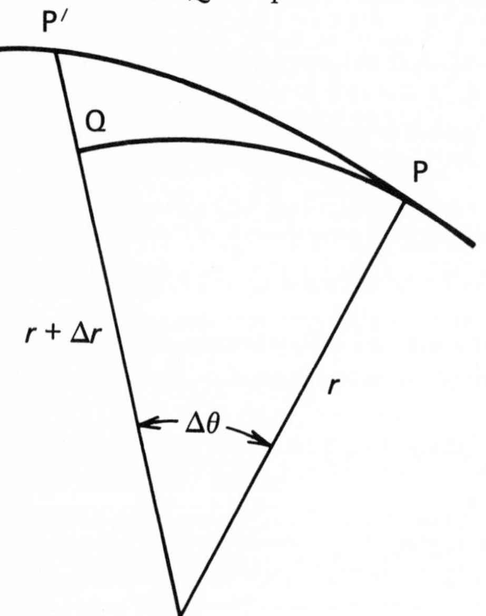

FIG. 7.19 Area swept out by a moving body.

full revolution is 2π [Eq. (G.13)], the area of the sector SPQ is $(\Delta\theta/2\pi)\pi r^2 = r^2\omega\,\Delta t/2$. Thus, according to Kepler's second law, the area swept out in unit time is

$$r^2\omega/2 = k,$$

where k is a constant for a given planet. If we multiply both sides of this equation by $2M_P$ where M_P is the mass of the planet, we find that

$$M_P r^2\omega = 2M_P k.$$

The right-hand side of this equation does not depend on the radius, so it is a constant for a given planet. On the left-hand side of the equation, notice that the product $M_P r^2$ is the moment of inertia of the planet about the sun (Eq. 7.6-1). The product of this moment of inertia by the angular velocity ω is the angular momentum L_P of the planet about the sun [Eq. (7.10-1)]. We therefore write

$$M_P r^2 \omega = L_P \tag{7.13-1}$$

and find that Kepler's second law is equivalent to the statement that the angular momentum of each planet about the sun is a constant. By combining this conclusion with the known fact that angular momentum remains constant only when no torques are acting, we see at once that any forces acting on a planet must be directed along the line joining the planet to the sun. Were this not so, the force would produce a torque and change the angular momentum of the planet. The fact that the planets do not move in a straight line with constant velocity indicates that forces must act on them, and we now find that these forces are directed toward the sun. Thus, we have taken two steps toward the formulation of Newton's law of universal gravitation, and this will be completed in Chapter 14.

The reader will note from Eq. (7.13-1) that the angular velocity of a planet varies inversely as the square of the distance of the planet from the sun. Thus, in Fig. 7.18 the distance of closest approach is $\frac{1}{8}$ of the remotest distance and the angular velocities are in the ratio 64 : 1. This is in accord with our discussion in Sec. 7.11.

EXERCISES

7.13-1 A ball is sliding on a smooth table and is attached to a taut string which passes through a small hole in the center of that table, so that the ball moves in a circle about the hole. Prove that if the length of the string is changed, the angular velocity of the ball about the hole varies inversely as the square of the distance of the ball from the hole.

7.13-2 The ball discussed in Ex. 7.13-1 is rotating at 30 rev/min when it is 50 cm from the hole. If the string is pulled until the radius is 30 cm, what will be the angular velocity of the ball? What will its speed be?

7.13-3 The ball of Ex. 7.13-2 has a mass of 150 g. By considering the kinetic energy of rotation, find how much work must be done in pulling the string.

7.13-4 What is the tension in the string of Exs. 7.13-1 to 7.13-3 when the radius is 50 cm? What is the tension when the radius is 30 cm? What is the average tension in the string as the radius is decreased from 50 cm to 30 cm (cf. Ex. 7.13-3)?

7.13-5 A man stands on a freely turning horizontal platform. He is holding a weight of mass M, which is attached to the end of a rope. He is initially at rest and then starts to swing the weight in a horizontal circle of radius R about his head. When the weight has acquired an angular velocity of magnitude ω_1 with respect to the ground, the man has acquired an angular velocity of magnitude ω_2, again with respect to the ground. What is the combined moment of inertia of the man and the platform about the axis of rotation?

7.13-6 In Ex. 7.13-5, what is the angular velocity of the weight with respect to the man?

7.14 *Rotational Equilibrium*

It is not difficult to see that two torques that tend to rotate a rigid body in opposite directions will cancel one another at least partially. If these two torques taken separately would produce equal and opposite accelerations on the body, then under their combined action it will remain at rest or in motion at constant angular velocity.

We noted in Sec. 7.9 that torque is an axial vector. If we now apply this notion to the forces applied to the disk in Fig. 7.20, we see that the cross product

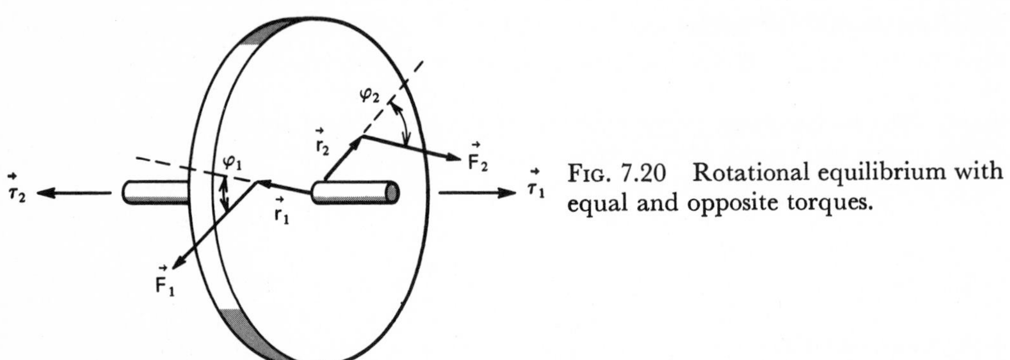

FIG. 7.20 Rotational equilibrium with equal and opposite torques.

$\vec{r}_2 \times \vec{F}_2 = \vec{\tau}_2$, an axial vector directed to the left along the axis of rotation of the disk. Similarly, $\vec{r}_1 \times \vec{F}_1 = \vec{\tau}_1$, an axial vector pointing to the right along the axis. The condition for equilibrium is $\vec{\tau}_1 + \vec{\tau}_2 = 0$ or

$$\vec{r}_1 \times \vec{F}_1 = \vec{r}_2 \times \vec{F}_2; \qquad r_1 F_1 \sin \phi_1 = r_2 F_2 \sin \phi_2. \tag{7.14-1}$$

It is easy to see that $\vec{\tau}_1 + \vec{\tau}_2 = 0$ is a special case of a more general result. We may say that the angular acceleration of a body will be zero—i.e., it will be in equilibrium as far as rotation is concerned—if

$$\sum_{j=1}^{n} \vec{\tau}_j = 0, \tag{7.14-2}$$

that is to say, if the vector sum of all the torques acting on the body is zero. The law expressed by Eq. (7.14-2) is often called the ***law of moments.***

A very simple example to which Eq. (7.14-2) may be applied is the equal arm balance (Sec. 4.16 and Fig. 7.21). The mass m_1 on the left-hand side exerts

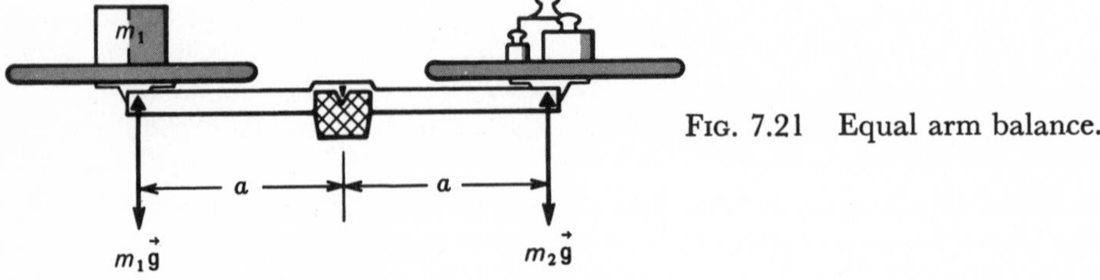

FIG. 7.21 Equal arm balance.

a torque $m_1 ga$, and that on the right-hand side is $-m_2 ga$. Applying Eq. (7.14-2), we have

$$m_1 ga - m_2 ga = 0,$$

if the arm does not rotate. This leads at once to $m_1 = m_2$, a result we have already obtained (Sec. 4.16) by a symmetry argument.

The see-saw (Fig. 7.22a) presents a simple example of the application of the law of moments. The reader can easily see that the condition for equilibrium is

$$m_1 x_1 - m_2 x_2 = 0, \qquad (7.14\text{-}3)$$

which we may rewrite as

$$x_1/x_2 = m_2/m_1.$$

Thus, the heavier person must sit closer to the center than the lighter. Figure 7.22b represents a more general type of see-saw in which a number of persons (or other heavy objects) are balanced on a plank. It is clear from the figure that the condition for equilibrium is

$$m_1 x_1 - m_2 x_2 - m_3 x_3 + m_4 x_4 = 0.$$

7.15 *Center of Mass*

Before we discuss any further problems in rotational equilibrium, there is one very important point to be understood. We know that if we try to balance a uniform plank on a log, the plank will tilt one way or the other unless the plank is located so that its center is exactly over the log (Fig. 7.23).

We can explain the behavior of the plank on the log by a further consideration of the see-saw of Fig. 7.22a. We know that the see-saw will balance at the point C provided that the distances x_1 and x_2 are related to the masses m_1 and m_2 by Eq. (7.14-3). Suppose now we try to support the see-saw at point D, which is a distance y to the left of C (Fig. 7.24), without changing the masses m_1 and m_2, which balanced the plank when it was supported at the center. If we neglect the mass of the plank, it is clear that the moment tending to turn the see-saw clockwise is

$$T = m_2 g(x_2 + y) - m_1 g(x_1 - y) = (m_1 + m_2)gy + (m_2 x_2 - m_1 x_1)g.$$

We know from Eq. (7.14-3) that the second term of this expression is zero, so that the moment tending to turn the plank is simply

$$T = (m_1 + m_2)gy. \qquad (7.15\text{-}1)$$

This moment is equal to that which would be produced by the two masses m_1 and m_2 concentrated at the point of balance C. It is left as an exercise for the reader to prove a similar result for the four masses of Fig. 7.22b. Since Eq. (7.15-1) holds for any value of y—i.e., for any location of D—it follows that as far as the moment due to gravity is concerned the two masses m_1 and m_2 of Figs. 7.22a and 7.24 behave exactly as though a single mass $(m_1 + m_2)$ were

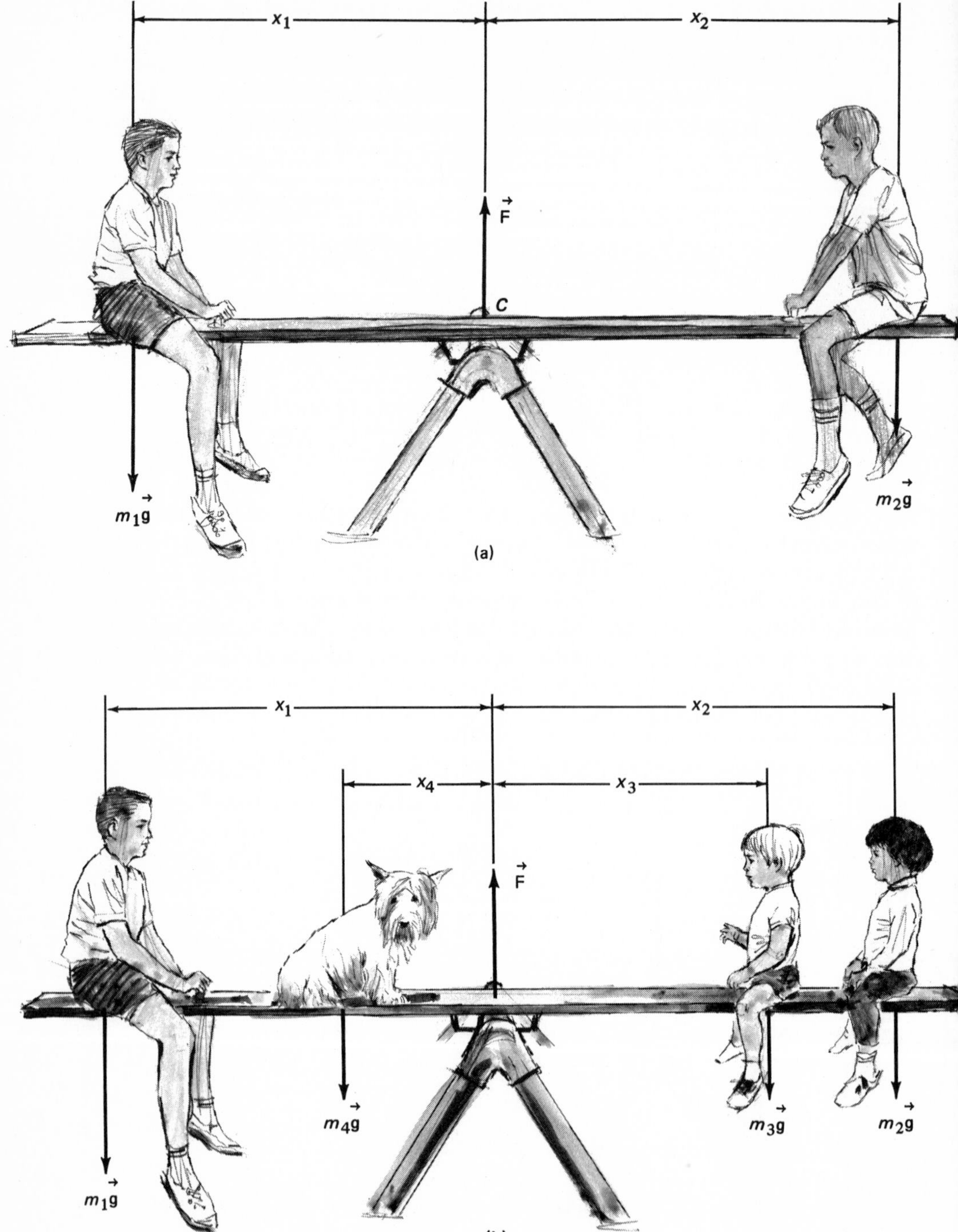

FIG. 7.22 Applications of the law of moments.

concentrated at C, and we notice that C is that point about which the total moment, due to the action of gravity on the masses m_1 and m_2, is zero.

We are thus led to define the ***center of mass*** of a system of bodies as that point in the system about which the total moment, due to the action of gravity on the system, is zero. As we have seen in the preceding paragraph, it follows

FIG. 7.23 Balancing a plank on a log.

that, as far as gravitational moment is concerned, any system of bodies behaves as though the total mass of all the bodies of the system were concentrated at the center of mass. This statement applies *only to moments due to gravitational forces.* It is clear, for example, that the moment of inertia would be changed if all the masses of an extended system were concentrated at their center of mass.

The location of the center of mass of many objects is quite simple. It is easy to see, for example, that the center of mass of a uniform plank is at its geometrical center, and this is true also for a sphere, or for a homogeneous circular disk, or for a homogeneous cylinder, as a symmetry argument (Sec. 4.16) will

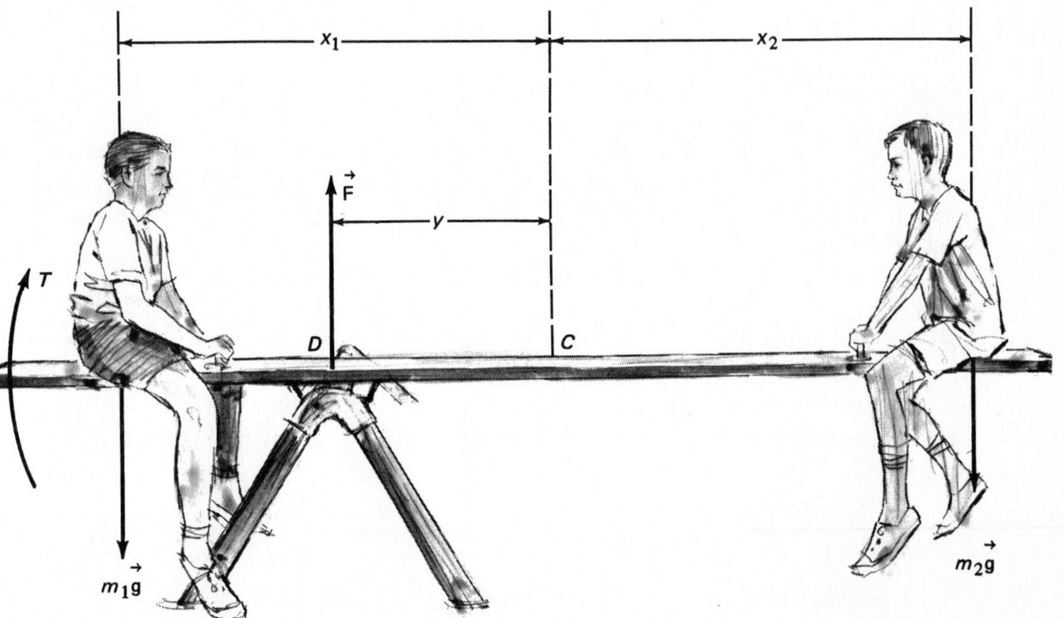

FIG. 7.24 Torque on an unbalanced see-saw.

easily prove. We shall not concern ourselves here with the location of the center of mass of more complicated bodies but merely point out that they can readily be determined by an experiment which the reader should be able to devise.

We are now able to face the question, which we avoided before, of the effect of the plank on the see-saws of Figs. 7.22 and 7.24. We shall, in fact, consider the extreme problem of the socially maladjusted child (scientifically rather precocious) who wishes to play on the see-saw by himself. He chooses a plank of mass M and adjusts it as indicated in Fig. 7.25 with the support D at a

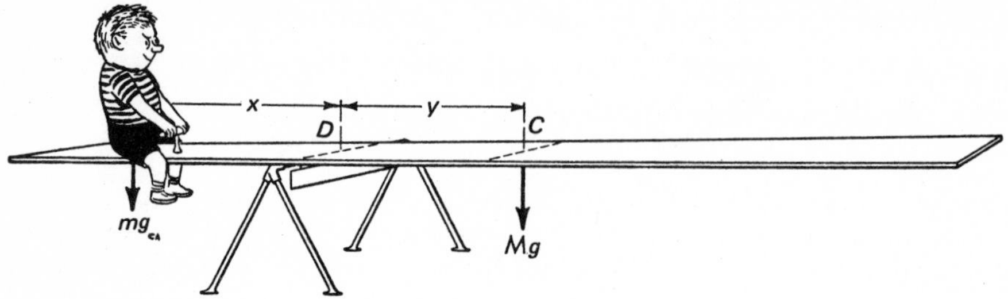

FIG. 7.25 Solitary see-saw (Courtesy and permission of Charles Addams).

distance y from the center of mass C of the plank. He seats himself at a distance x from the point of support D. He knows that the total mass M of the plank acts as a single concentrated mass M at the mass-center C and, if

$$mx = My,$$

he will be able to balance himself and the plank on the support D.

It is now easy to calculate the upward force that must be exerted by the support D of Fig. 7.25. The combined center of mass of the child and the plank is at D and the upward thrust of the support must, of course, be $(m + M)g$. In a similar way, one can easily compute the reactions of the support for the see-saw of Fig. 7.22 with due allowance for the fact that the center of mass of the plank is, in each of these cases, assumed to be directly over the point of support.

The concept of the center of mass is an important one for many problems other than those of rotational mechanics. For example, it is easy to show (Prob. 7.11) that the use of a coordinate system attached to the center of mass of two or more bodies simplifies the treatment of collisions. It should also be clear that a system of bodies on which no *outside* forces act must either remain at rest or continue in motion at constant velocity. We shall return to the consequences of this fact a number of times in the rest of this book.

7.16 General Conditions of Equilibrium

We can now write down the general conditions for the equilibrium of a system of bodies in space. We know from Sec. 6.4 *that the vector sum of all the forces acting on the system must be zero*, and we know from Sec. 7.14 that *the total moment or torque of all the forces acting on the system must also be zero* about every point in the system. We can thus write for the conditions of equilibrium

$$\Sigma\vec{F}=0 \qquad (7.16\text{-}1A)$$

and

$$\Sigma\vec{\tau}=0. \qquad (7.16\text{-}1B)$$

We can now apply these conditions to the solution of a simple problem. The plank of Fig. 7.26 has a mass M and is supported at two points C and D. Two

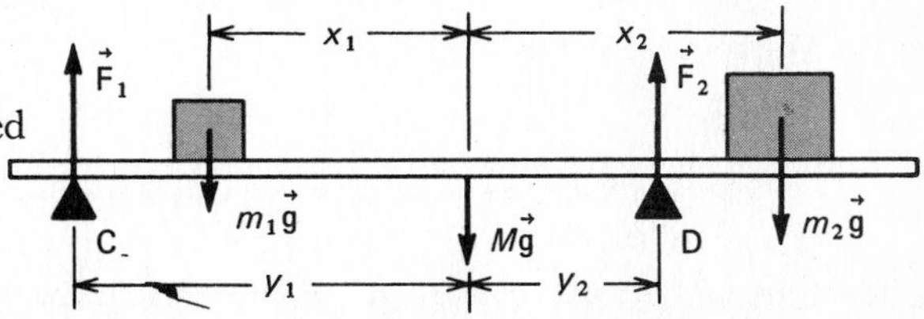

FIG. 7.26 Equilibrium of an extended body.

weights m_1 and m_2 are located as indicated in the figure. Using Eq. (7.16-1A), we can easily see that the combined upward force F_1+F_2 exerted by the supports is equal to the total weight of the system, i.e.,

$$F_1+F_2=g(m_1+m_2+M). \qquad (7.16\text{-}2A)$$

The total moment tending to rotate the plank about any point must also be zero. Taking moments about the point C, we have

$$F_2(y_1+y_2)-m_1g(y_1-x_1)-Mgy_1-m_2g(y_1+x_2)=0,$$

so that

$$F_2=\{Mgy_1+m_1g(y_1-x_1)+m_2g(y_1+x_2)\}/(y_1+y_2). \qquad (7.16\text{-}2B)$$

If the various masses and distances are known, Eq. (7.16-2B) will give us the value of F_2, the force with which the support D pushes up on the plank. Substitution of the value of F_2 into Eq. (7.16-2A) will then give a value for F_1, the reaction of the support C.

Although we chose above to consider moments about the point C, it is obvious that the plank, if it is in equilibrium, must not be rotating about *any* point. It follows that the total moment about any point must be zero. If we were to take moments about D, we would find that

$$F_1(y_1+y_2)-m_1g(x_1+y_2)-Mgy_2+m_2g(x_2-y_2)=0,$$

that is to say,

$$F_1=\frac{Mgy_2+m_1g(x_1+y_2)-m_2g(x_2-y_2)}{y_1+y_2}. \qquad (7.16\text{-}2C)$$

This equation, of course, will give the same value for F_1 as was obtained from the simultaneous solution of Eqs. (7.16-2A and B). We could, in fact, determine F_1 and F_2 from any of the three possible pairs of Eqs. (7.16-2). In any particular problem, there are generally a variety of moment equations that can be written, and the choice of the best equations for use is purely one of convenience. To show that the various pairs of Eqs. (7.16-2) lead to the same results, the reader may add Eqs. (7.16-2B and C) to obtain Eq. (7.16-2A).

Some points of interest can often be drawn from the equations for equilibrium without a detailed solution. For example, it is obvious that the supports in Fig. 7.26 can only push up on the plank. If either F_1 or F_2 were found to be negative, it would mean that the support would need to pull down and, since it cannot do this, equilibrium could not be maintained. Inspection of Eq. (7.16-2B) shows that F_2 is necessarily positive, but Eq. (7.16-2C) indicates that F_1 will be negative if

$$m_2(x_2 - y_2) > My_2 + m_1(x_1 + y_2).$$

It follows at once that there is an upper limit to the mass m_2 that will allow the plank to remain in equilibrium, if m_1, M, and the various distances are fixed.

EXERCISES

7.16-1 An improvized diving board is made of a uniform plank of mass 15.0 kg and of length 4.10 m. The board projects 2.70 m beyond the edge of a horizontal dock. A stone of mass 142 kg is used to hold down the plank and is located with its center of mass vertically above a point 0.40 m from the end of the plank. How close to the end of the diving board can a man of 60.0 kg walk without tipping the board?

7.16-2 The man of the previous exercise is dissatisfied with his diving board and replaces the previous stone with one of mass 190 kg, again placed 0.40 m from the end. How far can the same man walk out on this board without tipping it?

7.16-3 In the balance of Fig. 7.21, the two arms are unequal, having lengths a_1 on the left and a_2 on the right, and the beam is horizontal with the pans empty. Mass m_2 is unknown and is balanced by a mass m_1 when located as shown in the figure. If m_2 is transferred to the left-hand pan, a different mass m_1' is required to balance it. Show that $m_2 = (m_1 m_1')^{1/2}$.

7.16-4 A body is free to rotate about a horizontal axis. Its center of gravity is at a distance h from this axis. Show that there are two positions in which the body will be in equilibrium. Discuss what happens when the body is displaced slightly from each of these two positions.

7.16-5 Locate the center of mass of the four masses of Fig. 7.22b.

7.16-6 Devise an experimental method for the location of the center of mass of a piece of thin wood which is of uniform thickness and is cut in the shape of the ace of spades, the extreme height of the figure being about 25 cm.

7.17 *Angular Velocity and Angular Momentum*

In Tables 7.1 and 7.2 we made use of analogies that saved us much time in arriving at several valid expressions. We noted, however, that the analogies were valid only in a very special case of an axis fixed in space. We shall now show that the connection between angular momentum $(\vec{L})$ and angular velocity $(\vec{\omega})$ is somewhat different from that between linear momentum $(\vec{p})$ and linear velocity $(\vec{v})$.

In Figs. 7.6 and 7.12 we were careful to show only bodies that were symmetrical about the axis of rotation. Now let us consider a rotating rigid body that does not display such symmetry, say the system of two equal masses attached to an axle by light rods, as shown in Fig. 7.27a. Suppose that the axle is held in

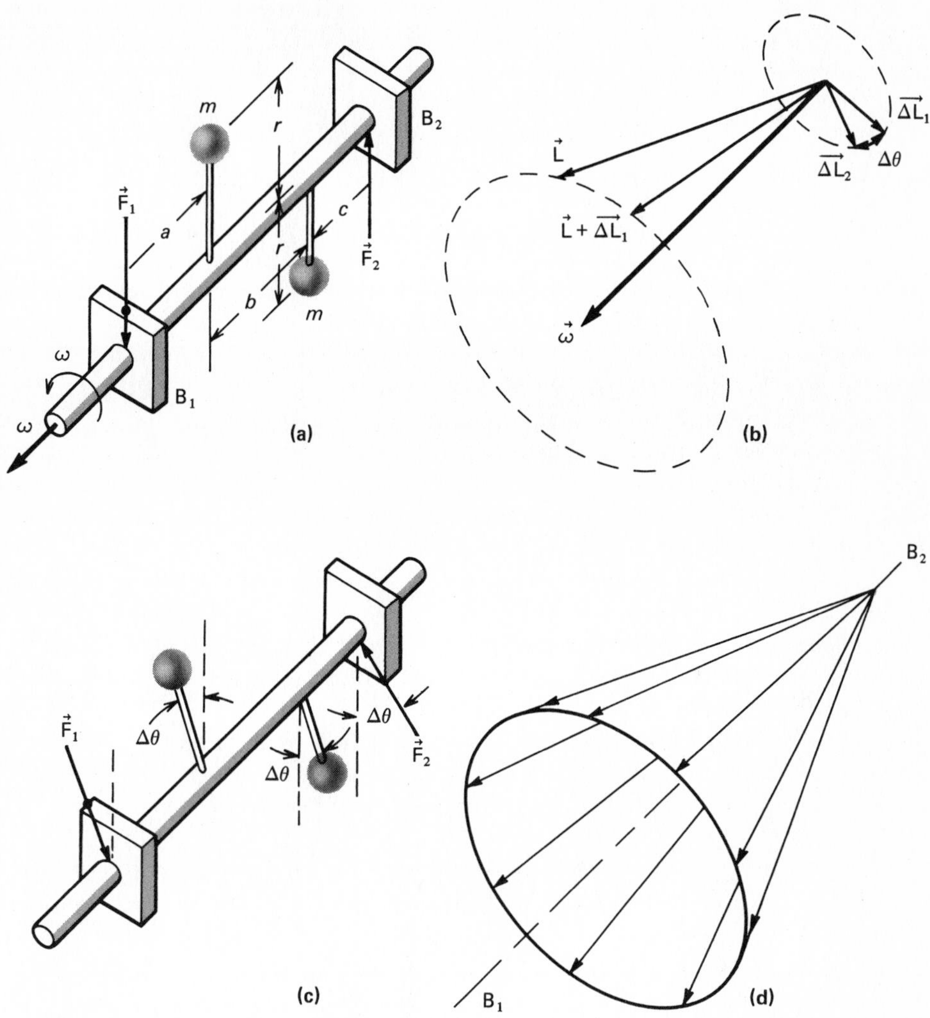

FIG. 7.27 Rotation of an asymmetrical body about a fixed axis.

place by two bearings, B_1 and B_2. For simplicity, we shall neglect gravitational forces and consider the masses of the axle and the two rods to be negligible and the masses m to be particles at distance r from the axis. The system is rotating with a constant angular velocity $\vec{\omega}$, which is an axial vector pointing forward along the axis of the shaft, as shown.

To hold the mass nearer to B_1 in uniform circular motion, it is necessary that a centripetal force, equal to $m\omega^2 r$, be exerted on it. This force is directed toward the axis of rotation, i.e., vertically downward in the figure. Similarly, a centripetal force of equal magnitude, but directed upward, must be exerted on the other mass. Because these two forces are equal in magnitude, no net force need act on the system. On the other hand, if we consider the torque necessary to hold the shaft stationary, we find that forces must be exerted by the bearings. Taking torque about the point B_1, for example, we find that the bearing B_2 must produce an *upward* force $\vec{F}_2$ such that

$$(a+b+c)F_2 = m\omega^2 r(a+b) - m\omega^2 ra = m\omega^2 rb.$$

Hence the reaction of the bearing B_2 on the shaft must be

$$F_2 = m\omega^2 rb/(a+b+c).$$

An exactly similar argument shows that there must be a *downward* force $\vec{F}_1$ acting on the shaft at bearing B_1, its magnitude being equal to F_2.

The existence of an external torque implies a changing angular momentum, according to Eq. (7.10-1). Apparently the angular momentum of the rotating system is not constant, although its angular velocity is constant!

At the instant pictured in Fig. 7.27a the forces $\vec{F}_1$ and $\vec{F}_2$ act in a vertical plane. Hence the torque that they exert, according to our right-hand screw rule, is horizontal, in the direction shown by the vector $\Delta\vec{L}_1$ in Fig. 7.27b. The magnitude of this vector is

$$\Delta L_1 = m\omega^2 rb\ \Delta t.$$

During the interval the angular momentum will therefore change from $\vec{L}$ to $\vec{L} + \Delta\vec{L}_1$, as shown in Fig. 7.27b. At the end of the Δt interval the system will have turned through some small angle $\Delta\theta$. Since the forces $\vec{F}_1$ and $\vec{F}_2$ are always in the plane that passes through the axis and through both masses, these forces will be acting at an angle $\Delta\theta$ with the vertical. Hence the torque will be directed at an angle $\Delta\theta$ with the horizontal, in the direction shown by $\Delta\vec{L}_2$ in Fig. 7.27b.

The situation is very much that considered in our discussion of centripetal force in Sec. 7.7. There a velocity vector was subject to a force that was constant in magnitude but changing in direction so that it was always perpendicular to the velocity. Here an angular momentum vector is subject to a torque that is constant in magnitude but rotating. In the case of motion in a circle the velocity returned to its original magnitude and direction at the end of each revolution because the *average* force during a full revolution was zero. In the case of the rotating asymmetrical body the *average* torque during a full revolution is also zero, so the angular momentum must return to its original magnitude and direction. It is easy to see that these conditions are met if the angular momentum vector behaves as shown in Fig. 7.27d. The tail of the vector stays fixed and the head moves around a circle, so that the vector always lies on a cone.

It should be clear from symmetry considerations that the cone described by the angular momentum vector must have the fixed axis of rotation as its axis. This axis is shown by the dot-dash line B_1-B_2 in Fig. 7.27d. It follows that the angular momentum vector makes a constant angle with the angular velocity vector. The angle ϕ between them depends on the exact distribution of the masses that make up the rotating system. We shall not bother to calculate it for the special system that we have considered. The important fact is that the angular momentum vector and the velocity vector are *not* necessarily in the same direction. It must therefore be true that the quantity by which the angular velocity must be multiplied to give angular momentum is not, in general, a scalar (cf. Sec. 5.5). The fact that we have been able to use a scalar moment of inertia as this quantity without getting ourselves into trouble has resulted only from our choice of bodies that were rotating about their axes of symmetry.

More advanced treatments than we care to engage in here show that each component of the angular momentum generally depends on all three components of the angular velocity, i.e.,

$$\begin{aligned} L_x &= A\omega_x + B\omega_y + C\omega_z, \\ L_y &= B\omega_x + D\omega_y + E\omega_z, \\ L_z &= C\omega_x + E\omega_y + F\omega_z, \end{aligned} \tag{7.17-1}$$

where A, B, C, D, E, and F are constants for a given body that has its angular momentum directed in a particular direction. These six quantities taken together define what is known as a ***symmetrical tensor***, just as three components define a vector. We shall not need to concern ourselves with tensors, other than to note their existence.

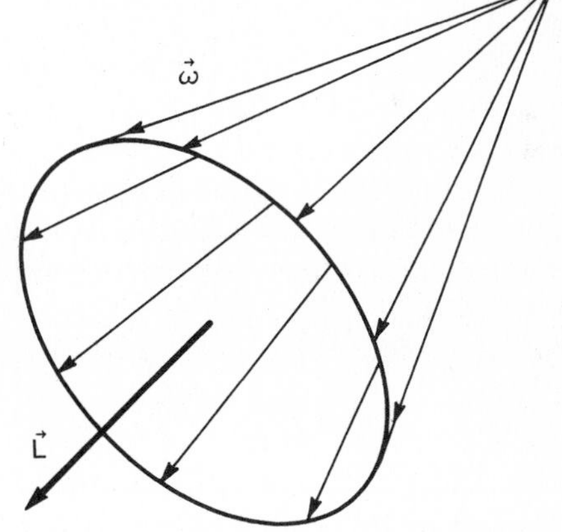

FIG. 7.28 With fixed angular momentum, the angular velocity may vary in direction.

It is interesting to consider what happens to a rigid body such as that of Fig. 7.27 when its rotation about a general axis is not constrained by bearings. Under these circumstances the angular momentum, being a conserved quantity, remains constant. Because the angle between the angular momentum vector and the angular velocity vector is fixed by the ***inertial tensor*** of Eq. (7.17-1), the axis of rotation will move on a cone, such as that shown in Fig. 7.28. The body is then said to ***precess*** about the angular momentum vector.

The system of Fig. 7.27 does have certain axes about which it could rotate with its angular momentum parallel to its angular velocity. These axes are shown in Fig. 7.29a, in which the masses m of Fig. 7.27 are shown as m-m in a side view of the system. An axis (A-A) through the two masses would require no forces at the bearings to hold the shaft in line because both masses are on this axis. Similarly, the axis C-C, which is in the plane of B_1, B_2, and the two masses and is perpendicular to A-A, is also perpendicular to the line m-m, so the centrifugal forces on the two masses balance each other if the system rotates about C-C. Finally, an axis through D, perpendicular to both A-A and C-C (and to the page) has the two masses on a common perpendicular to it, each at a distance $(\frac{1}{4}b^2 + r^2)^{1/2}$.

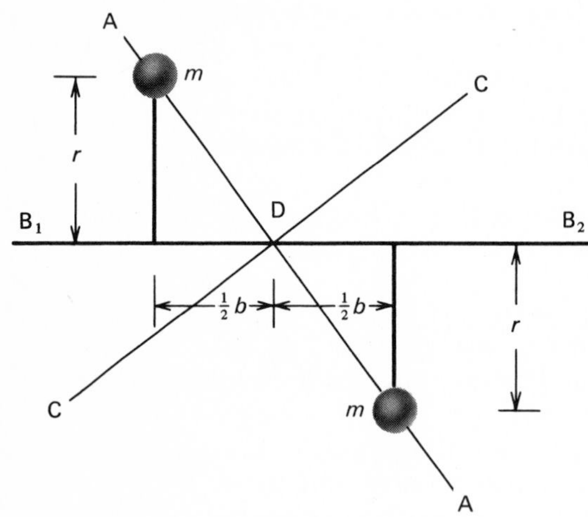

FIG. 7.29 Principal axes of an asymmetrical body.

It can be shown that a set of three such axes, for which all components of the inertial tensor of Eq. (7.17-1) except A, D, and F are zero, may be found for any rigid body, no matter how asymmetrical it may be. When the body rotates about any one of these three mutually perpendicular axes, its angular momentum is parallel to its angular velocity. These three axes are called the ***principal axes*** of the body. The three principal axes always pass through the center of mass of the body.

EXERCISES

7.17-1 Identify the principal axes of each of the following: (a) A meter stick. (b) A football. (c) The earth. (d) A baseball.

7.17-2 Take the three principal axes of the body shown in Figs. 7.27 and 7.29 as x, y, and z, x being along the line A-A of Fig. 7.29 and y along the line C-C. What are the constants in the inertial tensor for this system?

7.18 Summary

In this chapter we have considered the mechanics of rotation in some detail and have shown a very complete analogy between the mechanics of rotation about a fixed axis and the mechanics of motion along a line. We defined conventions for axial vectors and used them in relation to rotating systems. We discussed the important concept of moment of inertia and we expounded the law of conservation of angular momentum. This conservation law was applied in the rotational mechanics of planetary motions. We have also examined the centripetal force and the resulting centrifugal force that appear in a rotating system. Torque was defined and the conditions for rotational equilibrium were stated after which center of mass could be defined. Finally, we considered the applied torque required by a system that does not have symmetry about the axis of rotation and saw what would happen if this applied torque were no longer available.

PROBLEMS

7.1 If David's sling were 80 cm long and he whirled a stone whose mass was 0.10 kg about his head at 4.1 rev/sec, what would be the maximum speed with which the stone leaves the sling? What would be the angular velocity and the angular momentum just before the stone was released?

7.2 In the preceding problem what centripetal force was required just before David released the stone? What is the smallest amount of work David could have done in launching the stone?

7.3 Assume the height of the center of the circle in Prob. 7.1 to be 2.0 m, the height of Goliath's head to be 2.5 m, and the distance from David to Goliath to be 15 m. (a) What must be the angle between the plane of the circle and the horizontal if the stone is to strike Goliath's head? (b) With what speed will the stone strike Goliath?

7.4 An automobile whose mass is 1500 kg travels at 60 km/hr around a curve whose radius is 100 m. What centripetal force must be supplied to the car?

7.5 Curves in roads are often "banked," i.e., inclined to the horizontal, so that a component of the automobile's weight (rather than friction between the tires and the road) can support the car in a circular path. Consider a curve of radius R, intended for travel at a speed v.

(a) Show that the surface of the road must make an angle θ with the horizontal such that

$$\tan\theta = v^2/gR.$$

(b) Compute θ if $v = 60$ mi/hr and $R = 1320$ ft. (c) Suppose that a car rounds the curve of (b) at 30 mi/hr. What frictional force must act on the tires of the car to prevent it sliding to the low side of the road?

7.6 Consider a thin rigid rod of length L and mass m, rotating about a fixed axis that is perpendicular to it and that passes through its center. To find an approximate value for its moment of inertia, consider the rod to be divided into $2N$ sections, each of length $\Delta x = L/2N$.

(a) Show that the moment of inertia of the rod, I, is such that

$$\frac{mL^2}{4N^3}\sum_{j=0}^{j=N-1} j^2 < I < \frac{mL^2}{4N^3}\sum_{j=0}^{j=N-1} (j+1)^2,$$

where j is any integer: 0, 1, 2, ... $(N-1)$.

(b) Calculate upper and lower limits of I, taking $N = 10$.

(c) By approaching the limit, $\Delta x \to 0$, and integrating instead of summing, show that

$$I = mL^2/12.$$

7.7 Repeat Prob. 7.6 for rotation about an axis perpendicular to the rod and passing through one of its ends.

7.8 (a) By reasoning similar to that used in Prob. 7.6, show that the moment of inertia, I, of a uniform disk of mass m and radius R is such that

$$\frac{2mR^2}{N^4}\sum_{j=0}^{j=N-1} j^3 < I < \frac{2mR^2}{N^4}\sum_{j=0}^{j=N-1} (j+1)^3,$$

where N is the number of circular rings into which the disk has been divided, each disk having an inner radius jR/N and an outer radius $(j+1)R/N$, j being an integer.

(b) Show that the moment of inertia is $I = \frac{1}{2}mR^2$.

7.9 The speedometer of an automobile is driven by the driveshaft that connects the engine to the wheels. A particular car has its speedometer correctly calibrated for its original tires, which have an outer diameter of 28.0 in. If these tires are replaced by tires of 29.0 in. outside diameter, will the speedometer read high or low? By what percentage will its reading by incorrect?

7.10 The center of mass of a body may lie outside the body. (a) Consider the carpenter's square shown in the figure, which is made of a piece of steel that has uniform thickness and density. Locate the x- and y-coordinates of its center of mass. (b) Where is the center of mass of a uniform circular ring, of thickness t, inner radius R_1 and outer radius R_2?

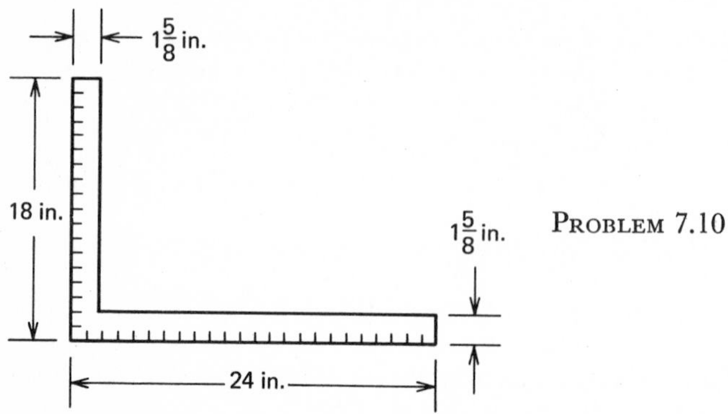

PROBLEM 7.10

7.11 Two cars, similar to those shown in Fig. 4.1, have masses m_1 and m_2. Each is moving with constant velocity, so that their respective displacements from an origin are

$$\vec{x}_1 = \vec{v}_1 t \quad \text{and} \quad \vec{x}_2 = \vec{x}_0 + \vec{v}_2 t,$$

where $\vec{x}_0$, $\vec{v}_1$, and $\vec{v}_2$ are constants and $v_1 > v_2$. (a) Find the location of the center of mass of the two cars as a function of time. (b) Show that the positions of the two cars, relative to the center of mass, are

$$x_1 = \frac{m_2(v_1 - v_2)t}{m_1 + m_2} - \frac{m_2 x_0}{m_1 + m_2}$$

and

$$x_2 = -\frac{m_1(v_1 - v_2)t}{m_1 + m_2} + \frac{m_1 x_0}{m_1 + m_2}.$$

(c) Show that the total momentum of the two cars in the center of mass system is zero. (d) Find the total kinetic energy of the two cars in the center of mass system, in terms of m_1, m_2, v_1, and v_2. (e) Suppose that the two cars collide perfectly inelastically. Show that the total kinetic energy, after the collision and measured in the center of mass system, is zero.

7.12 A uniform meter stick of mass m is initially at rest on a smooth horizontal table. It is acted upon for a short time by a horizontal force $\vec{F}$ that is perpendicular to the stick and that acts at a distance D from the center of the stick. This situation is exactly equivalent to one in which three forces, $\vec{F}$, $\vec{F}_1$, and $\vec{F}_2$ act on the meter stick, $\vec{F}_1$ being parallel to $\vec{F}$ and acting through the center of mass and $\vec{F}_2$ $(= -\vec{F}_1)$ also acting through the center of mass.

(a) Show that the force $\vec{F}_1$ will lead to a change in the linear momentum of the meter stick but to no rotation, while the combination of $\vec{F}$ and $\vec{F}_2$ will lead to a change in angular momentum but to no change in linear momentum.

(b) Show that $m\, d\vec{V}/dt$, where $\vec{V}$ is the velocity of the center of mass, is equal to $\vec{F}$.

(c) Show that $I\, d\omega/dt$, where I is the moment of inertia of the meter stick for rotation about a vertical axis through the center of mass and ω is the angular velocity of rotation about this axis, has a magnitude DF.

(d) Taking the length of the meter stick as 100 cm, $m = 100$ gm, $I = 8.35 \times 10^4$ gm cm^2, $D = 25.0$ cm, and $F = 2.00 \times 10^3$ dyne, compute the position of the center of mass and of each end of the meter stick at intervals of 0.100 sec from the time that the force is applied until 1.000 sec later. Plot these three positions on a single sheet.

7.13 (To be done after Prob. 7.12 has been completed.) A cylinder, of radius R, mass m, and moment of inertia I about its own axis, rolls without slipping on an inclined plane that makes an angle α with the horizontal. (a) What forces act on the cylinder? (b) If the cylinder starts from rest, find its kinetic energy when the speed of its center of mass has reached the value V. (c) Show that the acceleration of the center of mass is

$$a = \frac{g \sin \alpha}{1 + I/mR^2}.$$

(d) A solid cylinder and a cylindrical ring are made of identical material and have the same outer diameter. Both are started from rest on the inclined plane. Which will travel a given distance along the plane in the shorter time?

7.14 (a) Show that the change in angular momentum of the system of Fig. 7.27 as the system moves from the position shown in (a) to that shown in (c) is

$$\Delta L \approx L \sin \beta\, \Delta\theta,$$

where β is the angle between the angular momentum vector and the fixed axis of rotation.

(b) By passing to the limit $\Delta\theta \to 0$, show that

$$dL/dt = L\omega \sin \beta = m\omega^2 rb.$$

(c) Setting $L_z = 2mr^2\omega$, show that

$$\tan \beta = b/2r,$$

and hence that the angular momentum is along the axis of rotation if $b = 0$.

7.15 A figure skater is initially in the high-speed spin shown in Fig. 7.17b. He decreases his angular velocity by extending one arm only, instead of two arms as shown in Fig. 7.17a. Show that he must incline his body from the vertical so that his weight and the reaction of the ice to his skates supply a torque.

REFERENCES

7A Francis L. Friedman, *Velocity in Circular and Simple Harmonic Motion* and *Velocity and Acceleration in Circular Motion*, film loops produced by Educational Services, Inc. (Nos. 80-252 and 80-254, The Ealing Corp., Cambridge, Mass.)

7B J. N. Patterson Hume and Donald G. Ivey, *Frames of Reference*, a film produced by Educational Services, Inc. (No. 0307, Modern Learning Aids.) This filmed demonstration lecture has a section dealing with rotating coordinate systems.

7C AAPT College Physics Series, *Uniform Circular Motion*, McGraw-Hill, New York. A good animated film on centripetal force.

7D Aaron Lemonick, *Angular Momentum, A Vector Quantity*, a film produced by Educational Services, Inc. (No. 0451, Modern Learning Aids.) A clear demonstration that angular momentum is a vector quantity.

7E Franklin Miller, *Inertial Forces—Centripetal Acceleration.* An interesting $3\frac{1}{4}$-min film loop. (No. 80-214, The Ealing Corp., Cambridge, Mass.) The subject is illustrated by amusement park devices.

8 Special Relativity

8.1 *The Search for an Absolute Reference Frame*

Throughout our discussion of mechanics we have seen that the phenomena with which we deal can be described in any one of a number of frames of reference. For particular motions, one frame of reference may allow a simpler treatment than another, e.g., a projectile with both horizontal and vertical components of velocity moves in a vertical line in a reference frame that is moving horizontally with the same velocity as the projectile. We have also found that momentum is conserved and that Newton's laws of motion hold in any inertial frame and that every frame of reference that is moving at a uniform velocity relative to an inertial frame is itself an inertial frame. We sometimes state this by saying that the laws of Newtonian mechanics are invariant under the Newtonian relativity, i.e., that exactly the same laws hold when we use the Newtonian velocity transformation of Eq. (5.4-3) to translate our description from one inertial frame to another.

If all inertial frames are equivalent, is there any one of the infinite possible number of such frames that is better than another? By a "better" here, we mean a frame in which the physics is simpler. We know that the earth is revolving about the sun at about 3×10^4 m/sec, that the sun is moving relative to the other stars of the Milky Way galaxy, and that this entire galaxy is in motion relative to other galaxies. Would a reference frame attached to the center of the sun be better than one attached to the center of the earth? Would a still simpler description be possible if a frame were stationary with respect to the average position of all the stars?

If a preferred frame of reference does exist, it would be important to measure the velocity of the earth relative to it, for we could then transform our descriptions of phenomena to that reference frame in which physics became particularly simple. Because of this possibility, many physicists during the nineteenth century considered ways in which the velocity of a laboratory relative to "absolute space" could be determined.

8.2 *The Michelson–Morley Experiment*

We have paid special attention to measurements of the speed of light. One may ask whether there is any particular frame with respect to which this speed should be measured. During much of the nineteenth century, it was considered that light moved with a fixed speed c through a hypothetical medium called the "ether" (sometimes spelled "aether") which filled all space and which was presumably at rest with respect to the primary, or preferred, inertial frame. Granted this assumption, Newtonian relativity would predict that the measured speed should be $c + u$ if we are moving with a velocity $\vec{u}$ with respect to the ether in a direction opposite to the direction in which the light travels, and $c - u$ if $\vec{u}$ is in the same direction as that of the light. Any direct test of this prediction would require a measurement of as yet unattainable precision. The greatest speed with which we can move a bulky piece of apparatus is that of the earth in its revolution about the sun. As this is about 3×10^4 m/sec, the predicted fractional change in the speed of light would be only about $3 \times 10^4/3 \times 10^8$, or 0.01 percent. The problem is further complicated by the fact that all measurements of the speed of light are based on a "round trip" (cf. Sec. 3.5). As we found in Sec. 5.7, the effect of the Newtonian velocity transformation over a round trip leads to a fractional change of the order of u^2/v^2, where u is the speed of the observer's frame relative to some other inertial frame and v is the speed being observed. If we set $u = 3 \times 10^4$ m/sec and $v = c = 3 \times 10^8$ m/sec, we find that the fractional change that we would expect to result from our motion through the ether is about $(10^4/10^8)^2$, or one part in 10^8! This is far beyond the present limits of detectability.

One way out of this difficulty was developed by A. A. Michelson and E. W. Morley (1838–1923). Instead of trying to make two highly precise determinations of the speed of light, they developed a piece of equipment that measures directly the difference in the time taken by two light beams, travelling at right angles to each other, to make round trips over equal distances.

In discussing the Michelson–Morley experiment, we can make direct use of the results obtained for round trip aircraft flights in Sec. 5.7. We merely replace the air through which the plane flies by the ether in which the speed of light is c and consider that this space is drifting by us with a velocity $-\vec{u}$, i.e., that there is an "ether wind" passing us with a velocity equal in magnitude and opposite in direction to our velocity $\vec{u}$ through the ether. The entire apparatus of Michelson and Morley could be rotated about a vertical axis; the direction of this axis changed as the earth rotated. Even if we do not know in what direction we are moving, we can be sure that some orientation of the apparatus will be such that one of the two light beams will be moving along a line parallel to the ether wind and the other perpendicular to it. Under these circumstances we can use Eqs. (5.7-1) and (5.7-3) to predict the times of travel over a distance L and back:

$$t_{\parallel} = \frac{2L}{c} \cdot \frac{1}{1 - u^2/c^2} \tag{8.2-1}$$

and

$$t_{\perp} = \frac{2L}{c} \frac{1}{(1 - u^2/c^2)^{1/2}} \tag{8.2-2}$$

where $t_{\parallel}$ is the time for the beam travelling parallel to the ether wind and $t_{\perp}$

that for the beam at right angles to the ether wind. The difference of the two times is

$$t_{\parallel} - t_{\perp} = \frac{2L}{c}\left[\frac{1}{1 - u^2/c^2} - \frac{1}{(1 - u^2/c^2)^{1/2}}\right].$$

We can simplify this somewhat formidable expression by the use of the binomial theorem (Appendix H) to obtain

$$t_{\parallel} - t_{\perp} \approx \frac{2L}{c}\,[1 + u^2/c^2 - 1 - \tfrac{1}{2}u^2/c^2]$$

$$\approx Lu^2/c^3.$$

Again using $u/c = 10^{-4}$ and taking L as equal to 2 m, we find a predicted difference of about 10^{-16} second. The original apparatus was such that differences of as little as 2×10^{-17} second could be detected, so this experiment promised to show the effect of our motion through the ether. Much to the surprise of everyone, no difference in time that exceeded the experimental uncertainties was found!

8.3 Einstein's Assumptions

Mechanical experiments could not lead to a decision as to what the primary inertial frame might be, and now it turned out that even an ingenious optical experiment was equally powerless. Various attempts to explain the phenomena were made, particularly by H. A. Lorentz (1853–1928) and by G. F. Fitzgerald (1851–1901). The two physicists arrived independently at the same answer, which involved the assumption that the apparatus was distorted by its motion through the ether in just such a way as to cancel the expected effect. It appeared that one of the properties of the ether was an ability to conceal its own existence. We shall not discuss the details of the Lorentz–Fitzgerald treatment here, because they became unimportant after 1905, when the genius of Albert Einstein (1879–1949) furnished new insight into the problem.

Starting from the fact that all the physical phenomena with which we are acquainted depend on relative motion, Einstein asked what the consequences would be if the universe were so constituted that no absolute motion could be detected, i.e., if all possible reference frames moving at uniform velocity relative to each other were equally satisfactory for the statement of physical laws. If this is assumed, there is no possibility of identifying a primary inertial system. In particular, the speed of light cannot be affected by the motion of the observer. Not only will the same physical laws (such as conservation of momentum) hold in all inertial systems, but the same speed of light will be found by all observers who are in uniform relative motion.

Notice clearly that the speed of light, according to this Einstein assumption, has a unique relation to inertial systems which it shares with no other experimentally measurable speed. In the collision experiment of Figs. 4.3 and 4.4, we found that car B approached the collision with a speed of 0.05 m/sec, striking car A, which was initially at rest. After collision, car A moved off with a speed of 0.05 m/sec, while car B remained behind at rest. If the cars each had a mass of one kilogram, the momentum before collision was 0.05 kg-m/sec. Another observer, whom we will imagine to have been riding alongside car B before collision and who continued to move at the same velocity, says that before collision car B was at rest and car A had a momentum of 0.05 kg-m/sec, all of which it imparted to car B during the collision; after collision, he says car A was at rest. Thus, while the reader and the other observer will disagree about the before and after speeds of the cars, they will agree that *no momentum was lost during the collision.*

The Einstein assumption says further, however, that if the reader and the observer had also measured the speed of light during the experiment, they would have found the same speed. Thus, *while the speed of light will be the same, as measured by two such observers, all other speeds will be different.*

The balance of this chapter deals with the consequences of these Einstein assumptions. The reader will anticipate, of course, that we are dealing with good contemporary physics and that the results expressed are in the best modern scientific tradition. All of the results are grouped under the rubric of ***special relativity.*** It is special because it is restricted to inertial frames of reference—that is, to those frames of reference which move past one another with uniform or constant velocities.

To find the consequences of the Einstein assumptions, suppose that two physicists, O and O′, decide to measure the speed of light in each of two reference frames that are in uniform relative motion. One (O) has a laboratory fixed to the earth; the other (O′) has his laboratory on a rapidly moving train, which has a velocity $\vec{u}$ with respect to O. They have interchanged the clocks and the measuring rods that they use and have compared them, so that they agree that all the rods used are identical, as are all the clocks. They also can communicate results and descriptions of their experiments by radio. We shall consider in the next two sections what results they might obtain if the assumption about the speed of light is correct, but for our purpose neither O nor O′ has heard of the assumption.

8.4 Time Dilation

Suppose that both physicists measure the time taken for light to make a round trip over a path perpendicular to the velocity $\vec{u}$. Then the paths, each as seen in the reference frame of the person doing the experiment, will be those shown as AB and A′B′ in Fig. 8.1.

When O does his experiment, he measures the time t taken for a round trip and uses it to compute the speed of light, $c = 2L/t$. According to the Einstein assumption, the speed will be the same for O′, so he also finds a time equal to $2L'/c$. When he communicates to O his measurements of length and time, the latter cannot believe that a mistake has not been made. He has concluded from his measurements that the speed of light has the value c in his frame of reference. He also knows that the path followed by the light in the O′ experiment, as viewed in the O frame, is that shown in Fig. 8.2. He expects the light to travel

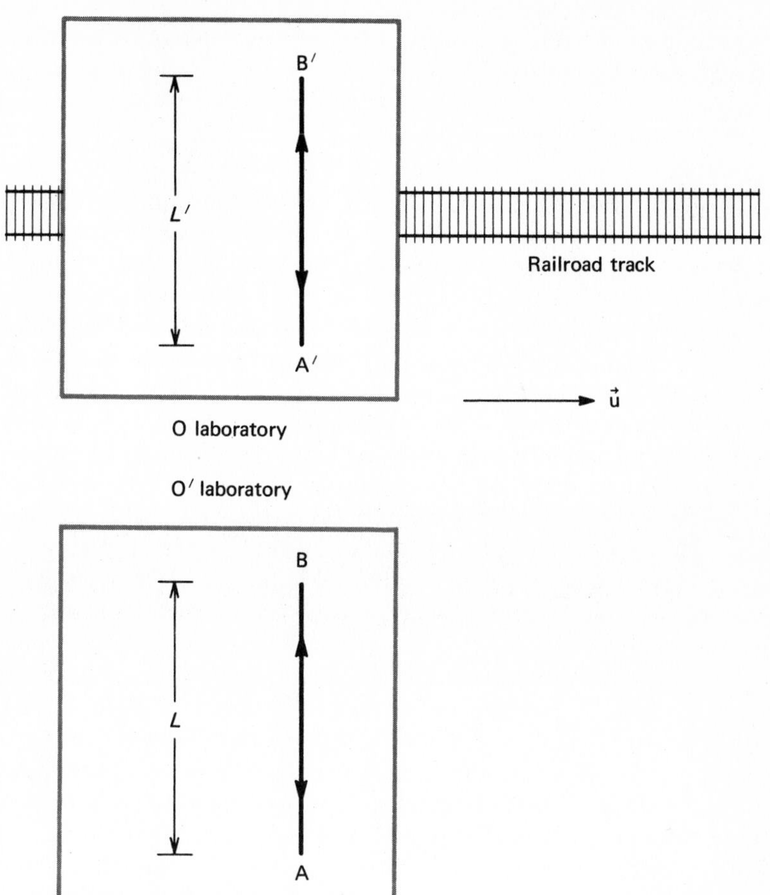

FIG. 8.1 Measurement of the speed of light by two observers.

FIG. 8.2 The first O′ experiment as seen by O.

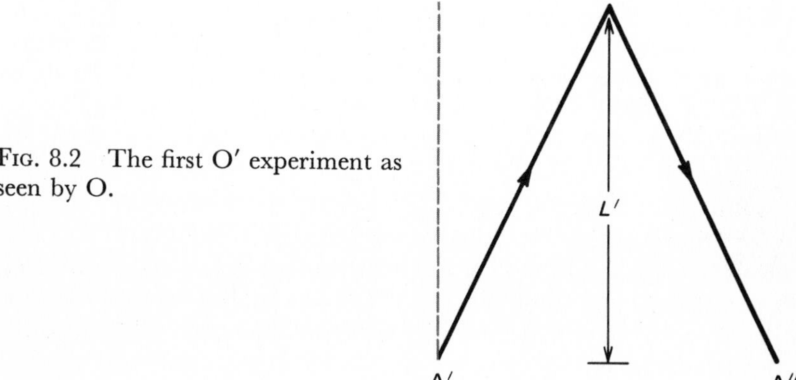

with speed c over this path, and therefore believes that O′ should have found the time as given by Eq. (8.2-2),

$$t=\frac{2L}{c}\cdot\frac{1}{(1-u^2/c^2)^{1/2}},$$

a time longer than O′ reported. He asks for a repetition of the message from O′; when he gets the same message as was received before he asks O′ to repeat the experiment; the earlier result is confirmed.

When he is finally convinced that both his own determination of c and the time found by O′ are the results of honest and careful experiments, he tries to decide what has caused the discrepancy. He finally realizes that O′ would have obtained a time shorter than that expected if the clocks used by O′ were *running slow.** In fact, if they were running just slowly enough so that any time interval $\Delta t'$ measured by O′ is, in terms of Δt, the interval as measured by O,

$$\Delta t' = \Delta t(1-u^2/c^2)^{1/2} \tag{8.4-1}$$

then

$$\frac{2L}{c}=\frac{2L}{c}\cdot\frac{1}{(1-u^2/c^2)^{1/2}}\cdot(1-u^2/c^2)^{1/2}$$

and the disagreement is explained.

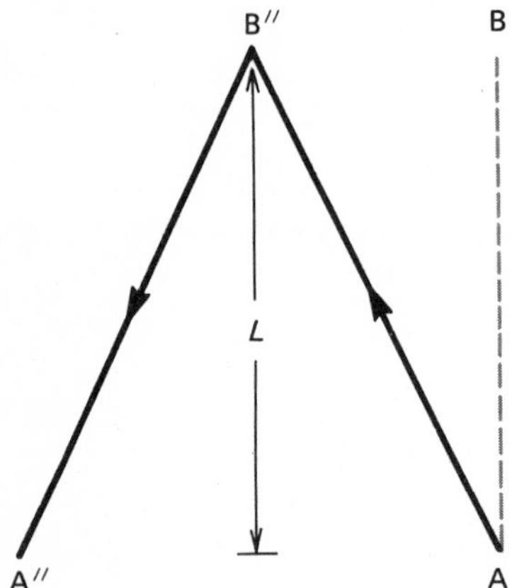

FIG. 8.3 The first O experiment as seen by O′.

If they stopped at this point, O and O′ might conclude that something had gone wrong with all the clocks used by O′, changing their periods in exactly the same way. In the meantime, however, O′ has been puzzling over the fact that O reported a time $t=2L/c$ as a result of his measurement. The path of the light in the O experiment, as seen in the O′ frame is that shown in Fig. 8.3. The distance traveled is greater than L, and measurements made by O′ indicate

* Alternatively, he might have guessed that the measuring rods used by O′ had expanded, so that the distance measured by O′ was less than the length L that O′ reported. We shall see later that this assumption would not be consistent with a later experiment, hence we shall not investigate it at this time.

to him that the speed of light in his reference frame is c. Hence he expected that O would report a longer time than he did. By the same reasoning as was used by O, O′ becomes convinced that the clocks used by O are running slow in the ratio $(1-u^2/c^2)^{1/2}$.

The two physicists now find themselves in a peculiar position. *Each says that the other's clocks are running slow.* How can both be right? We can reconcile the two statements only if we suppose that the rate at which a clock is *observed* to run depends on the speed with which the clock is moving with respect to the observer. This seems contrary to our experience until we realize that we have had few, if any, opportunities to read clocks that are moving past us at speeds sufficiently great so that u^2/c^2 is big enough to cause 1 and $(1-u^2/c^2)^{1/2}$ to differ by as much as the uncertainty in our observations. We could test the conclusion only if we observe very fast-moving clocks—as we shall see later, observations of this sort have been made and are found to confirm the prediction.

The effect predicted by Eq. (8.4-1) is known as the ***Einstein time dilation.*** We cannot explain it—we can only say that it is a consequence of our acceptance of the Einstein postulates and of the comparison of the results of imaginary experiments.* Until the predictions made by the use of Eq. (8.4-1) have been checked by actual experiments, we must hold our complete acceptance of it in abeyance. We shall, however, tentatively accept the behavior of clocks that the equation implied, so that we can investigate further the consequences of the Einstein assumptions.

8.5 The Lorentz Contraction

Having reached the interesting conclusion about clocks in motion relative to an observer, O and O′ decide on another pair of experiments. They make new measurements of the time taken for light to complete a round trip over a measured path, but this time they choose a path parallel to the velocity $\vec{u}$, as shown in Fig. 8.4. Again O finds a speed c and O′ reports a time t' for a path of length L', where $t' = 2L'/c$.

The time that O would have expected O′ to find, had he not learned about the slowness of the O′ clocks, would have been that corresponding to the distance $2L'/(1-u^2/c^2)$ given by Eq. (8.2-1):

$$\frac{2L'}{c}\,\frac{1}{1-u^2/c^2}.$$

Knowing about the behavior of the clocks, he anticipates that O′ will have found a time less than this, so he expected that the time reported would be

$$t' = \frac{2L'}{c}\cdot\frac{1}{1-u^2/c^2}\cdot(1-u^2/c^2)^{1/2} = \frac{2L'}{c}\cdot\frac{1}{(1-u^2/c^2)^{1/2}}.$$

* Such imaginary, or thought, experiments are often of great value in physical reasoning. They are commonly called *gedanken* experiments, after the German word for thought.

Apparently something else has now changed—the time found by O′ is again less than that expected by O! It seems impossible to blame any further difference on the clocks, as one cannot expect the rate of a clock that is stationary in a given reference frame to depend on the direction in which the light travels.

Having learned to accept the unexpected, O quickly reaches the conclusion that the measuring rods used by O′ are shorter than his rods by a factor

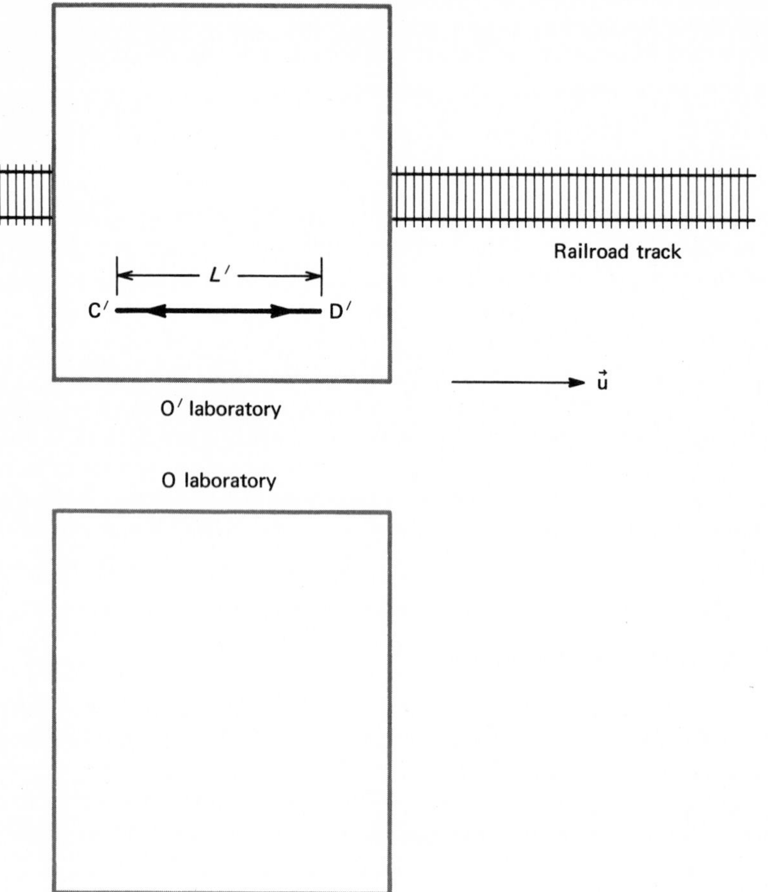

FIG. 8.4 The second speed of light experiment.

$(1 - u^2/c^2)^{1/2}$. If the rods are short, O′ will measure L' as *longer* than it would be measured by O, in the ratio $1/(1 - u^2/c^2)^{1/2}$. If O corrects the value of L′, he finds that the t' that he expects is exactly $2L'/c$, as reported by O′.

We may now consider the second O experiment as seen by O′. If he corrects for the slowness of the clocks used by O and assumes that the rods used by O are shorter than his own rods, he finds that the time reported by O agrees precisely with what he would predict on the basis of his measured value of c.

As a result of this second pair of experiments, each of the two physicists decides that the other's rods are shorter than his, in such a way that a rod of length ΔL, as measured when it is at rest in his own system, will have a length

$$\Delta L_u = \Delta L(1 - u^2/c^2)^{1/2} \tag{9.5-1}$$

when it is moving past him with a velocity $\vec{u}$, parallel to the length of the rod. This shortening of measuring rods is known as the ***Lorentz contraction.***

Notice that rods are shortened only in the direction of motion. Had they shortened when they were at right angles to this direction, the lengths measured in the first pair of experiments would not have agreed, unless a different time dilation had been assumed. The question of what happens to a rod that is neither parallel nor perpendicular to the direction of motion is left as an exercise.

An observer who is at rest with respect to an object he is measuring, or with respect to a clock he is reading, is called a ***proper observer.*** The terminology is slightly unfortunate because it may imply that the ***proper length*** or the ***proper time interval*** measured by such an observer is a "true" value, in a sense in which a measurement by another observer is not. Actually, one cannot say that either of two observers, in motion relative to each other, is right and that the other is wrong. Our whole concept of length, as was pointed out in Chapter 2, is an operational one. We can speak of the length of an object only as a result of the operation of successively applying measuring rods and a count of the number of applications. The term "length" has no meaning except in terms of this operation. We therefore have no justification for speaking of the "real" or "true" length of an object as something characteristic of the object and independent of the motion of the observer relative to the object. A similar remark applies to any time interval.

8.6 The Lorentz Transformation

Although direct evidence of the contraction of measuring rods and the slowing of clocks, when they are in motion relative to an observer, is not easy to obtain, certain consequences of the Einstein time dilation and the Lorentz contraction can be verified. As a step toward this verification, we may consider the effects of these two relations on the problem of comparing observations made in two different reference frames. Suppose that the observer O′ is moving with a velocity $\vec{u}$ relative to the observer, O, the direction of motion being along the x-axis of the O frame. Suppose further that O′ has set up a coordinate frame with an x'-axis in the same direction as the x-axis of O and that both observers have set their clocks to read zero at the instant that the origins of their coordinate frames coincide, i.e., that $x = x' = 0$ when $t = t' = 0$. Note that we are priming the symbols that stand for measurements made by O′ in his own frame and leaving unprimed the symbols that represent measurements made by O in his own frame.

Suppose that O observes an event that happens at point x, y, z and at time t, and that O′ observes the same event at point x', y', z' relative to his own origin and at time t' as measured by his own clocks. If we adopt the "common sense" view that clocks and measuring rods are unaffected by motion relative to the observer, it is obvious from Fig. 8.5 that the two observations are connected by a simple set of relations:

$$\begin{aligned} x' &= x - ut, \\ y' &= y, \\ z' &= z, \\ t' &= t. \end{aligned} \tag{8.6-1}$$

This set of equations constitute the ***Galilean transformations***. They allow us to determine the place and time of an event in one reference frame if the event has been located in a different frame, moving with respect to the first. They are based on the implicit assumption of the classical mechanics developed by Galileo and Newton.

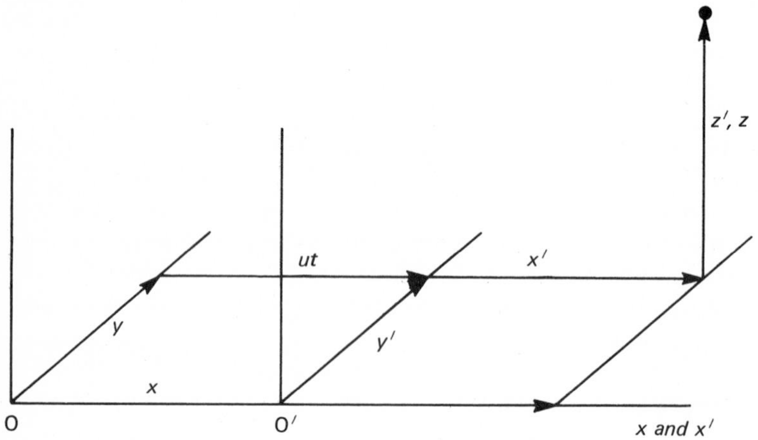

FIG. 8.5 Description of an event in two reference frames.

If, on the other hand, we accept the existence of the Einstein time dilation and of the Lorentz contraction to be consistent with the Einstein assumptions, we cannot arrive so quickly at appropriate transformations. Observer O has measured the component x of the displacement of the event from his origin. He also knows that the origin of the primed system was at the position $x = ut$ at the time of the event relative to his own origin, since he has measured the velocity of O′. He may ask, "What is the component x' of the displacement of the event from the origin of the primed system as measured by O′, i.e., what value of x' will O′ report to me if I ask him to locate the event?" At this point, he realizes that O′ must measure x' by laying rods along a line parallel to $\vec{u}$ and that he has already found that the rods used by O′ in this position are shortened. Hence he will see that x' will be greater as measured by O′, than it would be if he measures it, in the ratio $1/(1 - u^2/c^2)^{1/2}$. He must therefore reduce in this ratio the value reported by O′ before he can expect the first of Eqs. (8.6-1) to hold. He therefore rewrites that equation as

$$x'(1 - u^2/c^2)^{1/2} = x - ut,$$

so that

$$x' = \frac{x - ut}{(1 - u^2/c^2)^{1/2}}. \tag{8.6-2}$$

Similarly, O′ might have located the event at x', y', z', t' and might ask where O would have located it. He now says that the origin of the O reference frame was at $-ut'$ when the event occurred. (Note that he uses the time t' as measured by his own clocks.) When he asks what the value of x, as measured by O, may be, he recognizes that he has found that the rods used by O are short, hence he must reduce x in the ratio of $(1 - u^2/c^2)^{1/2}$. He therefore writes the equation

$$x(1 - u^2/c^2)^{1/2} = x' + ut',$$

so that he predicts that

$$x = \frac{x' + ut'}{(1 - u^2/c^2)^{1/2}}. \tag{8.6-3}$$

Equations (8.6-2) and (8.6-3) have been derived using the Lorentz contraction alone; they imply the Einstein time dilation only by using two times, t and t', at which the same event occurs in the two frames of reference. Actually, however, the contraction of measuring rods and the slowing of clocks are so intimately related that the latter effect can be found from these two equations. If the value of x' given by Eq. (8.6-2) is substituted into Eq. (8.6-3), a little algebraic manipulation yields a relation between t', t and x:

$$t' = \frac{t - ux/c^2}{(1 - u^2/c^2)^{1/2}}. \tag{8.6-4}$$

Similarly, substitution of the value of x from Eq. (8.6-3) into Eq. (8.6-2) shows that

$$t = \frac{t' + ux'/c^2}{(1 - u^2/c^2)^{1/2}}. \tag{8.6-5}$$

To show that the two equations just derived are consistent with the expression for time dilation, let us suppose that two events take place at the origin of the unprimed reference frame, i.e., at $x = 0$, that the first takes place at $t_1 = 0$, and that the second takes place at time t_2, as measured by O. The time interval between the two events, again as measured by O, is then t_2. If we use Eq. (8.6-4) to find the times at which O′ observes the two events, we find $t'_1 = 0$ and

$$t'_2 = \frac{t_2}{(1 - u^2/c^2)^{1/2}}.$$

Thus O′ observes a time interval longer than that observed by O, in the ratio of $(1 - u^2/c^2)^{1/2}$. He finds, in other words, that the clocks used by O, moving past him at a speed u, are running slow.

We can add two other equations to the four found for x', x, t', and t. Because rods are shortened only when they move along their own length, the Galilean transformations $y = y'$ and $z = z'$ still hold. The resulting set of equations is known as the ***Lorentz transformation.*** The entire set is collected below for convenience.

$$x' = \frac{x - ut}{(1 - u^2/c^2)^{1/2}} \qquad x = \frac{x' + ut'}{(1 - u^2/c^2)^{1/2}}$$

$$y' = y \tag{8.6-6}$$

$$z' = z$$

$$t' = \frac{t - ux/c^2}{(1 - u^2/c^2)^{1/2}} \qquad t = \frac{t' + ux'/c^2}{(1 - u^2/c^2)^{1/2}}$$

When using the Lorentz transformation in this form, one must remember that $\vec{u}$ is the velocity of the primed system relative to the unprimed system and that $-\vec{u}$ is the velocity of the unprimed system relative to the primed system. One must also remember that the direction of the x- and x'-axes is taken parallel to that of $\vec{u}$.

Illustrative Example

To study some of the consequences of the theory of special relativity, we shall consider the famous twin paradox. Suppose that one of two twins, at age exactly 20, goes off in a rocket that accelerates quickly to a speed that is $0.50c$ and travels in a straight line at that speed. He covers a distance of 1.50×10^{16} m (as measured by the stay-at-home twin), after which he accelerates quickly to a velocity just equal in magnitude and opposite in direction to his earlier velocity, and so returns to earth over the same path.

According to the measurements made by the twin who stayed on earth, the time taken for the round trip is

$$t = \frac{3.00 \times 10^{16}\text{ m}}{1.50 \times 10^{8}\text{ m/sec}} = 2.00 \times 10^{8}\text{ sec} \times \frac{\text{yr}}{3.16 \times 10^{7}\text{ sec}} = 6.33\text{ yr.}$$

If the earth-bound twin receives signals from any clock carried by his traveling brother, he will find that clock running slow. This applies to mechanical clocks and, equally to biological clocks, such as pulse beats or breathing. Applying Eq. (8.4-1), we find that the time interval shown by any such clock on the rocket is

$$t' = 6.33\text{ yr}\,[1 - (\tfrac{1}{2})^2]^{1/2} = 5.48\text{ yr.}$$

It follows that the traveling twin will be 25.5 years old when he returns to earth, while his brother will be 26.3 years old!

This result may seem surprising, but there is every reason to believe it to be correct. As a check on our reasoning, we may use Eq. (8.6-4) to find at what time (T') the traveling twin reaches the turn-around point of his trip. Letting T be the time as measured by his brother, we have

$$T' = \frac{T - (\frac{1}{2}c)(x)/c^2}{[1 - (\frac{1}{2})^2]^{1/2}} = \frac{T - \frac{1}{2}x/c}{0.866},$$

where x is the extreme distance of travel as measured by the twin on earth. Substituting 1.00×10^8 sec for T and 1.50×10^{16} m for x, we find $T' = 8.66 \times 10^7$ sec $=$ 2.75 yr, which is half of t' to the accuracy of the three significant figure data. The rocket-borne twin has aged only 2.75 years on the outward trip, while his brother has aged 3.16 years.

Part of the apparent paradox is resolved if we ask how far the traveling twin has traveled, as measured by him. Because of the Lorentz contraction of the earth-bound twin's measuring rods, he has the distance as greater than would be measured from the rocket. Hence we may apply Eq. (8.5-1) to find

$$\begin{aligned} x' &= x(1 - u^2/c^2)^{1/2} = (1.50 \times 10^{16}\ \text{m})(0.866) \\ &= 1.30 \times 10^{16}\ \text{m}. \end{aligned}$$

Since he travels this distance in a time $T' = 8.66 \times 10^7$ sec, his speed is 1.30×10^{16} m/ 8.66×10^7 sec $= 1.50 \times 10^8$ m/sec $= \frac{1}{2}c$. His speed relative to his brother is indeed the same, as measured by either twin.

8.7 *Simultaneity*

It is an interesting consequence of the Lorentz transformations that two events which occur simultaneously in one reference frame are not necessarily simultaneous in a second reference frame that is in motion relative to the first. To quote an example put forward by Einstein, suppose that two lightning strokes hit the opposite ends of a moving train at the same instant, as observed by some one on the train. If we imagine a coordinate system with its origin attached to the center of the train and its x-axis along the direction of motion, we can say that the two strokes hit at the same time, t, but at different locations, $x_1 = \frac{1}{2}L$ and $x_2 = -\frac{1}{2}L$, where L is the length of the train. If we use the Lorentz transformation for t' to determine the times as observed by an observer on the ground, who is moving with a velocity $-\vec{u}$ with respect to the train, we find that the stroke that hit the front of the train struck at time

$$t'_1 = \frac{t + \frac{1}{2}uL/c^2}{(1 - u^2/c^2)^{1/2}},$$

while the stroke that hit the rear of the train struck at time

$$t'_2 = \frac{t - \frac{1}{2}uL/c^2}{(1 - u^2/c^2)^{1/2}}.$$

It is clear from these two expressions that the stroke at the rear of the train occurred earlier than the stroke at the front, the difference in time being

$$t'_1 - t'_2 = \frac{uL/c^2}{(1 - u^2/c^2)^{1/2}}.$$

EXERCISES

8.7-1 Show that the Lorentz contraction leads to a relative change of length of less than one percent unless the speed of the moving rod is greater than 14 percent of that of light. Hint: Expand $(1-u^2/c^2)^{1/2}$ by the use of the binomial expansion of Appendix H.

8.7-2 A rod has a length of 1.000 m when it is stationary with respect to the observer. Calculate the length as measured by an observer with respect to whom it is moving with a speed 0.20 c, the motion being along the direction of the rod. Repeat for 0.40c, 0.60c, 0.80c. 0.90c. Plot the observed length of the rod as a function of u/c.

8.7-3 A measuring rod is known to have a length L as measured by an observer O who is at rest relative to the rod. One end of the rod is at $x=0$ and the other at $x=L$. Suppose that another observer, O′, measures the length of the rod while it is moving past him with a velocity $\vec{u}$, in the direction of the length of the rod. To accomplish this he must observe the two ends of the rod simultaneously. For simplicity, let the time at which he makes his observations be $t'=0$. Show that the length L' found by O′ is

$$L' = L(1-u^2/c^2)^{1/2},$$

in agreement with the expression for the Lorentz contraction.

8.7-4 (To be done after Ex. 8.7-3 has been completed.) A rod is fastened rigidly in a reference frame, with its ends at $x_1=a, y_1=0$ and at $x_2=a, y_2=b$ $(z_1=z_2=0)$. If light signals from the two ends of the rod are observed simultaneously at $t=t'=0$ in a second reference frame, which has its x'-axis coincident with the x-axis of the first frame, the rod will not be perpendicular to the x'-axis. Show that the rod will make an angle ϕ with the y-direction such that

$$\tan\phi = -(u/cb)[(a^2+b^2)^{1/2}-a]/(1-u^2/c^2)^{1/2},$$

where u is the speed of the second frame relative to the first.

8.8 The Einstein Velocity Transformation

If one accepts the validity of the Lorentz transformations, he might expect that the simple Galilean rule for the addition of velocities, as it was developed in Sec. 5.4, might no longer hold. We can easily show that such is the case.

We shall first consider the one-dimensional case of a body moving with a velocity directed along the x- and x'-axes of two coordinate systems that coincided at $t=t'=0$. Let the primed coordinate system be moving with a velocity $\vec{u}$ with respect to the unprimed system and let the body under consideration be moving with a velocity $\vec{v}'$, relative to the primed system. At any instant t', the position of the body in the primed system will be

$$x' = a + v't',$$

where a is a constant. According to the Lorentz transformation, its position in the unprimed system will be

$$x = \frac{x'+ut'}{(1-u^2/c^2)^{1/2}} = \frac{a+(v'+u)t'}{(1-u^2/c^2)^{1/2}}.$$

To find the velocity in the unprimed system we need to express t' in terms of t, u, and v'. We write

$$t = \frac{t' + ux'/c^2}{(1 - u^2/c^2)^{1/2}} = \frac{(ua/c^2) + t'(1 + uv'/c^2)}{(1 - u^2/c^2)^{1/2}},$$

so that

$$t' = \frac{t(1 - u^2/c^2)^{1/2} - (ua/c^2)}{1 + uv'/c^2}.$$

Substituting this value of t' into the expression for x, we obtain

$$x = A + \frac{v' + u}{1 + uv'/c^2}\, t,$$

where A is dependent only on a, u, and v', not on time. The velocity in the unprimed system is, by inspection,

$$v = \frac{dx}{dt} = \frac{v' + u}{1 + uv'/c^2}, \qquad (8.8\text{-}1A)$$

which is the ***Einstein velocity transformation.***

We may solve Eq. (8.8-1A) for v' to obtain the transformation from the velocity in the unprimed system to that in the primed system:

$$v' = \frac{v - u}{1 - uv/c^2}. \qquad (8.8\text{-}1B)$$

Some immediate consequences of the velocity transformations are of particular interest. If we compare v with the speed predicted by the Galilean velocity transformation of Eq. (5.4-3), we find that the Einstein velocity transformation always gives a lower resultant speed than the Galilean, if $\vec{u}$ and $\vec{v}$ are in the same direction. To see this we merely divide both sides of Eq. (8.8-1A) by $v' + u$, the speed predicted by the classical equation. We then get as the ratio of speeds, $1/(1 + uv'/c^2)$. Since both $\vec{u}$ and $\vec{v}$ have the same sign, uv'/c^2 is intrinsically positive and the denominator of the fraction is greater than unity.

If both u and v' are much smaller than c, the quantity $1 + uv'/c^2$ is very nearly unity. The Galilean and Einstein transformations then give essentially the same result, as is necessary if the new transformation is to agree with the old one for low speeds. The Galilean transformation is perfectly adequate for most purposes —the Einstein transformation need be used only if either u or v' is an appreciable fraction of the speed of light.

An interesting case arises if we suppose that both u and v' are very nearly equal to c, and that the two have the same sign. Then $uv'/c^2 \approx c^2/c^2 = 1$, so that the speed v measured in the unprimed system is half that predicted by the Galilean transformation. The latter, moreover, is essentially $2c$, so the new transformation law predicts that the addition of two velocities, each equal to or less than c, can never lead to a velocity of magnitude greater than c. It appears that the speed of light plays a very critical role in the addition of velocities. This will be confirmed later, when we find that the speed of light represents an upper limit to the speed with which any material object may be moved, *relative to any observer.*

EXERCISES

8.8-1 We may test the consistency of Eqs. (8.8-1) with the Einstein assumption of the constancy of the speed of light by letting $v' = c$ and then finding the speed v as measured in the unprimed system. Show that v always equals c under these circumstances.

8.8-2 Suppose that a body is moving with a velocity of 1.50×10^8 m/sec toward the left in some coordinate frame and that an observer is moving to the right with a speed 1.00×10^8 m/sec in the same frame. What is the speed of the body relative to the observer?

8.8-3 We have restricted ourselves in Sec. 8.8 to motions along the x-axis, i.e., parallel to $\vec{u}$, the velocity of the primed system relative to the unprimed system. Suppose that $\vec{v}'$ is along the yz axis, i.e., is perpendicular to $\vec{u}$. Show that the velocity component v_y as observed in the unprimed system is

$$v_y = v_y'/(1 - u^2/c^2)^{1/2}.$$

Hint: Remember that rods perpendicular to $\vec{u}$ do not exhibit a Lorentz contraction, but that time dilation affects all velocity measurements.

8.8-4 It has been tacitly assumed throughout this chapter that there is only a single relative speed of two systems, i.e., that the velocity of a primed system with respect to an unprimed system is equal in magnitude and opposite in direction to that of the unprimed system with respect to the primed. The validity of this assumption may be tested by considering two systems each in motion relative to a third system. Suppose that O′ is moving with a velocity $\vec{u}$ relative to O and that O″ is moving with a velocity $\vec{U}$ relative to O. Find the velocity of O″ with respect to O′ and that of O′ with respect to O″. Do the two velocities agree with the assumption above?

8.9 The Dependence of Mass on Relative Motion

In our discussion of the effect of the Einstein assumption of the independence of the speed of light of the motion of the coordinate frame in which it is measured, we have found that measurements of the fundamental quantities of length and time are affected when the systems being studied are in motion relative to the observer. One may ask whether the third fundamental quantity, mass, is similarly affected.

We cannot answer this question by considering the comparison of masses on an equal arm balance, since both masses might be expected to change together. The use of a spring balance is also not possible because we have not yet seen how forces may be affected by relative motion. We shall therefore return to the definition of mass developed in Chapter 4, and compare masses by allowing them to collide and by measuring their velocities before and after impact.

Consider two observers, O and O′, and let O′ be moving with a velocity $\vec{u}$ relative to O. Each of these observers has one of two balls, which have been compared by means of collisions at low speeds and have been found to have identical masses m_0. The balls are thrown in the manner shown in Fig. 8.6. The first observer (O) throws his ball in the direction of motion of the second observer, with a velocity $\vec{u}$, as measured in his own coordinate system. This ball is thus at rest with respect to O′. The second observer (O′) throws his ball in the opposite direction with a velocity $-\vec{u}$ as measured in his own system, so that it collides head-on with the ball thrown by O. The ball thrown by O′ is obviously at rest in the system of O. Each observer thus observes a collision between a stationary ball and one moving with a speed u, as shown in the top

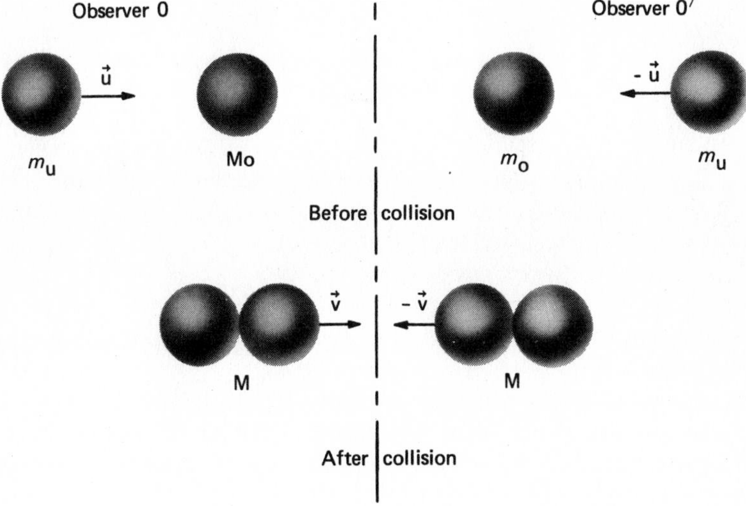

FIG. 8.6 Tolman relativistic collision.

diagrams of Fig. 8.6. Finally, suppose that the balls are of such a nature that their collision is perfectly inelastic, i.e., that they stick together and move as a unit after the collision.

According to the Einstein postulates (cf. Sec. 8.3), the two coordinate systems are equivalent, so both mass and momentum must be conserved in both systems. We may allow for the possibility of a change of mass with speed by writing m_0 for the mass of the ball when it is at rest (or moving very slowly) with respect to the observer and m_u for the mass of the ball when it has a speed u with respect to the observer. Considering first the observations made by O, we see that the combined mass M of the two balls after the collision is

$$M = m_0 + m_u. \tag{8.9-1}$$

Since momentum must be conserved, the balls after the collision must be moving with a velocity $\vec{v}$, which satisfies the relation

$$Mv = (m_0 + m_u)v = m_u u. \tag{8.9-2}$$

This last equation can be rewritten as

$$(m_0 + m_u)/m_u = m_0/m_u + 1 = u/v. \tag{8.9-3}$$

Because of the exact symmetry between the two systems, a consideration of the mass and momentum relations by O′ will lead to equations identical with Eqs. (8.9-1)–(8.9-3). We can now determine the ratio m_0/m_u from the fact that the velocity $-\vec{v}$ of the two particles together as observed by O′ must be related to the velocity $\vec{v}$ as observed by O, since the two observers are observing the same pair of particles. This relation, of course, is provided by the Einstein velocity transformation, Eq. (8.8-1B). Substituting $-v$ for v' in that equation, we find that

$$-v = \frac{v-u}{1-uv/c^2},$$

which can be rewritten

$$1 - uv/c^2 = u/v - 1,$$

where both sides of the equation have been multiplied by $-(1 - uv/c^2)/v$. For convenience, we multiply both the numerator and denominator of the fraction on the left by u, to obtain

$$1 - \frac{u^2 v}{c^2 u} = \frac{u}{v} - 1. \tag{8.9-4}$$

We now substitute the value of u/v from Eq. (8.9-3) to find that

$$1 - \frac{u^2}{c^2} \cdot \frac{m_u}{m_0 + m_u} = \frac{m_0 + m_u}{m_u} - 1 = \frac{m_0}{m_u}.$$

Finally, putting the terms of this equation over a common denominator, $(m_0 + m_u)m_u$, we obtain

$$m_0 m_u + m_u{}^2 - u^2 m_u{}^2/c^2 = m_0{}^2 + m_0 m_u,$$

so that

$$m_u{}^2 = \frac{m_0{}^2}{1 - u^2/c^2}$$

or

$$m_u = \frac{m_0}{(1 - u^2/c^2)^{1/2}}. \tag{8.9-5}$$

This important result, which was derived for a particular collision, can be shown to hold for any collision (cf. Ex. 8.9-4). It tells us that a body whose mass is m_0 when observed at rest has the mass m_u given by Eq. (8.9-5) when it is moving at a speed u with respect to the observer. The mass m_0 is known as the ***rest mass*** of the body, and the mass m_u is known as the ***observed mass***. The observed mass is always equal to or greater than the rest mass, since $\gamma = (1 - u^2/c^2)^{1/2}$ is always less than or equal to one.

We shall find later that not only will the observed mass of a particle vary during a collision, but that actually the rest mass m_0 may vary during this process (cf. also Exs. 8.9-3 and 8.9-4). It was in anticipation of this result that the footnote was added to our early discussion of mass in Sec. 4.3. In the derivation of Eq. (8.9-5), the law of the conservation of mass was used, so we must realize that *the total observed mass of any isolated system of particles remains constant,* even though the total rest mass changes and some of the particles gain observed mass while others lose observed mass. Consequently, the law of conservation of mass as stated in Sec. 4.7 is valid even when speeds comparable with that of light are involved, provided that we use *observed mass,* rather than rest masses. Unless we are dealing with particles moving at very high speeds, the observed and rest masses differ by negligible amounts. Therefore we do not need to make a distinction between the two in dealing with most physical or chemical processes.

The notion of momentum, however, remains unchanged in special relativity. We still say that the ***momentum*** of a body is the product of its observed mass by its velocity, and that Eqs. (4.5-1) and (6.1-2) and the succeeding equations maintain their validity, with the proviso that the observed mass of a given particle may now be different after the collision from what it was before. The law of conservation of momentum thus holds for all possible velocities of the particles of the isolated system.

EXERCISES

8.9-1 An electron is known to have a mass of 9.1×10^{-31} kg when it is at rest relative to the observer. Find its mass when it is moving at a speed $\frac{1}{2}c$ relative to the observer. At $0.8c$. At $0.9c$.

8.9-2 How fast must a body be moving relative to the laboratory in order that its mass be increased by one percent above the rest mass?

8.9-3 Two particles have rest masses of m_0 and $2m_0$. The first is moving with a velocity $2\vec{v}$ (directed to the right) and the second with a velocity $-\vec{v}$ (directed to the left) just before they collide head-on and perfectly inelastically. Will the combined mass be moving to the left, to the right, or be at rest after the collision?

8.9-4 Apply Eq. (8.9-5) to consider the head-on elastic collision of two masses that are identical when compared on an equal arm balance. Before the collision, one of the masses is moving with a speed v relative to the laboratory and the other is at rest; after the collision, the first is at rest and the second has a speed v. Show that both momentum and the combined mass of the two particles are conserved.

8.10 ***Forces in Special Relativity***

We are now in a position to consider what forces are necessary to accelerate a body according to special relativity theory. We have seen that momentum is conserved in any inertial reference frame; hence, the requirement that the force with which one body acts on another is to be equal and opposite to the force with which the other acts on it will be satisfied if we retain the definition of force established in Sec. 4.9, i.e., if we take the force as

$$\vec{f} = d\vec{p}/dt,$$

and define the momentum as

$$\vec{p} = m\vec{v}.$$

Here, of course, m is the observed mass, which depends on the speed v. We therefore have[1]

$$\vec{f} = \lim_{\Delta t \to 0} \frac{\Delta(m\vec{v})}{\Delta t}$$

$$= \lim_{\Delta t \to 0} \frac{(m + \Delta m)(\vec{v} + \Delta\vec{v}) - m\vec{v}}{\Delta t}$$

$$= \lim_{\Delta t \to 0} \frac{m\,\Delta\vec{v} + \vec{v}\,\Delta m + \Delta m\,\Delta\vec{v}}{\Delta t}.$$

The last term in the numerator becomes negligible as Δt (and hence Δm and Δv) becomes small, so we can express the force as

$$\vec{f} = m\frac{d\vec{v}}{dt} + \vec{v}\frac{dm}{dt}. \qquad (8.10\text{-}1)$$

In applying Eq. (8.10-1) we must take into account the difference between cases in which the force is parallel to the velocity and those in which it is perpendicular.

Let us first consider that $\vec{f}$ is parallel to $\vec{v}$. Then, since the mass changes with time only because the speed changes, we can replace dm/dt by $(dm/dv)(dv/dt)$. Differentiating Eq. (8.9-5), we find that

$$\frac{dm}{dv} = \frac{m_0 v/c^2}{(1 - v^2/c^2)^{3/2}}.$$

We also note that the velocity does not change in direction, so we can replace $\vec{v}$ by the speed v. Equation (8.10-1) then becomes

$$f_L = \frac{m_0}{(1 - v^2/c^2)^{1/2}} \cdot \frac{dv}{dt} + \frac{m_0 v^2/c^2}{(1 - v^2/c^2)^{3/2}} \frac{dv}{dt},$$

where the subscript on f indicates that this is a ***longitudinal force***, i.e., a force in the direction of the velocity. Collecting terms, we have

$$f_L = \frac{m_0}{(1 - v^2/c^2)^{1/2}} \left[1 + \frac{v^2c^2}{1 - v^2/c^2}\right] \frac{dv}{dt}$$

$$= \frac{m_0}{(1 - v^2/c^2)^{1/2}} \frac{1}{1 - v^2/c^2} \frac{dv}{dt}$$

$$= \frac{m_0}{(1 - v^2/c^2)^{3/2}} \frac{dv}{dt}. \qquad (8.10\text{-}2)$$

This expression for the force reduces to the Newtonian expression $f = m_0(dv/dt)$ when $v \ll c$. On the other hand, the ratio of f_L to the acceleration (dv/dt) becomes large without limit as v approaches c. This seems to confirm our guess

[1] The reader who is familiar with the derivative of a product can go directly from the first step of this derivation to Eq. (8.10-1).

in Sec. 8.8 that c is an upper limit to the speed to which any material body can be accelerated.

Consider next the case in which the force acts at right angles to the velocity, in which the ***transverse force*** is

$$\vec{f}_T = m\frac{d\vec{v}}{dt} + \vec{v}\frac{dm}{dt}.$$

In this case the acceleration, and hence also the change in velocity, is perpendicular to the initial velocity, as shown in Fig. 8.7. When the velocity has changed from $\vec{v}$ to $\vec{v} + \Delta\vec{v}$, the speed has changed from v to $[v^2 + (\Delta v)^2]^{1/2}$. We can therefore write

$$\frac{dv}{dt} = \lim_{\Delta t \to 0} \frac{v[1 + (\Delta v/v)^2]^{1/2} - v}{\Delta t} \approx \lim_{\Delta t \to 0} \frac{1}{2}\frac{\Delta v}{\Delta t}\frac{\Delta v}{v}.$$

Here the factor $(\Delta v/v)$ approaches zero as Δt, and hence Δv, approaches zero, so $dv/dt = 0$. The speed does not change as the result of an acceleration that is always perpendicular to the velocity. Furthermore, because the speed does not

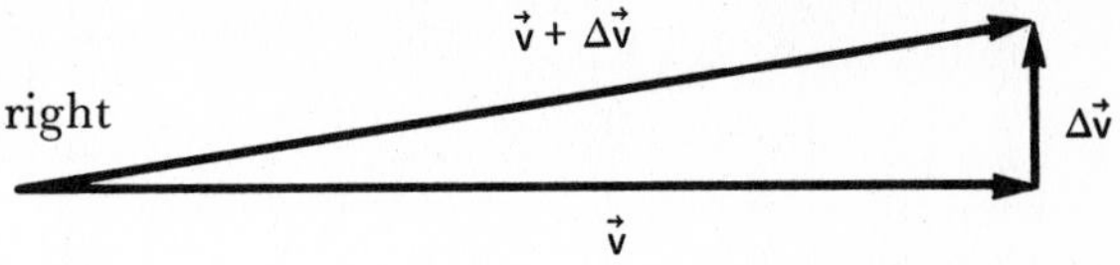

FIG. 8.7 Effect of acceleration at right angles to the velocity.

change and because the mass changes only as a result of a change of speed, dm/dt must be zero. We shall return to the discussion of forces that produce accelerations without changes of speed in Chapter 17. In the meantime, we have, for a transverse force,

$$\vec{f}_T = m\frac{d\vec{v}}{dt} = \frac{m_0}{(1 - v^2/c^2)^{1/2}}\frac{d\vec{v}}{dt}. \tag{8.10-3}$$

The $d\vec{v}/dt$ in Eq. (8.10-3) represents a change only in the direction of the velocity, with no change in its magnitude. Thus $m_0(1 - v^2/c^2)^{1/2}$ is constant. We see, as in the case of longitudinal acceleration, that the force approaches $m_0(d\vec{v}/dt)$ when $v \ll c$ and increases without limit as v approaches c.

When a force acts on a body in a direction neither parallel nor perpendicular to the velocity, it can be resolved into two components, one of which is determined by Eq. (8.10-2) and the other by Eq. (8.10-3). The two components of acceleration can then be added to give the magnitude and the direction of the acceleration, which will not, in general, be parallel to the force producing it.

8.11 Kinetic Energy

Since we suppose, in accordance with the Einstein assumptions, that energy is conserved in every inertial reference frame, we can calculate the change in kinetic energy of a body as it changes its speed from v to $v + \Delta v$ by computing the work necessary to change the speed. Suppose that a body is moving at speed

v and that a force of magnitude f acts upon it in the direction of motion for a short time Δt. The work done, and therefore the increase in kinetic energy, will be

$$\Delta E = f\,\Delta x \approx fv\,\Delta t,$$

where the last expression follows from the fact that the distance traveled, Δx, will be very close to $v\,\Delta t$ if Δt, and hence Δv, is small. We substitute for f from Eq. (8.10-2) to show that

$$\Delta E \approx \frac{mv}{1 - v^2/c^2}\frac{dv}{dt}\,\Delta t,$$

where we have replaced m_0 by $m(1 - v^2/c^2)^{1/2}$. If Δt is sufficiently small, we replace $(dv/dt)\,\Delta t$ by dv, the change in velocity, and write ΔE as the differential dE, so that

$$dE \approx \frac{mv\,dv}{1 - v^2/c^2}. \tag{8.11-1}$$

A more convenient expression for the change in energy may be obtained if we use Eq. (8.9-5), replacing m_u by m and u by v. We then have, after slight rearrangement,

$$m^2v^2 = m^2c^2 - m_0{}^2c^2.$$

Differentiation of this expression gives

$$2m^2v\,dv + 2v^2m\,dm = 2c^2m\,dm,$$

so that

$$mv\,dv = dm(c^2 - v^2) = c^2\,dm(1 - v^2/c^2),$$

Finally, substituting for $mv\,dv$ in Eq. (8.11-1), we find that

$$dE = c^2\,dm. \tag{8.11-2}$$

We thus conclude that the change in kinetic energy during any stage of the acceleration of a body is directly proportional to the change of observed mass during the same stage. Therefore, the total kinetic energy of any body whose observed mass is m and whose rest mass is m_0 is

$$E = c^2(m - m_0). \tag{8.11-3}$$

An interesting comparison with Newtonian mechanics is apparent if we substitute for m from Eq. (8.9-5) and then expand the denominator with the help of the binomial theorem of Appendix H:

$$E = m_0c^2\left[\frac{1}{(1 - v^2/c^2)^{1/2}} - 1\right]$$

$$= m_0c^2\left[1 + \frac{v^2}{2c^2} + \frac{3}{8}\frac{v^4}{c^4} + \cdots - 1\right] \tag{8.11-4}$$

$$= \frac{1}{2}m_0v^2 + \frac{3m_0v^4}{8c^2} + \cdots. \tag{8.11-5}$$

We see that the first term on the right is exactly the kinetic energy given by Newtonian mechanics. When $(v^2/c^2) \ll 1$, the two treatments give the same kinetic energy to a high degree of approximation.

Notice that the last term in Eq. (8.11-5) is positive, as are all succeeding terms not written there. The kinetic energy as computed in special relativity is always higher than that computed in Newtonian mechanics. Further, as inspection of Eq. (8.11-4) shows, the energy increases without limit as v approaches c. There is now final evidence that no material body can be accelerated to a speed as great as the speed of light; to do so would require infinite energy.

8.12 The Mass-Energy Relation

When Einstein discovered Eqs. (8.11-2) and (8.11-3) in 1905, he recognized that his result was capable of a most important generalization. If every increase in the energy of a body is equivalent to a change of mass of the body, it is clear that mass and energy are not really independent quantities, but rather that they are different measures of the same thing. We therefore express the entire mass of a body, instead of just the increase of its mass, in units of energy, and write the total energy E of a body as

$$E = mc^2, \tag{8.12-1}$$

where m is the observed mass of the body. Equation (8.12-1) is known as ***the Einstein mass-energy relation.*** According to this relation, the creation of matter requires the expenditure of energy, and the destruction of matter will result in the production of energy.

Notice that we speak of the creation or destruction of matter, *not* of mass. According to the mass-energy relation, mass and energy are merely different measures of the same quantity, which may be manifest as pure energy (e.g., in a beam of light or radio waves) or as matter (e.g., a baseball or an electron at rest).

The changes in mass that occur in commonly observed physical phenomena are extremely small. As an example, consider the case of an airplane of the future, whose mass is 10^5 kg (about 100 tons) and whose speed is 680 m/sec, about twice the speed of sound (Sec. 10.8). The kinetic energy of such an airplane is then about 2×10^{10} J, and this corresponds to an increase in mass over its mass at rest of $(2 \times 10^{10}\text{ J})/(9 \times 10^{16}\text{ m}^2/\text{sec}^2) = 2 \times 10^{-7}$ kg, a mass about that of a very small raindrop. Although balances are available that will weigh such a mass taken alone, no known instrument could detect such a small change in the large mass of a flying airplane.

According to the mass-energy relation, a body at rest has an energy

$$E_0 = m_0 c^2 \tag{8.12-2}$$

where m_0 is the mass of the body at rest. The energy E_0 is known as the ***rest energy*** of a mass m_0. If such a body could be destroyed, an amount of energy equal to 9×10^{16} J would appear for every kilogram of matter destroyed. The explosion of atomic bombs has given striking evidence of the truth of this assertion, but in addition there are countless laboratory experiments which give precise evidence for the correctness of the Einstein mass-energy relation.

EXERCISES

8.12-1 The electrical energy consumption of the United States during a particular week in 1965 was 19.2×10^9 kW hr [see Eq. (6.8-6)]. How much matter would need to be destroyed to produce this power?

8.12-2 Verify that the quantity c^2 can be expressed either in m^2/sec^2 or in J/kg.

8.12-3 The positron, a particle with the same mass as the electron, 0.91×10^{-30} kg, was discovered when a pair of particles (a positron and an electron) were created simultaneously. What is the minimal amount of energy required for the creation of the pair? Why can this be stated only in terms of a *minimal* energy?

8.12-4 Compute the ratio of the kinetic energy of a body to its rest energy if the body is moving at a speed of $0.10c$ relative to the observer. Compare this with the ratio of the Newtonian kinetic energy to c^2 times the rest mass. To what percentage accuracy would the mass of this body need to be measured to allow a direct test of the lack of validity of Newtonian mechanics?

8.12-5 Repeat Ex. 8.12-4 for a body moving with a speed of $0.5c$.

8.13 Conservation in Special Relativity

In the discussions of mass in Sec. 4.7 we have come to the conclusion that mass is a conserved quantity under all ordinary circumstances. Similarly, in the considerations of Sec. 6.10, we have concluded that energy is conserved in certain idealized systems. The mass-energy relationship now tells us that the laws of the conservation of mass and of conservation of energy are only approximate statements of a single more general law, that of ***the conservation of mass-energy***. We can say that the energy of an isolated system is constant only if we include an amount of energy E given by Eq. (8.12-1) for every mass m. Alternatively, we can say that the total mass of a system is conserved only if we use *observed masses*, which include the masses produced by the addition of energy to the system, rather than rest masses.

A consideration of the general conservation law in connection with the collision of two bodies is particularly revealing. If we let E_1 and E_2 be the energies of the two masses before collision and E_1' and E_2' the energies afterward, the law of conservation of energy tells us that

$$E_1 + E_2 = E_1' + E_2', \tag{8.13-1}$$

and the Einstein relation leads to

$$m_1 c^2 + m_2 c^2 = m_1' c^2 + m_2' c^2,$$

that is to say,

$$m_1 + m_2 = m_1' + m_2'. \tag{8.13-2}$$

We thus see that the statement that energy is conserved is equivalent to the statement that observed mass is conserved. We notice that Eq. (8.13-2) does not necessarily mean that $m_1 = m_1'$ and $m_2 = m_2'$, although that will be the case in collisions that take place at low speeds.

To recapitulate, in the relativity theory it can be said that the total energy in an isolated system is constant if we include in our calculation the rest energies of all the masses in the system. We can also make the entirely equivalent statement that the total mass of an isolated system is constant, but this statement does not imply that the total rest mass is constant.

The relativistic interchange of mass and energy is illustrated especially well in the case of an inelastic collision. Suppose that two identical bodies, each of rest mass m_0, are moving with the same speed v, but with oppositely directed velocities, $+\vec{v}$ and $-\vec{v}$, and that they collide head-on, perfectly inelastically. We know from the discussion of Secs. 4.2 and 8.9 that the bodies will come to rest, since their total momentum is zero. All of the initial kinetic energy has therefore been used in deforming and heating the bodies (cf. Sec. 11.6). Treating the problem on the basis of Newtonian mechanics, we would say that the combined mass of the bodies, both before and after the collision, is $2m_0$, that the kinetic energy before is $2(m_0 v^2/2) = m_0 v^2$, and that the kinetic energy after the collision is zero.

Let us now examine the same collision in the light of relativity. In this case, the total mass before the collision is given by Eq. (8.9-5) as

$$M = 2m_v = \frac{2m_0}{(1 - v^2/c^2)^{1/2}}, \tag{8.13-3A}$$

a quantity in excess of the rest mass. The excess mass, of course, is exactly equivalent to the work done in accelerating the bodies from rest to the speed v. Alternatively, we could state that the energy of the bodies before the collision is

$$E = 2m_v c^2 = \frac{2m_0 c^2}{(1 - v^2/c^2)^{1/2}}. \tag{8.13-3B}$$

The two equations (8.13-3) are exactly equivalent, and the first difference resulting from the relativity theory is that we no longer need to state the mass and energy separately, since a statement of one includes the other. According to the conservation law, the mass and energy given by Eqs. (8.13-3) must be those after the collision as well as before. From this and the symmetry of the problem, we arrive at the conclusion that each body after the collision has a mass m_v equal to its mass before the collision. This is true in spite of the fact that the bodies are at rest after the collision. Hence the rest mass of each body has changed from m_0 to $m_0/(1 - v^2/c^2)^{1/2}$ as a result of the processes of acceleration and collision that the body has undergone. At first glance this may seem surprising, but it is entirely clear as soon as we realize that the kinetic energy given to the bodies during their acceleration has gone into changes (deformation and heating) in the bodies themselves, and it is this energy that accounts for the increase in rest mass.

8.14 Evidence for the Validity of Special Relativity

We have seen at various stages of our discussion that direct laboratory measurements of the Lorentz contraction or of the Einstein time dilation, using bodies of common size and mass, would involve unattainable precision. Under such circumstances, on what sort of evidence can we decide whether Newtonian or Einsteinian mechanics is the better description?

The most convincing evidence in support of special relativity theory probably comes from the fact that accelerators (devices used to bring electrically charged particles to speeds approaching that of light; see Chapter 19) actually work. These machines are designed on the assumption of the validity of the relativistic equations that we have obtained for forces and energies, as well as those for time and space transformations. It would indeed be surprising if an accelerator designed on the basis of incorrect equations were to operate.

Direct evidence for the mass-energy relation is supplied by experiments in which matter is created or annihilated (again, see Chapter 19). The minimal energy necessary to create a pair of elementary particles, each of rest mass m_0, is found to be $2m_0c^2$; any extra energy supplied appears as kinetic energy of the particles (see Prob. 8.6).

Finally, it has been found possible by refined optical experiments to test the time dilation predicted by Eq. (8.4-1) (see Ref. 8E) and to make tests of both time dilation and of the Lorentz contraction by using particles of very low mass, moving at very high speeds (see Refs. 8C and 8D).

We conclude that the evidence for the validity of special relativity theory has been established as thoroughly as that for any other part of physics. If at some future time the postulates of Einstein's special theory are found to be incorrect, it will be necessary to replace them with other postulates that lead to essentially the same final predictions.

8.15 A Note on General Relativity

Throughout this chapter we have been concerned only with transformations between coordinate frames that are moving at uniform velocities relative to each other, excluding frames that are accelerated with respect to other frames. This, of course, is a severe limitation. Einstein in 1913 developed a theory of general relativity to deal with accelerated systems; we shall give some consideration of this general relativity theory in Chapter 14.

PROBLEMS

8.1 It was pointed out in Ex. 8.7-3 that a *measurement* of the length of a moving body requires that the two ends be observed simultaneously. This requirement may be restated as a condition that the light signals by which the two ends of the body are observed must *start* from the two ends simultaneously in the reference frame of the observer. On the other hand, the "apparent" length of a body is determined by the fact that light signals from the two ends of the body *reach the observer* simultaneously. A rod with a proper length L' is moving along its own length with a speed u relative to an observer who is located in line with the rod. Show that the apparent length of the rod will be decreased, approximately in the ratio $(1 - u/c)$, if the rod is moving away from the observer, and it will be increased in the approximate ratio $(1 + u/c)$ if the rod is moving toward him. Neglect all terms proportional to $(u/c)^2$ or higher powers of u/c.

8.2 By a quantitative consideration of the situations stated in Prob. 8.1, show that the apparent length of the rod is

$$L_A = L'\left(1 - \frac{u}{c}\right)/\gamma,$$

where u is considered positive when the rod is moving away from the observer and γ is an abbreviation for $(1 - u^2/c^2)^{1/2}$.

8.3 A μ-meson is an elementary particle found in cosmic radiation. A typical μ-meson disintegrates in $(2.2 \pm 0.2) \times 10^{-6}$ sec as measured by an observer with respect to whom it is at rest. If a typical μ-meson is traveling at a speed of 0.995 c relative to an observer on the ground, how long will it take to disintegrate?

8.4 Call the "lifetime" of the μ-meson τ_0 as found by a proper observer and τ that found by the observer on the ground. During its lifetime the meson travels a distance $0.995\tau c$ downward through the atmosphere as seen by the observer on the ground. During the lifetime τ_0, the atmosphere has moved upward a distance $0.995\ \tau_0 c$, according to an observer "riding" the meson. Reconcile the apparent discrepancy, making use of the Lorentz contraction.

8.5 A moving body has velocity components v_x' and v_y' in the primed coordinate system of Fig. 8.5. (a) Show that its velocity components in the unprimed system are

$$v_x = \frac{v_x' + u}{1 + uv_x'/c^2}$$

and

$$v_y = v_y' \frac{(1 - u^2/c^2)^{1/2}}{1 + uv_x'/c^2}.$$

(b) Find the speed of the body as measured by an observer in the unprimed system.

8.6 A photon may be considered to be a particle with zero rest mass (see Sec. 12.11), whose energy ε is equal to c times its momentum p. Imagine a process of "pair-production" in which a photon is annihilated and two particles, of equal rest mass m_0, are created. The two particles of the pair move off at identical speeds v in directions that are symmetrical about the original direction of motion of the photon, each velocity making the same angle θ with this original direction.

(a) Prove that the process cannot take place unless there is another particle involved to carry off some of the energy and momentum of the photon. (b) Assume that another particle of mass $M \gg m$ is involved in the pair production. For simplicity, suppose that this particle is initially at rest. Show by symmetry arguments that the particle must be moving in the original direction of motion of the photon after the pair production. (c) Again for simplicity, assume that M is so great that the speed u of the extra particle after the pair production is so much less than c that Newtonian mechanics gives valid expressions for the kinetic energy and momentum of this particle. (Use relativistic expressions for the two particles of the pair). Show that

$$u = c - [c^2(1 - 4m/M) + (4m/M)cv \cos \theta]^{1/2}.$$

(d) Suppose that $M \gg m$. What is the least energy of the photon (ε) that will produce a pair of particles?

8.7 According to Newtonian mechanics, the kinetic energy T and the momentum p of a particle of mass m are related by the equation $T = p^2/2m$. Show that the corresponding relativistic relation is

$$T = c(m_0{}^2c^2 + p^2)^{1/2} - m_0 c^2,$$

where m_0 is the rest mass of the particle.

REFERENCES

8A A. Einstein, *Relativity*, Crown, New York, 1920 (paper). A very readable and good discussion of relativity theory.

8B R. S. Shankland, "The Michelson-Morley Experiment," *Scientific American*, November 1964, pp. 80–94.

8C A. Einstein and L. Infeld, *The Evolution of Physics*, Simon and Schuster, New York, 1938. Pages 160–203 deal with special relativity.

8D William Bartozzi, *The Ultimate Speed*, a film produced by Educational Services Inc., 1962. (No. 0452, Modern Learning Aids.) A filmed experiment demonstrating the relation between kinetic energy and the speed of electrons.

8E David H. Frisch and James H. Smith. *Time Dilation—An Experiment with μ-Mesons*, a film produced by Educational Services, Inc., 1962. (No. 0453, Modern Learning Aids.) A filmed experiment showing direct evidence for time dilation.

8F Robert Katz, *An Introduction to Special Relativity Theory* (Momentum Book No. 9), Van Nostrand, Princeton, N.J., 1964. A treatment of relativity theory that extends beyond the discussions of this chapter.

8G Edwin F. Taylor and John Archibald Wheeler, *Spacetime Physics*, W. H. Freeman, San Francisco, 1966. A very good introduction to the ideas of relativity.

9 Some Properties of Matter

9.1 Introduction

In Chapters 4, 5, and 6 we restricted ourselves to cases in which we could treat bodies as particles. During uniform motions, accelerations, or collisions, we generally contrived that there be no rotation or that the rotation, if any, be ignorable. In a sense that part of our study of mechanics could be called a mechanics of centers of mass, the bodies, whether falling balls or cars on a track, were regarded as particles or points of mass.

Then, in Chapter 7, as we considered rotation itself, we saw immediately that the manner in which mass is distributed within a body becomes significant. And, although we were no longer talking as if the mass were concentrated in a point, we were still employing a simplifying restriction, namely, that the bodies be rigid. But real bodies stretch, warp, compress, or bend, so they are not perfectly rigid.

In this chapter we shall be concerned with a few of the properties of matter as it occurs in bulk. Some of these properties are inherent in the fact that no bodies, not even solid ones, are completely rigid, and the nonrigidity of matter makes it possible to transfer energy through it in the form of waves. Using Chapter 9 as preparation, we shall devote Chapter 10 to a study of waves.

9.2 Density and Specific Gravity

If we observe familiar materials, we find that they can be divided into two classes: homogeneous and nonhomogeneous (or heterogeneous). In the ***homogeneous*** materials, every portion of the material has the same properties as every other portion. In the ***nonhomogeneous*** materials this is not true. Thus water, air, iron, and gold are homogeneous, whereas granite and meat are nonhomogeneous. These definitions are true only if the volume considered contains many molecules. It will be seen later that all materials are nonhomogeneous if a fine enough division is made.

Probably the most fundamental property of all matter is its mass. It is found that all bodies composed of the same homogeneous material are characterized by the fact that their masses are proportional to their volumes. The ratio of the mass of a body to its volume, or the mass per unit volume of a material, is known as the ***density*** of the material of which the body is formed. Density is often represented by the Greek letter ρ (rho). The dimensions of density are

$$[\rho] = [m/\text{vol}] = [m\ell^{-3}]. \qquad (9.2\text{-}1)$$

The unit in which density is measured in the mks system is thus kg/m³. In many density tables the density is expressed in gm/cm³, the unit of density in the cgs system. The reader will have no difficulty in verifying that

$$10^3 \text{ kg/m}^3 = 1 \text{ gm/cm}^3. \tag{9.2-2}$$

The density of a solid may be computed after its mass and its volume have been determined. The density of a liquid or a gas may be found by weighing an evacuated closed vessel of known volume and then weighing the same vessel after it has been filled with the fluid being studied.

Because the volume of any material changes with the temperature and pressure, while the mass remains constant, the density also changes. It is therefore necessary, in giving the densities of substances, to specify the value of the temperatures and the pressures at which they are correct. Unless otherwise indicated, densities are stated for atmospheric pressure (small variations in pressure have little effect on solids and liquids). The temperature, however, must be given explicitly. The densities of a number of materials are given in Table 9.1.

Table 9.1 *Densities of Various Materials* ($T = 20°C$)(10^3 kg/m³ $= 1$ gm/cm³)

Material	Density ρ (kg/m³)
Aluminum	2.70×10^3
Carbon, diamond	3.52
Carbon, graphite	2.25
Copper	8.92
Gold	19.3
Lead	11.35
Magnesium	1.74
Mercury	13.55
Platinum	21.4
Silver	10.50
Sodium	0.97
Steel	7.8
Wood, balsa	0.11–0.33
oak (red)	0.60
teak (Africa)	0.78
ebony (Venezuela)	1.2
Ethyl alcohol	0.79
Gasoline	0.67
Seawater	1.025

When the metric system of measurements was set up, it was intended that the mass of exactly 1 cm³ of water at the temperature of its maximum density (i.e., 3.98°C) should be exactly 1 gm. However, the standard kilogram, a block of platinum-iridium, and the standard meter, the distance between two scratches on a metal bar, as they were constructed, did not have precisely the intended relation to one another. Subsequent careful measurements have shown that the density of water at 3.98°C is $0.999\,973 \times 10^3$ kg/m³, or 0.999 973 gm/cm³.

As a result of the attempt, mentioned in the previous paragraph, to connect the units of volume and mass in the metric system, there is in use a second unit of volume, called the liter, which is approximately equivalent to 1000 cm³. The ***liter*** is defined as the volume occupied by exactly 1 kg of pure water at the temperature of its maximum density (3.98°C). Using the figure given above for the maximum density of water, we see that

$$1 \text{ liter} = (0.999\,973 \times 10^3)^{-1} \text{ m}^3 = 1.000\,027 \times 10^{-3} \text{ m}^3,$$

or that

$$1 \text{ kiloliter} = 1.000\,027 \text{ m}^3. \qquad (9.2\text{-}3)$$

Thus the kiloliter and the cubic meter differ as units of volume by 27 parts in one million, and this small difference can be neglected in all but the most precise volume and density measurements. We must be careful, however, to remember the difference in the definitions of the two units and that the liter is not a unit of the mks system.

Traditionally, there have been many units of volume in use in various countries, and often several systems of units are used in the same countries for different commodities. For example, the ***U.S. fluid gallon*** is defined as 231.00 in.³, and by definition it contains 128 ***U.S. fluid ounces.*** It is encouraging to note that, by legislative procedures, these unnecessarily complex systems of measure are beginning to be replaced by the mks system. In physics, we shall use the mks and cgs units of volume almost exclusively.

The ***specific gravity*** of a substance is obtained by dividing the density of the substance by the density of some standard substance. For liquids and solids, the standard substance is usually water at 3.98°C (maximum density), although some tables refer to water at some other temperature or to other liquids. Gases may be referred to air or to some other gas at a standard temperature and pressure.

EXERCISES

9.2-1 What is the mass of solid right circular cylinder of aluminum whose radius is 8.0 cm and whose height is 30 cm?

9.2-2 A piece of metal is in the form of a sphere of diameter (5.00 ± 0.05) cm. Its mass is found to be (1.25 ± 0.01) kg. What is the probable nature of the metal?

9.3 The Elasticity of Solids

We ordinarily think of those bodies which we call solids as having a definite shape and size. Actually, however, even the most rigid steel bar can be noticeably bent, twisted, stretched, or compressed under the action of sufficiently large

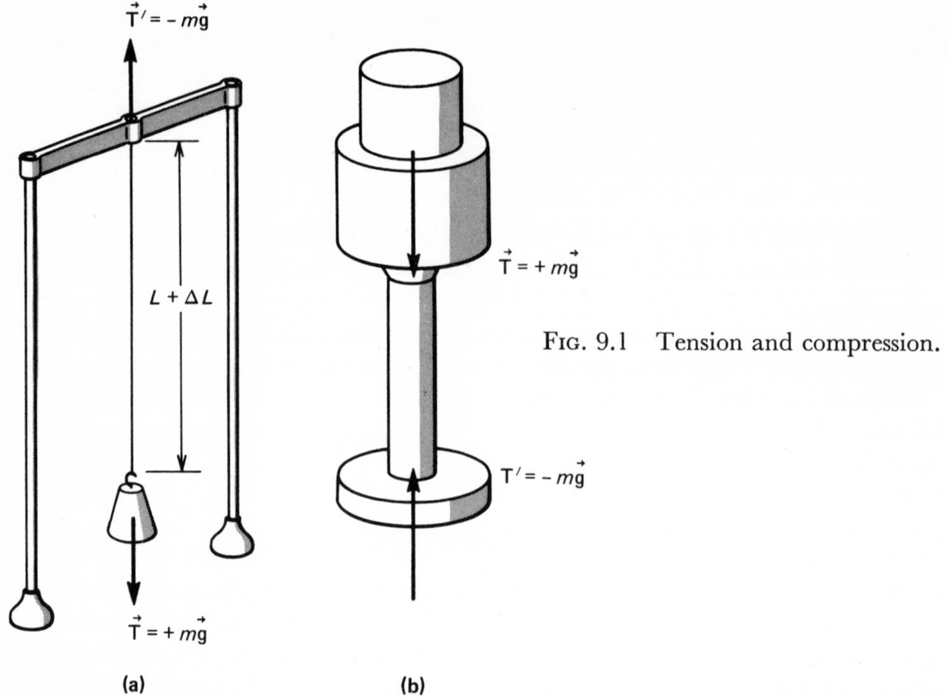

FIG. 9.1 Tension and compression.

forces. The distortion of a solid by a force is easily shown by stretching a rubber band or a helical spring of wire with a weight hung from it. Delicate measurements indicate that similar distortions take place even when small forces are applied to heavy metal rods. Thus there is no such thing as a perfectly rigid body, and the "rigid rods" used for measuring lengths (Sec. 2.3) must be handled in such a way that the forces tending to distort them are kept as small as possible.

Whenever a solid body is distorted by forces acting upon it, one of two things may happen. If the forces are not too large, the body will return to its original shape and size when they are removed. Under these circumstances, we say that the body is behaving ***elastically***. On the other hand, if larger forces are used, the body may retain some or all of its deformation after the forces have ceased to act. We then say that the body has experienced a ***plastic deformation***.

The simplest type of elastic deformation is a simple stretch or compression, such as the ones shown in Fig. 9.1. In both illustrations, the force deforming the material is supplied by the weight of the mass m, so that the force $\vec{T}$ has a magnitude mg. To maintain equilibrium, the wire pulls up on the weight in Fig. 9.1a with a force $\vec{T}' = -m\vec{g}$, and the rod in Fig. 9.1b pushes up on the weight with the same force. This force results from the stretching of the wire or the compression of the rod and is known as an ***elastic force***.

If the length of the wire in Fig. 9.1a is measured before the weight is attached and again while the wire is supporting the weight, it is found that the length is increased by the application of the force. If the original length of the wire is L, the increase in length, under a given tensile force $T = mg$, may be called ΔL. If various forces are applied to the wire by hanging different weights on it, the extension of the wire is found to be proportional to the tension T applied to the wire, provided that no plastic deformation takes place. Thus for a given wire and for small forces, we write

$$T/\Delta L = k, \tag{9.3-1}$$

where k is a constant for the wire. This fact was first noted by Robert Hooke (1635–1703) in 1676, when he stated his law of elasticity, *Ut tensio, sic vis* (As the distortion, so the force). A precise statement of ***Hooke's law*** is that *the elastic deformation produced in a given body is proportional to the force producing it.* If measurements are made of the behavior of the rod of Fig. 9.1b under the action of a ***compressive force*** T, it will be found that Hooke's law is obeyed in compression as well as in tension.

Since the support at the top of the wire must exert an upward pull of magnitude T, the same force acts across every cross section of the wire. That is to say, *any* two parts of the wire are being pulled apart by the tensile force T. Similarly, the stretch is uniformly distributed over the length. This is shown if a number of equidistant marks are placed along the length of the wire before it is stretched. If the distances between these marks are measured with the tension applied, it is found that all of the distances increase equally. We should therefore expect, if the wire of Fig. 9.1a were replaced by a longer wire of the same material and cross section, that the change of length with a given tensile force would be increased in the same ratio as the length was increased. This expectation can be verified by experiment. We therefore write

$$LT/\Delta L = K, \tag{9.3-2}$$

where K is a new constant, characteristic of the cross section and material of the wire. The same relation holds in compression.

Let us now perform a further series of experiments. We take a number of wires, all of the same material but with different areas and shapes of cross section (square, triangular, circular, etc.), and stretch them. We can thus determine a constant K for each wire. In studying the values of K obtained, we shall find that two uniform wires having *the same area of cross section* will have the same value of K, no matter what the shape of their cross sections. If the areas are different, we find that the value of K is proportional to the area S of the cross section, i.e., $K = YS$, where Y is again a constant. We then see that

$$Y = (LT)/(S\,\Delta L). \tag{9.3–3}$$

So far, we have changed the length and the cross-sectional area of the wire and found how these affect the relationship between T and ΔL. The only thing left to change is the material of the wire. If we change the material, Y will change, but for the same material it will always have the same value. Y is thus a constant for a given material, and it is known as ***Young's modulus*** for that material. The name honors Thomas Young (1773–1829). The values of this modulus for some common materials are given in Table 9.2. It will be a useful exercise for the reader to show that the dimensions of Y are given by

$$[\mathscr{Y}] = [m\ell^{-1}t^{-2}]. \tag{9.3-4}$$

Table 9.2 *Values of Young's Modulus (Y) for Various Solids*

Material	Modulus Y (N/m²)
Aluminum	7×10^{10}
Brass	9
Copper	11
Glass	5
Iron (drawn)	20
Nickel	21
Steel	19
Wood	0.5–1.0

The values given in the table apply equally for tension or compression. The units of Young's modulus as given here are the mks units N/m^2. If the reader uses any of the more extended tables given in various handbooks, he will find that some state the modulus in other units, which can be converted readily to these (cf. Ex. 9.3-1).

It is interesting to examine Eq. (9.3-3) in more detail. We can rewrite it, if we wish, in the form

$$Y = \frac{T/S}{\Delta L/L}. \tag{9.3-3A}$$

The quantity T/S is the ratio of the force T to the cross-sectional area S, and it is called the ***stress***. If the force is in such a direction as to elongate the wire, the latter is said to be under ***tension***. If it is so directed that it shortens the rod, the latter is said to be under ***compression***. The unit in which stress is measured in the mks system is the newton per square meter, N/m^2, and the dimensions of stress are $[m\ell^{-1}t^{-2}]$. The ratio $(\Delta L/L)$ is called the ***strain*** and is a pure number, since it is the ratio of two lengths. It is a convenient aid to memory to express Eq. (9.3-3A) in the form

$$Y = \text{stress/strain}. \tag{9.3-3B}$$

It must be emphasized that Eqs. (9.3-3) are valid only if no plastic deformation occurs. The value of the stress at which plastic deformation begins to occur is called the ***elastic limit*** of the material.

The behavior of a helical spring is somewhat more complicated than that of a straight wire. It can, however, be shown theoretically, or demonstrated experimentally, that many springs obey Hooke's law and that

$$T = kx, \tag{9.3-5}$$

where T is the force extending the spring, x is the amount of the extension of the spring, and k is a constant for the spring. This constant is often called the ***stiffness constant***. In the notation of Eqs. (9.3-1) and (9.3-3) the stiffness constant of a straight wire is given by

$$k = T/\Delta L = YS/L. \tag{9.3-6}$$

The property of the coiled spring just described enables us to construct a useful physical instrument called a ***spring balance.*** A spring is mounted in a rigid frame (Fig. 9.2), which is provided with a scale. The pointer indicates the zero mark on the scale when the tension T on the spring is zero. As the tension T increases, the pointer moves down the scale, which can be calibrated to read directly in newtons or in other units of force. The spring balance is thus a simple instrument for the measurement of force.

A spring balance can be used for *comparing* the masses of two bodies. Suppose the masses of the bodies are m_1 and m_2. Then if we hang these bodies successively on the balance, the force readings will be given by $T_1 = m_1 g$ and $T_2 = m_2 g$. We then see that if these two measurements are made at the same place on the earth's surface, the value of g is the same in both equations, and we have

$$T_1/T_2 = m_1/m_2.$$

The readings of the spring balance are therefore proportional to the masses. Many balances are calibrated directly in terms of the mass that will produce a given extension under the action of gravitation, i.e., in terms of the force in grams weight, etc. (Sec. 4.15). In principle, such a calibration is good only at the point at which it was made or at other points where the value of g is the same. In practice, g does not vary by more than 0.5 percent from the average value 9.80 m/sec^2, and this figure is within the accuracy of almost all spring balances. On such balances, a reading of 1.00 kg would indicate a force of 9.80 N, since a mass of 1.00 kg is attracted by the earth with a force of 9.80 N (cf. Appendix D.3).

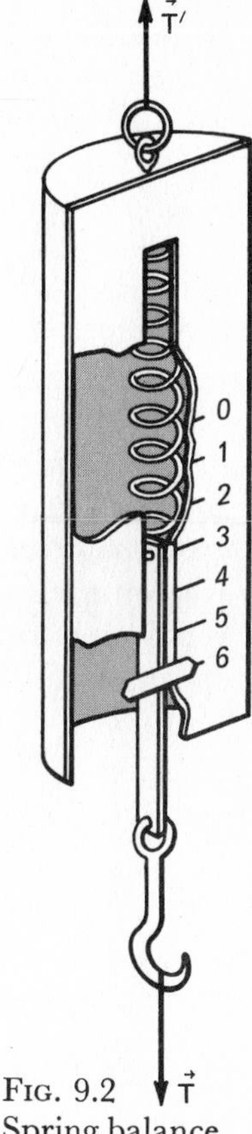

FIG. 9.2 Spring balance.

EXERCISES

9.3-1 Derive the conversion formulae:

$$1 \text{ N/m}^2 = 10 \text{ dyne/cm}^2 = 0.0102 \text{ gm wt/cm}^2.$$

9.3-2 A steel wire, of diameter 1.00 mm and length 1.26 m, has a mass of 100 kg hung from it. It is observed to stretch by 0.73 cm. What is the value of Young's modulus for this wire?

9.3-3 A weight of 400 kg mass is being lifted slowly into a building by means of a drawn iron wire. The wire is 0.254 cm in diameter and is 12.7 m long. By how much will it stretch?

9.3-4 An automobile, of 1000 kg mass, is being towed by means of a steel cable. The diameter of the cable is 8.0 mm and its length is 5.0 m. If the towed car is being accelerated at 0.5 m/sec^2 and frictional forces are neglected, by how much will the cable stretch?

9.4 Work and Elastic Potential Energy

Work is required in any situation in which some kind of a change is produced by a force acting through a displacement. In Sec. 4.11, we considered the force $\vec{\mathbf{F}}$ and the displacement $\vec{ds}$ to occur along the same line, and the increment of work dW is simply $dW = F\,ds$. Or, if the force is constant throughout the displacement, the work is $W = Fs$. In Sec. 6.6, we noted that more generally $\vec{\mathbf{F}}$ and $\vec{ds}$ need not be in the same direction in space. The definition of the increment of work then becomes $dW = \vec{\mathbf{F}} \cdot \vec{ds} = F\,ds \cos\theta$, where θ is the angle between $\vec{\mathbf{F}}$ and $\vec{ds}$. Again, if $\vec{\mathbf{F}}$ is constant throughout the displacement and if the displacement occurs along a straight line, we can write $W = \vec{\mathbf{F}} \cdot \vec{\mathbf{s}} = Fs \cos\theta$. We have seen several examples of the utility of work as a concept. We might recall particularly the work required to produce a change in kinetic energy (Sec. 4.11) and the definition of gravitational potential energy as the work that a weight could do in falling (Sec. 4.18).

In the preceding section we saw that the strain produced in the stretching of a wire or a helical spring requires a force to act through a displacement. Thus, work is required to produce the strain. Let us now analyze the stretching of a helical spring from the point of view of the work involved.

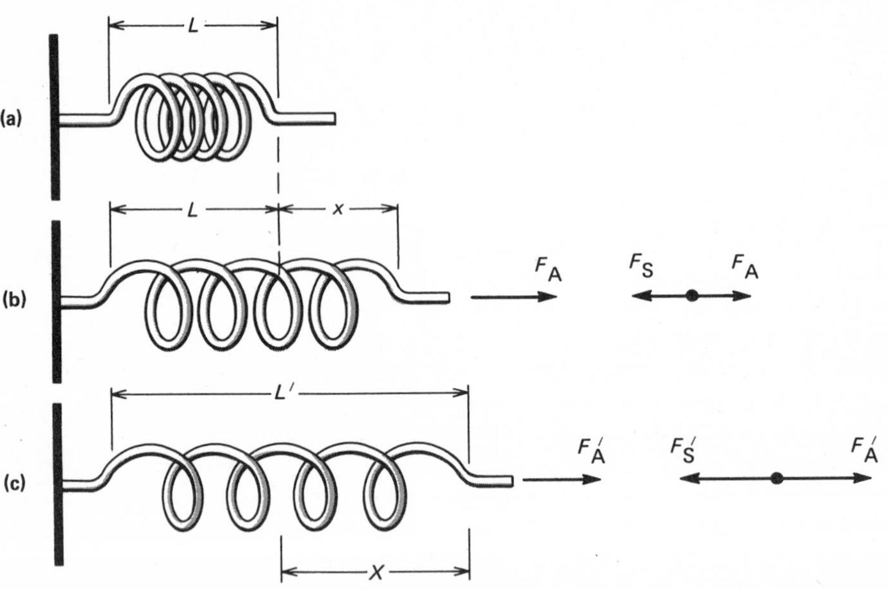

FIG. 9.3 Elastic deformation of a helical spring, (a) to (b) to (c). Force vectors for the equilibrium of the end of the spring are shown.

Suppose that we have a helical spring whose relaxed length is L, as shown in Fig. 9.3a. We apply a force F_A, as in Fig. 9.3b, stretching the spring to its new length $L + x$. According to Hooke's law and Eq. (9.3-5), the relation between F_A and x is given by

$$F_A = kx, \qquad (9.4\text{-}1)$$

where k is the stiffness constant of this particular spring. A graph of the stretching force F_A plotted against the elongation x is shown in Fig. 9.4.

Our problem is to determine the total work done in stretching the spring to a given length, say, L'. Since the relaxed length of the spring is L, the elongation will be $X = L' - L$, and the total stretching force required will be F_A'. We illustrate these conditions in Fig. 9.3c, and we graph them by a point P on Fig. 9.4.

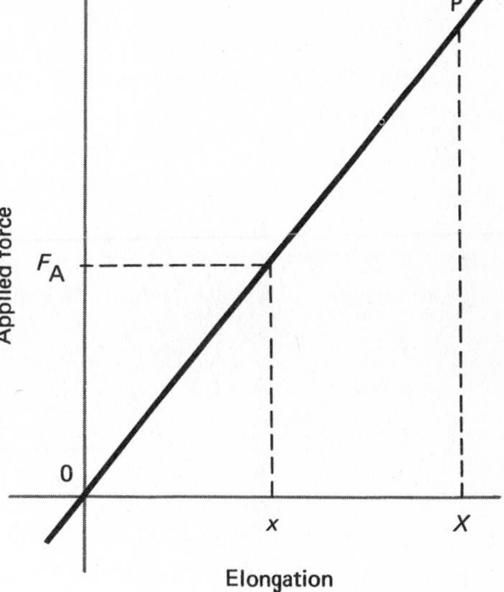

FIG. 9.4 Graph of applied force vs. elongation for a helical spring for which Hooke's law is valid. With suitable relabeling, the graph will serve equally well for the restoring force exerted by the spring.

From Eq. (9.4-1) we see that

$$F_A' = kX = k(L' - L). \qquad (9.4\text{-}2)$$

It should be immediately evident that we cannot compute the total work required to stretch the spring by multiplying F_A' by X. The work is not that much because the force changes continuously, according to Eq. (9.4-1) and Fig. 9.4, as x varies from *zero* to $(L' - L) = X$.

In order to analyze the situation, suppose that the spring has already been stretched to an elongation x and compute the work Δw required to increase the elongation to $x + \Delta x$. If the ***average*** force acting through the additional displacement is F_{av}, then

$$\Delta w = F_{av}\,\Delta x. \qquad (9.4\text{-}3)$$

We can draw a complete analogy between our present problem and that treated in Sec. 3.16. Compare Fig. 9.4 with Fig. 3.15b and Eq. (9.4-3) with Eq. (3.16-1). We note that the graphs are both straight-line graphs passing through the origin. The right sides of the equations are both the product of an ordinate by a small change of its associated abscissa. Thus, the left sides may be regarded as narrow vertical rectangles of area under the curve. Furthermore, the ordinates in each of Eqs. (9.4-3) and (3.16-1) are proportional to their abscissas as, of course, the graphs say they must be; that is, $F = kx$ and $v = at$, respectively.

Since the mathematical analyses are completely analogous, we can repeat in all details the kind of argument which we made in Sec. 3.16. The former argument concluded that $s = \frac{1}{2}at^2$. In our analogy, then, we must conclude that

$$W = \tfrac{1}{2}kX^2. \tag{9.4-4}$$

Thus, the work required to stretch a helical spring is equal to one-half the spring constant times the elongation squared. This work is represented by the total area in the right triangle OPX.

If the spring is stretched to any given elongation and held there, the system of spring, wall, and applied force must be in equilibrium. Hence, in Fig. 9.5, point P_1, at the end of the spring where F_A' is applied, is in equilibrium. Since

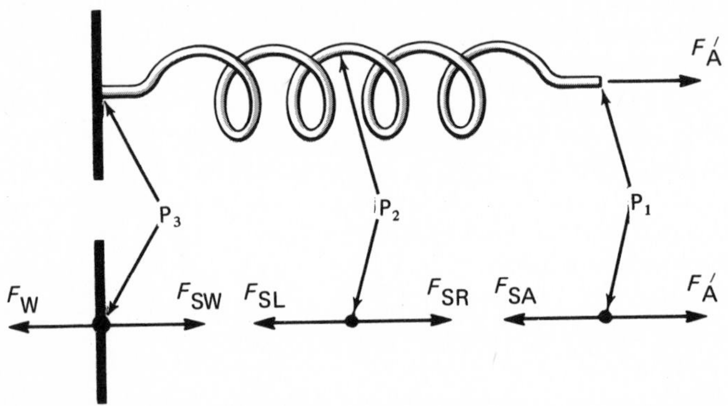

FIG. 9.5 Every point on the spring is in equilibrium under a constant strain.

F_A' acts to the right, there must be an equal and opposite force by the spring toward the left: $F_A' - F_{SA} = 0$. Similarly, any point P_2 in the spring itself is in equilibrium, so at that point the pull of the spring to the right F_{SR} must be balanced by the pull of the spring to the left F_{SL}: $F_{SR} - F_{SL} = 0$. Finally, point P_3, where the spring joins the wall, is also in equilibrium. The spring as a whole, being pulled to the right by F_A', transmits the force F_{SW} to the wall; for P_3 to be in equilibrium, an equal and opposite force F_W, by the wall, must act to the left: $F_{SW} - F_W = 0$.

For any elongation of the spring, as in Fig. 9.3b, the force F_S to the left is equal in magnitude to F_A, as in Fig. 9.3d. Hence, it follows that Fig. 9.4 would do equally well, with relabeling, to graph F_S against the elongation. And, if the spring has been stretched to elongation X, the work it will do in returning to *zero* elongation is again represented by the area of the right triangle OPX and is given quantitatively by Eq. (9.4-4).

We defined gravitational potential energy as the work that an elevated weight could do in falling. In a similar manner we define ***elastic potential energy*** as the work that a strained body does in returning to its unstrained condition. Thus, if a helical spring with stiffness constant k is stretched to elongation X, the potential energy of the strained spring will be

$$PE = \tfrac{1}{2}kX^2. \tag{9.4-5}$$

EXERCISES

9.4-1 A spring is stretched from its unstrained length of 1.500 m to 1.625 m, and the work required is found, 3.75 J. Find the stiffness constant of the spring.

9.4-2 Using the data from Ex. 9.4-1, compare the increase in potential energy as the spring is stretched from 1.500 m to 1.625 m with that when it is stretched from 1.625 m to 1.750 m.

9.4-3 If the cross section of a piece of steel wire is 1.00 mm² and the wire without strain is 10.00 m long, what potential energy will be stored in the wire when it is stretched to a length of 10.01 m?

9.4-4 If all data of Ex. 9.4-3 are the same except that the cross section is 2.00 mm², what potential energy will be stored?

9.4-5 If the energy stored in the spring of Ex. 9.4-1 when the spring is stretched to 1.750 m is used to propel a stone of 0.05 kg mass, with what speed will the stone be projected?

9.4-6 Making use of the analogies used to derive Eq. (9.4-4) carry through a complete derivation of this equation in a manner similar to that used in Sec. 3.16. Replace both the symbolism and the wording of that section by those appropriate to the elastic problem. (Hint: Consider both $(w + \Delta w) = \frac{1}{2}k(x + \Delta x)^2$ and $(w - \Delta w) = \frac{1}{2}k(x - \Delta x)^2$ in calculating Δw.)

9.4-7 Derive Eq. (9.4-4) directly, without the use of analogies, but note that the work done in stretching the spring is the area under the force vs. displacement curve, i.e., $W = \int \vec{f} \cdot d\vec{s}$.

9.4-8 An elastic, helical spring is pulled by a steady force at one end, the other end being free. Discuss qualitatively what happens, including an answer to the question of whether the spring stretches.

9.5 *The Elasticity of Liquids*

The principal property of liquids which distinguishes them from solids is the ease with which their shapes can be changed. If we pour a liquid into a vessel, the liquid fills every nook and cranny of the container, however peculiar its shape. Further, the liquid will slop around in response to the slightest disturbance. We have seen, in Sec. 9.2, that this property of liquids does not interfere seriously with the determination of their densities but, since the elastic constants defined in Sec. 9.3 were based on changes of length, they will not be applicable to liquids. Since the volume of a liquid, rather than any linear dimension, is useful in its description, we shall investigate the changes of volume which accompany changes of pressure on the liquid.

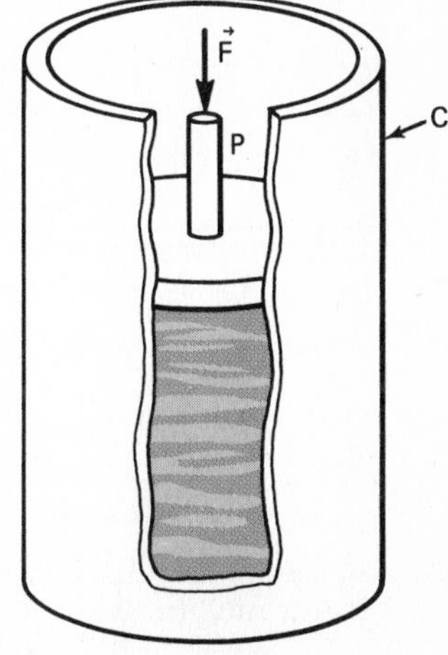

FIG. 9.6 Compression of a liquid.

If we construct a hollow cylinder C of heavy metal, as shown in Fig. 9.6, provide it with a close fitting piston P of area S, and fill the cylinder with a volume V of some particular liquid, we can use the apparatus to study the elasticity of the liquid. If we push down on the cylinder with a known force F, we find that the volume of the liquid changes by a small amount ΔV. We also find that ΔV is proportional to the magnitude F of the force applied to the piston unless the force is very large. We get our clue to the rest of the experiment from the procedure we adopted in establishing Young's modulus for a wire (Sec. 9.3). We vary the volume V of the liquid, the area S of the piston, and the shape of the cylinder. We find that for a given force the compression ΔV does not depend on the shape of the cylinder but that it does depend on the area S of the piston and the volume V of the liquid. We find, in fact, that the ratio

$$M_B = -FV/S\,\Delta V = -\frac{F/S}{\Delta V/V}, \tag{9.5-1}$$

is constant over a considerable range for a given liquid. The minus sign occurs because a positive pressure produces a negative change Δv. This ratio is known as the ***bulk modulus*** of elasticity for the liquid. Notice that the definition of this modulus is very similar to the definition of Young's modulus in Eqs. (9.3-3). The ***stress*** is now the ratio F/S, a force per unit area, and the ***strain*** is the change in volume per unit volume, i.e., the ratio $\Delta V/V$. Values of the bulk moduli M_B for a few liquids and solids are given in Table 9.3 for relatively low pressures. These moduli change somewhat at high pressures. In measuring the bulk moduli for solids, care must be taken to see that the pressure is applied uniformly in all directions. This is usually done by immersing the solid to be tested in a liquid whose modulus is known. The bulk modulus of a gas is by no means a constant. We shall discuss its variation in Chapter 20.

Table 9.3 *Bulk Moduli (M_B) for Various Liquids and Solids*

Material	Bulk Modulus M_B (N/m^2)
Mercury	27×10^9
Paraffin	1.2
Water	2.1
Aluminum	71
Copper	133
Steel	181
Lead	41

The notion of stress takes on a particular significance in a liquid or a gas. We can understand the reason for this by studying the experiment of Fig. 9.7. We construct a hollow vessel equipped with a number of pistons of different areas (S_1, S_2, etc.) and fill it with a small volume of a liquid. We then press any one of the pistons and experiment to find out what forces will be needed to hold the

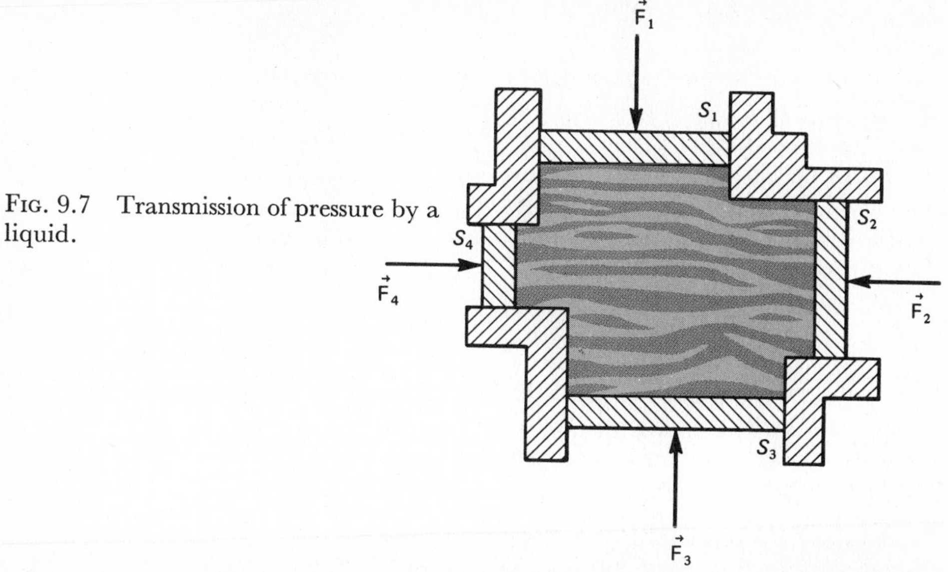

FIG. 9.7 Transmission of pressure by a liquid.

other pistons in place. We find that different forces are required for each piston, but that the forces are always proportional to the area of the pistons, that is, the ratios

$$F_1/S_1 = F_2/S_2 = F_3/S_3 = F_4/S_4 = p$$

are all constant. The stress anywhere in a small volume of a liquid is thus a constant, and it is the same in any direction. We call this constant stress p the ***pressure*** in the liquid. We shall obtain the same result if we repeat the experiment with a gas in the cylinder, and we can give a similar definition for the pressure in a gas. The dimensions of pressure are the same as those of stress, i.e., $[m\ell^{-1}t^{-2}]$.

Another way of expressing the result of the previous paragraph is seen from the experiment of Fig. 9.8. In this experiment, we make a small cylinder with a piston and equip it with a spring balance so that we can measure the force on

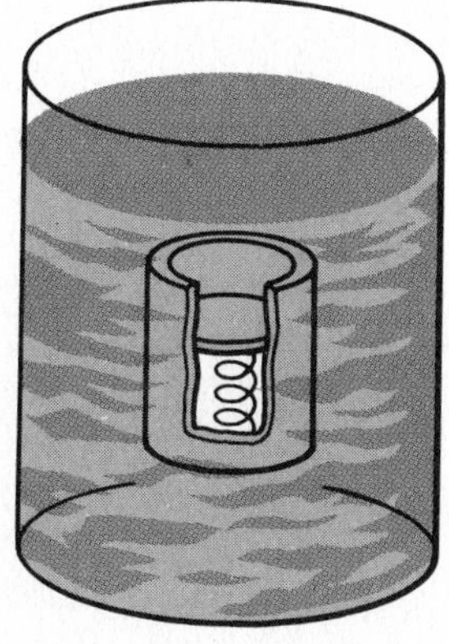
FIG. 9.8 Pressure gauge.

the piston. We find that however we turn this measuring device around, we obtain the same force on the piston and consequently the same pressure, or force per unit area, in any small region in the liquid.

The principle just found, that *any pressure applied to the surface of a liquid is transmitted throughout the liquid in all directions*, was first enunciated by Blaise Pascal (1623–1662) in the middle of the seventeenth century, and it is known as ***Pascal's principle.***

9.6 Hydrostatic Pressure

In the preceding section we said that the pressure is the same in all directions in a small volume of a liquid. The reason that we insisted on a small volume is readily seen from the following argument. Consider a long uniform cylinder closed by a piston at the bottom, shown in Fig. 9.9. It contains a liquid whose

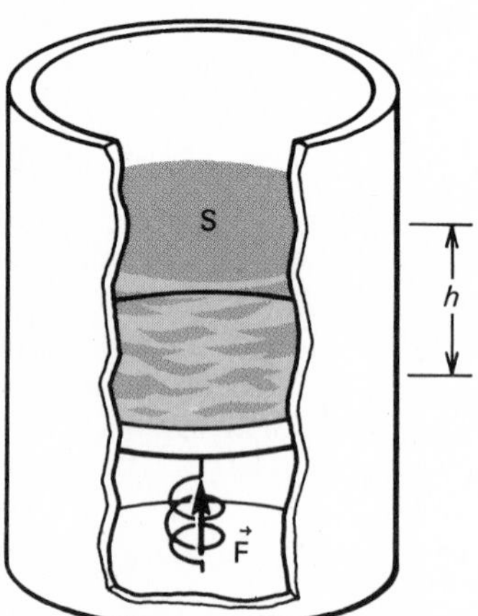

Fig. 9.9 Variation of pressure with depth.

weight must be supported by the piston. As more liquid is poured into the cylinder, the weight, and therefore the upward force necessary to support the piston, must increase. Since this force $F = pS$, where p is the pressure on the piston and S is the area of the piston, it follows that the pressure in a liquid varies with the depth beneath the surface. Only when the total depth of the liquid is so small that the pressure due to its weight is negligible compared with external pressures can we say that the pressure is constant.

In order to find the force acting on the piston of Fig. 9.9, we need merely to compute the weight of the liquid. Since the mass of the liquid is the product of its density by its volume, the weight is ρghS, where ρ is the average density of the liquid. To some extent, of course, the density will vary with depth, since the liquid at the bottom of the container is under a higher pressure than that at the top and is therefore slightly compressed. However, the values of the bulk moduli of liquids (Table 9.3) are so large that enormously great depths are required before the density is changed appreciably. For example, the density of water is increased at a depth of 2000 m (over a mile), by about one percent by the pressure upon it and by correspondingly smaller amounts in shallower water.

We shall therefore not make an appreciable error if we consider most liquids to be ***incompressible*** and use the densities determined at atmospheric pressure.

Using the definition of pressure, we find that the pressure on the piston of Fig. 9.9 is

$$p = F/S = \rho ghS/S = \rho gh. \qquad (9.6\text{-}1)$$

Notice that the area of the piston has disappeared from this expression for the pressure. This might lead us to suspect that the pressure depends only on g, the depth h beneath the surface, and the density ρ of the liquid. That this conclusion is correct may be inferred from the consideration of a noncylindrical vessel, such as that shown in Fig. 9.10. The volume actually supported by the piston is simply that directly above it, enclosed within the dotted lines. The remainder of the liquid is supported by the floor and the sides of the vessel. Hence, the pressure on the piston is independent of the shape of the containing vessel, and the pressure at a given depth below the surface is constant, its value being given by Eq. (9.6-1).

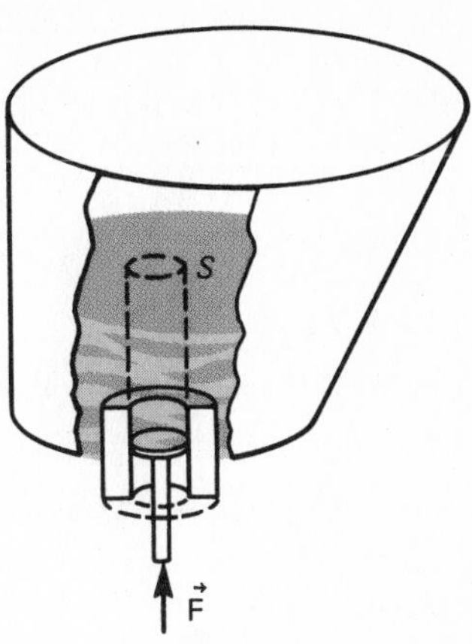

Fig. 9.10 Hydrostatic pressure depends only on the depth below the surface.

This last result leads us to a very elegant method for the comparison of the densities of two liquids. We bend a glass tube into the form of a U and pour into it the denser liquid A (Fig. 9.11). Into one side we pour the second liquid B, which we assume does not mix with A. If what we have said so far is true, the pressure on both sides of the U-tube at the level of the dotted line must be the same. We can therefore write

$$\rho_A g h_A = \rho_B g h_B$$

and consequently

$$\rho_A/\rho_B = h_B/h_A. \qquad (9.6\text{-}2)$$

If the two liquids mix the method is obviously not applicable, but the reader should have no difficulty in devising a similar method for the comparison of the densities of two miscible liquids, provided a third liquid can be found which mixes with neither (Ex. 9.6-2).

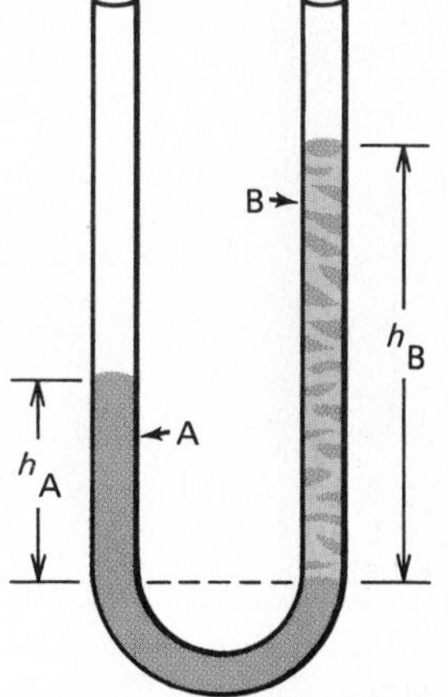

Fig. 9.11 Comparison of densities of two liquids.

EXERCISES

9.6-1 Compute the change in the density of water at a temperature of 20°C when the pressure is changed from normal atmospheric pressure to 156×10 N/m². (Hint: Find the fractional change in density in terms of the fractional change in volume, using the results of Appendix H, before substituting any numerical values.)

9.6-2 Devise one or more methods for the comparison of the densities of two miscible liquids as suggested at the end of Sec. 9.6.

9.6-3 A device similar to that shown in Fig. 9.7 has only two pistons, S_1 and S_2. The area $S_1 = 1.00$ in.^{2} and $S_2 = 1.00$ ft^2. If a force of 800 N is exerted on S_1, what force will be necessary to hold S_2 in place?

9.6-4 If in Prob. 9.6-3 S_1 is moved 1.00 cm, how far will S_2 be moved under the same forces?

9.6-5 What would be the depth in the ocean at which the pressure would be that given in Ex. 9.6-1? Hint: To compute the depth, consider the density to be constant.

9.7 A Preliminary Study of the Atmosphere

In the discussion of the preceding section, we have ignored the fact that we live in a gas called air. It takes only a little consideration to convince us that what we have said about the pressure of liquids must apply equally to gases, the only appreciable differences being that gases are much less dense and that they cannot be considered as incompressible. We should therefore expect that the surface of the earth must support the weight of the atmosphere, and that this weight would produce a pressure.

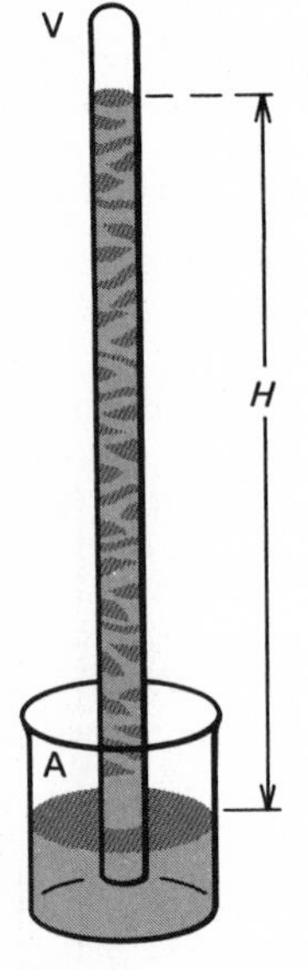

Fig. 9.12 Mercury barometer.

The existence of ***atmospheric pressure*** was demonstrated by Evangelista Torricelli (1608–1647) in 1643 by the use of a device identical in principle with the U-tube of Fig. 9.11. Torricelli's apparatus is shown in Fig. 9.12. The long tube is first filled with mercury and then inverted, without allowing any air to enter, into a shallow vessel which also contains mercury. It is then found that the mercury does not leave the tube completely, but remains at a height H above the level A of the mercury in the dish. We must infer that, since there is nothing to produce pressure at V, the pressure at A must equal ρgH, where ρ is the density of mercury. On an "average day" at sea level the height H is 0.760 m. The pressure corresponding to this height is

$$p = 13.55 \times 10^3\ (\text{kg/m}^3) \times 9.80\ (\text{m/sec}^2) \times 0.760\ (\text{m})$$
$$= 1.013 \times 10^5\ \text{N/m}^2$$

since the density of mercury at 20°C is 13.55×10^3 kg/m^3. The instrument shown in Fig. 9.12 is known as a ***mercury barometer***. Because of the historical importance of this instrument, atmospheric pressures are often referred to as ***barometric pressures***, and are usually expressed in terms of the height of the mercury column which the atmosphere will support, expressed in millimeters, centimeters, or inches. In physics, we often wish to know this pressure in N/m^2. A pressure of 760 mm of mercury is called one ***atmosphere*** (atm), and from the above calculation we have

$$1\ \text{atm} = 0.7600\ \text{m (of mercury)} = 1.013 \times 10^5\ \text{N/m}^2. \qquad (9.7\text{-}1)$$

In recent years another unit of pressure has appeared in the publication of barometric pressures by the Weather Bureau. This unit is the ***bar***, and we have the equivalence:

$$1 \text{ bar} = 1 \times 10^5 \text{ N/m}^2 = 0.7502 \text{ m (of mercury)} = 0.9869 \text{ atm.} \qquad (9.7\text{-}2)$$

Notice that one atmosphere is only a little greater than one bar. Pressure on weather maps are usually given in ***millibars***.

The pressure of the atmosphere varies from day to day as the air that covers the earth circulates from one place to another. Because the barometric pressure is a measure of the average density of the air overhead, its changes indicate whether warmer or colder air masses are moving into a given location, and so it may be used as part of the information necessary in weather prediction. We cannot calculate the depth of the atmospheric layer over a given point from Eq. (9.6-1) because the assumption of incompressibility, on which it was derived, is not valid for gases.

Atmospheric pressure can also be measured by a device similar to that shown in Fig. 9.8, if the interior of the pressure gauge is evacuated so that the force on the piston due to the pressure of the air is balanced only by the force of the spring. A device built on this principle is known as an ***aneroid barometer***. Such instruments are usually calibrated in terms of the height of an equivalent mercury column.

EXERCISES

9.7-1 Suppose a barometer of the type shown in Fig. 9.12 is constructed using water instead of mercury. What will be the height H of the water column on an "average day"?

9.7-2 Eq. (9.6-1) takes no account of the atmospheric pressure on the surface of the liquid. Supposing that the atmospheric pressure is 750 mm of mercury, find the pressure at the bottom of a tank of water 8.00 m deep.

9.7-3 Two barometers, one on the ground and the other on the top of a building 350 m high, are read simultaneously. Their respective readings are 75.92 cm and 72.64 cm. What is the average density of the air surrounding the building?

9.8 ***The Principle of Archimedes***

It is a matter of common experience that light bodies float when immersed in a liquid and that heavy bodies sink. A little thought about the behavior of a balloon will show that gases behave similarly to liquids in this respect. Even those bodies that sink in a fluid experience upward forces that decrease their weights, as may be verified by lowering a heavy piece of aluminum or other low-density metal into a tank of water and noticing the difference in the forces required to hold it up before and after submersion. It is now our purpose to investigate the forces that act on bodies immersed in liquids and gases.

The basic principle involved in ***buoyant forces*** was discovered by Archimedes (287–212 B.C.), when he realized that the forces within the fluid would be the same whether or not the foreign body was present. Thus the ship of Fig. 9.13a is supported by the pressure of the water on its hull. If the ship moves elsewhere (Fig. 9.13b), the water fills the "hole" left by the removal of the ship. However, we know that the pressure under the surface of the water depends only on the depth beneath the surface, and it follows that the weight of water within the "hole" is now supported by the same forces which previously supported the ship. The same argument applies to any body floating on the surface of a fluid or immersed beneath the fluid. Thus, *any body immersed in a fluid must be subject to a buoyant force equal to the weight of the displaced fluid.* This statement is known as ***Archimedes' principle.***

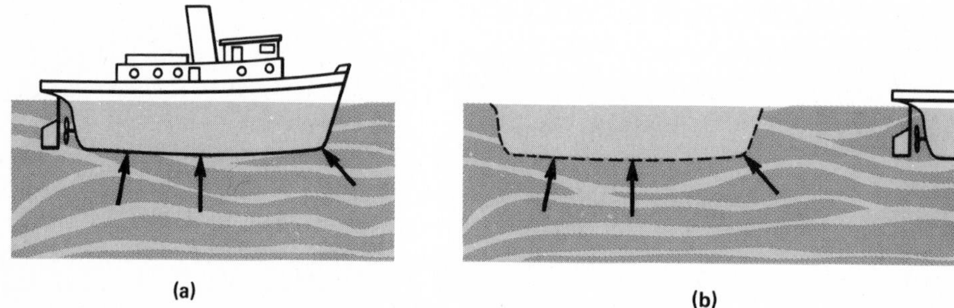

FIG. 9.13 The principle of Archimedes.

Since the volume of the displaced fluid is identical with the volume of a totally immersed body, the net weight of the body in the fluid is

$$F = mg - \rho_L V g, \tag{9.8-1}$$

where m is the mass and V the volume of the body, and ρ_L is the density of the fluid. The ***net weight*** or ***apparent weight*** of the body is thus the resultant of the actual weight of the body and the buoyant force, and is therefore the force tending to accelerate the body downward. If the immersed body is more dense than the fluid, i.e., if its density

$$\rho = (m/V) > \rho_L,$$

the net weight given by Eq. (9.8-1) will be positive and the body will sink. If the density of the body is less than that of the fluid, the net force on it will be upward, and the body will rise through the fluid. The boundary between these two cases occurs when the body has the same density as the fluid, so that the buoyant force just balances the gravitational attraction. Under these circumstances, the body will be in equilibrium. This provides us with a simple way of determining the density of an irregularly shaped solid. By mixing two liquids, one denser and one lighter than the solid, we can make a liquid in which the body neither rises nor sinks, although it is totally submerged. We may then obtain the density of the liquid mixture by weighing a known volume on a balance, as suggested in Sec. 9.2, and so determine the density of the solid. A second and more commonly used method of determining density involves the weighing of the solid first in air or in a vacuum, then while it is submerged in a liquid of known density less than that of the solid. The problem of determining the volume of the body from Eq. (9.8-1) is left as an exercise for the reader (Ex. 9.9-1).

If we wish to study in more detail the nature of the hydrostatic forces whose resultant is the buoyant force, we can consider the forces acting on a cylinder immersed in a liquid. Suppose that the mass of the cylinder is m and the density of the liquid is ρ_L. Suppose further that the cross-sectional area of the cylinder is S, that its height is h, and that its base is horizontal, as shown in Fig. 9.14. Now let us consider the forces acting on the cylinder. First, there will be a force $m\vec{g}$

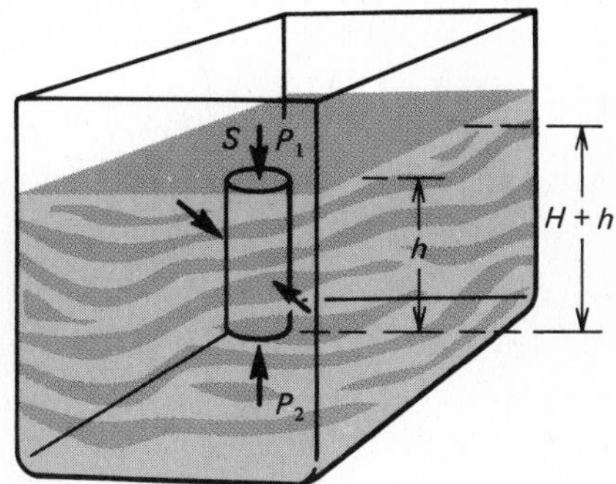

FIG. 9.14 Forces on immersed cylinder.

acting downward on the cylinder due to the attraction of the earth. On the lower end of the cylinder, there will be an upward force of magnitude $P_2 S = g\rho_L(H + h)S$. On the upper end, there will be a downward force of magnitude $P_1 S = g\rho_L HS$. These forces are due to the pressure of the liquid. We now see that the total downward force $\vec{F}$ on the body has a magnitude

$$F = mg - P_2 S + P_1 S = mg - g\rho_L(H + h)S + g\rho_L HS = mg - g\rho_L hS, \qquad (9.8\text{-}2)$$

while the sideways forces on the cylinder will cancel one another out. It will readily be seen that Eq. (9.8-2) is identical with Eq. (9.8-1).

9.9 *Application to Floating Bodies*

We saw from Eq. (9.8-1) that a body less dense than a fluid in which it was totally submerged would have "negative apparent weight" and would rise. As soon as such a body breaks the surface, however, the immersed volume decreases, and, according to Archimedes principle, the buoyant force also decreases. Equilibrium will be obtained when the buoyant force exactly equals the weight in air, mg. Hence, any body whose average density is less than that of the liquid, such as the ship of Fig. 9.13, will float on the liquid with part of its volume submerged. The volume immersed can readily be calculated by setting $F = 0$ in Eq. (9.8-1), since the body is in equilibrium, i.e.,

$$F = mg - \rho_L Vg = 0.$$

Thus, we have

$$V = m/\rho_L. \tag{9.9-1}$$

This relation is used in the design of an instrument called a ***hydrometer***, which is employed to determine densities of liquids. A glass bulb with projecting stem is loaded at the lower end so that it will float vertically as shown in Fig. 9.15. The immersed volume and hence the length of the stem that projects above the surface of the liquid will, according to Eq. (9.9-1), depend upon the density of the liquid. The stem can therefore be provided with a scale on which the density of the liquid may be read directly.

FIG. 9.15 Hydrometer.

A body can also float on the boundary between two fluids. Thus, the average density of a submarine can be adjusted so that it is less than that of sea water and greater than that of fresh water. If such a submarine is operating near the mouth of a river, where the fresh water of the river flows over the salt water of the ocean, it can "float," totally submerged, at the boundary between the two liquids. Any upward motion will result in a decreased buoyant force, so that the net weight of the submarine will become positive; any downward motion will result in an increased buoyant force and a consequent negative net weight. The submarine therefore will remain in equilibrium. The same effect can take place in a calm tropical sea, where the heat of the sun often results in a sharply defined warm layer of water on top of much cooler water below. The decrease of the density of water with increasing temperature (cf. Sec. 11.4) allows the submarine to float at the boundary.

EXERCISES

9.9-1 Derive an equation for the density of a solid body which has an apparent weight $M_O g$ in air and $M_L g$ when totally submerged in a liquid of density ρ_L.

9.9-2 A solid body is weighed on a spring balance and found to have a weight of 5000 N. The system is then lowered until the body is under water and the balance is still outside. The apparent weight is then 3400 N. What is the density of the solid?

9.9-3 Given a solid of unknown density, a liquid of unknown density, a spring balance, and some water, devise a method for determining the density of the liquid.

9.9-4 An unloaded ship, whose sides are vertical near the water line, floats at a given level in fresh water. After it has been loaded with a cargo of mass 5.0×10^5 kg, it sinks a distance of 33 cm. What is the cross-sectional area of the ship at the waterline?

9.9-5 The maximum mass of a submarine is 1.0×10^6 kg. What is the maximum value for its volume?

9.9-6 A body of density ρ_B is weighed on an equal arm balance against a set of standard masses of density ρ_M and its apparent mass is found to be m. What correction should be applied to this mass due to the buoyant force of the air, of density ρ_A?

9.9-7 By consideration of the forces acting on a cylinder similar to that shown in Fig. 9.14, but floating in virtue of its density being less than that of the liquid, derive Eq. (9.9-1). What is the ratio of the volume immersed to the whole volume of the cylinder?

9.10 ***Summary***

This chapter has been concerned with some of the mechanical properties of solids and of fluids (liquids and gases). A number of ways have been discussed for the measurement of the density (mass per unit volume) which is characteristic of a homogeneous material.

Any attempt to change the shape of a solid or the density of a fluid sets up within the substance elastic forces that resist the change. For the elastic change in length of a solid wire or bar and for the change in volume of a solid or a fluid, it has been found (Hooke's law) that the stress (force per unit area) and the strain (fractional change in dimensions) are proportional to one another if the strain is small.

Both experimental evidence and simple reasoning have been used to determine how the pressure varies within a fluid at rest. The hydrostatic pressure due to the weight of the fluid has been illustrated by the behavior of the atmosphere and by the buoyant effects of fluids on submerged objects.

PROBLEMS

9.1 The density defined in Sec. 9.1 is clearly the *average* density of the material contained in the volume V. If the density varies from place to place within a material, the density at any point may be defined as

$$\rho = \frac{dm}{dV} = \lim_{\Delta V \to 0} \frac{\Delta m}{\Delta V},$$

where Δm is the mass of the material within the volume ΔV that includes the point in question. Suppose that the density of the air near the ground on a given day decreases with height above the ground in such a way that

$$\rho = \rho_0 - kz,$$

where z is the height, ρ_0 is the density at $z = 0$, and k is a constant.

(a) Show that the mass of air in a column of uniform (horizontal) cross-sectional area A and of height h is

$$m = Ah(\rho_0 - \tfrac{1}{2}kh).$$

(b) Show that the difference between the atmospheric pressure at $z = 0$ and that at $z = h$ is

$$p_0 - p_z = \rho_0 gh - \tfrac{1}{2}kgh^2.$$

9.2 A steel measuring tape, having a thickness of 0.025 cm and a width of 1.00 cm, was calibrated when it was under no tension. A surveyor uses the tape to measure the distance between two points and reads this distance as 25.315 m. To keep the tape essentially straight between the two points, he was to pull on each end with a force of 200 N.

(a) Will the distance as read by the surveyor be greater or less than the true distance between the two points? (b) What is the true distance?

9.3 A steel wire of negligible mass is stretched between two points at the same height and 10.0 m apart. The diameter of the wire is 0.100 cm. A weight of mass 10.0 kg is then hung from the middle of the wire. (a) By how much will the length of the wire be changed? (b) What will be the height of the middle of the wire, relative to the points of support?

9.4 Hooke's law is an approximate generalization that is never strictly obeyed for real materials. Suppose that the force required to stretch a spring from its unstretched length l_0 to a new length l is

$$f = k(l - l_0) + k'(l - l_0)^2.$$

Find an expression for the potential energy of the stretched spring.

9.5 A solid cylinder of radius a and original length L rests on a firm foundation and is compressed by a weight resting upon it. The cylinder is made of material of density ρ and having Young's modulus Y.

(a) Find the force necessary to compress the cylinder to a length $L - \Delta L$.

(b) How much elastic potential energy is stored in the cylinder in its compressed state?

(c) Suppose that the weight is suddenly removed. Show that the cylinder can rise to a height h given by

$$h = (\Delta L)^2 Y / 2L^2 g\rho,$$

where g is the acceleration due to gravity.

(d) Find h if the cylinder is made of steel, $L = 30$ cm, and $\Delta L/L = 10^{-3}$.

9.6 A long, thin, uniform bar of length L, cross-sectional area A, and mass m is rotating about an axis that passes through the center of mass and is perpendicular to the bar. The angular velocity is constant and is equal to ω.

(a) Consider a small piece of the bar, extending from a plane perpendicular to the bar at a distance r from the center of mass to a parallel plane at a distance $r + \Delta r$ from the center of mass. Show that the centripetal force necessary to hold this piece in uniform circular motion is

$$\Delta F \approx m\omega^2 r \, \Delta r / L.$$

(b) By passing to the limit $\Delta r \to 0$, to make the approximate equality exact, show that

$$dF/dr = m\omega^2 r / L.$$

(c) Show that the bar must be under tension, and show that the tension T (force per unit cross-sectional area) varies with the distance from the axis in such a way that

$$T = (m\omega^2/8AL)(L^2 - 4r^2).$$

(Use the fact that the tension must be zero when $r = \frac{1}{2}L$.)

(d) Show that the section between r and $r + \Delta r$ stretches by an amount

$$\frac{T\Delta r}{Y} \approx \frac{m\omega^2}{8ALY}(L^2 - 4r^2)\,\Delta r,$$

where Y is the value of Young's modulus.

(e) Show that the length of the bar increases by an amount

$$\Delta L = m\omega^2 L^2/12AY.$$

(Hint: Pass to the limit $\Delta r \to 0$ and integrate.)

9.7 A tank of water has a small hole of area A in its wall, at a depth z below the surface of the water inside. Consider that a small mass of water (m) emerges from this hole during some short time interval. Neglect frictional effects. (a) Show that the potential energy of the water in the tank decreases by an amount mgz during the time interval. (b) Find the speed with which the water leaves the hole. (c) Show that the rate at which water leaves the tank is

$$\frac{dm}{dt} = A\rho\sqrt{2gz},$$

where ρ is the density. (It may be of some help to read the first paragraph of Sec. 17.2 before doing this part of the problem.)

9.8 A balloon filled with helium has a density less than air. It is inside a closed automobile. (a) If the car is moving with uniform velocity, will the balloon rest on the floor or against the top of the car? (b) If the car rounds a curve will the balloon move toward the inside or outside of the curve? (c) What can be expected to happen to the balloon if the brakes are applied suddenly?

9.9 One might improve the solution obtained in Ex. 9.6-5 by taking the compressibility of the water into account.

(a) Using the binomial theorem of Appendix H, show that

$$\rho_2 = \rho_1\left(1 + \frac{P_2 - P_1}{B}\right),$$

where ρ_2 is the density of the liquid under a pressure P_2, ρ_1 is its density under a pressure P_1, and B is the bulk modulus.

(b) Using this result and the pressure as given by Eq. (9.6-1), show that the density at a depth z below the surface is

$$\rho_z \approx \rho_0\left(1 + \frac{\rho_0 gz}{B}\right),$$

where ρ_0 is the density at the surface.

(c) Prove that the more exact solution for the pressure at depth h is

$$P = P_0 + \int_0^h \rho_z g\, dz.$$

(d) Find the pressure at the depth given in Ex. 9.6-5 and recalculate the density at this depth. By what fraction of the total density was the approximate result in error?

9.10 A log may be approximated as a cylinder of radius a and length L. It has a density of 500 kg/m^3 and is floating in fresh water. At some instant it is in the position shown in (I).

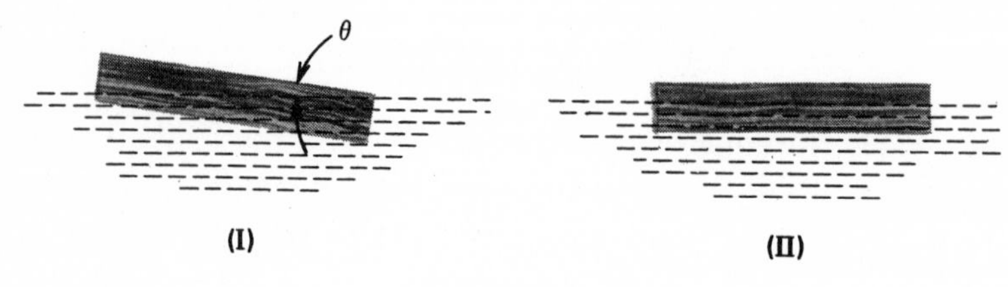

PROBLEM 9.10

(a) Show that there is no net force on the log in this position. (b) Show that a torque does act on the log and that it has such a direction that it will cause θ to decrease. (c) Show that no force and no torque are exerted on the log in the position shown at (II), and hence that the log is in equilibrium in this position.

(Hint: Remember that the buoyant force may be considered to act through the center of mass *of the displaced water*. Qualitative reasoning is sufficient for this problem.)

REFERENCES

9A Ernst Mach, *The Science of Mechanics*, 6th edition, Open Court, La Salle, Ill., 1960. Pages 106–150 pertain to properties of matter.

9B William Francis Magie, *A Source Book in Physics*, Harvard, Cambridge, Mass., 1935. The behavior of fluids is treated by selections appearing in pp. 70–84, and a discussion of elasticity follows in pp. 93–97.

9C Reginald J. Stephenson, *Mechanics and the Properties of Matter*, 2nd edition, Wiley, New York, 1960. Chapter 7 is commended to the reader as a more extensive introduction to the macroscopic properties of matter.

9D George Hidy, *The Winds* (Momentum Book No. 19), Van Nostrand, Princeton, N.J., 1967. Applications of the principles covered here and others to the study of the atmosphere.

9E John Stewart, *The World of High Pressure* (Momentum Book No. 17), Van Nostrand, Princeton, N.J., 1967. Methods of producing very high pressures and effects of such pressures on solid bodies.

10 ⇨ *Wave Motion*

10.1 The Transmission of Energy

In earlier chapters we were concerned with kinetic and potential energy and we discussed the properties of energy in isolated systems. We can now investigate the ways in which energy can be transmitted from one part of the system to another.

The simplest method for the transmission of energy uses projectiles of various sorts. A bowler exerts himself to give kinetic energy to a ball, which travels down the alley carrying its energy with it. When it hits the pins at the end of the alley, it gives up some of its energy to them and expends the rest in the backstop. The bowler has exerted the energy which finally scattered the pins, but he has done it indirectly through the agency of the ball. Other examples of this process are the projectile weapons, such as the bow and arrow and the slingshot, in which the energy to kill or injure is provided by the man using them, and the rifle or shotgun, in which the energy is provided by the burning of gunpowder in the barrel. In each case the energy is carried through space by the projectile. Other examples of projectile motion are streams of water, of air, and of other fluids. An electric fan on one side of a room can remove papers from a table on the other side. A hose in the hands of a fireman can knock down a man or tear the shingles from a burning roof.

A second method for the transmission of energy is somewhat more subtle than the projectile method in that it does not involve the transportation of matter from one place to another, but merely the transportation of a disturbance of some sort. An earthquake occurs in the Aleutian Islands and causes a tidal wave in Hawaii. This does not mean that water from the Aleutians has been hurled at the shores of Hawaii. It means that the Pacific Ocean has been disturbed in one place and the disturbance has traveled across the surface of the water, finally causing damage on the beaches of another shore. Other examples are musical instruments. A pianist expends energy in disturbing the strings of a piano which then agitates the air around them. This disturbance spreads through the concert hall until it reaches the ears of the listener. Some of the energy originally expended by the pianist stimulates a physiological process in the ear of the listener. This process is analyzed by the ear and the brain and gives the sensation we call musical sound. Disturbances of these types, which carry energy from place to place without the transport of matter, are called ***waves***.

10.2 Waves in a Train

We can obtain an extensive understanding of the nature of waves by considering the starting of a train. Suppose that all the cars of the train (Fig. 10.1a) are alike and that they are connected together by springs that are initially unextended so that no car is exerting a force on its neighbors. As the train starts, the locomotive, pulling toward the right, exerts a force on car 1, rapidly accelerating it so that before car 2 starts to move the spring between cars 1 and 2 is stretched as in Fig. 10.1b.

Figure 10.1b was taken 0.36 sec after the locomotive started to move, as indicated by the one rev/sec clock. A careful study of the photographs shows that car 1 has moved forward by a considerable amount from its starting position and that car 2 is just starting to move. The photograph in Fig. 10.1c, taken 0.70 sec after the starting of the locomotive, shows that car 2 has moved about half as far as car 1, that car 3 has started to move, and that car 4 is just starting.

Let us designate the spring between the locomotive and car 1 as 01, that between cars 1 and 2 as 12, etc. As soon as spring 12 is extended as in Fig. 10.1b, it exerts a force to the left on car 1 and so decreases its acceleration, but at the same time, it exerts a force to the right on car 2 and so accelerates it. We see in the photographs that the two springs 01 and 12 were stretched appreciably in 0.36 sec and that the fourth spring (34) was starting to stretch at the end of 0.70 sec. It therefore seems that the number of springs stretched (and the number of cars put into motion) is at least approximately proportional to the time interval since the locomotive started, i.e., that the disturbance created by the locomotive passes along the train with a constant speed.

Let us now consider the starting wave in some detail. In Fig. 10.2a the train, with the locomotive off the page to the left, is shown before any motion is started. In Fig. 10.2b, however, the locomotive pulling to the left has rapidly accelerated the first car to a velocity $-\vec{V}$, and the locomotive then keeps the car moving at this constant speed. If the acceleration is so rapid that this happens before the second car has time to move appreciably, the state of affairs will be shown in Fig. 10.2b. This condition cannot last, however, since the stretched spring 12 exerts a force pulling car 2 to the left. This force will accelerate the car. When car 2 is moving at the same speed as car 1, the state of affairs will be that shown in Fig. 10.2c. Car 2 will no longer experience any further acceleration, because spring 23 is pulling on it to the right with a force equal to that with which spring 12 pulls to the left; i.e., the net force on car 2 is zero. Consequently, car 2 will continue to move at the same speed as car 1 and spring 12 will remain at its stretched length, so that the cars will be further apart than they were with the train at rest. Spring 23, however, will accelerate car 3 until the latter is moving with the same speed as cars 1 and 2, as shown in Fig. 10.2d.

Notice that the whole train does not start in motion at once. Rather, the disturbance created by the locomotive—i.e., the motion of the cars and the stretching of the springs—gradually moves along the train. In Fig. 10.2a it

Fig. 10.1 Starting a train of cars joined by spring couplings.

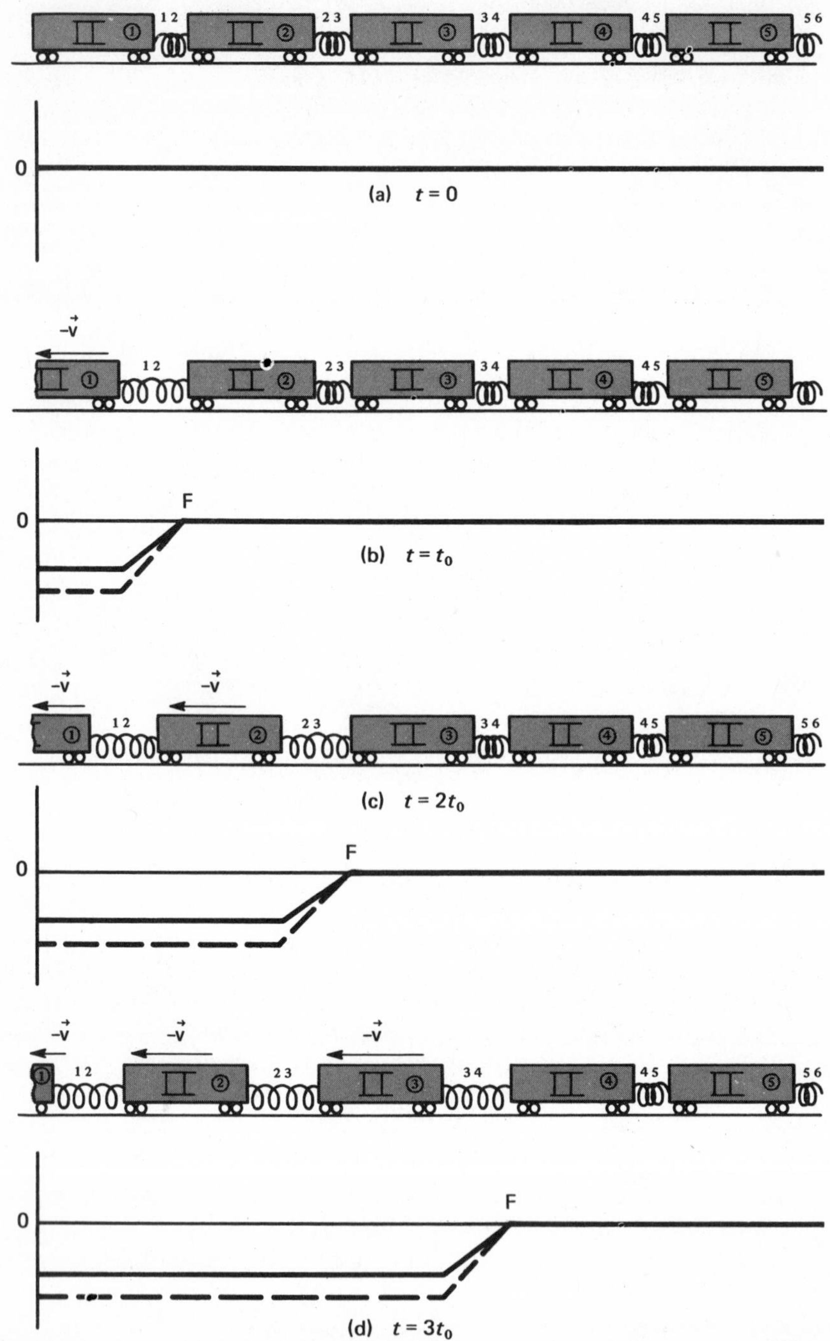

Fig. 10.2 Starting an ideal train with locomotive pulling to the left. Velocity and compression waves shown at times $t = 0$, t_0, $2t_0$, and $3t_0$.

has not appeared among the cars shown; in Fig. 10.2b it has reached car 1 and spring 12; in Fig. 10.2c it has arrived at car 2 and spring 23, etc. This motion of a disturbance is a feature of all wave motions.

We can represent the process just described by a succession of graphs. In Fig. 10.2 the speed of the cars is plotted as a solid line and the compression of the springs between the cars as a dotted line. Note that speed to the left is plotted as a negative quantity as is the compression; stretching is negative compression. The points labeled F are the front of the disturbance as it progresses along the train. The heavy line along the axis, to the right of F in each instance, indicates those parts of the train that are as yet undisturbed by the speed and compression waves.

If, instead of pulling the train to the left, the locomotive pushes the train to the right, it is easy to see that the situation will be that represented by Fig. 10.3; both the velocity and the compression will now be positive.

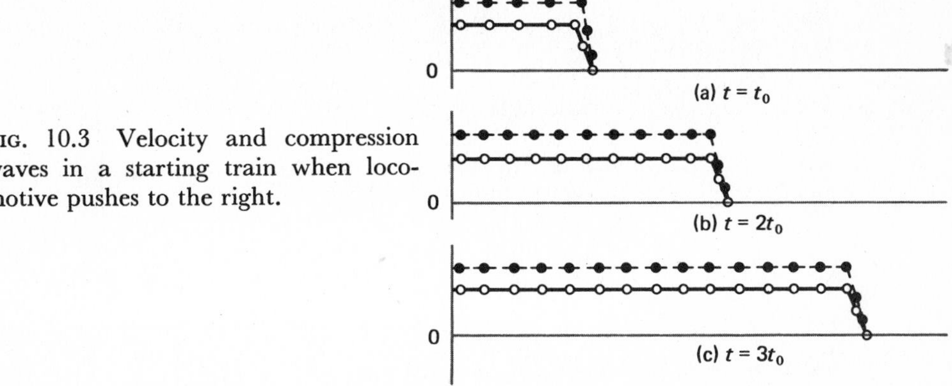

FIG. 10.3 Velocity and compression waves in a starting train when locomotive pushes to the right.

As an extension of these notions, it is easy to imagine an engineer starting and stopping the train according to some complicated routine and thus sending a complicated set of motions down the length of the train, We can, for example, consider the case in which the engineer starts (at $t = 0$) to push the train to the right with the velocity $+\vec{V}$, then at $t = t_0$ he reverses his velocity to $-\vec{V}$, and finally at $t = 2t_0$ he stops the train. The wave he sends down the train is that shown in Fig. 10.4. Notice that in a wave of this type some cars are moving to the right while others are moving to the left. Those who have been on a train run by an inexperienced or nervous engineer will recognize this phenomenon without difficulty.

The reader may have noticed that all the discussions of this section will break down when the last car of the train starts to move. We have purposely avoided this issue and shall return to it in Sec. 10.11. For the present we shall assume that the train is very long and that we are considering disturbances that have not yet had time to reach the end of the train.

EXERCISES

10.2-1 Draw a graph of the same type as those of Figs. 10.2 and 10.3 for the wave propagation along a train pulled by an engine toward the right. (Hint: Note carefully the signs of the compression of the strings and of the velocity.)

10.2-2 Repeat Ex. 10.2-1 for the case in which the engine pushes the train toward the left.

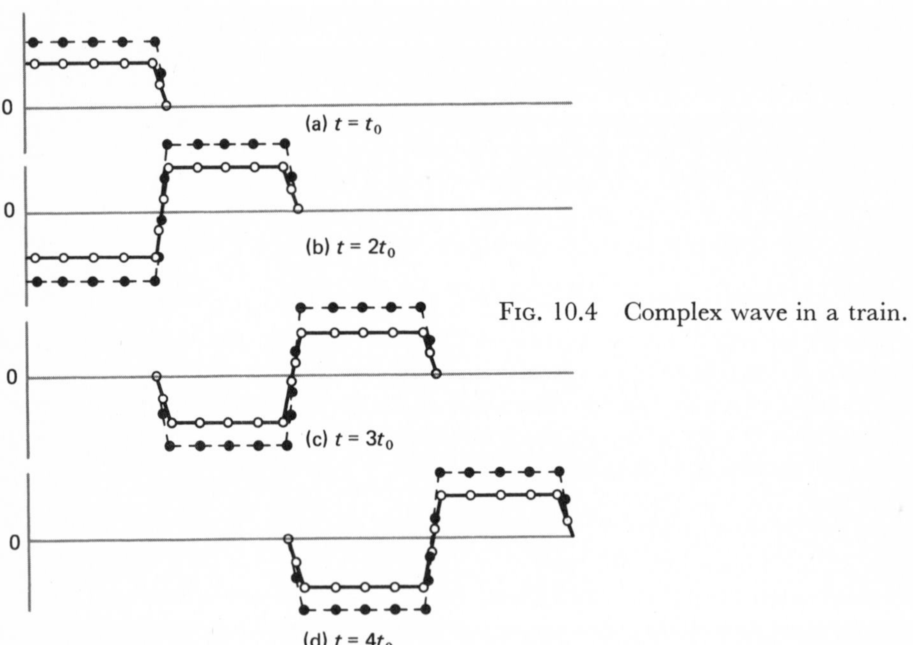

FIG. 10.4 Complex wave in a train.

10.3 Calculation of the Wave Speed in a Train

The qualitative discussion of Sec. 10.2, while it displayed the mechanism by which a disturbance traveled along the train, was unsatisfactory in the sense that it gave us no indication of the rate at which the starting wave progressed. We now consider the problem in somewhat greater detail. It is easy to see that the rate of propagation of the wave must depend on the mass of the cars and the stiffness of the springs that couple them. This follows directly from Eq. (4.9-4) which relates the force F, the mass m on which it acts, and the acceleration a produced by the force

$$F = ma.$$

The time taken for any car to be accelerated to its final velocity will obviously be inversely proportional to the acceleration, and we see that this acceleration is directly proportional to the force exerted by the spring and inversely proportional to the mass of the car. If more massive cars are used, the time will be increased because the acceleration will be decreased; if stiffer springs are used, giving greater forces for the same extension, the time will be decreased. Since the time taken for one car to be accelerated to its final velocity is obviously equal to the time taken for the wave to travel one car length, we see that the wave speed must increase as the springs are made stiffer and must decrease as the cars are made heavier.

Although a consideration of the forces shows us on what factors the speed of propagation depends, the calculation of this speed is most easily carried out with the help of energy considerations. The starting of the train is accomplished by a transfer of energy from the locomotive to the cars. Initially, neither the cars nor the springs had any energy. Each car in motion, however, has acquired a kinetic energy $\frac{1}{2}mV^2$, where m is the mass of the car and V is its speed [cf. Eq. (4.11-6)]. Similarly, each spring that has been stretched or compressed has acquired a potential energy $\frac{1}{2}k(\Delta x)^2$, where k is the stiffness constant of the spring and Δx is the amount by which it is stretched or compressed [cf. Eq. (9.4-4)]. If n cars have been set in motion and n springs have been stretched or compressed, the total energy acquired by the train is therefore

$$E = n\{\tfrac{1}{2}mV^2 + \tfrac{1}{2}k(\Delta x)^2\}. \tag{10.3-1}$$

The source of this energy is the work done by the locomotive in accelerating the train. To compute the work, suppose that the locomotive pulls or pushes the train with a constant force F. The work done during any time t is F times the distance that the locomotive has moved. Since the locomotive is moving with constant speed V, the work done is therefore

$$w = FVt. \tag{10.3-2}$$

If n cars have been put into motion in the time t, n springs have been stretched or compressed during the same time, since the $(n + 1)$ car has not yet moved. The distance traveled by the locomotive is exactly the amount that n springs have stretched, i.e.,

$$Vt = n\Delta x. \tag{10.3-3}$$

The force exerted by the locomotive is exactly the force stretching each spring, since the first n cars are no longer accelerated and therefore have no net force acting on them. Assuming that Hooke's law [Eq. (9.3-5)] holds, we know that

$$F = k\Delta x.$$

Inserting the values just found for Vt and F into Eq. (10.3-2), we see that the work done by the locomotive in starting n cars into motion is

$$w = nk(\Delta x)^2.$$

The conservation law tells us that this work must be equal to the energy acquired by the n cars that have started into motion and the n springs that have been distorted. Equating this work to the energy, as given by Eq. (10.3-1), we find that

$$k(\Delta x)^2 = \tfrac{1}{2}mV^2 + \tfrac{1}{2}k(\Delta x)^2$$

or that

$$\tfrac{1}{2}k(\Delta x)^2 = \tfrac{1}{2}mV^2. \tag{10.3-4}$$

This expression can be rewritten as

$$(V/\Delta x)^2 = k/m.$$

Finally, substituting the value of $V = n\Delta x/t$ from Eq. (10.3-3), we find that

$$n/t = (k/m)^{1/2}. \tag{10.3-5}$$

We thus see that the number of cars that have started in motion at the end of a time t (after the locomotive starts) is proportional to the time, the constant of proportionality being $\sqrt{k/m}$. It is a remarkable and interesting fact that the speed at which the disturbance moves along the train is not dependent on the speed of the locomotive, but depends only on the stiffness constant of the springs and the mass of the cars—i.e., on the physical characteristics of the train.

10.4 The Speed of a Longitudinal Wave in a Rod

The argument of the two preceding sections can immediately be applied to a discussion of the waves in a solid rod which is struck at one end by a hammer, as shown in Fig. 10.5. When the hammer strikes, the solid immediately underneath

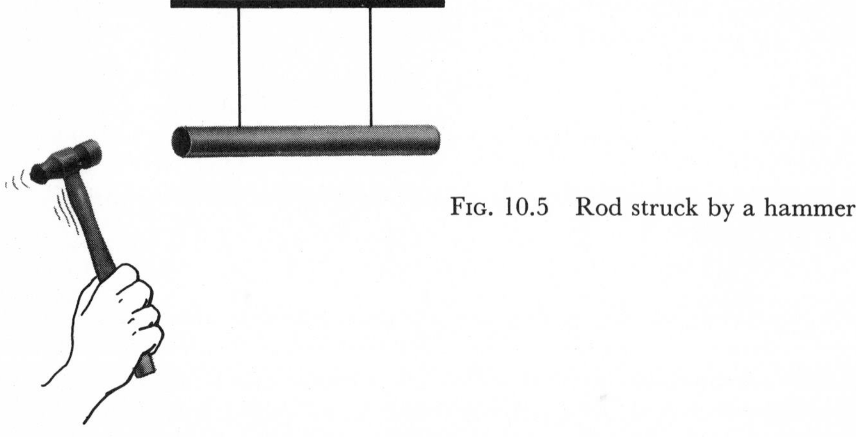

FIG. 10.5 Rod struck by a hammer.

it will be moved to the right and be compressed. This compression will result in a motion and a compression of the material next to it, and a disturbance will travel down the rod. As the disturbance proceeds, each part of the rod must be accelerated and compressed, and it is easy to see that the process is strictly analogous to the problem of starting a train. It is true that the rod is not made up of a number of "cars," connected by "springs," but it does possess mass, as did the cars, and the rod is capable of exerting elastic forces, as did the springs. If we think of the rod as being divided into very short identical sections, each of these sections can be considered analogous to a single car. Moreover, each section, if it is to transmit a force from the section on its left to the section on its right, must be compressed while the force acts. It will therefore be analogous to a spring, as well as to a car. The net result of the process is that the whole rod eventually moves to the right, but this discussion shows that, as in the case of the train, all parts do not start at the same time.

Let the length of each of the sections into which the rod is mentally divided be a. Each of these lengths a, which can be said to correspond to a single car of the train, has a mass m given by the density of the material times the volume of the section, i.e.,

$$m = \rho S a, \tag{10.4-1}$$

where S is the cross-sectional area of the rod and ρ is the density of the material of which it is made. By Eq. (9.3-6) we know that the stiffness constant of a rod of length a, of cross section S, and Young's modulus Y is given by

$$k = YS/a. \tag{10.4-2}$$

Substituting Eqs. (10.4-1) and (10.4-2) in Eq. (10.3-5), we get

$$\begin{aligned} n/t &= (k/m)^{1/2} = (YS/\rho Sa^2)^{1/2} \\ &= \frac{(Y/\rho)^{1/2}}{a}. \end{aligned} \tag{10.4-3}$$

This result gives us the number of sections, each of length a, traversed by the disturbance in time t. The distance traveled in a time t is then na, and consequently the speed W with which disturbance moves is given by

$$W = na/t = (Y/\rho)^{1/2}. \tag{10.4-4}$$

The speed W is called the ***wave speed for compression waves*** in a rod of the material in question. Because the motions of the individual parts of the material in such compression waves are in the same direction as that in which the wave progresses, compression waves are also called ***longitudinal waves.***

In Ex. 10.4-2 below, the reader is asked to verify that, in the case of a fluid, the compression wave speed W is given by

$$W = (M_B/\rho)^{1/2}, \tag{10.4-5}$$

where M_B is the bulk modulus of the fluid and ρ is its density.

It is useful to note by Eqs. (10.3-5), (10.4-4), and (10.4-5) that the wave speed in each case is given by the square root of a ratio that always has an elasticity factor in its numerator and an inertial factor in its denominator. It turns out that wave speeds can always be expressed by a ratio of this sort no matter what kind of wave is considered.

EXERCISES

10.4-1 Verify that Eqs. (10.4-4) and (10.4-5) are dimensionally correct.

10.4-2 By considering the compression of a fluid in a vessel such as that depicted in Fig. 9.3, prove that the ratio of the force F to the displacement Δx of the piston is given by

$$F/\Delta x = -M_B\, S/a,$$

where a is the length of the vessel, and hence verify Eq. (10.4-5).

10.4-3 Compute the wave speeds for rods of aluminum and steel, and for mercury and water.

10.4-4 In a certain train, the mass of each car is 30×10^3 kg, and the cars are coupled by springs in which a force of 1200 N produces a compression of 1.0 cm. If the length of each car is 10.0 m, what time will elapse before the 50th car is started?

10.5 Periodic Waves

Most of the waves we have been discussing have been the result of sudden disturbances propagated along the train, rod, or other material body in the form of a pulse. In physics, we are particularly interested in waves that result from periodic disturbances, i.e., disturbances that repeat themselves identically again and again. Examples of such waves are the surface waves on a large body of water, in which the surface rises and falls regularly with monotonous, and sometimes painful, regularity.

Had the engineer of Sec. 10.2 continued his process of reversing the train at regular intervals, as illustrated in Fig. 10.4, he would have kept disturbances moving along the train, and there would always be some cars moving to the right, while others were moving to the left. An especially interesting case arises if the engineer varies the velocity of the locomotive in a continuous and continual fashion. For example, suppose that he oscillates the engine so that its position varies in a manner similar to that of the weight of Fig. 2.12. The velocity wave in the train then has the appearance of Fig. 10.6. Because of the identity of the shape of this curve with a sine curve (Fig. G.3 of Appendix G) such a wave is called a ***sinusoidal wave.***

In the case of the train, the frequency with which the motion could be reversed would be somewhat limited, since a single car cannot be moving in two directions at once. If the sinusoidal disturbance is applied to the end of a continuous rod like that of Sec. 10.4, the result is somewhat clearer. The instantaneous velocity of any point along the length of the rod will then vary sinusoidally.

The distance λ between any two successive points behaving identically is called the ***wavelength*** of the sinusoidal wave (Fig. 10.6). Thus, the wavelength

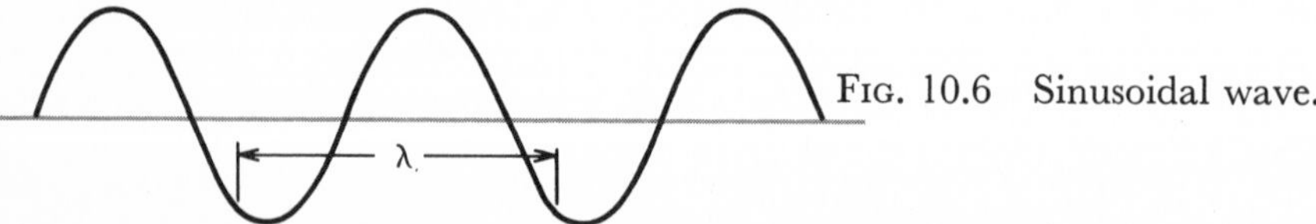

FIG. 10.6 Sinusoidal wave.

is the distance between successive crests, or successive troughs, or between any two points of the same slope and the same distance from the axis. If a sinusoidal wave is moving with a speed W, then the time taken by one complete wave in passing a fixed observer is called the ***periodic time*** τ of the wave (cf. Sec. 2.19). During this time the wave shown in Fig. 10.6 will have moved a distance λ to the right at a speed W. Hence,

$$\lambda = W\tau. \tag{10.5-1}$$

Successive stages of the wave as it progresses through the material are shown in Fig. 10.7. Each of these curves represents the state of affairs as it would be caught by a snapshot taken at a particular instant. The instants chosen here are simple fractions of the period. If we focus our attention on any point in the material such as A (Fig. 10.7), we see that the velocity at that point varies through one complete cycle from $+\vec{V}$ through zero to $-\vec{V}$ and back through

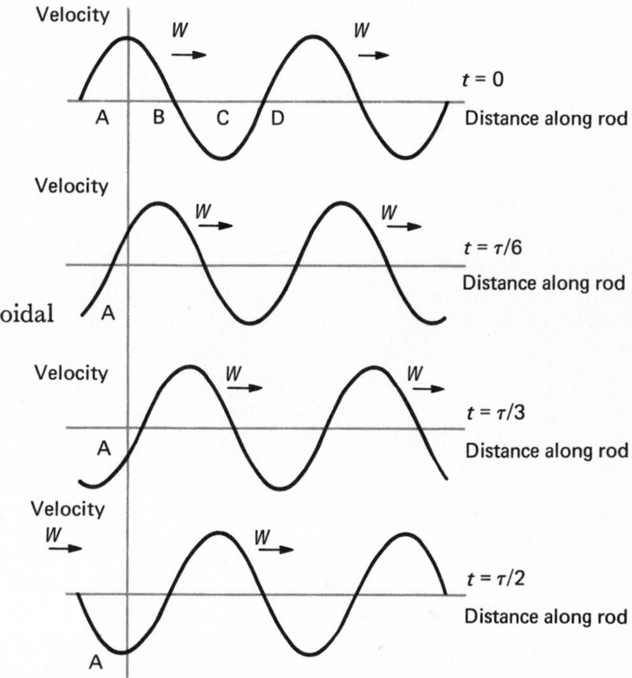

Fig. 10.7 Progression of a sinusoidal wave.

zero to $+\vec{V}$ again during the time τ. The velocity thus varies with time in the same manner as did the displacement of the weight of Sec. 2.19, and we see from Eq. (2.19-1) that the frequency of oscillation at any point in the material is given by

$$\nu = 1/\tau. \tag{10.5-2}$$

This is called the ***frequency*** of the wave. By substituting the value of τ from Eq. (10.5-1) into Eq. (10.5-2), we find that

$$\nu\lambda = W. \tag{10.5-3}$$

This relation among the frequency, wavelength, and speed of propagation expresses one of the most important properties of sinusoidal waves. It is valid not only for compression waves in a rod, but also for all other waves in which the quantities involved vary sinusoidally with time. We shall meet a number of such waves in our later studies.

In Figs. 10.6 and 10.7, the sinusoidal wave was used to graph the instantaneous velocities of the points along the rod at a given time. Thus, at $t = 0$ point A has a maximum positive velocity, while point B, $\lambda/4$ farther out along the rod is momentarily at rest. At the same instant ($t=0$), point C has an extreme negative velocity and point D is at rest. The sinusoidal wave form could also be used to graph other features of the wave motion, say, the displacement or the compression. We should note, however, that the crest of the velocity wave corresponding to a given point, say A, at a given time, say $t=0$, will not coincide with the crest of the displacement wave at $t=0$. A little thought will convince the reader that a point cannot have a maximum displacement and a maximum velocity at the same time; if the displacement is a maximum, the velocity at that moment must be zero and changing in direction. We then say that the velocity wave and the displacement wave do not have the same phase. We shall deal more with phase difference in Chapter 22.

As an example of the use of a sine curve to represent a compression wave consider Fig. 10.8. In Fig. 10.8b, the equidistant lines represent arbitrarily

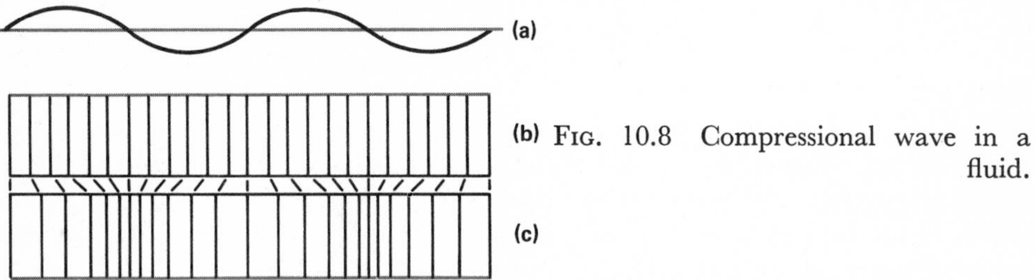

FIG. 10.8 Compressional wave in a fluid.

marked layers in a fluid before a compression wave passes. The sine curve of Fig. 10.8a represents the displacement of each layer at some particular instant. The resulting position of the layers is shown in Fig. 10.8c. It is clear from the figure that the distance between two successive regions of compression or two successive regions of rarefaction, is one wavelength.

The maximum displacement of any portion of the material from its rest position is defined as the ***displacement amplitude*** of the wave (cf. Sec. 2.19). We also speak of the maximum departure of the velocity from zero (Figs. 10.6 and 10.7) as the ***velocity amplitude***, and in a similar way the ***compression amplitude***, would be the maximum departure of the compression from its normal value.

10.6 Waves in Space

Thus far we have considered waves that have only one direction of travel, and we have seen how such waves continue to travel in the one direction when once they are started. It is easy, however, to see that if a small volume of a solid or a fluid such as the air undergoes expansion or contraction, it will impart that expansion or contraction to the surrounding fluid and will send out waves in all directions. Since the speed of the wave will always be the same in a given fluid [Eq. (10.4-5)], the waves will spread out spherically from the pulsating region. A section through such a system of spherical waves surrounding a pulsating source S is shown in Fig. 10.9, in which the full lines may be taken to represent regions of maximum compression and the dotted lines represent regions of maximum rarefaction. The process of the spreading of spherical waves from a small pulsating body in space is of course quite similar to the spreading of circular waves on the surface of a pond when a pebble is thrown into the water.

We shall see in Sec. 10.8 that sound is transmitted by a compression wave originating from a pulsating source. Such waves are, of course, examples of disturbances which spread in three dimensions. Figure 10.10 includes two photographs that show the regions in which the air is compressed by a wave

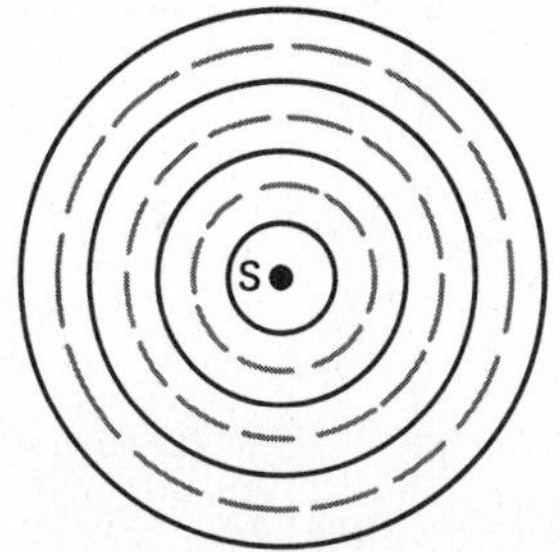

Fig. 10.9 Section through a spherical wave.

spreading out from an explosive sound behind the round shield in the center of the picture. Figure 10.10a shows the state of affairs 11×10^{-5} sec after the sound originated. The wave has spread out spherically from the source, except where it has impinged on a plane solid surface at the left, from which it has been reflected. Figure 10.10b was photographed 9×10^{-5} sec later than Fig. 10.10a, and we may notice that both the direct and the reflected waves are continuing to spread out. We shall return later to this figure in discussing the reflection of waves.

10.7 Energy in Waves

From the discussion of waves in the preceding sections it is obvious that wave motion provides a means of transmitting energy from one part of space to another. Thus, if an engineer sends the pulse of Fig. 10.4 down a long train, the resulting motion of the last car can be made to do work long after the engine has ceased to move. In a more delicate way, the waves spreading out from a pulsating source such as that discussed in Sec. 10.6 can be made to do work, and in this way a source of energy in one location can be made to do work in a region far away.

10.8 Sound Sources and Sound Waves

Suppose that a bar of metal is clamped at one end and then bent elastically into the form shown by the solid lines of Fig. 10.11. After it is released, it will oscillate between the limits shown by the solid lines and the dotted lines. Whenever the bar is moving to the right, it will compress the air on that side of it and allow the air on the other side to expand. The opposite happens when the motion reverses. These disturbances will be propagated through the air with a speed determined by Eq. (10.4-5). We shall see in Chapter 20 that the bulk modulus and the density of air are such that the speed of sound in air is 331.4 m/sec at 0°C, and that it increases with increasing temperature in accordance with the equation

$$W_t = (331.4 \text{ m/sec}) \sqrt{(273° + t)/273°}, \qquad (10.8\text{-}1)$$

where W_t is the speed of a longitudinal wave in air at the temperature t, measured in degrees Celsius (Centigrade).

The alternate compressions and rarefactions produced in a fluid can be detected in many ways, but one of the best is by the ear. If the frequency of the

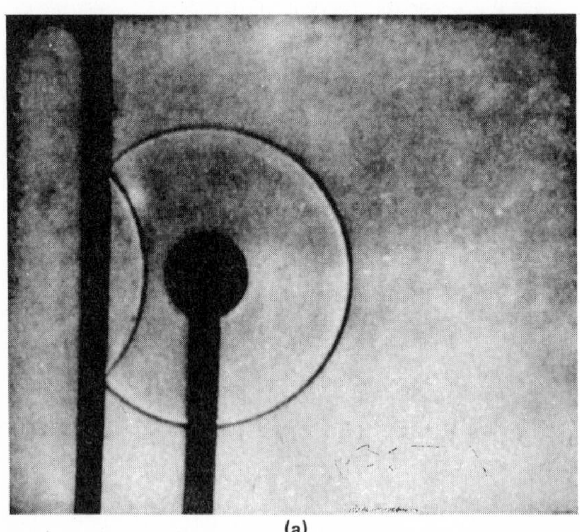

(a)

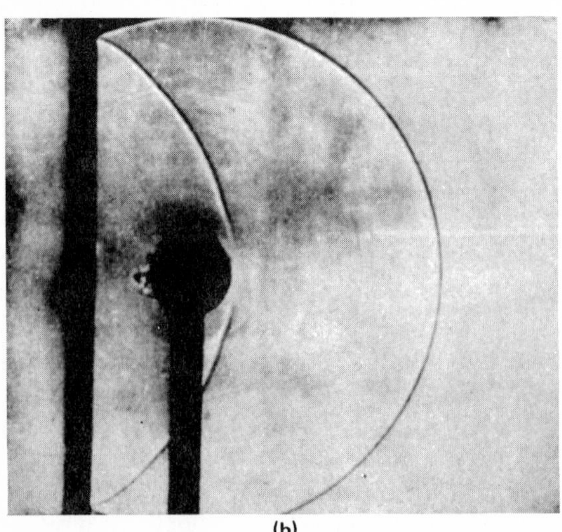

(b)

FIG. 10.10 Photographs of a sound wave. (By permission of Central Scientific Company.)

compressional wave is roughly between the limits of 50/sec and 20,000/sec, the sensation of sound is produced. (The sensitivity of the ear to sound is not uniform over this range of frequencies, and the limits vary not only from person to person but also with age.) Compressional waves, whether in air or in some other medium, are often spoken of as ***sound waves.***

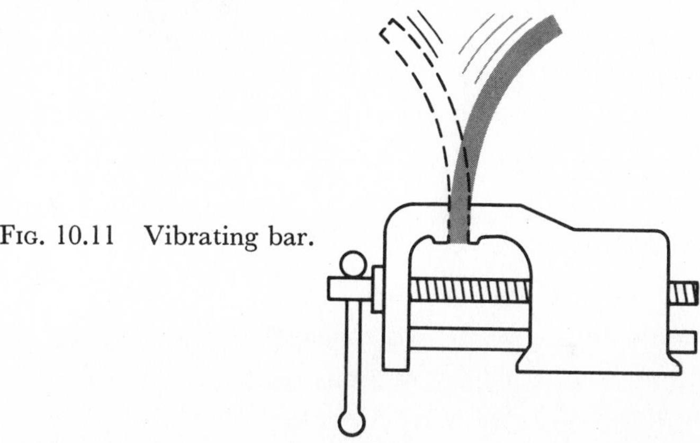

FIG. 10.11 Vibrating bar.

Not only the vibrating bar of Fig. 10.11 but also any other body vibrating with a frequency within the audible range can act as a source of sound. We shall have occasion later in this chapter to investigate in some detail the behavior of various sound sources.

10.9 Relations between Sound Waves and Hearing

The sensation produced when a sound wave reaches the ear depends not only on the characteristics of the wave but also on the physiology of the ear and the brain. The wave motion itself can be described in terms of its speed of propagation, its frequency, and its amplitude. We describe musical sounds, in the simplest terms, as having pitch and loudness. What is the relation between these two descriptions?

While an exact answer to this question cannot yet be given, certain approximations to it have been established by experiment. The frequency of the sound wave is found to determine, almost entirely, the pitch of the note heard. Increasing frequency corresponds to increasing pitch, and a doubling of the frequency results in an increase of pitch of one octave. Thus, most modern musical instruments when they sound middle A emit a sound wave of frequency 440/sec, and one of 880/sec for A one octave higher.

The amplitude of the disturbance reaching the ear is the principal factor in determining the loudness, particularly if two sounds of the same pitch are compared. The loudness does not increase as rapidly as does the amplitude, however. It has been found that the relative loudness of two sounds of the same pitch but of different amplitudes is closely proportional to the logarithm of the ratio of the amplitudes.

EXERCISES

10.9-1 A rule for finding one's distance from a lightning flash is to count seconds from the time that one sees the flash until one hears the thunder, and to divide the count by 5. The result gives the distance in miles. Justify this rule and compute the percentage error in it at 20°C.

10.9-2 A car stands at some distance from a plane vertical cliff. The temperature is 26°C. If a short blast is sounded on the horn, an echo is heard 13.0 sec later. How far away is the cliff?

10.9-3 What is the wavelength of the wave that results in air at 20°C from the sounding of middle A?

10.9-4 Two musical notes are separated by two octaves. What is the ratio of their wavelengths, and which note (in terms of its pitch) has the longer wavelength?

10.10 The Principle of Superposition

Sound waves, like many other waves in which the effect is less obvious, can be superposed upon each other. For example, when a chord is played on the piano, the several strings vibrating at different frequencies send out waves of different frequencies and wavelengths, all of which are disturbances propagated through the same body of air at the same time. Similarly, when two musical instruments are played in unison, each sends out a separate wave, but the two waves travel through the air together. In either case, the wave that strikes the ear of the listener is a complex wave resulting from the combination of the waves from the individual sources, and it is this complex wave which produces the sensation of sound in the ear. In order to investigate these phenomena and many others in wave motion, it will be necessary for us to consider the way in which waves combine, or superpose on each other.

The simplest assumption in regard to the combination of two or more waves is that the effect of the combination is just the sum of the effects that the individual waves would produce if each were present alone. It is fortunate that this simple idea, known as the ***principle of superposition***, can be verified experimentally and theoretically for all materials in which Hooke's law (Secs. 9.3 and 9.4) is obeyed—i.e., for those materials for which the displacement and the force on the surroundings produced by a displacement of material are proportional to one another. It is only such ***elastic waves*** with which we shall be concerned at the present time.

Before we consider the principle of superposition as applied to waves in space, it will be worth while to illustrate it by simple waves that travel along a straight line, such as those involved in the starting of a train (cf. Secs. 10.2 and 10.3). Consider a long train with two identical locomotives, one at each end. Suppose that the two locomotives simultaneously start into motion in the same direction and with the same speed, the one at the left pushing the train and the one at the right pulling it. As we have seen in Sec. 10.2, the disturbance set up by either locomotive will move along the train with a finite speed, and there will be a considerable time during which the central portion of the train will not have felt the effect of either locomotive. During this period the two waves will be approaching each other without any interactions between them. The two waves will then be as represented in Fig. 10.12b. The locomotive on the left will have started the cars near it moving with a positive velocity, $+\vec{V}$ and will have given the springs joining these cars a positive compression $+C$. The locomotive on the right will also have started the cars near it into motion with a positive velocity

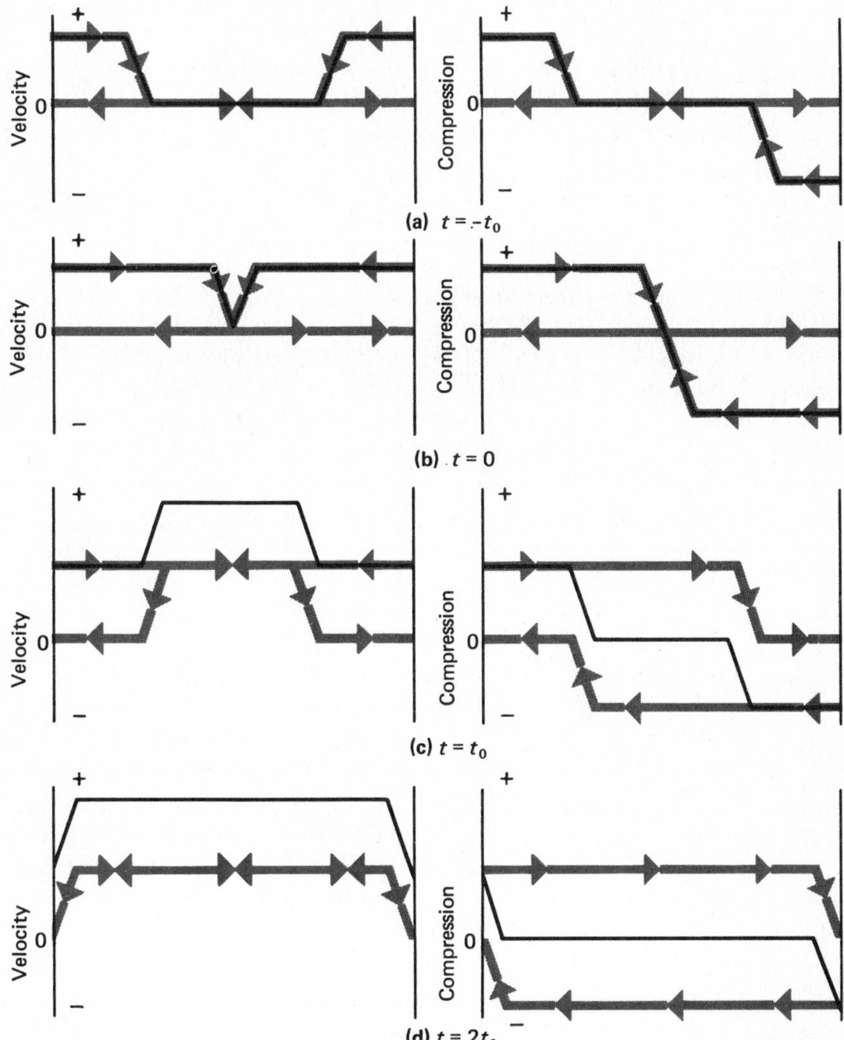

FIG. 10.12 Superposition of two waves with opposite compressions. The broad gray lines indicate the two independent waves, the arrow heads showing the direction of propagation of each wave. The solid black lines show the combined effect of the two waves. Plots at the left show the velocity as a function of position at four different times; plots at the right show the compression as a function of position at the same times.

$+\vec{V}$, but it will have stretched the springs, so the compression in the wave is negative, $-C$.

At the time represented by Fig. 10.12b, which we shall call $t=0$, the two waves will have just met at the center of the train. According to the principle of superposition, the combined effect of the two waves in that region into which both have penetrated will be the sum of their individual effects. It is easy to see that the sum of the two velocities in most of the train is exactly $+\vec{V}$, and the solid line through the circles in the figure shows that the whole train is, at this particular instant, moving with a velocity $+\vec{V}$. The compression of the springs, on the other hand, is not uniform throughout the train. As shown by the dashed line, which represents the sum of the compressions in the two waves, the compression changes suddenly from a positive value, $+C$, on the left to a negative value, $-C$, on the right. Hence, all springs to the left of the middle of the train will be uniformly compressed, and all to the right of the middle will be uniformly stretched.

At the time $t=t_0$ (just as long after the time of Fig. 10.12b as the time of Fig. 10.12a was before it), the two waves will have moved into each other to a considerable extent, as shown in Fig. 10.12c. Since both waves result in positive velocities, the cars in the middle of the train will be moving with a velocity $+2\vec{V}$. The compressions in this section cancel each other, leaving the springs between the cars unstretched, as shown by the dashed line. These conditions are easily understood physically, as either locomotive alone would have given the cars a velocity $+\vec{V}$, one stretching the springs and the other compressing them. Working together, the locomotives add the velocities $(\vec{V}+\vec{V}=2\vec{V})$ and they also add the compressions $(C-C=0)$.

Figure 10.12d shows the distribution of velocities and compressions along the train at time $t=2t_0$. We notice that with increasing time more and more of the cars are moving with a velocity $2\vec{V}$, and it is easy to see that the whole train will eventually be moving with this velocity.

As a second example, consider the case of a train in which the locomotive on the left end starts pushing with a velocity $+\vec{V}$ and the one on the right also pushes, but with a velocity $-\vec{V}$. Although this seems to indicate a certain lack of cooperation between the two engineers, it does lead to an interesting physical case, as illustrated in Fig. 10.13. The two locomotives produce equal compressions of the springs but opposite velocities, so that, when the two waves combine, a region of zero velocity and double compression results.

10.11 The Reflection of Waves

We may now take up an important problem which we have avoided thus far (cf. last paragraph of Sec. 10.2). What happens when a wave reaches the end of the train, or the rod, or the wire in which it is being propagated? As before, it will be enlightening to consider the train example, and then to transfer to other systems the knowledge obtained from this investigation.

We first notice that, until the spring between the last car and the one before it starts to stretch, the fact that there is a last car has had no effect upon the motion. The wave has been propagated in exactly the same way in the short train as it would have been if the train had been indefinitely long.

There are two problems of special interest to us. In one, we consider the usual case in which the last car is quite free to move. The last car then differs from the other cars only in that it does not have another car following it. The other case is that in which the last car is anchored firmly to the ground so that it cannot move. This is somewhat ridiculous from the point of view of railroad engineering, but it is very important in other branches of physics.

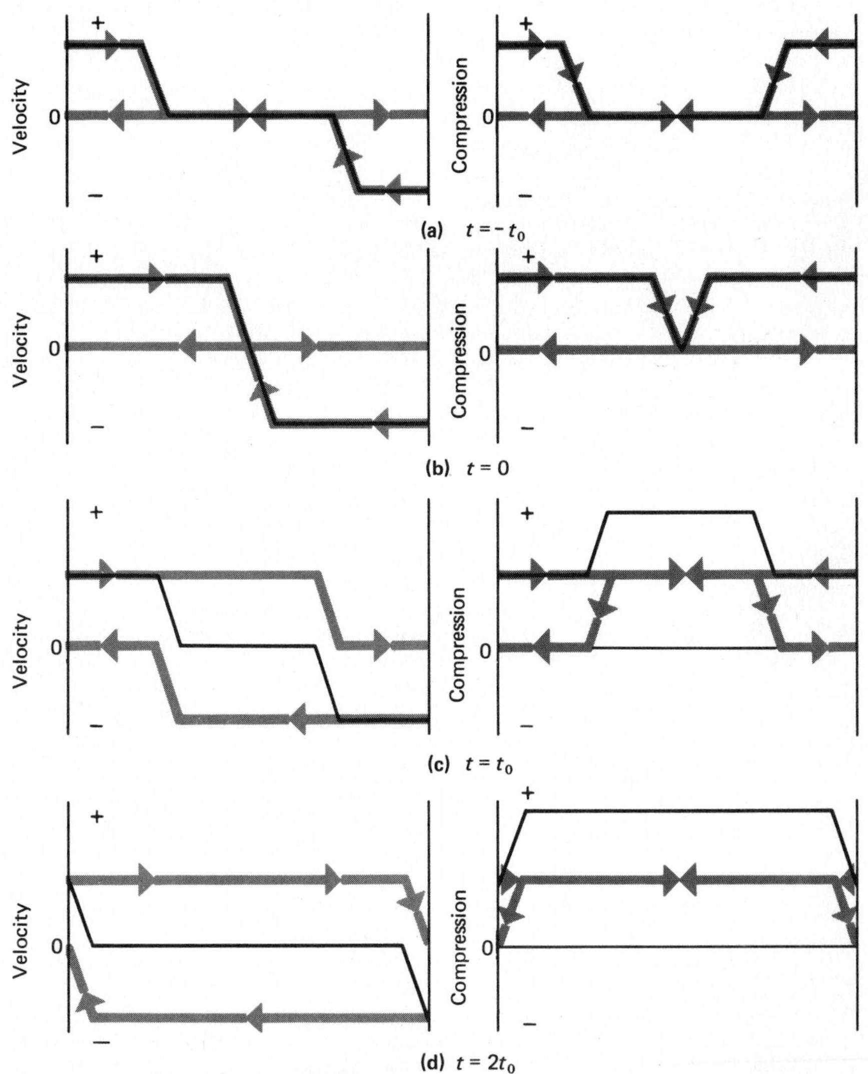

FIG. 10.13 Superposition of two waves with opposite velocities. The notation is that of Fig. 10.12.

Let us assume that the locomotive is pushing the train to the right, and that the last car of the train is free to move—i.e., that the spring beyond it has a completely free end. Until the wave has reached this car, the finite length of the train has no effect, and the disturbance moves along the train exactly as in Fig. 10.3. When it reaches the last car, however, there is an important difference from the conditions previously encountered. When the spring to the left of this car is compressed, it exerts on the car a force just as great as that exerted by earlier springs on the cars following them. Now, however, the spring beyond the last car is free and cannot be compressed, and therefore it can exert no force. Thus, the force on the last car due to the spring on the left is not compensated by a compression of the spring beyond it. The net force on the last car is therefore greater than that on the cars ahead. The acceleration will therefore be greater and the car will acquire a speed higher than V. As soon as it begins to move at this higher speed, it will gain on the car to its left, and it can do this only by stretching the spring between them. This will continue until the second car from the end has reached the same velocity as the end car. In the meantime, the spring to the left of the second car will be stretched, and so on along the whole train. In other words, the fact that the original disturbance has reached the end of the train, where the last spring could not be compressed, has resulted in a new disturbance being set up and being propagated through the train in the opposite direction to the original wave. We say that the wave has been ***reflected*** from the free end of the train, and we refer to the new disturbance as the ***reflected wave***.

In order to study the reflected wave in more detail, we next notice that the conditions in this train with a free end are very similar to those shown in Fig. 10.12 and discussed in Sec. 10.10. We have seen that the thing which leads to the existence of the reflected wave is the fact that the last spring of the train cannot be compressed. It follows that the reflected wave must be of such a nature that, when it is superposed on the original wave, it must cancel the compression of this spring. In other words, it must produce a compression that is equal in magnitude and opposite in sign to the compression produced by the original wave, in this one spring. At the same time, it must increase the velocity of the last car. Referring now to Fig. 10.12, we see that the one spring in the middle of the long train always has zero compression. This state of affairs was brought about by the superposition of the wave (with positive velocity and positive compression) coming from the left and the wave (with positive velocity and negative compression) coming from the right. The wave therefore satisfies completely the conditions that the reflected wave must meet, and the train with a free end is equivalent to the left-hand half of the train illustrated by Fig. 10.12. Figure 10.14 therefore shows the effect produced by the superposition of the original wave and reflected wave. The original wave is shown by the blue lines with arrows pointing to the right and the reflected wave by the blue lines with arrows pointing to the left. Notice that the compression of the springs becomes zero along the train as the two waves combine. The combined effect of the two velocity waves is to produce a velocity $2\vec{V}$ in the cars at the right-hand end of the train (heavy solid line).

If the engineer were to double his speed just at the instant that the reflected wave reaches the locomotive, he could do so without exerting any force on the train, and the whole train would then move along uniformly with a speed of $2V$. If he does not adjust his speed in this way, the reflected wave will itself be reflected from the locomotive at the left end of the train. We shall postpone the discussion of the multiple reflections of a wave (first from one end and then from the other) to Secs. 10.13–10.15.

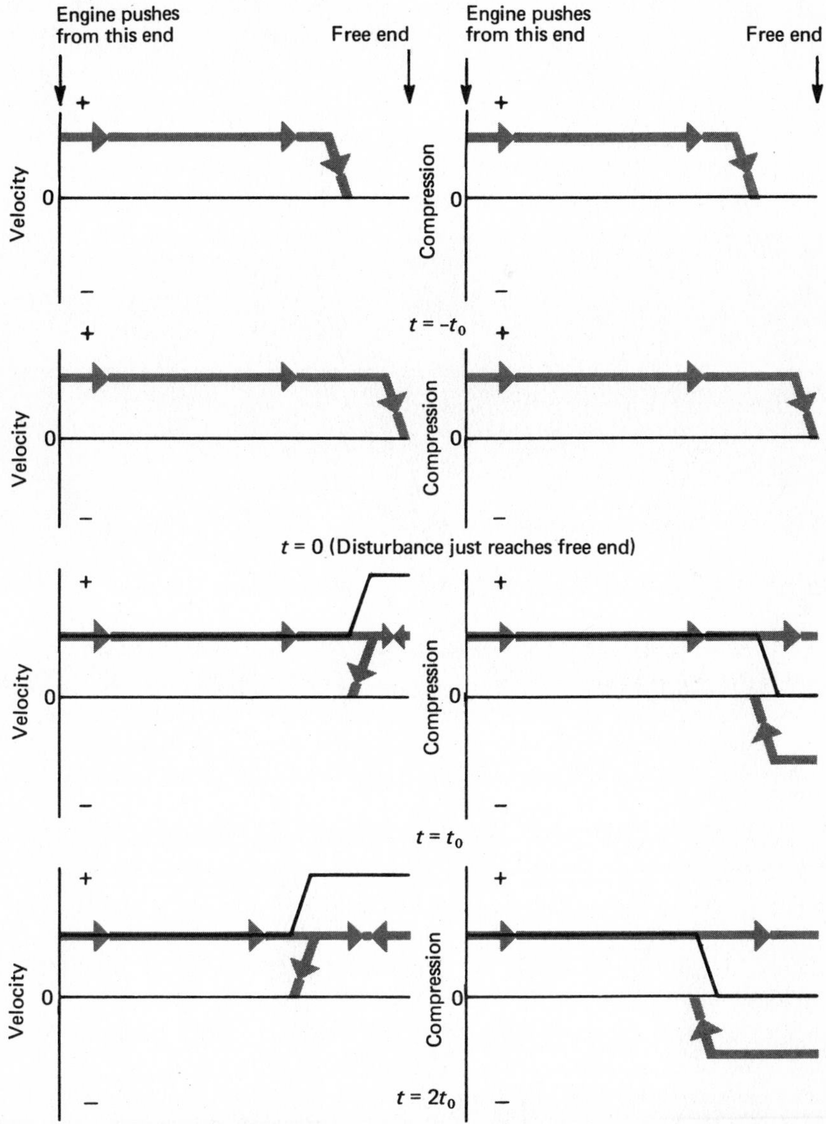

FIG. 10.14 Reflection at the free end of a train (cf. Fig. 10.12). The notation is that of Fig. 10.12. Notice that the waves coming from the right are in this case reflected waves.

Figure 10.15 shows the same train shown in Fig. 10.1. The first photograph was taken 1.52 sec after the locomotive started to pull to the right. The starting wave has already reached the free end of the train and has been reflected as a positive compression wave. This is indicated by the fact that the spring between cars 4 and 5 has returned to its unstretched length and *both* cars are in motion. In the second photograph, taken 2.97 sec after the locomotive was started, the reflected wave has traveled the entire length of the train and the compression in all springs is zero. Measurements on the photographs indicate that the average velocity of car 5 in the interval between 1.52 sec and 2.97 sec is about 1.5 times that of the locomotive. This is somewhat less than 2.0 V which we would expect if the system were without friction.

Now consider the second case, in which the spring of the last car is fastened to a bumper attached to the track. The locomotive is again pushing the train to the right. In this case, as before, the wave travels along the train until it reaches the last car. Here, however, the critical condition is that the last car cannot

FIG. 10.15 Reflection of a compression wave.

move. Its velocity must be zero, and this can be brought about only if the spring that attaches it to the track is compressed more than the other coupling springs were compressed by the original wave. When the next to last spring is compressed, the force exerted will not move the last car appreciably but will merely result in an excessive compression of the spring attached to the bumper. Thus, the next to last car will gain on the last and will cause an additional compression of the spring between these two cars. This additional compression will propagate backward through the train, and as in the case of the train with a free end, a reflected wave is set up by the fixed end. This wave, in order to satisfy the conditions at the fixed end, must be characterized by a velocity equal in magnitude and opposite in direction to that of the initial disturbance, and its compression must have the same sign as the original compression. A glance at Fig. 10.13 shows that these conditions are met by the wave coming from the right in that figure and that the train with a fixed end is therefore equivalent to the left half of the train there illustrated. Figure 10.16 shows the progress of the reflected wave in the train and the effect produced by its superposition on the original wave. Notice that the cars stop (heavy black line) and the compression of the springs double (heavy black line) as the waves combine. If the engineer stops the locomotive just as the reflected wave reaches it, the whole train will be brought to rest with all the springs highly compressed. Otherwise, a second reflection will take place at the left end of the train.

We can summarize the results of this section by the following statement: *When a wave reaches the boundary of any continuous system (the end of a train), a reflected wave will be set up. The nature of this wave will be such as to satisfy the conditions prescribed by the boundary.* Thus, if the boundary is fixed, the reflected and the incident waves will combine to produce no motion at the boundary (Fig. 10.16). If the boundary is free, the reflected and the incident waves will combine to produce no compression at the boundary (Fig. 10.14). More complicated boundary conditions can, of course, arise—consider the case in which two trains with different masses for the cars and different coupling springs are fastened together—and in such cases both a transmitted and a reflected wave will be needed to satisfy the conditions at the boundary. Such problems are of much interest in both physics and engineering but we shall not go into them here. (However, see Probs. 10.6–10.8.) The present brief remark will aid, however, in the understanding of the partial reflections we shall be discussing in Chapters 12 and 13.

When waves are traveling in space, instead of along a straight line, reflection may also take place. For example, when the compression wave of Fig. 10.10 strikes the plane solid surface, at which the velocity must be zero, a reflected wave is set up. If the initial wave is itself considered to be a superposition of two waves, one traveling perpendicular to the surface and the other parallel to the surface, the phenomenon shown in the figure is easily understood. The wave traveling perpendicular to the surface is reflected, whereas that traveling parallel to the surface is not affected by the presence of the surface. The superposition of this unaffected wave with the reflected wave results in the pattern shown. We shall discuss this problem in greater detail in Chapter 12.

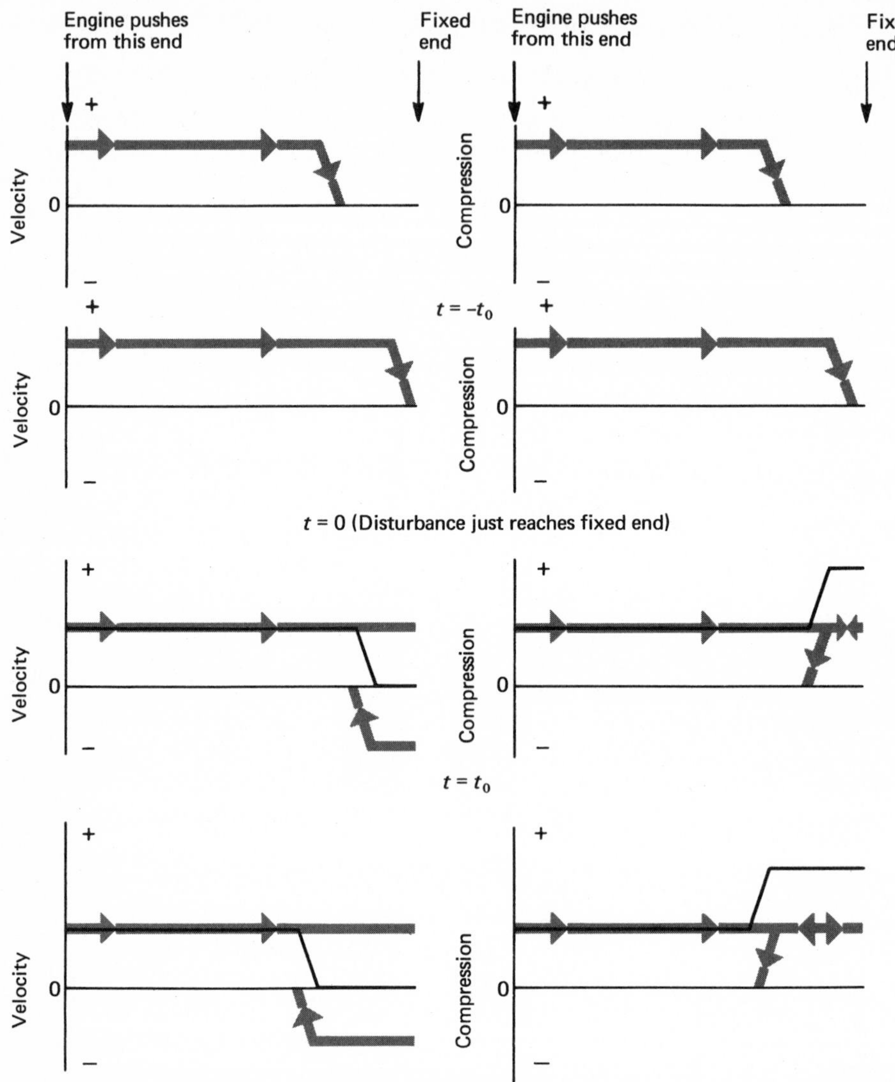

FIG. 10.16 Reflection at the fixed end of a train (cf. Fig. 10.13). The notation is that of Fig. 10.12. Notice that the waves coming from the right are in this case reflected waves.

EXERCISES

10.11-1 Draw curves analogous to Fig. 10.14 for the reflection of the wave shown in Fig. 10.4 at the free end of a train. Include curves for the times $t = -t_0$, at which time the initial disturbance has not reached the end of the train; $t = 0$, when it has just reached the end; $t = +t_0$; and $t = +2t_0$.

10.11-2 Draw curves analogous to Fig. 10.16 for the reflection of the wave shown in Fig. 10.4 at the fixed end of a train. Include curves for the same times as were specified in Ex. 10.11-1.

10.12 Transverse Waves

In the longitudinal waves considered up to this point, the to-and-fro motion of the particles of the material takes place in the same direction as that in which the wave is traveling. In another type of wave, the oscillatory motion is at right angles to the direction of propagation. Such waves are called ***transverse waves.*** Waves on the surface of deep water provide typical examples of transverse waves. A simpler form of transverse wave motion is presented by the disturbance that travels along a stretched string or wire when a part of it is displaced sideways.

Suppose that the stretched string of Fig. 10.17a is struck a sharp blow in the middle so that it is deformed into the shape of Fig. 10.17b. Elastic forces between

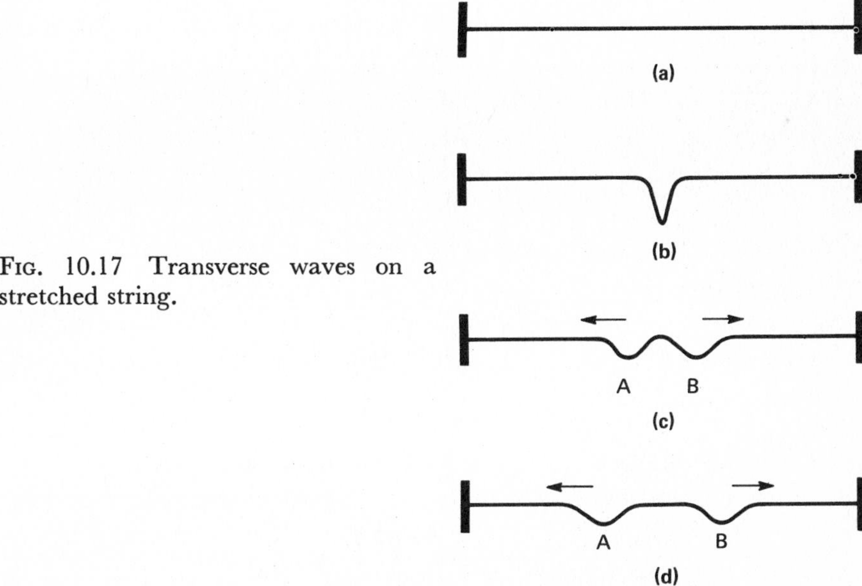

FIG. 10.17 Transverse waves on a stretched string.

the displaced and the undisplaced portions tend to return the former to their equilibrium positions. At the same time, the adjoining portions of the wire are pulled in the direction of the displacement. As a result of this process, two pulses A and B (Fig. 10.17c and d) are formed as the original displacement dies down. Each of these in turn will act on the neighboring portions of the string. Thus, the two pulses will travel along the string as wave motions.

The tension in the string provides the force that accelerates the neighboring parts of the string, and therefore plays the same role as the springs of the train or the elasticity of the rod in which a longitudinal wave is progressing. Similarly, the mass per unit length of the string corresponds to the mass of a car in the train or the density in the elastic rod.

The speed of propagation of a transverse wave on a string or wire can be derived in a manner very similar to that used in Secs. 10.3 and 10.4 to find the speed of a longitudinal wave. Because we wish to illustrate a slightly different method and because the computation of the potential energy of a stretched string is somewhat more involved than that of the springs of the train (see Prob. 10.9), we shall here use the conservation of momentum instead of the conservation of energy as the basis of our derivation.

Suppose that the string shown in Fig. 10.18a is stretched between two fixed points in such a way that the tension is T. At $t = 0$ one starts pulling upward on the string at some point, such as O, in such a way that this point moves upward with a uniform velocity $\vec{V}$. At some time later than $t = 0$ the string can be expected to be deformed to the shape shown in Fig. 10.18b. We shall suppose that the string is stretched so little by this motion that the tension is increased only negligibly.

Now consider a small part of the string, of length ΔL, centered at O. This piece of string has a mass $\mu \Delta L$, where μ is the mass per unit length of the string.

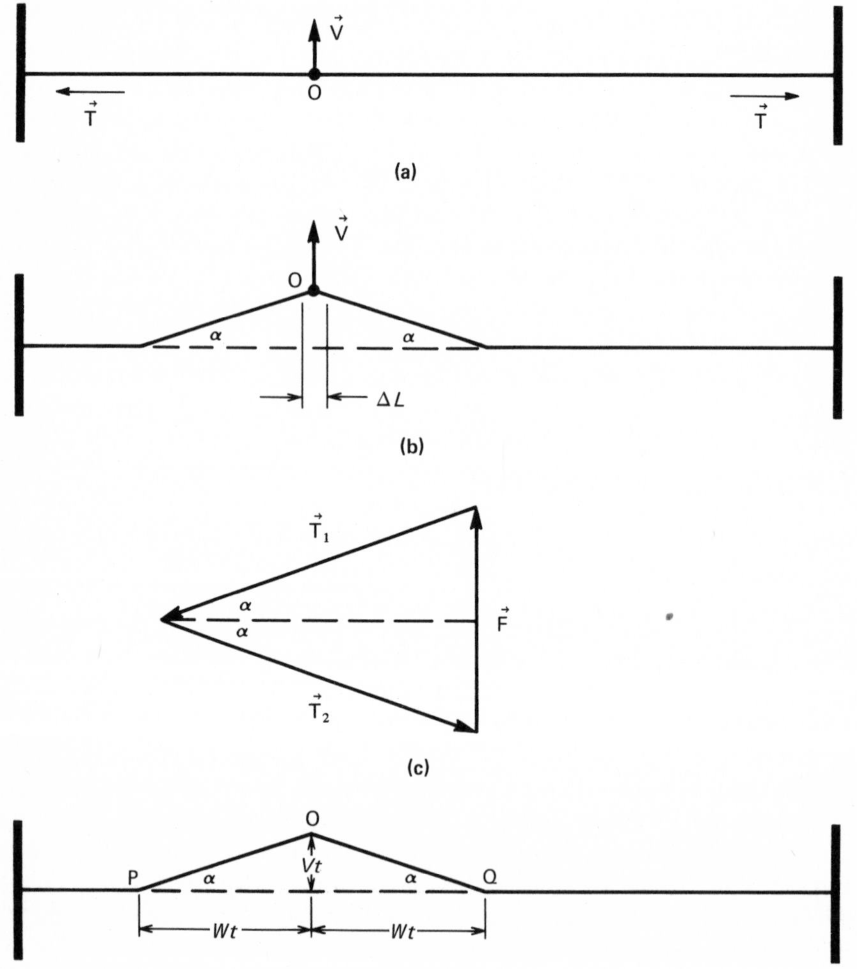

FIG. 10.18 Derivation of the wave speed of a transverse wave on a string.

The mass is moving upward at uniform speed; hence it is in equilibrium (cf. Sec. 6.4), and we know that the vector sum of the forces on it must be zero. The vector diagram of Fig. 10.18c shows that the magnitude of the force $\vec{F}$ that must be exerted to pull the point O upward is

$$F = T_1 \sin \alpha + T_2 \sin \alpha,$$

where α is the angle between either of the two disturbed sections of the string and the original, undisturbed direction. In accordance with our assumption of little stretch, $T_1 = T_2 = T$, so

$$F = 2T \sin \alpha.$$

After this force has been exerted steadily for some time t, the amount of momentum transferred to the string will be given by Eq. (4.11-2) as

$$p = Ft = 2Tt \sin \alpha. \qquad (10.12\text{-}1)$$

In drawing Fig. 10.18b we have assumed that the disturbance spreads out from O at some constant speed of propagation. Letting this speed be W, the geometry at time t is seen to be that shown in Fig. 10.18d. During the time t the point O has moved upward a distance Vt and the disturbance has moved outward a distance Wt in each direction. Hence the section of the string, of length $2Wt$, between P and Q is moving upward with a speed V, and none of the string outside this section is yet moving. The magnitude of the momentum is given by the mass of the moving sections, $2Wt\mu$, times its velocity

$$p = 2Wt\mu V.$$

We now equate the impulse given by Eq. (10.12-1) to this momentum, to find that

$$T \sin \alpha = W\mu V. \qquad (10.12\text{-}2)$$

We next notice in Fig. 10.18d that

$$\tan \alpha = Vt/Wt = V/W.$$

It is shown in Appendix G that $\sin \alpha \approx \tan \alpha$ when α is small, as it must be here. Hence we can replace $\sin \alpha$ in Eq. (10.12-2) by V/W, to find that

$$TV/W = W\mu V,$$

so that

$$W = (T/\mu)^{1/2}. \qquad (10.12\text{-}3)$$

Notice that the tension in this expression for the speed of propagation of a transverse wave plays a role similar to that of Young's modulus in a longitudinal wave, and the mass per unit length is analogous to the density in the earlier case.

The discussion of the last few paragraphs can be applied to transverse disturbances of any nature, including periodic ones. Thus, if the wire is so disturbed that the displacement of some point on it varies sinusoidally with time, the wave will be sinusoidal, and a snapshot of a portion of the wire at any time will look very much like Fig. 10.6.

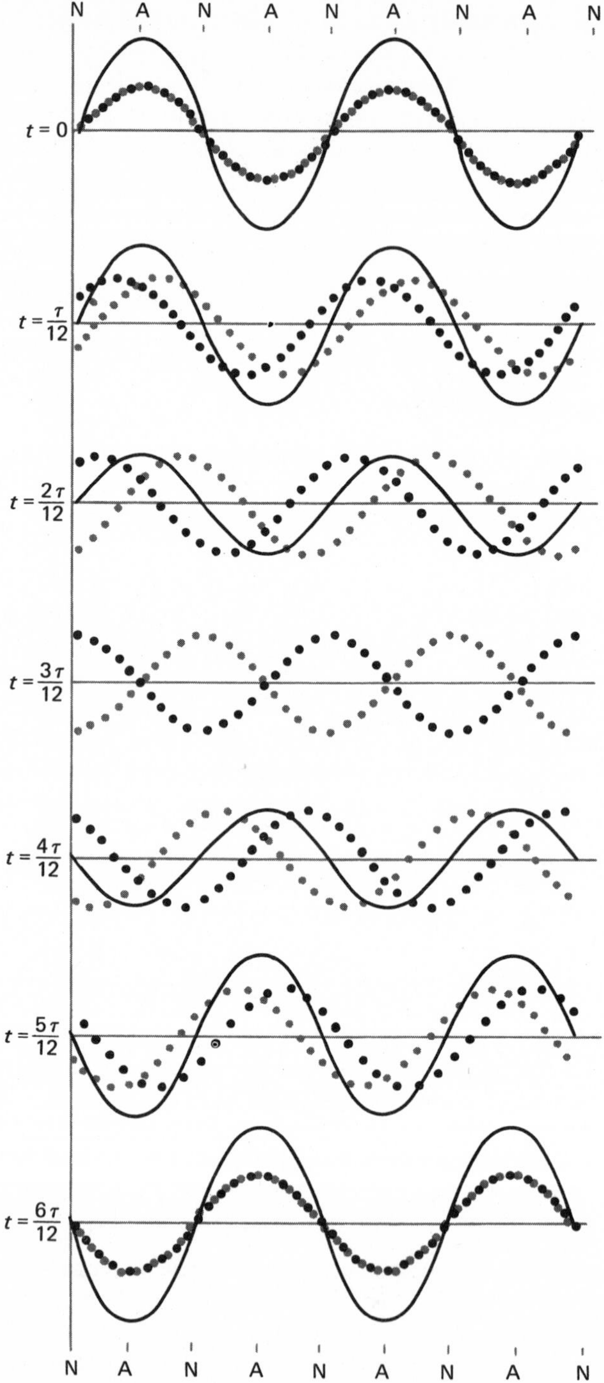

Fig. 10.19 Stationary wave produced by two oppositely directed waves of identical frequency and amplitude. The plot shows displacement as a function of position.

When a wave on a string or a wire reaches an end of the wire, which is fastened in place, a reflected wave is established in exactly the same way that it was at the fixed end of the train of Sec. 10.11. It should be clear from the discussion of that section that the reflected wave must produce a displacement equal and opposite to that of the incident wave.

EXERCISES

10.12-1 Verify that Eq. (10.12-1) is dimensionally correct.

10.12-2 Calculate the wave speed for transverse waves in the wire of Ex. 9.3-3, assuming that the density of iron is 8.0×10^3 kg/m³.

10.13 Standing Waves

As an introduction to the study of musical instruments, it is interesting to examine what happens when two identical sinusoidal waves travel along the same string with the same speed, but in opposite directions.

In Fig. 10.19, the two identical sinusoidal waves, one represented by light circles and the other by black circles, moving in opposite directions, are assumed to be superimposed additively at $t = 0$. We shall denote the wave moving to the right (light circles) by R, and the wave moving to the left (black circles) by L. These two waves combine, according to the principle of superposition, to give the wave indicated by the full curve. A little later (at $t = \tau/12$ in the figure) L has moved to the left and R has moved to the right. These two waves now combine to produce a new wave (full line) which is of smaller amplitude than that at $t = 0$. As the R wave and the L wave separate still further, the amplitude of the combined wave decreases until, at $t = 3\tau/12 = \tau/4$, the two waves are directly opposed to one another, and the amplitude of the resultant wave is zero

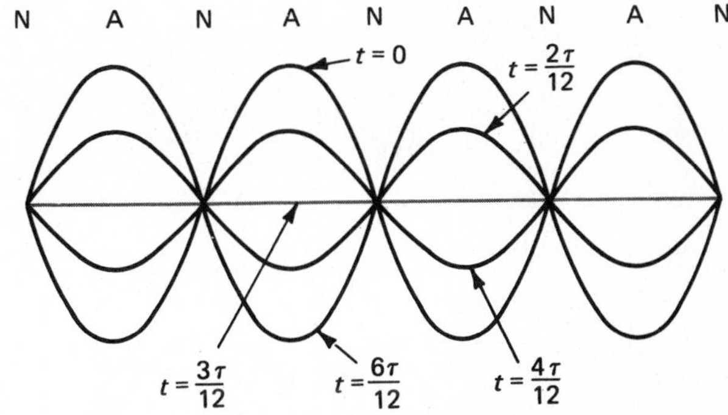

FIG. 10.20 Stationary sinusoidal wave.

everywhere. Later still, the combination of the two waves produces troughs in the full line curve at the points where the peaks originally occurred and produces peaks where the troughs were. It is now clear from Fig. 10.19 that the combination of the two waves moving in opposite directions is a ***stationary wave***, or ***standing wave***. In such a standing wave, the disturbance does not move along the string, but each point on the string vibrates with an amplitude dependent on its position. The successive shapes of the full line curves of Fig. 10.19 are plotted together in Fig. 10.20.

Notice that in the stationary wave of Figs. 10.19 and 10.20, there are points (marked N in the figures) which never move, despite the fact that the two component waves are continually passing through them. At these points, called the ***nodes***, the two component waves always produce equal and opposite effects and thus always cancel one another (cf. Sec. 10.10). The distance between adjacent nodes is $\lambda/2$, where λ is the wavelength of the component waves. Midway between the nodes, the string undergoes a maximum vibration, and the points where this maximum vibration occurs are called ***antinodes.*** These are marked A in Figs. 10.18 and 10.19.

10.14 Vibrating Strings

There is an immediate application of the result of the preceding section to the discussion of the vibration of a string stretched between two fixed points P_1 and P_2 (Fig. 10.21). If we start a sinusoidal wave from left to right along the string,

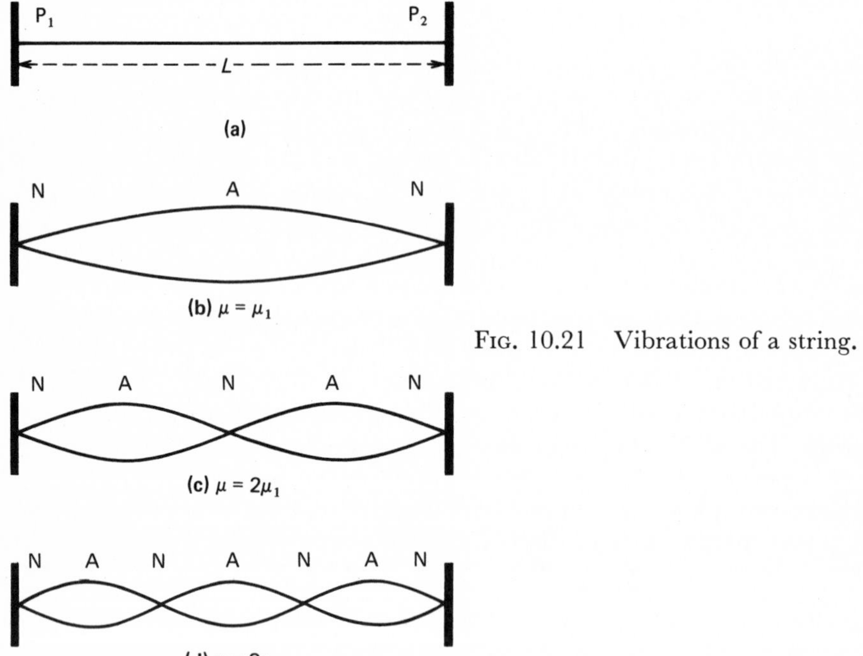

FIG. 10.21 Vibrations of a string.

we see by the argument of Sec. 10.11 that a wave must be reflected at the right-hand end in such a way that the end does not move, and this reflected wave in its turn must be reflected at the left end of the wire in such a way that the left end does not move. Furthermore, this twice reflected wave must reinforce the original wave so that the cycle of repeated reflections can go on indefinitely. It is easy to see that, if the nodes of the stationary waves discussed in Sec. 10.13 are located at the fixed ends of the string, then the component waves of which the stationary waves were built up satisfy the conditions for reflection at the fixed ends (Sec. 10.11)—i.e., the reflected wave produces a displacement that is equal and opposite to that of the incident wave.

Since the distance between the nodes is $\lambda/2$, we must have

$$L = n\lambda/2, \tag{10.14-1}$$

where n is a whole number and L is the length of the string, if a node is to be located at each end of the string. It is then easy to see that only certain wavelengths λ_n satisfy the reflection conditions given above. These are

$$\lambda_n = 2L/n. \tag{10.14-2}$$

To each of these wavelengths corresponds a frequency ν_n given by Eq. (10.5-3) as

$$\nu_n = W/\lambda_n = nW/2L,$$

where W is the wave velocity for a transverse wave in the string. With the aid of Eq. (10.12-3), this can be written as

$$\nu_n = (n/2L)(T/\mu)^{1/2}, \tag{10.14-3}$$

in which T is the tension in the string and μ is its mass per unit length.

The discussion of the last paragraph tells us that there are a number of ***characteristic frequencies*** with which a wire will vibrate freely. In the lowest of these frequencies, ν_1, the vibration is as indicated in Fig. 10.21b, with a node at each end and an antinode in the middle of the string. At a frequency $\nu_2 = 2\nu_1$, a node has appeared in the middle of the string, and there are now two antinodes (Fig. 10.21c). The number of antinodes is thus equal to n, and the number of nodes, not counting those at the ends, is equal to $(n - 1)$.

It can be shown that any possible vibration of the string can be made up of the characteristic vibrations we have described. Thus, a plucked string will vibrate in a combination of the various frequencies ν_n. All of these frequencies are whole number multiples of the lowest, ν_1, which is called the ***fundamental frequency***. The multiples of the fundamental are called the ***harmonics***. The relative importance of the various harmonic frequencies in the vibration of the string depends on how the vibration is started. Thus, if the string of Fig. 10.21a is struck in the middle with a hammer, the vibrations of Figs. 10.21b and d will be started, but that of Fig. 10.20c will not. The resulting note emitted will be characterized by the first, third, and other odd harmonics, but not by the second, fourth, etc. On the other hand, if the string is struck one quarter of the way from one end, the second harmonic vibration of Fig. 10.21c will be strongly excited.

10.15 Organ Pipes

In the preceding section, we saw how the reflection conditions at the ends of a stretched string require that the string possess certain characteristic frequencies of vibration. We can now apply exactly the same reasoning to the discussion of the longitudinal vibrations in organ pipes. If we consider a pipe open at both ends (Fig. 10.22), we realize that a wave traveling in the air in the pipe will be reflected at the ends. At these ends, the pressure will be fixed at atmospheric pressure while the velocity of the air will be free to change. In accordance with the discussion of Sec. 10.11, there will be pressure nodes at the ends of the pipe, and the wavelength and frequency of the characteristic vibrations of the open pipe (open at both ends) will be given by

$$\lambda_n = 2L/n \tag{10.15-1}$$

and

$$\nu_n = W/\lambda_n = nW/2L. \tag{10.15-2}$$

The harmonics of the open pipe are thus whole number multiples of the fundamental, just as in the case of the string (Sec. 10.14).

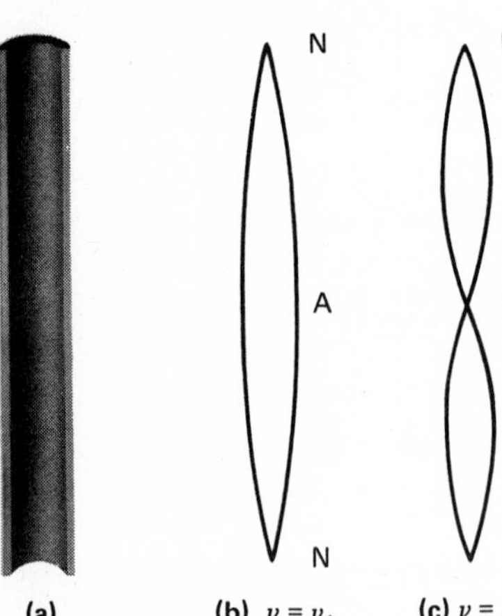

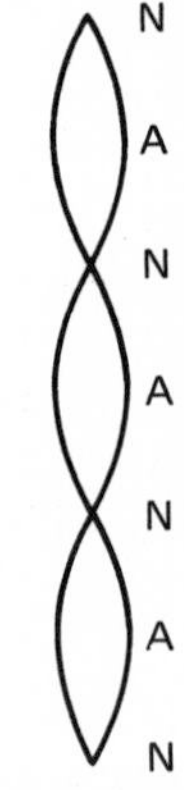

FIG. 10.22 Pressure variations in an organ pipe open at both ends.

The organ pipe closed at one end and open at the other is treated by a slight variation of the same reasoning. At the open end, there will be a pressure node, as in the case of the open pipe. At the closed end the velocity must be zero, but the pressure may vary. Hence, there will be a pressure antinode at the closed end (Fig. 10.23). Since the distance between a node and an antinode is $\lambda/4$, $3\lambda/4$, $5\lambda/4$, etc. (i.e., an odd number of quarter wavelengths), we can write

$$L = (2n + 1)\lambda/4,$$

and it follows that the characteristic wavelengths for a closed pipe are given by

$$\lambda_n = 4L/(2n + 1), \tag{10.15-3}$$

and the characteristic frequencies ν_n are given by

$$\nu_n = (2n + 1)W/4L. \tag{10.15-4}$$

The harmonics for the closed pipe therefore have frequencies that are the odd multiples of the fundamental frequency, $W/4L$.

All musical instruments are based on the existence of standing waves of some sort. The basic theory outlined for the string is directly applicable to the stringed instruments of the orchestra, and the theory of the organ pipe is applicable to the wind instruments. We have seen that in these instruments harmonic frequencies may be emitted at the same time as the fundamental. The relative energies associated with the various harmonic frequencies enable us to distinguish between the different orchestral instruments, say, a violin and a clarinet, even though they are playing the same fundamental note. We say that ones having different harmonic content differ in quality or timber.

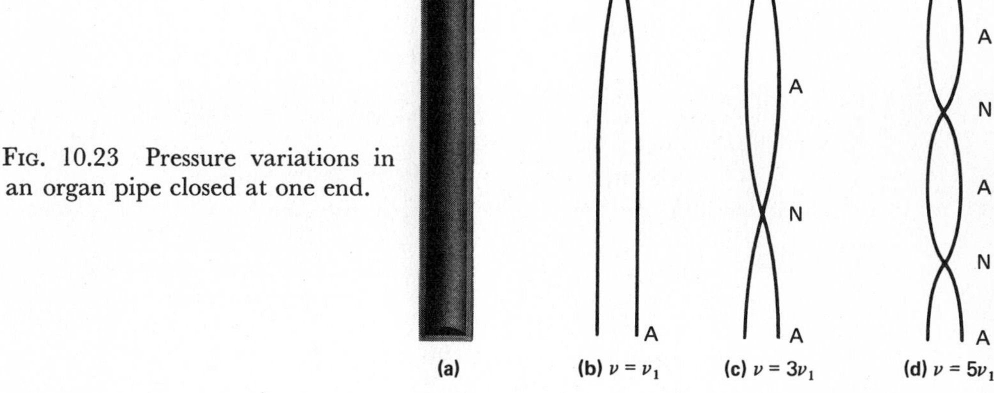

FIG. 10.23 Pressure variations in an organ pipe closed at one end.

In some instruments, such as the percussion instruments and the bells, the higher frequencies or overtones are not whole number multiples of the fundamental frequency.

10.16 Summary

In this chapter wave motion has been discussed as a means of propagating energy from one part of space to another. The transmission of sound is an interesting example of such wave motion. In particular we have considered the propagation of longitudinal waves in elastic solids and fluids and of transverse waves in a stretched string and have found the wave speeds for these two types of waves. We have also discussed in some detail the process of reflection of waves and have made use of the results so obtained to determine the characteristic frequencies of vibrating strings and of organ pipes.

PROBLEMS

10.1 Equation (10.3-5), which was derived by the consideration of energy, can also be derived by considering the momentum given to the train by the engine. If n cars have been set in motion with a velocity $\vec{V}$ during a time t, the total momentum acquired by the cars in this time, nmV, must be equal to Ft, where F is the force with which the engine pulls (or pushes) on the first spring. Starting from this relation, derive Eq. (10.3-5).

10.2 Starting from the expressions for F and V that were used in deriving Eq. (10.3-5), show that the ratio

$$F/V = (mk)^{1/2}.$$

This ratio is known as the ***mechanical impedance*** of the train. It is often denoted by the letter Z.

10.3 (a) Using the result of Prob. 10.2 and reasoning similar to that used in Sec. 10.4 show that the mechanical impedance of a rod, for longitudinal waves, is

$$Z = S(\rho Y)^{1/2}.$$

(b) The ***characteristic impedance*** z_0 of the material of which a rod is made is defined as the ratio of the impedance of the rod to the cross-sectional area. Find an expression for the characteristic impedance of the rod considered in (a) and show that it depends only on the characteristics of the material of which the rod is made, not on the dimensions of the rod.

(c) What are the dimensions of characteristic impedance?

10.4 Suppose that a wave moving to the right in a train similar to that of Figs. 10.1 and 10.2 gives a positive velocity $+\vec{V}$ to each car. Show that this wave must be a compression wave, so that $\vec{F} = +Z\vec{V}$, where Z is the mechanical impedance of the train. Similarly, show that a wave moving to the left must be a tension wave, so that $\vec{F} = Z\vec{V}$.

10.5 (a) Compute the range of wavelengths in air of audible sounds within the frequency range given in Sec. 10.8. (b) Using data from Chapter 9, compute the speed of sound in water. (c) What is the range of wavelengths in water of audible sounds?

10.6 Suppose that a train, or a rod, consists of two parts having different mechanical impedances. Everywhere to the left of some point A the impedance is Z_1; everywhere to the right of A it is Z_2. Suppose that an incident wave is coming from the left and, at some instant, is causing A to move with a velocity V_i. A transmitted wave will move past A into the second part of the system, and a reflected wave will move to the left from A. Let the velocities of the transmitted and reflected waves by V_t and V_r, respectively. Since A can have only one velocity, we must have

$$V_i + V_r = V_t.$$

Similarly, the force acting on A from the left must be equal in magnitude to the force acting on it from the right, so that

$$F_i + F_r = F_t,$$

where the three forces listed are respectively those exerted by the incident wave, the reflected wave, and the transmitted wave.

(a) Use the results of Prob. 10.4 to eliminate F_i, F_r, and F_t from the equations above and then eliminate V_t from the resulting pair of simultaneous equations. Hence show that

$$V_r = \frac{V_i(Z_1 - Z_2)}{Z_1 + Z_2}.$$

(b) Show that

$$V_t = \frac{2V_i Z_1}{Z_1 + Z_2}.$$

10.7 (a) Apply the results of Prob. 10.6 to the special case of $Z_2 = 0$, i.e., to the free end of a train, and hence justify the statement of Sec. 10.11 that the velocity resulting from the reflected wave is equal to that of the incident wave.

(b) Apply the results of Prob. 10.6 to the special case of $1/Z_2 = 0$, i.e., to the fixed end of a train.

10.8 A rod of uniform cross section is made by joining a steel rod and a copper rod end to end. A wave characterized by a particle velocity V_i approaches the junction from the steel side of the rod. Use the results of Prob. 10.6 to find the velocity amplitudes of the reflected and transmitted waves.

10.9 (a) Show that the work done in stretching the string of Fig. 10.18, and hence the potential energy of the string, is

$$2TWt\left(\frac{1}{\cos\alpha} - 1\right),$$

where t is the time during which the force F has been acting, and T, W, and α have the same meanings as in Sec. 10.12. Using the first two terms on the right of Eq. (G.16) of Appendix G as an approximation to $\cos\alpha$ and Eq. (H.3) of Appendix H, show that this potential energy is

$$PE = TWt\alpha^2.$$

(b) Show that the work done by the force F during the time t is

$$w = 2TVt\alpha = 2TWt\alpha^2.$$

(c) Hence demonstrate that half of the work done by the force F goes into potential energy and half into kinetic energy.

10.10 By use of the results of Prob. 10.9 and reasoning similar to that of Sec. 10.3, show that the conservation of energy leads to Eq. (10.12-3).

10.11 Show that the mechanical impedance (cf. Probs. 10.2 and 10.3) of a stretched string for a transverse wave is $Z = (\mu T)^{1/2}$, where μ is the mass per unit length and T is the tension. Hint: Remember that the transverse force F in Fig. 10.18 is establishing two waves, one to the right and one to the left.

10.12 A steel nail 8.0 cm long is struck on the head by a hammer. How much time will elapse between the first contact of the hammer and the instant when the point of the nail begins to move?

REFERENCES

10A Dayton C. Miller, *Anecdotal History of the Science of Sound*, Macmillan, New York, 1935. A classic by one of the pioneers in acoustics.

10B Charles A. Culver, *Musical Acoustics*, 4th edition, McGraw-Hill, New York, 1956. A useful introduction to the physics of music.

10C C. A. Taylor, *The Physics of Musical Sounds*, American Elsevier, New York, 1965. Interested readers can easily pursue the subject either descriptively or mathematically by means of this book.

10D Jess Josephs, *The Physics of Musical Sound* (Momentum Book No. 13), Van Nostrand, Princeton, N.J., 1967. Good discussions of vibrations, hearing, and musical instruments.

10E John Shive, *Similarities in Wave Behavior*, Bell Telephone Laboratories. (Available on loan from local Bell Telephone operating companies.) A filmed demonstration lecture illustrating superposition, reflection, impedance, etc.

11 ⇨ *Thermal Phenomena*

11.1 The Notion of Temperature

In most of our discussions up to this point we have paid little attention to one important aspect of material bodies—that which we ordinarily describe when we say that a body is hot or cold. Following our usual procedure, we will refine common usage until we have created satisfactory physical definitions. Before doing this, we shall need to make qualitative observations on the characteristics that distinguish a hotter body from a colder one.

The most obvious property of a hot body is that it gives off heat to cooler bodies near it. This effect can be observed physiologically when we get near a fire or radiator. The effect can be observed also when we put an overheated pan or spoon into cold water in order to cool it; the pan will cool and the water will warm until they are equally warm (or cool).

A second difference between hot and cold bodies, which is of great value in the study of heat, is that bodies generally expand when heated. Suppose two rigid metal rods are carefully machined to exactly the same length when they have been kept side-by-side for some time. If now one of the rods is strongly heated, it is usually found that the hot rod is longer than the colder one. As the hot rod cools it will shorten. If the rods are again placed side-by-side and left for some time, they will again be equal in length.

We have just described the property of ***thermal expansion***, and this property can be used to measure temperature. If we take a rod of some material that always expands as it becomes hotter, we can use the length of the rod as a measure of its temperature. If the length of the rod under some standard set of conditions, which we may use to define the zero of temperature, is L_0, and if its length under any other set of conditions is L_t, we can define the ***temperature*** t of the rod under the second set of conditions as

$$t = k(L_t - L_0), \tag{11.1-1}$$

where k is a constant chosen at our convenience. As soon as we have defined the constant of Eq. (11.1-1), we have converted the rod into a ***thermometer***.

We have just described a set of operations by means of which we can measure temperature. Methodologically, this operational definition is similar to all other operational definitions, such as those by which length and time are measured.

So far we have implied that *any* rod will do for making a thermometer, if only it expands upon heating. Obviously, it must not first expand and then contract as heating continues, for then the same length would correspond to two different temperatures. This, however, is not a problem, since few substances actually contract upon heating. There are practical considerations, though, which make it desirable to prefer certain substances over others. We shall return to this matter in Sec. 11.5.

11.2 The Celsius (Centigrade) Temperature Scale

The choice of a set of standard conditions that can be used to define the zero of temperature is quite arbitrary, as long as the conditions are completely and easily reproducible. If the rod thermometer is repeatedly dipped into well-stirred mixtures of ice and water, it is found that it always assumes the same length while it is totally submerged in the mixture, regardless of the relative amounts of ice and water present, regardless of the temperature outside the ice-water bath, regardless of any other ways in which we can conveniently vary the surroundings.* Because of the constancy of temperature of an ice-water bath, and because of the general availability of ice and water, such a bath is used to define the zero of temperatures on the ***Celsius (Centigrade) temperature scale***, which is employed almost universally in scientific work. This temperature scale is named for its inventor, Anders Celsius (1701–1744), a Swedish astronomer. The temperature of a mixture of ice and water, under normal atmospheric pressure, is defined as ***zero degrees Celsius*** (Centigrade) (°C). Zero degrees Celsius is frequently referred to as the ***ice point***, because of the way in which it is defined.

As was pointed out above, the constant k in Eq. (11.1-1) may be chosen in any way. We might therefore set k at some arbitrary value, say 1,000,000° per meter change of length, but this procedure would have the disadvantage that the thermometer thus established might not agree with one of a different initial length, or one made of a different material. In order that workers everywhere may be able to construct thermometers that agree among themselves, it is better to choose two standard and easily reproducible sets of conditions, and to define the temperature under both of these conditions. A convenient temperature point, other than the ice point, is that at which water boils in an open vessel under the standard atmospheric pressure that will support 760 mm of mercury. This ***steam point***, like the ice point, is found to be quite reproducible, and its temperature on the Celsius scale is defined as 100°C. If the length of our rod thermometer is read when the thermometer is in boiling water under the proper pressure,† or in the steam just above the water, the constant k can be determined

* Changes in the pressure on the ice-water bath (cf. Sec. 11.14) do affect the length of the rod, but only to a very slight extent unless the changes are many times normal atmospheric pressure.

† It might first appear that we should have to wait for a day when the barometer stands at exactly 760 mm in order to determine the steam point under normal atmospheric pressure. Fortunately, it is possible to correct the temperature of boiling water for variations in pressure, so the calibration of the thermometer can be carried out at any time (cf. Table 11.9).

from the difference between this length and that of the thermometer at the ice point. Letting L_{100} be the length at the steam point, and letting $t = 100°C$ in Eq. (11.1-1), we have

$$100°\text{C} = k(L_{100} - L_0),$$

or

$$k = \frac{100°\text{C}}{L_{100} - L_0}. \qquad (11.2\text{-}1)$$

We have now introduced a new fundamental quantity, temperature, into our discussion in addition to length, time, mass, and angle. If we denote this quantity by $[\mathscr{T}]$, we see that the dimensions of k are $[\mathscr{T}\ell^{-1}]$. To give some idea of the magnitude of k, we can note that, had we used a rod of steel which was 0.10000 m long at 0°C for our thermometer, its length at 100°C would be about 0.10011 m. Hence, for this thermometer

$$k = \frac{100°\text{C}}{0.00011\ \text{m}} = 0.91(10)^6\,°\text{C/m}.$$

11.3 Coefficients of Thermal Expansion

With a temperature scale defined, we can now investigate thermal expansion more thoroughly. Suppose that we take a number of rods of the same material but of different lengths and with different cross-sectional shapes and sizes. We might measure the lengths of the rods at 0°C, then heat them to various temperatures as measured with the steel thermometer, and at each new temperature determine the new lengths. We should find that the cross section of a rod has no effect on its change of length but that this change, over a given temperature range, is directly proportional to the original length of the rod (i.e., if one rod was originally twice as long as another, it would expand twice as much). We should also find, if we limited ourselves to temperatures that are not too much above the steam point or too far below the ice point, that the change of length of a given rod, as its temperature is changed over various ranges, is almost exactly proportional to the change in temperature. We can combine these results into a very simple expression. If we let L_t and L_0 be the lengths of a rod at the respective temperatures t and t_0, we have

$$L_t - L_0 = aL_0(t - t_0), \qquad (11.3\text{-}1)$$

where a is an experimentally determined constant. In order that the units be the same on both sides of the equation, it will be necessary that a have the dimension $\mathscr{T}^{-1}$. We shall commonly use $(°\text{C})^{-1}$ as the unit of a. This quantity a is called the ***coefficient of linear thermal expansion***, and it is defined as the relative change in length of a given material per degree rise in temperature. Different materials have different coefficients of expansion, and a number of experimentally determined values are given in Table 11.1.

Table 11.1 *Coefficients of Linear Thermal Expansion*
(Valid for temperatures from −80°C–200°C)

Material	Coefficient a (per °C)
Aluminum	2.30×10^{-5}
Brass	1.8–2.1
Copper	1.66
Marble	1.0–3.0
Nickel	1.28
Oak (across grain)	5.4
(along grain)	0.49
Pyrex glass	0.32
Soda glass	1.2
Steel	1.1

With the help of these known values and Eq. (11.3-1), we can predict the change in length which a body will undergo as its temperature changes by a fixed amount. It may sometimes be more convenient, when we know the length at one temperature, to calculate the new length directly, rather than the change, and for this purpose we can solve Eq. (11.3-1) for L_t obtaining

$$L_t = L_0[1 + a(T - T_0)]. \tag{11.3-2}$$

Thermal expansion is important not only because of its effect on measuring rods, but also because it brings about changes in length in all devices and structures subject to varying temperatures. These changes may be of considerable magnitude. For example, suppose that a steel bridge has a length of 300 ft at 20°C and that it is subject to temperatures that vary from −20°C to 40°C during the year. At the highest temperature, its length will be

$$L_{40} = L_{20}[1 + a(40°\text{C} - 20°\text{C})] = L_{20}[1 + a(20°\text{C})],$$

where L_{20} is the length at 20°C and a is the coefficient of linear expansion for steel. At the lowest temperature, the length will be

$$L_{-20} = L_{20}\{1 - a[20°\text{C} - (-20°\text{C})]\} = L_{20}[1 - a(40°\text{C})].$$

Consequently, the difference between the longest and shortest length of the bridge will be

$$L_{40} - L_{-20} = L_{20}\,a(60°\text{C}).$$

Substituting the value of a from Table 11.1, we find that the bridge changes its length by 0.20 ft. If both ends of the bridge were fixed to the earth, such a change in length would result in severe buckling of the bridge in hot weather or in the bridge pulling loose from its foundations in cold weather. For this reason, one end of a bridge structure is often left free to slide on its supports, or some other means of allowing for thermal expansion is provided.

Since the length of a body generally increases as the temperature rises, a heated solid must also increase its volume with increasing temperature. We now investigate the relation between this change and the coefficient of linear expansion. For simplicity, consider that we have a cubical body, of length L_0 on a side, at temperature t_0. Its volume is then $V_0 = L_0^3$. If the temperature is now raised to t, we can find the new length of an edge by the use of Eq. (11.3-2) and can then show that the new volume is

$$\begin{aligned} V_t &= L_0^3[1 + a(t - t_0)]^3 \\ &= V_0[1 + 3a(t - t_0) + 3a^2(t - t_0)^2 + a^3(t - t_0)^3]. \end{aligned}$$

In the expression in brackets, since a is seldom much larger than $10^{-5}/°C$, the product $a(t - t_0)$ will only be about 0.001 for a temperature rise of as much as a hundred degrees. The square of this quantity, which occurs in the next term, will be less than 10^{-5}, and this is so small compared with unity that its effect on the volume will be less than the uncertainty of most physical measurements. The last term is still smaller, so we can usually neglect these two terms and write

$$V_t = V_0[1 + 3a(t - t_0)],$$

to a sufficient accuracy for almost all measurements. Since this is so very much like Eq. (11.3-2), we may find it convenient to rewrite it as

$$V_t = V_0[1 + b(t - t_0)], \tag{11.3-3}$$

where

$$b \approx 3a. \tag{11.3-4}$$

The quantity b is known as the ***coefficient of volume thermal expansion.*** Since any volume can be approximated as closely as desired by the combination of a number of cubes, i.e., even a sphere of a given material can be approximated by gluing together a great number of very small, equal-size cubes of the same material, Eq. (11.3-4) shows us that the coefficient b for any solid is three times the coefficient of linear expansion.

Before we can discuss the volume expansion of a liquid, we shall have to consider the expansion of the container that holds the liquid. This leads us to an interesting question. Suppose we have a solid with a cavity in it and that we heat the solid. Will the cavity become larger or smaller? We can probably answer this question most easily by considering that we draw a closed line on the walls of the cavity. Now the length of this line is a linear quantity, and we know that any linear dimension of a solid expands on heating. Consequently, the line must grow longer as the temperature rises, and therefore we know that the cavity must expand. As a matter of fact, thermal expansion causes the volume of a hole in a piece of matter to increase at exactly the same rate as the piece of material necessary to fill it would have expanded had it been present.

11.4 Differential Expansion and the Expansion of Liquids

Since different materials may have different coefficients of thermal expansion, two rods of unlike composition with identical lengths at one temperature will, in general, not be of the same length at a different temperature. For example, suppose a thin flat rod of steel and another of aluminum are of identical lengths at 0°C. Imagine further that the two rods are rigidly fastened together at one end. Then, at any temperature other than 0°C, the other ends will not coincide, but the aluminum rod will be the longer at positive Celsius temperatures, whereas the steel rod will be the longer at negative ones. It may have occurred to the reader that the length of our steel thermometer would have been inconvenient to measure. The combination of aluminum and steel provides a *difference* of two lengths which may be used to measure temperature and this can frequently be more conveniently used than the measurement of a total length.

As indicated in the preceding section, the question of differential expansion is of particular interest when we wish to investigate the expansion of liquids. Since the liquid must be kept in a container of some sort, and since this container expands along with the liquid, the quantity actually observed is the difference of the expansions of the liquid and the container. If the coefficient of volume expansion of the container material is greater than that of the liquid, the surface level of the liquid will actually drop as the temperature increases. This seldom happens, however, since most liquids expand far more than solids for a given temperature rise. Table 11.2 gives the measured values of the coefficient of volume expansion for a number of commonly used liquids.

Table 11.2 *Coefficients of Volume Thermal Expansion*

(Valid only for the liquid state)

Liquid	Coefficient b (per °C)
Alcohol	11×10^{-4}
Acetone	15
Benzene	12
Mercury	1.82
Motor oil	9

Water is omitted from Table 11.2 because its behavior is not like that of most other liquids. Just above the ice point, water contracts with rising temperature, reaching a minimum volume at 3.98°C, above which it expands at a rate that changes as the steam point is approached. This behavior makes it impossible to assign a coefficient of thermal expansion to water except over a very small range of temperature, so we include in Table 11.3 a list of the relative volumes of a given quantity of water at various temperatures.

Table 11.3 *Thermal Expansion of Water*

(Quantities given are ratios of volumes to that at 0°C)

Temperature (0°C)	Relative Volume
0	1.00000
1	0.99994
2	0.99990
3	0.99988
4	0.99987
5	0.99988
10	1.00014
20	1.00164
30	1.00421
40	1.00768
50	1.01196
60	1.01694
70	1.02259
80	1.02888
90	1.03579
100	1.04332

11.5 Thermometers

For practical use, the steel rod thermometer, or even the steel-aluminum thermometer that we have mentioned, is too cumbersome and not sufficiently sensitive. For this reason, the common ***mercury-in-glass thermometer*** is the common instrument over the range of temperatures at which we ordinarily work. This instrument, a typical form of which is shown in Fig. 11.1, is made very sensitive by using a large bulb of thin glass to hold a considerable volume of mercury and having the differential volume change take place in a long tube of very small cross section. In this way very small changes of temperature are made to result in appreciable changes in the length of the mercury column in the tube. The thermometer is calibrated by the same method used for the steel thermometer—i.e., the position of the top of the mercury column is observed in melting ice and then in steam. These two points are marked on the stem, and the distance between them is divided into one hundred equal divisions, each of which is defined as ***one Celsius degree.*** If the thermometer is to be used for temperatures below 0°C or above 100°C, divisions of equal length to those within this range are marked off in either direction.

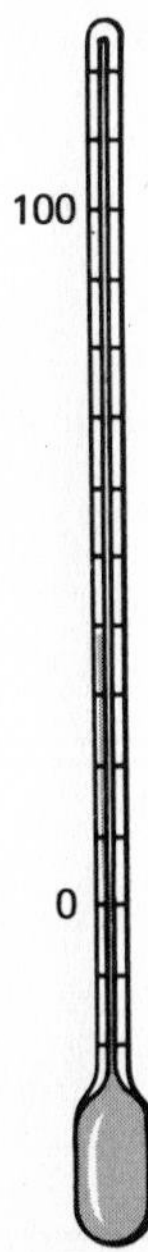

Fig. 11.1 Mercury-in-glass thermometer.

Other liquids, such as alcohol or glycerine, may be used as thermometric substances. If such thermometers are cheap instruments for giving the approximate room or outdoor temperature, they, too, may have a printed scale bearing 100 equal divisions between 0°C and 100°C. However, if such nonmercurial liquid thermometers are used in precision work, they must be calibrated at more than two points to make sure that the scale will agree with the Celsius scale. This is necessary because the coefficient of expansion over a large range of temperature may not be quite constant. In fact, even mercurial thermometers for the highest precision are referred to the hydrogen (or helium) gas thermometer, which is taken as the standard. Gas thermometers will be discussed in Chapter 20.

Another thermometer which is frequently used for less accurate work is the ***bimetallic thermometer***. This is constructed of two metals of different coefficients of expansion in the manner shown in Fig. 11.2. The strips are firmly

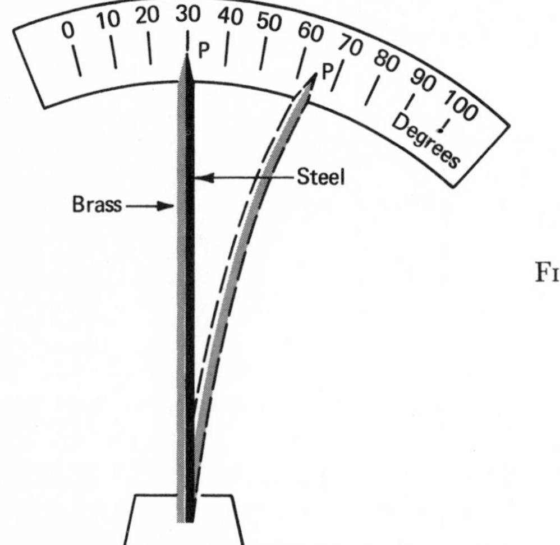

FIG. 11.2 Bimetallic thermometer.

fastened together along their entire lengths. If the combination is heated, the metal strips cannot slide over one another, as they did in the differential thermometer of Sec. 11.4. The only possibility is that the bimetallic strip curl into an arc, with the higher coefficient metal on the outside, as shown by the dotted line in the figure. Similarly, at lower temperatures the lower expansion metal will be the longer, and the strip will curl in the opposite direction. This curving may be used to move a pointer P which reads temperature.

Although we have chosen to introduce the concept of temperature measurement in terms of the expansion of solids, liquids, and gases, we shall later see that many properties of material bodies, other than their dimensions, depend upon temperature. Thus changes in electrical resistance (Sec. 16.18) are used as measures of temperature in the ***resistance thermometer***. Electromotive forces (Secs. 17.5 and 18.16) are produced when electrical circuits consisting of more than one kind of conducting material connect regions at different temperatures

—this effect is the basis of the ***thermocouple.*** Changes of the magnetic properties of some materials (Sec. 16.11) are used for thermometric purposes. Measurement of the radiation from heated bodies (Sec. 12.1) is employed in ***radiation pyrometers***, among which the most commonly used is the ***optical pyrometer.*** We shall not discuss such thermometers in detail, but only note that any property of a substance that depends on temperature may allow a thermometer to be constructed.

EXERCISES

11.5-1 A rod of unknown metal has a length of 0.526 m at 21.0°C. When it is surrounded by steam at 99.5°C, it expands by 0.00074 m. What is its coefficient of linear thermal expansion?

11.5-2 The ***Fahrenheit scale of temperatures*** is based on a mercury-in-glass thermometer with the ice point defined as 32°F and the steam point as 212°F. What are the relative sizes of the Fahrenheit and Celsius degrees?

11.5-3 Using the result of the preceding exercise, convert the following Celsius temperatures to Fahrenheit temperatures: (a) 0°C, (b) 100°C, (c) 37.0°C, (d) −40°C, (e) −273°C.

11.5-4 The telescope at Mt. Palomar Observatory has a Pyrex glass mirror 200 in. in diameter, and the temperatures here range from −5°C to 45°C. By how much will the diameter of the mirror change from one extreme to the other?

11.5-5 A graduated Pyrex flask is filled with motor oil up to the 100-cm³ mark at 20.0°C. What will be the volume of the oil at 31.2°C, as read on the graduations of the flask?

11.6 ***Friction***

In order to connect our study of heat with the laws of mechanics, we shall find it worth while to investigate in some detail one process by which heat can be obtained by mechanical means. This is the process of friction, which is the one used to start a fire by rubbing two sticks together.

From the very start of our study of mechanics, we have observed that a solid body which is rolling or sliding over another is retarded in its motion, and we have ascribed this resistance to friction. We now have enough knowledge of physics to begin a more detailed study of the class of phenomena grouped under this name.

We first consider the motion of a solid body sliding over a surface, as shown in Fig. 11.3. In the absence of friction, we would expect that the moving body would continue indefinitely at constant speed in a straight line, once it had been given an initial velocity. But we actually find that such a motion can be maintained only if a constant force $\vec{f}$ is applied in the direction of the motion. We must therefore suppose that there exists a ***frictional force***, of magnitude f, in the opposite direction—i.e., opposed to the motion.

In spite of the great importance of frictional forces and the long period during which they have been studied, the exact mechanisms which constitute them are still imperfectly understood. It is probable that there are at least two major causes of friction between solid bodies sliding over each other. The first of these is the fact that even the most finely polished surface has small irregularities, and part of the area of contact between the two bodies can be visualized as similar to the section shown in Fig. 11.3b. As the upper body slides over the lower, either it must rise and fall slightly with the surface irregularities or it must grind them off. Both processes take place and both require work. This work can only be achieved by an external force producing the displacement. The second major cause of friction is connected with the forces that hold solid bodies together. We shall see in Chapter 21 that these forces are attractions among the molecules of which the bodies are made, that they exist between unlike as well as between like molecules, and that they become very large when the molecules are

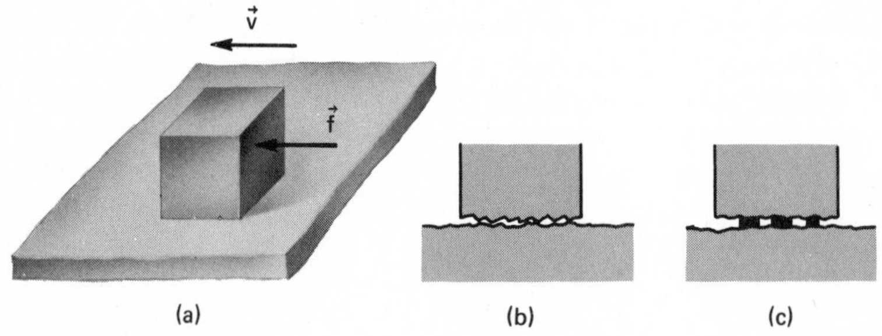

Fig. 11.3 Friction.

separated by very small distances. It seems probable that the state of affairs illustrated in Fig. 11.3c occurs where two solids are in contact. At the points of closest contact, the attractive forces become great enough so that the two materials are actually welded together. During the sliding, joints between the two materials are continually being broken and new ones formed. Each breaking of a joint requires work that must be supplied through the agency of the external force. It is possible that a third type of force, which is electrostatic in nature (cf. Chapter 15), also plays a role. It is the work done against these various impediments to motion that accounts for the decrease in the energy of mechanical systems, which we discussed in Secs. 4.9 and 6.10.

When a solid body is moving through a liquid or a gas, it also experiences a frictional resistance to motion. At low speeds, this resistance is directly proportional to the speed of the body and to a constant of the fluid, known as the ***viscosity***. Studies of motion through a fluid can be made by introducing some opaque material, such as smoke particles in air, or a nonmiscible dye in water, and photographing the paths of this material around the body with a motion picture camera. By such experiments, it is found that the fluid flows smoothly around the body at speeds such that the above relationship holds. At higher speeds, there occurs a phenomenon known as ***turbulence***, in which the fluid whirls and eddies around the body. The resistance then increases much faster than the speed. The speed at which turbulence begins depends upon the shape of the body. A ***streamlined body*** is one so shaped, for motion in a particular direction, that turbulence is set up only at very high speeds. Whether or not streamlining is desirable in a body depends on the motion the body is expected to undergo. Thus, an airplane, a rocket, or a projectile must be streamlined in the direction of its motion, whereas a parachute should be as far from a streamlined body as possible.

The mention of a parachute suggests an interesting consideration. Suppose that a body is falling through the atmosphere. As it starts from rest, the frictional force is zero and the acceleration is $\vec{g}$. As the speed of fall increases, the retarding force also increases, and the net force on the body is its weight less this retarding force. Hence, the acceleration becomes less than g and, instead of varying according to Eq. (3.11-1B), the speed will increase more and more slowly. Finally, when the frictional force is just equal to the weight, the speed will become constant. This vertically downward speed is known as the ***terminal velocity*** of the body. Another case of a body that reaches a terminal speed is furnished by the data of Table 3.4 on the motion of a car starting from rest. The terminal velocity will vary, of course, with the shape and mass of the body. The existence of a terminal velocity is very fortunate in many instances, as the reader may verify by calculating the speed at which a raindrop would strike the earth after falling freely from a height of a kilometer.

11.7 Heat as a Form of Energy

In each of the examples of friction we have considered, energy was consumed in overcoming the frictional force. Thus, in the case of a body falling at terminal velocity, the body loses $mg\,\Delta x$ of potential energy for every Δx that it falls. But, since the speed is constant, the kinetic energy does not increase, and mechanical energy is therefore disappearing at the rate

$$P = \Delta(PE)/\Delta t = mg(\Delta x/\Delta t) = mgv_t,$$

where v_t is the terminal speed. What happens to this energy? If we observe any frictional process carefully, we usually find that the temperature of the bodies involved increases as the process goes on. You can readily verify this by applying a piece of sandpaper vigorously to a block of hardwood. We know that heat is necessary to increase the temperature of a body, so our observations of friction may lead us to expect that heat is another form of energy and that the mechanical energy that disappears in friction is converted into heat. This idea was first proposed in 1798 by Count Rumford (Benjamin Thompson, 1753–1814), who had made observations on the heat produced during the boring of cannon. In the following year, Sir Humphrey Davy (1778–1829), while observing the increased rate of melting of two blocks of ice when they were rubbed together, arrived independently at a similar conclusion.

Before we can accept the equivalence of heat and mechanical energy, it will be necessary to find whether the loss of a fixed amount of mechanical energy always produces the same amount of heat. This, in turn, requires that we find a quantitative method of studying heat. Finally, it will be interesting to see whether the inverse transformation, of heat into mechanical energy, can take place. All of these problems will be discussed in the next few sections.

11.8 The Experiments of Joule

Rumford performed some rather crude experiments to test the quantitative relation between mechanical energy and heat, but it remained for James Prescott Joule (1818–1889), nearly fifty years later, to place the equivalence on an exact basis. The apparatus used in some of his experiments is shown schematically in Fig. 11.4. A paddle wheel, free to turn about a vertical axis, is used to

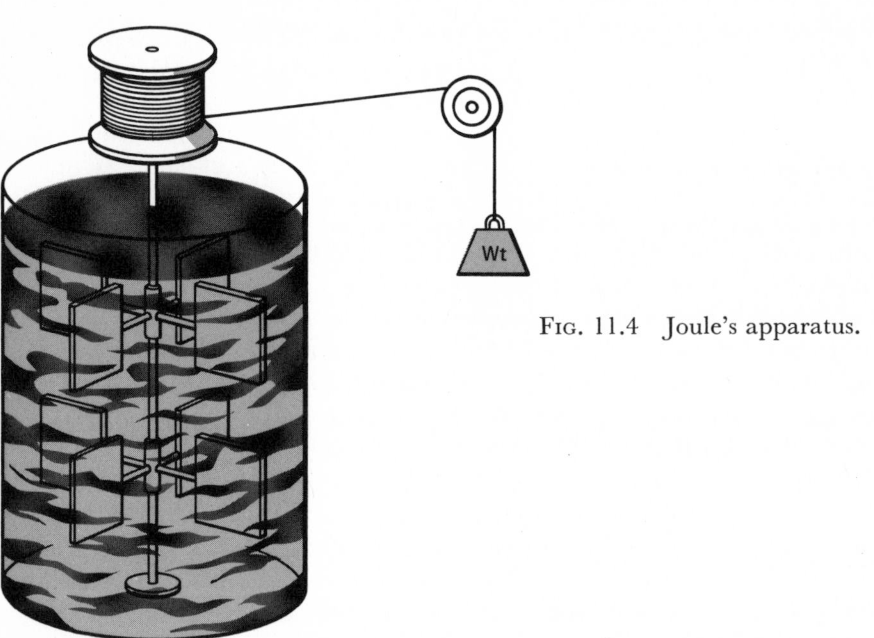

FIG. 11.4 Joule's apparatus.

churn the water in a container. Fixed vanes attached to the walls of the container are arranged so that there is maximum stirring when the paddle wheel is turning. The paddle wheel is driven by the falling of a weight attached to a drum by a cord over a pulley. As a result of the frictional heat developed by the paddle in the water, the water is warmed. If the friction is sufficiently great so that the weight falls very slowly, with practically constant velocity, no potential energy will be converted to kinetic energy. All of the potential energy lost by the weight is used against friction. Thus, if m is the mass of the weight and h is the height through which it has fallen, an amount of energy mgh has been expended in heating the water. Joule found the temperature rise of the water to be directly proportional to the amount of energy lost by the falling weight and inversely proportional to the mass of water employed. Writing the constant of proportionality as $(1/\kappa_W)$, we can express his result by the equation

$$t_2 - t_1 = mgh/\kappa_W M, \tag{11.8-1}$$

where M is the mass of the water, and t_1 and t_2 are the initial and final temperatures. This equation was obeyed very closely for various amounts of water, for different values of the falling mass, and for different distances of fall. Joule's experiments therefore indicate not only that a given amount of mechanical energy always produces the same thermal effect, but also that the temperature rise of water may be used successfully to measure thermal energy. The constant κ_W (Greek letter *kappa*) is obviously the amount of energy necessary to raise 1 kg of water 1°C. We shall call this constant the ***specific heat of water***. Joule found that a 772.5-lb mass, in dropping one foot, could heat a pound of water by 1°F. Converting these measurements into units we are using, we find that the specific heat of water is 4177 J/kg °C.

11.9 *The Specific Heat of Water*

Although we stated that Eq. (11.8-1) was obeyed very closely in the Joule experiments, it is true that small departures from it may be found in an experiment of this type if extreme precision is used. The temperature rise that accompanies a given loss of potential energy is slightly dependent on the initial temperature, but for a given temperature range the results are entirely concordant. This indicates that the specific heat of water is not quite a constant, but that it varies slightly with temperature. Accurate measurements of the energy necessary to heat water give the results summarized in Table 11.4. It is evident from this table that the

Table 11.4 *The Specific Heat of Water*

Temperature (°C)	κ_W (J/kg °C)
0	4215
10	4193
15	4185
20	4179
30	4174
40	4175
50	4178
60	4182
70	4184
80	4187
90	4190
100	4193

specific heat of water is almost constant. For most purposes, we can take the value

$$\kappa_W = 4.18 \times 10^3 \text{ J/kg °C}. \tag{11.9-1}$$

This is never in error by more than one percent, and by that much only at the very ends of the temperature range (0°C–100°C) within which liquid water ordinarily exists.

11.10 Heat Engines

While the demonstrated conversion of mechanical energy into heat leads us to believe that the latter is a form of energy, it is not sufficient to give us complete confidence in the equivalence of heat and energy. It is necessary to inquire whether the reverse conversion—i.e., the conversion of heat into mechanical energy—can also occur. One of the simplest devices for accomplishing the transformation is shown in Fig. 11.5. A closed cylinder with a closely fitted

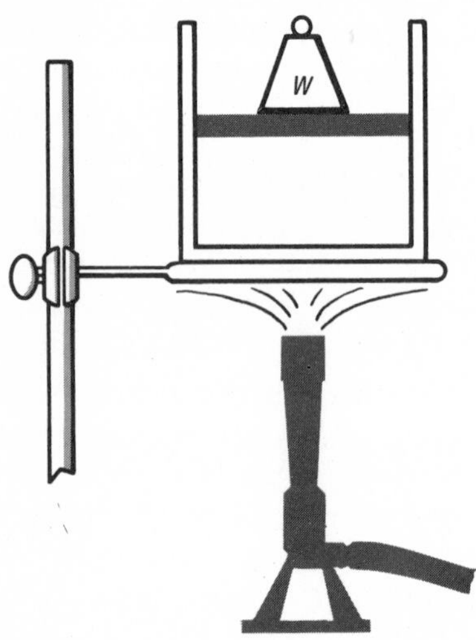

FIG. 11.5 Simple heat engine.

piston, which is free to move, contains a gas. When the gas is heated, its temperature rises and it expands. In so doing it pushes the piston upward, lifting the weight w and doing work. We shall see in Chapter 20 that more heat must be supplied to do this than would be needed merely to heat the gas, and that the amount of work done by the expansion is exactly equivalent to the amount of this excess heat.

Any device that converts thermal energy into other forms of energy is called a ***heat engine***. The engine shown in Fig. 11.5 would not be very useful, since it is not fitted for continuous operation. In most practical heat engines, a cyclic process is carried out so that the engine works continuously without an undue amount of attention. The steam engine uses the expansion of steam, which has been produced from water by heat, to push a piston. The internal combustion engine uses the expansion of the gas resulting from the burning of gasoline or some similar substance within the cylinder.

We have not yet investigated the methods necessary for measuring the amount of heat supplied to a heat engine. We shall therefore merely state here that measurements of this heat show that part of the thermal energy appears as mechanical energy and that the balance of it reappears as thermal energy. Since the heat engine supplies the last link needed in the chain of evidence, we can now say that *heat is energy*.

11.11 The First Law of Thermodynamics

The general study of the relations between other forms of energy and heat is known as ***thermodynamics***. The principles underlying this study have been stated as very general laws. By putting together the results of the last few sections and the considerations of Chapter 6, we can now make a complete generalization of ***the law of the conservation of energy***, which is often called the ***first law of thermodynamics***: *In any isolated system of bodies, the total energy remains constant, regardless of any processes that may take place.*

The term energy, of course, includes all forms: mechanical, mass, thermal, etc. Practically all of the reasoning of physics and chemistry assumes the validity of the first law, and no observation has ever been found to be in conflict with it. A single experiment in disagreement with this conservation law would practically remove the foundations from under theoretical science.

One of the immediate consequences of the first law is the statement that the creation of energy *de novo* is impossible. Thus, a machine that could deliver more energy than was put into it cannot be built. Such a device is known as a ***perpetual motion machine of the first kind***. (This terminology is used to distinguish it from a ***perpetual motion machine of the second kind***, which would merely run indefinitely without delivering energy or having energy supplied to it.) In fact, one of the alternative statements of the first law is: *It is impossible to construct a perpetual motion machine of the first kind.*

EXERCISES

11.11-1 In a Joule experiment, a mass of 5.00 kg falls through a height of 40.0 m. In falling, the mass rotates a paddle wheel that stirs 0.598 kg of water, initially at a temperature of 20°C. Calculate the rise in temperature of the water.

11.11-2 Raindrops are falling vertically downward with a constant speed of 5.00 m/sec onto a flat horizontal surface of 3.00 m^2 area. The total amount of water falling onto the surface each minute is 500 g. Calculate the rate at which heat is developed at the surface, assuming that the water does not run off.

11.11-3 A waterfall is 30 m high, and 8.3×10^3 kg of water flows over it per minute. The water comes to rest in a pool at the bottom. Assuming that no heat is lost to the surroundings, what temperature difference would you expect between the water at the top of the fall and that at the bottom?

11.11-4 Raindrops fall from a height of 1.00 km and strike the ground with a speed of 2.5 m/sec. Assuming that no water is lost from a drop during its fall, and that the heat produced is divided equally between the drop and the air, what will be the rise in temperature of the drops during the fall?

11.12 Specific Heats

We saw in Secs. 11.8 and 11.9 that the amount of energy necessary to raise the temperature of a mass of water was proportional to the mass of water used and to the temperature rise. We shall now consider some experiments to test whether a similar relation holds for other substances. We know that when two bodies at different temperatures are placed in contact, the hotter substance is cooled and the cooler substance is warmed. We explain this by saying that heat flows from the hotter to the cooler body. Suppose that we place any body of known mass m, at temperature t_1, in contact with a mass m_W of water, at a higher temperature t_W. The system (water plus other body) will eventually reach a new temperature t, intermediate between t_1 and t_W. If the system is isolated (i.e., if no heat is lost to or gained from the surroundings), the heat lost by the water in cooling from t_W to t must be just equal to the heat required by the other body to raise its temperature from t_1 to t. Assuming for the moment that we can ascribe to this body a constant ***specific heat*** κ, defined as the quantity of heat required to raise the temperature of one kilogram of the substance through one degree Centigrade, we shall have

$$m\kappa(t - t_1) = m_W \kappa_W (t_W - t). \tag{11.12-1}$$

The assumptions we made in deriving Eq. (11.12-1) can be tested only de seeing whether the equation is verified by experiments in which various values of m, m_W, t_1, and t_W are used. If different combinations of these quantities all give the same value of κ, we are justified in assuming both that no appreciable amount of heat is lost or gained and that the substance has a constant specific heat. Experiments in the range of room temperature and above show a very good check with Eq. (11.12-1) for almost all substances, provided only that the material does not change its state. Examples of such a change of state would be the melting of a solid or the vaporization of a liquid.

In the actual experiments, of course, t_W can be either greater or less than t_1. If the mass of water is relatively large compared with the mass of the other substance, t_1 may be far higher than 100°C, at which water boils, or lower than 0°C, at which it freezes. In such cases, it is only necessary that t_W and t lie in the range from 0°C to 100°C. The requirement that there be no heat exchange with the surroundings is sometimes difficult to satisfy. If we conduct the process rapidly and do the mixing in a carefully insulated vessel, the heat loss or gain may be minimized. If heat exchange does take place, methods may be devised for measuring its magnitude and correcting for it. The details of such experiments will be left to the reader's experience in the laboratory.

After the specific heats of a number of substances have been determined, those of new substances can be obtained by comparison with those already known, just as well as by comparison with water. Moreover, the result of mixing any number of substances, of known specific heats and at known initial temperatures, can be predicted, since the total heat lost by the hotter bodies must be equal to that gained by the cooler bodies. If the initial temperature of a mass

m_n of one of the substances, which has a specific heat κ_n, is t_n, and the final temperature of the mixture is t, then the heat gained by that substance is

$$m_n \kappa_n (t - t_n),$$

if no changes of state take place. If the substance is cooled in the mixing process, t is less than t_n, and the substance gains negative heat—i.e., it loses heat. In any mixing process in which no heat is gained or lost and no changes of state take place, the sum of the terms of this type for all substances involved must be zero.

When we defined the specific heat, we gave it the unit of joules per kilogram degree. The energy, of course, could equally well be measured in some other unit than the joule. One such unit, which is of considerable historical importance, is the ***calorie***, which is defined as the amount of heat necessary to raise the temperature of one gram of water one begree. Because of the small variations in the specific heat of water (cf. Table 11.4), it is necessary in precise work to specify the limits of the temperature range over which the water is heated. Thus, the ***fifteen degree calorie*** is the amount of heat required to raise one gram of water from 14.5°C to 15.5°C. Other ranges are occasionally used in the definition, but we shall use the term calorie in this book only for the fifteen degree calorie. This unit is inconveniently small for many purposes, and the ***kilocalorie***, or ***large calorie***, equal to 1000 calories, is frequently used. If the specific heat of water is measured in terms of the kilocalorie (ordinarily abbreviated "kcal" in distinction to "cal" for the calorie), it has a value of exactly 1.000 kcal/kg °C at 15°C and is very near to this value for all other temperatures between 0°C and 100°C. By reference to Table 11.4, we see that

$$1 \text{ kcal} = 4185 \text{ J}. \tag{11.12-2}$$

Measurements of the specific heats of most solids have been made with high accuracy and can be found in any of the handbooks of physics or chemistry. A list of the values for a number of common materials is given in Table 11.5.

Table 11.5 *Specific Heats of Common Solids*
(The values given are valid at room temperature and above)

Material	Kilogram Specific Heat κ (J/kg °C)	(kcal/kg °C)
Aluminum	9.2×10^2	0.21
Brass	3.1–3.9	0.074–0.094
Copper	3.88	0.093
Glass	8.4	0.20
Iron	4.6	0.11
Lead	1.3	0.031
Nickel	4.3	0.103
Platinum	1.3	0.033
Water	41.8	1.00

Although the specific heats of most solids are approximately independent of temperature at room temperature and above, it is found that they decrease rapidly at low temperatures, approaching zero as the temperature approaches −273°C. A few substances, of which diamond is a notable example, have specific heats which increase rapidly with increasing temperature at ordinary temperatures. The temperature variation of thermal capacities has found an interesting explanation in modern theoretical physics, but the treatment is beyond the scope of this chapter.

Illustrative Example

A lump of lead, of 0.200 kg mass, is set upon a solid anvil and is then flattened to a sheet by dropping a hard 100-kg mass upon it from a height of 1.00 m. What happens to the temperature of the lead?

To apply the law of the conservation of energy, we need first to determine how much mechanical energy is available. This is clearly equal to the potential energy of the hard mass before it is released:

$$W = Mgh = (100\text{ kg})(9.80\text{ m/sec}^2)(1.00\text{ m})$$
$$= 9.80 \times 10^2\text{ J}.$$

One might ask whether all of this energy is really available. Air friction will certainly cause little dissipation of energy in this short fall. It is certainly possible that the hard mass may bounce from the lead, recovering some of the kinetic energy that it had before striking, but this will make no difference—the mass will merely fall again, giving up any mechanical energy that it may have, as it eventually comes to rest on the lead.

All of the mechanical energy originally present must reappear in some form, according to the conservation law. Let us first suppose that *all* of it goes into heating of the lead. Then, the temperature rise will be

$$\Delta T = W/\kappa m,$$

where κ is the specific heat and m is the mass of the lead. Taking κ from Table 11.5, we have

$$\Delta T = (9.80 \times 10^2\text{ J})/(1.3 \times 10^2\text{ J/kg deg})\ (0.200\text{ kg})$$
$$= 3.77°\text{C}.$$

This is an upper limit to the temperature rise. If the internal mechanical energy of the lead is changed as a result of the flattening, or if any heat is transferred to the anvil or to the hard mass, the temperature rise will be less than we have calculated. During the short time of impact, thermal transfer is probably small, so we can be pretty sure that the lead will experience a temperature rise of about 3°C. It is doubtful if more than one significant figure is justified in the result, and 3° has been taken, rather than 4°, because any effects that we have neglected would result in a smaller temperature rise than the 3.77° computed as an upper limit.

EXERCISES

11.12-1 The water coming from a cold tap has a temperature of 15°C, and that from a hot tap has a temperature of 95°C. How much water must be drawn from each tap to draw a bath of 75 kg of water at 45°C?

11.12-2 A mass of lead shot at 150°C is added to 0.342 kg of water at 21.2°C. After the lead shot is added, the mass of the water and the shot together is 0.568 kg. Assuming that no heat is lost, calculate the temperature of the water and of the shot after they have been mixed.

11.12-3 A copper bucket has a mass 1.32 kg and is at a temperature of 20.0°C. Water at 43.2°C is poured into it until the total mass is 6.57 kg. Assuming that no heat is lost, calculate the temperature of the water in the bucket.

11.12-4 The bucket of Ex. 11.12-3 contains water at 20.0°C, the total mass of water and bucket being 5.40 kg. A piece of hot steel at 1500°C is dropped into the bucket, and the resultant temperature is found to be 29.6°C. If the mass of the steel is 253 g and no heat is lost, what is the specific heat of the steel?

11.12-5 Five hundred grams of a liquid of unknown specific heat are contained in a glass beaker which has a mass of 150 g. The temperature of the liquid is 20.5°C. After 200 g of aluminum shavings at 100°C are added to it, the temperature is found to be 33.8°C. What is the specific heat of the liquid?

11.13 Fusion

When we started discussing specific heats in Sec. 11.12, we stated that the considerations of that section were valid only if none of the substances changed state during the measurements. We shall here use the term ***state*** to indicate the physical characteristics of a substance. Most substances can exist in three different states, solid, liquid, and gas.* For example, we have ice, water, and steam as three states of the same substance. We shall now investigate the thermal changes that take place when a substance changes from one state to another.

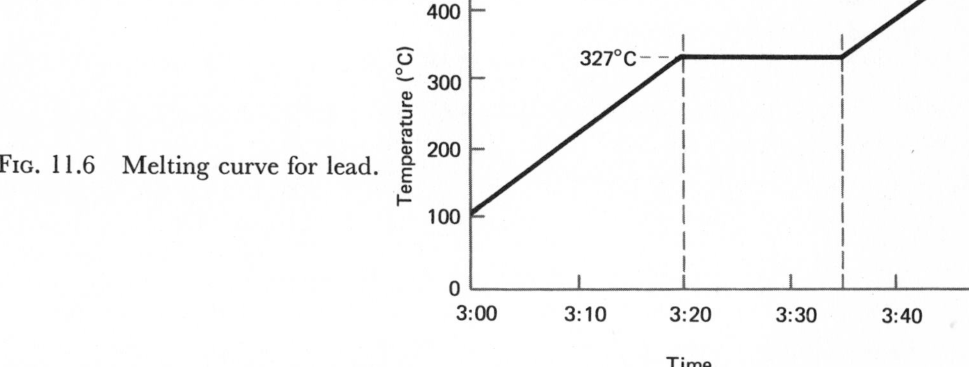

FIG. 11.6 Melting curve for lead.

Let us first consider the process known as ***melting***, or ***fusion***—i.e., the change from a solid to a liquid. We place a piece of some solid substance, such as lead, in a crucible and supply heat to it at a constant rate. If we observe the temperature of the lead at regular intervals, we obtain data that can be plotted in a curve such as that in Fig. 11.6. The temperature rises steadily at first. In

* Some materials may have more than one solid state, depending on their internal arrangement. We shall not be concerned with such cases here.

the experiment illustrated, 1.00 kg of lead was used and the rate of rise was 11°C/min. If we combine this figure with the specific heat of lead as given by Table 11.5, we find that heat was being supplied at the rate of 1.5×10^3 J/min, or 25 watts. When the temperature reaches 327°C, the increase stops. If we were to examine the lead at this point, we would discover that it has begun to melt. The temperature stays constant for 15 min, during which the lead continues to melt. At the end of this time, only liquid is present in the crucible, and the temperature again begins to rise as heat is supplied to the liquid. Since we know the rate at which energy is supplied to the lead, we can compute the amount of heat that goes into the material during the melting, without changing the temperature. This is found to be 2.3×10^4 J.

If a large number of experiments of the type just described are carried out, using various masses of different *pure* substances, two interesting results are obtained:

(1) During the process of melting, a fixed temperature, known as the ***melting point***, is maintained, regardless of the quantity of heat supplied.
(2) The quantity of heat necessary to melt a solid is directly proportional to the mass of the substance melted.

In consequence of the last statement, we can write the energy necessary to melt a mass m of a pure substance as

$$E = mL_f, \tag{11.13-1}$$

where L_f is a constant of the substance, called the latent heat of fusion. The ***latent heat of fusion*** is therefore the quantity of heat necessary to melt one kilogram of the substance without increasing the temperature. A number of observed latent heats of fusion are given in Table 11.6.

Table 11.6 *Latent Heats of Fusion*

Material	Melting Point (°C)	Latent Heat of Fusion L (J/kg)	(kcal/kg)
Copper	1083	20.5×10^4	49.0
Gold	1063	6.61	15.8
Water	0	33.3	79.7
Lead	327	2.29	5.47
Mercury	−39	1.18	2.82
Silver	961	10.9	26.0
Sulfur	119	5.52	13.2
Tin	232	5.79	13.8

From the fact that heat is necessary to melt a solid, we are led to expect that a substance in the liquid state contains more internal energy than the same quantity of the substance in the solid state. If this interpretation is correct, we should expect from the conservation law that, when a mass m of a liquid ***freezes*** to a solid, an amount of heat mL_f should be given to the surroundings. We can test this by observing freezing curves in much the same way that we observed the melting curve of Fig. 11.6. If we do so, we find that *exactly as much heat is given up by a liquid when it freezes as it required to melt the same mass of the solid.* We also find that the ***freezing point*** of a pure substance is identical with its melting point.

In view of what has just been said, it should be apparent that the process of melting cools the surroundings and that of freezing warms them. It is for this reason that a location near water is usually warmer in the winter and cooler in the summer than a spot further inland. As the temperature drops, heat is given off by the large mass of water as it cools. As soon as the freezing point is reached, ice starts to form and very large quantities of heat are released. This prevents the temperature from dropping as rapidly as it would otherwise. With increase of temperature, the ice starts to melt, takes up much of the available energy, and lowers the rate of increases. These effects are especially pronounced because water has abnormally high specific and latent heats, as are seen from Tables 11.5 and 11.6. It is the high latent heat of fusion of ice that makes this substance a good refrigerant.

11.14 Variation of the Melting Point

Had we measured the melting points of different solids under different conditions and with high precision, we might have found that the melting point does not remain quite constant but depends slightly on the pressure. We can see a reason for this if we notice that almost all substances have a higher density as solids than they do as liquids, i.e., they expand upon melting. If the pressure is increased, this expansion will be more difficult, and we might expect the melting point to be raised. As a matter of fact, exactly this behavior is observed for all of the substances which expand on melting. However, there are a few anomalous substances, of which water is the prime example, in which the solid is less dense than the liquid at the melting point. Using the same reasoning as before, we should predict that the melting point would be lowered for these materials as the pressure increases. This behavior is observed for substances like water. The effect of pressure on the melting point is very small. The ice point, for example, is lowered by about 0.008°C by a doubling of the normal atmospheric pressure.

Impurities have a much larger effect on the melting point than pressure. Relatively small amounts of dissolved substances can produce appreciable changes in the freezing temperature of a liquid. Many impure substances do not have a fixed melting point at all, but change their temperature with the ratio of the amount of solid to the amount of liquid present. We shall not discuss this phenomenon in detail, but we mention it in order to point out that the purity of a substance is important if the melting point of the substance is to be determined.

EXERCISES

11.14-1 Heat is supplied to a block of ice at a uniform rate. The temperature of the ice is initially −10°C. It takes 72 sec for the temperature to rise to 0°C. The temperature then remains at this level for 1200 sec, after which the ice is all melted and the temperature again rises. What is the specific heat of ice as determined by this experiment?

11.14-2 A glass has a mass of 110 g and contains 190 g of water at 21.0°C. One ice cube (at 0°C) of mass 27 g is added and the water is stirred. What is the resulting temperature?

11.14-3 Under the conditions of Ex. 11.14-2, three identical ice cubes are added instead of one. What is the final temperature?

11.14-4 A piece of copper of mass 52 g at a temperature of 100°C is placed in contact with a large block of ice which is initially at 0°C. How much ice will melt?

11.15 Vaporization and Vapor Pressure

When a quantity of liquid is left with a surface exposed to the atmosphere, the amount of liquid in the container generally decreases with time. We can show, by means of a simple experiment, that this liquid is not lost but rather passes into the surrounding atmosphere in the form of a ***vapor***, a name given to the gaseous state of a liquid. Suppose that we have a closed glass bulb of the shape shown in Fig. 11.7, with a small amount of liquid sealed into it but with the air

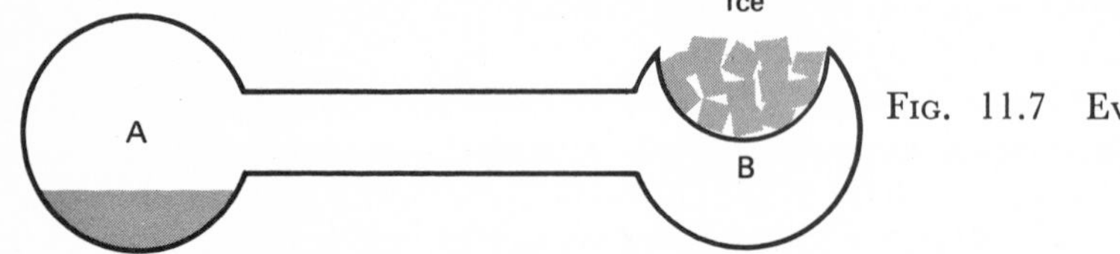

FIG. 11.7 Evaporation and condensation.

removed by a vacuum pump. We first tip the bulb to bring all the liquid into chamber A, and then restore the bulb to the position shown in the figure. If chamber A is heated slightly or if chamber B is cooled, no liquid will appear between the two, but the quantity of liquid in A will decrease and liquid will start to collect in B. The substance passes from A to B in the form of a vapor and is recondensed to the liquid state in B.

Another illustration of the presence of the vapor over a liquid is the ***vapor pressure tube***, shown in Fig. 11.8. This is a tube with one closed end. It is first filled with mercury and inverted into a container of mercury to form an ordinary barometer. If air bubbles and impurities have been avoided, the column of mercury will stand at barometric height h. If a small quantity of liquid is now introduced under the bottom of the tube with a medicine dropper, it will rise and float on the mercury. As it does so, the mercury column will drop to a new level, height h'. After one has introduced just enough of the liquid so that only a thin layer rests on the surface of the mercury column, the new level of the mercury is independent of the amount of liquid introduced. Now, from the conditions of hydrostatic equilibrium (Sec. 9.6), we know that there must be a pressure p on the top of the mercury surface, such that

$$p = \rho g(h - h'),$$

where ρ is the density of mercury and g is the acceleration due to gravity. This pressure, in general, is far greater than is the hydrostatic pressure resulting from the minute amount of liquid floating on the mercury, so we are forced to assume the existence of a vapor over the liquid.

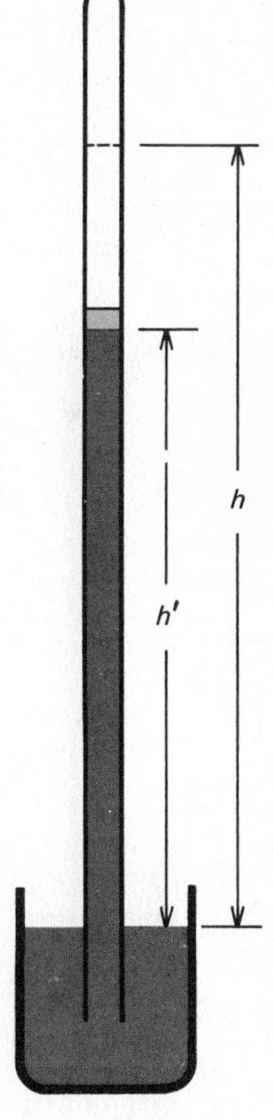

FIG. 11.8 Vapor pressure tube.

With the vapor pressure tube we can also study the way in which vapor pressure varies with temperature. If we surround the upper portion of the tube with heating coils or with a water jacket that carries warm water, we can control the temperature of the vapor at will. If enough liquid is introduced so that there is always some left on top of the mercury, we find that the level of the mercury column drops quite rapidly as the temperature increases. We measure p at a series of known temperatures to determine the ***vapor pressure curve.*** Figure 11.9 shows such a curve for water. It will be noticed that the pressure of the vapor increases much faster than does the temperature. This is typical of all vapor pressure curves. For highly volatile substances such as ether, the observed pressures would be much higher than those shown in Fig. 11.9, whereas for a substance like motor oil they would be exceedingly low. In any case, there is a fixed pressure that a pure liquid and its vapor will maintain, for a given temperature, when they are in contact in a closed space.

We may suppose that the process of ***vaporization*** consists of the escape of some of the molecules of the liquid through the surface. If the liquid is exposed in a large room, the vapor thus formed can spread out, away from the liquid, and the process can continue indefinitely. If, on the other hand, the space over the liquid is limited, the pressure of the vapour increases as evaporation takes place. The fact that a definite equilibrium pressure is reached indicates that some of the vapor again ***condenses*** to form liquid. The rate at which this ***condensation*** takes place depends upon the pressure of the vapor. When the rate at which vapor is formed and the rate at which it condenses are just equal, equilibrium will be established and the pressure will remain constant.

On the basis of the discussion of the preceding paragraph, we are led to suppose that the rate at which a liquid evaporates depends both on the temperature of the liquid and on the pressure of the vapor above it. We can check the first conclusion by heating chamber A, in Fig. 11.7, to various temperatures and measuring the rate at which liquid collected in B, which is always kept cooler than A. The dependence of the rate of evaporation on the vapor pressure above the liquid is the reason that water in a room evaporates at different rates, depending upon the humidity or the water content of the atmosphere. Air in contact with water always contains water vapor as one of its constituents. The pressure of the atmosphere is thus partially due to the other constituents (oxygen, nitrogen, carbon dioxide, etc.) and partially due to water vapor. If the

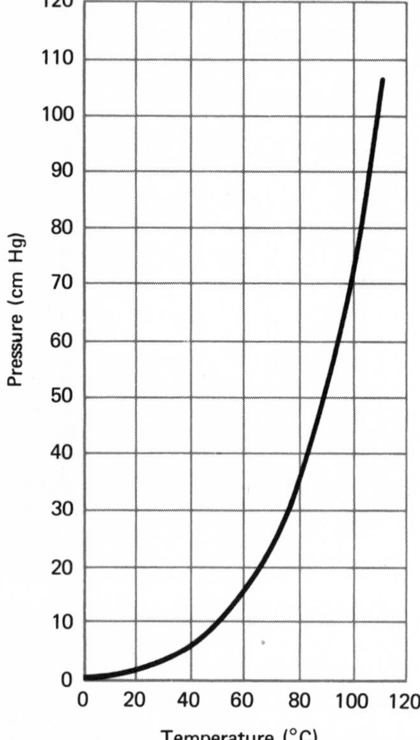

FIG. 11.9 Vapor pressure of water.

pressure of the water vapor alone is the equilibrium vapor pressure for the given temperature of the air, the air is said to be ***saturated (100 percent humidity).*** Under these circumstances, water will not evaporate, since vapor will condense at the same rate that vaporization takes place. If water is brought into contact with ***completely dry air (0 percent humidity)***, no condensation takes place, and the net rate of vaporization is high. The pressure of the water vapor at 20°C for complete saturation is about 2000 N/m^2, or 15 mm of mercury.

11.16 The Latent Heat of Vaporization

From our conclusions regarding the energy necessary for a change from the solid to the liquid state of matter, we might be inclined to speculate on the possibility that energy is also required to change a substance from a liquid to a vapor. One of the simplest ways of demonstrating this fact is sketched in Fig. 11.10. A container of liquid is placed under a bell jar connected to a vacuum pump. The container is insulated from the surroundings so that little heat transfer can take place. A thermometer is in contact with the liquid. If the region above the liquid is now evacuated, the vapor will be removed as fast as it forms, and continual evaporation will take place. It is found under these circumstances that the temperature of the liquid drops very rapidly. This implies that a heat of vaporization is required to produce the vapor and that this has been supplied

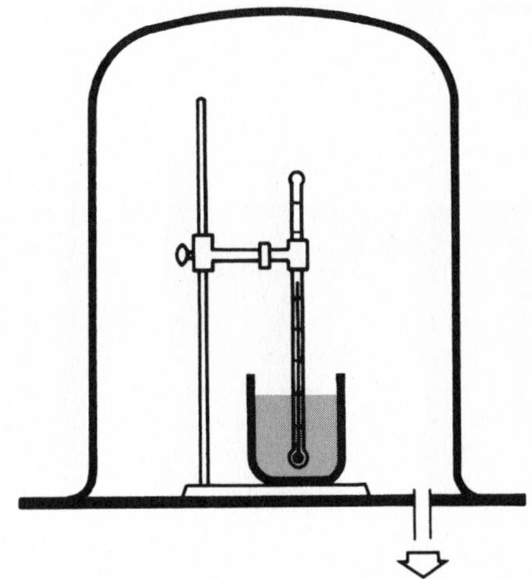

FIG. 11.10 Cooling by vaporization.

by the cooling of the liquid. We define the ***latent heat of vaporization*** as the quantity of energy necessary to convert one kilogram of a liquid completely into a vapor, without a change of temperature. With the help of this definition, we can find a relation between the temperature drop of the liquid and the amount of vapor formed. If a mass m of a liquid of specific heat κ is present, and if a very small quantity, Δm, is vaporized, the first law tells us that

$$L_V(\Delta m) = -m\kappa(\Delta t),$$

where L_V is the latent heat of vaporization and Δt is the small temperature change resulting from the process.

In the process of condensation, an amount of energy equal to the latent heat of vaporization is released for every kilogram of vapor condensed into the liquid. The values of the latent heats of vaporization of a number of liquids are given in Table 11.7. The heats of vaporization are somewhat dependent on the temperature at which the vaporization takes place. Notice that most of the values in the table are given for the boiling temperature. In most cases, the change of the value with temperature is small over most of the liquid range.

Table 11.7 *Latent Heats of Vaporization*
The values given apply at the boiling point (at 760 mm Hg) unless otherwise specified

Material	Latent Heat of Vaporization L_v	
	(J/kg)	(kcal/kg)
Ammonia	13.6×10^5	327
Ether	3.51	83.9
Ethyl alcohol	8.54	204
Hydrogen	4.51	108
Mercury	3.0	71
Nitrogen	1.99	47.6
Oxygen	2.12	50.9
Water (0°C)	24.94	595.9
(50°C)	23.78	568.5
(100°C)	22.58	539.6

11.17 Boiling

Suppose that a liquid in an open container is gradually heated. As the temperature increases, the vapor pressure also increases and vaporization takes place at an increasing rate. If the temperature rise is continued long enough, the vapor pressure may become equal to that of the atmosphere over the liquid. As soon as this happens, the process of vaporization changes from something that takes place only on the surface to a phenomenon occurring throughout the volume of the liquid. The reason for this is that the vapor pressure is now great enough so that bubbles of vapor can form anywhere within the liquid and can push aside the liquid against atmospheric pressure. Moreover, further heat supplied to the liquid cannot increase its temperature, since any increase would result in a higher vapor pressure. Such a pressure is impossible, for the vapor could expand indefinitely against the atmosphere if its pressure increased above atmospheric pressure. We call this vaporization process ***boiling***. It takes place at a constant temperature, regardless of the amount of heat supplied. The temperature at which boiling takes place is known as the ***boiling point***. Table 11.8 lists the boiling points of several common liquids.

The discussion of the preceding paragraph should make it clear that the boiling point depends upon the pressure over the liquid. It was for this reason that we specified in Sec. 11.2 the pressure at which thermometers were to be calibrated. If the liquid is placed in a closed container and the region above it is evacuated, the boiling point can be lowered to any temperature, if the substance is still liquid, depending only upon the rate of pumping. On the other hand, if the container is closed and not evacuated, the vapor pressure will build up inside it and the boiling point will be raised. Both of these schemes are used commercially: the first when it is desired to evaporate water rapidly without undue heating, as in the crystallization of sugar from syrup; the second when

Table 11.8 *Boiling Points of Liquids* (at 760 mm Hg)

Liquid	Boiling Point (°C)
Air	−190
Ether	34.6
Ethyl alcohol	78.3
Gold	2600
Mercury	356.9
Nitrogen	−195.8
Oxygen	−183.0
Sulfur	444.6

temperatures higher than 100°C are needed, as in processes of sterilization. Values for the boiling point of water at several pressures are given in Table 11.9.

Table 11.9 *Boiling Point of Water*

Pressure (mm Hg)	Temperature (°C)
720.0	98.493
730.0	98.877
740.0	99.255
750.0	99.630
760.0	100.000
770.0	100.366
780.0	100.728
790.0	101.087

11.18 Sublimation

Under some circumstances, it is possible for a substance to pass directly from the solid state to the vapor state, or vice versa, without passing through the liquid state. Perhaps the most familiar example of this occurs with "dry ice" (solid carbon dioxide). It happens that liquid carbon dioxide can exist only at pressures well above atmospheric, so at ordinary pressures only the solid and the gas may be observed. Another example occurs when ordinary ice is placed in a cold, dry atmosphere. If the temperature is kept below 0°C and the humidity is kept low, the ice will gradually disappear without melting. We call such processes ***sublimation*** and say that the vapor has sublimed from the solid. As with melting and vaporization, a given quantity of energy is needed to change one kilogram of the solid to the vapor state, without change of temperature, and this is known as the ***latent heat of sublimation***. An equivalent amount of heat is released when the vapor condenses to the solid. Condensation of vapor to solid occurs, of course, on cold, clear nights when frost forms on grass, leaves, and roofs.

EXERCISES

11.18-1 The container of Ex.11.12-3 contains sufficient water to make the total mass 4.76 kg. The temperature is 20.3°C, and the atmospheric pressure is normal. Steam is passed into it until the total mass has been increased to 5.03 kg. What is the final temperature?

11.18-2 When a glass of ice water stands in a room, moisture often condenses on the outside. Why does this happen? Does the condensation have any effect on the energy content of the glass of water?

11.18-3 When a glass contains ice in a mixture of water and alcohol, ice sometimes forms on the outside. What conclusion can you draw from this phenomenon concerning the freezing point of a water-alcohol mixture?

11.18-4 A block of solid carbon dioxide (dry ice) of mass 10 g is dropped into a mass of 450 g of water at an initial temperature of 18.4°C. The temperature of the water after all the carbon dioxide has sublimed and the gas has escaped is 16.5°C. What is the latent heat of sublimation of this solid?

11.19 Heat Transfer

We have discussed thermal energy at some length in this chapter, but we have not yet touched upon the methods by which heat may be communicated from one body to another. While we must reserve the detailed discussion of the mechanism of this transfer until we discuss the structure of solids and liquids in Chapter 21, we may outline here the observed facts regarding the phenomena.

Probably the simplest way in which thermal energy is moved from point to point is by the actual transfer of heated matter. This process is known as ***convection.*** The most familiar example of convection occurs in liquids and gases. If heat is applied to the bottom of a container that holds a fluid, the temperature of the bottom layer of liquid increases. This temperature rise is accompanied by thermal expansion, which lowers the density of this part of the fluid with respect to the main body. The fluid of lower density therefore floats upward (cf. Sec. 9.9), carrying the heat with it, while the cooler fluid on top sinks to the bottom and is in turn warmed. The phenomenon of convection is largely responsible for winds in our atmosphere.

The second method of heat transfer is by a process known as ***thermal conduction.*** When any material body is heated at one point, other portions of the body also become warmer. The quantitative laws of thermal conduction are studied most easily by the use of a block of material shaped like a parallelepiped (Fig. 11.11). If one face of this block is maintained at a temperature t and the other at a temperature $t + \Delta t$, heat will flow through the block at a steady rate. The amount of energy transferred per second can be measured by the rate of vaporization of a liquid on the cooler face or, better, by electrical methods. If this is done, it is found that the results can be expressed in the form of an equation:

$$P = \sigma_{\mathrm{T}} A(\Delta t)/L, \tag{11.19-1}$$

where P is the rate of energy transfer, A is the cross-sectional area of the block, and L is its thickness. The quantity σ_{T} (Greek letter *sigma*) is characteristic of the material and is known as the ***thermal conductivity.*** The thermal conductivities of a number of important materials are given in Table 11.10.

Table 11.10 *Thermal Conductivities of Solids*

Material	Thermal Conductivity σ_T (W/m °C)
Aluminum	210
Asbestos paper	0.2
Brick, red	0.6
Copper	380
Glass	0.8
Gold	290
Oak (across grain)	0.14
Paper	0.1
Pine (across grain)	0.11
Rock wool	0.04
Silver	410
Steel	46

Notice that the metals have much higher thermal conductivities than other materials.

The third method of heat transfer, the one by which heat reaches us from the sun, is ***radiation.*** Every heated body continually sends out radiant energy that falls on other bodies and is absorbed by them. Since radiation is discussed at considerable length in Chapter 12, we shall not go into the properties of radiant

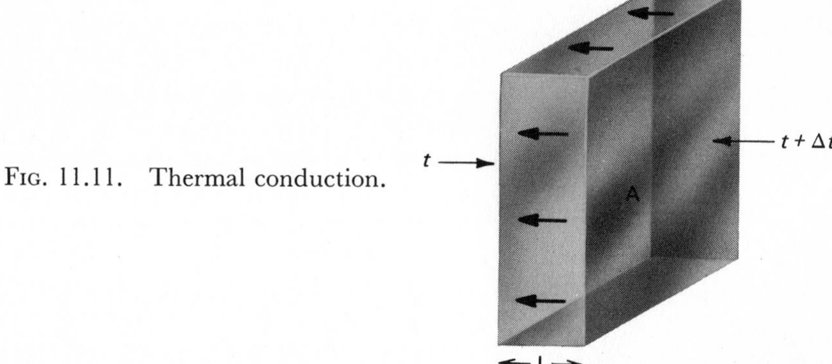

FIG. 11.11. Thermal conduction.

energy here to any great extent. We may say, however, that this form of heat transfer is effective even without a medium to carry the energy, as in the vacuous space between the sun and the earth. Radiant energy also passes quite freely through many transparent bodies, such as glass. Most materials that are transparent to light are also transparent to thermal energy.

EXERCISES

11.19-1 Account for the fact that a tropical island frequently has breezes from the sea during the day and from inland at night. Illustrate with diagrams.

11.19-2 Show that the unit of thermal conductivity as given in Table 11.10 is dimensionally correct. If we are to use the values of this table directly, in what units must A and L in Eq. (11.19-1) be expressed?

11.19-3 A greenhouse has an area of glass of 55 m^2. The glass is 4.0 mm thick. If the temperature outside is −20°C and the inside is to be maintained at 18°C, how many 500-watt lamps must be kept burning if we assume that these are the only source of heat?

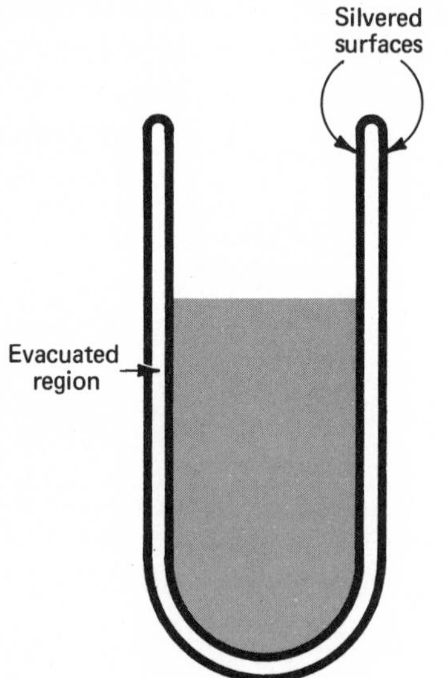

Fig. 11.12 Dewar flask.

11.20 The Dewar Flask

One of the most interesting applications of our knowledge of heat transfer mechanisms is the ***Dewar flask***, invented by Sir James Dewar (1842–1923) for the storage of liquefied gases and popularized as the ***Thermos bottle***. Such a flask is shown in Fig. 11.12. It consists essentially of a double-walled vessel, usually made of glass. The region between the two walls is evacuated, and the surface of the glass is coated with silver to give a mirror finish. Since there is practically no air in the space separating the two walls, no convection can take place. The glass may be made quite thin around the neck of the flask, and thus conduction to or from the outside is minimized. Finally, the mirror surface reflects radiant heat. Thus, all three forms of heat transfer are reduced to very low levels. For the storage of such materials as liquid hydrogen or liquid helium (boiling points −252.8°C and −268.9°C, respectively, at 760 mm of Hg) even these precautions are hardly sufficient, and it is sometimes necessary to enclose the entire flask in a larger second flask, with liquid nitrogen (boiling point −195.8°C at 760 mm of Hg) in the intervening space.

EXERCISE

11.20-1 If one wishes to store liquid hydrogen for as long as possible, why does it make good sense from the physical point of view to put the liquid hydrogen in a Dewar vessel which, in turn, is placed in liquid nitrogen contained within a larger, outer Dewar vessel?

11.21 Summary

This chapter has been concerned with the study of heat. We have investigated the expansion that takes place when bodies are heated and have used this expansion to construct thermometers and to establish temperature scales. Heat is a form of energy and must therefore be included in discussions of the conservation of energy. Heat is required to increase the temperature of a body, to change a solid to a liquid or a gas, or to vaporize a liquid. In the reverse processes, heat is given off. We have also discussed briefly the ways in which heat can be transferred from a hotter to a cooler body.

PROBLEMS

11.1 Suppose that a rod of length L_0 is fastened rigidly at both ends at a temperature t_0, so that the distance between its ends cannot change. Its temperature is then raised to t. For simplicity, consider that the rod bends into a circular arc, of radius R that subtends a central angle of 2θ. Show the following equations to hold:

$$R^2 \approx L^2/12\alpha(t - t_0),$$

$$\theta \approx L/2R,$$

$$\Delta h \approx L\theta/4,$$

where α is the coefficient of linear expansion of the rod and Δh is the distance that the center of the rod departs from its original position (at t_0) as a result of the expansion. Hint: Use the approximate relationship

$$\sin\theta \approx \theta - \theta^3/3$$

from Appendix G and neglect all terms smaller than $\alpha(t - t_0)$.

11.2 Apply the results of Prob. 11.1 to the bridge discussed in Sec. 11.3 to find by how much its center will be moved at 40°C if the bridge is straight at 20°C and is rigidly fastened at both ends.

11.3 (a) Suppose that the two ends of a rod of length L_0 are fastened rigidly to firm supports at a temperature t_0 and that the rod is then cooled to some new temperature t. The rod will then be in tension. The tension can be calculated by supposing that the rod was allowed to contract and then was stretched by the application of a tensile force to its original length. Show that this force is

$$F = \alpha YA(t_0 - t),$$

where α is the coefficient of linear expansion, Y is Young's modulus, and A is the cross-sectional area of the rod.

(b) Apply the result obtained in (a) to a vertical steel rod of 1.0 cm^2 cross-sectional area, taking $(t_0 - t)$ to be 5.0°C. What would be the mass, in pounds, that would need to be hung from the rod to produce an equal tension?

11.4 A cavity of volume V_0 in a steel container is just filled with water at 4°C. The cavity is then plugged tightly and the temperature of the container and water is raised to 80°C. What will the hydrostatic pressure on the water be at this temperature? (Hint: Do Prob. 11.3 before attempting this problem.)

11.5 (a) A Dewar flask of the type shown in Fig. 11.12 is partially filled with ice and water. It is then left uncovered in a room at a temperature of 25°C. At the end of eight hours it is found that 300 g of ice has melted. At what average rate has heat entered the flask?

(b) The same flask is partially filled with 1200 g of water at 90°C. Again it is left uncovered in a room at 25°C. At the end of eight hours the temperature of the water is found to be 60°C. At what rate has heat left the flask?

(c) Discuss the difference between the results found in (a) and in (b). Give at least two reasons that the difference occurs.

11.6 Suppose that the inner wall of the Dewar flask of Fig. 11.12 is a glass tube of inner radius r_i and outer radius r_0. It is filled up to a distance h from the top with liquid nitrogen. Supposing that the top of the flask is at room temperature (20°C) and that convection and radiation are negligible compared with heat conduction, find an expression for the rate at which the mass of the liquid nitrogen will decrease in terms of the dimensions given, the thermal conductivity of the glass, and the latent heat of vaporization of nitrogen.

REFERENCES

11A Peter Fong, *Foundations of Thermodynamics*, Oxford, New York, 1963. A short book discussing thermodynamics from the viewpoint of physical principles rather than mathematical formulation.

11B Franklin Miller, *Critical Temperature.* A 5-min film loop. (No. 80-205, The Ealing Corp., Cambridge, Mass.) The demonstration shows the disappearance and reappearance of the interface between ether liquid and ether vapor as the temperature passes through a range including the critical temperature, above which the liquid does not exist.

11C F. Palmer, "What About Friction?" *American Journal of Physics*, vol. 17, 1949. The causes and laws of friction are discussed in pp. 181–187 and 327–342.

11D Morris Shamos, editor, *Great Experiments in Physics*, Holt, New York, 1960. Chapter 12 gives a thorough discussion of Joule's determination of the mechanical equivalent of heat.

11E Hans Thirring, *Energy for Man*, Harper Torchbook (TB 556), New York, 1962. A nontechnical discussion of the physics, economics, and technological development of heat engines.

11F Mark W. Zemansky, *Temperatures Very Low and Very High* (Momentum Book No. 6), Van Nostrand, Princeton, 1964. A description of the application of thermodynamics to the production of extreme temperatures, including "negative" temperatures.

12 Radiation

12.1 Light and Heat Radiation

When we observe an extremely hot body such as the sun, a campfire, or the heated wire in an electric heater, two effects are apparent. First, the light affects our eyes, enabling us to see not only the glowing object itself but also any other nearby object on which the light falls. Secondly, heat from the glowing object affects the sensory receptors in the skin so that we feel the heat directly; but in addition to this direct effect, we observe that a stone close to a campfire or the pavement in the open sunlight becomes warm to the touch. Whenever we seek shade on a hot, sunny day, we interpose a screen between us and the sun, cutting off not only the light but also the heat. We are easily led to assume that there is some mechanism by which energy, in the form of light and heat, is transferred from the glowing body to other objects. Before we consider in detail how this energy transfer takes place, there are a few simple properties of light which we must describe.

As we shall see in Sec. 12.16, light is usually accompanied by heat radiation. Furthermore, heat radiation (Sec. 11.19), even when unaccompanied by light, obeys laws quite similar to those obeyed by light. We shall therefore use the term "light" to mean heat, visible light, and all forms of radiation that obey the same laws; thus we include x-rays, γ-rays, ultraviolet light, infrared light, radio waves, etc. (cf. Table 23.1).

12.2 The Rectilinear Propagation of Light

A very simple experiment (Fig. 12.1) will seem to prove to us that light travels in straight lines. If we drill small holes in each of three screens, A_1, A_2, and A_3, and align them so that the source of light S, the three holes in the screens, and the eye E of the observer are all in the same straight line, then the observer will

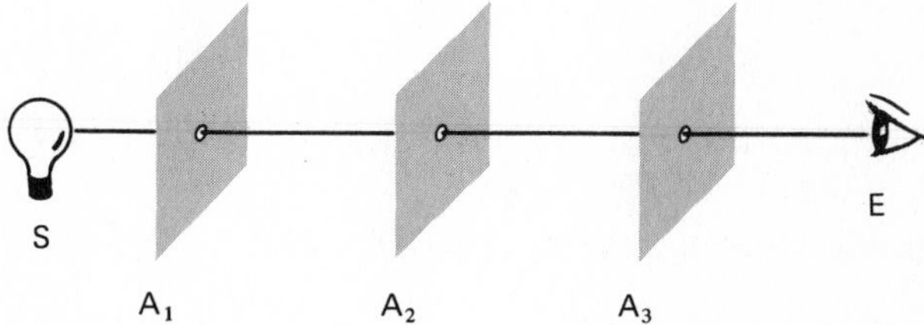

FIG. 12.1 Rectilinear propagation of light.

see light from the source. If one of the holes, say that in the screen A_2, is moved out of line, then the light will be cut off.

We make continual use of this property of light in everyday life. We sight along the edge of a ruler, or a row of plants, or the seam of a stocking to see that it is straight. The formation of shadows is another example of this phenomenon. We find that the shadow of a telephone pole (Fig. 12.2) can be constructed by drawing straight lines from the sun past the outline of the pole to form the shadow.

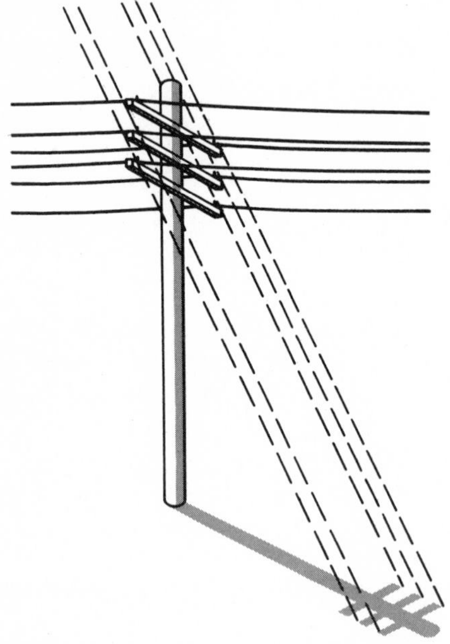

FIG. 12.2 Shadow formation.

Since it is so easy for us to observe that light travels in a straight line unless some object is in the way, we refer to this property of light as ***rectilinear propagation.*** But we can also show that light travels in other than straight line paths. We demonstrate this by another simple experiment. If a very small pinhole (0.1 mm or less) is made in an opaque window shade, and if light from the sun illuminates the outside of the shade, an observer located inside the darkened room (Fig. 12.3) will see light coming from the pinhole even though the sun, the pinhole, and the eye are not in the same straight line. It is true that the light observed under these conditions is by no means as bright as that observed if the source, the pinhole, and the eye are in the same straight line. This phenomenon is known as ***diffraction*** and will be discussed in greater detail in Sec. 12.20. We shall find there that, unless the pinhole P (Fig. 12.3) is extremely small, the amount of light seen by an eye at E is negligibly small as compared to that seen by an eye in the straight line direction at E′.

It will be noticed that if the holes in the screens A_1 and A_2 of Fig. 12.1 are small compared to the distance between them, then the light which gets through them both will be traveling only in directions that are very nearly parallel to the line joining the centers of the holes. The light beyond the second aperture A_2 is then confined to a space which is actually conical but which is nearly

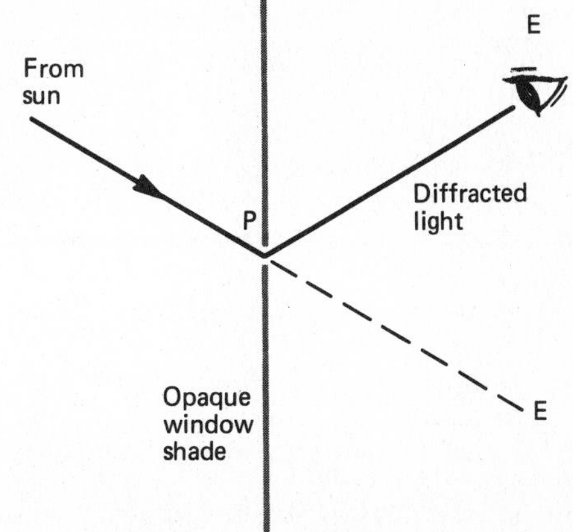

FIG. 12.3 Diffraction by a pinhole.

cylindrical. Such a cylindrical, or nearly cylindrical, bundle of light is called a ***pencil*** of light. A straight line which represents the direction in which light is traveling is called a ***ray.***

12.3 The Laws of Reflection

If a pencil of light is allowed to fall on a plane sheet of polished metal (Fig. 12.4), that is to say on a ***mirror***, a reflected pencil of light is observed. The

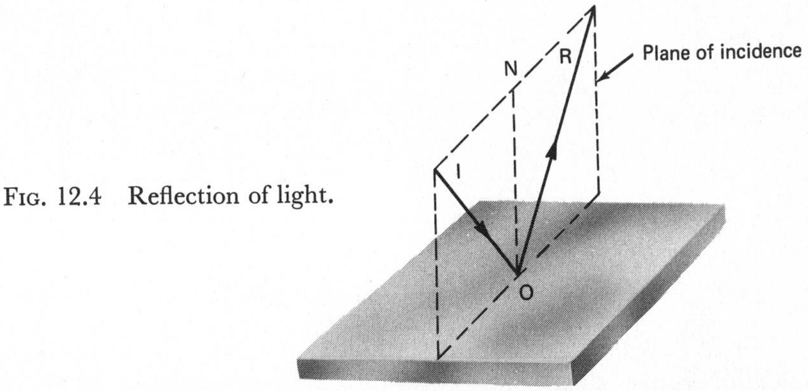

FIG. 12.4 Reflection of light.

direction of the ***incident pencil*** is represented by the ray IO, and that of the ***reflected pencil*** by the ray OR. The dotted line ON—called the ***normal***—is drawn perpendicular to the reflecting surface. It is observed experimentally that the ***angle of incidence*** ION and the ***angle of reflection*** NOR are equal, and that the incident ray IO, the reflected ray OR and the normal ON all lie in the same plane, called the ***plane of incidence***. These two experimental results illustrate the ***laws of reflection*** and were known to the Greeks of the 4th century B.C.

EXERCISES

Illustrate all answers to these exercises and to other exercises in this chapter with diagrams.

12.3-1 If $\vec{I}$ is a vector of unit length in the direction of the incident pencil of light falling on a mirror and $\vec{R}$ is a vector, also of unit length but in the direction of the reflected ray, prove that the normal to the mirror is in the direction of the vector $(\vec{R} - \vec{I})$.

12.3-2 Show that, for a direction of incidence that is fixed in space, a rotation of a mirror through an angle ϕ, about an axis perpendicular to the plane of incidence, produces a change of angle 2ϕ in the direction of the reflected ray.

12.3-3 A long tube is pointed toward the sun at noon. How must a mirror be located so that the light from the sun will be reflected from the mirror and will then pass down the tube at some other time of day? At what angular velocity (cf. Sec. 7.2) in revolutions per day must the mirror rotate if the light from the sun is to shine down the tube from sunrise to sunset on a clear day? (Hint: Use the results of Ex. 12.2-2.)

12.4 The Law of Refraction

If a pencil of light (IO in Fig. 12.5) is allowed to fall on the plane surface AOB of a transparent medium such as glass or water or one of the transparent plastics, a reflected pencil OR is observed as in the case of the mirror, and in

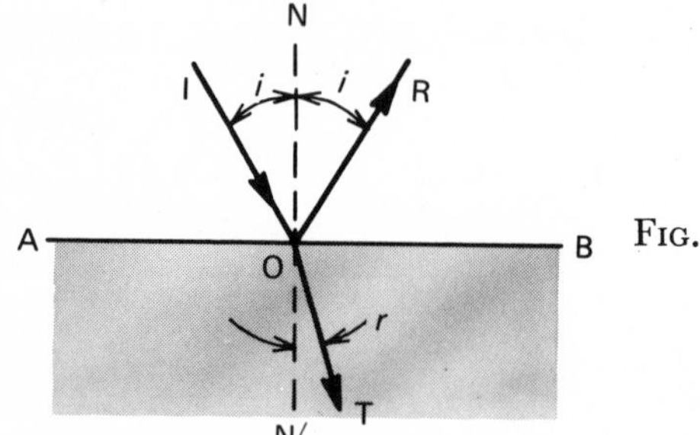

FIG. 12.5 Refraction of light.

addition, a ***transmitted pencil*** (OT) is also observed. The directions of the incident and the reflected pencils are related by the law of reflection. The transmitted pencil OT is not in the same direction as the incident pencil, although it does lie in the same plane as IO, ON, and OR. If we vary the angle of incidence i (ION), we find that the ***angle of refraction*** r (N′OT) varies according to the law

$$\sin i/\sin r = \mu, \qquad (12.4\text{-}1)$$

where μ is a pure number called the ***relative refractive index*** of the second material with respect to the first material. This experimental result is known as the ***law of refraction***, or ***Snell's law***. It was discovered by the Dutch physicist Willebrord Snell (1591–1626).

The relative refractive index depends not only on the nature of the two media on either side of the boundary AOB (Fig. 12.5) but also on the nature of the light. For example, the refractive index for an air to window glass boundary varies between 1.53 for violet light and 1.51 for red light. The variation of refractive index with the color of the light is known as ***dispersion***, and we shall refer to it again in Secs. 12.19 and 13.15, but for the present we can assume that μ is approximately constant for visible light (e.g., 1.52 for glass). For water the refractive index varies between 1.331 and 1.343. Again, for most purposes, we can use an approximate value of 1.33 as the relative refractive index from air to water.

We notice that if μ is greater than 1, as it is for light passing from air to water, or glass, or almost any other transparent body, the pencil is bent toward the normal on entering the denser medium. As a pencil of light leaves a dense medium and returns to air, the reverse process takes place and the pencil is bent away from the normal. Thus, in the case of a plane parallel plate (Fig. 12.6), it is found that light incident in the direction IO emerges in the direction

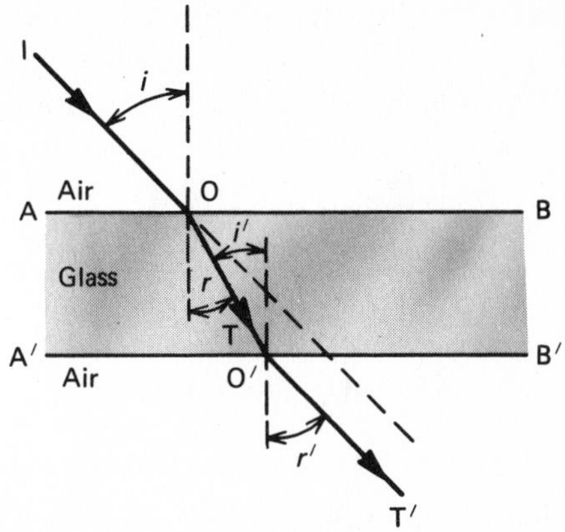

FIG. 12.6 Refraction by a plane parallel plate.

O′T′, which is parallel to IO. Since AOB is parallel to A′O′B′ and IO is parallel to O′T′, it follows that the angle of incidence i at the first surface is equal to the angle of refraction r' at the second surface (i.e., $i = r'$), and hence, $\sin i = \sin r'$. It also follows that $r = i'$ and that $\sin r = \sin i'$. If we insert these two values for $\sin i$ and $\sin r$ in Eq. (12.4-1), which we know must hold at the first surface, we find that

$$\sin r'/\sin i' = \mu,$$

which may be rewritten as

$$\sin i'/\sin r' = 1/\mu. \tag{12.4-2}$$

We see then that Eq. (12.4-2) is of the same form as Eq. (12.4-1) and that the relative refractive index for light going from the medium B (glass) into the medium A (air) is the reciprocal of the relative refractive index for light going from the medium A into the medium B.

The symmetry of Fig. 12.6 enables us to state an important principle of optics. According to the ***principle of reversibility***, any light path can be traversed in either direction. Thus, if light can travel along the path IOO′T′, it can also travel along the path T′O′OI. It is also worth noting that, if we use the principle of reversibility, we can arrive at Eq. (12.4-2) by putting $i' = r$ and $r' = i$ in the situation of Fig. 12.5, or in Eq. (12.4-1).

12.5 The Speed of Light in Material Bodies

The index of refraction μ, which was defined in the preceding section, has another interesting meaning. If the speeds of light in various transparent media are determined experimentally, it is found that the speeds in any two media are connected by the relative refraction index according to the relation:

$$C_1 = \mu C_2, \tag{12.5-1}$$

where C_1 is the speed in one medium, C_2 is the speed in the other, and μ is the relative refraction index for light passing from the first medium to the second. Thus, the speed of light in water is $(3.00 \times 10^8 \text{ m/sec})/1.33 = 2.25 \times 10^8$ m/sec. It is interesting to note that the refractive index of air (under normal conditions) relative to that of a vacuum is only 1.00029, so that little error is made by taking the speed of light in air as equal to c [cf. Eq. (3.7-1)].

If the speed of light in medium B is less than the speed of light in medium A, then we frequently say that medium B has a greater ***optical density*** than medium A. If the sense of usage is clear so that we know that we are concerned with optical properties, we sometimes say *density* when we mean *optical density.* The reader should be cautioned, however, that there is no simple relation between material density (kg/m³) and optical density.

12.6 Total Reflection

We saw in Sec. 12.4 that, when light leaves an optically dense medium such as glass and enters a rarer medium, the angle of refraction r' is greater than the angle of incidence i'. A particularly interesting case arises when the angle of incidence i' has such a value that $\sin i' = 1/\mu$, μ being the relative index of the dense medium with respect to the less dense, i.e., $\mu > 1$. For this angle of incidence, Eq. (12.4-2) tells us that $\sin r' = 1$, i.e., $r' = 90°$, and the refracted pencil emerges parallel to the surface. Figure 12.7 is drawn for the case in which $\sin i'$

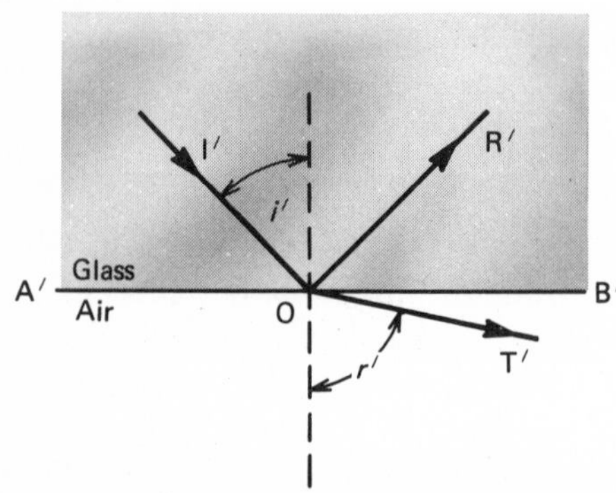

FIG. 12.7 Total reflection.

is slightly less than 90°; the refracted ray OT′ is then nearly parallel to the surface. As sin i' approaches the value $1/\mu$, the direction of OT′ approaches OB′. For values of sin i' greater than $1/\mu$, Eq. (12.4-2) would lead to values of sin r' greater than 1, which we know to be impossible for any real angle r' (cf. Appendices E–G). Under these circumstances, there is no transmitted pencil and the light is said to undergo ***total reflection*** (See Fig. 12.8). All of the light in the incident pencil I′ appears in the reflected pencil T′. The smallest angle of incidence i_t at which total reflection appears is called the ***critical angle*** or ***angle of total reflection.*** It follows that

$$\sin i_t = 1/\mu. \tag{12.6-1}$$

Examples of total reflection which can be demonstrated easily are referred to in some of the following exercises.

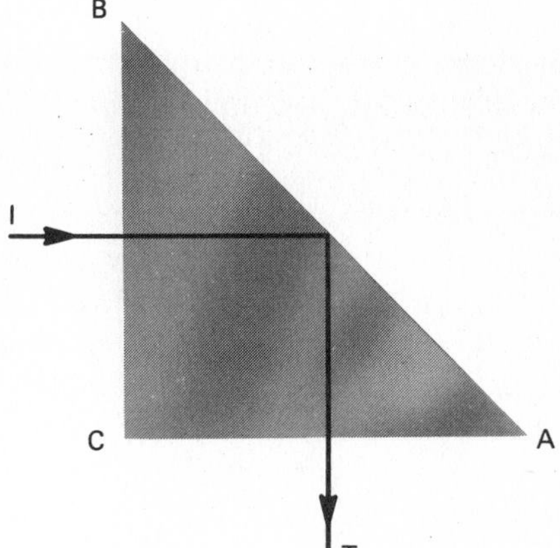

FIG. 12.8 Totally reflecting prism.

EXERCISES

12.6-1 At a particular time the sun is at an angle of 52° from the zenith (the point vertically overhead). An underwater swimmer in a lake, whose surface is smooth, opens his eyes and looks upward. What will he find for the apparent angle of the sun with the zenith?

12.6-2 An underwater swimmer is at such a depth that his eyes are 5.0 m beneath the smooth water surface. When he looks upward, he sees a bright circle surrounded by a mirror-like surface that reflects the lake bottom. Explain this. What is the diameter of the circle in terms of the index of refraction and his depth? What does he see within this circle if the lake surface is quite smooth?

12.6-3 A prism is cut in the form of a 45° triangle right-angled at C (Fig. 12.8). What is the smallest value of μ for the material of the prism if a pencil normal to the face BC is to be totally reflected at the face AB?

12.6-4 An aquarium has vertical end walls. In what direction must a pencil of light strike one of these end walls if it is to be totally reflected back into the water from the water-air boundary at the surface? Assume that the walls of the aquarium are plane parallel glass plates.

12.7 The Intensity of Light

As we have seen in Sec. 12.1, a hot body is continually sending out energy in the form of light and heat. It is important for us to be able to measure the total amount of energy emitted by such a body and also the amount of energy intercepted (per unit area) by any body placed in the way of the radiation emitted. In the preceding sections, we have considered some materials which reflect the light that falls on them and others which both reflect and transmit light. We know, as a matter of experience, that bodies with rough surfaces scatter the light that falls on them and that, if the body is black with a matte surface, it will absorb almost all the light that falls on it.

If we wish to make a measurement of the energy carried by radiation, we can do this with the aid of a blackened disk of metal, in the shape of a penny but smaller, which we expose to the radiation. We measure the rise in temperature of the disk while it is exposed and so obtain a measure of the amount of energy per unit time carried to the disk. The disk is located so that it faces the source of radiation, for example, the sun, and is shielded from all other sources of heat as indicated in Fig. 12.9.

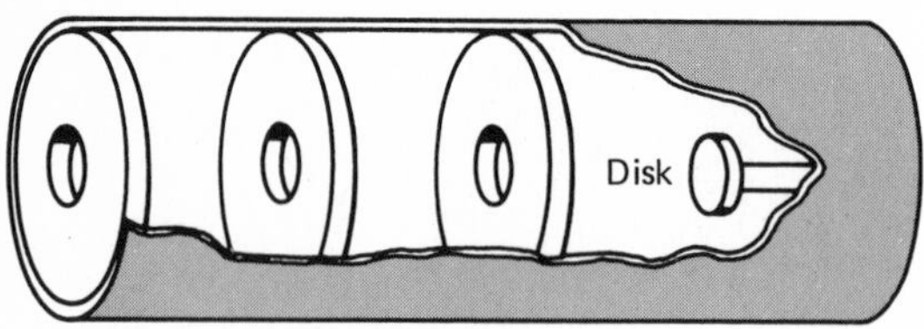

FIG. 12.9 Measurement of light intensity.

We first make a measurement of the ***thermal capacity*** H of the disk, i.e., of the amount of heat required to raise the temperature of the disk 1°C. If we then expose the disk to the radiation for a time Δt and observe that the temperature of the disk rises by an amount ΔT, we know that the energy ΔE falling on the disk in this time is given by

$$\Delta E = H\Delta T. \tag{12.7-1}$$

The rate at which the disk is receiving energy—i.e., the power P which the radiation is supplying to the disk—is then

$$P = \Delta E/\Delta t = H\Delta T/\Delta t. \tag{12.7-1A}$$

If we vary the size of the disk, keeping all other things constant, we find that the power P is proportional to the area S of the disk, and it becomes convenient to define a quantity called the intensity I of the radiation. We have

$$I = P/S \tag{12.7-2}$$

and notice that the ***intensity*** of the radiation is the energy per unit time per unit area which is carried by the radiation. As Eq. (12.7-2) shows, intensity has the dimensions $[mt^{-3}]$. In the MKS system it is measured in watts per meter squared

(W/m^2). The intensity of the radiation can be directly measured by means of the apparatus of Fig. 12.9. Substituting Eq. (12.7-1A) into Eq. (12.7-2) and taking the limit of $\Delta T/\Delta t$, we find that

$$I = (H/S)(dT/dt), \tag{12.7-2A}$$

where dT/dt is the *initial* rate of temperature increase (cf. Prob. 12.2). An instrument such as the one just described for the direct measurement of intensities is called a ***radiometer.***

It is interesting to consider a few of the results of radiometer measurements. The maximum intensity of solar radiation in the latitude of Washington, D.C., is about 1.05×10^3 W/m², whereas the intensity of the radiation received from one of the brightest stars—other than the sun—is about 1.2×10^{-9} W/m². A candle at a distance of one meter from the disk would produce an intensity of roughly 1.5×10^{-3} W/m².

There are many other instruments that give us a notion of the intensity of the radiation received from the sun or from any other light source. The most important of these is of course the eye, and we shall make use of it in what follows as a qualitative instrument for estimating light intensity without bothering, for the time, about the way in which it operates.

12.8 The Inverse Square Law

If we measure the intensity of the light given off by a hot body such as the filament of a lamp or the flame of a candle, we shall find that the intensity is inversely proportional to the square of the distance from the source, provided that the

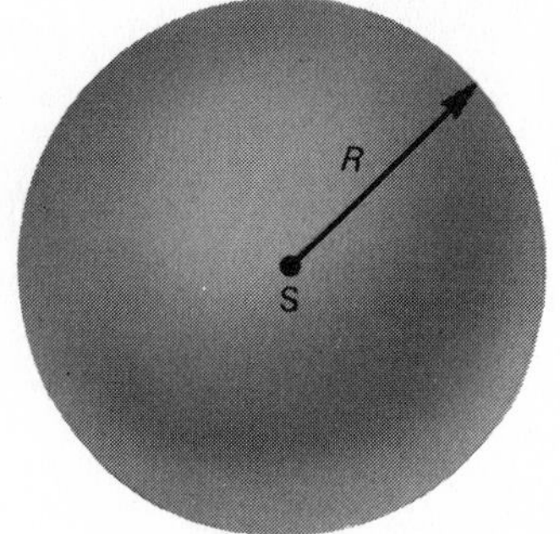

FIG. 12.10 Inverse square law for light intensity.

distance is much greater than any dimension of the source. That is to say, if we double the distance, the intensity is divided by four; for three times the distance the intensity is divided by nine, etc. That this is not unreasonable is seen by a simple argument based on the law of conservation of energy. Suppose that a source of light S (Fig. 12.10) is emitting light at a rate of P and is sending this

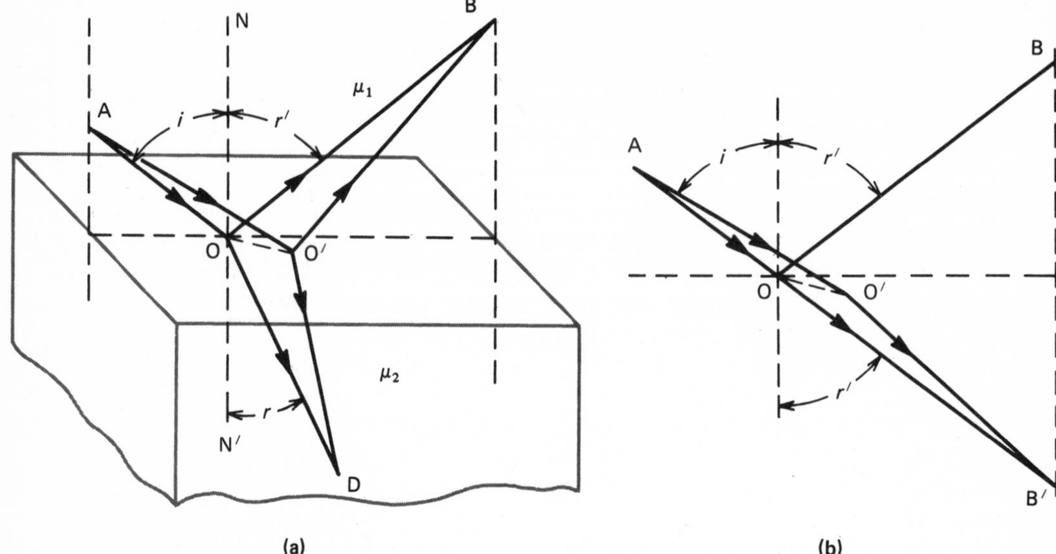

energy equally in all directions. The intensity I of the light on the surface of a sphere of radius R with its center at the source S will thus be uniform, and the product of this intensity by the surface area of the sphere ($4\pi R^2$) will be equal to the power P emitted by the source, since no energy can escape from S unless it goes through the sphere under discussion. We thus have

$$4\pi R^2 I = P$$

and

$$I = P/4\pi R^2. \tag{12.8-1}$$

In this way, we have proved the ***inverse square law*** for the variation of light intensity for small sources which send light equally in all directions. This law does not necessarily hold if for any reason the light from the source is emitted nonuniformly in direction, if the medium through which the light passes is one that absorbs radiation, or if the source is large enough so that it cannot be well approximated as a point.

12.9 Fermat's Principle

In the last few sections we have seen the experimental evidence for many of the most striking properties of light. Before we go on to the construction of theories, or models, of light, it will be worth our while to notice that the apparently different laws of reflection and refraction can be included in a single, more general, principle.

Figure 12.11a shows a light ray that passes through point A and meets the surface of a medium of higher index at O. Part of the light is then reflected and

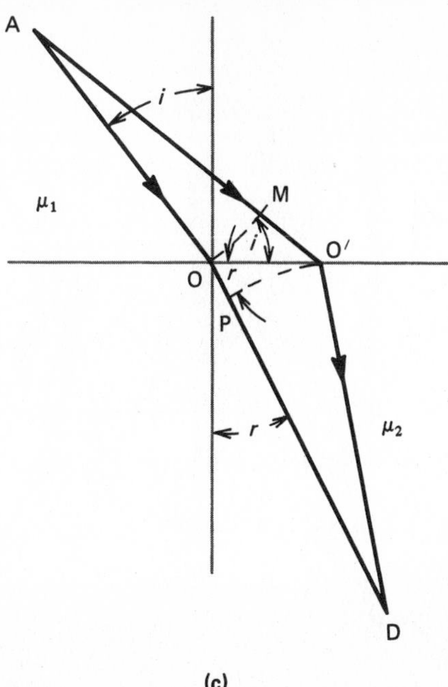

Fig. 12.11 Fermat's principle.

eventually passes through point B; the rest is refracted and passes through point D. We remember that the points A, O, B, and D all lie in the same plane and that the angle of reflection r' is equal to the angle of incidence i. Now suppose that the ray had traveled from A to B by some slightly different path, either moving along other than straight lines or being propagated in a rectilinear manner but being reflected from point O′ instead of O. In the former case, the time taken for the light to go from A to B would be obviously increased—a straight line is the shortest distance between two points. If the light had been reflected from O′, the path would be greater than in the actual case and the time taken from A to B would be longer. To see that the path is increased, refer to Fig. 12.11b. The path length along AOB is exactly equal to the distance AOB′, where B′ is in the plane of incidence and is as far behind the surface as B is in front of it. Because of the equality of i and r', AOB′ is a straight line. Therefore the path AO′B′ is not a straight line and is longer than AOB′ or AOB.

Were the light refracted at O′ instead of O, the total path AO′D might be either longer or shorter than the path AOD but the time taken to traverse the path would be increased. To see this, consider either of two ways in which O′ can be displaced from O. Suppose first that O′ is moved in a direction at right angles to the plane of incidence. Then, because A, O, and D are all in the plane of incidence, both AO′ > AO and O′D > OD. The time taken for the light to go from A to D is clearly increased. Next, consider that O′ is displaced *in* the plane of incidence, as shown in Fig. 12.11c. The circular arcs OM and O′P are shown with centers at A and D, respectively. The change in the time required for passage from A to D is clearly

$$\Delta t = \frac{(\mathrm{MO'})}{C_1} - \frac{(\mathrm{OP})}{C_2},$$

where C_1 and C_2 are the respective speeds in the two media. If the angles OAO′ and ODO′ are small, the figures OMO′ and O′PO will approximate triangles, with acute angles i and r as shown. We therefore have

$$\Delta t \approx \frac{(\mathrm{OO'})\sin i}{C_1} - \frac{(\mathrm{OO'})\sin r}{C_2}.$$

By Eqs. (12.4-1) and (12.4-2), $\sin i/C_1 = \sin r/C_2$, so Δt, to this approximation, vanishes. The approximation that OMO′ and O′PO are triangles has resulted in a slight underestimation of both MO′ and OP. A more detailed consideration shows that Δt is always greater than zero. Any displacement of O from O′ can be made up of two successive displacements, one in the plane of incidence and one at right angles to it. Both increase the time taken for the light to go from A to D, so any displacement of the point of refraction, O, increases this time.

We have arrived at a law first stated by Pierre de Fermat (1601–1665). It is called ***Fermat's principle of least time***:

> The actual path taken by light in going from one fixed point to another fixed point is such that the time taken is less than it would be over a neighboring path that departs slightly from the real path.

As we have seen, Fermat's principle is equivalent to both the laws of reflection and the laws of refraction. It can therefore be used as a more compact statement of these laws. We shall have occcasion to use it in Chapter 13.

We cannot say that the light starting from A and headed for B or D *chooses* the point O, at which it shall be reflected or refracted, in such a way as to make the total travel time minimal, tempting as such a teleological idea may appear. We must recognize, rather, that the principle of least time is merely a very brief way of combining several empirical laws into a single statement.

12.10 Theories of Light

One of the earliest systematic studies of the nature of light was made by Isaac Newton and was discussed by him in his *Optiks* (1704). He believed that light consisted of large numbers of rapidly moving particles which were emitted by the source of light and which thus carried energy from it. Later, research by Thomas Young (1773–1829), Augustin Jean Fresnel (1788–1827), James Clerk Maxwell (1831–1879), and others convinced physicists in the 19th century that light was a wave motion sent out by the source. In the present century, investigations by Max Planck, Albert Einstein, Arthur Compton, Louis de Broglie, Werner Heisenberg, Erwin Schroedinger, and many others have shown that neither the wave theory nor the particle theory alone provides a complete explanation and that it is necessary to set up a new theory that combines the particle and wave descriptions. This theory tells us that very small particles and very high-frequency waves have many properties in common. This approach provides the basis for the quantum mechanics, and its understanding requires a good deal of information about light and electricity and atomic structure, some of which we shall develop later in the book (Chapters 24 and 25.) Therefore, we shall confine ourselves here to a few simple ideas about the particle theory and some important ideas from the wave theory. This will give us enough background to continue and extend our studies of light and to make use of the information it gives us about atomic structure.

12.11 The Propagation of Photons

In Sec. 3.7 we saw that light signals travel with the speed $c = 2.998 \times 10^8$ m/sec, and we know from the discussion of Chapter 8 that this speed c is a limiting speed that cannot be attained by any material particle. If we wish to assume that light consists of particles which travel with a speed c, we shall have to assume that these particles possess rather peculiar properties. What is their rest mass? To answer this we remember that a particle with a mass m at a speed u must have a rest mass m_0 given by [cf. Eq. (8.9-5)]

$$m_0 = m\,(1 - u^2/c^2)^{1/2}. \tag{12.11-1}$$

If the particle is to travel at a speed $u = c$ and still have a finite mass m, it is clear that it must possess a zero rest mass, $m_0 = 0$. This is an unusual property for a material particle, yet it is still possible for light particles to possess an energy ε and a mass m connected by the Einstein relation [Eq. (8.12-1)]:

$$m = \varepsilon/c^2. \tag{12.11-2}$$

Since such particles are traveling at a speed c, their momentum p will be given (Sec. 8.10) as

$$p = mc = \varepsilon/c. \tag{12.11-3}$$

Particles of zero rest mass which travel at a speed c in a vacuum and which have mass, energy, and momentum connected by Eqs. (12.11-2) and (12.11-3) are called ***photons***.*

If a photon is undisturbed in its motion, it will, of course, travel in a straight line (Sec. 4.9—Newton's first law of motion), and for all terrestrial observations the effect of gravitation will be quite negligible (Ex. 12.11-1).

If we assume for simplicity that each of the photons emitted by a light source has the same energy ε, then the total number N of photons that fall in unit time on unit area in a light beam of intensity I will be given by the equation

$$I = N\varepsilon. \tag{12.11-4}$$

If all these particles are absorbed in a disk such as that of the radiometer, each photon must transfer all of its momentum, i.e., an amount of momentum $p = \varepsilon/c$, from the light beam to the disk. Thus the decrease in momentum of the light beam per unit area per second will be $N\varepsilon/c$. The disk must therefore exert an

* This definition, though satisfactory for present purposes, is not quite complete, since it would include neutrinos as well as photons. The two kinds of particles differ in the angular momentum that they carry (cf. Sec. 19.20).

opposing force [Eq. 4.9-1)] on the light beam of amount $N\varepsilon/c$ $(=I/c)$ per unit area, and consequently the light beam exerts a pressure P_1 (force per unit area) on the disk given by

$$P_1 = I/c. \tag{12.11-5}$$

This light pressure is extraordinarily small. Thus for full sunlight (Sec. 12.7) in which $I = 1.05 \times 10^3$ W/m^2 the light pressure is $P_1 = 0.35 \times 10^{-5}$ N/m^2. This very small pressure was measured early in the present century by Peter Lebedew (1866–1911) in Russia and by Edward Nichols (1854–1937) and Gordon Ferrie Hull (1870–1956) in the United states, and the latter observers were able to verify, within a few percent, the relation of Eq. (12.11-5). These remarkable experiments do not, however, lead to any decision between a wave and a particle theory of light, since the wave theory as developed by Maxwell also leads to Eq. (12.11-5).

EXERCISES

12.11-1 Calculate the deviation from the straight line (due to gravitation) of a photon, which is initially traveling horizontally, while it moves through a distance of 1.0 m near the surface of the earth.

12.11-2 Prove that if light of intensity I falls at normal incidence on a totally reflecting disk, the pressure due to the light will be $2I/c$.

12.12 The Reflection and Refraction of Photons

The problem of the reflection of photons by a mirror has already been solved in Sec. 6.2, in which we discussed the elastic collision of a billiard ball with a cushion. We saw there that the angle of incidence is equal to the angle of reflection so long as there is no loss of kinetic energy in the collision and there is no change of the component of momentum of the ball in a direction parallel to the reflecting surface. The reflection of photons is the same as the reflection of elastic balls. This is indicated both by the laws of reflection (Sec. 12.3) and by measurements of light pressure (cf. Ex. 12.11-2). In Chapter 24 we shall discuss methods by which the energies of individual photons can be measured directly. Such measurements confirm the fact that no energy is lost in reflection.

The refraction of photons may be considered in a similar manner. Suppose that a photon having a momentum $\overrightarrow{p_1}$ impinges on the plane boundary, AOB in Fig. 12.12, between two media, the angle of incidence being i. On crossing the boundary, the photon changes its direction, and it then continues its motion into the second medium with an angle of refraction r. If there is no change of any component of momentum parallel to the surface AOB, it follows that the momentum $\overrightarrow{p_2}$ in the second medium can have no component perpendicular to the plane of incidence, because $\overrightarrow{p_1}$ has no component in this direction. Thus $\overrightarrow{p_1}$, $\overrightarrow{p_2}$, and NON′ must all lie in the same plane—the plane of incidence—in accord with the observed law of reflection. Again, if there is no change of momentum parallel to the boundary, then the component $(p_1 \sin i)$ of $\overrightarrow{p_1}$

parallel to the boundary and in the plane of incidence must be equal to the component ($p_2 \sin r$) of $\vec{p_2}$ parallel to the boundary and in the same plane. We therefore have

$$p_1 \sin i = p_2 \sin r,$$

which may be written

$$\sin i / \sin r = p_2/p_1. \tag{12.12-1}$$

Comparison with Snell's law then tells us that

$$p_2/p_1 = \mu, \tag{12.12-2}$$

and that the momentum of the photon must increase as the photon enters the second medium if μ is greater than unity. We know from Eq. (12.5-1), however, that

$$\mu = C_1/C_2 \tag{12.12-3}$$

and that the speed of light is lower in the medium of high index than in that of low index. Equations (12.12-2) and (12.12-3) together tell us that the momentum of the photon must increase at the same time that the speed decreases. This

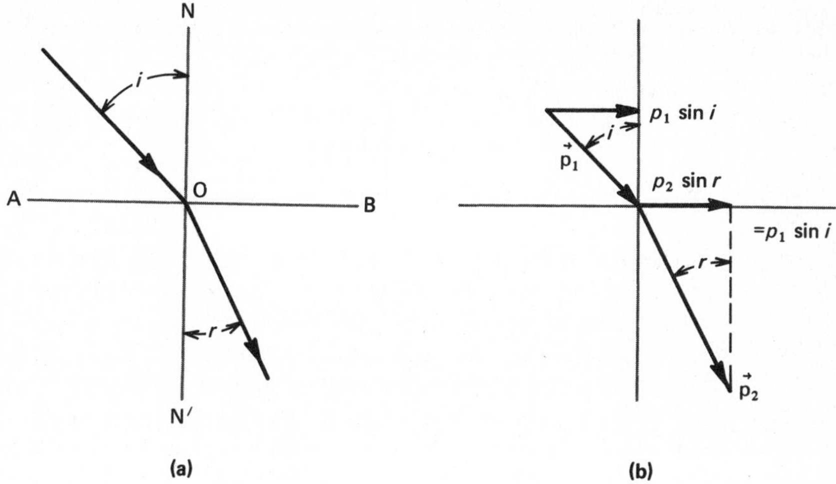

FIG. 12.12 Refraction of photons.

apparent contradiction provided one of the strongest objections to the particle model of light originally proposed by Newton, since the mass of any particle had to be constant in classical mechanics and an increase of momentum necessarily meant that the speed had increased. In relativity theory the mass is not necessarily constant, so an increase in momentum at the same time as a decrease in speed is entirely possible if the mass of the photon can increase at the same time.

The theory of the refraction of photons is by no means simple, even in terms of relativity theory, and no completely satisfactory solution has been obtained. It may be seen, however, that one can develop at least a partial model. Suppose that the *observed* mass of the photon changes from m_1 to m_2 as it passes from the first medium to the second. The momenta in the two media are then, respectively, of magnitudes

$$p_1 = m_1 C_1 \qquad \text{and} \qquad p_2 = m_2 C_2 .$$

Substitution of these values into Eq. (12.12-2) gives

$$m_2/m_1 = C_1 \mu / C_2 = \mu^2,$$

where the last equality follows from Eq. (12.12-3). We may now use Eq. (8.9-5) to find m_{02}, the rest mass of the photon in the second medium:

$$m_{02} = m_2(1 - C_2{}^2/c^2)^{1/2} = m_1\,\mu(\mu^2 - 1)^{1/2},$$

where μ now denotes the index of the second medium relative to a vacuum. Because none of the factors on the right-hand side is zero unless $\mu = 1$, we are forced to conclude that a photon in any medium other than a vacuum must be ascribed a nonzero rest mass. The increase of mass that occurs as a photon moves from a vacuum into the medium can be explained if we consider that the medium exerts an attractive force, normal to the surface, on the photon. Work is then done on the photon as it passes the boundary; the photon acquires extra energy; this is manifested as an increase in the rest mass. If the photon is stopped within the medium so that it loses all of its kinetic energy, the additional energy (the rest energy) must remain in the medium.

Although the model just proposed for the refraction of photons seems sound, it does not account for the fact that some of the photons that strike the boundary of a transparent medium are refracted and that the others are reflected. This difference between the behavior of two identical photons cannot be explained on the basis of any current theory that describes the photons purely as particles.

12.13 Recapitulation of the Particle Theory

In Secs. 12.10–12.12, we compared several properties of high-speed particles with properties which we observed for light. We can certainly explain the rectilinear progagation of light in terms of a photon theory, but there are undoubted difficulties in attempts to explain diffraction (Sec. 12.2). We saw that the inverse square law for the intensity at a distance from a light source can be derived on energy considerations alone, so that it must hold equally well for waves or for photons as the carriers of light energy (cf. Sec. 12.8). The photon theory gives a vivid picture of the nature of light pressure and of the process of the reflection of light. The explanation of refraction leads to some difficulties that have not yet been overcome, but they may well be resolved in the future.

In our future studies we shall find many other phenomena that receive an adequate explanation on a particle theory. But before we consider them, it is necessary to discuss the wave theory in further detail, since it will give us a great deal of information necessary in developing the wave-particle compromise referred to in Sec. 12.9.

12.14 Interference of Waves

In Secs. 10.13–10.15 we saw that two waves of equal amplitude can combine to form standing waves on a wire or in an organ pipe. We have to consider now the more complex problem of what happens when two spherical waves combine in space (cf. Sec. 10.6). In order to have something concrete to think about, let us consider what happens when a plane wave of sound (Fig. 12.13) falls on two

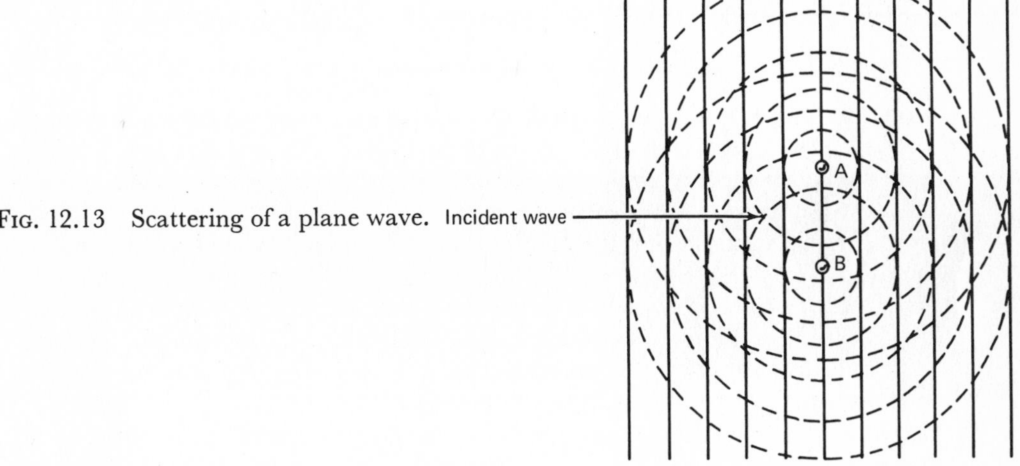

FIG. 12.13 Scattering of a plane wave.

rigid balls located at a distance *a* apart. The maxima of the incident wave are represented by the parallel straight lines in the figure. When this wave hits the balls, a situation will arise which is closely similar to that which occurred when the wave in the train reached the fixed end of the train (Sec. 10.11). The air at the surface of the balls is unable to move as would be required by the incident wave alone. A reflected wave is therefore set up by each ball, and these waves (indicated by the dashed lines in the figure) go out in all directions from the balls.* These two waves from the two balls (A and B Fig. 12.13) will be "in phase,"—when a maximum of the reflected wave starts out from A, a maximum will also start out from B at exactly the same time.

Figure 12.14 is Fig. 12.13 redrawn on a larger scale with the distance *a* equal to 2.5 times the wavelength of the incident wave. The incident wave is omitted for clarity, and the two families of scattered waves from the two balls are redrawn with full lines indicating the pressure maxima of the waves and dotted lines indicating the pressure minima. By the principle of superposition, the two

* Actually, these waves reflected from the obstacles are not uniform in all directions of space unless the size of the balls is negligibly small compared with the wavelength, but we shall assume for the moment that this condition is satisfied and that the reflected waves are uniform in all directions.

scattered waves will move independently of one another, and the resultant pressure will be the sum of the pressures due to the individual waves. The way in which these two systems combine is indicated in Fig. 12.14. The crosses indicate the points at which the pressure peaks of the two waves coincide. At these points, the excess of pressure is the sum of the excesses due to the single scattered

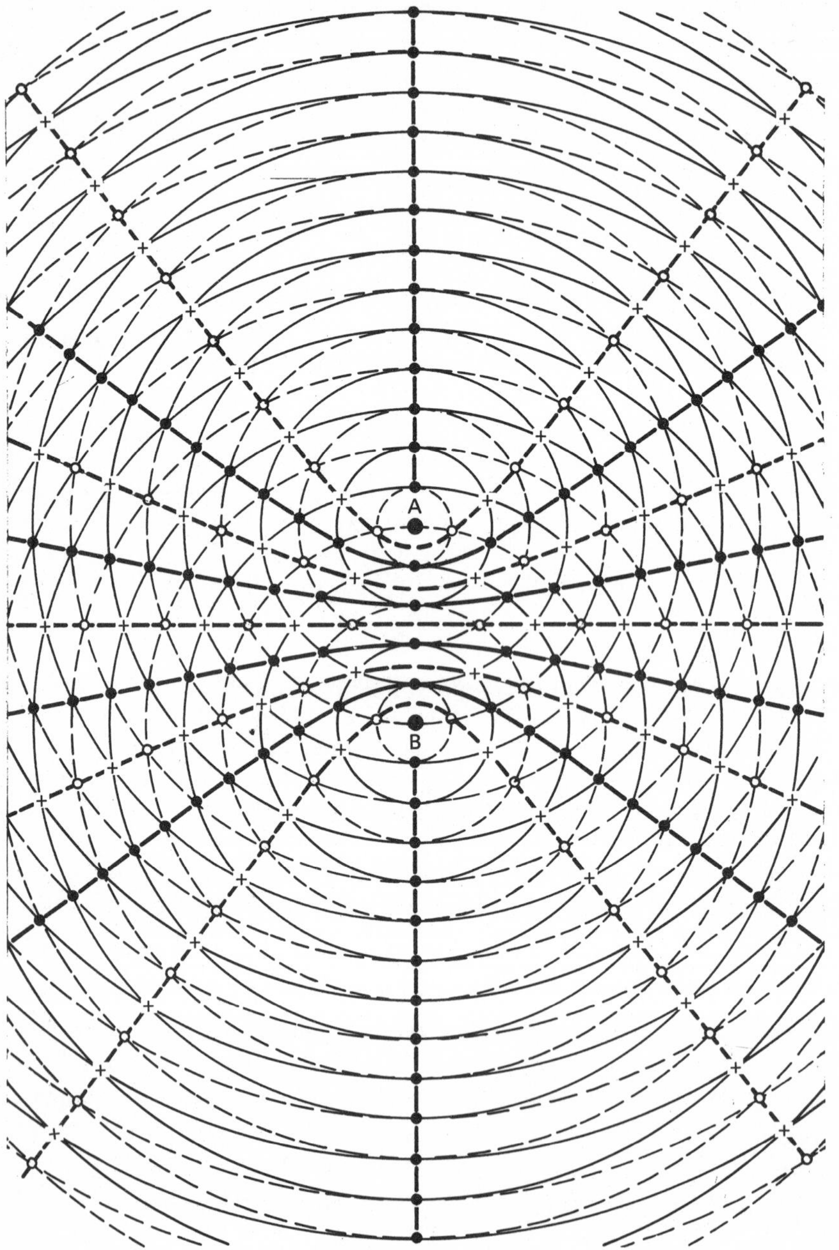

FIG. 12.14 Interference of two scattered waves.

waves. The circles indicate the points at which two pressure minima coincide. At such points the two waves combine to form a pressure minimum at which the pressure deficit is the sum of the deficits due to the single scattered waves. The dots indicate the points at which a maximum of one wave coincides with a minimum of the other and the two pressure waves tend to cancel one another.

The two waves thus ***interfere*** with one another. At the circle points and the cross points in which the two waves reinforce, the interference is said to be ***constructive.*** At the dot points in which two waves oppose one another, the interference is said to be ***destructive.***

It will be noticed in Fig. 12.14 that the dots lie along a family of curves* separated by a similar system of curves defined by the circles and crosses taken together. It is not difficult to see that the pressure variation along one of the circle-cross curves of Fig. 12.14 will look like the lowest curve ($t = 6\tau/12$) of Fig. 10.19 in which two waves in phase combine to produce one of double the amplitude. The pressure variation along one of the dot curves of Fig. 12.14 will look like the middle curve ($t = 3\tau/12$) of Fig. 10.19 in which two waves of opposite phase combine, and all the way along the dot curve the pressure disturbance will be zero.

As the two scattered waves proceed outward from the balls at which they were produced, the pressure along the dot curves will always remain undisturbed. Along the circle-cross curves, the crosses corresponding to the peaks and the circles corresponding to the troughs in the pressure curve will move outward at the same time as the two interfering waves move outward. Thus, there will be a flow of energy along the circle-cross curves on which the wave motion is a maximum, and there will be no flow of energy along the dot curves on which there is no wave motion.

In Figs. 12.13 and 12.14 the diagrams indicate what happens when plane waves are scattered by two small spheres A and B. We supposed that the incident plane waves are sound waves. Sound waves cannot easily be made visible, and even a photograph such as that in Fig. 10.10 shows only a shock wave—i.e it is simply a pulse and not a periodic wave. It may be useful in connection with Figs. 12.13 and 12.14 to see a photograph in a situation where the waves can be made visible. Figure 12.15 is a photograph of plane ripples produced by two sources that are vibrating in phase. The similarity between Fig. 12.15 and Fig. 12.14 is apparent.

It is now profitable to analyze the pattern of Fig. 12.14 in more detail. Consider a point P (Fig. 12.16a) which is near the two scattering centers A and B. The condition for constructive interference at P is that the distance r_1 from A to P differs from the distance r_2 from B to P by a whole number of wavelengths. In such a case, a peak of one wave will always coincide with a peak of the other, or a trough with a trough, or a zero value with a zero value. We can express this condition by the relation

$$r_1 - r_2 = n\lambda, \qquad (12.14\text{-}1)$$

* The student of analytic geometry will be able to prove that these form a system of confocal hyperbolae (Eqs. 12.14-1 and 12.14-2).

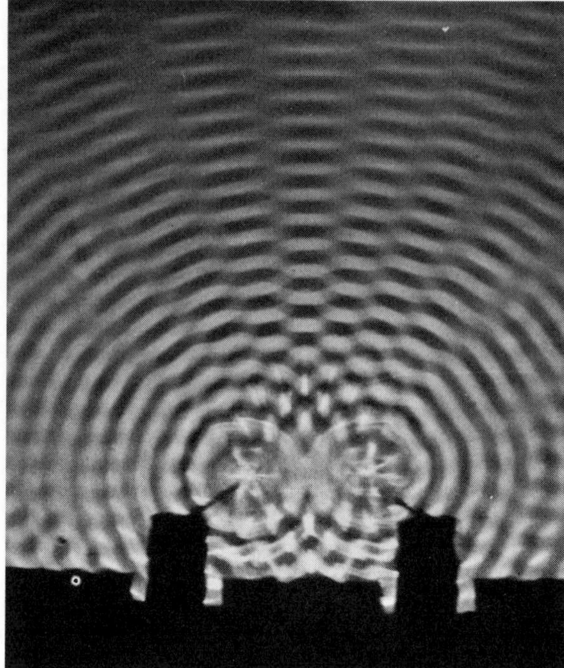

Fig. 12.15 Interference pattern in a ripple tank.

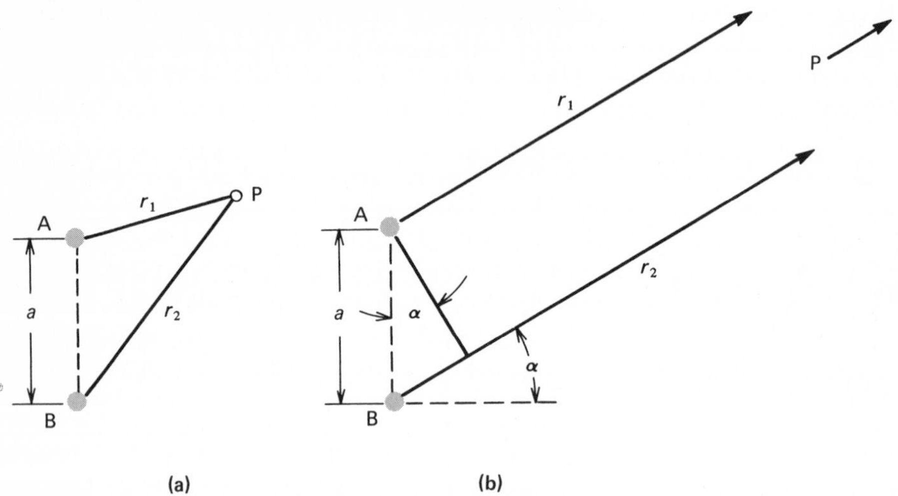

Fig. 12.16 Path difference.

where n is a whole number and λ is the wavelength. All points along the circle-cross curves of Fig. 12.14 must satisfy this relation.

We can also see that the condition for destructive interference is that the difference in the paths of the two waves must be an odd number of half wavelengths, or

$$r_1 - r_2 = (2n + 1)\lambda/2, \tag{12.14-2}$$

where n is again a whole number. Thus, when the difference between r_1 and r_2 is an odd number of half wave lengths, a peak of the wave from A will always correspond to a trough from B, and vice versa. All points along the dot curves of Fig. 12.14 must satisfy this relation.

A particularly interesting case arises when r_1 and r_2 both become large with respect to a, the distance between the two scatterers. The curves of constructive and destructive interference then approach straight lines, as will be seen by an examination of the outer edges of Fig. 12.14. We can calculate the angle these straight lines make with the line joining the two sources by reference to Fig. 12.16b. If P is very remote from A and B, we can treat r_1 and r_2 as parallel, meeting at P, which is effectively at an infinite distance. The difference in length between r_1 and r_2 will then depend on the angle α between either r_1 or r_2 and the line normal to AB. We can see from the figure that

$$r_2 - r_1 = a \sin \alpha.$$

Equations (12.14-1 and 12.14-2) then tell us that for constructive interference we must have

$$n\lambda = a \sin \alpha, \tag{12.14-3}$$

and for destructive interference,

$$(2n + 1)\lambda/2 = a \sin \alpha. \tag{12.14-4}$$

In this section we have discussed in some detail the diffraction of an incident plane wave of sound by two rigid balls (Fig. 12.12) and have found that there are a number of directions (given by Eq. 12.14-3) in which there is a maximum intensity in the diffracted waves. These directions are separated by others (given by Eq. 12.14-4) in which the intensity is zero.

The reader will realize that, although we have chosen one particular problem to provide concreteness, the argument applied to the diffraction of sound by two spheres is applicable to many other problems. We can, for example, replace the two balls by a screen in which two small holes are located (Fig. 12.17). Each of the holes is the source of a system of spherical waves, and these

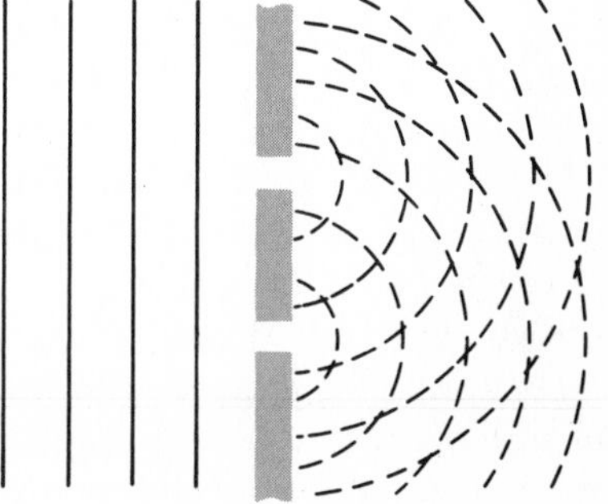

FIG. 12.17 Diffraction from two holes in a screen.

two systems will interfere to give a diffraction pattern of very much the same nature as the right-hand side of Fig. 12.14. Similarly, the same argument can be applied to any type of wave motion, for example, the diffraction of surface waves on water by two obstacles (Fig. 12.15) or the diffraction of compression waves within a solid by two holes in the solid.

So far we have made no statement of the nature of the wave motion which we must postulate to carry light and heat energy and we shall be unable to do so until Chapter 23, in which we shall show that it must be electromagnetic in origin. We can be sure, however, that if it is a wave motion of any sort, it will give a pattern like that of Fig. 12.14 when diffracted by two obstacles. We shall discuss the experimental verification of this prediction for light in Sec. 12.16.

12.15 *The Diffraction Grating*

If instead of the two scatterers discussed in the last section, we allow plane waves to fall on a straight row of many such scatterers or on a row of holes in a screen (Fig. 12.18), we obtain a diffraction pattern which is of great interest and importance to us. Such an arrangement of scatterers or holes is called a ***diffraction***

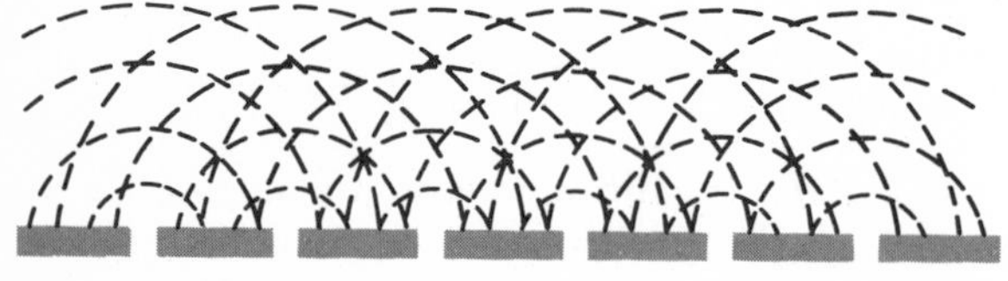

FIG. 12.18 Diffraction grating.

grating. It is easy to see that the directions of maximum intensity for a diffraction grating are the same as those for the two scatterers and are given by Eq. (12.14-3):

$$n\lambda = a \sin \alpha,$$

where n is an integer, λ is the wavelength, α is the angle that the direction of observation makes with the normal to the grating, and a is the distance between the holes of the grating—i.e., the ***spacing*** of the grating. The maxima of intensity thus occur when the path differences from two neighboring holes differ by exactly a whole wavelength (Fig. 12.16b), as in the case of the two scatterers discussed in the preceding section. The ***zero order*** from the grating is formed in the direction in which the difference in path between successive holes is zero—i.e., for $n = 0$, $\sin \alpha = 0$, and $\alpha = 0$. In Fig. 12.19a, circles, whose radii are whole number multiples of one wavelength, are drawn from each of the apertures A_1, A_2, A_3, A_4, etc. All the waves with the same radii will ultimately interfere constructively at a large distance to form a plane wave proceeding from the grating in the direction $\alpha = 0$. Figure 12.18b, indicates how spherical waves whose path difference from adjacent apertures is one wavelength combine to produce plane waves moving in a direction such that α is given by $\sin \alpha = \lambda/a$; this is the ***first order*** diffracted wave. In a similar manner, Fig. 12.19c indicates the way in which the ***second order*** diffracted wave is produced from spherical waves whose radii differ by two wavelengths. The direction of the second order wave, of course, is such that $\sin \alpha = 2\lambda/a$. Similar figures can

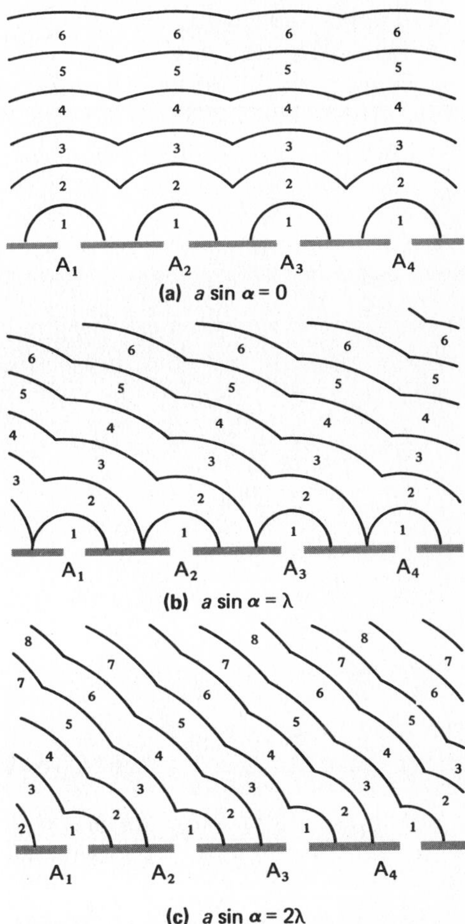

FIG. 12.19 Formation of diffracted waves by a grating.

be drawn for higher orders if they exist, although the reader should verify (Ex. 12.16-1) that the highest order n which a grating can produce is always less than a/λ.

So far we have concerned ourselves solely with the directions in which the maxima of the diffracted waves appear when waves fall on a diffraction grating. If the number of holes in the grating is large, the intensity of the diffracted light falls off very rapidly as the angle α departs from those values which satisfy Eq. (12.14-3). A detailed discussion of the intensity in the regions between the maxima is rather complicated, and we shall avoid it here. We merely state that, for the directions other than those of the maxima, the waves from the holes cancel one another almost completely when the number of holes is large.

Thus, an incident plane wave consisting of only one wavelength will be split up into several distinct plane waves corresponding to various values of n. If the incident wave contains several wavelengths, each of these will be diffracted in a different set of α values, and the grating will enable us to analyze any beam of light according to wavelength. This will be discussed in more detail in the next section.

If we wish to test whether light or any other form of radiation consists of wave motion, we should be able to do so by allowing it to fall on a diffraction grating. If maxima in the intensity of the light beyond the grating appear in directions that depend on the spacing of the grating in accordance with Eq. (12.14-3), then we should have evidence for the wave nature of the radiation being investigated.

A photograph of ripples on water, diffracted by a diffraction grating, is shown in Fig. 12.20.

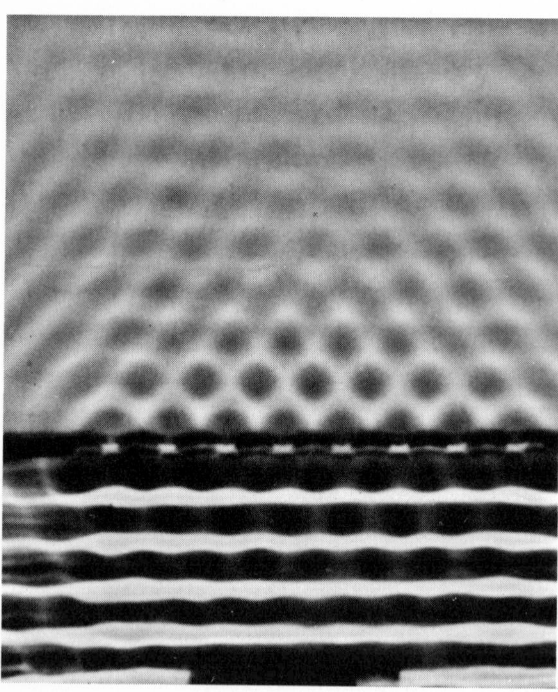

Fig. 12.20 Diffraction grating in a ripple tank.

12.16 Determination of the Wavelength of Light

A particular form of diffraction grating which is of greatest use in ***spectrum analysis***—that is to say, in the analysis of light into its constituent wavelengths—is the ***ruled grating***. Such gratings are of two types. In the ***transmission grating***, a plane plate of glass or other transparent material is ruled with a large number of equally spaced, parallel grooves by means of a sharp V-shaped diamond cutter to give a surface of the type shown in Fig. 12.21. In the ruled portion, the transmission of light is either blocked entirely or modified very considerably, while in the unruled portion the transmission takes place quite normally. In a ***reflection grating***, a mirror is ruled in the same way, and the usual type of reflection takes place from the unruled portions of the grating and the reflections from the ruled portion are highly modified. The diffraction grating as used for the study of light was invented by Joseph von Fraunhofer (1787–1826), but most of the best modern gratings have been ruled on machines of the type developed by the American physicist Henry Rowland (1848–1901). In such machines, as many as 10,000 lines can be ruled in one centimeter.

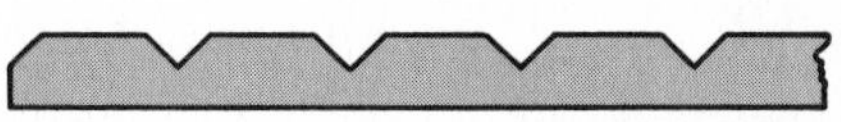

FIG. 12.21. Cross section of ruled grating—groove size and spacing magnified about 10^4 times.

Since the number of lines ruled per unit of length on a ruled grating can be measured with very great accuracy, the spacing a is accurately determined, and the diffraction grating can be used as a method of measuring the wavelength of any radiation which falls on it. In Eq. (12.14-3) a is known, α can be measured accurately, and n can be determined by counting. Thus, the only unknown λ can be calculated directly.

The details of the use of the grating for spectrum analysis must be left to Chapter 13, but for the present we wish to make use of some of the results obtained with the aid of this very useful device. If we allow sunlight or the light from any other white-hot body to fall on a grating, we find that first-order diffraction consists of a continuous sequence of visible wavelengths in the range $4000–7000 \times 10^{-10}$ m, or (as it is more usually expressed), 4000–7000 Å where Å stands for the ***Ångström unit***, named after the Swedish physicist Anders Ångström (1814–1874), an early worker in spectrum analysis. According to Eq. (12.14-3), the shortest wavelength will give the smallest value of $\sin \alpha$ and consequently, the value of α, closest to 0°—that is to say, the closest to the direction of the incident beam. If we examine this light by eye, we find that the short wave end of the spectrum appears violet to us. As α gets farther from 0°, $\sin \alpha$ gets larger and, consequently, λ gets larger. As we go through the wavelength range of visible light from the shortest (about 4000 Å) to the longest (about 7000 Å), we meet the "rainbow" of color: violet, indigo, blue, green, yellow, orange, red. The sequence of wavelengths from any source of light is called the ***spectrum*** of that source, and the sequence of wavelengths (and colors) to which we have just referred is called the ***visible spectrum.*** If we use the radiometer (Sec. 12.7) as a means of detection of radiation, we find that in the light of the sun there is radiation of longer wavelength than the extreme red of visible light. This is called ***infrared radiation.*** There is also radiation of wavelength shorter than the extreme violet of visible light. This is called ***ultraviolet radiation.***

The light from the sun, and from all hot solids and hot liquids, exhibits a continuous sequence of wavelengths known as a ***continuous spectrum.*** Spectra from hot gases and from electrically excited gases, such as is obtained from the neon, argon, and mercury lamps used in advertising signs and from the sodium lamps used in highway lighting, consists of ***line spectra*** in which a finite number of discrete well-defined wavelengths are present. The spectrum of sodium is particularly interesting since it contains only two strong lines in the visible range at wavelengths 5890 Å and 5896 Å. These two lines (called the ***D-lines***) are so close together that a sodium lamp is often used as a ***monochromatic source***, a source of light of one wavelength, although in precise work account must be taken of the fact that two wavelengths are present. Full tables of all the wavelengths in the spectra of the various chemical elements are given in the *Handbook of Chemistry and Physics* and in many other places. The recognition of the wavelengths of light emitted by a given element provides a very simple and trustworthy means for identification of the element.

The demonstration of diffraction of light by a line grating is essentially a demonstration of a wave nature for light. We shall give an explanation of reflection and refraction on the wave hypothesis, but first we must present an important principle that applies to all types of wave motion.

EXERCISES

12.16-1 Prove the statement made in the text (Sec. 12.15) that the order n of a diffracted wave is always less than a/λ.

12.16-2 Construct a diagram such as that of Fig. 12.14 for two scatterers whose distance apart is $a = 6\lambda$.

12.16-3 Calculate the angles at which the curves of constructive interference of Fig. 12.14 will diverge from the two sources at large distances from them. How many orders will appear in addition to the zero order?

12.16-4 Answer the questions of Ex. 12.16-3 as applied to the solution of Ex. 12.16-2.

12.16-5 Two powerful sources of sound are 5.00 m apart and are emitting sine waves in phase with one another of frequency 172 sec^{-1}. Calculate the directions in which intense sound will be heard at a distance of 500 m from those sources. In what directions will the sound intensity be a minimum? The air temperature is 21°C.

12.16-6 Light from a sodium lamp is incident normally on a grating with 5000 lines per centimeter. Assuming that the wavelength of the sodium doublet can be taken as a single line for which $\lambda = 5893$ Å, calculate the angular position of the first three orders of the diffraction pattern from this grating. What is the maximum number of orders that may be expected?

12.17 Huygens' Principle

In discussing wave motion in Chapter 10, we saw that the ability of a material to transmit a wave depends on the fact that a disturbance at any point in the medium affects neighboring points and so is propagated through the material. It follows that every such disturbance behaves like a source that sends out a spherical wave in a homogeneous medium. The Dutch physicist Christian

Huygens (1629–1665) realized that a disturbance is taking place at any point in a medium through which a wave is passing, and therefore, that the point in question can be taken as a source of new spherical waves. He thus concluded that each point in a wave crest or trough could be considered as a new source of radiation, and that, if all the contributions from all parts of the original wave were added together at a later time, the original wave would be reconstructed as it would have appeared at that later time. This important result is known as ***Huygens' principle.*** Two very simple cases of Huygens' construction are exhibited in Fig. 12.22. In Fig. 12.22a, the plane wave AB is treated as a plane of sources. From every point of the wave front AB, a spherical wave goes out. For

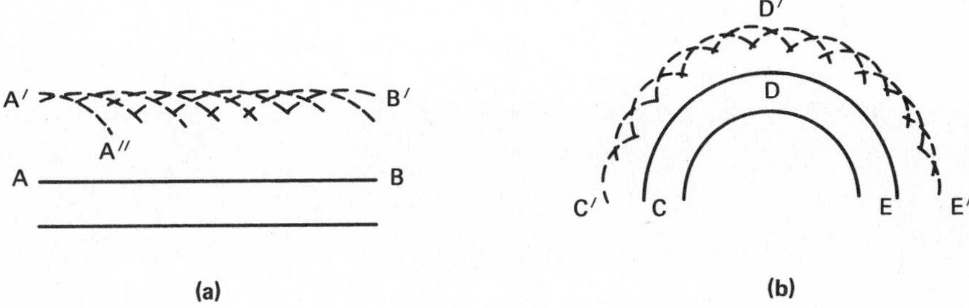

Fig. 12.22 Huygens' construction (a) for plane wave, (b) for spherical wave.

example, the spherical wave A′A″ originates at A. These waves recombine to form the new plane wave A′B′, which in this case is simply the original wave AB that has progressed two wavelengths farther on (the radius of the spheres is 2λ). In Fig. 12.22b, a spherical wave CDE is reconstructed as in C′D′E′ by using spheres of radius λ. In the figures, the centers for the Huygens' spheres have been taken a relatively large distance apart. The new wave front, of course, is fully developed only when these centers are taken very close together. The results of Sec. 12.15 and Ex. 12.16-1 tell us that when the sources are very close together, as they are in Huygens' argument, only the zero order in the diffraction spectra will appear.

It is not difficult to see that Huygens' construction can be generalized. Consider a line abcdef (Fig. 12.23) drawn across a plane wave system moving from left to right. The successive positions of a single crest of a wave system are shown by the vertical lines and are numbered from 0 to 5. Suppose now that the crest when in the 0 position sends out a wave from point a. As the crest moves into the 1 position, a wave is sent from b, and so on until a wave is sent out from f, when the original crest is in the 5 position. It will be noticed that the wave from b is sent out a certain time t_0 later than that from a. The value t_0 will depend on the speed of the wave and the distance between a and b measured in the direction in which the wave is traveling. The waves from c, d, e, f, etc., will follow at successive intervals of t_0. We can then see that all these waves will combine to form a new wave crest at AB which is a position which would have been occupied by the original wave if it had been allowed to progress without obstruction. We can thus assume that as each part of the original wave meets the line abcdef, it is annihilated and replaced by a circular wave diverging from the point of collision. The spherical waves then unite to reconstruct the original wave.

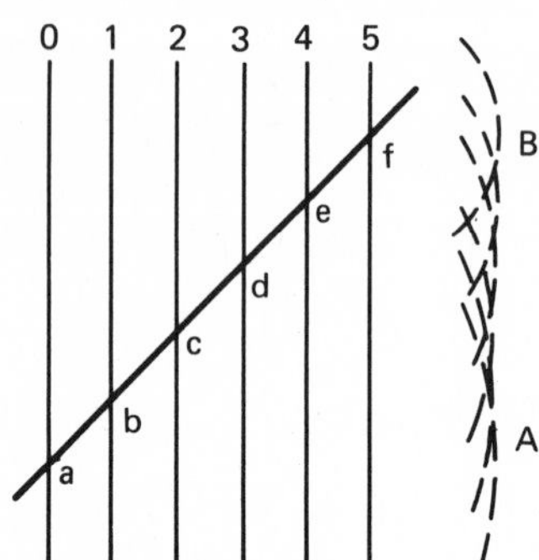

FIG. 12.23 Reconstruction of a wave.

12.18 Wave Theory of Reflection and Refraction

In studying the reflection of waves, we shall make application of Huygens' principle and its extensions discussed in the preceding section. We saw in Sec. 10.11 that, whenever a wave hits a rigid obstacle, a reflected wave is set up. We now see that when a plane wave hits a rigid obstacle, each point in every

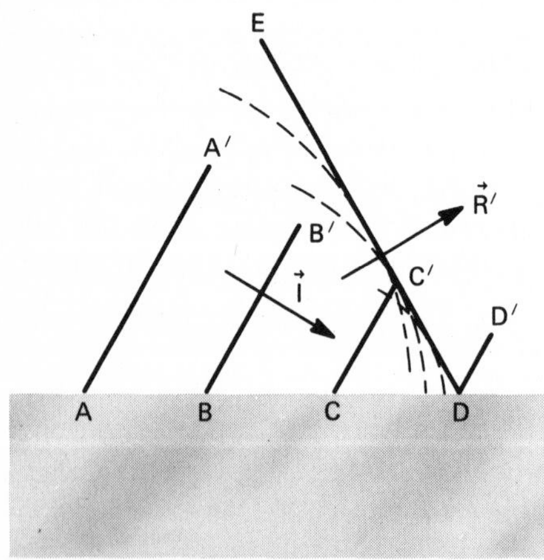

FIG. 12.24 Reflection of a wave.

crest may, according to Huygens' construction, be considered as a source of a spherical wave. Thus, in Fig. 12.24, a given wave crest AA′ is incident on a rigid surface ABCD with the wave normal in the direction of the vector $\vec{I}$. The incident crest takes up successive positions BB′, CC′, DD′. When the incident crest is in the position AA′, it sends out a spherical wave from A. A little later, when this crest is at BB′, a spherical wave starts from B, and so on for C and D and for all intermediate points. All these spherical waves will combine to form a new crest DE, whose direction of motion is the direction of the vector $\vec{R}'$, which is drawn perpendicular to the new wave front DE.

Figure 12.25 now allows us to relate the directions of the vectors $\vec{I}'$ and $\vec{R}'$ In this figure, A′D is drawn perpendicular to the wave front AA′—i.e., in the direction of the vector $\vec{I}$—which makes an angle i with the normal ON to the

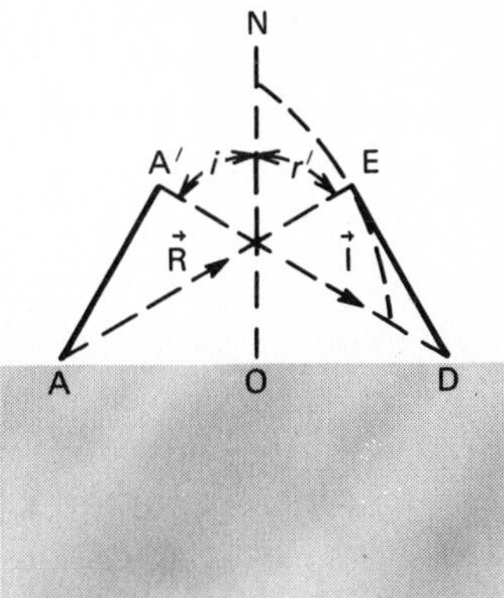

Fig. 12.25 The law of reflection.

surface. When the crest AA′ is in the position shown, a spherical wave starts out from A and, during the time it takes point A′ to move from A′ to D (cf. Fig. 12.24), the spherical wave will have expanded to a radius AE such that AE = A′D. At this instant, a wave will be starting from D, so that the new wave front must lie along ED with ED perpendicular to AE, since the new wave (cf. Figs. 12.22, 12.23) is always tangent to its constituent waves. Thus, the line AE gives the direction in which the wave is traveling or the direction of the vector $\vec{R}'$. The angle that $\vec{R}$ makes with ON is r'. Now, the two triangles ADA′ and DAE are both right-angled with AE = DA′ and AD as a common side. They are therefore congruent and the angle A′AD is equal to the angle EDA. It is easy to see that the angle A′AD is equal to i and that EDA is equal to r'. It therefore follows that

$$i = r'. \tag{12.18-1}$$

Hence, we obtain the important result that the law of reflection for plane waves is the same as the law of reflection for light (Sec. 12.3). It is also the law for reflection of a photon (Sec. 12.12). This result may at first seem surprising, but it is less surprising when we consider that waves, photons, and material particles all possess the common property of transporting energy in their direction of motion. When we study a reflection of waves or of particles, we are merely studying the way in which an energy flow is reflected under the circumstance that no energy is lost in the reflection.

Consider now what happens when a plane wave crest falls obliquely on the boundary between two media as indicated in Fig. 12.26. We assume that in the first medium the speed of the wave is C_1 and in the second C_2. We suppose that the initial direction of the normal to the plane wave makes an angle i (angle of incidence) with the normal to the surface, and we assume that AA′ is a crest in such a wave (Fig. 12.26). When point A on the initial wave hits the boundary AB′ between the two media, a disturbance will start out from A into the second region. As the initial wave AA′ progresses, each portion of it will in succession start a wave into the second medium as it strikes the boundary.* When point A′ hits the boundary at B′, a new wave will be just starting into the second

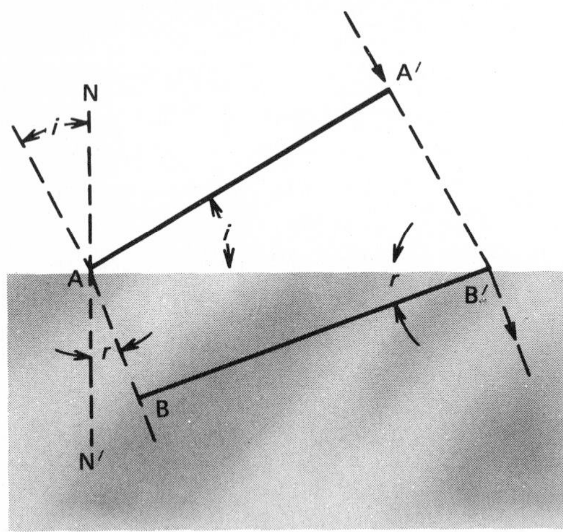

Fig. 12.26 Refraction of a wave.

medium from that point. In the meantime, the wave that started from A will have combined with all the waves starting from points between A and B′ to form a new plane wave in the second medium. We can locate this wave by the generalized Huygens' construction and by the following argument. It can be seen that the time t taken by point A′ in traveling from A′ to B′ will be given by

$$\mathrm{A'B'}/C_1 = t. \tag{12.18-2}$$

In the same time t, the wave in the second medium that started from A will have traveled a distance AB given by

$$\mathrm{AB}/C_2 = t. \tag{12.18-3}$$

The wave crest in the second medium must therefore be along the line BB′ with AB perpendicular to BB′. Assume that AB makes an angle r (angle of refraction) with the normal to the surface.

It is now easy to see that the angle A′AB′ is i and the angle AB′B is r, and it follows that A′B′ = AB′ sin i and AB = AB′ sin r. We may thus write

$$\sin i/\sin r = \mathrm{A'B'/AB}. \tag{12.18-4}$$

* There will also be a wave reflected back into the first medium. This wave, of course, will obey the law of reflection.

Combining Eqs. (12.18-2) and 12.18-3), we see that

$$A'B'/AB = C_1/C_2 = \mu,$$

(cf. Eq. 12.4-1) and it follows that

$$\sin i/\sin r = \mu. \tag{12.18-5}$$

Thus, the laws of reflection and refraction can both be explained on the basis of the wave theory.

12.19 Dispersion

In Secs. 12.4 and 12.5, we mentioned that the speed of light C and the refractive index μ for various media depend on the nature of the light. We can now correlate this dependence with the wavelength. It is found that, if we measure the refractive index μ for light of a single wavelength, we always get the same value for a given pair of materials, and in general, if we vary the wavelength, the refractive index and the wave speed C will vary.

In Sec. 12.5 we defined the relative refractive index μ as the ratio of the speed of light in the first medium to that in the second. In tabulating refractive indices, it is convenient to have one of these two media always the same. The absolute refractive index n of a medium is defined as the relative refractive index of the medium with respect to vacuum as the first medium. Thus, the ***absolute refractive index*** n for a given medium and a given wavelength is given by

$$n = c/C, \tag{12.19-1}$$

in which C is the wave speed in the medium for a given wavelength, and c is the wave speed of light in a vacuum. The quantity c is the same for all wavelengths. If the absolute refractive indices of the first and second media are n_1 and n_2, respectively, then the relative refractive index μ will be given by

$$\mu = n_2/n_1. \tag{12.19-2}$$

In Table 12.1 are listed the refractive indices for a number of materials and for three different wavelengths.

Table 12.1 *Dispersion of Refractive Indices* (n)

	$\lambda = 4861$ Å*	$\lambda = 5893$ Å*	$\lambda = 6563$ Å*
Crown glass	1.5233	1.5171	1.5146
Light flint glass	1.5903	1.5804	1.5764
Dense flint glass	1.6691	1.6555	1.6501
Fused quartz	1.4632	1.4584	1.4564
Water	1.3371	1.3334	1.3311

* The wavelength of light of a given frequency depends on the medium. Unless otherwise specified, wavelengths given in tables, etc., are those in a vacuum.

If we measure the wavelength of light in vacuum by means of the diffraction grating, we can determine the frequency ν of the light by means of Eq. (10.5-3), i.e.,

$$\nu = c/\lambda. \tag{12.19-3}$$

When light travels from vacuum into a refractive medium, its frequency will be unaltered. If this were not true of any wave that passes from one medium to another, it would be impossible to satisfy at every instant boundary conditions such as those that were discussed in Prob. 10.6. Hence the wavelength must change to a new value λ' given by

$$\lambda' = C/\nu; \tag{12.19-4}$$

and

$$\lambda'/\lambda = C/c = \mu. \tag{12.19-5}$$

12.20 Diffraction and Rectilinear Propagation

In order to explain the results of Sec. 12.2 on the basis of the wave theory, we must consider what happens when a plane wave of light falls on a single hole in a screen (Fig. 12.27). Suppose we assume that the hole is divided into two halves

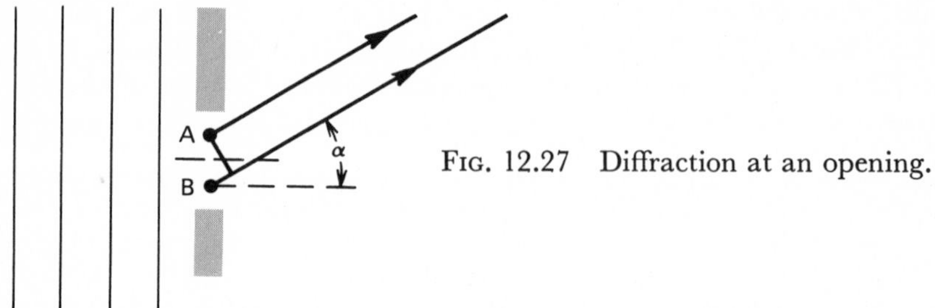

FIG. 12.27 Diffraction at an opening.

as indicated by the dotted line in the figure. Then we can consider all the light from the top half of the hole as coming from points A and all the light from the bottom half as coming from points B, point A and B being approximately in the middle of the top half and bottom half of the hole, respectively. Obviously, two sources at A and B will interfere constructively in the direction in which the wave was originally traveling ($\alpha = 0$). This gives us the rectilinear propagation. If we now depart from that direction until

$$\lambda/2 = (AB) \sin \alpha,$$

we see that the condition of Eq. (12.14-4) is satisfied, and we get destructive interference between the two halves of the hole. If the distance AB is very large compared with λ, Eq. (12.14-4) will be satisfied for very small values of α, the minimum will occur very close to the original direction of the beam, and almost all the light will travel in the direction $\alpha = 0$. If on the other hand AB is only a small multiple of the wavelength, the minimum angle for destructive interference is quite large, and we shall get an appreciable intensity at quite large angles (Fig. 12.3.)

12.21 The Wave-Particle Duality

In this chapter we have studied a few of the simple properties of light radiation. We have found that reflection, refraction, rectilinear propagation, and the inverse square law of the falling off of intensity for a small source can all be explained on either a photon theory or a wave theory. The diffraction of light receives a very direct explanation in the wave theory and seems at first sight to be impossible to explain in a purely particle theory. For a long time the diffraction experiments were thought to be conclusive evidence for the wave theory, but experiments made in the early part of this century indicated that light energy was not transmitted continuously but in discrete units. Direct measurements were made of the size of these units, or ***quanta*** (singular, ***quantum***) of energy. It was found that when light energy was absorbed or emitted, the absorption or emission always took place in bundles, or quanta, of energy ε given by

$$\varepsilon = h\nu, \tag{12.21-1}$$

where h is a constant known as ***Planck's constant*** and ν is the frequency of the light absorbed or emitted. This constant is named for the German physicist Max Planck (1858–1947), the originator of the quantum theory. In Chapters 24 and 25 we shall present the experimental evidence for this important result and shall also describe the experiments by means of which the magnitude of h is found to be

$$h = 6.624 \times 10^{-34}\ \text{J sec.} \tag{12.21-2}$$

Since light is absorbed or emitted in bundles of size ε given by Eq. (12.21-1), it is only reasonable to suppose that it is propagated in such bundles and that the energy ε of the quantum is also the energy of the photon (Secs. 12.12 and 12.11). The momentum p of the photon will then be given by Eqs. (12.11-3) and (12.21-1) in the form

$$p = \varepsilon/c = h\nu/c$$

With the aid of Eq. (12.19-3), this momentum can be written

$$p = h/\lambda. \tag{12.21-3}$$

This expression is known as the ***de Broglie relation.***

As a result of these considerations, we are faced with two theories of light, the wave theory and the photon theory, or particle theory, and we are unable to decide between them. In the wave theory, light is characterized by two quantities, wavelength λ and frequency ν, connected by Eq. (12.19-3), i.e.,

$$\nu\lambda = c. \tag{12.21-4}$$

In the photon theory, light is also characterized by two quantities, the energy ε and momentum p, connected by Eq. (12.11-3), which can be written as

$$\varepsilon/p = c. \tag{12.21-5}$$

The solution to the wave-particle dilemma was offered by the French physicist Louis de Broglie (1892–) in 1924. He suggested that the difficulty was not with the wave-particle duality in light, but that we had failed to observe that duality in ordinary material particles. According to de Broglie, *all particles, photons or material particles, must be associated with a wavelength* λ as given by Eq. (12.21-3); or, alternatively, *all particles must be associated with a frequency* ν as found from Eq. (12.21-1), in which we must put ε equal to mc^2. The verification of this remarkable hypothesis will be discussed in Chapter 24.

EXERCISES

12.21-1 Compute the photon energy and momentum for light of wavelengths (a) 4861 Å, (b) 5893 Å, (c) 6563 Å.

12.21-2 Compute the de Broglie wavelength for a rifle bullet of mass 1.00 g traveling at a speed of 400 m/sec.

12.22 The Doppler Effect

There is one phenomenon connected with all waves that we have not yet mentioned, although we might have considered it in Chapter 10. It is observed whenever there is relative motion between the source of a wave and the observer, or the device an observer uses to detect the wave.

Suppose that a source of sound (or of any other periodic disturbance), S in Fig. 12.28a, is at rest with respect to the medium in which the wave is propagated with the speed W. Suppose also that the source is sending out a sinusoidal wave of frequency ν_S and wavelength λ_S. If the observer (O in Fig. 12.28) is

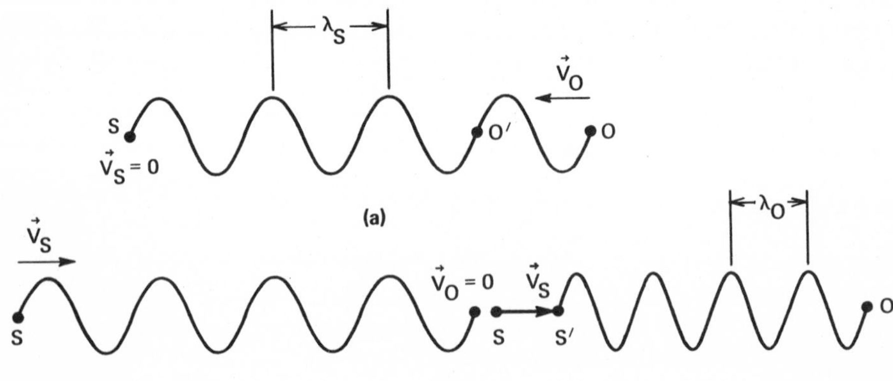

FIG. 12.28 The Doppler effect.

also at rest with respect to the medium, he will receive as many vibrations per unit time as are emitted by the source, so he will receive a disturbance characterized by the frequency ν_S. Suppose on the other hand that he is moving toward the source with a speed V_O. In a time $\tau = \lambda_S/V_O$, where λ_S is the wavelength, he will have moved from O to O′. Hence he will have encountered one full vibration more than he would have received had he been at rest. Hence he will receive the wave at a frequency $\nu_O > \nu_S$. The number of vibrations that reach him in time τ is

$$\nu_O\tau = \nu_S\tau + 1,$$

so that

$$\nu_O = \nu_S + 1/\tau.$$

We may now substitute for τ its value

$$\tau = \lambda_S/V_O = W/\nu_S V_O$$

where the last expression results from Eq. (10.5-3). We then find that the observed frequency is

$$\nu_O = \nu_S + \nu_S V_O/W = \nu_S(1 + V_O/W). \tag{12.22-1}$$

Had the observer been moving away from the source, he would have encountered one less, instead of one more, vibration in a time τ, and Eq. (12.22-1) would be replaced by

$$\nu_O = \nu_S(1 - V_O/W). \tag{12.22-2}$$

A slightly different relation between the emitted and the received frequencies is established if the source is moving relative to the medium and the observer is stationary. Were both S and O stationary, during any time interval t the source would emit $\nu_S t$ vibrations and the observer would receive an equal number. During this time, however, the source has moved a distance $V_S t$, so that the $\nu_S t$ periods of the wave have been crowded into a distance $L - V_S t$, where L is the distance from S to O at $t = 0$. The crowding of the waves is shown in Fig. 12.28c. Hence the wavelength as seen by O is

$$\lambda_O = \frac{L - V_S t}{\nu_S t}$$

and the frequency as observed by O is

$$\nu_O = \frac{W}{\lambda_O} = \frac{W\nu_S t}{L - V_S t}.$$

Setting $L = Wt$, we find that

$$\nu_O = \frac{W\nu_S}{W - V_S} = \frac{\nu_S}{1 - V_S/W}, \tag{12.22-3}$$

so that $\nu_O > \nu_S$. Had the source been moving away from the observer, we would have found that

$$\nu_O = \frac{\nu_S}{1 + V_S/W} \tag{12.22-4}$$

Equations (12.22-1) to (12.22-4) are the expressions for the change in frequency known as the ***Doppler effect***, after the German physicist who first called attention to it, Christian Doppler (1803–1853).

The difference between Eqs. (12.22-1) and (12.22-2) is the change in the sign of V_O/W. Similarly, Eqs. (12.22-3) and (12.22-4) differ only in the sign of V_S/W. The correct sign to use in any of the equations is determined easily if we notice that the observed frequency is always increased if the observer and source are approaching each other and is always decreased if they are separating. It is probably simpler to obtain the correct signs this way than it is to set up and remember special sign conventions. Thus, if the source is moving *toward the observer* with a speed V_S relative to the medium, and the observer is moving *away from the source* with a speed V_O, again relative to the medium, the observed frequency will be

$$\nu_O = \frac{\nu_S(1 - V_O/W)}{1 - V_S/W}. \tag{12.22-5}$$

Notice that the negative sign of V_O/W in the numerator would, by itself, cause ν_O to be less than ν_S, whereas the negative sign of V_S/W in the denominator would, by itself, cause ν_O to be greater than ν_S.

The Doppler effect is easily observed in connection with sound waves. For example, a train whistle or an auto horn decreases in pitch as the vehicle passes an observer, the frequency being given by Eq. (12.22-2) as the vehicle is approaching and by Eq. (12.22-4) as it recedes from him.

The Doppler effect for light is not quite in accordance with Eqs. (12.22-1) to (12.22-5). The reason is that the speed of light, as we have seen in Chapter 8, is c relative to *both* source and observer, whereas the speed of a sound wave is $W \pm V_S$ relative to the source and $W \pm V_O$ relative to the observer. We can arrive at the correct expression for the optical Doppler effect if we recognize that the difference between ν_S and ν_O that is given by Eqs. (12.22-1) and (12.22-2) results purely from the fact that the speed of the wave relative to the observer is $W \pm V_O$. We therefore can expect the effect predicted by those two equations to be absent in the case of light. On the other hand, the crowding or stretching of the waves that led respectively to Eqs. (12.22-3) and (12.22-4) is a phenomenon involving distance, rather than velocity. These two equations are therefore equally valid for sound waves or light waves, except that one additional correction must be made to make the equations consistent with special relativity. We saw in Sec. 8.4 that the Einstein time dilation causes the observed time interval read by a clock to be greater for an observer moving relative to the clock than for an observer who is stationary with respect to it. Any source vibrating with a fixed frequency ν_S may be considered to be a clock, as we saw in Sec. 2.16. Hence, if the frequency of the source is $\nu_S = 1/\tau_S$ for an observer at rest with respect to it, the frequency for an observer moving with a speed v *relative to the source* will be

$$\nu' = 1/\tau' = \left(\frac{\tau_S}{(1 - v^2/c^2)^{1/2}}\right)^{-1} = \nu_S(1 - v^2/c^2)^{1/2}.$$

Substitution of this value for ν_S in Eq. (12.22-4) and the changing of V_S to v and W to c gives

$$\nu_O = \frac{\nu_S(1 - v^2/c^2)^{1/2}}{1 + v/c}.$$

Factoring the numerator, we find

$$\nu_O = \frac{\nu_S(1 - v/c)^{1/2}(1 + v/c)^{1/2}}{1 + v/c}$$

$$= \frac{\nu_S(1 - v/c)^{1/2}}{(1 + v/c)^{1/2}} = \nu_S[(c - v)/(c + v)]^{1/2} \qquad (12.22\text{-}6)$$

as the relation between the observed and emitted frequencies if the relative motion of source and observer is taking them apart. If the relative motion is such that it brings them toward each other, the sign of v changes and we have

$$\nu_O = \nu_S[(c + v)/(c - v)]^{1/2}. \qquad (12.22\text{-}7)$$

EXERCISES

12.22-1 A train whistle emits a note of frequency 300 sec^{-1} as heard by an observer on the train. The temperature is 27°C. If the train approaches a station at a speed of 25 m/sec, what will be the frequency of the sound from the whistle as heard by an observer at the station?

12.22-2 What will be the frequency of the sound heard by the stationary observer as the train recedes from the station at 25 m/sec?

12.22-3 The train of Ex. 12.22-1 is approaching a second train, which is moving toward it at a speed of 20 m/sec relative to the ground. What will the frequency of the whistle be as heard by an observer on the second train?

12.22-4 A sodium lamp, observed in a laboratory, emits light of two wavelengths; 5889.95 Å and 5895.92 Å. In a spectrogram of a star, two wavelengths, 5878.17 Å and 5884.13 Å are observed. What can be deduced about the motion of the star relative to the earth?

12.23 Summary

The simpler properties of light have been considered from an experimental point of view, and the laws of rectilinear progagation, reflection, and refraction have been obtained. The interpretations of these laws on the photon theory and on the wave theory have been presented and, in the course of this presentation, the inverse square law, light pressure, and diffraction were discussed. No decision has been reached between the wave and particle theories, and the wave-particle picture presented by de Broglie was offered for future discussion.

PROBLEMS

12.1 Real shadows are seldom as sharply defined as would be indicated by Fig. 12.2.

(a) Part (a) of the figure for this problem shows the shadow of a vertical rod as it occurs on a horizontal surface. Note that there is a dark region in the center of the shadow and a less dark region bordering it. What can be said of the nature of the light source?

(b) The shadow of the same rod, under different conditions of illumination, is shown at (b). Discuss the nature of the source or sources of illumination.

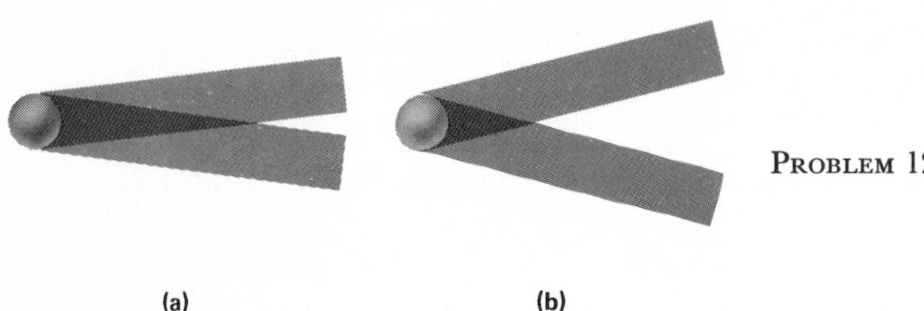

PROBLEM 12.1

12.2 The blackened disk of a radiometer, similar to that shown in Fig. 12.9, is made of aluminum. It's mass is 0.200 g. The instrument is pointed toward a source of radiation with the front hole covered. The hole is uncovered at $t = 0$, allowing the radiation to reach the disk. The temperature rise (ΔT) of the disk is measured at various times, with the following results:

Time (t) in seconds:	0.0	0.5	1.0	1.5	2.0	4.0	6.0	10.0	20.0
Temperature rise (ΔT) in C°:	0.00	2.40	4.28	5.74	6.88	9.41	10.34	10.88	10.88

(a) What is the intensity of the radiation? (b) What phenomenon causes the curve of ΔT vs. t to level off? Discuss this behavior in as quantitative a fashion as you find possible.

12.3 A light source is in the form of a very long vertical column of glowing gas. Show that the intensity in a plane near the center of the column falls off as the inverse first power of the distance if the medium surrounding the source does not absorb any light.

12.4 A glass prism has a cross section shown in the figure. Light strikes one face of the prism, traveling in the plane of the paper and making an angle α with the normal

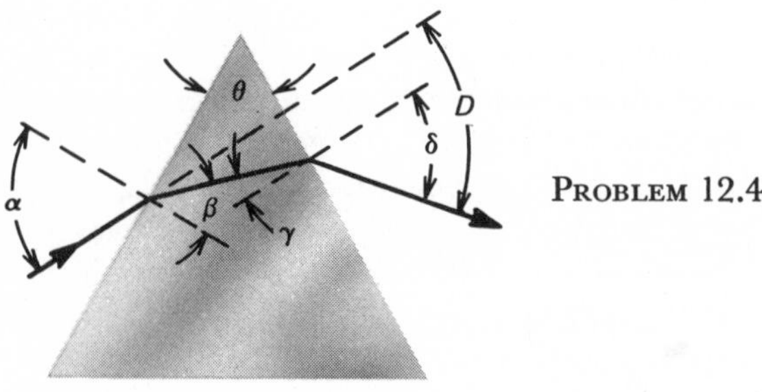

PROBLEM 12.4

to a prism face. Take the index of refraction of the prism as 1.50, $\theta = 60.0°$ and $\alpha =$ 45.0°. Show that the *angle of deviation D* is

$$D = \alpha - \beta - \gamma + \delta = 37.4°.$$

12.5 Find the least value of α if light striking the prism of Prob. 12.4 is not to suffer total internal reflection at the second face of the prism.

12.6 When a sheet of Polaroid is placed in a light beam, its plane being perpendicular to the beam, the intensity of the light is cut to one-half of its previous value. If a second sheet of Polaroid is then introduced, parallel to the first sheet, it is found that rotation of the second sheet about an axis in the direction of the beam changes the intensity of the transmitted eight. In two orientations of the second sheet, between which a rotation of 180° takes place, the intensity is essentially the same as if the sheet were not present; in orientations corresponding to 90° rotation from these, the transmitted intensity drops essentially to zero.

(a) Draw a set of diagrams illustrating this experiment.

(b) On the basis of these experiments, can you decide whether light is a longitudinal wave, a transverse wave, or some combination of the two?

(The light after passing through the first Polaroid sheet is said to be *plane polarized.* This phenomenon will be discussed further in Chapter 23.)

12.7 It is possible to rule a diffraction grating in such a way that all adjacent slits are not separated by the same distance. Suppose that each line of a grating is identified by a number n ($=1, 2, 3, 4, \ldots$). The distance between the slits for which $n = 4j + 1$, j being an integer, and those for which $n = 4j + 2$ is a, as is the distance between those slits for which $n = 4j + 2$ and $n = 4j + 3$. The distance between those slits for which $n = 4j + 3$ and those for which $n = 4j + 4$ is $2a$. Light of wavelength λ falls on the grating at normal incidence, as in Fig. 12.19.

(a) Show that this grating will produce maxima of intensity in the same directions as if the slits had equal spacing, a. (b) Show that the grating will also produce maxima, of lower intensity, at angles θ from the normal such that

$$\sin\theta = (2n + 1)\lambda/2a.$$

12.8 Light strikes a reflection grating, with spacing a between adjacent slits, at an angle θ with the normal to the grating. (a) Show that the zeroth order maximum of intensity occurs when the diffracted ray makes an angle ϕ with the normal (ϕ being positive if the diffracted and incident rays are on the same side of the normal) when $\phi = -\theta$. (b) Show that the other maxima occur at angles ϕ such that

$$\sin\theta + \sin\phi = n\lambda/a,$$

where n is an integer. (c) What is the highest order that can be observed when the grating is used in this way with a given value of θ? For what θ is the highest order obtained?

12.9 Light of wavelength λ falls at normal incidence on a slit of width $w = 3\lambda$. Show that diffraction maxima will be observed, at distances much larger than w, at angles θ with the normal such that

$$\sin\theta_n = (2n + 1)\lambda/2w,$$

where n is an integer, and show that diffraction minima will occur at angles θ such that

$$\sin\theta_m = m\lambda/w,$$

where m is an integer.

12.10 Light of wavelength λ falls, at normal incidence, on a screen containing two slits, each of width $w = \lambda$. The centers of the slits are separated by a distance $a = 10\lambda$. The interference pattern is observed at a distance large compared with a.

(a) Find the directions at which maxima of intensity will occur.

(b) Show that the maxima of the n order will be less intense than that of the $(n-1)$ order, for any possible value of n. (Hint: Remember that the amplitude that any slit can contribute to the interference pattern is limited by the diffraction pattern of the slit.)

12.11 The Doppler effect was treated in Sec. 12.22 in terms of the wave theory. It can equally well be considered as a photon phenomenon. Consider a particle of mass m that is moving with a velocity $\vec{v}$ and that emits a photon of frequency ν in the direction in which it is moving. Assume that the particle is so massive that Newtonian mechanics can be used to find its momentum and kinetic energy. At the emission of the photon, the mass of the particle is decreased by an amount ε_0/c^2, where ε_0 is the energy released by the emission of the photon.

(a) Show that the speed of the particle after the emission is determined by momentum conservation as

$$V = c(mvc - h\nu)/(mc^2 - \varepsilon_0).$$

(b) Using the conservation of energy, and assuming both (ε_0/c^2) and $(h\nu/c^2)$ to be much less than m, show that the energy of the photon is

$$h\nu = \frac{\varepsilon_0}{1 - v/c}.$$

(c) Hence show that the frequency (ν_O) of the emitted photon is related to the frequency (ν_S) that would be emitted if m were at rest by the equation

$$\nu_O = \frac{\nu_S}{1 - v/c},$$

in agreement with Eq. (12.22-3).

12.12 (a) Repeat Prob. 12.11, taking $v = 0$, but not neglecting terms proportional to (ε_0/c^2) and $(h\nu/c^2)$. Hence show that the energy of the emitted photon is always less than ε_0 when the particle of mass m is at rest before the emission.

(b) Suppose the emitting particle to be an atom of mass $\approx 10^{-25}$ kg. Show that $(h\nu/c^2)$ is negligible for a photon of visible light, of wavelength ≈ 5000 Å, but that it is not negligible for a gamma-ray photon of wavelength ≈ 0.01 Å.

REFERENCES

12A A. Einstein and L. Infeld, *The Evolution of Physics*, Simon and Schuster, New York, 1938. See pp. 272–286.

12B A. A. Michelson, *Studies in Optics*, University of Chicago Press, Chicago, 1927. Pages 1–19 relate to radiation.

12C Franklin Miller, *Diffraction—Single Slit; Diffraction—Double Slit;* and *Michelson Interferometer.* (Nos. 80-206, 80-207, and 80-209, The Ealing Corp., Cambridge, Mass.) Three appropriate film loops, each of about 4 min duration.

12D Morris Shamos, editor, *Great Experiments in Physics*, Holt, New York, 1960. Chapters 7 and 8 deal with the work of Thomas Young and A. J. Fresnel, respectively.

12E James Strickland, *ESI Ripple Tank Series*, fourteen 2- to 4-min film loops produced by Educational Services, Inc. (Set No. 89-918, The Ealing Corp., Cambridge, Mass.) Refraction, reflection, interference, diffraction, and the Doppler effect are illustrated.

12F Morton S. Roberts, "Hydrogen in Galaxies," *Scientific American*, June 1963, pp. 94–106. Applications of the Doppler effect.

12G Gerald Oster and Yasunori Mishijima, "Moire Patterns," *Scientific American*, May 1963, pp. 54–63. Some interesting optical effects.

13 ⇨ *Optical Instruments*

13.1 The Plane Mirror

The laws of reflection and refraction discussed in Chapter 12 are basic to the design of optical instruments. These instruments, which include such devices as lenses, mirrors, microscopes, telescopes, cameras, and spectroscopes, are used to redirect beams of radiation in predetermined ways. Through them we can exercise very useful controls over radiant energy.

The simplest of all such optical instruments is the ***plane mirror*** which we have already discussed in connection with the law of reflection in Sec. 12.3. When we look into a mirror, we see a reflection of ourselves and of the objects in the room around us. What we see appears to be behind the mirror and is of course not really there. The light starting from an object in front of the mirror is reflected by the mirror and reaches our eyes from such directions that it seems to come from behind the mirror. To understand how these images are formed we must consider briefly how the human eye locates an object in space. We shall confine ourselves here to a discussion of what the eye does and postpone the consideration of the mechanism of the eye to Sec. 13.10.

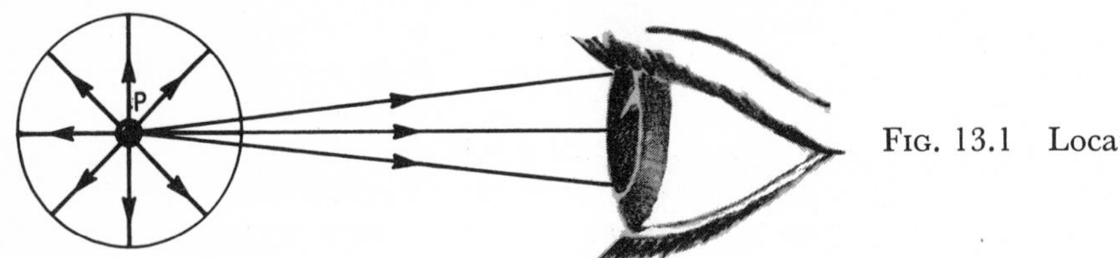

Fig. 13.1 Location of a point source.

We know that a luminous point P (Fig. 13.1) sends out light in all directions. A small cone of this light falls on the clear opening in the iris or colored portion of the eye. This opening is called the ***pupil*** (cf. Sec.13.10). The eye establishes the direction of the point P by the direction of the axis of the cone, and it locates the distance of point P by the divergence of the cone, i.e., the angle between the extreme rays in the cone of light that reaches the eye will be larger if the object is near the eye than it will be if it is far from the eye. The two eyes aid one another in the accurate estimate of distance, but for the moment we need consider only one eye. *If light falls on the eye in the form of a cone diverging from* P *(Fig. 13.1), the eye will perceive a luminous point at the vertex of the cone, i.e., at* P.

Consider now an ***object*** O (Fig. 13.2) located to the left of the plane mirror MM′. Light from the object O which travels along OA will be reflected along

AB to make the angle OAN equal to the angle NAB, according to the law of reflection (Sec. 12.3). The ray OD which is normal to the mirror will be reflected back on itself. If now we extend the lines OD and BA behind the mirror they will intersect at I. It is then easy to see that the two triangles ADO and ADI are congruent since they are both right-angled at D, have the same base DA, and have the same angles at O and I, respectively. It then follows that OD = DI and that the point I is the same distance behind the mirror as O is in front, with the line OI perpendicular to the mirror. This will be true wherever A is located. It follows that all rays that leave O and are reflected by the mirror will appear to diverge from I, and in particular the small cone of light that diverges from O and falls on the mirror at C will be reflected to fall on the eye at E. This eye will

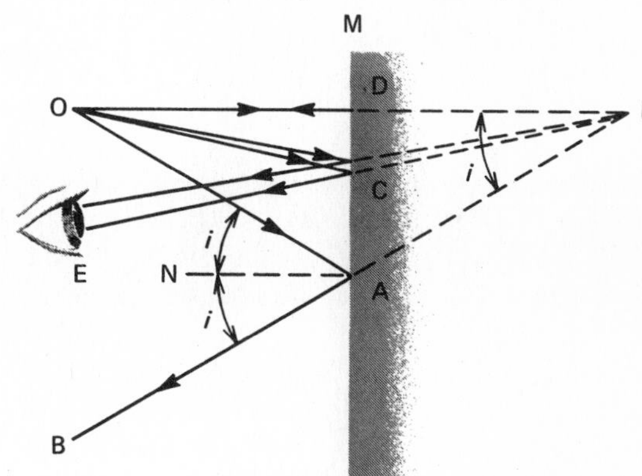

FIG. 13.2 Image formation by a plane mirror.

see light which diverges from I and will therefore perceive a luminous ***image*** at I. If the eye is moved, the light that reaches it will be reflected from different parts of the mirror, but the image will remain fixed at I as long as the object and the mirror remain fixed. It should be noted that the eye uses only that portion of the mirror near C to locate the image at I. It is therefore not necessary for image formation that any portion of the mirror lie on the line ODI, perpendicular to the plane of the mirror. The image formed by a plane mirror is called a ***virtual image***. The term virtual is used because the rays of light by which the image is perceived do not actually pass through the image. We shall see in Sec. 13.3 that other optical instruments form ***real images*** in which the rays of light actually pass through the image point before they diverge to be seen by the eye. The object O is called a ***real object***, since the rays actually diverge from it. The definition of a virtual object will be given in Sec. 13.7.

In the case of an extended object, the image of each point of the object is, formed separately (Fig. 13.3). In such a diagram the reversing effect of a mirror which interchanges left and right between object and image, is made clear.

An image formed by one mirror can act as the object for a second mirror. In Fig. 13.4 two mirrors are drawn at right angles to one another. The object O forms an image I_2 in M_2M. However, the eye at E can see I_1 reflected in M_2M, so that it will see an image I_3 that is the image of I_1 in M_2M. If the eye is moved to the other side of O, it will see I_3 as the image of I_2 reflected in $M_1 M$. If the angle between the mirrors is exactly 90°, the image I_3 seen in the two ways will have the same location. This will not be true if the angle is slightly different from 90°. If the angle between the mirrors is $180°/n$, the number of images formed will be $(2n - 1)$ if n is an integer (cf. Ex. 13.1-3).

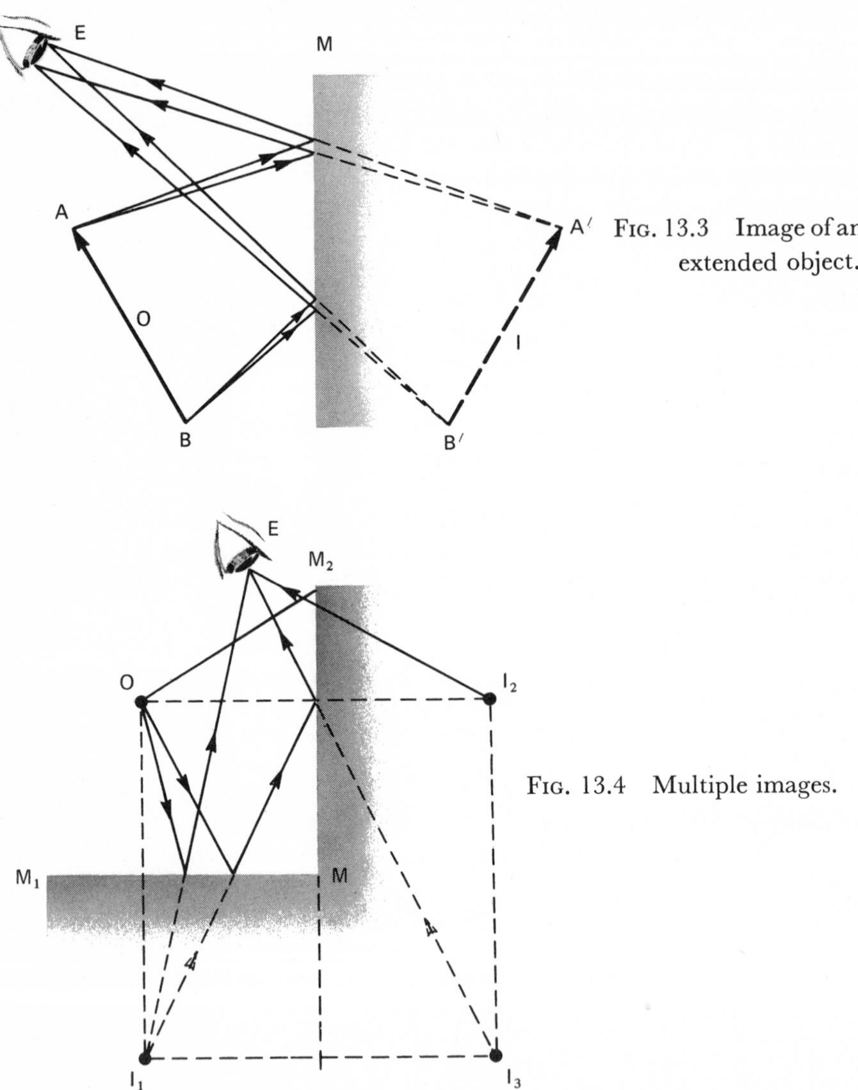

FIG. 13.3 Image of an extended object.

FIG. 13.4 Multiple images.

EXERCISES

13.1-1 A person holds a meter stick in a vertical position with his eye close to the 50-cm mark. What is the minimum height of a vertical mirror in which he can see the entire meter stick?

13.1-2 What is the minimum length of the vertical mirror in which a person of height h standing upright can see his full length? What must be the levels of the top and bottom of this mirror? Does it matter how far from the mirror he stands?

13.1-3 Two plane mirrors meet at a common edge and are inclined at an angle of 60° to each other. A point object is placed within the 60° angle, equidistant from the two mirrors. Show that five images will be formed, and find their locations.

13.1-4 Two mirrors are parallel and facing each other at any distance apart. How many images of an object placed between them will be formed in each mirror?

13.1-5 A simple periscope can be constructed from a tube and two plane mirrors. The tube has a vertical axis and the mirrors, which are parallel to each other and at an angle of 45° to the axis of the tube, are placed above and below it. Sketch the arrangement and show that a person looking into the lower mirror will see erect images of the objects reflected in the upper mirror.

13.1-6 By replacing the object O of Fig. 13.4 by an extended object, show that different aspects of the object may be seen in the images in the different mirrors.

13.1-7 Devise an arrangement of two or more mirrors that will enable an observer to see a full face, a profile, and a back view of himself without moving his head. Draw an accurate diagram showing the paths of the rays by which these images are seen.

13.2 Lenses

The fact that light rays can be concentrated by a piece of transparent material, so shaped that it is thicker at its center than at the edges, was known to the classical world, long before the discovery of Snell's law or Fermat's principle of least time.

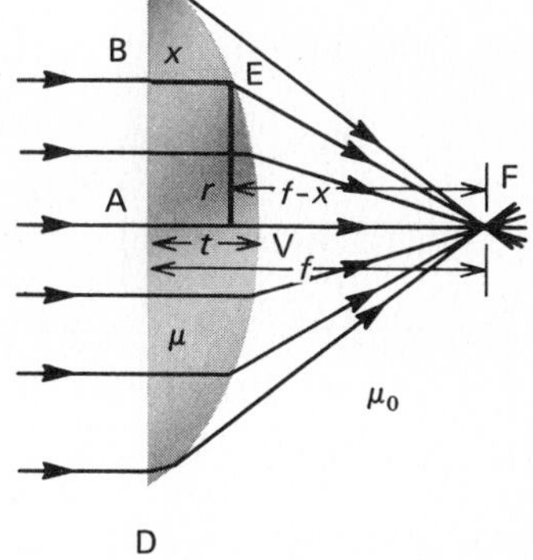

FIG. 13.5 Convergence of initially parallel rays to a focus.

Consider a piece of glass or other transparent material with a cross section shown by the curve ABCVD in Fig. 13.5. Let the index of refraction of the material be μ and that of the surroundings μ_0. Suppose that the surfaces are ***figures of revolution***, i.e., that *all* planes through the ***axis*** AV cut identical cross sections. Assume also for the moment that the left hand face is a plane, but we shall show later that this restriction is not necessary.

Suppose that a bundle of light rays falls on the lens from the left, coming from an object so small and so distant that all the rays are essentially parallel to each other. Suppose also that the lens has been oriented in such a way that the rays are parallel to the axis AV. Since these rays strike the plane surface at normal incidence, they will suffer no refraction at this surface. After passing through the lens, they will be bent away from the normal to the surface, toward the axis of the lens. We now ask whether it is possible to shape the curved surface of the lens so that every ray in the bundle passes through the same spot F, on the axis of the lens.

This problem could be solved by using Snell's law to calculate the angles of refraction, but it is somewhat simpler to do so by applying Fermat's principle (Sec. 12.9). The rays are parallel to each other and perpendicular to the surface, hence each ray has traveled for the same time when it reaches the plane surface of the lens. It then travels through the lens at a speed c/μ. In the case of the ray passing through the point B, this distance is $x =$ BE, and the time taken is $T_1 = x\mu/c$. The ray then must travel along the path EF at a speed c/μ_0, taking a time T_2 to do so. According to Fermat's principle, the total time $T = T_1 + T_2$ must be minimal—it must be less than that taken over any slightly different path. This, in turn, demands that each ray take the *same* time as any other ray. Were this not so, one of two closely neighboring rays could travel from the plane face to F in a lesser time than it takes along its actual path, by changing its path to approximate that of its neighbor.

Before going on with the application of Fermat's principle, it may be worth while to note that the same result—that all rays take the same time to reach the focus F—can be arrived at in another way. If we wish to have the brightest spot that we can obtain at F, it is necessary that all of the rays passing through the lens interfere constructively at that point. This can be achieved only if the paths taken by any two rays differ by 0, 1, 2, 3, ... wavelengths. But no two closely neighboring paths can differ by as much as a single wavelength. They must therefore differ by zero wavelengths and, if this is true for *any* two neighboring paths, it must be true of *all* paths. This requires that the number of wavelengths in the distance BE plus the number of wavelengths in the distance EF must be independent of the distance r of the ray from the axis. Since the wavelength is proportional to the speed of light in the lens, the number of wavelengths along any portion of the path is inversely proportional to the speed, and, therefore, directly proportional to the time taken to traverse that portion of the path. The requirement of constructive interference is exactly equivalent here to that of minimal time.

Let us now take the times of two rays, one of which passes through B at a distance r from the axis. The time taken for it to pass from B to F is

$$\frac{x}{(c/\mu)} + \frac{[(f-x)^2 + r^2]^{1/2}}{(c/\mu_0)}.$$

For a second ray, we may choose the one that passes through A along the axis. The time required for it to travel from A to F is

$$\frac{t}{(c/\mu)} + \frac{f-t}{(c/\mu_0)},$$

where t is the maximal thickness of the lens. Equating the two times, we find that

$$\mu x + \mu_0[(f - x)^2 + r^2]^{1/2} = \mu t + \mu_0 f - \mu_0 t.$$

The equation may be simplified by rearrangement and squaring to give

$$[\mu x - (\mu - \mu_0)t - \mu_0 f]^2 = \mu_0^2(f^2 - 2fx + x^2 + r^2). \qquad (13.2\text{-}1)$$

Were we to solve Eq. (13.2-1) for x, we would then be able to compute the necessary thickness of the lens at various radii r. As may be guessed by the appearance of the equation, the necessary surface is not a simple one. It would be very expensive to grind a piece of glass to such a surface and it would seldom be worth the cost, because the lens would work perfectly only for light coming from an object at essentially infinite distance and then only for light of a given wavelength, since the equation involves μ, which depends on wavelength. Almost all real lenses are made with surfaces that are different enough from ideal so that the rays pass through points close to the focus F, rather than exactly through it.

We can simplify Eq. (13.2-1) greatly by supposing that the lens is *thin*, in the sense that t (and hence x) is much less than either R or f. Most simple lenses satisfy this condition to at least fair accuracy. If we carry out the squaring operation indicated on the left of the equation and then throw away, as negligible, all terms proportional to x^2, t^2, or xt, we arrive at the much simpler equation:

$$-2\mu\mu_0 xf + 2\mu_0(\mu - \mu_0)tf = -2\mu_0^2 fx + \mu_0^2 r^2.$$

This is solved for x to yield

$$x = \frac{-r^2 + 2tf(\mu - \mu_0)/\mu_0}{2f(\mu - \mu_0)/\mu_0} \qquad (13.2\text{-}2)$$

In deriving Eq. (13.2-2), we considered that the rays met the first, plane surface of the lens at normal incidence, so that no refraction took place at this surface.

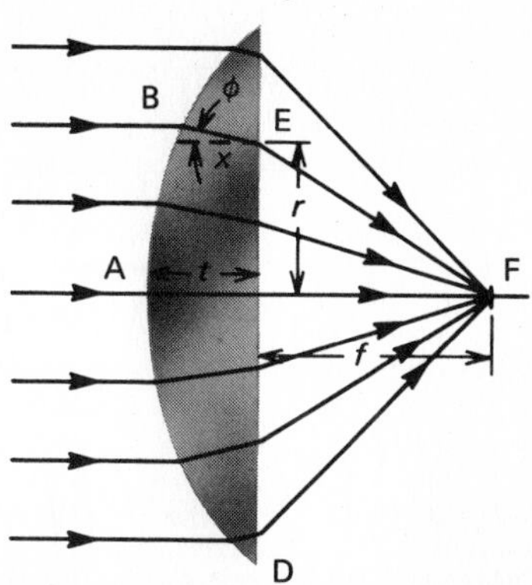

FIG. 13.6 Rays incident on the curved face.

This was done to simplify our first treatment, but it is not a necessary restriction, as we see by considering the lens shown (in cross section) in Fig. 13.6. This is merely the lens of Fig. 13.5 reversed, so that the light impinges on the curved surface and emerges from the plane one. The ray entering at B now is refracted to the path BE. This path clearly is not exactly equal in length to x, the thickness of the lens at distance r from the axis. However, if we limit ourselves to rays that make only a small angle ϕ with the axis, BE is very nearly equal to x, and we approximate the distance that the ray travels within the lens by x.

If the lens were not present, all rays would reach the plane surface after traveling equal distances from the distant object. Under such circumstances the ray that strikes at B would reach that point at a time $x/(c/\mu_0)$ before reaching the plane CD. With the lens in place, the ray takes a time $x/(c/\mu)$ instead, so the delay resulting from the presence of the lens is approximately

$$\frac{x}{(c/\mu)} - \frac{x}{(c/\mu_0)} = \frac{x(\mu - \mu_0)}{c}.$$

The corresponding delay for the ray that strikes at A is

$$\frac{t}{(c/\mu)} - \frac{t}{(c/\mu_0)} = \frac{t(\mu - \mu_0)}{c}.$$

After leaving the lens, the first ray requires a time

$$\frac{\mu_0(f^2 + r^2)^{1/2}}{c}$$

to reach the focus F and the second requires a time $\mu_0 f/c$. Hence the requirement of equal times for the two rays is expressed by the equation

$$(\mu - \mu_0)x + \mu_0(f^2 + r^2)^{1/2} = (\mu - \mu_0)t + \mu_0 f.$$

After this is rearranged, it reads

$$[(\mu - \mu_0)x - (\mu - \mu_0)t - \mu_0 f]^2 = \mu_0^2(f^2 + r^2),$$

and we can perform the squaring operation and neglect all terms proportional to t^2, x^2, or tx as before. When the resulting expression is solved for x, it is found that the result is identical with that given by Eq. (13.2-2). As long as we deal only with rays making small angles with the axis, the way that the thickness of the lens must vary with the distance from the axis to focus the rays at a given distance from the plane face does not depend on which face points toward the source.

13.3 Thin Lenses with Spherical Surfaces

Equation (13.2-2) is that of a parabolic surface, but it approximates that of a sphere if $t \ll r$ and $t \ll f$. To show this, consider the spherical surface of radius R shown in Fig. 13.7. Using the Pythagorean theorem, we find that

$$(R - t + x)^2 = R^2 - r^2.$$

If we again neglect terms in x^2, t^2, and xt, after performing the squaring operation, we obtain

$$2xR - 2Rt = -r^2, \tag{13.3-1}$$

so that

$$x = \frac{-r^2 + 2Rt}{2R}. \tag{13.3-2}$$

This equation for x becomes identical with Eq. (13.2-2) if we set

$$R = f(\mu - \mu_0)/\mu_0. \tag{13.3-3}$$

The point F at which rays that are initially parallel to the axis converge after passing through the lens is called the ***first principal focus*** of the lens. The distance f of this principal focus from the lens is known as the ***focal length*** of the lens. Notice that the focal length depends on the radius of curvature and the indices of refraction of the lens (μ) and of the surrounding medium (μ_0).

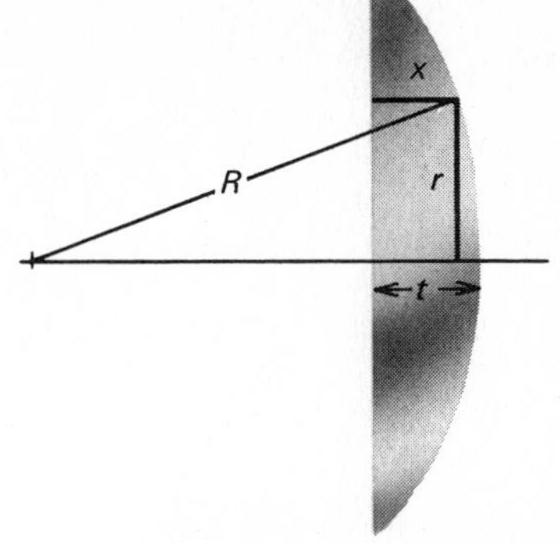

FIG. 13.7 Relation between thickness and distance from the axis.

Nearly all lenses are made with spherical surfaces. The reason is a simple one —such surfaces are easier to grind and polish than any others. If two pieces of glass are separated by an abrasive powder and are rubbed together, each will be ground away and the shape of its surface changed. Suppose that the direction of motion is varied, so that the two pieces move in different relative directions at different times. The surfaces in contact must then take such shapes that one will slide over the other in any direction. This can happen if, and only if, one surface takes the shape of a convex sphere and the other that of a concave sphere of the same radius of curvature.* As the abrasion continues, the radii of curvature will gradually become less. The process just described is basically the one used to grind lenses.

The entire treatment that we have been through above is based on the fact that a lens has a thickness that changes as we go farther from the axis. The light goes more slowly within the lens than it does outside, if the index of refraction of

* Two *plane* surfaces will, of course, slide over each other in any direction. This is not, however, an exception to the general rule stated. A plane is a special case of a sphere, one in which the radius of curvature is infinite.

the lens is greater than that of the surroundings. The resulting delay of the light passing through the thicker parts the of lens must be compensated by a shorter distance from the lens to the focus.

All of the lenses discussed thus far had one spherical and one plane surface. We have seen, however, that the important characteristic of a lens, other than the index of refraction of the material of which it is made, is the way that its thickness varies with the radial distance from the axis. Assuming that the surfaces are spherical, we can show that the thickness varies in the same manner

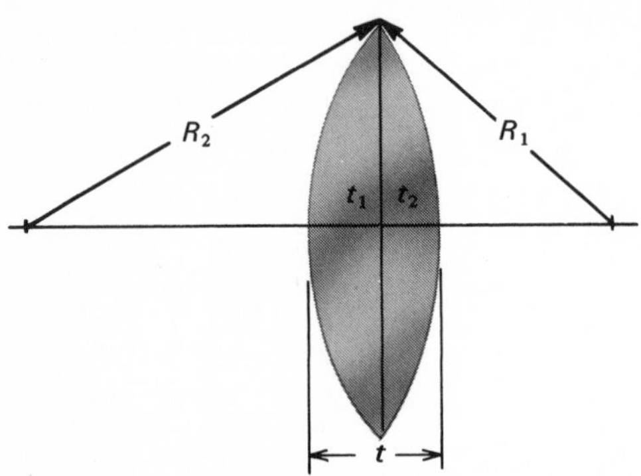

FIG. 13.8 Double convex lens.

whether one or both surfaces are spherical. Consider the ***double-convex lens*** whose cross section is shown in Fig. 13.8. This lens is exactly equivalent to two ***plano-convex lenses*** joined on their plane faces. According to Eq. (13.3-2), these two lenses have thicknesses at distance r from the axis equal to

$$x_1 = t_1 - \frac{r^2}{2R_1} \qquad \text{and} \qquad x_2 = t_2 - \frac{r^2}{2R_2}.$$

Hence the thickness is

$$x = x_1 + x_2 = t_1 + t_2 - \frac{r^2}{2}\left(\frac{1}{R_1} + \frac{1}{R_2}\right) = t + \frac{r^2}{2}\left(\frac{1}{R_1} + \frac{1}{R_2}\right). \tag{13.3-4}$$

We see that Eq. (13.3-4) is exactly equivalent to Eq. (13.3-2) if $1/R$ in the latter is replaced by $(1/R_1) + (1/R_2)$. Hence the focal length of the double convex lens is given by Eq. (13.3-3) as

$$\frac{1}{f} = \left(\frac{\mu - \mu_0}{\mu_0}\right)\left(\frac{1}{R_1} + \frac{1}{R_2}\right), \tag{13.3-5}$$

where R_1 and R_2 are the radii of curvature of the two faces. Notice that Eqs. (13.3-2) and (13.3-3) are special cases of Eqs. (13.3-4) and (13.3-5), obtained if we set one of the two radii equal to infinity, the radius of a plane surface.

A somewhat more revealing form of the equation for the focal length of a double convex lens is obtained if we express the latter in terms of the difference between the maximal and minimal thicknesses of the lens. Suppose that the diameter of the lens is $2r_0$, as shown in Fig. 13.9, that the thickness at the center is t, and that the thickness at the outer edge is t_0. Replacement of x by t_0 and of r by r_0 in Eq. (13.3-4) and substitution of the value of f from Eq. (13.3-5) to eliminate R_1 an R_2 gives

$$f = \frac{\mu_0 r_0^2}{2(\mu - \mu_0)(t - t_0)}. \tag{13.3-6}$$

We have dealt thus far with double convex lenses whose index of refraction (μ) is greater than that (μ_0) of the surroundings. Suppose that any of the lenses of Figs. 13.5–13.9 had $\mu < \mu_0$, or that the lens with $\mu > \mu_0$ were ***double concave***, as shown in Fig. 13.10a. Then Eq. (13.3-6) would show the focal length to be negative. What does this result mean?

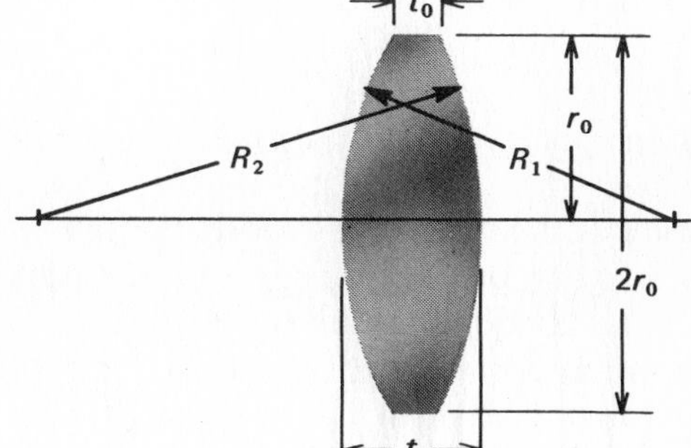

FIG. 13.9 Double convex lens with finite thickness at edge.

Let us return for the moment to our treatment of the lens in terms of Fermat's principle. In the double concave lens, the ray striking the lens at A must pass through a greater thickness of the lens than the ray that strikes it at C. Hence the ray at C must travel a longer path in the medium outside of the lens than the ray at A, to take an equal time over the whole path. Since this is an opposite state of affairs from that encountered in the double convex lens, we might anticipate that the initially parallel rays would diverge (i.e., bend away from the axis) instead of converging as they did before.

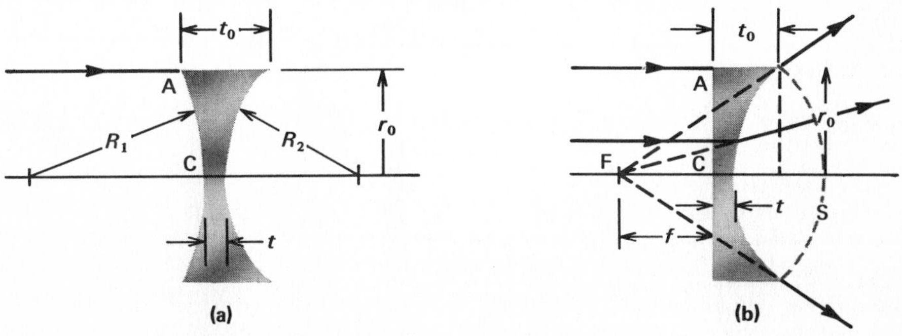

FIG. 13.10 Diverging lens.

To check on this assumption, suppose that the initially parallel rays, after passing through the lens, appear to be diverging from a common point F. Then the rays that strike the lens at A and C should reach the sphere S, centered at F, at the same time. The radius of this sphere is clearly equal to $[(f+t_0)^2+r_0{}^2]^{1/2}$. The ray striking at A takes a time

$$t_A = \mu t_0/c$$

to travel from the point of its first contact with the lens to the point at which it reaches the sphere. On the other hand, the ray striking at C requires a time

$$t_C = \frac{\mu t + \mu_0\{[(f+t_0)^2+r_0{}^2]^{1/2} - f - t\}}{c}$$

to travel from C to the sphere. When we equate t_A and t_C, neglect terms in t^2 and $t_0{}^2$, and solve for f, we find that Eq. (13.3-6) is satisfied. A lens of negative focal length refracts rays that are initially parallel to the axis in such a way that they appear to be diverging from the first principal focus, which is on the side of the lens that the light reaches first. Such a lens is often called a ***diverging lens***, in contrast to a ***converging lens***, which has a positive focal length and whose first principal focus is on the opposite side of the lens from the object.

The image of the infinitely distant object formed at F by a diverging lens is called a ***virtual image*** because the refracted rays do not actually pass through it as they do through the ***real image*** formed by a converging lens—they merely travel in such directions that they appear to be diverging from the image.

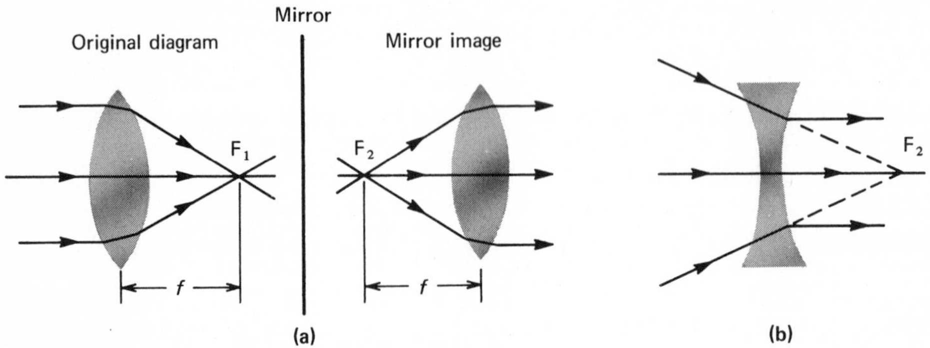

FIG. 13.11 Positions of principal foci.

If we consider the mirror image of any of the ray diagrams that we have discussed, as shown in Fig. 13.11a, all ray paths in the mirror image will have the same lengths as in the original diagram. It follows that rays diverging from the ***second principal focus***, which is a point on the axis at a distance f from a thin lens but on the opposite side of the lens from the first principal focus, will be refracted by a converging lens in such a way that they travel parallel to the axis after passing through the lens. Similarly, rays that are converging toward the second principal focus of a diverging lens will travel parallel to the axis after refraction (see Fig. 13.11b).

EXERCISES

13.3-1 Suppose that the lens of Fig. 13.5 is made of a transparent material having an index of refraction μ that is *less* than that μ_0 of the surroundings (e.g., the surroundings might be ice and the lens a cavity within the ice). Show, by direct application of Fermat's principle and with the approximations that the lens is thin and that all rays make only small angles with the axis, that the first principal focus is to the left of the lens and that the focal length is given correctly by Eq. (13.3-3).

13.3-2 It was suggested in Sec. 13.2 that the properties of lenses could be derived on the basis of the laws of refraction, rather than by the use of Fermat's principle. Consider the ray passing through B and E in Fig. 13.5. Suppose the surface CEVD to be spherical, of radius R. By considering the refraction of the ray at E, and by considering all angles to be small enough that each angle is equal to its sine, compute the position of the first principal focus F. (Hint: Draw the line from the center of curvature of the surface to E. This is the normal to the surface at E.)

13.4 *Images of Point Objects*

We have dealt thus far only with point objects on the axis of a lens, either at infinite distance from the lens or located at a principal focus. We now need to consider a more general case. What happens, after refraction by a lens, to the rays that originate from a single point located anywhere in space? Consider, for example, a point object at O in the system shown in Fig. 13.12. Are all the rays

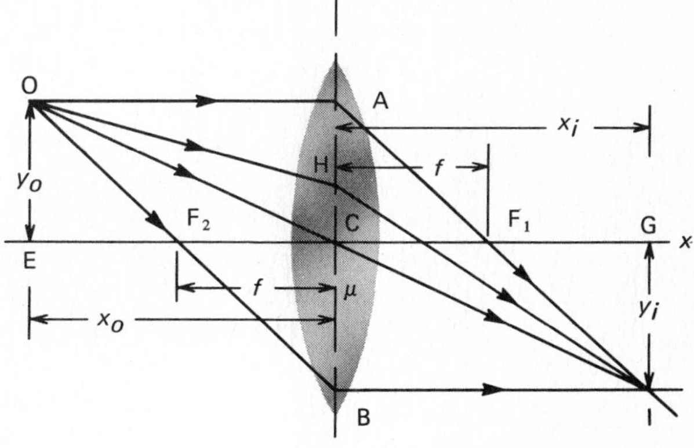

FIG. 13.12 All rays from an object point pass through the same image point.

starting from this point so refracted that they pass through (or at least very close to) some image point I? If so, it will be possible for the lens to form an image of any object, with each point of the image corresponding to a particular point of the object.

If the image point I does exist at all, it is easy to find its location. We know that the ray OA, initially traveling parallel to the axis, will be refracted so as to pass through the first principal focus F_1. Similarly, ray OB, which passes through the second principal focus F_2, cannot be distinguished from a ray starting from that point, so it will be parallel to the axis after refraction. We shall suppose, as before, that the lens is so thin that we can neglect its thickness in comparison with the distances x_o and x_i of the object and image points from it. By the similarity of triangles AF_1C and AIB, we find that the distance y_i of I from the axis is related to that of O from the axis:

$$\frac{y_o}{f}=\frac{y_o+y_i}{x_i}.$$

Also, from the similarity of triangles BF_2C and BOA, we have

$$\frac{y_i}{f}=\frac{y_o+y_i}{x_o}.$$

We may solve the second of these equations for

$$y_i=\frac{fy_o}{x_o-f} \tag{13.4-1}$$

and substitute this value into the first equation to get

$$x_i=\frac{fx_o}{x_o-f}. \tag{13.4-2}$$

Finally, we find the ratio

$$\frac{y_i}{x_i}=\frac{y_o}{x_o}. \tag{13.4-3}$$

The equality of the two ratios tells us that the triangles OCE and ICG are similar, so point I must lie on the line drawn from O through the center of the lens C.

We now ask whether any other ray, such as OH, will be refracted so as to pass through I. In other words, does ray OHI take the same time to travel from O to I as does ray OAI? That this is *possible* can be seen quite easily. The part of the path OAI that is in the medium of index μ_0 is obviously shorter than is the corresponding part of the path OHI. On the other hand, the path OHI travels through a greater thickness of the lens (of index μ) than does OAI. We shall not bother to go through the algebra necessary for a quantitative check, but a calculation of the travel times does show them to be the same, to the accuracy of the approximations we used in Secs. 13.2 and 13.3 (thickness of lens much less than f, x_o, or x_i and rays making only small angles with the axis). We may therefore conclude that to any object point, such as O, there corresponds an image point I, at a location specified by Eqs. (13.4-1), (13.4-2), and (13.4-3). The rays starting from O do not pass exactly through I, but they do pass very close to it (cf. Sec. 13.8).

13.5 Formation of Extended Images

We are now in a position to determine what kind of an image of an extended object, such as the arrow AB in Fig. 13.13, will be produced by a thin lens. From any point off the axis, such as A, we can draw any two of the three

principal rays, AMA′ (initially parallel to the axis and refracted through the first principal focus F_1), ANA′ (through the second principal focus F_2, and refracted to be parallel to the axis), and ALA′ (through the center of the lens). Their intersection locates the image A′ of A. The same construction cannot be used for a point on the axis, because the three principal rays coincide, but the fact that y_0 does not appear in Eq. (13.4-2) tells us that the distance of the image point from the lens is the same whether the object point is on the axis or off it. Hence the image B′ of B can be located by drawing the line A′B′ perpendicular to the axis from B′.

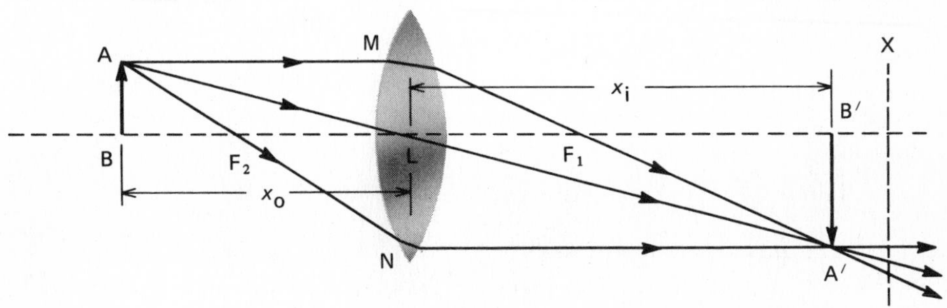

FIG. 13.13 Image of an extended object.

Notice that Eq. (13.4-2) tells us that the image of a plane object perpendicular to the axis will also lie in a plane perpendicular to the axis. It is this fact that makes it possible to focus a camera lens on a plane photographic film or plate or to focus a slide or film projector on a plane screen. When a three-dimensional scene is being photographed, light rays coming from two fixed points at different distances from the camera will not both be focused to points in the plane of the film. Thus, were the camera focused on an object slightly nearer than AB in Fig. 13.13, the film would be in a plane such as that indicated at X. Rays from point A would not converge to a point in this plane, but rather to a small spot, the intersection of the cone of rays with the plane of the film. The size of this spot depends both on the distance of the focus from the film and on the angle between the extreme rays that come from opposite edges of the lens. The spot is therefore most tolerable if a lens of small diameter is used. This is the reason that one "stops down" a lens to produce sharp images of three-dimensional objects.

Equation (13.4-2) may be put into a more easily remembered form:

$$\frac{1}{x_o}+\frac{1}{x_i}=\frac{1}{f}, \tag{13.5-1}$$

which is sometimes known as the ***Gaussian lens equation.*** It is named for Karl Friedrich Gauss (1777–1855), who developed the theory of thin lenses to the same approximations that we have used. Equation (13.5-1) may be used for any thin lens to find the image position for a known object position. It is necessary, however, that one be very careful about signs. According to one convention, object distances (x_o) are positive if the object is on the left of the lens and negative if it is on the right. The opposite signs are used for image distances. Converging lenses have positive f; diverging lenses have negative f. Because of the complications of the needed sign conventions, it is suggested that image positions be found by sketching ray diagrams similar to Fig. 13.13 and then using the properties of similar triangles, as was done in Sec. 13.4.

13.6 *Magnification*

One of the useful properties of lenses, which will be immediately apparent from a careful examination of Fig. 13.13, is that the image and the object are generally not of the same size. Since the triangles ABL and A′B′L are similar, it follows that

$$\mathrm{A'B'/AB} = -x_i/x_o,$$

where the minus sign indicates the inversion of the image. As the object is moved closer and closer to the principal focus F_2, the image moves farther from the lens, and the ratio of the image size to the object size increases. This ratio is known as the ***lateral magnification***, and it is expressed by

$$M = -x_i/x_o. \tag{13.6-1}$$

The reader will be able to verify the fact that the magnification of a lens of the type shown in Fig. 13.13 varies from zero, when the object is at infinite distance, to minus infinity, when the object is at principal focus.

Not only are distances transverse to the axis magnified or diminished by the action of a lens, but distances along the axis are similarly affected. Suppose that an object of thickness Δx_o along the axis is imaged by a lens, as shown in Fig. 13.14. The front face of the object is focused at a distance x_i from the lens, given by Eq. (13.5-1);

$$1/x_o + 1/x_i = 1/f. \tag{13.6-2}$$

Correspondingly, the rear face of the object will be focused at a distance $x_i + \Delta x_i$ from the lens, where

$$1/(x_o + \Delta x_o) + 1/(x_i + \Delta x_i) = 1/f. \tag{13.6-3}$$

By eliminating f from these two equations we can prove that the ***axial magnification*** is

$$M_a = \Delta x_i/\Delta x_o = -x_i^2/x_o^2 = -M^2. \tag{13.6-4}$$

We omit the derivation here and indicate two methods for carrying it out in Exs. 13.6-5 and 13.6-6.

Since the axial and the lateral magnifications are not the same, except in the special case of $M^2 = 1$, it follows that a lens cannot produce an undistorted three-dimensional image of a three-dimensional object. This is not a severe limitation, however, since two-dimensional images are ordinarily all that we require of lenses.

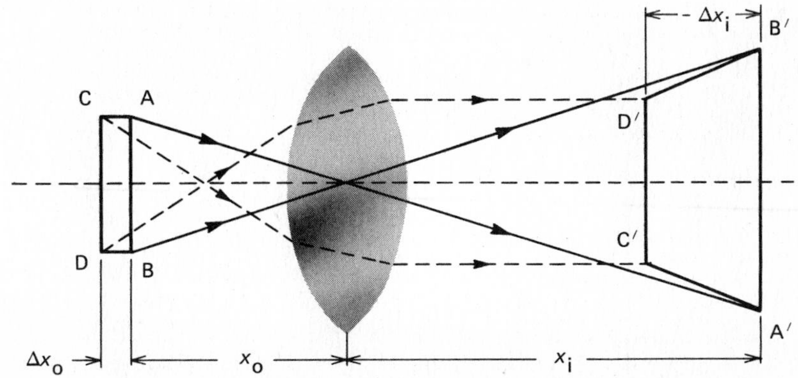

FIG. 13.14 Axial magnification.

Illustrative Example

A slide projector uses slides whose area (inside the masking or frame) is 2.75 in. × 3.25 in. It uses a thin lens of focal length 16.0 in. The distance from the lens to the screen on which the image is shown is 40 ft. What are the dimensions of the smallest screen that must be used?

To answer this question, we need to know the lateral magnification [Eq. (13.6-1)]. To find this, in turn, we need to know the distance from the lens to the slide (the object), as well as the given distance from the lens to the image. We start with a diagram like that shown in Fig. 13.12, letting f be 16.0 in. and letting y_o be half the slide height, equal to 1.625 in. We see at once that triangles OF_2E and BF_2C are similar. Also the distance BC $= y_i$, so

$$(y_i/y_o) = f/(x_o - f).$$

Triangles OCE and ICG are also similar, so we obtain a second expression for the ratio

$$(y_i/y_o) = (x_i/x_o).$$

Equating the two ratios, we may solve for the unknown x_o:

$$x_o = \frac{fx_i}{x_i - f}.$$

We could substitute in this equation to find that $x_o = 16.5$ in., but we can save time and gain accuracy by avoiding this step. Substituting the algebraic expression for x_o into the first equation for y_i/y_o, we find

$$\frac{y_i}{y_o} = \frac{f}{fx_i/(x_i - f)} = \frac{x_i - f}{f}.$$

Substitution of the values of x_i and f gives

$$\frac{y_i}{y_o} = \frac{464 \text{ in.}}{16.0 \text{ in.}} = 29.0.$$

The image has linear dimensions that are 29.0 times those of the object. Hence the minimal height of the screen is

$$29.0 \times 2.75 \text{ in.} = 79.8 \text{ in.},$$

and the minimal width is

$$29.0 \times 3.25 \text{ in.} = 94.2 \text{ in.}$$

EXERCISES

13.6-1 A lens is to be used to form a real image of a motion picture film on a screen which is 20 m away from the film. A single picture on the film is 24 mm × 35 mm and the image on the screen is to be 3.6 m × 5.0 m. What must be the focal length of the lens?

13.6-2 A small rectangular box, of dimensions 2 cm × 3 cm × 5 cm, is arranged with its shortest dimension parallel to the axis of a lens with a focal length of 10 cm. The distance from the front of the box to the lens is 40 cm. A screen is set up on the opposite side of the lens and is adjusted until a sharp image of the front of the box is obtained on it. What must be the position of this screen?

13.6-3 It is desired to move the lens of Ex. 13.6-2 to such a position that the back face of the box will be focused on the screen, neither the box nor the screen having been moved. How far and in what direction must the lens be moved to accomplish this?

13.6-4 The distance $X_o = x_o - f$ is the distance of the object from the second principal focus, and $X_i = x_i - f$ is the distance of the image from the first principal focus. Prove that

$$X_o = \frac{x_o^2}{x_o + x_i},$$

that

$$X_i = \frac{x_i^2}{x_o + x_i},$$

and that

$$X_o X_i = f^2. \tag{13.6-5}$$

This is known as the ***Newtonian form of the lens equation.***

13.6-5 By considering an object at $(X_o + \Delta X_o)$ and an image at $(X_i + \Delta X_i)$, prove that the axial magnification in the Newtonian form is given by

$$M_a = \Delta x_i/\Delta x_o = \Delta X_i/\Delta X_o = -X_i/X_o \tag{13.6-6}$$

and hence prove Eq. (13.6-4).

13.6-6 In Eq. (13.6-3), write $1/(x_o + \Delta x_o)$ in the form

$$(1/x_o)(1 + \Delta x_o/x_o)^{-1}$$

and apply Eq. (H.1) of Appendix H ($m = -1$), assuming $\Delta x_o / x_o \ll 1$. Carry out a similar manipulation on the term in x_i. Hence eliminate $1/f$ between Eq. (13.6-2) and the rewritten form of Eq. (13.6-3) and so prove Eq. (13.6-4).

13.6-7 An object is placed at a distance equal to twice the focal length to the left of the lens similar to that shown in Fig. 13.13. Show that the lateral magnification is minus one and locate the image.

13.7 Virtual Objects

When the light from one lens falls on a second lens, the image formed by the first lens may act as an object for the second lens, which will then form a second image. In Fig. 13.15, in which we have primed all symbols associated with the

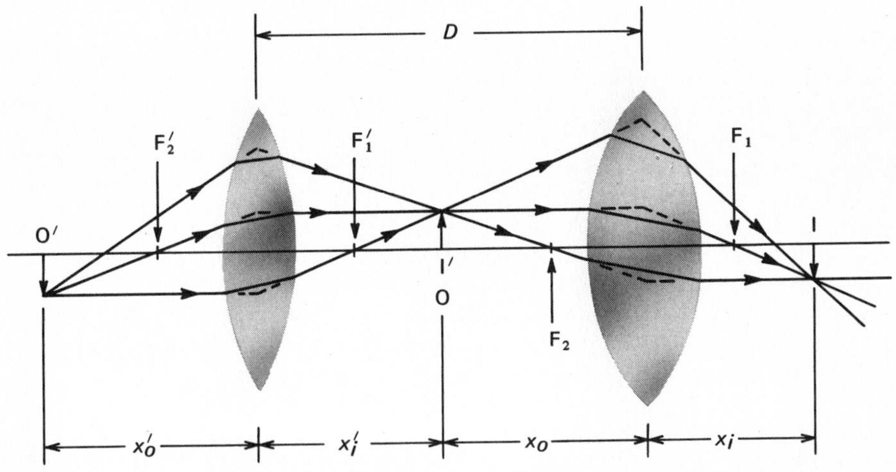

FIG. 13.15 Image formation by two lenses.

first lens and have used unprimed symbols for the second, the object O′ is imaged at I′. This image can also be labeled O, since it is the object for the second lens, which will image it at I. If the separation of the lenses is D, it is clear that

$$X_o = D - X_{i'},$$

and Eq. (13.6-2) can be used to calculate the position of I. Alternatively, a ray diagram similar to Fig. 13.15 may be *sketched* and similar triangles used to calculate the position of the final image.

An interesting case occurs when the second lens is located closer to the first and D is less than x_i', that is, the formation of the real image I′ is prevented by the fact that the lens L intercepts the light before this can take place. In this case the image I′ still acts as an object for the second lens. The construction of the image for such a virtual object is clear from Fig. 13.16. As illustrated by this case, a ***virtual object*** is one toward each point of which rays are converging before they meet the lens.

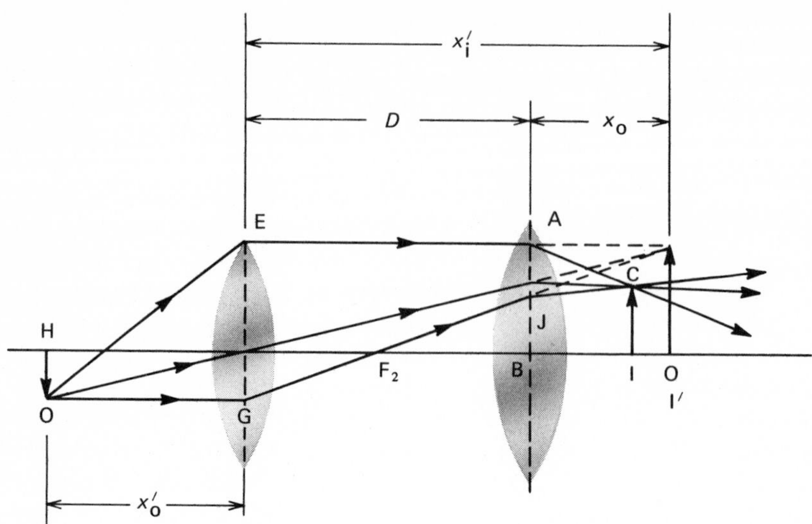

FIG. 13.16 Virtual object.

EXERCISES

13.7-1 Two lenses, each of focal length $f = 20$ cm, are located so that they have a common axis. They are 100 cm apart. An object O is placed at a distance of 40 cm to the left of the first lens. Sketch a ray diagram and calculate the following:

(a) the position of the image I formed by the first lens;

(b) the position of the image I′ formed by the second lens, the object being I:

(c) the lateral magnification produced by each lens and the lateral magnification produced by the system of two lenses (i.e., the ratio of the size of I′ to that of O).

(d) Is the image I produced by the first lens real or virtual? Is it erect or inverted with respect to O? Is this image a real or a virtual object for the second lens? Is the final image I′ real or virtual? Is it erect or inverted with respect to O?

13.7-2 Repeat Ex. 13.7-1, keeping all conditions the same *except* that the distance between the lenses is 20 cm.

13.7-3 Show that a thin convergent lens produces a virtual image of an object placed between the second principal focus and the lens. If the object is at a distance $x_o = -f/2$ from the lens, what will be the position of the image? What will the lateral magnification be?

13.7-4 A thin divergent lens has a virtual object at a position two-thirds of the distance from the lens to the second principal focus. Where will the image be formed? Will the image be virtual or real? Inverted or erect? Enlarged or diminished?

13.8 Defects of Lenses

All of the properties of lenses that we have deduced have resulted from approximate formulae. In particular, we have made three assumptions, none of which is exactly true for real lenses:

1. That all angles of incidence and refraction and of the various rays with the axis are so small that the sines and tangents of these angles are proportional to each other and to the angles.
2. That the thickness of the lens may be neglected as compared with the object and image distances and the radii of curvature.
3. That the relative index of refraction between the lens and its surroundings is independent of the wavelength (or photon momentum) of the light.

Since it is impossible to construct lenses that satisfy these conditions perfectly, all lenses that can be made produce somewhat imperfect images. The imperfections of the images are known as ***aberrations***. While these aberrations are generally small, they are important when a detailed correspondence between the image and object is desired, as in the microscope, the astronomical telescope, or the camera. Fortunately, it is often possible, when the purpose of a lens is known, to combine two or more lenses in such a way that the error in image formation resulting from one lens compensates the error resulting from the other. For example, the ***chromatic aberration*** that results from the dependence of index of refraction on color may be partially overcome by combining two or three lenses of different glasses to do the work of a single lens.

A common defect of lenses, known as ***spherical aberration***, results from the fact that the spherical surfaces demanded by practicality are only approximations to the ideal surfaces demanded by relations similar to Eq. (13.2-1). The smaller the surface of a lens of given focal length, the more closely can the desired surface be approximated by a spherical one. Hence spherical aberration can be reduced by "stopping down" the lens, i.e., by allowing light to pass through only a portion of it, near the axis. As we saw in Sec. 13.5, stopping down the lens also increases the ***depth of focus***, i.e., the range of object distances than can be tolerated without too much blurring of the image.

Other lens defects, such as curvature of the focal plane, ***astigmatism*** (the imaging of a point as a short line segment), and ***coma*** (a distortion of the image for objects not on the axis of the lens), are always present, but they may be reduced by a careful design that uses a combination of two or more lenses whose individual aberrations compensate. The design of lenses to reduce aberrations to a minimum under specific conditions requires detailed tracing of the exact ray paths and, while tedious, involves no new principles beyond those we have studied. Further, the resulting complex lenses are essentially equivalent to idealized thin lenses of the type we have discussed. We shall therefore not discuss lens design in further detail but shall treat the lenses which we shall have occasion to discuss as if they were perfect thin lenses.

EXERCISES

13.8-1 Show that a thin convergent lens produces a virtual image of an object placed between the second principal focus and the lens. If the object is at a distance $x_0 = f/2$, what will be the position of the image? What will the lateral magnification be?

13.8-2 A thin divergent lens has a virtual object at a position $\frac{2}{3}$ of the distance from the lens to the second principal focus. Where will the image be formed? Will the image be virtual or real? Inverted or erect? Enlarged or diminished?

13.9 The Camera

One of the simplest of all optical instruments is the ***camera***, the essential parts of which are a convergent lens, or system of lenses, and a screen. The lens is usually located in an opening in one end of a light-tight box (Fig. 13.17). At the other end of the box is placed a screen upon which the lens forms a real image.

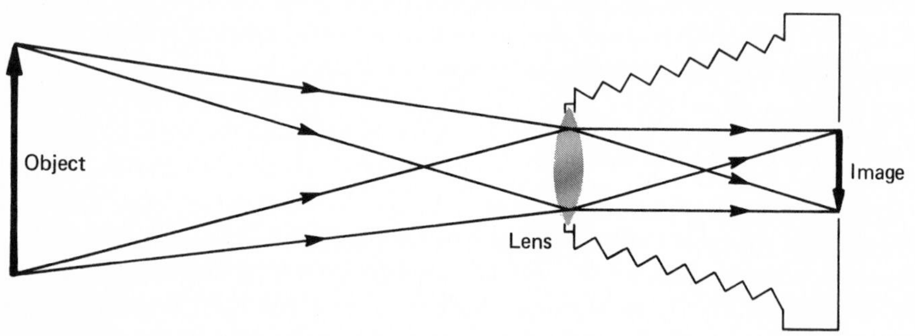

FIG. 13.17 The camera.

Some mechanism is usually provided to move the lens back and forth in order that the image may be sharply focused on the screen, and a shutter is provided to open and close the lens opening. If the image is to be recorded, the screen is replaced by a sensitive film or plate. On this film or plate is a thin gelatin emulsion in which is embedded a large number of microscopic grains of silver chloride and silver bromide. When the light strikes the emulsion, the photons remove electrons from the grains through the photoelectric effect (Chapter 24), and the chemical nature of the grains which have been struck is altered by the loss of electrons. When the film or plate is treated by a chemical reagent called a developer, those grains which have been illuminated are reduced to metallic silver, while those grains which have not been struck are unaffected. A fixing solution then dissolves out the unaffected grains. The result is a negative picture in which the parts that have been illuminated are blackened by the presence of the silver, and those parts that have been in the dark are left clear. The negative is then reversed by the familiar process of printing.

The amount of blackening produced at any point on the film depends on the amount of light reaching that point during the exposure. The greater the diameter of the lens for a given focal length, the more light will the lens collect and focus on the film, under a given set of conditions. It can be shown by simple geometry that the same blackening will be produced, other things being equal, by two lenses with the same ratio of focal length to diameter. This ratio is called the ***speed***, or the ***f-number***, of the lens. As the *f*-number of the lens is reduced, the same pictures can be taken with shorter exposures, but the lens must also become more complicated and expensive in order to reduce the aberrations which result from the larger angles between the various rays and the axis.

Almost all cameras are equipped with a ***diaphragm***, which is simply an opening of adustable diameter placed before or behind the camera lens. The purpose of this diaphragm is merely to increase the effective *f*-number of the lens. Two reasons make it necessary to do this. One is to reduce the speed of the lens when the illumination is so high that the shutter cannot be made to give a short enough exposure. The other is often more important, having to do with spherical aberration, and this has been discussed in Secs. 13.5 and 13.7. For a still object, such as a building, it is almost always better to use a large *f*-number and a long exposure than a small *f*-number and a short exposure, since the lens will be much freer of errors in the former case.

13.10 The Eye as a Camera

Perhaps the most remarkable camera known is the human eye. The analogy between the eye and the simple camera will be clear from a comparison of the schematic cross section of the eye shown in Fig. 13.18 with the diagram of a camera in Fig. 13.17. In the eye the lens L receives light which has entered through the cornea C. Both the lens and the front curved surface of the cornea refract the rays to focus them on the retina R. The end organs on the retina are excited by the light and send impulses through the fibers of the optic nerve N to the brain.

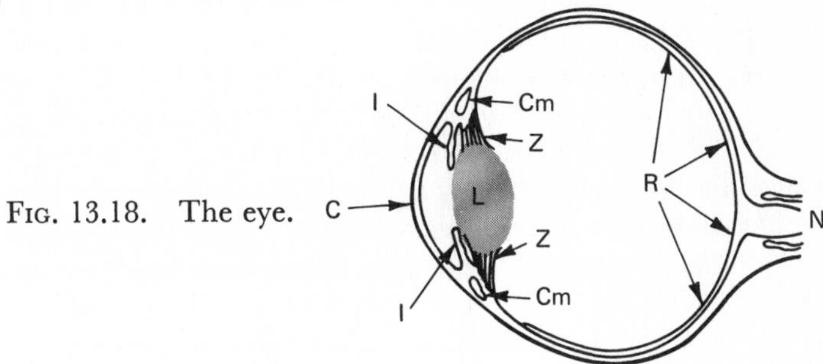

Fig. 13.18. The eye.

The iris (I in Fig. 13.18) is a diaphragm which changes the effective diameter of the lens, adjusting the amount of light that falls on the retina. This variable opening in the iris is called the pupil (cf. Sec. 13.1). In very dim light the iris may open to a pupil diameter of as much as 8 mm; in bright light it may contract the pupil to a diameter of about 2 mm. Since the amount of light admitted depends on the area of the pupil, this corresponds to a variation of 16 times in the sensitivity of the eye.

One of the major differences between the eye and the camera is the way in which focusing is accomplished. Instead of using a lens of fixed focal length and varying the distance between it and the image, the eye keeps this distance very nearly constant and changes the focal length of the lens. The lens L is a body of highly refractive elastic material. When it is freed from its attachment to the eye it takes a spherical shape. The lens is attached to the wall of the eyeball by a large number of radial fibers called the zonula (Z). The internal pressure of the fluid within the eyeball is considerably greater than that of fluids in the rest of the body, so that the wall of the eyeball is under tension. This tension is communicated to the lens by the zonula, and the lens L is kept in a flattened form which is its normal shape in the eye. In this state the lens has its largest radii of curvature and can focus distant objects on the retina R. The zonula is surrounded by a ring of muscle called the ciliary muscle Cm. When this muscle is contracted, it relieves the tension on the zonula fibers and hence on the lens, which takes a more nearly spherical shape. Its radii of curvature therefore decrease and the focal length of the lens decreases, enabling the eye to focus nearby objects. The relaxed state of the normal eye is that in which distant objects are focused. By the variation of the focal length of its lens the eye can adjust itself to produce nearly perfect images of an object which lies anywhere between an infinite distance and a location known as the ***near point***, which is usually a few inches from the cornea. As an object is moved toward the eye, the size of the image on the retina increases and more detail can be observed, provided that the eye can continue to focus the light rays from the object. It would therefore appear that the most detailed examination could be accomplished when the object was at the near point. Actually the strain required to keep the eye focused at this distance is sufficiently great so that a better examination of the object can usually be accomplished at a slightly greater distance. This distance, which is called the ***normal reading distance***, varies among individuals, but averages about 25 cm for normal adults in the age range 20–40 years.

13.11 Oculars

The human eye is a remarkably versatile optical instrument, but it is subject to limitations and defects. These can frequently be remedied, in part at least, by appropriate lenses, which, when used in positions close to the eye, are known as ***oculars***.

The most commonly used oculars are spectacle lenses, used to correct abnormalities in vision. For example, an eye that cannot focus on close objects may be aided by a convergent lens which produces magnified virtual images of close objects, and so makes such objects appear to be at a more distant position than that which they really occupy. Similarly, an eye that is focused on a nearby object instead of one at infinity when it is in its relaxed state requires a divergent lens which will produce a virtual image of a distant object at the location at which it can be focused by the eye. Examples of the lenses required in such cases will be furnished by Exs. 13.11-1 to 13.11-3.

Even the normal eye occasionally needs help, and one of the most common uses of the eye lens is a ***magnifier***, used for the detailed examination of nearby objects. If an object, at a distance of less than the focal length of a convergent lens, is viewed through the lens as shown in Fig. 13.19, an enlarged, erect, and virtual image of the object will be formed. Since the best position of this image for detailed examination is at the normal reading distance, we should adjust the position of the object so that the image will be formed at the normal reading distance from the eye, which we may denote by d_n. If the lens is held close to the eye, as it usually is, the image distance x_i will be very closely equal to d_n. Substitution of this value into Eq. (13.5-1) shows that

$$x_o = d_n f/(d_n + f). \tag{13.11-1}$$

The lateral magnification is given by Eq. (13.6-1) as

$$M = -x_i/x_o = (d_n/f) + 1. \tag{13.11-2}$$

If the focal length of the lens is considerably less than d_n, x_o will be very slightly less than f. The object must therefore be placed just inside the second principal focus, as shown in Fig. 13.19, and the magnification will be large. This is the customary way in which magnifying lenses are used.

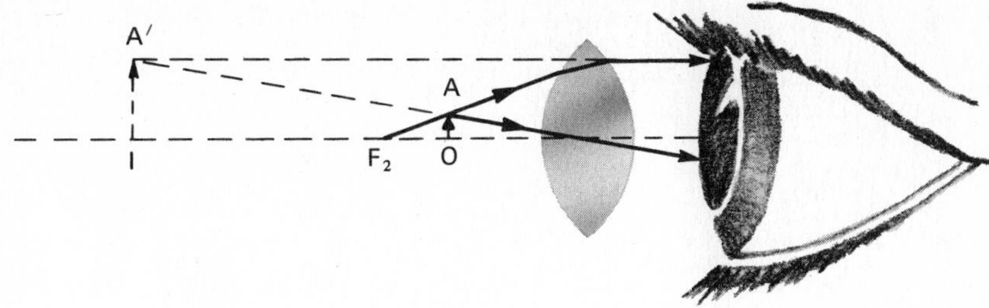

FIG. 13.19 Ocular used as a magnifier.

Many oculars are constructed of two or more lenses, in order to reduce aberrations, but we shall not concern ourselves here with these compound oculars (however, see Prob. 13.6).

EXERCISES

13.11-1 The near point of a defective eye has receded to 2.00 m. What will be the focal length of the eye glass necessary to enable such an eye to examine objects at the normal reading distance?

13.11-2 An eye with a far point of 5.00 m is to be corrected. What focal length should an eyeglass have in order to bring objects at infinity within the range of this eye?

13.11-3 The far point of an eye is at infinity and the near point is at 1.00 m. If a lens that brings the near point to 0.20 m is used, what will happen to the far point?

13.11-4 A simple magnifier of the type shown in Fig. 13.19 gives a magnification of 6.0 for a normal eye. What will be its magnification if used with the uncorrected eye of Ex. 13.11-3? (Assume that the lens is adjusted to produce the image at the near point of the abnormal eye.)

13.11-5 Show that, if a divergent lens is used close to the eye to view a real object, it acts as a reducing lens.

13.11-6 Calculate the magnifying power M of a single convergent lens of focal length f, if the lens is placed at a distance d from the eye instead of close to it. Assume that the image viewed by the eye is at the normal reading distance of 25 cm and is virtual.

13.12 The Microscope

The simplest microscope, of course, is the single eye-lens of Fig. 13.19. The magnification that can be attained by such an instrument is relatively small, and it is subject to many errors. The ***compound microscope*** consists of two parts, an ***objective*** and an ***ocular***, each of which may be either a single lens or a system of lenses. Both of these systems are usually convergent. The simplest compound microscope, in which the objective has a focal length f_1 and the ocular has a focal length f_2, is illustrated in Fig. 13.20. The object is located at a distance

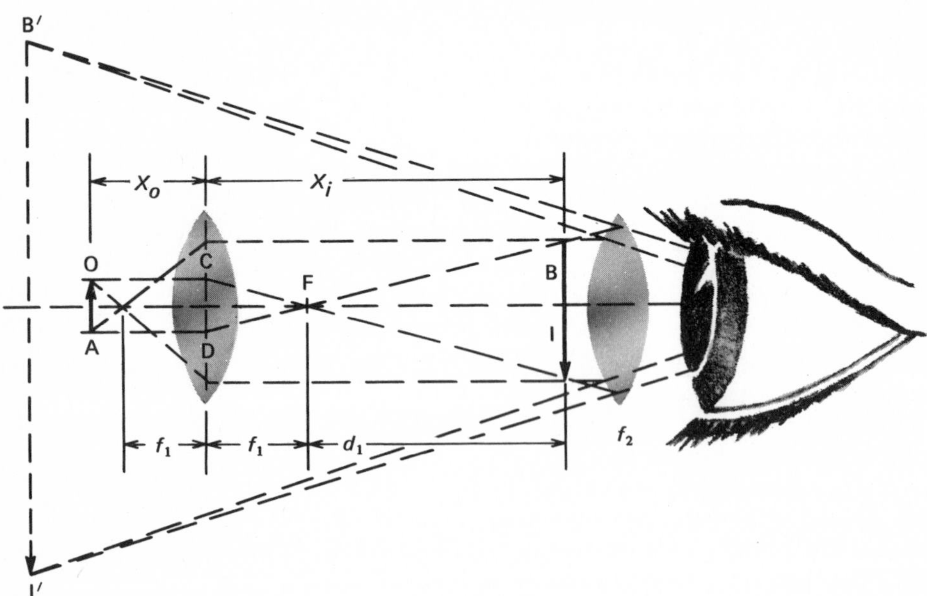

FIG. 13.20 The compound microscope.

slightly greater than f_1 from the objective and forms an inverted, enlarged, real image at BI. The distance x_i from the objective is $(f_1 + d_1)$ where d_1 is a constant for a given microscope, known as the ***optical tube length***, and is equal to the distance from the first principal focus of the objective to the image BI. Most commercially available microscopes are designed for use with $d_1 = 18$ cm. From the similarity of the triangles CFD and IFB, it is seen that the magnification of the objective is

$$M_1 = -d_1/f_1. \qquad (13.12\text{-}1)$$

The value of this magnification, disregarding the minus sign, is usually marked on the lens mount by the manufacturer as, say, $30\times$.

The image BI is viewed through an ocular in the same manner that an object is seen through a magnifier (Sec. 13.11), i.e., a virtual image B′I′ is formed at the normal reading distance d_n. According to Eq. (13.11-2) the magnification M_2 of the ocular is

$$M_2 = (d_n/f_2) + 1, \tag{13.12-2}$$

so that the overall magnification is

$$M = M_1 M_2 = -(d_1/f_1)(d_n/f_2 + 1). \tag{13.12-3}$$

It would appear from this formula that by making f_1 and f_2 sufficiently small we could obtain any magnification, however large, with a microscope. Actually, however, the useful magnification is limited by the diffraction that results from the light passing through the openings in which the lenses are mounted. This diffraction always causes some blurring of the image and, when very high magnification is attempted, detail is lost faster than it is gained. Further, a very short focal length lens is needed for the objective of a high-magnification microscope. The problems of constructing such a lens are troublesome, and it is particularly difficult to correct its aberrations.

In a microscope of high magnification the problem of illumination is important. First, it is seen that only a fraction of the light leaving the object will enter the first lens and proceed through the system, and, since the final image on the retina is so much larger than it would be if the image were viewed directly, the amount of light per unit area of that image is very much reduced. If a high magnification is to be used, the object must be intensely illuminated, and to make this possible, all microscopes are provided with a third lens system called a ***condenser***, which is usually provided with an adjustable diaphragm. The purpose of the condenser is to concentrate light from a lamp or other source on the object under examination.

If a microscope is to be used to full advantage, it is essential that the condenser, the objective, and the ocular be designed and used in such a way that all the surfaces of all the lenses are completely illuminated. Microscopes are often used at a low efficiency simply because of ignorance of this fact. There are many manuals of microscopy that discuss this point, and they should be consulted by the microscopist who wishes to make the best use of his instruments.

13.13 The Telescope

The simple ***telescope***, which is used for the examination of distant objects, differs from the microscope in that it employs a long focal length lens for its objective, instead of one of short focal length. The process of image formation is illustrated in Fig. 13.21, in which light from a very distant object is falling on the objective. Because the object distance is very large as compared with the focal length of the objective, it can be set equal to infinity (i.e., $1/x_o = 0$) without appreciable error. The rays from any point of the object may therefore be considered as being parallel to each other, and the image F_1I of the object will be formed at the first principal focus F_1 of the objective.

The real image F_1I is imaged and magnified by the ocular in much the same way that the real object OA of Fig. 13.19 was imaged by the magnifier, or the real image BI of Fig. 13.20 was imaged by the microscope ocular. There is, however, one very important difference. The telescope is usually adjusted so that the final image is also placed at such a large distance that it may be considered to be at infinity. This, of course, requires that the light rays from any single point be parallel to each other after passing through the ocular. If the second principal focus of the ocular coincides with the first principal focus of the objective, the rays will be parallel, and this is the customary adjustment of a telescope.

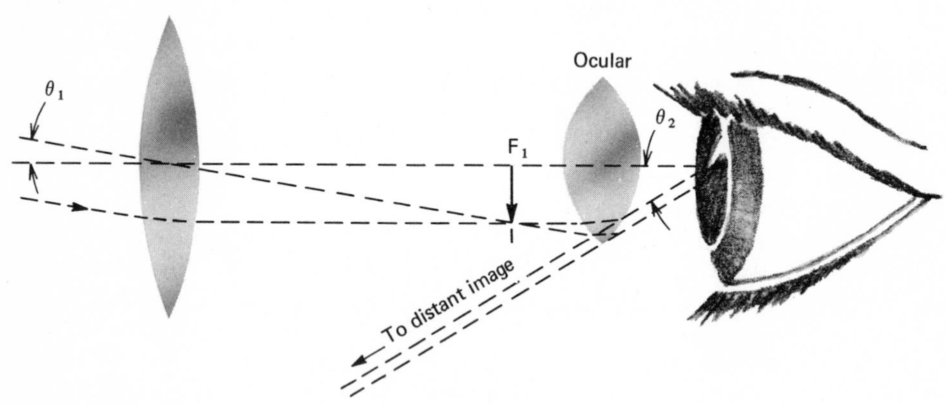

FIG. 13.21 The telescope.

When a very distant object is observed, its size is better described in terms of the angle which the object subtends at the eye than in terms of its linear dimensions. The effect of a telescopic system is therefore better expressed in terms of magnifying power, instead of lateral magnification. The ***magnifying power*** is defined as the ratio of the angle subtended by the final image to the angle subtended by the object itself. The magnifying power of the telescope shown in Fig. 13.21, for example, is θ_2/θ_1.

In order to compute the magnifying power, refer to Fig. 13.22, which shows the same telescope as Fig. 13.21 but omits all rays except those that pass centrally through one or the other of the lenses. If h is the lateral size of the real image F_1I formed by the objective,

$$\tan \theta_1 = h/f_1 \qquad \text{and} \qquad \tan \theta_2 = h/f_2$$

where f_1 and f_2 are the focal lengths of the objective and ocular, respectively. If, as is usual, both θ_1 and θ_2 are small angles, we may take the angles as proportional to their tangents, in accordance with Eq. (G.14), so that the magnifying power

$$T = \theta_2/\theta_1 = f_1/f_2. \tag{13.13-1}$$

Notice that the image formed by the telescope of Figs. 13.21–13.22 is inverted with respect to the object. This causes no great inconvenience in telescopes used for astronomical observation, but it is disconcerting to see inverted images of terrestrial objects. As a result, the terrestrial telescope (or its close relative, the binocular) is usually equipped either with a system of prisms that serve the double purpose of erecting the image and decreasing the overall length of the telescope or with an ocular that forms an inverted image of F_1I (see Prob. 13.6).

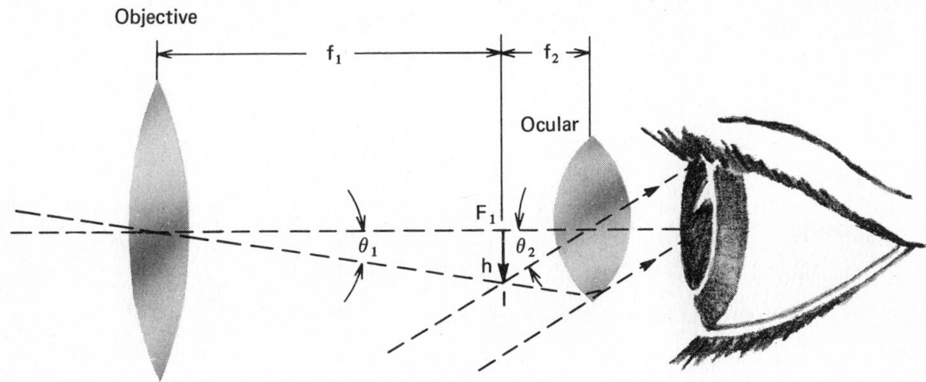

FIG. 13.22 Magnifying power of the telescope.

EXERCISES

13.13-1 A microscope has an objective of focal length +1.00 cm and a simple ocular lens of focal length +2.50 cm. These lenses are mounted 25.0 cm apart. What is the magnification if the final image is viewed at the normal reading distance? (Hint: Compute the distance of the real image from the ocular and then the optical tube length before making other computations.)

13.13-2 In the microscope of standard length discussed in Sec. 13.12, $f_1 = 2.00$ mm and $f_2 = 2.0$ cm. A cross hair whose diameter is 12 microns is stretched perpendicularly to the axis through the points BI of Fig. 13.20. What will be the width of the image of the cross hair? How wide a band of the object will be hidden by the cross hair?

13.13-3 A particular section of biological material cut for microscopic examination has a thickness of 10 microns. It is studied with a microscope whose overall transverse magnification is −500. What is the thickness of the final image?

13.13-4 The moon has a diameter of 3.4×10^6 m and is at a distance of 3.8×10^8 m from the earth. What is the angle subtended by the moon at the eye of an observer? The moon is observed through a telescope whose objective has a focal length of 2.50 m and whose ocular has a focal length of 2.00 cm. What is the apparent angle subtended by the moon as seen through this instrument?

13.13-5 Show that the effect on the apparent size of the object (i.e., the angle subtended by the object at the eye), obtained by observing an astronomical body through a telescope of magnifying power T, is the same as that which would be obtained if the object could be brought to a distance of $(1/T)$ times its actual distance and were then observed without the telescope.

13.14 Spherical Mirrors

Mirrors with spherical reflecting surfaces are frequently used instead of lenses to form images. An example is furnished by the ***concave mirror*** of Fig. 13.23, which has its center of curvature at C and which produces a real image of the point object O at I. We shall not discuss spherical mirrors in any detail here, except to say that they have many properties in common with lenses and that the images produced by them are subject to the same limitations (except for chromatic aberration) as are those produced by lenses. A few simple properties of spherical mirrors are illustrated by Exs. 13.14-1 and 13.14-2.

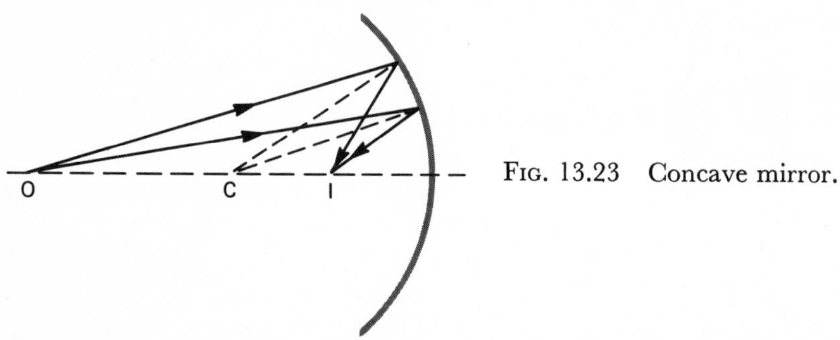

FIG. 13.23 Concave mirror.

Curved mirrors find particular application in astronomical telescopes, since objectives of great diameter are needed to collect light from very distant stars. Such reflecting telescopes are easier to construct than are refracting telescopes, both because large pieces of perfectly clear glass are required for the objective lenses of the latter and because the mirror of a reflecting telescope may be supported over its entire back, whereas a lens is supported only at its edges in order that light transmission is not blocked.

EXERCISES

13.14-1 By detailed tracing of the rays, as was done in Secs. 13.2–13.3, considering all angles of incidence and reflection to be small, show that light rays parallel to the axis and falling on the mirror of Fig. 13.23 from the left will be focused at a point halfway between C and the mirror. As a result, show that the focal length of a concave mirror is $R/2$, where R is the radius of curvature.

13.14-2 By methods similar to those used in Ex. 13.14-1, show that a convex mirror (i.e., one with its radius of curvature on the opposite side of the mirror from the object) produces a virtual image of the object. Show that this virtual image is at a distance $R/2$ behind the mirror for an object at infinite distance.

13.15 The Spectroscope

We saw in Secs. 12.15–12.16 that a diffraction grating could be used to break a complex light beam up into its constituent wavelengths, and so to analyze spectra. Throughout our treatment of the grating, we assumed that the rays of light that fell upon it were parallel to each other and that they were examined at an infinite distance from the grating after being diffracted. When we first met the grating, we had no way of satisfying these conditions unless we worked with a very distant light source and observed the diffraction pattern at a great distance from the grating. Such an arrangement would not only be cumbersome, but it would have the further disadvantage that the observable intensities of the light would be prohibitively low. Fortunately, it is possible to use a set of lenses to bring about the conditions under which we derived the grating equation (Eq. 12.14-3) without great sacrifice either of space or of light intensity.

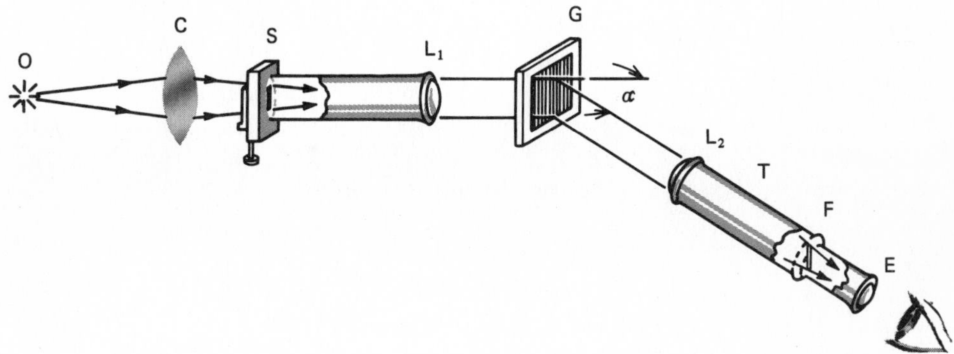

FIG. 13.24 Grating spectroscope.

In the ***grating spectroscope*** shown schematically in Fig. 13.24, light from a source O is focused on a vertical slit S, which is of adjustable width, by a condensing lens C. Another lens L_1 is mounted on the axis that passes through the centers of C and S at such a distance that S is exactly at its second principal focus. Since the slit acts as an object for this lens, the image of the slit will be produced at infinity and the rays of light emerging from the lens will be parallel. The production of a parallel light beam in this way is known as ***collimation***, and the combination of a convergent lens with a slit at its principal focus is called a ***collimator***.

The light from the collimator falls on the diffraction grating G. Let us now suppose that the angle α is one which satisfies the grating equation [Eq. (12.14-3)]:

$$n\lambda = a \sin \alpha$$

for a wavelength λ that is present in the light from the source. Parallel light rays emerging from the grating in this direction will interfere so as to produce a maximum of intensity at infinite distance. In order that these rays may be observed from reasonably close at hand, the telescope T, consisting of an objective L_2 and an ocular E, is mounted with its axis along the direction of the diffracted rays. The objective forms a real image of the slit at F, and this can be examined through the ocular.

In most spectrometers, which are intended for the precise measurement of wavelength, the telescope is mounted on an arm pivoted directly under the center of the grating. By swinging this arm around its pivot, various values of α may be obtained. Whenever α has a value satisfying Eq. (12.14-3), an image of the slit will be observed. Since this image is formed by light of a single wavelength, it will be colored. By locating the series of images formed, the various wavelengths emitted by the source can be measured.

In the ***spectrograph***, the ocular E is omitted and a photographic plate is mounted at F. This plate will show, after development, a series of images of the slit, formed by the various wavelengths present, and the wavelengths can be determined by subsequent measurement of the image positions. Because the images appear as along narrow rectangles, the images are often referred to as ***spectral lines***.

A second type of spectroscope uses a prism instead of a grating to break the light up into its components. The ***prism*** used is a plane-faced wedge of transparent material, and its action depends on refraction, instead of diffraction. If a light ray strikes one face of such a prism, as shown in Fig. 13.25a, it will be

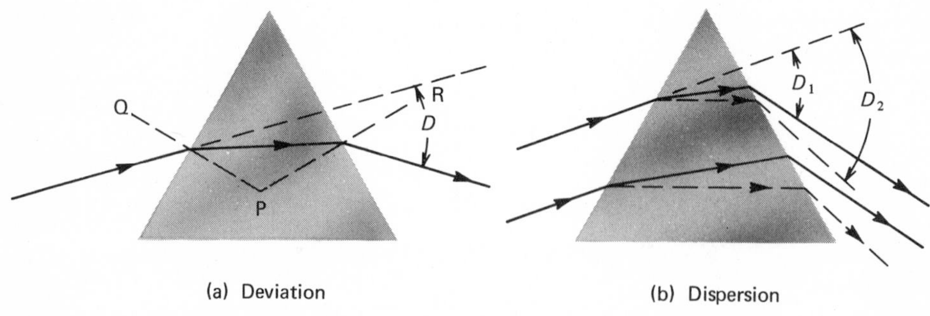

FIG. 13.25 Deviation and dispersion by a prism.

refracted toward the normal PQ. When it strikes the second face, it will be refracted away from the normal PR. Since the two faces are not parallel, the emergent ray will not be parallel to the incident ray, and the angle D between them is known as the ***angle of deviation***. Since the index of refraction of the prism depends on the wavelength of the light (cf. Sec. 12.19), the refractions at the two surfaces will also depend on the wavelength, and so will the angle of deviation. Therefore, if a parallel beam of light rays falls on the prism, as shown in Fig. 13.25b, the different wavelengths in the beam will be deviated by different amounts, and more than one parallel beam will result, as shown in the figure.

If the grating of Fig. 13.25 is replaced by a prism, each of the parallel light beams will produce an image of the slit in the telescope, so that spectra can also be obtained with a ***prism spectroscope***. When a prism is used, however, there will be but one image for each wavelength, instead of the multiple images which correspond to various values of n in Eq. (12.14-3).

The appearance of the spectrum observed in a spectroscope will depend upon the nature of the light source. If the light is given off by a luminescent gas which emits a few discrete wavelengths, the spectrum will consist of a few separate colored images of the slit. If the source is a luminescent solid or liquid which emits a continuous spectrum of all wavelengths, there will be an infinite number of slit images, and the overlapping of these will result in a continuous band of color, ranging from red at one end to violet at the other.

13.16 Summary

The present chapter has been devoted to a study of optical instruments, which depend on applications of the laws of reflection, refraction, and diffraction. Particular emphasis has been placed on lenses with spherical surfaces, and it has been found that such lenses can produce images of objects, the images being enlarged or reduced optical reproductions of the objects, depending on the relative positions of the object, lens, and image. Further, a ray diagram or a single simple equation can be used to find the position of the image with respect to the lens, if the position of the object is known. The uses of such lenses in eyeglasses, cameras, telescopes, and microscopes has been investigated. Finally, a short discussion of spectroscopes, which analyze complex light into its component wavelengths, has been given.

PROBLEMS

13.1 We have considered only "front surface mirrors," those in which light strikes the reflecting surface without passing through glass. Most mirrors are "back surface." Suppose that a reflecting surface has a piece of glass of thickness t and index of refraction μ relative to the surroundings. An object is at a distance D in front of the glass. Considering only rays that fall on the mirror at small angles of incidence, show that the distance of the image behind the reflecting surface is

$$D' = D - t(1 - 2/\mu).$$

13.2 Show that two plane mirrors, making an angle of $360°/n$, where n is an integer, will form $(n - 1)$ images of an object placed in front of them.

13.3 In most cameras the lens is compound. One design uses a thin front lens (i.e., the lens nearest to the object) that is diverging and of focal length $-3f$. The thin rear lens is converging and of focal length f. The two lenses have a common axis and are separated by a distance $f/4$.

(a) Find the position of the image formed by this compound lens of an object at a large distance x_0 from the front lens. (b) Compute the magnification of the compound lens. (c) Show that the image of a very distant object (i.e., one for which $x_0 \gg f$) is formed at a distance $13f/9$ behind the rear lens. (d) Show that the ratio of the size of the image to the angle subtended by the very distant object at the front lens (i.e., h_0/x_0, where h_0 is the size of the object) is $4f/3$.

13.4 Suppose that the front and the rear lenses of the camera of Prob. 13.3 are interchanged. Compute the same distances and the magnification that were found in parts (a), (b), and (c) of Prob. 13.3 for the normal arrangement of the lens. Also show that the quantity computed in (d) is again $4f/3$.

13.5 The definition of the focal length given in Sec. 13.3 is useful only for thin lenses, because the plane from which one measures the distance to the first principal focus is not determined for a compound lens or for a thick one. A more general definition states that the focal length is the size of the image divided by the angle subtended at the lens by infinitely distant object.

(a) Show that this new definition is in agreement with the definition given in Sec. 13.3 for a thin lens. (b) What is the focal length of the compound lens of Probs. 13.3–13.4? (c) Does this focal length depend on the order of the two thin lenses?

13.6 One form of telescope ocular consists of two thin diverging lenses, each of local length $-f$, separated by a distance f.

(a) Show that this ocular will form a virtual image of a virtual object that is at a distance $(2f/3)$ from the first lens and $(f/3)$ from the second lens.

(b) Show that the image formed by the ocular is inverted with respect to the virtual object and that this ocular will therefore produce an upright image of distant objects and is suitable for a terrestrial telescope.

(c) Where should the first lens be placed relative to the objective of the telescope if the latter has a focal length F?

(d) What is the magnifying power of the telescope formed by this combination of lenses?

13.7 A thin lens, of index of refraction μ and with thickness t at the center and zero at the edges, has a radius r_0. The lens is in a wall that separates air (index of refraction $= \mu_0$) from water (index of refraction $= \mu_1$).

(a) The image of an infinitely distant object, located on the air side of the lens, is formed in the water. Find the position of the image.

(b) The image of an infinitely distant object, located in the water, is formed in the air. Find the position of this image.

(c) Does a lens that has different media on the two sides of it possess a unique focal length? (Cf. Prob. 13.5.)

13.8 A lens made of light flint glass (cf. Table 12.1) has radii of curvature of 20.00 cm and 40.00 cm for its two faces, the first face being convex and the second concave. A source of light is placed 2.000 m to the left of the lens. If a filter that passes red light of $\lambda = 6563$ Å is inserted in the beam, where will the image of the light source be formed? If the red filter is replaced by a blue filter that passes light of $\lambda = 4861$ Å, where will the image be?

REFERENCES

13A Franklin Miller, *Resolving Power.* (No. 80-208, The Ealing Corp., Cambridge, Mass.) A 4-min film loop that bears on the instruments of this chapter.

13B O. Stuhlman, Jr., *Introduction to Biophysics*, Wiley, New York, 1943. The eye is discussed in pp. 100–132 and microscopes in pp. 310–330.

13C Arthur I. Berman, "Observations in Space," *Scientific American*, August 1963, pp. 28–37. A discussion of telescopes on earth-satellites.

13D A. C. Crombie, "Early Concepts of the Senses and the Mind," *Scientific American*, May 1964, pp. 108–116. (Reprint No. 184, W. H. Freeman.) A history of theories of vision.

14 ➾ *The Gravitational Field of Force*

14.1 Action at a Distance

Most of the forces we have been discussing so far have involved the actual, or at least apparent, contact of two bodies. The one exception to this was the gravitational force that accounts for the weight of bodies on the surface of the earth. Little consideration was given to this force, however, except to recognize its existence and its proportionality to mass. The idea of forces resulting from physical contact ties in very well with our primitive conception of force as a muscular push or pull. But it was not long after the foundation of the science of mechanics until it became clear that forces can act between two bodies that are at a distance from each other. These forces, as we shall see, may be gravitational forces (Sec. 14.5) due to the masses of the bodies, or electrical forces (Sec. 15.5), or magnetic forces (Sec. 15.13). It has since been found that even contact and elastic forces are best described in terms of *forces acting at small distances* between the small particles of which matter is constructed. It is therefore important that we study in some detail the forces that bodies exert on each other when they do not touch.

When one body, due to its mass, electrical charge, or other property, can exert forces on other bodies in its neighborhood, we say that a ***field of force*** exists around it. This chapter and the next will be devoted to the properties of some of the more important fields of force.

14.2 Kepler's Laws and Gravitation

We saw in Sec. 7.13 that the existence of a centripetal force, directed toward the sun, is necessary in order to explain the fact that a planet moves in a closed orbit. Otherwise, according to Newton's first law, we should expect the planet to travel off in a straight line into space. Newton's great contribution to the study of planetary motion was to establish firmly that this centripetal force is a gravitational force. Making extensive use of Kepler's laws, Newton showed that the gravitational force between the sun and a planet depends on the masses of the two bodies and on the distance between them.

In order to consider the essentials of Newton's argument, we have to think more about Kepler's laws. We restate them as follows:

1. The orbits of the planets are ellipses, having the sun at one focus.
2. The area swept out per unit time by the radius vector from the sun to the planet is a constant.
3. The squares of the periodic times of the planets are proportional to the cubes of the semimajor axes of their elliptical orbits.

Note that these laws are only descriptive. They state how the planets move and make no reference to why they so move. The sun occupies a unique place in Kepler's laws, being at one focus of every planetary orbit. Moreover, there is nothing special about the earth; it is simply one of the planets that revolve about the sun.

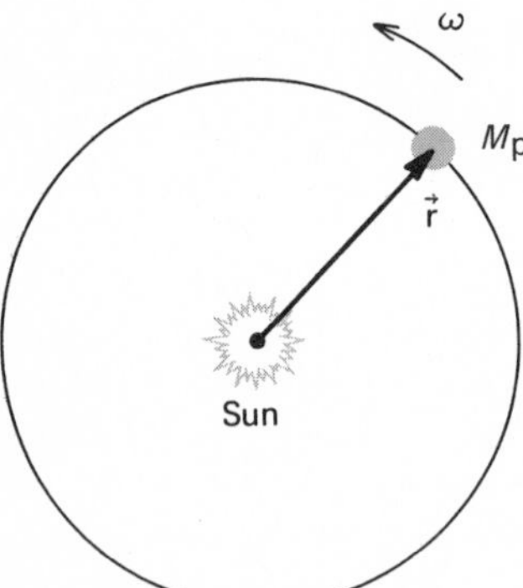

FIG. 14.1 Circular orbit of a planet.

To follow Newton's reasoning, consider first a very special case, seldom observed exactly but approximated closely by most of the planets. Let us suppose that a planet of mass M_p is moving in a *circular* orbit such as that shown in Fig. 14.1. We know that a centripetal force, $-M_p\omega^2\vec{r}$, where ω is the angular velocity and $\vec{r}$ is the vector to the planet from the sun,* is needed to keep the planet in this orbit. Such a force will be supplied if the planet is attracted toward the sun with a force that may depend on r but is of constant magnitude at a given r. We have, for the force

$$\vec{F} = -M_p\omega^2\vec{r}.$$

We can now apply Kepler's third law of planetary motion (Sec. 7.13) in the form $\tau^2 = Kr^3$, where τ is the period of the planet, equal to $2\pi/\omega$, and K is a constant for all planets in the solar system. We thus find that

$$\vec{F} = -\frac{4\pi^2 M_p\vec{r}}{\tau^2} = -\frac{4\pi^2 M_p\vec{r}}{Kr^3}. \qquad (14.2\text{-}1)$$

* Strictly speaking, r is the distance from the planet to the center of mass of the sun-planet system (see Prob. 14.12). The sun, however, is so massive compared with any planet that the center of mass nearly coincides with the center of the sun.

Since $-\vec{r}/r^3$ is a vector of magnitude $1/r^2$, we thus see that the circular motion will be accounted for if a force of magnitude

$$F = \frac{4\pi^2 M_p}{K r^2} \tag{14.2-1A}$$

continually pulls the planet toward the sun.

Note that the force we have postulated is always directed inward along the radius. It therefore exerts no torque on the planet; the angular momentum therefore remains constant, as is required by Kepler's second law. Also, because the force is always at a right angle with the velocity, the force does not work on the planet (cf. Secs. 6.6 and 6.10). Hence the kinetic energy of the planet remains constant, as it must if both ω and r remain constant.

We have found that a force that varies as the inverse square of the distance will hold a planet in a circular orbit, but we cannot consider that the existence of such a force is established unless we can show that it will also account for the observed elliptical orbits, which are not circular. Let us first look at the situation in a qualitative fashion—we can return to it in more detail later.

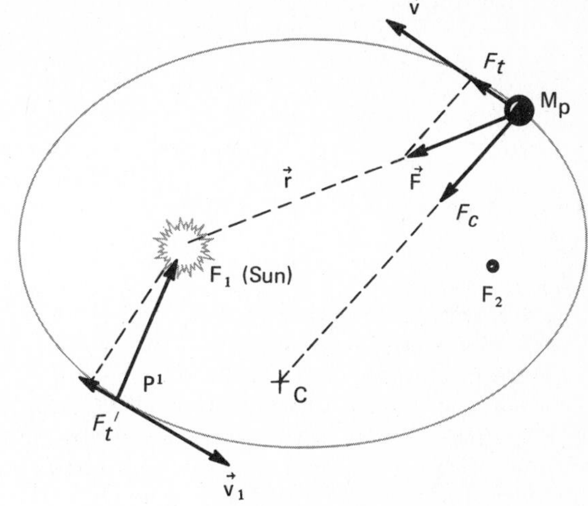

FIG. 14.2 Resolution of the central force into components.

Suppose that the planet in an elliptical orbit is at some instant in the position shown at M_p in Fig. 14.2. Its instantaneous velocity $\vec{v}$ is directed along the tangent to the ellipse and is therefore not perpendicular to $\vec{r}$, the vector from the sun. If the force $\vec{F}$ is inward along that vector, as we have supposed, we can break it into two components, F_c at right angles to $\vec{v}$ and F_t along $\vec{v}$. The former of these does not work on the planet; it is a centripetal force holding the planet in a path that is at the instant along the arc of a circle centered at some point such as C. The component F_t, however, does do work. Being directed along the velocity, it increases the speed of the planet. This is exactly what is required—the planet in the position shown is clearly getting nearer the sun as it moves in its orbit and it must therefore be increasing its speed to satisfy

Kepler's second law (of equal areas). Note that the component F'_t at some later time, when the planet is in the position P′, will be directed opposite to the velocity $\vec{v}'$. It will then be decreasing the speed of the planet, as required by Kepler's second law.

The qualitative arguments that were just considered make it *plausible* that elliptical orbits are consistent with an inverse square law of force. Before we can produce a quantitative discussion, we shall need to consider some properties of ellipses.

14.3 Some Properties of Ellipses

In order to define an ***ellipse***, locate two points, F_1 and F_2 in Fig. 14.3; each of these points is a ***focus***, and as a pair they are called the ***foci*** of the ellipse which we shall draw. Actually, we shall see in Exs. 14.3-1–14.3-3 that we could

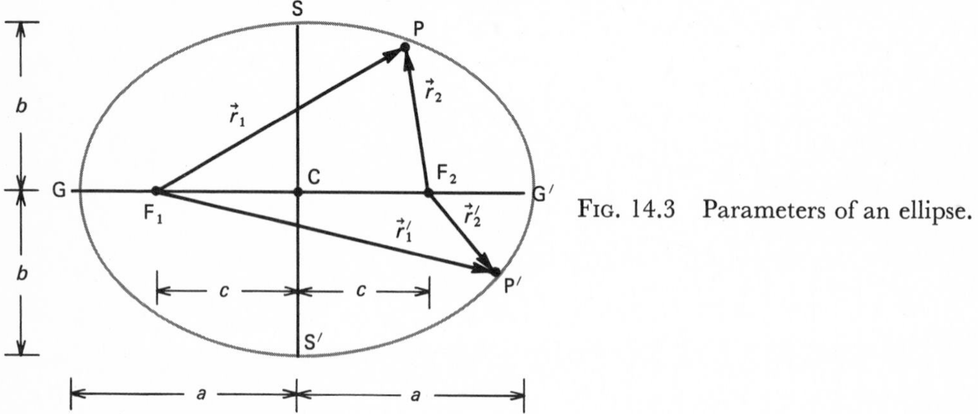

FIG. 14.3 Parameters of an ellipse.

draw an infinite number of ellipses of various sizes and shapes belonging to these two foci. Let us start reasonably, however, by picking some point P as in Fig. 14.3. Lines F_1P and F_2P are the radius vectors $\vec{r}_1$ and $\vec{r}_2$, respectively, which establish the displacement of P from F_1 and F_2, respectively. If we now draw the locus of all points P such that the sum of the lengths of $\vec{r}_1$ and $\vec{r}_2$ is always the same constant, the closed curve so described is an ellipse. Thus, in Fig. 14.3, $r_1 + r_2 = r'_1 + r'_2 = \Lambda$, where Λ is the constant. Thus,

$$r_1 + r_2 = \Lambda, \tag{14.3-1}$$

where r_1 and r_2 range over all possible pairs of values, is an equation for an ellipse. Obviously, if a different constant Λ is chosen, Eq. (14.3-1) will give a different ellipse.

Point C, midway between the foci, is called the ***center*** of the ellipse, and the line segment GG′ is called the ***major axis***; either half, GC or CG′, of the major axis is a ***semimajor axis***. The line segment SS′, normal to the major axis at C, is the ***minor axis*** of the ellipse, and each half of it is the ***semiminor axis***.

For simplicity, let us define the following lengths: semimajor axis $= \mathrm{GC} = \mathrm{CG}' = a$; semiminor axis $= \mathrm{SC} = \mathrm{CS}' = b$; $\mathrm{F_1C} = \mathrm{CF_2} = c$. We have already specified that $r_1 + r_2 = \Lambda$. By selecting point P at convenient places on the ellipse, it will be easy for the reader to show that $\Lambda = 2a$ and that $a^2 = b^2 + c^2$.

We can now show that the area enclosed by an ellipse is πab. First note that an ellipse can be regarded as that closed curve which we see when we look at a circle drawn on a page that is tilted. Figures 14.4a and b illustrate the

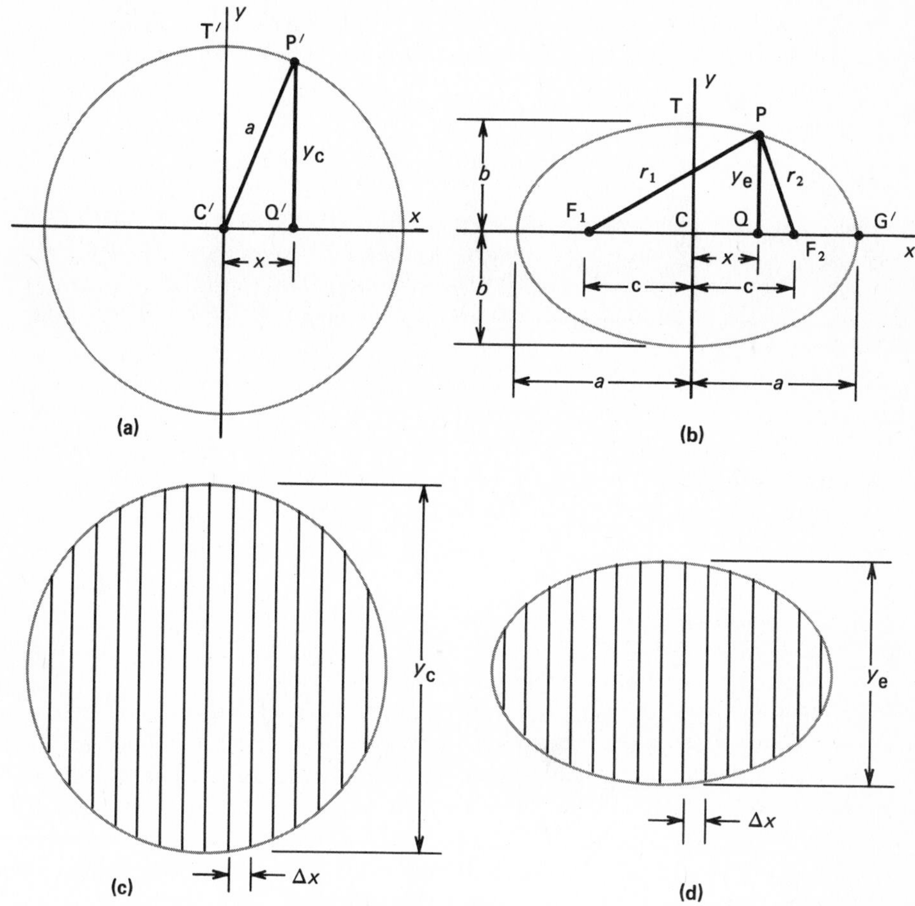

FIG. 14.4 The area of an ellipse is πab.

effect. In Fig. 14.4a, for example, you might be looking straight down at the top of a drinking glass, while in Fig. 14.4b, your head has been moved back so that you see the circular edge of the glass from an angle. Figure 14.4b is drawn with a semimajor axis a, which is equal to the radius of the circle in Fig. 14.4a. Our problem now is to prove that a circle, viewed in projection as in Fig. 14.4b, is indeed an ellipse and not simply some other oval figure.

Pick any point Q on the major axis of the ellipse and let the distance $CQ = x$. An equal distance $C'Q' = x$ is laid off on the x-axis of the circle to locate Q′ to correspond with Q. Points P and P′ are chosen so that PQ and P′Q′ are each normal to their corresponding x-axes; of course, $PQ = y_e$ and $P'Q' = y_c$. If the ellipse can be regarded as a tilted circle, then, for all corresponding points P and P′,

$$y_e = (b/a) y_c. \tag{14.3-2}$$

It is clear that this is true for T and T′, for we have $CT = (b/a)\ C'T'$ and $b = (b/a)a$ or $b = b$, since $CT = a$ and $C'T' = b$. Figure 14.5 shows that, if a is tilted through angle θ, it looks like a length b. The ratio $(b/a) = \cos\theta$ is a measure of the tilt.

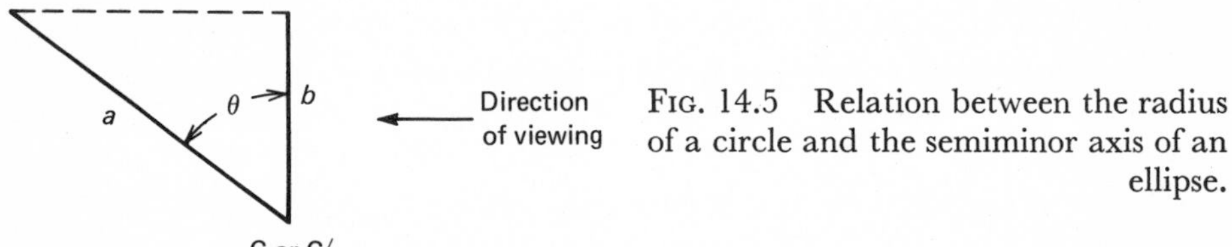

FIG. 14.5 Relation between the radius of a circle and the semiminor axis of an ellipse.

We shall now show that, if we take various y_c from the circle and compute the corresponding y_e from Eq. (14.3-2), the points P so determined fit our equation for the ellipse—i.e., their distances from the foci will satisfy the equation

$$r_1 + r_2 = 2a. \tag{14.3-1A}$$

Since $b^2 = a^2 - c^2$, we have

$$y_e^2 = \frac{b^2}{a^2} y_c^2 = \frac{(a^2 - c^2)}{a^2} y_c^2, \tag{14.3-3}$$

and from the circle we get

$$y_c^2 = (a^2 - x^2)$$

so that

$$y_e^2 = \frac{(a^2 - c^2)(a^2 - x^2)}{a^2}. \tag{14.3-4}$$

From Fig. 14.4b we see that

$$r_1^2 = y_e^2 + (c + x)^2 \tag{14.3-5}$$

and

$$r_2^2 = y_e^2 + (c - x)^2. \tag{14.3-6}$$

If we now substitute y_e^2 from Eq. (14.3-4) into Eqs. (14.3-5) and (14.3-6), we get

$$r_1 = \frac{(a^2 + cx)}{a} \tag{14.3-7}$$

and

$$r_2 = \frac{(a^2 - cx)}{a}. \tag{14.3-8}$$

It is clear that Eqs. (14.3-7) and (14.3-8) satisfy Eq. (14.3-1A), so Fig. 14.4b is indeed an ellipse.

If we imagine the area of the circle in Fig. 14.4a divided into narrow rectangular strips of width Δx as shown in Fig. 14.4c, a typical strip will have the dimensions Δx by $2y_c$. If the area of this strip is projected as in Fig. 14.4b, its dimensions will then be Δx by $2y_e = (b/a)y_c$. (See Fig. 14.4d.) Since each such rectangle will have its area reduced by the factor b/a, the area of the circle projected into the ellipse will be reduced in the same ratio. Thus,

$$\pi a^2(b/a) = \pi ab = \text{area of ellipse.} \tag{14.3-9}$$

Finally, let us relate ellipses to planetary orbits. According to Kepler's first law, the sun is located at one focus; let us suppose that this is F_1 in Fig. 14.3. When the planet is at point G, it is said to be a ***perihelion***, the closest point to the sun. When the planet is at G′, it is at ***aphelion***, the farthest point from the sun. It can be seen from Fig. 14.3 that at perihelion $r_1 = r_p = a - c$ and at aphelion $r_1 = r_a = a + c$.

One further useful relation can be obtained from Eqs. (14.3-7) and (14.3-8). Multiplying them together gives

$$r_1 r_2 = \frac{a^4 - c^2x^2}{a^2}. \tag{14.3-10}$$

If in this equation we put $x = a$—i.e., point P is at the end of a semimajor axis, so it is either at perihelion or aphelion—we get

$$r_p r_a = a^2 - c^2 = b^2. \tag{14.3-11}$$

We can conclude this brief discussion of Kepler's laws by making a couple of short comments about the second and third laws. In Sec. 7.13 we noted that Kepler's second law can be written as Eq. (7.13-1); that is, $r^2\omega/2 = k$, where at any given instant, r is the length of the radius vector, ω is the angular velocity, and k is a constant for a given planet.

In a similar way, we can express Kepler's third law in the form of an equation. Thus, if τ_1 and τ_2 are the periods of two different planets, and a_1 and a_2 are the semimajor axes of their elliptical orbits about the sun, we can write

$$\tau_1^2/a_1^3 = \tau_2^2/a_2^3. \tag{14.3-12}$$

Since Eq. (14.3-1) can be applied to any two planets of our solar system, we can write a more useful equation by noting that the ratios in Eq. (14.3-12) define a constant $\tau_1^2/a_1^3 = \tau_2^2/a_2^3 = K$; then, more generally, we can say that

$$\tau^2 = Ka^3, \qquad (14.3\text{-}13).$$

where τ is the period of any planet and a is the corresponding semimajor axis. Note that $a = \frac{1}{2}(r_p + r_a)$—that is, the semimajor axis is the mean of r_p and r_a.

EXERCISES

14.3-1 For a given pair of foci, F_1 and F_2, what would be the smallest possible value of $r_1 + r_2 = \Lambda$? What would be the corresponding values of a, b, and c, and what would be the shape of the ellipse? Also, what would be the corresponding values of r_p and r_a?

14.3-2 Consider the effect on a, b, c, r_p, and r_a and on the shape of the ellipse of choosing a very large Λ—i.e., as $\Lambda \to \infty$—for a given pair of foci.

14.3-3 Considering the results of Exs. 14.3-1 and 14.3-2, how many ellipses can there be belonging to a given pair of foci, F_1 and F_2? Prove that no two of these ellipses can intersect each other.

14.3-4 Show that r_p and r_a can be found from Eqs. (14.3-9) and (14.3-10).

14.3-5 Show that the law of equal areas applies to the situation in the figure. Particle P moves with constant velocity along lath TT′. Show that from some arbitrary point C the displacement vector $\vec{r}$ sweeps out equal areas in equal intervals of time.

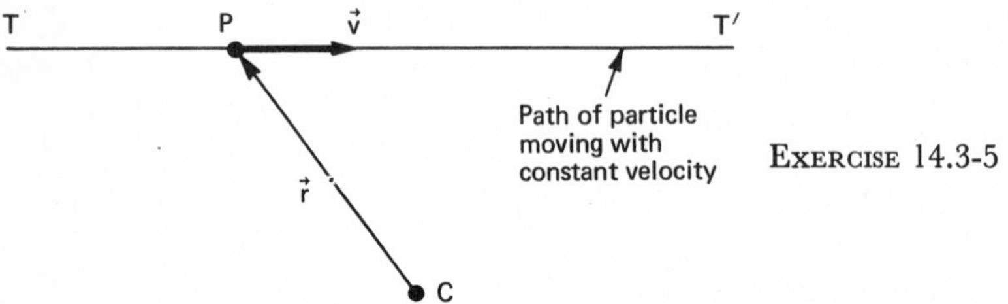

EXERCISE 14.3-5

14.3-6 The eccentricity of an elliptical orbit is defined by the ratio $e = c/a$. If for the earth $e_e = 0.0167$ and $a_e = 1.50 \times 10^8$ km, and for Pluto $e_p = 0.249$ and $a_p = 5.9 \times 10^9$ km, make rough calculations to compare the distances between the orbital foci and the r_p and r_a in the two cases.

14.3-7 If one rounds off the data of Ex. 14.3-6 to say that $a_p = 40a_e$, and if one measures the orbital period of the earth as $\tau_e = 1$ year, what is the period of Pluto measured in our years?

14.4 Conservation of Energy in Planetary Motion

By considering the conservation of energy as a planet moves in its orbit, we can show that the inverse square law allows elliptical orbits. We begin by noting that in Sec. 7.13 we obtained

$$L = Mr^2\omega$$

from Kepler's second law, the law of equal areas. In this equation L is the angular momentum and M the mass of the planet, and both are constant. But in Sec. 14.3 we saw that the planet moves from perihelion where $r_p = a - c$ out to aphelion where $r_a = a + c$; both r and ω must vary. Does the kinetic energy of M also change as r and ω vary? We can answer this question by computing the kinetic energy of M at perihelion and at aphelion.

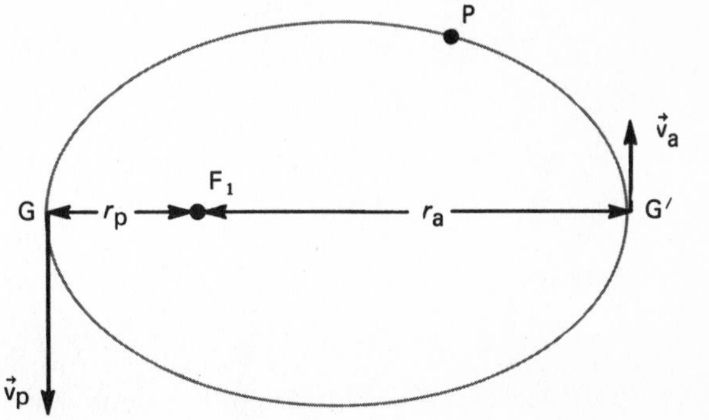

FIG. 14.6 Relation between speeds at aphelion and perihelion.

At the instants when M moves through perihelion and aphelion, the motion is pure rotation; as is apparent in Fig. 14.6, there is no component of velocity along the radius at those points. We have

$$KE_p = \tfrac{1}{2}Mv_p{}^2 = \tfrac{1}{2}Mr_p{}^2\omega_p{}^2 \tag{14.4-1}$$

and

$$KE_a = \tfrac{1}{2}Mv_a{}^2 = \tfrac{1}{2}Mr_a{}^2\omega_a{}^2. \tag{14.4-2}$$

But from Eq. (7.13-2) we can say that $r_p\omega_p = L/Mr_p$ and $r_a\omega_a = L/Mr_a$. Thus, Eqs. (14.4-1) and (14.4-2) become

$$KE_p = \frac{L^2}{2Mr_p{}^2} \tag{14.4-3}$$

and

$$KE_a = \frac{L^2}{2Mr_a{}^2}. \tag{14.4-4}$$

The kinetic energy at perihelion is obviously greater than that at aphelion, since $r_p < r_a$. Since no external forces or torques act on this sun-planet system, the difference in kinetic energies, $KE_p - KE_a$, must equal the differences in potential energies, $PE_a - PE_p$. We are assuming, of course, that the sun and any one planet constitute an isolated sun-planet system and that the effects of all other planets on this system are negligible.

We now apply the law of conservation of energy at perihelion and at aphelion to write

$$KE_a + PE_a = KE_p + PE_p \tag{14.4-5}$$

or

$$PE_a - PE_p = KE_p - KE_a. \tag{14.4-6}$$

Using Eqs. (14.4-3) and (14.4-4) in the right side of Eq. (14.4-6), we get

$$PE_a - PE_p = \frac{L^2}{2M}\left(\frac{1}{r_p^2} - \frac{1}{r_a^2}\right)$$

$$= \frac{L^2}{2M}\frac{r_a^2 - r_p^2}{r_p^2 r_a^2}$$

$$= \frac{L^2}{2M}\left(\frac{r_a + r_p}{r_p r_a}\right)\left(\frac{r_a - r_p}{r_p r_a}\right). \quad (14.4\text{-}7)$$

From Eqs. (14.3-1A) and (14.3-11), it follows that Eq. (14.4-7) gives

$$PE_a - PE_p = \frac{L^2 a}{Mb^2}\left(\frac{r_a - r_p}{r_p r_a}\right) = \frac{L^2 a}{Mb^2}\left(\frac{1}{r_p} - \frac{1}{r_a}\right). \quad (14.4\text{-}8)$$

In Eq. (14.4-8) the factor L^2a/Mb^2 is obviously constant. However, we can use Kepler's laws and various properties of an ellipse in order to express this constant in a more convenient form. Starting with Kepler's second law, Eq. (7.13-1), we write, as the rate at which area is swept out,

$$\Delta A/\Delta t = r^2\omega/2 = k$$

or

$$\Delta A = k\,\Delta t. \quad (14.4\text{-}9)$$

Now if we add up the small equal increments of area ΔA all the way around the ellipse, we will get for the left side of Eq. (14.4-9) just the area of the ellipse, $A = \pi ab$, as we found in Eq. (14.3-9). On the right side of Eq. (14.4-9), adding all of the corresponding equal time intervals Δt will give the period τ for revolution of the planet once around the orbit. Thus, Eq. (14.4-9) leads to

$$A = k\tau = \frac{r^2\omega}{2}\tau = \frac{L}{2M}\tau = \pi ab. \quad (14.4\text{-}10)$$

Finally, using Kepler's third law, $\tau^2 = Ka^3$, we get

$$\frac{L^2}{4M^2}\tau^2 = \frac{L^2Ka^3}{4M^2} = \pi^2a^2b^2 \quad (14.4\text{-}11A)$$

or

$$\frac{L^2a}{Mb^2} = \frac{4\pi^2M}{K} = 4\pi^2MC, \quad (14.4\text{-}11B)$$

where we have placed $C = 1/K$.

Returning now to Eq. (14.4-8), we use the result of Eq. (14.4-11B) to write

$$PE_a - PE_p = 4\pi^2MC\left(\frac{1}{r_p} - \frac{1}{r_a}\right). \quad (14.4\text{-}12)$$

In Sec. 4.18 we discussed the gravitational potential energy of a body near the surface of a massive body, such as the sun or the earth. Eq. (14.4-12) may be regarded as removing the restriction that the mass be within a few kilometers.

We see that we can satisfy this equation if we set the potential energy at any distance r from the sun equal to

$$PE = -4\pi^2 MC/r. \tag{14.4-13}$$

As r gets larger and larger, the potential energy approaches zero. Hence we have chosen a point at infinite distance from the sun as one at which the potential energy is zero. We saw in Sec. 4.18 that we could choose the position of zero potential energy arbitrarily, because we are concerned only with differences of potential energy. Hence we lose nothing by expressing PE in the form of Eq. (14.4-13).

The significance of the minus sign in Eq. (14.4-13) is clear. If the potential energy is zero at $r = \infty$, and if the force between the sun and the planet is attractive, the system will do work as the planet moves in closer to the sun; its potential energy will become less than zero, or negative.

At the outset we chose to apply the law of conservation of energy to the particular points G and G′. At any other point such as P in Fig. 14.6, the law applies, of course, but there $\Delta KE = -\Delta PE$, and both of these depend on Δr in ways that are more difficult to treat mathematically. This compromise in our derivation in no way restricts Eq. (14.4-13); it applies everywhere in the sun-planet system, even though we have demonstrated this only for two particular points in the orbit.

Also, in Eq. (14.4-13) the only factor that applies to a particular planet is the mass M; therefore, in order to apply the equation to the sun and some other planet, we need only substitute the mass of the other planet.

We can now show that Eq. (14.4-13) is exactly the gravitational potential energy that we expect if the gravitational force depends on the inverse square of the distance.

To do this, we suppose that the planet moves from a distance r from the sun to a distance $r + \Delta r$. Its potential energy has then changed by an amount $\Delta(PE)$. It must therefore have done work equal to

$$-\Delta(PE) = \overline{\mathrm{F}}\,\Delta r,$$

where $\overline{\mathrm{F}}$ is the average force that it exerts during the change of position. We can rewrite this equation as $\overline{\mathrm{F}} = -\Delta(PE)/\Delta r$. We then let $\Delta r \to 0$, to find that $F = -d(PE)/dr$. Substituting from Eq. (14.4-13) for PE, we have

$$F = \frac{d}{dr}\left(\frac{4\pi^2 MC}{r}\right) = (4\pi^2 MC) \lim_{\Delta r \to 0}\left(\frac{1}{r + \Delta r} - \frac{1}{r}\right)\Big/\Delta r.$$

We can write the first term in the parentheses as $(r + \Delta r)^{-1} = r^{-1}(1 + \Delta r/r)^{-1}$. When $(\Delta r/r)$ is small, we can use Eq. (H. 3) of Appendix H, with $n = -1$, to show that

$$\left(1 + \frac{\Delta r}{r}\right)^{-1} = 1 - \frac{\Delta r}{r} + \left(\frac{\Delta r}{r}\right)^2 + \text{higher powers of } \frac{\Delta r}{r}.$$

Hence

$$\frac{1}{r+\Delta r}-\frac{1}{r}=\frac{1}{r}\left[1-\frac{\Delta r}{r}+\left(\frac{\Delta r}{r}\right)^2+\cdots\right]-\frac{1}{r}$$

$$=-\frac{\Delta r}{r^2}+\frac{(\Delta r)^2}{r^3}+\cdots,$$

and

$$\lim_{\Delta r\to 0}\left(\frac{1}{\Delta r}\right)\left(\frac{1}{r+\Delta r}-\frac{1}{r}\right)=-\frac{1}{r^2},$$

because all the higher-order terms vanish as $\Delta r \to 0$. Substitution of this value into the expression for the force shows that

$$F=-\frac{4\pi MC^2}{r^2}. \qquad (14.4\text{-}14)$$

The dependence of the force on distance in order that energy be conserved in elliptical orbits is exactly that which we found for circular orbits. An inverse square law of force is completely consistent with Kepler's laws.

14.5 Newton's Law of Universal Gravitation

According to Eq. (14.4-14), the force pulling a planet of mass M_{p} toward the sun is

$$F_{\mathrm{s}}=-\frac{4\pi M_{\mathrm{p}}C}{r^2}. \qquad (14.5\text{-}1)$$

i.e., the force that the sun exerts on the planet is directly proportional to the mass of the planet and inversely proportional to the square of the distance between the planet and the sun.

The minus sign in Eq. (14.4-14) has emerged straightforwardly from the algebraic development.

By Newton's third law, not only does the sun exert a force F_{s} on the planet, but the planet exerts an equal and opposite force F_{p} on the sun. Thus, Eq. (14.5-1) becomes

$$F_{\mathrm{p}}=\frac{4\pi^2 M_{\mathrm{p}}C_{\mathrm{p}}}{r^2}, \qquad (14.5\text{-}2)$$

where F_{p} is the force *on* the sun *by* the planet, M_{p} is the mass of the planet, and C_{p} is the constant $C_{\mathrm{p}}=1/K$ applicable to the equation for any of the planets. Similarly,

$$F_{\mathrm{s}}=-\frac{4\pi^2 M_{\mathrm{s}}C_{\mathrm{s}}}{r^2}, \qquad (14.5\text{-}3)$$

where the subscripts s have obvious meanings. But $C_s \neq 1/K$! Let us now, by Newton's third law, equate magnitudes: $F_s = F_p$ and

$$\frac{4\pi^2 M_s C_s}{r^2} = \frac{4\pi^2 M_p C_p}{r^2}$$

or

$$M_s C_s = M_p C_p . \tag{14.5-4}$$

Since action and reaction are symmetrical, we might expect that C_p in Eq. (14.5-2) should somehow involve M_s and that C_s in Eq. (14.4-5) should contain M_p. We can make this be the case if we rewrite Eq. (14.5-4) as

$$M_s M_p \frac{C_s}{M_p} = M_p M_s \frac{C_p}{M_s} \tag{14.5-5}$$

and set $C_s/M_p = C_p/M_s = G'$. Then, Eq. (14.5-3) becomes

$$F_s = -\frac{4\pi^2 G' M_s M_p}{r^2} \tag{14.5-6A}$$

$$= -\frac{G M_s M_p}{r^2} \tag{14.5-6B}$$

$$= -\frac{M_s M_p}{4\pi\gamma r^2} . \tag{14.5-6C}$$

The Eqs. (14.5-6) are all expressions of Newton's law of gravitation. It is most commonly written either in form B or form C. Most generally, M_s and M_p need not be the masses of the sun and a planet. They may be the masses of any two bodies, and the Eqs. (14.5-6) then give the forces of attraction between those two bodies; thus, Eqs. (14.5-6) are expressions of ***Newton's law of universal gravitation.*** We may state Newton's law of gravitation as: *Every body attracts every other body with a force which is directly proportional to the product of their masses and inversely proportional to the square of the distance between their centers.*

Newton's law of gravitation provides an example of the way in which a quantity defined in one way may exhibit properties which are entirely different from those implied by the original definition. In Sec. 4.16 we mentioned the fact that there are two distinct ways of comparing masses—by collision and by weighing. We have been dealing in this chapter with gravitational mass, i.e., the measure of the attraction that a body exerts on other bodies, rather than with the inertial mass, a measure of the momentum at a given velocity, that we emphasized in Chapter 4. The remarkable fact that these very different physical properties depended on the same property of a material object was no doubt recognized by Newton at the end of the seventeenth century, although he did not use the same language as we have in presenting the problem. The equivalence of these two aspects of mass was a subject of continued speculation by philosophers until the beginning of the twentieth century, when Einstein provided the first clarification of this point (Sec. 14.12). The physics of the twentieth century, following the lead of Einstein, has been characterized by the consideration of a large number of other physical quantities that make their appearance in connections far remote from those in which they have been originally defined.

EXERCISES

14.5-1 Discuss the physical meaning of the minus sign in Eq. (14.5-1). Comment on the sign of ΔF as a small change Δr is made in r.

14.5-2 Between Eqs. (14.5-5) and (14.5-6A), we set $C_s M_p = C_p/M_s = G'$. Argue that C_p and M_s are independent of the particular planet which is being considered but that C_s and M_p will vary from planet to planet.

14.5-3 Since only the separation r enters into Newton's law of universal gravitation, *directions* in space do not enter into energy calculations; thus the calculation of potential energies may be simplified by laying out r along the same line segment as shown in the figure. Compute the work done in moving a mass M from B to F.

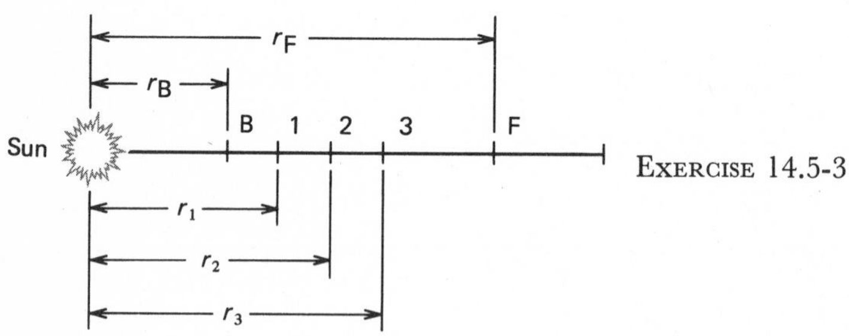

EXERCISE 14.5-3

First, argue that in computing the work between adjacent positions whose distances are, say, r_2 and r_3, $F_{23} = -GM_s Mp/r_2 r_3$ is a better average value to use than $F_{22} = -GM_s Mp/r_2^2$ or $F_{33} = -GM_s Mp/r_3^2$.

Second, if n is chosen very large—if points 2 and 3 are very close together—F_{23} becomes even better as an expression for the average force between points 2 and 3.

Third, express the work from point 2 to point 3, starting with $\Delta W_{23} = -F_{23}\,\Delta r_{23}$.

Fourth, show that, since $\Delta r_{12} = r_2 - r_1$, $\Delta r_{23} = r_3 - r_2$, etc., a lucky simplification results whereby we can add $\Delta W_{B1} + \Delta W_{12} + \Delta W_{23} + \cdots =$ total work and $(-F_{B1}\,\Delta r_{B1} - F_{12}\,\Delta r_{12} - F_{23}\,\Delta r_{23} + \cdots) =$ total work. Fifth, compare your results with Eq. (14.4-12).

14.6 The Gravitational Constant

We have not heretofore had to express a numerical value for G or for γ in Eqs. (14.5-6). This is because we have been concerned only with proportionalities and we needed to know only that the constant of proportionality exists—not what its numerical value is. As a matter of fact, astronomical observations cannot determine the gravitational constant. The laboratory determination of the constant also presents difficulties, since the gravitational forces between masses that can be handled in the laboratory are extremely small.

About a century and a half after Newton's discovery of the inverse square law, Henry Cavendish (1731–1810) succeeded in measuring the force of attraction between two known masses separated by a measured distance. As the result of his work and that of later investigators, we now know that

$$G = 6.67 \times 10^{-11}\ \text{Nm}^2/\text{kg}^2, \tag{14.6-1}$$

$$4\pi\gamma = 1.50 \times 10^{10}\ \text{kg}^2/\text{Nm}^2, \tag{14.6-2}$$

and

$$\gamma = 1.19 \times 10^{9}\ \text{kg}^2/\text{Nm}^2. \tag{14.6-3}$$

One of the important consequences of the knowledge of the gravitational constant is that it enables us to determine the mass of the earth. Since a mass m is attracted to the earth by a force of magnitude mg, we have from Eq. (14.5-6C)

$$-mg = -mM_e/4\pi\gamma R_e^2$$

where M_e is the mass of the earth and R_e is its radius; therefore,

$$M_e = 4\pi\gamma R_e^2 g. \tag{14.6-4}$$

Substitution of the measured value $R_e = 6.37 \times 10^6$ m and the known values of γ and g into this equation shows that the ***mass of the earth*** is 5.98×10^{24} kg.

Illustrative Example

An artificial satellite of the earth is in such an orbit that its closest approach to the earth is at a height of 150 km and its farthest distance is at a height of 1500 km. What is its period?

We may solve this either by brute force or by the much easier use of an analogy. Let us try brute force first. It follows from Eq. (14.5-6C) and the argument leading to it that the potential energy of a satellite of mass m in the gravitational field of the earth, whose mass is M_E, is

$$PE = -\frac{M_E m}{4\pi\gamma r}.$$

Inserting this value into Eq. (14.4-8) and using Eq. (14.4-11A), we find that

$$\frac{M_E m}{4\pi\gamma} = \frac{4\pi^2 a^3 b^2 m^2}{m b^2 \tau^2},$$

so that

$$\tau^2 = \frac{16\pi^3\gamma a^3}{M_E}. \tag{14.6-5}$$

The period, then, depends only on the mass of the earth and on the semimajor axis of the elliptical orbit.

To find a, we note that ***apogee***, or the greatest distance of the satellite from the center of the earth, is

$$1.50 \times 10^6 \text{ m} + 6.37 \times 10^6 \text{ m} = 7.87 \times 10^6 \text{ m}.$$

Similarly, the ***perigee***, or the least distance of the satellite from the center of the earth, is

$$6.37 \times 10^6 \text{ m} + 0.150 \times 10^6 \text{ m} = 6.52 \times 10^6 \text{ m}.$$

The sum of these two (cf. Fig. 14.3), is $2a$, so

$$a = \frac{7.87 + 6.52}{2} \times 10^6 \text{ m} = 7.20 \times 10^6 \text{ m}.$$

We now substitute this value, $\gamma = 1.19 \times 10^9 \text{ kg}^2/\text{Nm}^2$, and $M_E = 5.98 \times 10^{24}$ kg into Eq. (14.6-5) to get

$$\tau^2 = \frac{(16)(\pi^3)(1.19)(10)^9 \, (\text{kg}^2/\text{Nm}^2)(7.20)^3(10)^{18} \text{ m}^3}{(5.98)(10)^{24} \text{ kg}}$$

$$= 36.70 \times 10^6 \text{ sec}^2.$$

$$\tau = 6.069 \times 10^3 \text{ sec} = 101.2 \text{ min}.$$

Having obtained this result, we note that Eq. (14.6-5) is equivalent to Kepler's third law of planetary motion. It applies to all satellites of the earth, provided only that their masses are much less than that of the earth (cf. Prob. 14.12). We know that the moon orbits the earth in a nearly circular orbit, of radius $r_m = a_m = 3.85 \times 10^8$ m, with a period $\tau_m = 27.55$ days $= 3.967 \times 10^4$ min. (see Ex. 14.6-3). Applying Eq. (14.6-5), we have

$$\tau^2/\tau_m{}^2 = a^3/a_m{}^3,$$

$$\tau^2 = \frac{(3.967)^2(10)^8 \, (\text{min})^2(7.20)^3(10)^{18} \text{ m}^3}{(3.85)^3(10)^{24} \text{ m}^3} = 1.029 \times 10^4 \text{ min}^2$$

Hence, we find

$$\tau = 101.4 \text{ min}.$$

The two answers that we have obtained agree to three significant figures.

EXERCISES

14.6-1 What is the force of attraction between two masses of 1.00 kg each, with their centers at a distance of 1.00 m?

14.6-2 Assuming Newton's law of gravitation and that the moon travels around the earth in a circular orbit of radius r_m, show that the moon is continually accelerated toward the earth with an acceleration of magnitude

$$a = -M_e/4\pi\gamma r_m{}^2.$$

Further, if the period of revolution of the moon is τ_m, show that the mass of the earth must be

$$M_e = 16\pi^3\gamma r_m{}^3/\tau_m{}^2.$$

14.6-3 By combining the result of Ex. 14.6-2 with Eq. (14.6-4), calculate the value of g you would expect at the surface of the earth. Take $r_m = 3.85 \times 10^8$ m and $\tau_m = 27.55$ days. How closely does your computed value of g agree with the average observed value?

14.6-4 Taking the period of revolution of the earth about the sun as 365.26 days,* and the distance of the earth from the sun as 14.9×10^{10} m, find the mass of the sun.

14.6-5 One of the moons of Jupiter travels in an orbit that is approximately circular. The radius of the orbit is 4.27×10^5 km and the periodic time of rev is 1 day: 18 hr: 28 min. From these data and the value of γ find the mass of Jupiter.

14.6-6 Show that the dimensions of γ are given by

$$[\gamma] = [m\ell^{-3}t^2].$$

14.6-7 The mass of Jupiter is 315 times that of the earth. The sidereal period of the moon about the earth is 27.5 days, and the mean radius of the moon's orbit is 38×10^4 km. Determine the period of a satellite of Jupiter if the orbital radius is the same as that of our moon.

14.6-8 Calculate the relative magnitudes of the gravitational attraction between the sun and the earth and the sun and Jupiter.

14.7 Field Strength

The derivation of the law of gravitation, Eqs. (14.5-6), from Kepler's laws implicity makes use of the fact that the sun and the planets are at a distance apart that is very large compared with their sizes. Otherwise we would not know between which two points in the bodies r should be measured. In deducing Eq. (14.6-4), we have assumed that the appropriate value of r for a body on the surface of the earth is the distance of the body from the center of the earth, and in this case we certainly cannot say that the distance between the bodies is large compared with the radius of the earth. We must now proceed to justify this assumption, and in doing so we shall obtain a number of important and useful results.

We are assured by our astronomical results that the law of gravitation, given by Eqs. (14.5-6), holds if the linear dimensions of the two masses m_1 and m_2 are very small compared with the distance r that separates them. We shall therefore study first the behavior of two small bodies. Suppose that we fix ourselves with respect to one of these bodies, of mass M and observe a second body, of mass m, which we call a ***test body***, in the neighborhood of the first. We find that the test body m is always attracted to the body M by a force given by

$$F = -mM/4\pi\gamma r^2.$$

We then see that the force per unit mass on the test body is given by

$$g = -M/4\pi\gamma r^2. \qquad (14.7\text{-}1)$$

* Compare Sec. 2.17. This is the sidereal year, i.e., the time for one revolution with respect to the stars. The tropical year, or the time for one revolution with respect to the seasons, is slightly less than the sidereal year. This is because the axis of rotation of the earth very slowly describes the surface of a cone with respect to the stars.

It is now possible to make a generalization from the ideas expressed in the three preceding sentences. We can say that the presence of the mass M has produced a change in the nature of the space surrounding it. This change is such that any mass placed in that space will experience a force per unit mass given by $\vec{g}$, where the magnitude of $\vec{g}$ depends on the position of the test mass. We describe this change in the properties of space by saying that the mass M has produced a ***gravitational field*** in the space surrounding it. The usefulness of this notion can readily be demonstrated. Obviously the single mass M produces one special type of gravitational field. Let us now consider a case in which a large number of masses surround a test body m (Fig. 14.7). The test

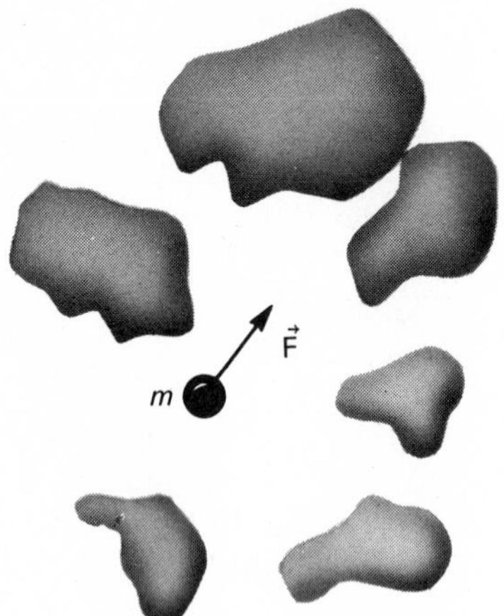

FIG. 14.7 Measurement of gravitational field strength.

body will be attracted by each one of these masses, and as a result it will be subject to a force $\vec{F}$ which is the resultant (Sec. 6.3) of all the forces of attraction of the surrounding masses. The presence of this force tells us that there is a gravitational field at the point at which the test body m is located.

We may describe the effect of the surrounding masses on the test body by saying that *if a test body of mass m experiences a force* $\vec{F}$, *at a given point, as a result of the gravitational attraction of other bodies, then a gravitational field exists at that point.* The ***gravitational field strength*** $\vec{g}$ is then given by

$$\vec{g} = \vec{F}/m, \tag{14.7-2}$$

and we can determine that strength by the use of any test object m.* The unit in which g is measured is N/kg or its equivalent m/sec^2. We can thus say that the gravitational field strength on the surface of the earth is 9.80 N/kg directed toward the center of the earth.

* Since the presence of the mass m of the test body, even though small, will distort the gravitational field in the neighborhood of m, Eq. (14.7-2) is sometimes stated more rigorously as $\vec{g} = \lim_{m \to 0} \vec{F}/m$. In this case, we can make the distortion as small as we wish by taking m as small as we wish. The ratio $\vec{F}/m$ will still be finite, however, and will be the strength of the gravitational field at the positition of m.

14.8 Lines of Force and Gravitational Displacement

It is sometimes helpful to supplement the notion of gravitational field strength by a pictorial representation. To arrive at the latter, consider that we have a small test body at some point such as P (Fig. 14.8a) in the neighborhood of the mass M. The gravitational force on this test body is in the direction shown by the arrow. If we allow the body to move very slowly in the direction of the force, it will be displaced along the path PP′P″M. This continuous path, which is always in the direction of the force on a test body, is known as a ***line of force.***

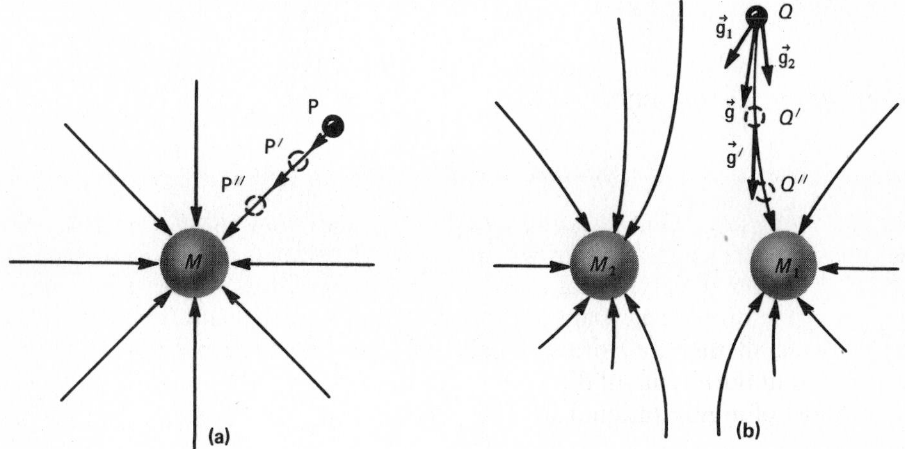

FIG. 14.8 Gravitational lines of force.

Depending on the starting points chosen, we can draw an infinite number of lines of force in the neighborhood of a small concentrated mass such as M in Fig. 14.8a. Furthermore, these lines of force will all be radial lines, since the field strength vector always points toward the mass. In the case of extended masses, or of a combination of masses, however, the situation is not so simple. For example, at point Q in Fig. 14.8b, the test body is attracted by both of the masses M_1 and M_2 and the resulting field strength is

$$\vec{g} = \vec{g}_2 + \vec{g}_1,$$

where $\vec{g}_1$ and $\vec{g}_2$ are the field strengths due to M_1 and M_2, respectively. As the body moves from Q to Q′, it is approaching M_1 relatively faster than it is M_2. Hence, at Q′ the field strength is $\vec{g}'$, which is not, in general, parallel to $\vec{g}$ nor does it have the same magnitude as $\vec{g}$. Tracing the path of the test body farther, we find that the line of force passing through Q is curved along the path QQ′Q″M_1. Lines of force passing through other points than Q are also shown in the figure.

We shall find it convenient to use another vector, in addition to the field strength, for defining a gravitational field. This vector, known as the ***gravitational displacement***, will be useful to us in what follows. It is defined as

$$\vec{G} = \gamma \vec{g}. \tag{14.8-1}$$

The gravitational displacement vector is parallel to and proportional to the field strength $\vec{g}$, since it is simply a constant multiple of $\vec{g}$. The dimensions of G are $[m\ell^{-2}]$ (cf. Ex. 14.6-6), a fact that can also be emphasized by writing Eq. (14.7-1) in the simple form

$$G = \gamma g = -M/4\pi r^2. \tag{14.8-2}$$

The magnitude of the displacement at a distance r from a concentrated mass M is thus equal to the mass divided by the area of a sphere of radius r (cf. Eq. 12.8-1), and there is a clear analogy between the gravitational displacement due to a mass M and the intensity of light due to a source of power P.

It should be observed that $|\vec{G}| = G$ as used in the preceding paragraph is distinctly different from the Cavendish constant of Eq. (14.6-1). Since we shall usually employ $4\pi\gamma$ or γ rather than the latter [Eqs. (14.6-2) and (14.6-3)], there will be no confusion.

14.9 Lines and Tubes of Displacement

We saw in the preceding section that an infinite number of lines of displacement (or lines of force) could be drawn in the neighborhood of any mass M (Fig. 14.8a). In order to arrive at a more useful representation of the field, suppose that we agree quite arbitrarily to draw n lines of displacement for every unit of mass. We shall therefore draw, in all, nM lines, all pointing toward M and distributed uniformly in all directions. We may take n to be as large as we wish. This model of a gravitational field is illustrated by Fig. 14.9. In this figure we

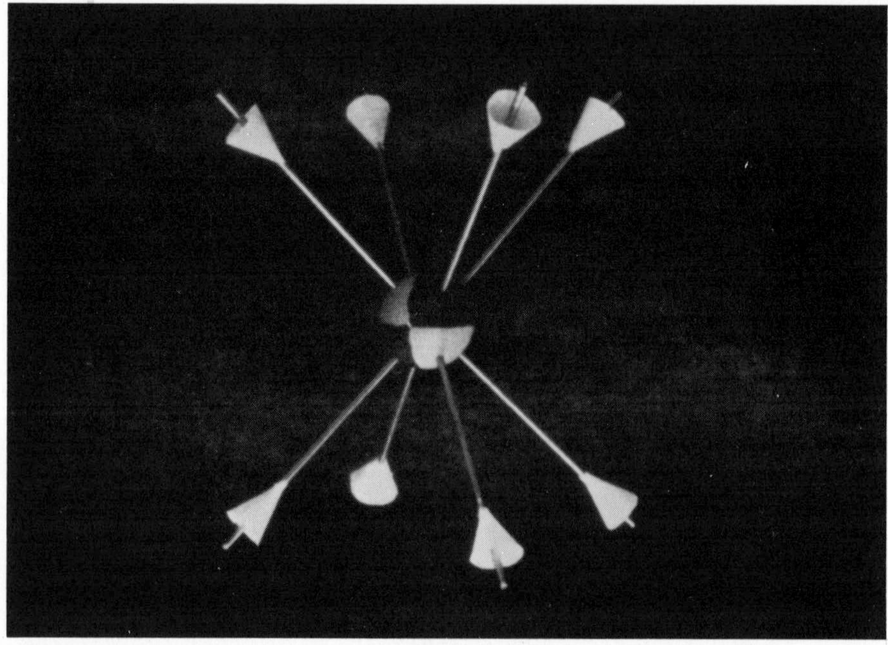

FIG. 14.9 Tubes of gravitational flux.

have chosen $n = 8$. The surface of the ball is divided into eight equal areas—"triangles" whose sides are segments of great circles. Each such "triangle" has a line of displacement directed toward its center and the center of the ball. These lines of displacement, then, are uniformly distributed in space around the particle mass. *By any suitable scheme we can devise in order to distribute the lines of displacement uniformly in space, we can make n as large as we wish.* We can accomplish this task in thought more easily than in practice.

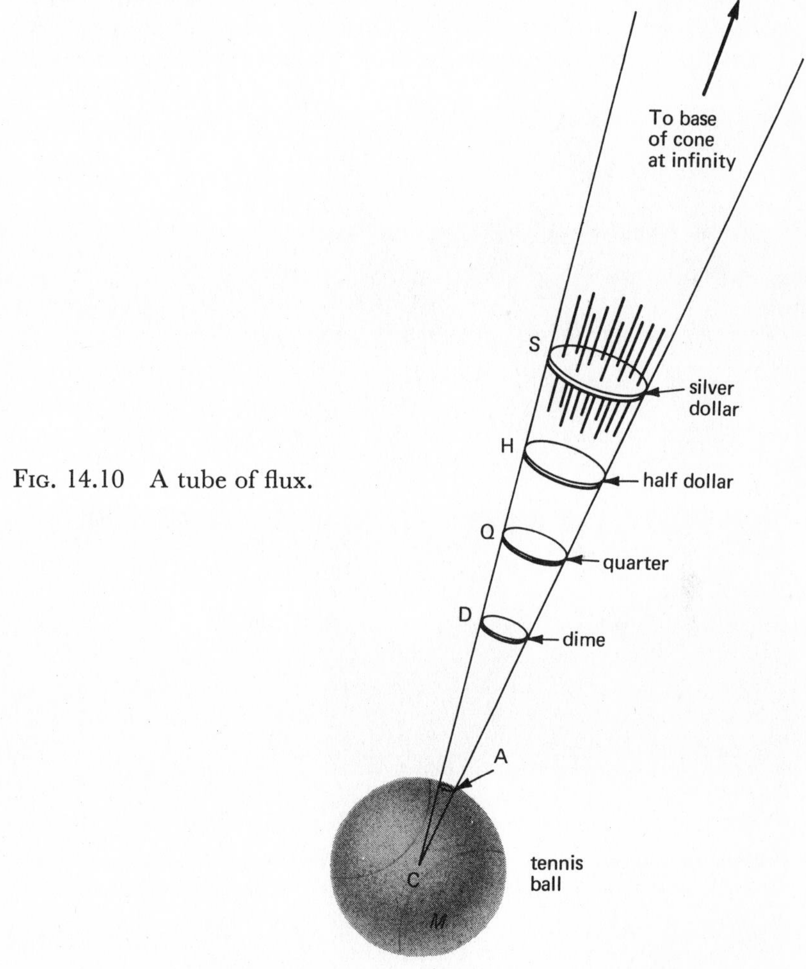

FIG. 14.10 A tube of flux.

In order to illustrate the usefulness of this model of lines of displacement for discussing gravitational fields, let us consider Fig. 14.10. If, say, the mass M is a tennis ball, we can *imagine* that we inscribe small equal areas A all over the surface of the ball. There would then be about 60 such equal areas covering the entire surface of the ball. Now suppose that each area A has ten lines* of

* For the purposes of the model, we could just as well have chosen one line or a hundred lines to converge into each area A.

displacement distributed uniformly over it; these lines, of course, will be radial, all pointing inward toward C, the center of the ball. The analogy with a cocklebur comes to mind, one with 600 prickles.

But let us give our attention to the ten lines that will point into the area A shown in Fig. 14.10. Since these lines are radial, all pointing inward toward C, they will all lie inside the frustrum of a cone whose apex is at C and whose cross section at the surface of the ball is A; the base of the frustrum should be considered to be at infinity. Now if we imagine a dime, a quarter, a half dollar, and a silver dollar fitted into the cone as shown (the figure is approximately to scale), we may discuss the number of lines per square centimeter at each position.

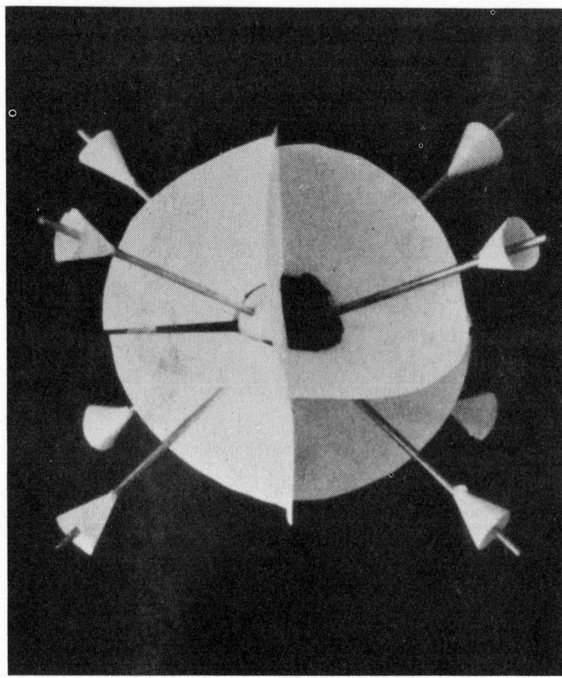

FIG. 14.11 Division of space into tubes.

Thus, since the area of a dime is about 2.4 cm^2, there are 10/2.4 or about 4.2 lines/cm^2 at position D. Similarly, at position Q, we get $10/4.5 = 2.2$ lines/cm^2, the area of a quarter being about 4.5 cm^2. And, since the areas of a half dollar and a silver dollar are 7.1 cm^2 and 11.0 cm^2, respectively, we get line densities of 1.4 and 0.91 lines/cm^2, respectively.

A little thought should convince the reader that the number of lines/cm^2 becomes a measure of field strength. Thus, if we are twice as far from C in the cone, the cross section of the cone is four times as great; hence, the number of lines per square centimeter is one-fourth as great. It works just the same as the inverse square law [cf. Eqs. (14.5-1) and (14.5-6)].

A cone such as that in Fig. 14.10, which contains a number of lines, none of which pass into or out of the cone through its walls, is called a ***tube of displacement***. A tube of displacement is a pictographic representation of *relative* field strengths where, in effect, we compare field strengths by making an inverse comparison of cross sections.

Tubes of displacement need not be conical. For example, we can extend the model of Fig. 14.9 by attaching a pyramidal tube as shown in Fig. 14.11. The walls of this tube of displacement are four planes that make a symmetrical four-sided pyramid, the angle between opposite faces at the center of the ball being 90°. We emphasize that the size and shape of the tube and the number of lines it contains is arbitrary and is determined only by the convenience for pictography.

We should note, however, that not all situations will yield such axially symmetric tubes of displacement as those in Figs. 14.10 and 14.11. Thus, in Fig. 14.12, we see two tubes of displacement attached to the mass M_2 of Fig. 14.8b. Note that one tube is a sort of "bent" cone while the other tube is horn-shaped.

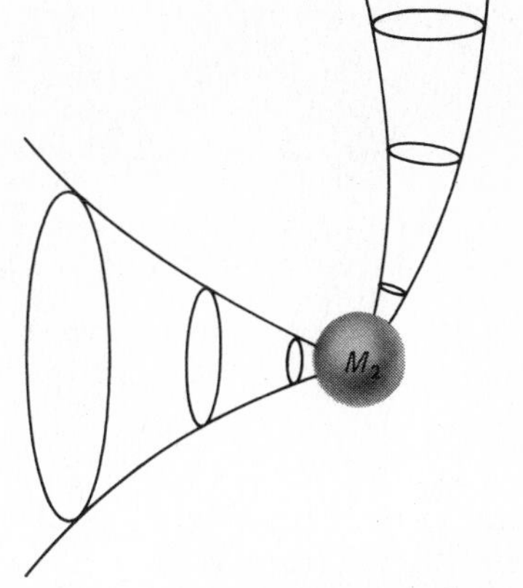

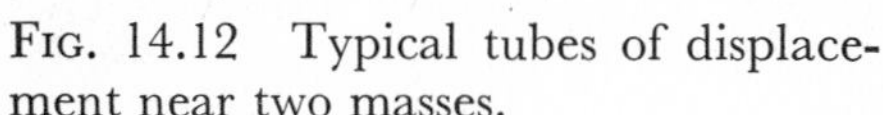
FIG. 14.12 Typical tubes of displacement near two masses.

14.10 *Gravitational Flux*

Let us again consider a single particle as in Fig. 14.13. Let M be the mass of the particle and draw n lines of displacement per unit of mass. There will then be nM lines of displacement pointing radially into the particle. If we construct a sphere S of radius r surrounding the particle, the number of lines passing *inward* through the surface of the sphere will be nM. We can construct tubes of displacement by grouping sets of n neighboring lines together. If this is done for all of the lines, then we shall have M tubes of displacement passing *into* the sphere, or we shall have $-M$ tubes passing *outward* through the sphere.

The number of tubes that pass outward through each unit area of the sphere will thus be $-M/4\pi r^2$ and, from Eq. (14.8-2), we see that this is equal to the magnitude of the gravitational displacement $\vec{G}$ at any point on the surface of the sphere. We have thus shown that the gravitational displacement at a point is equal to the number of tubes crossing the unit area of a surface perpendicular to them. If we set Γ (Greek capital *gamma*), the ***gravitational flux***, equal to the total number of tubes of displacement crossing any surface, we find for the sphere that

$$\Gamma = 4\pi r^2 G = -M. \tag{14.10-1}$$

The great value of the concept of gravitational flux is that it gives us a convenient method of finding the field due to many extended distributions of mass. We shall study that method shortly.

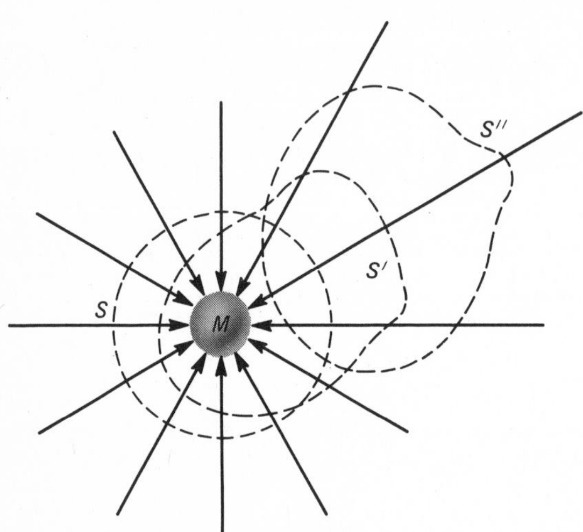

FIG. 14.13 Gauss' law for a single mass.

14.11 Gauss' Law

Before proceeding with the study of the field due to extended distributions of mass, we shall consider the flux through any surface in the neighborhood of a mass. If the surface totally surrounds the mass, as does S' in Fig. 14.13, every tube of displacement crossing the spherical surface S must also pass through the surface S'. Hence, the gravitational flux through S' is $-M$, regardless of the shape of S'. On the other hand, if the surface is such as that shown by S'', and does not include M, every tube of displacement due to M either misses the surface entirely or passes through the surface as many times inward as outward. If we count inward passages as negative and outward as positive, as we did in Eq. (14.10-1), the total flux through S'' due to the presence of M is therefore zero.

Since any mass M located totally within a surface contributes a flux $-M$ through the surface and any mass outside contributed no flux, the flux through any surface can be computed easily by adding up all the masses enclosed by the surface. Thus, in Fig. 14.14, the flux through the arbitrary surface S is

$$\Gamma = -M_1 - M_2 - M_3 - M_4.$$

The conclusion just reached, that *the flux through any surface is the negative of the total mass enclosed within the surface*, is known as ***Gauss' law***, after its discoverer, Karl Friedrich Gauss (1777–1855).

With the help of Gauss' law, we can compute the gravitational field due to an extended symmetrical mass, without the condition that the dimensions of the mass shall be small compared with the distance from its center (cf. Sec. 14.7). For example, consider the solid homogeneous spherical mass M of

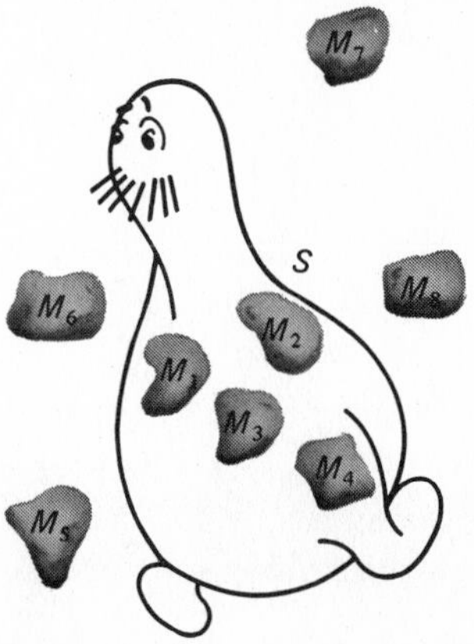

FIG. 14.14 Gauss' law for a number of masses. (Courtesy of Al Capp, copyright, United Features Syndicate.)

radius a shown in Fig. 14.15. If we surround this sphere by a spherical surface of radius $r > a$, the total flux through this surface must be, by Gauss' law, $\Gamma = -M$.

In order to use this result to determine the value of g on this surface, we notice that the direction of the vector $\vec{G} = \gamma\vec{g}$ must be along the radius of the sphere. Consider, for example, the direction of $\vec{g}$ at the point P (Fig. 14.15).

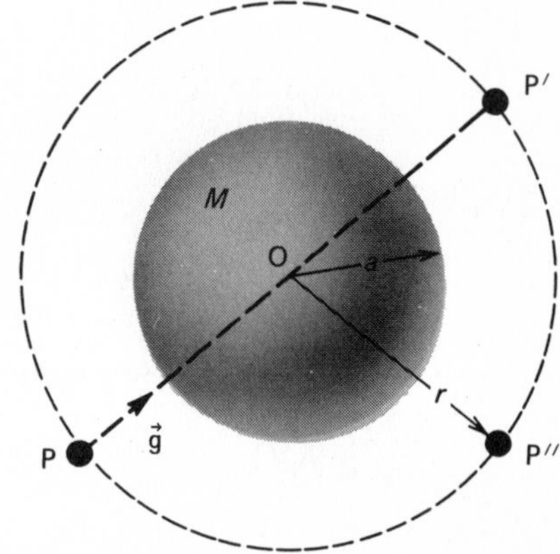

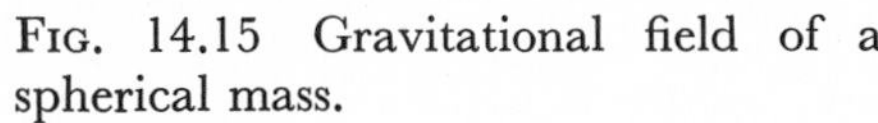
FIG. 14.15 Gravitational field of a spherical mass.

The force on a test mass is the sum of all the forces due to the individual attractions of all the parts of the sphere. If we draw any plane containing P and O, there is exactly the same amount of attracting matter above the plane as below, and these equal amounts are similarly situated above and below. Hence, $\vec{g}$ is certainly in this plane. Since this is true for any plane through P and O, $\vec{g}$ and $\vec{G}$ must lie in the line PO, which is the intersection of all planes through P and

O. In addition, any other point P′ or P″ on the sphere is situated in an exactly similar relation to the sphere as is P, so that $\vec{G}$ must have exactly the same magnitude at P′ or P″ as at P. We have thus made use of the symmetry of a sphere, which indicates that all properties of the sphere vary in the same way in all directions from the center, to prove that the gravitational field of a solid sphere is always directed along the radius and is constant over a sphere of constant radius. This means that the flux per unit area is constant over the sphere and is equal to G. The total flux is therefore

$$\Gamma = 4\pi r^2 G = -M,$$

and it follows that

$$G = -M/4\pi r^2 \tag{14.11-1A}$$

and

$$g = G/\gamma = -M/4\pi\gamma r^2. \tag{14.11-1B}$$

Comparison of the two Eqs. (14.11-1) with Eqs. (14.8-1) and (14.7-1) tells us then that *the gravitational field at any point outside a uniform sphere is exactly the same as that of an equal mass concentrated at the center of the sphere.*

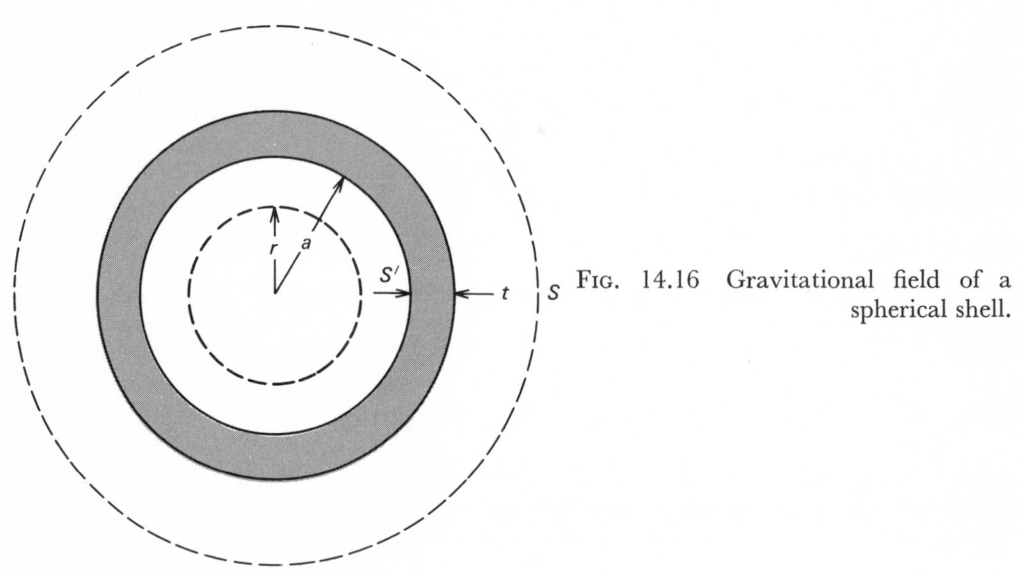

FIG. 14.16 Gravitational field of a spherical shell.

Another interesting application of Gauss' law can be made to the case of a hollow spherical shell (Fig. 14.16) of internal radius a and external radius $a + t$, where t is the thickness of the shell. If the reader considers a spherical surface S (of radius $> a + t$) drawn entirely outside the spherical shell, he shall have no difficulty in convincing himself that a spherical shell will have the same property as a solid sphere and will attract bodies outside it in exactly the same way as an equal mass concentrated at the center of the sphere (Ex. 14.11-3). In considering the sphere S' ($r < a$) drawn entirely within the shell, our symmetry argument again tells us that, everywhere on S′, $\vec{G}$ is of the same magnitude and must be radial. However, there is no mass within S′, so that there can be no flux through this surface. Thus $4\pi r^2 G = 0$ and since $4\pi r^2$ is not zero $\vec{G}$, and therefore $\vec{g}$, must be zero everywhere within the sphere. We thus obtain the rather surprising result that a *uniform spherical shell exerts no gravitational force on a body placed inside it.*

The results obtained in this section for spherical objects by the combined use of Gauss' law and symmetry arguments can also be obtained by splitting up the solid sphere or the shell into a large number of small particles and combining the attractions of all these particles on a single test mass. We shall not go into the details of such calculations here, but their nature can be indicated in a somewhat qualitative way. Thus, it is clear that the total gravitational force on a test mass *at the center* of a spherical shell will be zero. The individual particles of the shell do pull on the test mass, but they pull on it equally in opposite directions, and the resultant of all the forces they exert is zero. But now consider the force on a test mass at point P (Fig. 14.17) within a thin

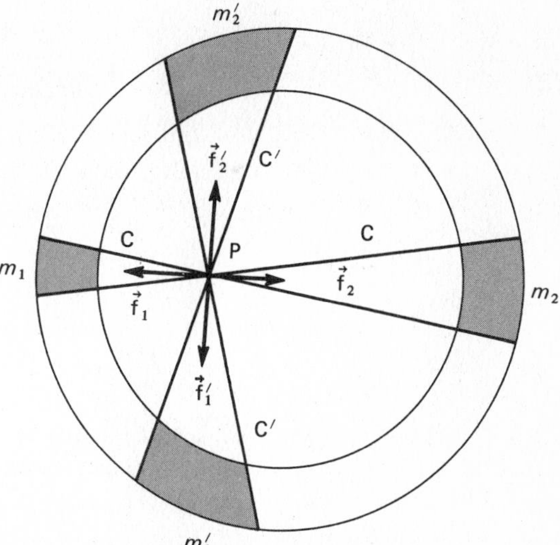

FIG. 14.17 Balancing of gravitational forces inside a shell.

spherical shell. Suppose that we draw the double cone CC, which cuts out the masses m_1 and m_2 from the shell. The mass m_1 is closer to P and is smaller, whereas the mass m_2 is farther from P and is larger. By an argument that depends on the well-known geometrical fact that the area of the base of a cone is proportional to the square of its height, we can show that the force $\vec{f}_1$, due to the attraction of the mass m_1, is exactly equal and opposite to the force $\vec{f}_2$ due to the mass m_2. In a similar way, it can be shown that the attractions $\vec{f'}_1$ and $\vec{f'}_2$ on a test mass at P due to the masses m_2' and m_1', cut out by any other double cone C′C′, are also equal and opposite. It is in this way that the combined attractions of all the particles of the shell result in zero force on a test mass at any point P inside the shell.

It is clear that Gauss' law enables us to demonstrate our results in a much simpler manner than that which discusses the attractions of all the particles of a sphere or a spherical shell on a test body. We must emphasize, however, the fact that Gauss' law as we have presented it requires some symmetry that tells us that G is constant over the surface under discussion. We shall see later (Chapter 15) that Gauss' law is also applicable in many other cases in which symmetry is present. But if there is no symmetry, we must revert to a consideration of all the attractions of the individual particles.

EXERCISES

14.11-1 Assuming that the radius of the moon is 1.74×10^6 m and that the mass of the moon is 7.33×10^{22} kg, calculate the value of g on its surface.

14.11-2 Calculate the position of the point on the line joining the earth and the moon at which the gravitational field strength, due to these two bodies alone, is zero. If a small body were placed a little closer to the moon than this distance, what would happen to it?

14.11-3 Show that the gravitational field strength outside the spherical shell of Fig. 14.16 is identical with that of a point mass located at the center of the shell. Show that this mass is

$$M = (4\pi\rho/3)[(t + a)^3 - a^3],$$

where ρ is the density of the spherical shell.

14.11-4 Show that the gravitational field strength inside the solid sphere of Fig. 14.15 is proportional to the distance from the center of the sphere. Assume uniform density.

14.11-5 Using the result of Ex. 14.11-4, show that, if the radius of the earth is a and its density is uniform, the value of g at the bottom of a mine of depth h is given by $g = g_0(1 - h/a)$, where g_0 is the value of g on the surface.

14.11-6 An airplane has a mass of 5.0×10^4 kg. What is its weight on the surface of the earth? By how much will its weight change if it flies to a height of 8.0 km?

14.11-7 Consider qualitatively the nature of the tube of force model of the gravitational field directly along the line joining the center of the earth to the center of the moon.

14.12 The General Relativity Theory of Gravitation

The Newtonian theory of gravitation discussed in the preceding sections gives an extremely accurate account of the behavior of almost all gravitating systems. In particular, it is sufficiently accurate to describe the motions of all the planets except one. It should be recognised that the orbit of a given planet is not exactly elliptical because it is subject to the attractions of other planets as well as the sun. The influences of these other planets produce perturbations in the orbit of any particular planet. The perturbation of one planet on another can be calculated with great accuracy. In fact, it was possible for the theoretical astronomers John Couch Adams (1819–1892) and Urbain Leverrier (1811–1877) to predict the existence of the planet Neptune by a study of the perturbations of the planet Uranus. In more recent years, unexplained perturbations in the orbits of Uranus and of Neptune led Percival Lowell (1855–1916) to predict the presence of yet another planet, and as a result the planet Pluto was discovered in 1930 by Clyde Tombaugh (1906–). At another extreme in the solar system, the perturbations on the motion of the planet Mercury remained unexplained for a long time. This planet moves in a rosette-like curve as though its elliptic orbit were rotating as a whole around the sun (Fig. 14.18). In the figure, the axis of the ellipse is shown to have rotated through quite a large angle in a single revolution of Mercury around the sun. Actually, the rotation of the axis of the ellipse is at the extraordinarily slow rate of 2.78×10^{-3} radians per century (= 0.159 deg/cent = 574 seconds of arc per century), whereas Mercury completes its orbit in 88 days. Of this amount, 2.58×10^{-3} radians per century is predicted from the influence of other planets, leaving an unexplained discrepancy of 0.20×10^{-3} radians per century. This small discrepancy is much larger than the experimental error.

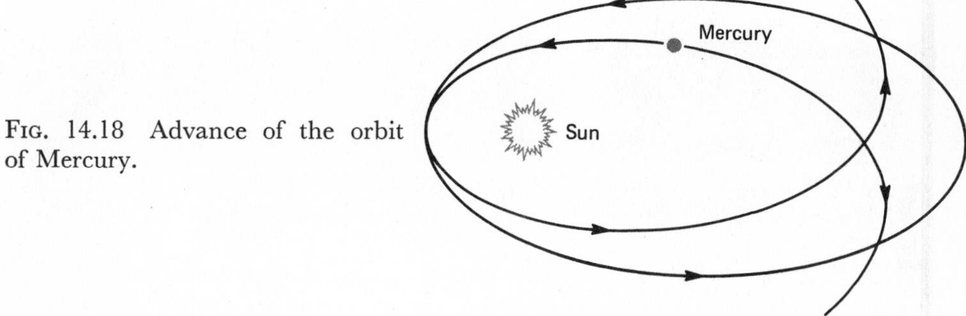

FIG. 14.18 Advance of the orbit of Mercury.

Einstein's success with the special relativity theory led him to develop the ***general relativity theory***, which deals with the transformation of the observations of two observers who are accelerated with respect to one another We cannot follow him in detail here, but we can give a qualitative picture of some of the ideas behind his work and of the results he obtained. Let us consider what sort of observations might be made inside a totally enclosed elevator. If the elevator is not moving, an observer inside it will find that a mass m will be subject to a force $-m\vec{g}$ in a vertical direction and that a body will fall to the floor with an acceleration $-\vec{g}$. The same will be true if the elevator is moving at a constant speed. However, if the cable is cut and the elevator falls freely with an acceleration $-\vec{g}$, then a mass m released inside the car will maintain its place in the car, since it, too, will be falling with an acceleration $-\vec{g}$ with respect to the earth. An observer in such a car would then say that no gravitational field existed inside his car, since a body released in the space in the car would simply stay where it was; or if the body were given a definite velocity, it would move in a straight line across the car.

Suppose that the same car were moved into interstellar space in a region remote from stars or planets In such a place, the value of the gravitational field strength will be extremely small and objects in the elevator car will not be subject to any appreciable gravitational attraction. Under these circumstances, suppose that the car is accelerated. The observer in the car will then find that every object in the car is apparently subject to a force $\vec{F}$ proportional to its mass m (Fig. 14.19) and to the acceleration $\vec{a}$ of the car. If the car were closed and he could not see outside, he might infer that the car was in a gravitational field of intensity $-\vec{a}$, since his test body is subject to a force $\vec{F} = -m\vec{a}$. It would be impossible for him to decide whether he is hanging at rest in a gravitational field of intensity $-\vec{a}$ or whether his system is accelerated as in Fig. 14.19. From

Fig. 14.19 Forces in an accelerated elevator.

such arguments as these, Einstein came to the conclusion that there is no difference between the properties of a system subject to a gravitational field and those of an accelerated system far removed from all other matter. This correspondence between the forces on a given mass resulting from an acceleration and from gravitation is known as the ***Einstein principle of equivalence*** of gravitational fields and accelerations. The effect of one is indistinguishable from that of the other, and it is clear that gravitational mass and inertial mass must be one and the same thing (cf. Sec. 14.5).

We must now make one more investigation in our accelerated car. Suppose a light source is located at S and an observer with a telescope is at O, both at the same height above the floor of the car (Fig. 14.20). During the time $t = D/c$ which the light takes to travel across the car, the velocity of the car will have increased by an amount

$$\Delta v = at = aD/c. \tag{14.12-1}$$

Thus, there is a relative velocity Δv between the observer O at the time when he receives the light and the source S at the time when the light was emitted.

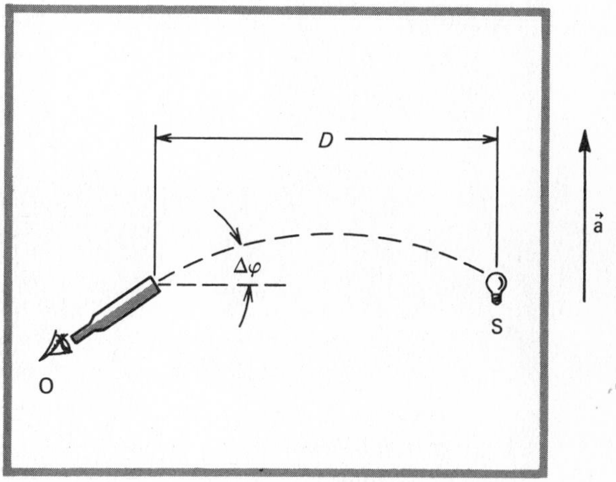

FIG. 14.20 Bending of light in an accelerated system.

In addition to the component c parallel to the floor of the car, the photons reaching the observer O have a downward component Δv given by Eq. (14.12-1). If this light is to enter a telescope at O, the latter must be tilted upward at an angle $\Delta\phi$ with the horizontal, given by

$$\Delta\phi = \Delta v/c = aD/c^2, \tag{14.12-2}$$

where the angle ϕ is measured in radians. Hence, the path of the light from S to O will appear curved. This curvature is too small to be detected except when very large accelerations or tremendous distances of light travel are involved. For example, if we set $a = g = 9.80$ m/sec^2 and $D = 100$ km, $\Delta\phi$ is found to be only 6.2×10^{-10} degrees. Near the sun the gravitational field is much stronger than that on the earth, and the presence of a curvature of light rays that pass close to the sun has been demonstrated. This is done by the observation of the apparent position of a star whose light passes close to the sun during a total solar eclipse. It is found that the star under these circumstances does not appear to be in its true position.

A result such as we have just obtained requires us to reconsider the geometry on which we have based our whole discussion of physics. If we hold to the notion that a light ray travels in a straight line, we see that in a gravitational field we must expect a different geometry from that to which we are accustomed. If we call a straight line the shortest distance between two points, we must consider carefully how a measuring rod behaves in a gravitational field. The discussion of this point takes us beyond the scope of this book, but it leads us to the result that the path of a light ray is also the shortest path between two points as measured by measuring rods. In discussing geometry in strong gravitational fields, therefore, we cannot maintain the notions of Euclid. We define a ***geodesic*** as a light path, or the shortest path between two points in a gravitational field. We may then consider figures (which we call triangles) bounded by three geodesics and find that these figures do not exactly obey the laws of Euclid's geometry. The sum of the three angles of a triangle in the accelerated car we have discussed would be greater than two right angles.

This discussion has been carried out in detail by Einstein and, as a consequence of his work, he was able to obtain three extremely important results:

1. He explained the motion of Mercury to an accuracy well within the experimental error.*
2. He predicted that a photon passing close to the sun will experience a gravitational deflection through an angle of 8.4×10^{-6} radians, where the best experimental values indicate a deflection between 7.8×10^{-6} and 9.6×10^{-6} radians.
3. He predicted also that the energy of a photon emitted by a given atom in the sun should be lower (due to the effect of gravitation on clocks) by 2 parts in 10^6 than that emitted by the same atom on the earth, with a correspondingly greater shift for heavier bodies. The question of the agreement of observation with this last prediction is more open to dispute than is the case of the other two, but it seems that there is evidence that would indicate that Einstein's notions provide a closer approach to the observations than that presented by other theories.

We cannot say that the general relativity theory is a final theory, because there are a number of fundamental physical ideas which are not yet included in it. Since the general relativity theory was developed by Einstein, he and many other physicists have attempted to set up a theory under the name of ***unified field theory***, which would include the results that we have just discussed and also the ideas of electricity and magnetism to be presented later. These attempts have not been entirely successful and, in fact, the relativity theory has not yet been able to present a completely clear account of the accelerations produced by rotations (Sec. 7.7). We can see, however, that relativity theory does represent an advance over earlier theories. It explains all the results that they were able to explain and, in addition, it gives a precise explanation of the previously unexplained effects referred to above. It also tells us that we must be extraordinarily careful not to take for granted the things that merely seem obvious without checking them by precise measurement.

* In 1967, R. H. Dicke (1916–) presented evidence that the sun is not quite spherical and that the slight bulge at its equator may account for the precession. If this result is confirmed, it may upset that part of general relativity theory that deals with the orbit of Mercury, but the principle of equivalence would still remain valid.

14.13 Summary

Using reasoning similar to that employed by Newton, we have shown that Kepler's laws of planetary motion are consistent with Newtonian mechanics only if there acts between the sun and any planet an attractive gravitational force that is proportional to the mass of the planet and that is inversely proportional to the square of the distance between them. It has been shown quite rigorously that this force will account for circular orbits, and it has been made plausible for elliptical orbits. By supposing that the solar system furnishes only a specific example of gravitational force and that all pairs of bodies show similar attractions, we have arrived at Newton's law of universal gravitation and shown that it will account for the motion of the moon, artificial satellites, and falling bodies on the surface of the earth.

We have found that the treatment of gravitational forces can be simplified if we introduce the concept of a field, i.e., of the modification of space by the existence of gravitating masses. The modification is described by a vector, the gravitational field strength, whose magnitude and direction vary from point to point. With the help of this idea we have been able to find connections between certain symmetrical mass distributions and the gravitational fields that they produce.

Finally, we have touched briefly on Einstein's general theory of relativity, which agrees with Newtonian mechanics in most cases but that makes a slightly different prediction for the orbit of the planet Mercury. We have found that the new theory predicts that light moving near a massive body travels in a curved line, a prediction that has been verified.

PROBLEMS

14.1 Given that the sidereal period of the moon is 27.3 days and its mean distance from the earth is 3.84×10^5 km, determine K for earth-satellite systems [Kepler's third law, Eq. (14.2-13)]. Now determine the period of an earth satellite in circular orbit of 7500 km radius.

14.2 Given a very long, thin, uniform metal rod of circular cross section, whose linear density is 1.0 kg/m. Show how to construct a Gauss' law surface around a portion of the rod in order to determine the gravitational field strength at a distance of 1.0 m from the axis of the rod. Compute the attraction of this rod for a 1.0 kg mass at a distance of 1.0 m from the axis of the rod.

14.3 Apply Gauss' law to determine the gravitational field near the center of a very large, plane, thin sheet of matter.

14.4 By combining the results of Secs. 14.2 and 14.4, show that the potential energy of a planet (reckoned as zero at infinity) in a circular orbit is equal to the negative of twice its kinetic energy. Hence show that the total energy is the negative of the kinetic energy.

14.5 (a) Show that the total energy of a planet of mass M_p, moving in an elliptic orbit of semimajor axis a and semiminor axis b about the sun is $E = -M_s M_p/8\pi\gamma a$, where M is the mass of the sun.

(b) This energy is always negative. Were it positive, how far from the sun would the planet get? Would the planet then be moving in a periodic orbit?

14.6 In Sec. 5.9, we assumed that the acceleration due to gravity was independent of the height above the earth's surface and found that a projectile in free flight should follow a parabolic path. This is true for most projectiles, which rise to heights that are negligible compared with the radius of the earth; it is not true for rockets that rise to heights comparable to this radius.

(a) Show that an ellipse is a better approximation to the true trajectory than is a parabola. (b) If the projectile rises to a maximal height h above the surface of the earth, where are the two foci of the elliptical path? (c) Find the ***velocity of escape***, i.e., the minimal vertical component of velocity, that a body must have at the surface of the earth if it is never to return.

14.7 A satellite of the earth has a mass m and is in an orbit that may be approximated closely as a circle of radius r. It is subject to a small and constant frictional force of magnitude F. (a) Show that the rate at which the satellite loses energy is

$$\frac{dE}{dt} = -F\omega r = \frac{Mm}{8\pi\gamma r^2}\frac{dr}{dt},$$

where ω is the angular velocity and M is the mass of the earth. (b) Find dr/dt and show that frictional force will cause the satellite to spiral inward toward the earth. (c) By consideration of the angular momentum, show that the angular acceleration is

$$\frac{d\omega}{dt} = \frac{F}{m}\left(\frac{16\pi\gamma r^2\omega^2}{M} - \frac{1}{r}\right).$$

(d) Find the value of $d\omega/dt$ in terms of F, m, and r and show that the angular velocity increases as the satellite spirals inward.

14.8 A satellite consists of two equal masses (each m) separated by a rigid rod of length a, whose mass is negligible. The rod makes an angle θ with the vertical, as shown in the figure, and the center of the rod is moving in a circular orbit of radius r. In answering the following questions, assume $a \ll r$.

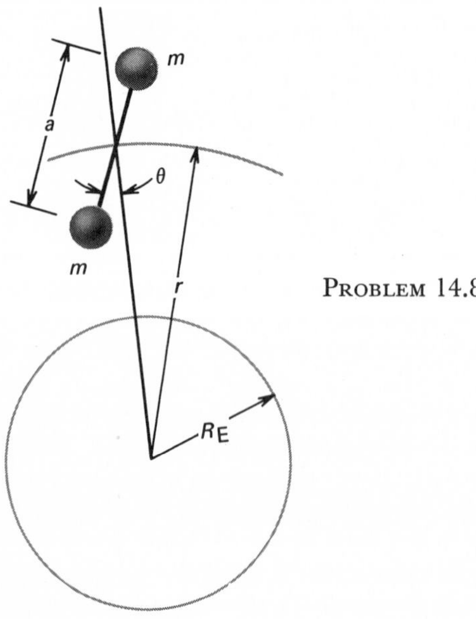

PROBLEM 14.8

(a) Show that the angular velocity of the satellite in its orbit is $\omega = g_0^{1/2}R_E/r^{3/2}$ where g_0 is the value of the acceleration due to the gravity *at the surface of the earth.*

(b) Show that a torque of magnitude

$$M \approx a^2 m g_0 R_E^2 \sin\theta \cos\theta / r^3$$

acts on the satellite and has such a direction that it tends to decrease the angle θ, and hence to cause the satellite to orient itself with the rod vertical.

14.9 An artificial satellite of mass m is in a circular orbit of radius r. At one point in its flight a short rocket burst is fired so that the speed is increased from V to $V + v$, where $v \ll V$. In answering the following questions, neglect terms of the order of v^2 in comparison with terms proportional to Vv.

(a) Show that the new orbit will be elliptical and find the semimajor axis in terms of the mass of the earth (M), the gravitational constant (γ), v, and r.

(b) Show that the semimajor axis lies along the line joining the point at which the rocket was fixed with the center of the earth.

(c) Show that the semiminor axis is equal to r to the accuracy of first-order terms in v/V. (Hint: Use the results of Prob. 14.5.)

14.10 Satellites used for communications are often put into such orbits that they revolve once a day, thus remaining always above a given spot on the earth's surface. If the orbit of such a satellite is in the plane of the earth's equator, show that the orbit must be circular, and find the radius of the orbit.

14.11 (a) Suppose that some region of space is so surrounded by various masses that the lines of force are curved, as in Fig. 14.8b. Suppose further that a particle of mass m is moving with velocity $\vec{v}$ in a direction tangent to a line of force at some point. If it were to continue to move *along* the line of force, it would experience a force that could be approximated as $m\vec{g}$ during a short time interval Δt, where $\vec{g}$ has the direction of the chord connecting the positions of the particle at the beginning and the end of the interval. This chord makes a small angle α with $\vec{v}$. By considering components of the force parallel and perpendicular to the original motion, show that the velocity at the end of the interval makes an angle $\beta \neq 2\alpha$ with $\vec{v}$, and hence that the particle cannot continue to move along the line of force.

(b) Show that there are two exceptions to the statement made above: (1) if the line of force is straight, and (2) if the velocity of the particle is vanishingly small.

14.12 The results of Secs. 14.2 and 14.4 were obtained by assuming the sun to be infinitely massive with respect to the planet.

(a) Show that Eq. (14.2-1) becomes

$$\vec{F} = \frac{4\pi^2 M_p M_s \vec{r}}{\tau^2(M_p + M_s)}$$

if one assumes correctly that both the sun and the planet rotate about their center of mass. The quantity $M_p M_s/(M_p + M_s)$ is called the ***reduced mass*** of the planet.

(b) By what fraction is the period predicted by Eq. (14.2-1) in error for the earth moving about the sun?

14.13 Satellites launched from Cape Kennedy are sent in an eastward direction. There are both physical and safety reasons for this choice. Discuss both reasons as quantitatively as possible.

14.14 If the earth possessed perfect spherical symmetry and were not rotating, the acceleration due to gravity would have the same magnitude at all points on the surface and would always be directed toward the center of the earth. In the following calculations, assume a spherically symmetrical but rotating earth.

(a) Show that a body of mass m on the equator of the earth has its weight reduced from $mg_0 = M_E\, m/4\pi\gamma R_E^2$ to

$$mg_0 - m\omega^2 R_E,$$

where M_E and R_E are, respectively, the mass and radius of the earth and ω is the angular velocity of rotation. Hence show that the apparent acceleration due to gravity is

$$g = M_E/4\pi\gamma R_E^2 - \omega^2 R_E.$$

(b) Show that $\vec{g}$ at any latitude θ has a magnitude

$$g \approx g_0 - \omega^2 R_E \cos\theta$$

and that the angle between $\vec{g}$ and the line to the center of the earth is

$$\alpha \approx \omega^2 R_E \sin\theta \cos\theta/g_0.$$

(Note that approximations can be made because $\omega^2 R_E \ll g_0$.)

(c) Calculate the value of g, as predicted by these assumptions for $\theta = 0°$, $\theta = 45°$, and $\theta = 90°$.

14.15 The fuel gauges in some cars are so constructed and calibrated that they read correctly when the car is standing on a level road, but read incorrectly when the car is parked on a hill. The driver of a car with such a gauge finds that the gauge reads 0.50 (half full) when the car is on the level, 0.44 when the car is pointed up hill at an angle of 5° with the horizontal, and 0.38 when the angle is 10°.

(a) Using the principle of equivalence, show that the fuel gauge may be used as an accelerometer.

(b) With the same amount of fuel that was in the tank when the above data were taken, and on a level road, the gauge reads 0.40. Is the car accelerating or decelerating? What is the magnitude of the acceleration?

(c) With the same amount of fuel in the tank, what will the gauge read when the car is moving at a constant velocity of 80 mi/hr on a level road?

REFERENCES

14A Albert Baez, *Planetary Orbits*, produced by Educational Services Inc. (No. 0310, Modern Learning Aids.) A filmed demonstration lecture about elliptical orbits.

14B George Gamow, "Gravity," *Scientific American*, March 1961, pp. 94–104. (Reprint No. 273, W. H. Freeman.)

14C Franklin Miller, *Measurement of "G"—Cavendish Experiment.* A film loop. (No. 80-212, The Ealing Corp., Cambridge, Mass.)

14D Morris Shamos, editor, *Great Experiments in Physics*, Holt, New York, 1960. Chapter 6 reproduces Cavendish's paper describing his measurements of the gravitational constant.

14E Harlow Shapley and H. E. Howarth, *A Source Book in Astronomy*, Harvard University Press, Cambridge, Mass., 1929. Excerpts from the work of Johannes Kepler appear in pp. 29–40.

14F Freeman J. Dyson, "Mathematics in the Physical Sciences," *Scientific American*, September 1964, pp. 128–146. Includes a discussion of Kepler's work.

15 ➩ *Static Electric and Magnetic Fields*

15.1 Introduction

In Chapter 14 we developed the notion of gravitational fields of force. We started with Kepler's laws for the planets, and by employing the law of conservation of energy, we arrived at Newton's inverse square law of gravitation. We went on then to define gravitational field strength, gravitational lines of force and displacement, and tubes of gravitational displacement. Finally, we developed Gauss' law for gravitational fields and used it to arrive at certain important ideas about the fields that belong to spherical distributions of mass.

All of these ideas which we have considered for gravitational fields are applicable to other kinds of fields as well. In this chapter, we shall extend these notions to include static electric fields and static magnetic fields. Before we can do this, however, it will be necessary to discuss some of the basic phenomena of electricity. As usual, we shall make certain definitions that will form the basis of our treatment of electric fields.

15.2 Some Electrical Phenomena

If a piece of amber is rubbed with a woolen cloth, it acquires the power of attracting small objects—lint, dust, small bits of paper. This fact was known to the ancients, and it is from the Greek name for amber, *elektron*, that electricity gets its name. Ebonite and other plastics rubbed with wool, or glass rubbed with silk, will give similar effects. Bodies showing this effect are said to be ***electrified***, or ***charged***.

Suppose we suspend a piece of glass rod by a piece of dry thread so that the rod is free to turn in a horizontal plane. If we electrify it by rubbing it with silk, we then find the silk and the rod, when brought close together, *attract* each other more strongly then do the rod and *some other* piece of silk. On the other hand, if the suspended glass rod and another glass rod are both electrified by rubbing with silk, the two rods *repel* when they are brought near to each other. The same experiment can be performed with two pieces of ebonite, one suspended and one held in the hand; again the two rods *repel*. If, however, we electrify a piece of glass by rubbing it with silk and suspend it so that it is free to move, and then bring near to it a piece of ebonite that has been rubbed with wool, we find that the two *attract* one another.

It seems, therefore, that there are two kinds of electrification or charge. It is traditional to follow the practice introduced by Benjamin Franklin (1706–1790), calling the charge produced on glass by silk ***positive*** and that on ebonite or amber rubbed by wool ***negative***. We can then sum up the experiments described in the preceding paragraph in the single statement: *Charges of like sign repel one another, and charges of unlike sign attract one another.*

We can now define what we mean by an *uncharged body* by stating that: *If two bodies, remote from other bodies, neither attract nor repel each other* (apart from the very small attraction due to gravity), *they are uncharged.* Furthermore, we may say that *if two bodies repel one another they are charged and are either both positive or both negative.* We may not say that two bodies that attract one another are of opposite sign, because as we shall see in Sec. 15.4 a charged body may attract an uncharged body or even one charged weakly with the same sign.

Suppose that we test a piece of glass and a piece of silk, as indicated above, and decide that they are both uncharged. We then rub them together and find that they are both charged. The charge on the glass is, of course, positive by definition; that on the silk we can show to be negative by testing it with a piece of ebonite which has been rubbed with wool. The glass and the silk that were previously uncharged have been charged with opposite signs by friction.

We can account for the results of these experiments if we make the following simple assumptions:

1. An uncharged body contains equal amounts of positive and negative electricity, whose effects neutralize one another.
2. A positively charged body contains an excess of positive electricity, and a negatively charged body contains an excess of negative electricity.

Our experiment can then be explained in one of two ways: either the glass has lost negative charge which has been gained by the silk, or the silk has lost positive charge which has been gained by the glass. We shall see later that the first explanation is probably correct.

15.3 Conductors and Insulators

Let us continue our efforts to charge various kinds of rods by rubbing them with pieces of fabric. There is no difficulty in producing a charge on a glass rod or an ebonite rod, particularly if the atmosphere is dry; it may be somewhat harder on a humid day. But if one holds a brass rod in one hand and rubs it with a piece of fabric held in the other, he cannot electrify the brass rod. However, if we fit a dry wooden or plastic handle to the brass rod and hold it carefully so that we do not touch the brass, a charge can be produced on it. Brass, too, or any other metal, will fit with Assumption 1 of the preceding section if we provide it with a suitable handle.

We can easily explain these simple observations by stating that, in some kinds of matter, the charges can easily move from place-to-place within the matter, whereas in other kinds of matter, they cannot. We classify as ***conductors*** those materials in which charges move easily and as ***insulators***, or ***nonconductors*** those in which the charges seem to be bound. We shall later want to correlate conduction and nonconduction with the electrical structure of atoms and molecules, and we shall do that when we study atoms and molecules in detail.

It is to be expected that the ability to conduct electricity will vary from material to material in a way that will depend on the ease with which the electricity is able to move from atom to atom. We may thus expect a continuous graduation from good conductors through poor conductors and poor insulators to good insulators. As extremes, we may list the metals such as gold, copper, silver, mercury as good conductors and glass, ebonite, amber, sulfur, and certain types of porcelain as good insulators. Pure water is a poor conductor. but solutions of acids, bases, and salts in water are generally good conductors,

It is important to notice that if we place a charge on a nonconductor by friction or otherwise, the charge will remain where it is placed. If on the other hand we place a charge on a conductor, this charge is free to move around on the conductor and will spread itself under the influence of its own repulsion. We can demonstrate this point by studying the behavior of an ***electroscope***, which is essentially a conductor that is able to indicate its own charge. A simple form of this instrument consists of a metal rod supported by an insulator (Fig. 15.1). At the lower end of the rod two thin leaves of gold leaf or aluminum foil are attached. If the rod and the foil are uncharged, the leaves will hang down side by side. If an electric charge is given to the rod, it will spread over the rod, and from the rod onto the leaves. The latter will thus both be charged with the same sign and will repel one another as indicated in the figure.

In the light of the preceding paragraphs, it is easy to understand why we have to attach a special handle to a brass rod before it can be charged by friction. The human body, being filled with saline solutions, is a good conductor, as is the brass itself. As fast as the fabric removes charge from the brass, more flows on from the hand; consequently, the brass seemingly cannot be charged by friction. However, if the brass is held by means of a nonconducting handle such as dry wood, glass, plastic, or wax, the charge cannot flow on from the hand. Brass or any conductor, under these circumstances, can be charged by friction.

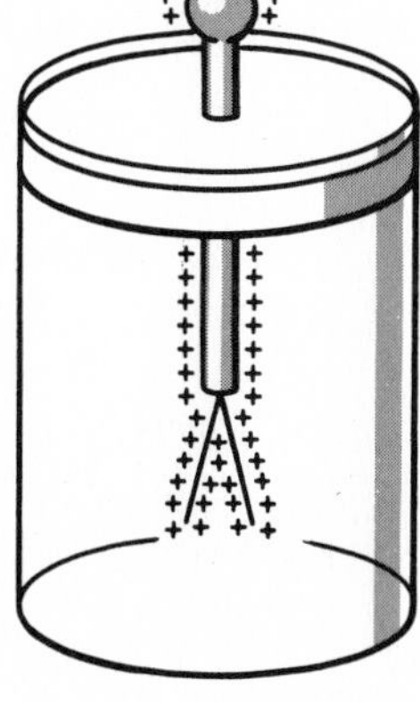

FIG. 15.1 Electroscope.

15.4 Electric Induction and Electrical Machines

We have said that in a conductor electric charge is free to move about within the boundaries of the conductor. Suppose that we mount a conductor on an insulating stand, as in Fig. 15.2, and bring a positively charged rod near to it.

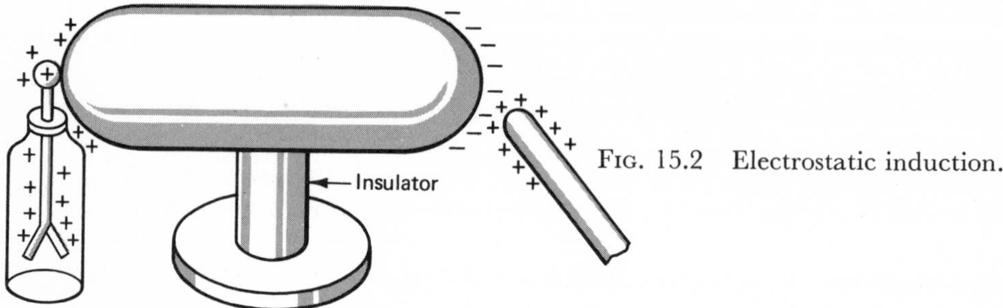

Fig. 15.2 Electrostatic induction.

The negative charges in the conductor will be attracted toward the positive rod and the positive charges will be repelled. Some of this charge will be able to move, and there will be an accumulation of negative electricity on the end of the conductor nearest the rod, with a corresponding accumulation of positive charge at the end farthest from the rod. The presence of this latter charge can be demonstrated by attaching an electroscope to the conductor as indicated in the figure.

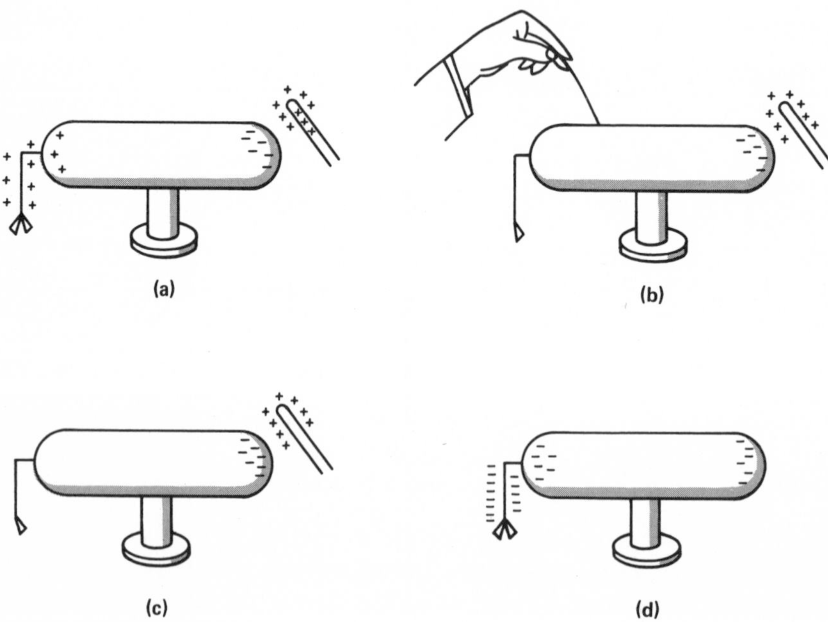

Fig. 15.3 Charging by induction.

We can show that the induced charges are equal and opposite to one another, because, if we remove the rod carrying the positive charge, we find that the conductor is again uncharged. The positive and negative charges neutralize one another.

We now repeat the above experiment as indicated in Fig. 15.3a, but this time, while the positive rod is near the conductor, we touch the latter with a conducting wire which is connected to earth (Fig. 15.3b). The leaves of an electroscope attached to the far end of the conductor will immediately collapse, indicating that there is no longer a charge there. It has been repelled through the conducting wire to the earth. It tries to get as far away as possible from the charge repelling it. If now we remove the wire and then the rod, in that order (Figs. 15.3c and d), the electroscope again diverges, showing the presence of a charge. But this time it is a negative charge. The negative ***induced charge*** was held by the attraction of the positive charge and did not escape to earth. After the removal of the rod, however, it spread itself over the conductor, every portion of charge repelling every other. We have thus left the conductor charged negatively, and we say that it has been ***charged by induction.*** Of course, if we had started with a rod charged negatively, we would have left the conductor with a positive charge.

If now we have two conductors, one charged and the other uncharged, and if we bring them into contact, the charge will spread itself under its own repulsion over both conductors; they will both be charged with the same sign. This process is called ***charging by contact.***

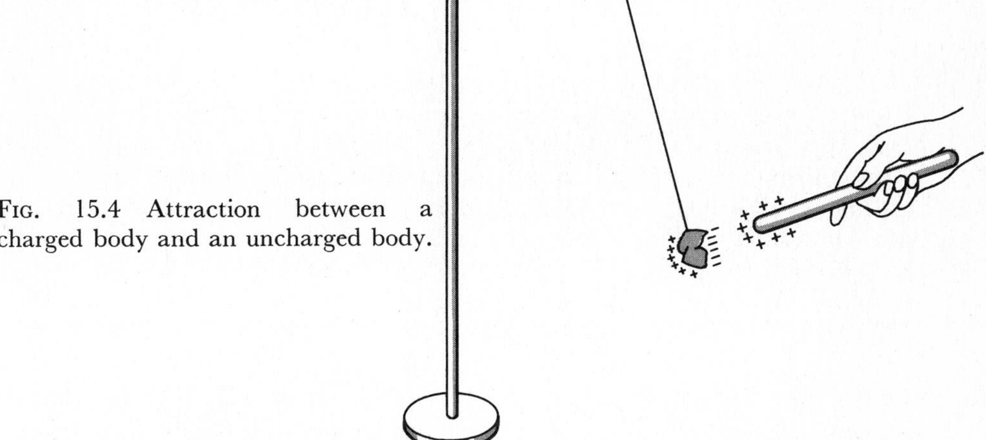

FIG. 15.4 Attraction between a charged body and an uncharged body.

Incidentally, we can now explain the attraction of uncharged bodies by a charged body. The charged body induces charges on the uncharged body (Fig. 15.4). The induced charge of unlike sign is much nearer to the charge on the inducing body than is the induced charge of like sign. Since the force of attraction and repulsion decreases markedly with distance, the resultant force on the induced charges is one of attraction, resulting in the attraction of the body on which the charges are induced.

We can also explain the action of the ***electrophorus***, one of the simplest of all electrical machines (Fig. 15.5). It usually consists of an ebonite plate which is given a negative charge of considerable strength by rubbing it with a woolen cloth or a piece of fur. A metal plate is placed on top of the ebonite by means of an insulating handle. The plate is then touched momentarily by a grounded wire or by the finger of the operator and thus it is charged positively by induction. If the plate is removed by the insulating handle, it will carry the positive charge with it, and this charge can be used to charge other conductors, either by induction or by contact. The charge on the ebonite plate has been left unaltered, however, by this operation (or very nearly so), so that if the metal plate is discharged by contact to another conductor, it can be recharged again and again by the above process.

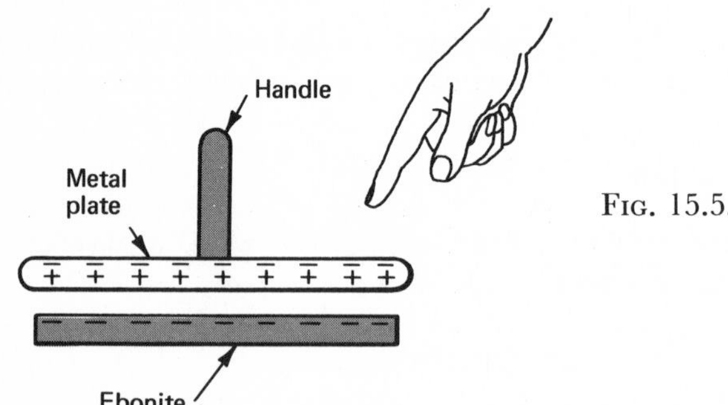

FIG. 15.5. Electrophorus.

It would be extremely tedious, however, to produce large charges by this method; consequently, many machines have been devised for that purpose. Some of them merely repeat the above process over and over again. In the Holtz machine, for example, a number of metal conductors are carried on a rotating disc. Each of these conductors is first charged positively by induction and then discharged by contact on to a positive storage conductor. They are then charged negatively by induction and discharged onto a negative storage conductor. As this cycle is repeated many times a second by each of several conductors, the storage or terminal conductors rapidly accumulate large amounts of positive and negative electrification.

Although very powerful electrostatic machines have been built (cf. Sec. 19.12), they are not the best available for producing large quantities of electricity. Another type of machine, known as a generator, or dynamo, is much better suited for that purpose, and it is by such machines that the electricity we use in everyday life is made. Chemical reactions can also be made to produce electricity, and sources of this type, called batteries or cells, will be discussed in Chapter 17.

Electrostatic machines, generators or dynamos, and batteries all possess the property of producing positive electricity at one terminal and negative electricity at the other and they can be used as sources of charge in our experiments.

15.5 *Quantity of Electricity and Coulomb's Law*

Suppose we have several small spherical conductors, identical in size and supported by insulating threads. Let us now charge one of these by contact with the charged metal plate of an electrophorus or the terminal of an electric machine. If we now touch this sphere to an identical uncharged sphere, the charge will distribute itself between the two. Since the spheres are identical, we would expect the charge to be divided equally between them. If we arbitararily call the charge originally on the first sphere one unit, we can say that we now have $\frac{1}{2}$ unit on each of the charged spheres. If we touch the second sphere to a third, we shall have $\frac{1}{4}$ unit on each of them. Touching the third to a fourth will obviously give us $\frac{1}{8}$ unit on each, and touching the first and the second will give us $\frac{3}{8}$ unit. If we assume that we can produce our original unit charge as often as we like by charging a number of spheres in exactly the same way from the same source, we can obviously obtain any fraction of our original unit.

Suppose that we have two conductors carrying charges of opposite sign. We touch them together and, as a result, we find them both to be uncharged. We can then say that they carried equal and opposite charges before contact, and in this way we may express negative and positive quantities of electricity in terms of the same unit.

Using an arbitrarily chosen unit of quantity and subdividing it as indicated at the beginning of this section, Charles Augustin de Coulomb (1736–1806) investigated the law of force between two charges. He carefully measured the repulsive force between two small spheres, carrying equal charges, as a function of the distance between them. He then reduced the charge on one of them to a fraction of its previous value and again measured the force of repulsion as a function of the distance. As a result of many such experiments, he concluded that the force between two charges varies directly as the product of the charges and inversely as the square of the distance between them. This law is expressed by the equation

$$F = kq_1 q_2/r^2, \qquad (15.5\text{-}1)$$

in which F is the force of repulsion between the two charges q_1 and q_2, and r is the distance between them. This relationship is known as ***Coulomb's law***. The value of the proportionality constant k will depend on the units in which we measure force, distance, and quantity of electricity. We must take the signs of the charges into consideration when applying Coulomb's law. Two negative charges, or two positive charges, will lead to a positive value for the repulsive force, while a positive charge and a negative charge will lead to a negative value for the repulsive force—i.e., to an attractive force.

With the help of Coulomb's law we can begin a systematic study of the fields of force in the neighborhood of electric charges. We must first, however, decide upon a unit in terms of which we can measure the charges on various bodies. Because charged bodies lose their charges in time, we cannot take a standard charge and store it for future comparison, as we did with the standards of mass and length. We might take as a unit the charge acquired by a metal sphere, of a specified size and shape, when charged in a particular fashion, but such a unit would be difficult to reproduce accurately. We could use Coulomb's law itself to define a unit of charge. For example, we could say that a unit charge is one which repels an identical charge, placed exactly one meter from it in a vacuum, with a force of one newton. Such a definition, while completely satisfactory in itself, would have the disadvantage of not being convenient for some of our future studies of electricity. We shall therefore adopt a definition of a unit charge which appears to be highly artificial but for which a justification will appear in Chapter 16. We shall call this unit the ***coulomb*** (Cb) and shall define it as the electric charge that repels an exactly similar charge, placed one meter from it in a vacuum, with a force of 8.986×10^9 N.

Letting $q_1 = q_2 = 1$ Cb, $r = 1$m, and $F = 8.986 \times 10^9$ N in Eq. (15.5-1), we find that

$$k = Fr^2/q_1^2 = 8.986 \times 10^9 \text{ kg m}^3/\text{sec}^2 \text{ Cb}^2.$$

In order to put Coulomb's law into a form similar to Newton's law of gravitation [Eq. (14.5-6C)], we shall make a change in the way that the constant k is expressed. Letting

$$k = 1/4\pi\varepsilon_0,$$

we find that

$$\varepsilon_0 = 8.855 \times 10^{-12} \text{ sec}^2 \text{ Cb}^2/\text{kg m}^3 \tag{15.5-2}$$

and that the expression for Coulomb's law is

$$F = q_1 q_2/4\pi\varepsilon_0 r^2. \tag{15.5-3}$$

The constant ε_0 is called the ***permittivity of free space.***

It is worthy of note that we have just introduced a new fundamental quantity, the coulomb, into our system of units, in addition to the meter, the second, and the kilogram. We shall denote the dimension of charge in dimensional equations by $[\mathscr{q}]$, so that the dimensions of the permittivity are

$$[\varepsilon_0] = [\mathscr{q}^2 \mathscr{t}^2 \ell^{-3} \mathscr{m}^{-1}]. \tag{15.5-4}$$

15.6 The Dielectric Constant

Although Coulomb's law (Eq. 15.5-3) expresses a law of force very similar to Newton's law, there are two very important differences between electrostatic and gravitational forces. We have already discussed the fact that, while all masses are positive, both positive and negative electric charges exist. The second difference becomes apparent whenever we repeat the Coulomb experiments with the charges totally submerged in a large volume of oil or any other nonconducting liquid. When this is done, it is found that the force between two charges depends on the medium surrounding them and is less in any material medium than it is in a vacuum. The force between two charges, q_1 and q_2, in any particular medium is

$$F = q_1 q_2/4\pi\varepsilon r^2, \tag{15.6-1}$$

where r is the distance between the charges and ε is a constant for the medium, known as the ***permittivity of the medium.*** Since the permittivity of free space is also a constant, we can express ε as

$$\varepsilon = \kappa_e \varepsilon_0 , \tag{15.6-2}$$

where κ_e is known as the ***dielectric constant of the medium.*** The constant is, of course, dimensionless and has the value of one for a vacuum. Values of ε and of κ_e for a number of common media are given in Table 15.1.

Table 15.1 *Dielectric Constants*

Medium	Permittivity ε (F/m*)	Dielectric Constant κ_e
Vacuum	(ε_0) 8.858×10^{-12}	1.00000
Air (at N.T.P.)	8.863	1.00059
Diamond	146	16.5
Glass	43–88	4.8–9.9
Mica	50–53	5.7–6.0
Paraffin	18.6	2.10
Sulfur	37.4	4.22
Ethyl alcohol (0°C)	252	28.4
Glycerine	498	56.2
Water	718	81.1

* The units used here are farads (F) per meter. These are equivalent to $sec^2Cb^2/kg\ m^3$ (cf. Chapter 16).

EXERCISES

15.6-1 Two small metal balls are charged with $+1.00 \times 10^{-6}$ Cb and $+3.00 \times 10^{-6}$ Cb. They are placed in a large tank of glycerine with their centers separated by a distance of 10.0 cm. What is the force between them?

15.6-2 If each of the metal balls in Ex. 15.6-1 has a mass of 30 g, compare the gravitational attraction between the masses with the electrical repulsion.

15.6-3 Two small balls are suspended from the same point by strings of length L. Each ball has a mass m and carries a charge Q. Show that the equilibrium position of each string will make an angle θ with the vertical, where

$$16\pi\varepsilon_0 mgL^2 \sin^3 \theta = Q^2 \cos \theta.$$

15.7 Electric Field Strength and Displacement

The close parallelism of Coulomb's law for electric charges (Eq. 15.5-3) and Newton's law for gravitating masses (Eq. 14.5-6C) allows us to apply to electrostatics the same definitions and procedures that we found to be useful in discussing the gravitational field. Thus, if we want to investigate the ***electric field*** in the neighborhood of a number of charged bodies, we may place an electric

test charge of magnitude q at any point and measure the force $\vec{F}$ that acts on it. The ***electric field strength*** at the point is then defined as

$$\vec{E} = \vec{F}/q, \tag{15.7-1}$$

in exact analogy with Eq. (14.7-2).* Similarly, the ***electric displacement*** is defined as

$$\vec{D} = \varepsilon\vec{E}, \tag{15.7-2}$$

which is like Eq. (14.8-1).

It should be noted that the magnitude of the field strength at a distance r from a point charge Q is

$$E = F/q = Q/4\pi\varepsilon r^2, \tag{15.7-3}$$

and that it therefore depends on the permittivity of the medium in which the charge is immersed. On the other hand, the magnitude of the displacement at the same point is

$$D = \varepsilon E = Q/4\pi r^2, \tag{15.7-4}$$

which is the same for any medium, depending only on the charge Q and the distance r. Because of this difference between E and D, the distinction between the field strength and displacement is more important in the electrostatic field than it is in the gravitational field. However, the field may be described equally well in terms of $\vec{E}$ or $\vec{D}$.

The electric field may, of course, be represented by lines of force and tubes of displacement, similar to those used for the gravitational field (Sec. 14.8). The ***lines of force*** are continuous curves which have at every point the same direction as the force on a positive test charge placed at that point, and the ***tubes of displacement*** are so chosen that they have the directions of the lines of force and that Q of them diverge from a positive charge Q. One important difference in the representation results from the existence of positive and negative charges.

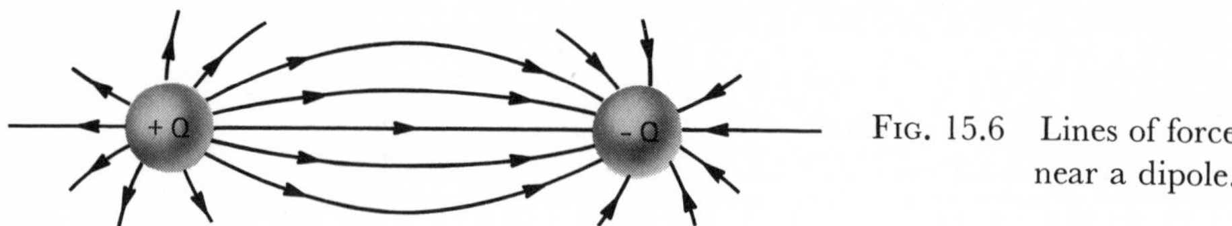

FIG. 15.6 Lines of force near a dipole.

Since a positive test charge is repelled by a positive charge and attracted by a negative charge, lines of force and tubes of displacement will be directed away from the former and toward the latter. For example, the lines of force in the neighborhood of two electric charges, of equal magnitudes and opposite signs, are shown in Fig. 15.6. A pair of charges, such as that shown in the figure, is called an ***electric dipole***.

* Following an argument similar to that of the footnote near the end of Sec. 14.6, we can express Eq. (15.6-1) more rigorously as $\vec{E} = \lim_{q \to 0} \vec{F}/q$.

15.8 Gauss' Law for Electrostatics

Continuing the analogy between the descriptions of the gravitational and electrical fields, we can define the ***electric displacement flux*** Ψ' through any surface as the total number of tubes of displacement that pass outward through the surface.

Thus, in analogy with Eq. (14.10-1), the electric flux through any surface which is everywhere normal to the lines of force is given by

$$\Psi' = DS, \tag{15.8-1}$$

where S is the area of the surface.

Because of the similarity between the two fields, the treatment of Sec. 14.11 can be applied at once, and ***Gauss' law for electrostatics*** can be stated: *The electric displacement flux through any surface is equal to the sum of all the electric charges enclosed by the surface.* In taking this sum, of course, the charges must be added with due regard for their signs. Thus, the flux through any surface surrounding the charge $+Q$ in Fig. 15.6 will be $+Q$ and that through any surface about $-Q$ will be $-Q$, while that through any surface surrounding both the charges Q and $-Q$ is zero, which means that as many tubes of displacement pass outward through the surface as pass inward.

As an example of the application of Gauss' law to the electrostatic field, consider a long cylindrical wire of radius a, which carries a charge μ per unit length (Fig. 15.7). In order to find the field strength near the wire, we construct a cylindrical surface which is coaxial with the wire and whose ends are plane surfaces perpendicular to the wire. Let the radius of the cylinder be r ($>a$) and its length be L. Since the charge within the cylinder is μL, the flux through it, by Gauss' law, is

$$\Psi' = \mu L.$$

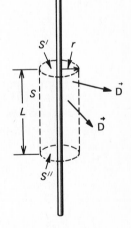

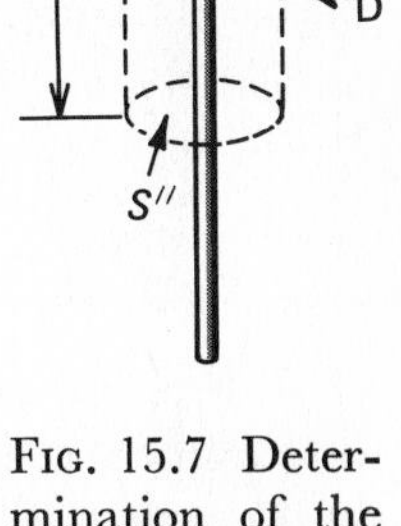

FIG. 15.7 Determination of the field near a wire.

We can arrive at some properties of the field by symmetry arguments. If the cylinder is far from the ends of the wire, the ends will have no effect on the field. Consequently, there is no reason that the field should have either an upward or a downward component (i.e., a component parallel to the wire), and the displacement vector must be perpendicular to the wire and to the cylindrical surface as shown in the figure. This, in turn, means that the displacement vector is parallel to the end surfaces S' and S'', and consequently no tubes of displacement pass through these surfaces. The entire flux Ψ', therefore, passes through the lateral surface of the cylinder.

Further, all radial directions about the wire are exactly equivalent, so the displacement must have the same magnitude everywhere on the lateral surface of S. Letting this value be D, and remembering that $\vec{D}$ is everywhere perpendicular to S, we see that

$$\Psi = \mu L = SD = 2\pi rLD,$$

or that

$$D = \mu/2\pi r. \tag{15.8-2}$$

The field strength at a distance r from the wire, therefore, has a magnitude

$$E = D/\varepsilon = \mu/2\pi\varepsilon r. \tag{15.8-3}$$

Thus the electric field about a long charged wire varies as the inverse first power of the distance from the wire.

EXERCISES

15.8-1 As we shall see in Chapter 23 any charged body possesses energy by virtue of its charge. If a body is charged by means of an electrophorus (Fig. 15.5), what is the source of its energy?

15.8-2 Show that the dimensions of electric field strength are $[m\ell t^{-2}q^{-1}]$ and that those of electric displacement are $[q\ell^{-2}]$. Show that the field strength may be expressed in units of newtons per coulomb.

15.8-3 By constructing a spherical Gauss' surface of radius r concentric with a sphere of radius a which carries a charge q distributed uniformly over its surface ($r > a$), show that the electric field outside such a sphere is identical with that of a point charge q located at the center of the sphere.

15.8-4 The electrostatic field strength at the surface of the earth is 300 N/Cb directed downward. Assuming that the earth is a uniformly charged sphere of radius 6.4×10^6 m, calculate the total electric charge on the earth.

15.8-5 A metal sphere of radius a carries a charge Q, which is distributed uniformly over its surface. It is surrounded by a spherical shell of uncharged paraffin, of inner radius a and outer radius b. What is the value of the field strength at a distance r if $a < r < b$? If $r > b$? (Hint: Construct spherical Gauss' surfaces.)

15.8-6 A very long cylindrical rod of radius a is made of a material of density ρ. Show that, at a distance $r > a$, which is small compared to the length of the rod, the gravitational field strength is $\rho a^2/2\gamma r$ and that within the rod this field strength is $\rho r/2\gamma$.

15.9 The Behavior of an Electric Dipole

If an electric dipole, such as that shown in Fig. 15.6, is placed in a uniform electric field of strength $\vec{E}$, equal and opposite forces will act on the two charges. Suppose that these charges are $+q$ and $-q$ and that they are separated by a distance $2a$, as shown in Fig. 15.8. If the dipole is parallel to the electric field (Fig. 15.8a), these forces will merely act to hold the dipole stationary in that position, the net force on it being

$$\vec{E}q - \vec{E}q = 0.$$

In any other position, such as that shown in Fig. 15.8b, the net force will still be zero, but there will be a torque that tends to decrease the angle θ between the dipole and the field—i.e., a torque that tends to rotate the dipole into the direction of the field. In accordance with Eq. (7.9-2), the torque due to each force will have the magnitude

$$T' = Eqa \sin \theta.$$

Both torques act to rotate the dipole in the same sense, so the full torque on the dipole is

$$T = -2Eqa \sin \theta, \tag{15.9-1}$$

where the negative sign indicates that the torque tends to decrease a positive θ.

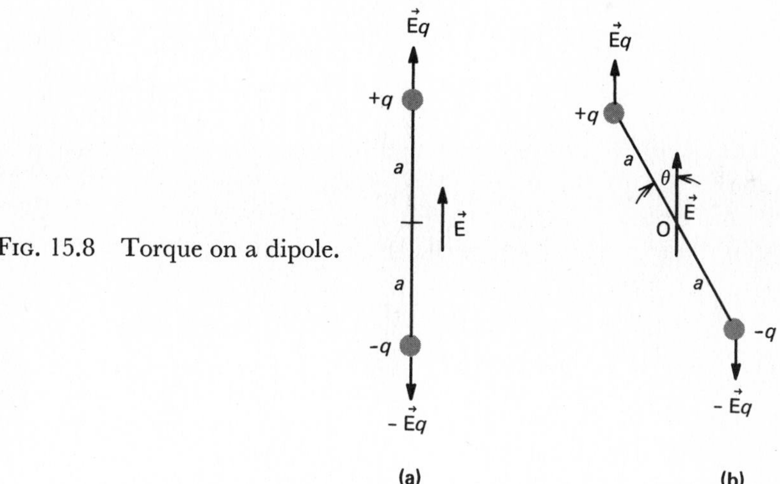

FIG. 15.8 Torque on a dipole.

We may now define the ***electric dipole moment*** p_e of the dipole as the product of one charge q by the distance between the charges, or as

$$p_e = 2aq. \tag{15.9-2}$$

Substitution of this value into Eq. (15.9-1) gives the torque as

$$T = -Ep_e \sin \theta. \tag{15.9-3}$$

EXERCISE

15.9-1 Express the quantities in Eq. (15.9-1) as vectors, and show how to determine the magnitude and direction of the torque vector as a vector product after the manner of Sec. 7.9.

15.10 The Use of Dipoles for Investigating Fields

A dipole is often a more convenient tool for the study of electric fields than is the single test charge that we used in Sec. 15.7. For example, if we wish to investigate in detail the field about the dipole of Fig. 15.9, we may bring a much smaller ***test dipole*** of known dipole moment p_e into the neighborhood of the dipole $+Q$, $-Q$. If this second dipole is placed at any point such as M, it will align itself parallel to the field at that point. Then, by moving the dipole along its own length (e.g., through the successive positions M, N, O, P), we can trace the line of force without making any quantative measurements.

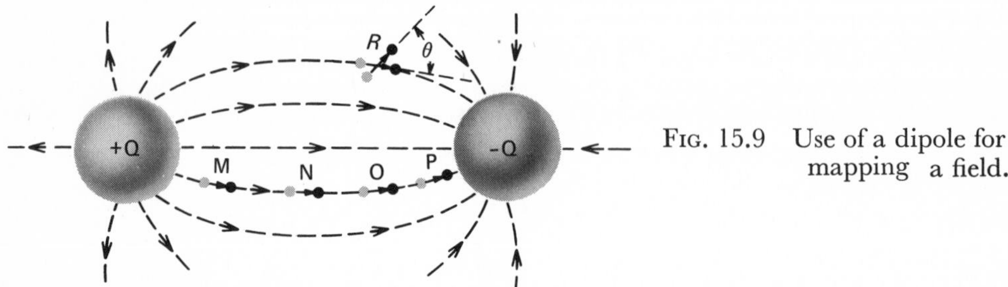

Fig. 15.9 Use of a dipole for mapping a field.

If we wish to measure the field at any point, such as at R in Fig. 15.9, we first find the direction of the field at that point by allowing the test dipole to take its equilibrium position. We then rotate the dipole through an angle θ, as shown at R, and measure the torque necessary to hold it in this position. If this torque is T, Eq. (15.9-3) gives the field at R as

$$E = -T/p_e \sin \theta. \tag{15.10-1}$$

EXERCISES

15.10-1 A small test dipole, of moment 1.00×10^{-10} Cb m, is mounted at a distance of 25.0 cm from the center of a metal sphere. The sphere has a radius of 5.00 cm and carries a charge of 2.50×10^{-9} Cb. The test dipole is held at right angles to the line joining it with the center of the sphere. What torque is necessary to hold the dipole in this position?

15.10-2 A very small electric dipole is mounted at the origin of a rectangular coordinate system in such a way that both of its charges are on the x-axis, the positive charge being on the positive x side of the origin and the negative charge on the negative side. A second dipole is mounted at the point $x = +10$ cm, $y = 0$, and is free to rotate. What will be the equilibrium position of this second dipole?

15.11 Magnets

We have thus far studied two types of forces that act between bodies. These are gravitational forces, which are an intrinsic accompaniment of mass, and electrostatic forces, which depend upon the presence of an electrical charge. A third type of force, which we shall later find to be related to electric forces, is also found in nature. This is the force known as ***magnetism***. Whenever a body exerts magnetic forces, we speak of it as being ***magnetized***. While many substances may be magnetized very weakly, the only materials that exhibit the phenomena sufficiently strongly to be important outside the laboratory are a few metals, of which iron, nickel, and cobalt are the prime examples.* Since iron is the most notable of these, such materials are known as ***ferromagnetic materials.***

Certain pieces of iron, or better, of steel (which is merely iron plus some slight impurities so distributed that they cause the iron to be much harder than normal), are found to have the property of attracting other pieces of ferromagnetic materials. To begin our discussion, assume that two such ***magnets***, each in the form of a long thin bar, have been found. If these two are brought near to each other, forces will be exerted between them, the exact nature of the forces depending on the relative orientation of the two magnets. If the two are kept parallel, as in Fig. 15.10, it will be found that they may initially either

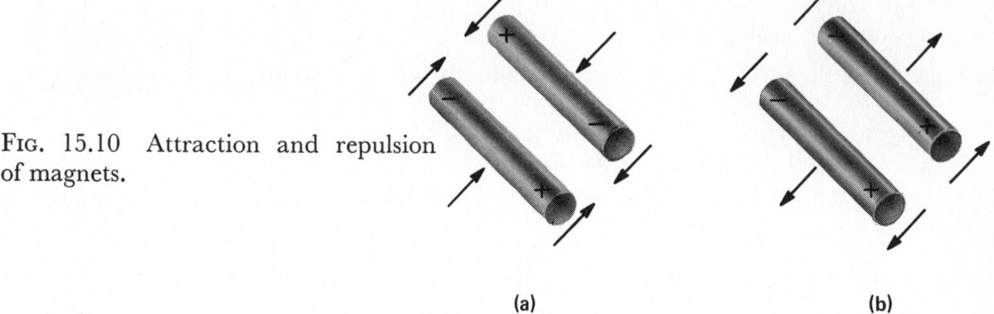

FIG. 15.10 Attraction and repulsion of magnets.

attract or repel. In either case, if one of the two is turned end-to-end, they will attract each other if they repelled before, and vice versa. This leads us to suspect that, as in the electrostatic case, we have two signs of magnetism. However, since merely turning a magnet end-for-end cannot be expected to reverse its magnetic "charge," we must look for a slightly more complicated explanation than we found in electricity. It will be seen that the phenomena are easily explained if we suppose that the forces between magnets are exerted principally between ***magnetic poles***, located near the ends of the magnets, that these poles have opposite signs, and that like poles repel each other and unlike poles attract each other. The magnets in Fig. 15.10 have been labeled in accordance with this concept.

The idea of poles can be tested further by bringing the same magnets near each other in the manner shown in Figs. 15.11a and 15.11b. If this is done, it is found that the attractions and repulsions observed are always in the direction that would be expected from our picture of the poles.

* This phenomenon is also exhibited by the iron oxide magnetite, the "lodestone" of the ancients, which was found by the Greeks in Magnesia.

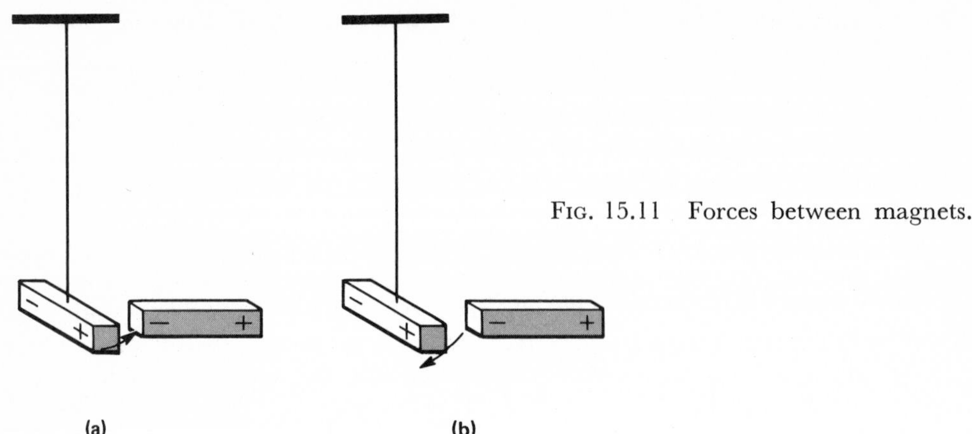

FIG. 15.11 Forces between magnets.

15.12 The Magnetic Dipole

Since the existence of two poles in each of the magnets that we have examined seems to complicate the explanation of the phenomena, we might conceive of the idea of separating the poles by breaking one of the magnets in two. If this is done, and each of the resulting pieces is tested by the remaining whole magnet, a surprising result is found. Each of the pieces, as shown in Fig. 15.12, has two unlike poles just as before! If we go further and break each of the short magnets in two, we find again that each resulting piece has two poles. It

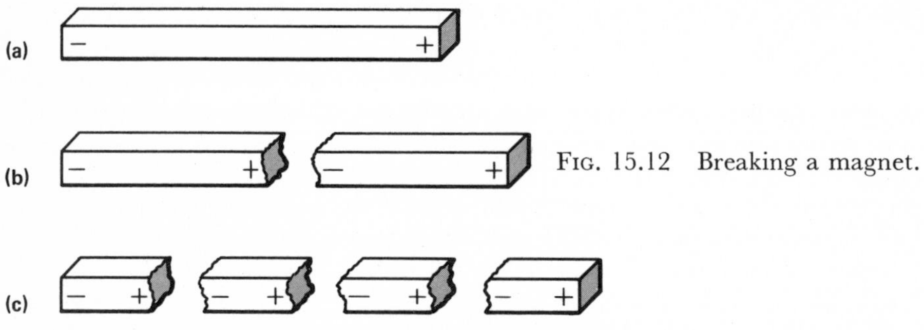

FIG. 15.12 Breaking a magnet.

appears from this that the poles must have been in the magnet before it was broken but that they were not apparent, since two unlike poles were so close together that their effects balanced when observed from outside the magnet. According to this picture, when the break occurred, a positive pole was exposed on one piece and a negative pole on the other. We might thus assume that the interior of a magnet consists of small regions, each of which is itself magnetized. In a strong magnet, these regions have their poles lined up in the same direction. Figure 15.13 shows an idealized sketch of such an arrangement, in which all the regions are of the same size and are perfectly aligned. Actually, these regions are not as simply arranged as this, but for the present we do not need to concern ourselves with the size or internal constitution of the regions, except to assume that they are very small compared with the magnet itself (cf. Sec. 21.9).

The magnetic phenomena that we have just considered indicate that *magnetic poles never occur singly, but always in pairs.* There are, as a matter of fact, many other data that point to the same conclusion. Such pairs of magnetic poles remind one of the electric dipoles considered in Secs. 15.7, 15.9, and 15.10. Guided by the obvious similarity, we may try a few experiments to find whether or not there is a close parallelism between the magnetic and electric dipoles.

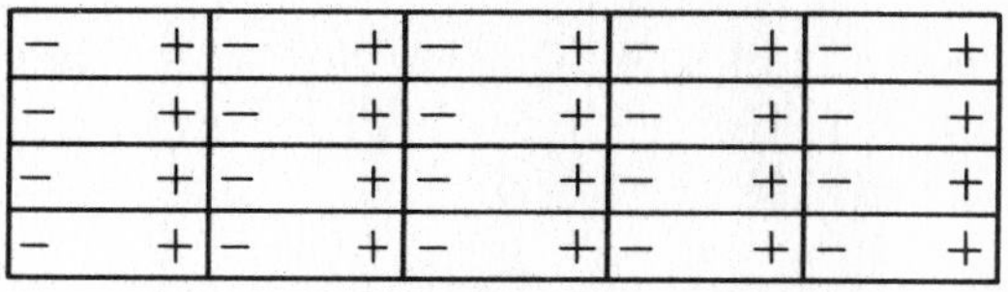

− +	− +	− +	− +	− +
− +	− +	− +	− +	− +
− +	− +	− +	− +	− +
− +	− +	− +	− +	− +

FIG. 15.13 Schematic arrangement of magnetic regions.

If we find that there is such a parallelism, we may be able to carry over to our study of magnetism some of the results that we have found in electrostatics, just as we used the theory of gravitation in developing electrostatics. Throughout our study, however, we must bear in mind the fact that isolated magnetic poles do not exist and that the ***magnetic dipole***, rather than the magnetic pole, is the simplest concept in magnetism. Otherwise, we shall find that the analogy between magnetic fields and electric fields is quite complete.

15.13 The Field About a Magnet

If the bar magnet we have been discussing is indeed a magnetic dipole, we should expect a field of force about it very similar to that indicated in Figs. 15.6 and 15.9. We should expect also that a small magnet, if moved to various locations near the first bar magnet and arranged so that it is free to rotate, would take an equilibrium position in which it is directed along the lines of force of the magnetic field, just as the electric dipole did in Fig. 15.9. By moving this small magnet, or test dipole, along its own length, we should be able to trace

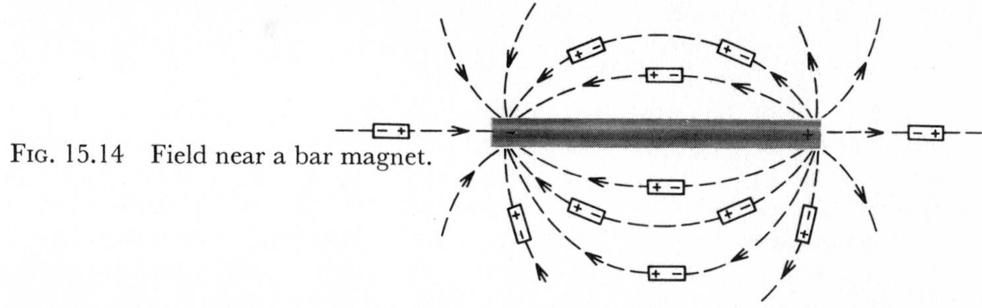

FIG. 15.14 Field near a bar magnet.

these lines of force and so to map the magnetic field. The result of such a mapping of the field about a bar magnet is illustrated in Fig. 15.14. The similarity between this figure and Fig. 15.9 certainly strengthens our belief that a bar magnet is a magnetic dipole very similar to an electric dipole.

The analogy just demonstrated is not sufficient to justify our description of a magnet as a dipole unless a measurement of the torque on a magnet in the magnetic field shows that it varies as shown by Eq. (15.9-3). To test this, we may rotate the small magnet of Fig. 15.14 from one of its equilibrium positions and measure the torque necessary to hold it at an angle θ with that position. Experiments of this sort show that the torque is

$$T = k \sin \theta, \tag{15.13-1}$$

where k is a constant for any fixed position of the center of the test magnet. The identity of this relation with Eq. (15.9-3) justifies our use of the term magnetic dipole.

If we had a unit magnetic dipole, we might carry the analogy with the electric dipole a bit further and use Eq. (15.13-1) to measure the magnetic field at any point. We shall see in Chapter 16 that the most convenient way to define a magnetic dipole is in terms of an electric current (i.e., of electric charge in motion), so we shall postpone the quantitative discussion of magnetic fields until we have obtained such a definition. In the meantime, we can use a test magnet to study magnetic fields qualitatively and to find the direction of the lines of magnetic force at any point in the neighborhood of a magnet or a set of magnets.

15.14 The Earth as a Magnet

Of the various magnets that occur in nature, one of the most striking is the earth itself. If the magnetic field of the earth is investigated, it is found that it is very closely the same as that which would be produced if a very powerful magnetic dipole were located at its center. This dipole is pointed along a direction at an angle of about 20° to the axis of the earth's rotation. The ***magnetic poles of the earth*** are the points at which a line drawn through this dipole would intersect the earth's surface. Due to the inclination of the dipole, these magnetic poles do not coincide with the geodetic poles. Moreover, they vary somewhat with time. At present, the magnetic pole in the Northern Hemisphere is located in the extreme northern portion of Canada, at longitude 96°W and latitude 70.5°N. The relation between the magnetic and geodetic poles is indicated in Fig. 15.15. The reader should remember that the dipole shown at the center of the earth in the figure is not actually there. The magnetic field of the earth, outside the surface, is, however, very close to the field that would be produced if all other magnetic material in the earth were removed and replaced by such a dipole.

Because of the magnetism of the earth, the poles of a magnet were long ago given the names ***north*** and ***south***, rather than positive and negative. That pole of a magnet which points toward the north when the magnet is free to rotate horizontally was first known as the ***north-seeking pole***; this was later abbreviated to ***north pole***. In the future, we shall often adopt this notation instead of the + and − notation used in Figs. 15.10–15.14. It may be well for the reader to go back over those figures now and label all the magnets with an "N" at the plus end and an "S" at the minus end.

The direction of the earth's magnetic field at any point can be determined by two instruments, the ***compass*** and the ***dip needle.*** The former is merely a permanent magnet arranged to rotate freely in a horizontal plane. It will, of course, place itself in an equilibrium position along the direction of the horizontal component of the magnetic field at the point where it is located. When the compass is used as an aid in navigation, it points toward the north magnetic pole,

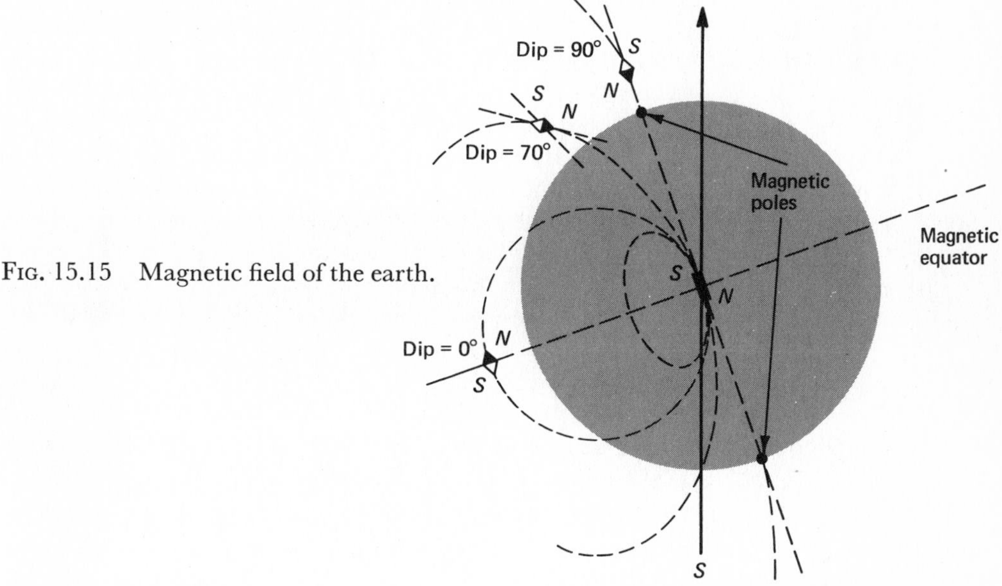

FIG. 15.15 Magnetic field of the earth.

rather than the geodetic pole. The angle between the direction in which the north pole of the compass points and the true north direction is known as the ***magnetic declination.*** This quantity has been carefully tabulated for different latitudes and longitudes and the tables are corrected at intervals by the various national surveys.

The dip needle is a bar magnet free to rotate about its center of mass in a vertical plane. If this plane is oriented in the direction of the compass needle at any point on the earth's surface, the equilibrium position of the dip needle will be that of the earth's field at that point. The ***angle of dip*** is the angle between the dip needle position and the horizontal. It varies from 0° at the geomagnetic equator (approximately halfway between the magnetic poles) to 90° at the poles.

15.15 Magnetization

Whenever a sample of ferromagnetic material is placed in a magnetic field, the elementary dipoles in the material are subject to torques which tend to line them up with the field. This process is known as ***magnetization by induction.***

It is due to this type of magnetization that pieces of previously unmagnetized iron or nickel are attracted to the poles of a magnet, since the part of the material nearest to a pole of the magnet will have a pole of opposite polarity induced in it. Magnetization by induction is thus similar in its effect to the electrification by induction, which we discussed in Sec. 15.4, although the mechanism is different in the two cases, the one involving the flow of charge and the other the rotation of dipoles.

The phenomenon of induced magnetization may be used for a qualitative investigation of the field due to a magnet. If a piece of glass or paper is placed over the magnet and iron filings are shaken onto it, each minute piece of iron will itself become a magnet and will therefore line up with the magnetic field. Hence, the filings arrange themselves in long chains, reaching from pole to pole, and they indicate, by the direction of these chains, the direction of the magnetic lines of force.

Some materials, such as soft iron or nickel, acquire a large magnetic moment in a relatively weak magnetic field but lose nearly all of this moment as soon as they are removed from the field. Other ferromagnetic materials, such as the hard steels, acquire a much smaller moment, apparently due to the fact that internal forces prevent the elementary magnets from coming into alignment. On the other hand, when such materials are removed from the field, they retain a large portion of their magnetism.

Materials that retain an appreciable part of their magnetism after the magnetizing field has been removed are said to have a high ***retentivity***. Such materials are naturally those suitable for the construction of permanent magnets, such as those discussed in Secs. 15.11–15.13.

15.16 Summary

We have seen in this chapter that forces other than those of gravitation may act between bodies separated from each other. In particular, electrostatic forces occur when one or more of the bodies has acquired an electrical charge and magnetic forces when the bodies are magnetized. Many of the concepts introduced in connection with gravitation in Chapter 14 can be applied directly to the discussion of electrical and magnetic phenomena—definitions of field strength and of displacement have turned out to be especially useful. Gauss' law also applies, as does the inverse square law of force.

In spite of the similarities of the three fields—gravitational, electrical, and magnetic—there are important differences. As a source of the gravitational field there exists only one type of mass, and all forces are attractive; the electric field may be produced by charges of different signs, and both attractive and repulsive forces occur; the sources of the magnetic field involve magnetic poles that exist only in pairs, or dipoles. The electric field depends upon the nature of the medium surrounding the charges or dipoles, whereas the gravitational law of force is universal and is not affected by intervening bodies. (We shall see later that the magnetic field resembles the electric field in this respect.)

PROBLEMS

15.1 The small sphere S_1 in diagram (a) carries a charge $+q$ and is suspended by a string of length L. The sphere S_2 carries an equal charge and is originally fixed at a point that is directly below the point of support at a distance L from that point. Under these circumstances, the suspension makes an angle 2θ with the vertical, and the centers of the two spheres are separated by a distance $2d$. Sphere S_2 is then moved to the left and raised slightly, until it is at the same height as S_1, and the separation of the two centers is d, as shown in (b). What is the horizontal component D of the displacement of S_2? (Neglect the small vertical component of motion if you wish to do so.)

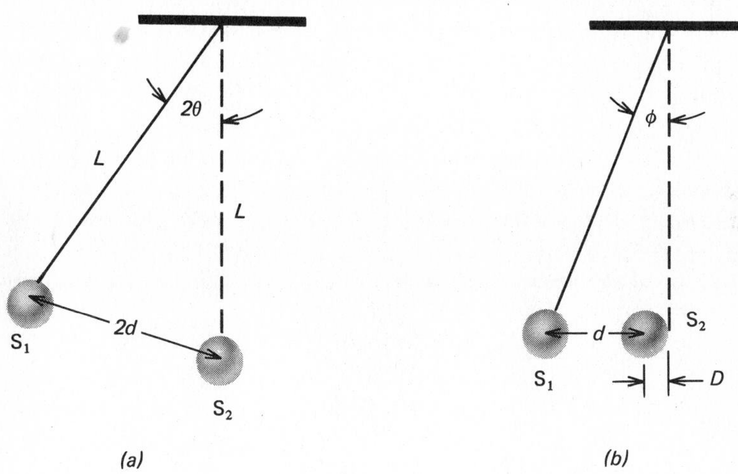

PROBLEM 15.1

15.2 A solid insulating sphere, of radius R and permittivity ε, is charged in such a way that the charge density ρ is uniform throughout its volume.

(a) What is the total charge within the sphere?

(b) By construction of appropriate Gaussian surfaces, show that the electric field inside the sphere is $\vec{E}_i = \rho\vec{r}/3\varepsilon$, where $\vec{r}$ is the radius vector from the center of the sphere to the point at which the field is measured.

(c) What is the field outside the sphere?

(d) Suppose that the sphere also carries a surface charge, uniformly distributed and equal to $-4\pi R^3\rho/3$. Which of the above results will be changed?

15.3 A ***spherical capacitor***, as indicated in the figure, consists of two hollow, metallic, spherical shells with a common center. The space between the two spheres is empty. The inner sphere is of radius a and carries a charge Q; the outer sphere has a radius b and carries a charge $-Q$. (a) Find the electric field at any point at distance r from the common center, when $b > r > a$. (b) Find the field at any point for which $r > b$.

15.4 Suppose that a fine insulating thread is stretched along a vertical radius between the tops of the two spheres of Prob. 15.3. This thread acts as guide for a small ball of mass m, which carries a charge q, of the same sign as Q, the charge on the inner sphere.

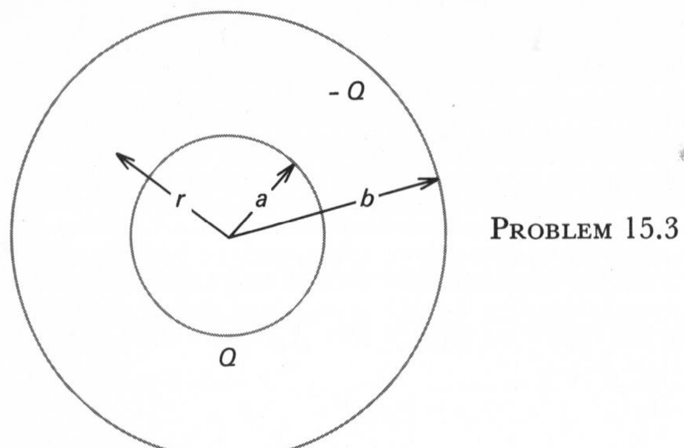

PROBLEM 15.3

(a) Find expressions for the maximal and minimal values of the product Qq that will cause the ball to come to an equilibrium position somewhere between the two spheres.

(b) Assuming that the product Qq is within the limits found in (a), find an expression for the equilibrium position.

15.5 Suppose that the small ball of Prob. 15.4 is made of metal and that it acquires its charge q by touching the inner sphere.

(a) Show that the ball will accelerate outward if the product Qq has a value greater than the minimum found in Prob. 15.4.

(b) Supposing the ball to be at rest in contact with the inner sphere at time $t = 0$, show that the velocity $\vec{v}$ at some later time will be such that

$$v^2 = \frac{Qq}{2\pi\varepsilon_0 m}\left(\frac{1}{a} - \frac{1}{r}\right) - 2g(r - a),$$

where r is the distance of the ball from the center.

(c) The expression found in (b) clearly can hold only for a limited range of time. Describe in a qualitative fashion what will happen to the ball at later times.

15.6 Using the figure of Prob. 15.3 to represent a cross section of two long concentric, metallic cylinders, which carry charges of λ and $-\lambda$ per meter of length, rework the problem.

15.7 (a) A hydrogen atom consists of a ***proton***, of mass 1.66×10^{-27} kg, and an ***electron***, of mass 0.911×10^{-30} kg. They are separated by a distance of 5.3×10^{-11} m. The proton carries a positive charge of 1.60×10^{-19} Cb and the electron carries a negative charge of the same magnitude. Compute the ratio of the gravitational force between the two particles to the electrical force betwen them. Are gravitational effects important in the hydrogen atom?

(b) To account for the fact that the hydrogen atom does not collapse under the action of the attractive forces, we may assume that the electron is rotating in a circular orbit about the proton. Show that the angular velocity of the electron is

$$\omega = (e^2/4\pi\varepsilon_0 m r^3)^{1/2},$$

where e is the magnitude of the electronic charge, m is the electronic mass, and r is the radius of the orbit.

15.8 An electric dipole similar to that shown in Fig. 15.9 has the two charges separated by a distance r. Choose a rectangular Cartesian coordinate system with its origin midway between the two charges and its $+z$-axis directed through the charge $+Q$. Find the direction and magnitude of the electric field at the following points:

(a) $x=y=z=0$.
(b) $x=y=0,\ z=3r/2$.
(c) $x=y=0,\ z=5r/2$.
(d) $x=z=0, y=r$.
(e) $x=r/\sqrt{3}, y=0,\ z=r/2$.

15.9 Show that the electric field anywhere on the z-axis of the dipole of Prob. 15.8 is parallel to the z-axis and has the magnitude

$$E=pz/2\pi\varepsilon_0[(\tfrac{1}{2}r)^2-z^2]^2$$

where p is the dipole moment, equal to Qr.

15.10 (a) Using the result of Prob. 15.9, show that the force exerted by the dipole on a charge q, placed on the z-axis at a distance $z \gg \frac{1}{2}r$ from the origin, is of magnitude

$$f_1 \approx pq/2\pi\varepsilon_0 z^3.$$

(b) What is the force (f_2) exerted on the dipole by the charge q?

(c) Show that the force found in (b) is equal to $p(dE/dz)$, where E is the magnitude of the electric field produced by q at the location of the dipole.

15.11 Suppose that the ball of Prob. 15.4 carries a dipole moment $\vec{p}$ instead of a charge q. The dipole moment is directed toward the center of the spheres. Assuming the result of Prob. 15.10(c) to be valid, find the equilibrium position of the dipole and the magnitude of the product Qp needed to place this position between the spheres.

15.12 Two identical compass needles are sufficiently near to each other so that the torque exerted on one by the other is comparable with the torque exerted on either by the earth's magnetic field. Make sketches of each of the following arrangements.

(a) Show that both needles will point north if their centers lie on a north-south line *or* on an east-west line.

(b) Show that neither compass will point north if their centers lie on a line that runs from southwest to northeast.

15.13 An ***electric quadrupole*** may be made up of a charge $+2Q$ at the origin of a coordinate system and two charges, each $-Q$, located on the z-axis, at $z=+d$ and $z=-d$.

(a) Find an approximate expression for the field produced by this quadrupole at any point on the z-axis for which $z \gg d$. Show that the field is directed inward along the axis and has a magnitude

$$E=3Qd^2/2\pi\varepsilon_0 z^4.$$

(b) What is the direction of the field at any point in the plane $z=0$?

15.14 A particle of mass m, which carries a charge $-q$, is moving at a certain instant with a velocity $\vec{v}$ that is perpendicular to the line joining the particle to a fixed origin. The distance from the origin at this instant is R. A charge of $+Q$ is fixed at the origin. The two charges have opposite signs. Use the laws of the conservation of energy and the conservation of angular momentum in proving the following statements:

(a) If the velocity is such that

$$v^2=Qq/4\pi\varepsilon_0 mR$$

the particle will move in a circular orbit.

(b) If v^2 is greater than twice that stated above, the particle will never again be as close as R to the origin. (Hint: Note Prob. 14.4.)

(c) If v^2 is greater than stated in (a) but less than twice that value, the particle will move in an elliptic orbit, the semiminor axis being greater than R.

(d) If v^2 is less than stated in (a), the particle will move in an elliptic orbit, the semimajor axis being less than R.

15.15 Suppose that v^2 in Prob. 15.14 is sufficiently great so that the condition of part (b) of that problem is satisfied. The path of the particle will then be that indicated by the heavy line in the figure (I). Show the following to be true for the time when the particle is at a point such as P, for which $r \gg R$:

(a) The speed V of the particle is such that

$$V^2 \approx v^2 - Qq/2\pi\varepsilon_0 mR.$$

(b) The perpendicular distance of the line of motion, AB, from Q is

$$b = Rv/V.$$

(c) The ***impact parameter*** b satisfies the relation

$$\frac{1}{b^2} = \frac{1}{R^2} - \frac{Qq}{2\pi\varepsilon_0 mR^3v^2}$$

15.16 Conditions are exactly the same as in Probs. 15.14 and 15.15, except that Q and q have the same sign. The path of the particle will then be that indicated by the heavy line in the figure (II). Prove the following statements: (a) The speed V of the particle at distances much greater than R from Q (e.g., at P′) is greater than v. (b) The impact parameter b' satisfies the relation

$$\frac{1}{b'^2} = \frac{1}{R^2} + \frac{Qq}{2\pi\varepsilon_0 mR^3v^2}.$$

(The path qP′B′ is a hyperbola. We shall return to this problem in Sec. 19.6.)

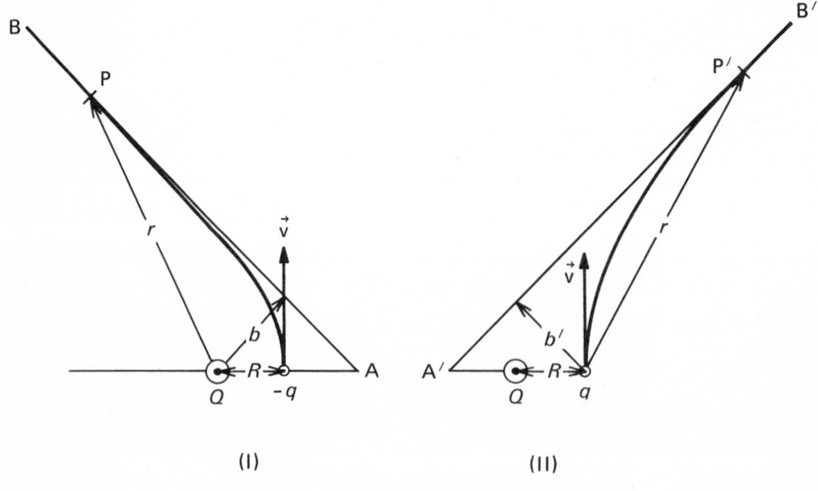

PROBLEMS 15.15 and 15.16

REFERENCES

15A *Electrostatics*. Ten 2- to 4-min loops. (Set No. 89-932, The Ealing Corp., Cambridge, Mass.)

15B A. Einstein and L. Infeld, *The Evolution of Physics*, Simon and Schuster, New York, 1938. The authors discuss field theories and general relativity in pp. 220–260.

15C William Francis Magie, *A Source Book in Physics*, Harvard, Cambridge, Mass., 1935. Some excerpts from William Gilbert's work on magnetism are presented in pp. 387–393 and from Charles Francois de Cisternay du Fay and Benjamin Franklin in pp. 398-403.

15D Morris Shamos, ed., *Great Experiments in Physics*, Holt, New York, 1960. Chapter 5 recounts the discovery of Coulomb's law.

15E Louis McKeehan, *Magnets* (Momentum Book No. 16), Van Nostrand, Princeton, 1967. History of magnets and magnetic materials.

16 ⇨ *Electric Currents and Potentials*

16.1 The Electric Current

In Chapter 15 we studied the properties of stationary electric charges and discussed the forces that these charges exert upon one another. We considered also the qualitative properties of magnets and showed that they behave according to laws that are very similar to those obeyed by electric dipoles. But magnetic effects are not physically connected with the forces between stationary electric charges; instead, they are explainable as a force that one moving electric charge exerts upon another moving charge. In order to show this, we must first study some of the phenomena that occur when charges move from one body to another.

When two equally but oppositely charged conductors, A and B in Fig. 16.1, are connected by a wire, they are discharged. We can observe the rate of this discharge process qualitatively by attaching an electroscope to either of the conductors.

If the two conductors are connected by a good third conductor, such as a copper wire, the discharge will be very rapid. It is difficult to measure the rate of flow of charge with an electroscope, but it is easy to define a unit in terms of

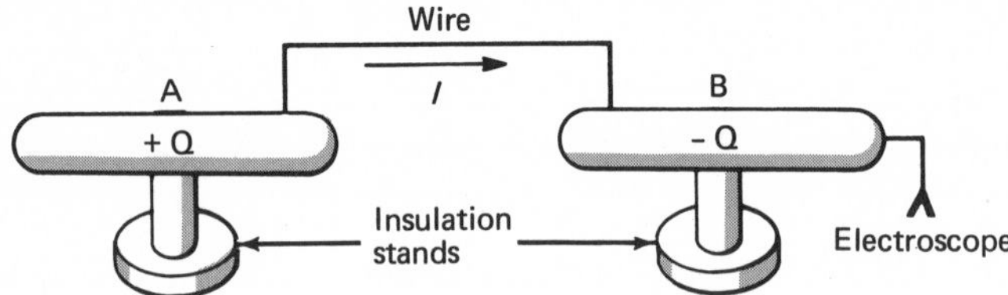

Fig. 16.1 Current flow during discharge. (a) Physical arrangement. (b) circuit diagram.

which such a flow can be measured by instruments that we shall meet later in this chapter. If an amount of charge Δq flows through the wire in a time Δt, we can say that the average time rate of flow of charge is $\Delta q/\Delta t$. We call this flow of charge the ***electric current*** I, and we measure the current as the rate of flow. Thus the average current in the wire is

$$I_{av} = \Delta q/\Delta t, \tag{16.1-1}$$

and the instantaneous current is

$$I = \lim_{\Delta t \to 0} (\Delta q/\Delta t) = dq/dt. \tag{16.1-2}$$

From Eq. (16.1-2), the unit of current follows logically as one coulomb per second (Cb/sec), which for convenience is called the ***ampere*** (A). This unit honors André Marie Ampère (1775–1836), a French physicist who contributed greatly to our knowledge of the magnetic effects of currents.

What moves while there is current? How are the charged bodies *before* the experiment of Fig. 16.1 different from the discharged bodies after the experiment? This is tantamount to asking: what is charge? We are not yet ready to give our best answers to these questions, for we must cite several other bits of evidence in the chapters to come. What we can do now is to state certain definitions that were made, somewhat arbitrarily, for the convenience of early investigations of electrical phenomena. This approach will not be lost motion, for these definitions lead immediately to the conventions now used in describing electrical phenomena.

We have already encountered the first definition, that the charge produced on ebonite when it is rubbed with wool is negative, and that the opposite charge, produced on glass when it is rubbed with silk, is positive. The second definition specifies the positive direction of the current—i.e., the direction of the flow of positive charge—as being from positive to negative. Thus, in Fig. 16.1, the current direction is from A (+) to B (−). Note that we can equally well say that a flow of negative charge from B to A constitutes a positive current. Either the flow of positive charge from A to B or that of negative charge from B to A results in the discharge and neutralization of the charged bodies. *This convention for the positive direction of current is the one we still use, despite the fact that we now interpret the current in a wire as being a flow of negative charges in the opposite direction.*

The production of an electric current by the discharge of electrostatic charges is not a convenient way to study the properties of current-carrying wires, because the discharge usually lasts for a very short time. However, if a wire is connected between the two terminals of an electrical machine or a battery, which were mentioned in Sec. 15.4, it is possible to produce a current that lasts for an indefinite time. The effects of the current can then be studied somewhat more leisurely. Figure 16.2a shows a simple arrangement for studying the properties of a current-carrying wire. The wire PMN is connected between the positive terminal P and the negative terminal N of the battery B. The symbol at B in Fig. 16.2b is the conventional one to denote a battery. An arrangement in which a conducting path (or paths) is connected between the terminals of a source of electricity is known as an ***electric circuit***, and "maps" such as that shown in Fig. 16.2b are known as ***circuit diagrams.***

In one sense, the circuit of Fig. 16.2 consists only of a battery and a wire and constitutes a ***short circuit***. We usually think of short circuits as mistakes which simply waste batteries. In the broader sense, however, we can recognize Fig. 16.2 as being representative of more practical circuits. For example, the effective part of a flashlight bulb is just a piece of wire which gets hot enough to glow brightly and to radiate energy in the visible spectrum.

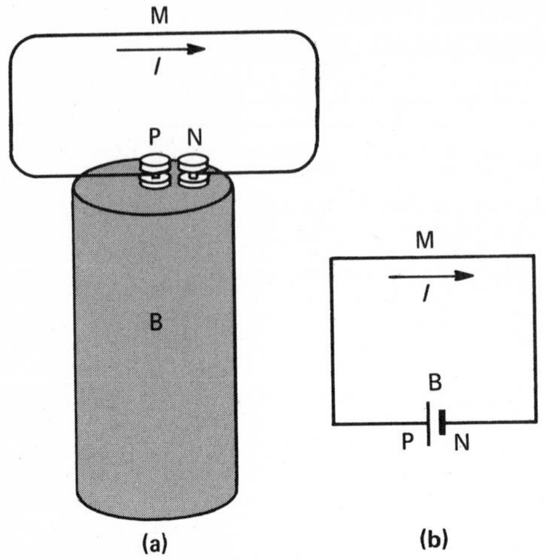

FIG. 16.2 Simple electric circuit.

16.2 Conductors in Series and Parallel

Although we have not yet discussed a practicable method to measure current, there are several results that we can readily deduce from our knowledge of electric charge.

In order to explain the continued production of light by the wire (the filament) in a flashlight bulb, we must assume that something within the battery operates continuously so that terminal P continues to be positively charged and terminal N, negatively charged. Later, we shall see that chemical activity within the battery results in a transfer of charge through the interior of the battery. Energy of chemical combinations is converted to electrical energy which, in turn, is converted to heat energy in the filament of the bulb. If the filament gets hot enough, the heat energy is radiated as visible light.

There is no current unless P and N are connected by conductors outside the battery. And if there is no current, the opposite charges on P and N do not continue to build up indefinitely. Actually, a battery may be exhausted after a time if P and N are continuously connected by a conducting path; but the battery can also be preserved for a long time if P and N remain unconnected. Thus, we can infer that the chemical activity within the battery occurs when there is a connection and that it ceases when the connection is broken.

In our study of electrostatics in Chapter 15, we found that positive and negative charges were always produced simultaneously. For example, when the glass became positively charged, the silk with which it was rubbed became negatively charged. We interpreted this by supposing that the charges were moved from one body to another, rather than being created anew. To put this in another way, we supposed that *electric charge is conserved*, in the same way that mass or momentum is conserved. In the rest of this chapter we shall accept the conservation of charge and base much of our reasoning upon this law. The fact that the conclusions we reach on this basis are in agreement with experiment will then be our basis for accepting charge conservation as a fundamental law of physics.

Suppose that, instead of using a single wire, PMN in Fig. 16.2, we use three pieces of wire—PA, AB, and BN in Fig. 16.3—to connect P to N. It is not

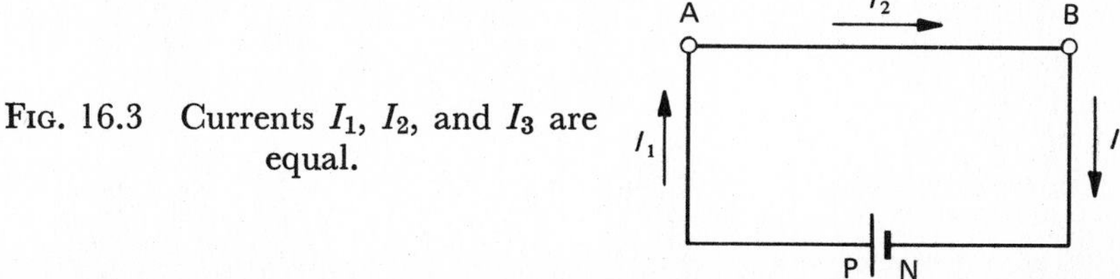

FIG. 16.3 Currents I_1, I_2, and I_3 are equal.

difficult to see that the current in each of these sections is the same. For, if the current I_1 from P to A were greater than the current I_2 from A to B, point A would become steadily more positive. But since the battery would continue to make N negative, current I_3 would continue making point B less positive—i.e., more negative. Our experiment of Fig. 16.1 indicated that there is a current when two oppositely charged conductors are connected by a wire. Points A and B are such conductors. Thus, if for a moment I_1 were greater than I_2, the increase in positive charge at A would tend immediately to increase I_2. Similarly, if I_1 were momentarily less than I_2, point A would become less positive in relation to B and the current I_2 would decrease. Thus, the only steady condition is for $I_1 = I_2 = I_3$.

Any number of conductors connected between two points in an electrical circuit in such a way that they provide one and only one path between the two points are said to be connected in ***series***. The discussion of the preceding paragraph enables us to state that *when a number of conductors are connected in series, the current in any one of them is the same as that in any other.* Thus, $I = I_1 = I_2 = I_3 = I'$ in Fig. 16.4.

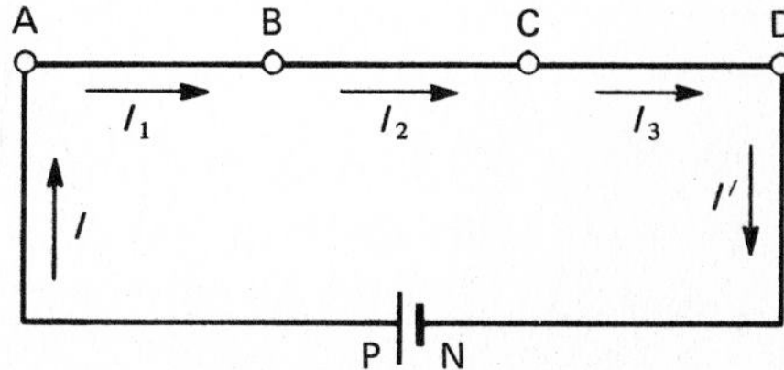

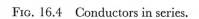

FIG. 16.4 Conductors in series.

If two alternative conducting paths are provided between P and N, as indicated in Fig. 16.5, it is apparent that the current will divide itself between the paths in some way that will depend on the nature of the wires which constitute these paths. We shall see later (Sec. 16.17) what determines this division. For the present, however, we need only apply the conservation of charge to decide that the total current leaving point A must be the same as the total current entering it. Thus, if I is the current from P to A, I_1 the current through branch ACB, and I_2 the current in branch ADB, then we must have

$$I = I_1 + I_2; \tag{16.2-1}$$

otherwise the charge at A would increase or decrease steadily. Similarly, the current from B to N must also have the value I, since the two currents I_1 and I_2 flow into the junction B. The two conductors ACB and ADB that provide two independent paths between A and B are said to be in ***parallel.***

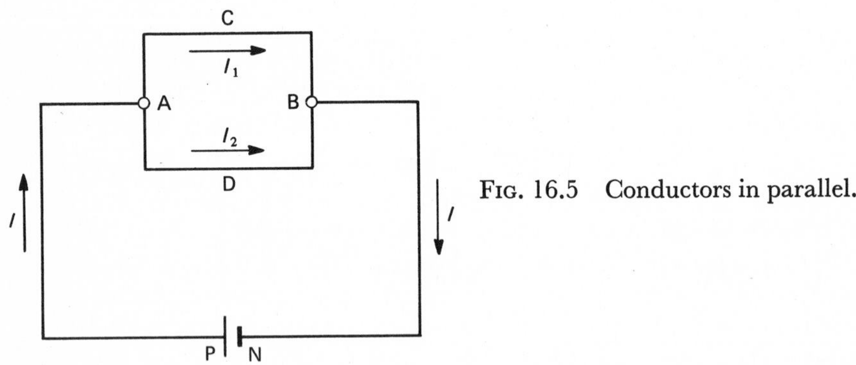

FIG. 16.5 Conductors in parallel.

We can immediately deduce by symmetry that, if the two paths are identical, the two currents will also be identical and we shall have

$$I_1 = I_2 = I/2. \tag{16.2-2}$$

If more than two identical conductors are connected in parallel, it follows that the current will divide itself equally among them.

EXERCISES

16.2-1 (a) Initially, an insulated conductor A has a charge +100 Cb, and a similar conductor B has a charge —100 Cb. If a charge +25 Cb is taken from A to B, what are the resulting charges on A and B?

(b) With the initial charges as before, a charge —25 Cb is taken from B to A. What are the resulting charges?

(c) Again, with the initial charges as before, a charge of +9 Cb is taken from A to B, and at the same time a charge of —16 Cb is taken from B to A. What is the resulting charge on each conductor?

16.2-2 During a time interval of 193 sec, a charge of +219 Cb flows through a wire connecting conductor A to conductor B. What is the average current from A to B during this time?

16.2-3 A charge of +19.3 Cb flows from A to B during an interval of 100 sec. During the same interval, a charge of −101.2 Cb flows from B to A. What is the average current from A to B during this time?

16.2-4 If two identical paths are provided for the current in Ex. 16.2-3, how much positive charge and how much negative charge will flow through each branch, and what will be the current in each branch?

16.3 Magnetic Effects of Currents

One of the most important properties of an electric current is its ability to produce magnetic effects. We can demonstrate these effects most vividly by winding a cylindrical coil of wire called a ***solenoid*** (Fig. 16.6). A solenoid is

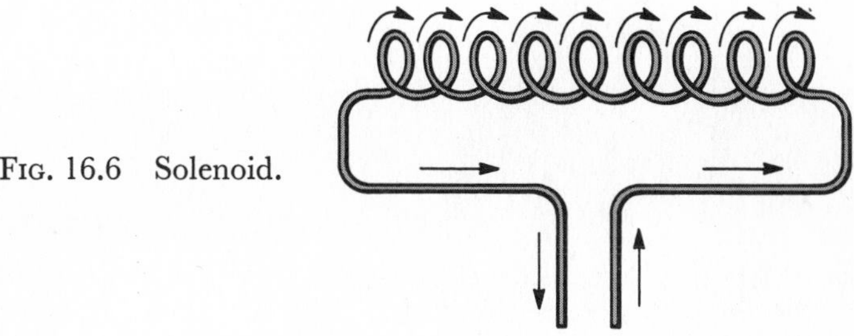

Fig. 16.6 Solenoid.

most conveniently made by winding one or more layers of wire on the outside of a cylindrical rod or tube. If we pass a current through a solenoid and use a small magnet to trace the magnetic field near it, we find that the magnetic field outside the solenoid is almost identical with that of a magnet of similar size and shape. In a similar way, if we pivot a very small solenoid about an axis perpendicular to its length, we may use it instead of a magnetic needle to map the magnetic field around a magnet or around another solenoid (Fig. 16.7).

Obviously, a solenoid is equivalent to a large number of circular coils of wire wound around the cylinder, so that we can simplify our thinking by studying a

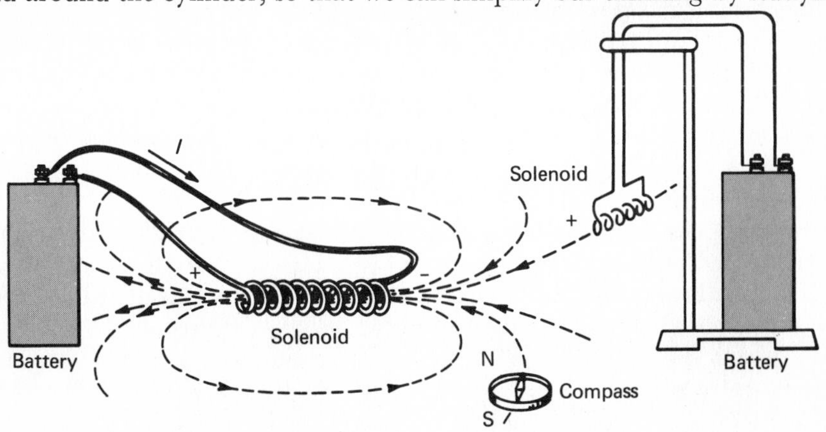

Fig. 16.7 Mapping of the field about a solenoid.

single circular loop of wire, or better, a number of circular loops or turns of wire bound together to form a circular coil of wire (Fig. 16.8). The two ends of the wire are brought out, as indicated in the figure, so that a current can be sent through the wire. This current then goes around the coil as many times as there are turns of wire around the coil. A circular coil of this sort behaves in exactly the same way in a magnetic field as do the small magnets or small solenoids already discussed. If a coil is suspended in a magnetic field, it will set its axis (AB, Fig. 16.8) parallel to the magnetic lines of force.

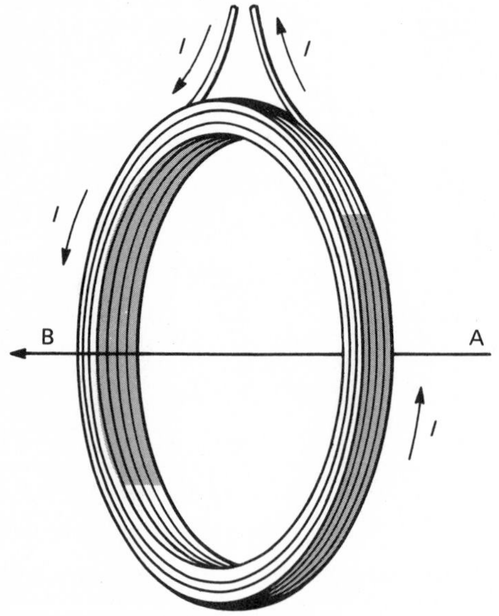

Fig. 16.8 Circular coil.

If we reverse the direction of the current through a coil freely suspended in a magnetic field, it will turn itself through 180°, indicating that the direction of the current in the coil determines which face of the coil is north-seeking (or +) in its magnetic properties. We can identify the north-seeking or positive face of a coil of wire by a simple rule which is consistent with all experiments that have been performed. *If we grasp the coil in the right hand as shown in Fig. 16.9 with the thumb in the direction of the current in the coil and the fingers through the coil, then the fingers point to the positive or north-seeking face of the coil.* This rule is known as the ***right-hand rule.***

It is more convenient to talk about the ***positive or north-seeking axis*** of the coil than to talk about its north-seeking face. This is simply the axis that comes out of the north-seeking face and is normal to it. The arrowhead at B in Fig. 16.8 indicates the positive axis for the coil and current as shown.

In applying the right-hand rule, we usually grasp the coil only in imagination. Many of the wires used in practical electricity are covered with a thin layer of cloth or rubber or other insulating material which protects the user from the effects of electrical shock, but many wires do not have such protection. The user of electrical equipment should grasp electric wires, when necessarily, only when he is absolutely sure that he is protected from harmful effects by appropriate insulation. Figure 16.9 should therefore be looked on simply as an aid to the imagination.

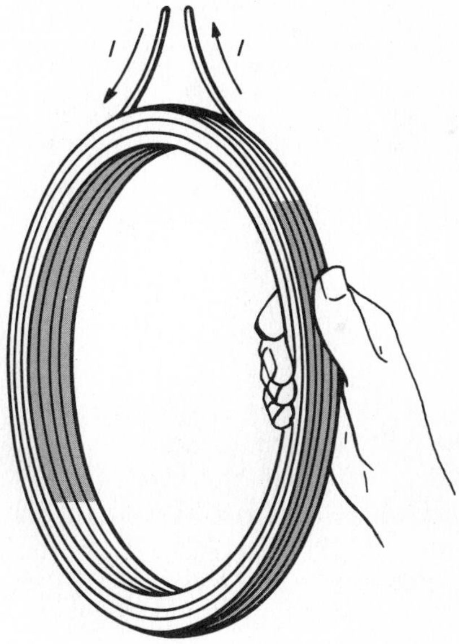

FIG. 16.9 The right-hand rule.

16.4 The Magnetic Dipole Moment of a Circular Coil

We saw in the preceding section that a freely-suspended, small circular coil, when placed in a magnetic field, rotates so that its north-seeking axis points in the direction of the magnetic field. We now define the ***positive direction of the magnetic field*** as that direction in which the north-seeking axis points. This is, of course, the direction of a magnetic line of force through the region and also the direction in which a compass needle would point.

If a small circular coil is freely suspended in a magnetic field, its equilibrium position will be that for which the north-seeking axis of the coil points in the direction of the field. If we attempt to turn the coil away from this equilibrium position, we find that a torque must be applied to do so. Measurement of this torque shows it to be proportional to sin θ, where θ is the angle through which the coil has been turned from its equilibrium position. In this respect, the behavior of the coil is identical with that of an electric dipole (Eq. 15.9-3) and with that of a small magnet (Eq. 15.13-1).

We can now prepare several circular coils of wire, some of which have different numbers of turns (N_1 and N_2) and the same radius a_1 (A, B of Fig. 16.10) and others of which have the same number of turns N_2 and different radii a_1, a_2 (B, C of Fig. 16.10). All of these coils are then connected in series to a battery so that the same current I flows through each one of them. They are then tested one by one in a given magnetic field (i.e., in the same location

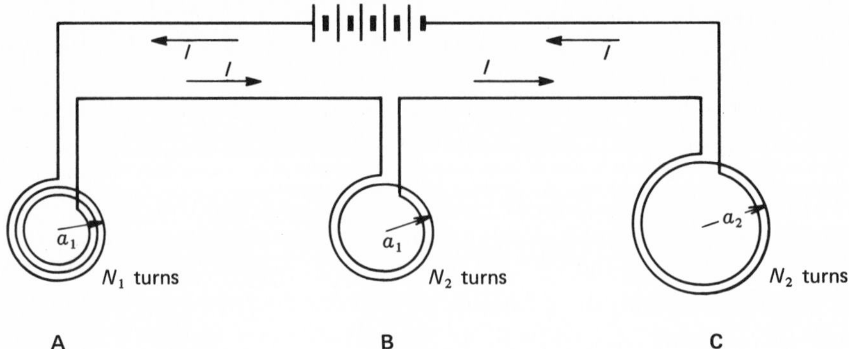

FIG. 16.10 Arrangement to study dependence of dipole moment on area and number of turns.

with respect to a given magnet). For coils A and B, the torques for a given angle of twist are always in the ratio N_1/N_2, whatever the angle and whatever the current. For the coils B and C, the torques are always in the ratio $a_1{}^2/a_2{}^2$. Since the area (πa^2) of a circular coil is proportional to the square of its radius, we are led to suspect that the ratio of the torques for the same current is A_1/A_2, where A_1 and A_2 are the areas of the coils. We can verify this by experimenting with coils of the same area and different shape (e.g., square, rectangular, or triangular coils). We find that the torque depends only on the area and the number of turns and not on the shape.

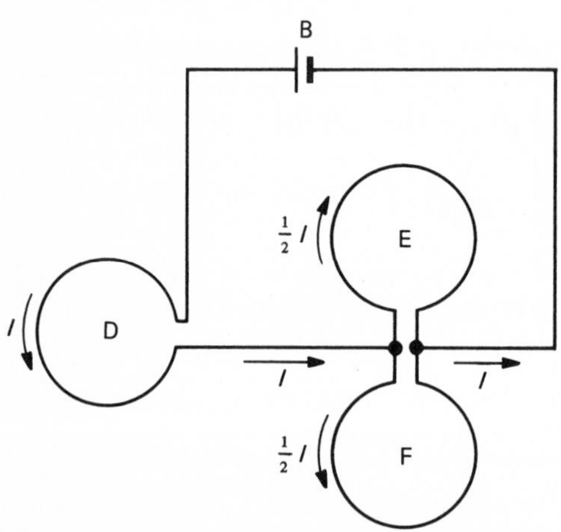

FIG. 16.11 Arrangement to study dependence of dipole moment on current.

We can now consider the effect of a change in current by constructing three identical coils (D, E, F) and connecting them as shown in Fig. 16.11. If a current I flows through D, equal currents $I/2$ flow through E and F. If we test these coils one by one in the same magnetic field, we can verify that the magnetic properties of coils E and F are identical by observing that they both require the same torque for a given angle of deflection. Furthermore, we find that the torque for coils E and F is one-half of that required to hold D in the same position, indicating that the torque on a coil is proportional to the current I flowing in the coil.

We have thus been able to show that the torque T' required to deflect a current-carrying coil in a given magnetic field is given by

$$T' = kNAI \sin \theta,$$

where k is a constant of proportionality, N is the number of turns in the coil, A is its area, I is the current in the coil, and θ is the angle through which the coil has been deflected from the position in which it comes to rest. Thus the torque T that the magnetic field exerts on the coil, tending to return it to its rest position, is

$$T = -T' = -kNAI \sin \theta. \tag{16.4-1}$$

Experiment has verified the fact that the only way in which the torque depends on the properties of the coil is through N, A, and I. No other properties *of the coil* have any effect on the torque on the coil in a magnetic field. The analogy with Eq. (15.9-3) leads us to define a quantity, which we call the ***magnetic dipole moment*** p_{m} of the coil, by the equation

$$p_{\mathrm{m}} = NAI. \tag{16.4-2}$$

The unit of dipole moment is (ampere-turns) (square-meters) and its dimensions are $[\ell^2 t^{-1} q]$, N being a dimensionless quantity. We can rewrite Eq. (16.4-1) in the form

$$T = -kp_{\mathrm{m}} \sin \theta, \tag{16.4-3}$$

in which we are assured that the constant k has nothing to do with the coil and can depend only on the magnetic field in which the coil is located.

16.5 Magnetic Flux Density and Magnetic Flux

We have defined the magnetic moment of a small coil in terms of the number of turns in the coil, the area enclosed by each turn of the coil, and the current in the coil. We found the dependence on the current simply by holding all other factors constant and contriving to reduce the original current to half its initial value. Thus, even though we have defined the ampere of current as a coulomb per second, we have not yet had to measure absolute values of current, i.e., to do more than to determine relative values in various cases. For example, we have been able to show that a current is half as great in one case as it is in another, or that it is the same in two cases.

We can continue to measure the relative torques on a small test coil, in which we always maintain a constant current, and thereby make qualitative explorations of magnetic fields. We find that the torque on such a coil increases as the coil is brought near to a large magnet and decreases as it is moved farther away. In analogy to the vector $\vec{\mathrm{E}}$, the electric field strength whose magnitude appears in Eq. (15.9-3), we can define a vector $\vec{B}$ which is a factor in the torque that tends to return the coil to its equilibrium position. Thus,

$$T = -Bp_m \sin\theta, \tag{16.5-1}$$

and B is identical to the k of Eq. (16.4-3). Vector $\vec{B}$ is called the ***magnetic flux density***, and its direction, of course, is the direction of the north-seeking axis of the test coil when it is in its equilibrium position. We can measure the magnitude of $\vec{B}$ at any point by determining the magnitude of the torque (T) on a test coil of known dipole moment (p_m) when the coil is twisted an angle θ from its equilibrium position. Thus, we have

$$B = -T/p_m \sin\theta; \tag{16.5-2}$$

hence, we can determine both the magnitude and direction of $\vec{B}$ by means of the coil.

In many ways, it would be better to call $\vec{B}$ the *magnetic field strength* in analogy with electric field strength $\vec{E}$ and gravitational field strength $\vec{g}$. But the historical development of our knowledge has fixed present usage and we shall conform to it.

In analogy with Eqs. (14.10-1) and (15.8-1), we treat vector $\vec{B}$ as the magnetic displacement and define the ***magnetic flux*** Φ through a surface S normal to $\vec{B}$ by the relation

$$\Phi = BS. \tag{16.5-3}$$

The unit of magnetic flux is called the ***weber*** (Wb) after Wilhelm Edward Weber (1804–1891), a German physicist noted for his experimental and theoretical work on magnetism. The unit in which B is measured is thus the weber per square meter (Wb/m^2). To express these units in terms of the mks Cb system, we observe that according to Eq. (16.5-2), the dimensions of B are

$$[B] = [T/p_m] = [m\ell^2 t^{-2}/\ell^2 t^{-1} q], \tag{16.5-4}$$

and the dimensions of flux are

$$[\Phi] = [BS] = [m\ell^2 t^{-1} q^{-1}]. \tag{16.5-5}$$

Thus, the unit Wb/m^2 is equivalent to one kg/Cb sec, and consequently one weber is equivalent to one kg m^2/Cb sec.

16.6 The Field Near a Long, Straight Wire

In 1820, Hans Christian Oersted (1777–1851) was the first to discover that a current produces a magnetic field. Above a compass needle, which was pointing to magnetic north, he stretched a wire that ran parallel to the needle. When a current was established in this wire from south to north, the north-seeking end of the compass needle was deflected toward the west. When the current was reversed, the deflection was toward the east.

Oersted's discovery was followed rapidly by detailed studies of the magnetic fields of currents by Ampère, Jean Baptiste Biot (1774–1862), and Felix Savart

(1791–1841). In deriving some of the interesting results that they obtained, we shall depart from the historical development. It is somewhat easier to consider torques on coils than forces on magnetic poles, so we shall start from Eqs. (16.4-2) and (16.5-2).

Figure 16.12 shows a long, straight, current-carrying wire, in which the current I is directed upward. If the magnetic field is investigated in the neighborhood of the wire by the use of a small compass needle, it is found that the

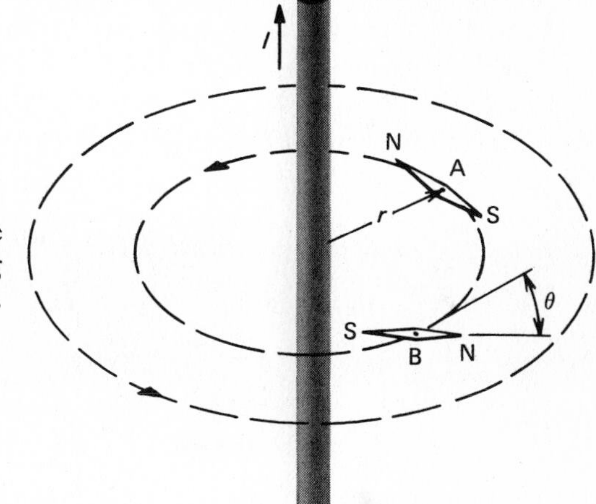

FIG. 16.12 Lines of magnetic force near a long, straight, current-carrying wire are circles centered on the wire.

direction of $\vec{B}$ is always in a plane perpendicular to the wire and in a direction perpendicular to the radius joining the point of observation (A) with the wire (r in Fig. 16.12). In other words, the lines of magnetic force are circles, centered at the wire, as indicated by the dashed lines. The sense of the lines of force, shown by the arrows, is that given by the right-hand rule of Sec. 16.3, with the thumb pointing in the direction of the current and the fingers in the direction of the lines of force.

The magnitude, as well as the direction, of the magnetic flux density may be studied if we apply a torque to the needle to twist it through an angle θ from its equilibrium position, as shown at B in Fig. 16.12. It is found that the needed torque is proportional to sin θ, as would be expected from Eq. (16.5-2), and that it is also inversely proportional to r, the distance from the wire. By using conductors in series and parallel combinations, as was done in Sec. 16.2, we can also show that B at a given location is proportional to I. Combining these results into a single expression, we have

$$B = \frac{\mu_0 I}{2\pi r}, \tag{16.6-1}$$

where $\mu_0/2\pi$ has been arbitrarily chosen as a constant of proportionality. The constant μ_0, of course, is still undetermined—we shall return to this point in the next section. Equation (16.6-1) is often called the ***law of Biot and Savart.***

16.7 Definition of the Ampere

Historically, there have been several different ways of defining units for measuring current. Each of these definitions has involved a set of operations, of course, and the definition to be preferred is the one that depends on the operations that can be carried out with the greatest precision using available laboratory techniques. Thus, from time to time as laboratory arts improve, a scientific community will shift to a new definition for a unit of a given kind. In the measurement of current, it is possible to construct coils with great accuracy and to use them in the measurement of current by its magnetic effects. By such operations it is possible to measure currents to an accuracy of a few parts in ten million. In this section, we outline the essential operations for defining the ampere in terms of the magnetic effects of a current.

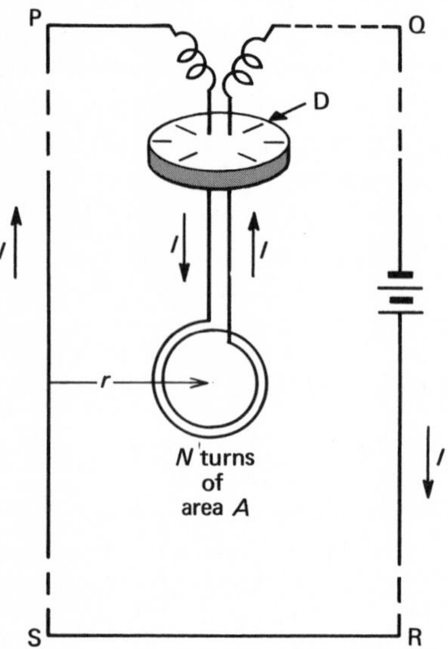

FIG. 16.13 Apparatus for the determination of the ampere.

Figure 16.13 shows an arrangement similar to that of Fig. 16.12, except that the compass needle of the earlier experiment is replaced by a small circular coil of N turns and of area A. The coil is mounted so that it can rotate about a vertical axis and so that torques can be applied to it by twisting the circular drum D, to which the wires supporting it are fastened. The dashed sections of the wiring are inserted to indicate that the wires PQ, QR, and RS are so far from the wire SP that their magnetic effects are negligible.

All of the studies that led to Eq. (16.6-1) can be repeated with the new apparatus. We now have the advantage, however, that we can express the magnetic moment p_m in terms of the current I, by the use of Eq. (16.4-2). We therefore have, by substitution of this moment in Eq. (16.5-1) and with the help of Eq. (16.6-1),

$$T = -Bp_m \sin\theta = \frac{\mu_0 NAI^2 \sin\theta}{2\pi r}. \tag{16.7-1}$$

In this expression, the torque T, the angle θ, and the quantities N, A, and r can all be measured. We are left with only two quantities, μ_0 and I, undetermined. The ampere is defined by choosing the first of these arbitrarily. We make an apparently strange choice, but one that will later be justified, by taking

$$\frac{\mu_0}{2\pi} = 2 \times 10^{-7}\ \text{kg m/Cb}^2. \tag{16.7-2}$$

The constant $\mu_0 = 4\pi \times 10^{-7}$ kg m/Cb² is called the ***permeability of free space.***

Comparison of Eq. (16.7-1) with Eq. (16.6-1) shows that the ***ampere*** is the steady current that, when present in a long straight wire, produces a magnetic flux density of magnitude 2×10^{-7} Wb/m² at a distance of one meter from the wire. The accuracy with which the ampere could be determined by the direct use of this definition would not be satisfactory, but we shall see later that we can derive from the experimental observations already discussed a value for the magnetic flux density inside a solenoid, a long helical coil of wire. Such solenoids can be constructed very precisely and are used to establish both the ampere and the coulomb.

EXERCISES

16.7-1 Verify the dimensions of μ_0 as given in Eq. (16.7-2).

16.7-2 Two long, straight, parallel wires carry currents of the same magnitude in opposite directions. They are separated by a distance a. Show that the magnetic flux density midway between them is given by

$$B_1 = 2\mu_0 I/\pi a,$$

and that the magnitude of the flux density at a point in the plane of the wires and at a point $\frac{1}{2}a$ distant from one wire and $\frac{3}{2}a$ distant from the other is given by

$$B_2 = 2\mu_0 I/3\pi a.$$

16.7-3 A small compass needle is mounted at a distance b below a long, straight horizontal wire that carries current I from magnetic south to magnetic north, as in the Oersted experiment. The magnetic flux density at the place of the experiment has a horizontal component B_e. Show that the needle will be deflected by an angle θ such that

$$\tan\theta = \mu_0 I/2\pi r B_e.$$

16.7-4 (a) In an experiment related to Oersted's observations, suppose that current in the wire is from east to west and that the horizontal component of the earth's flux density is B_e. Show that the needle will not be disturbed by the current if the latter is less than

$$I_0 = 2\pi b B_e/\mu_0,$$

where b is the distance from the wire to the needle.

(b) What will be the equilibrium position of the needle if the current is greater than I_0?

16.8 Some Remarks about μ_0, ε_0, 4π, and Systems of Units

In this section we will comment on the constants that appear in Newton's law of universal gravitation (Secs. 14.4 and 14.5), on Coulomb's law of electrostatic force (Sec. 15.5), and on the relation between a current and the magnetic field associated with it (Secs. 16.6 and 16.7). For convenience, we repeat the essential equations:

$$F = -M_S M_P/4\pi\gamma r^2; \qquad (14.5\text{-}6C)$$

$$4\pi\gamma = 1.50 \times 10^{10} \text{ kg}^2/\text{Nm}^2; \qquad (14.6\text{-}2)$$

$$F = q_1 q_2/4\pi\varepsilon_0 r^2; \qquad (15.5\text{-}3)$$

$$\varepsilon_0 = 8.855 \times 10^{-12} \text{ sec}^2 \text{ Cb}^2/\text{k gm}^3; \qquad (15.5\text{-}2)$$

$$B = \mu_0 I/2\pi r; \qquad (16.6\text{-}1)$$

$$\mu_0 = 4\pi \times 10^{-7} \text{ kg m/Cb}^2. \qquad (16.7\text{-}2)$$

We must remember that experimentally determined relationships usually determine only proportionalities, not equations. Whenever new physical quantities are defined in terms of such relationships, an arbitrary choice of the constants of proportionality must be made. We saw an example of this in Chapter 4, when we defined the newton as the force necessary to produce an acceleration of one meter per second squared of a mass of one kilogram. By so doing, we arbitrarily chose the constant of proportionality, k, in Newton's second law of motion,

$$f = kma,$$

as dimensionless and of unit magnitude, so that the law became

$$f = ma.$$

Each field of study develops its own language. The various fields of physics that we have encountered came into being somewhat independently. Mechanics was developed first. Once that mass and force had been defined, the introduction of Newton's law of gravitation made no new demands. Masses, forces, and distances were all measurable, and the determination of the constant of proportionality, which we have written as $1/4\pi\gamma$ in Eq. (14.5-6C), was straightforward. Its dimensions are determined by the equation itself, and its magnitude is strictly a matter for laboratory measurement.

With Coulomb's law [Eq. (15.5-3)], however, something new entered. A new quantity, electric charge, had been introduced—either it or the constant of proportionality could be chosen arbitrarily. Historically, the study of static electricity developed its own language, which was somewhat different from the one we have used. The ***esu system*** (*e*lectro*s*tatic *u*nits) was based on the centimeter as a unit of length, the dyne (1 gm cm/sec^2) as a unit of force, and the second as a unit of time. The constant of proportionality in Coulomb's law was chosen to be unity and dimensionless, instead of the $1/4\pi\varepsilon_0$ that we have used. With this choice made, one can set $q_1 = q_2 = q$ in Eq. (15.5-3) to obtain

$$q^2 = Fr^2.$$

One therefore defines the ***esu of charge***, or the ***statcoulomb***, as the charge which repels an exactly similar charge, located one centimeter from it in a vacuum, with a force of one dyne. The dimensions of charge in this system are clearly expressible in terms of the purely mechanical quantities, m, ℓ, and t (cf. Ex. 16.8-1).

The study of the magnetic effects of currents was initiated before it was established that currents in wires were a flow of the same electric charge that was responsible for electrostatic forces. Hence, the definition of current as the rate at which charge passes [Eq. (16.1-2)] was impossible. As a result, another system of units grew up. This system, known as the ***emu system*** (*e*lectro*m*agnetic *u*nits), also used the centimeter, the gram, and the second as mechanical units. It is obtained from Eq. (16.6-1) by replacing μ_0 with unity (dimensionless). The resulting unit of current is the ***abampere.*** Thus another language was developed.

When the connection between electrostatics and electromagnetism was thoroughly established in the last half of the nineteenth century, two completely different sets of electrical units had thus been established, the one based on ε_0 being dimensionless and the other on μ_0 also being dimensionless. These two choices are inconsistent, so some compromise was desirable.

To complicate the situation still further, while esu and emu systems were being employed extensively in laboratory investigations, electrical technology was giving wide currency to a set of units called ***practical units***—amperes, watts, joules, volts, etc.—and the coulomb is the practical unit of charge. Since electrical energy is used by the general public, many of the practical units entered everyday speech, *occasionally with their correct meaning!* And students who were beginning their study of physics had at least heard the words before.

The three systems of units—and there were still others—gave widely different sizes to the different units of each electrical quantity. The interrelations of charge units, for example, are 1 coulomb $= 0.1$ abcoulomb $= 2.998 \times 10^9$ statcoulombs. With some 12 to 15 other units in each system, the reader can easily imagine that the physicists themselves had trouble with units and conversion, to say nothing of the troubled students!

The ***mksCb system*** of units was developed in part as an effort to promote a common system for the use of all.* It incorporates most of the practical system

* Strictly speaking, this is the ***mksA system***, because the ampere, rather than the coulomb, is arbitrarily defined.

in a logical, straightforward manner and ties it directly to mks mechanical units. The awkward part comes in the rather artificial requirement that there be 8.986×10^9 N of force between two one-coulomb charges which are separated by one meter in a vacuum.

We shall not pursue this line of discussion here, but the same kind of justification can be made for setting μ_0 equal to $4\pi \times 10^{-7}$ kg m/Cb^2.

As usual, of course, one system of units is convertible to another. As an illustration of this point, we take $q_1 = q_2 = 1.000$ Cb, $4\pi\varepsilon_0 = 1.113 \times 10^{-10}$ sec^2 Cb^2/kg m^3, and $r = 1.000$ m, all appropriate to the mksCb system. Then, in Eq. (15.5-3), we get

$$F = \frac{1.00\ \text{Cb}^2}{(1.113 \times 10^{-10}\ \text{sec}^2\ \text{Cb}^2/\text{kg m}^3)(1.00\ \text{m}^2)}$$

$$= 0.898 \times 10^{10}\ \text{kg m/sec}^2 = 8.98 \times 10^9\ \text{N}.$$

On the other hand, using the *esu-cgs* system, we put $q_1 = q_2 = 2.998 \times 10^9$ statcoulombs, $r = 100.0$ cm, and $1/4\pi\varepsilon_0 = 1.000$ (no units or dimensions), which gives us

$$F = \frac{(2.998 \times 10^9\ \text{statcoulombs})^2}{(100.0\ \text{cm})^2} = \frac{8.98 \times 10^{18}}{10^4} \frac{\text{statcoulomb}^2}{\text{cm}^2}$$

$$= 8.98 \times 10^{14}\ \text{dyne} = 8.98 \times 10^9\ \text{N}.$$

The reason that 4π has been left explicit in $4\pi\gamma$, $4\pi\varepsilon_0$, and $\mu_0/4\pi$ is that, in more sophisticated instances of fields, the fields may be regarded as emanating from points. Now 4π is the total solid angle about a point. (Recall that the surface and volume of a sphere are $4\pi R^2$ and $4\pi R^3/3$, respectively.) Thus, the geometry or the spherical symmetry of the more complicated situation may bring in its own factor of 4π. If we sagaciously have kept 4π explicit in the constants, then 4π will be available later for cancellation, and most later equations can appear in simpler form.

To say this in another way, we are just pointing out that if we use $\gamma' = 4\pi\gamma$, $\varepsilon_0' = 4\pi\varepsilon_0$, and $\mu_0' = \mu_0/4\pi$ as the constants now, then more intricate situations later will involve the factors $\gamma'/4\pi$, $\varepsilon_0'/4\pi$, and $4\pi\mu_0'$. It is a matter of overall convenience to write the constants as we have.

Relations among the most commonly used systems of units are discussed in Appendices D.4 and D.5.

EXERCISES

16.8-1 If, in Coulomb's law, $1/4\pi\varepsilon_0$ is to be dimensionless, find the dimensions of [q].

16.8-2 Show that statcoulombs^2/cm^2 are dynes in the esu-cgs system of units.

16.8-3 Find the dimensions and magnitude of the quantity $(\varepsilon_0\mu_0)^{-1/2}$. Does this bear any relation to another physical quantity that we have met?

16.9 Ampère's Law

A very useful law, which follows from the work of Biot, Savart, and Ampère, expresses the line integral of the magnetic flux density around any closed path as a function of the current that flows across the surface bounded by that path.

We may get the form of this law by considering the circular lines of force around a long current-carrying wire, such as those shown in Fig. 16.12. Let the circle DEF in Fig. 16.14 represent such a line of force surrounding a wire

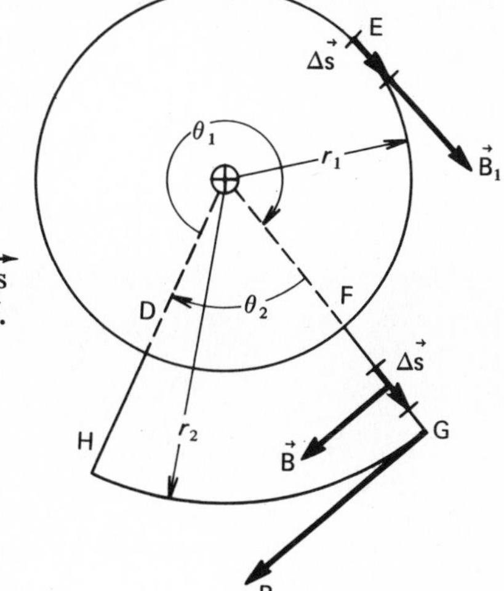

FIG. 16.14. The line integral of $\vec{B}\cdot\vec{ds}$ around a current I is $\mu_0 I$.

carrying a current I, directed into the page. The magnetic flux density at any point, such as E, is directed tangentially to the circle. We define the ***line integral*** of $\vec{B}$ around any closed path as

$$\oint \vec{B}\cdot\vec{ds} = \lim_{\Delta s\to 0} \sum B\,\Delta s \cos\theta, \tag{16.9-1}$$

where $\vec{\Delta s}$ is a small bit of path, $\vec{B}$ is the flux density in the immediate neighborhood of $\vec{\Delta s}$, and θ is the angle between $\vec{B}$ and $\vec{\Delta s}$. The symbol $\oint$ is read as "integral around a closed path," and the dot between $\vec{B}$ and $\vec{ds}$ indicates a scalar product. Let us now consider the scalar product $\vec{B}\cdot\vec{\Delta s}$ as Δs becomes very small. As this happens, $\vec{B}$ and $\vec{\Delta s}$ approach each other in direction, $\theta\to 0$, $\cos\theta\to 1$, and $\vec{B}\cdot\vec{\Delta s}\to B\,\Delta s$. But B has the same magnitude, B_1, everywhere on the circle DEFD; it is therefore a constant and may be removed to the front of the summation sign. Hence,

$$\oint \vec{B}\cdot\vec{ds} = B_1 \lim_{\Delta s\to 0} \sum \Delta s.$$

The expression on the right is clearly $\int ds$, where the integral is taken all around the circle, and this is the length of the path, or $2\pi r_1$. Substituting for B_1 from Eq. (16.6-1), we find that

$$\oint \vec{B}\cdot\vec{ds} = (\mu_0 I/2\pi r_1)(2\pi r_1) = \mu_0 I.$$

This is ***Ampère's law.***

We have derived this simple result by following a very special, circular path, but it can easily be shown to be true for a more general path. To see this, consider the line integral around the more complex path, DEFGHD. We can write this as the sum of four integrals:

$$\oint \vec{B} \cdot \vec{ds} = \int_D^F \vec{B} \cdot \vec{ds} + \int_F^G \vec{B} \cdot \vec{ds} + \int_G^H \vec{B} \cdot \vec{ds} + \int_H^D \vec{B} \cdot \vec{ds}.$$

In the first integral on the right, $B = B_1 = \mu_0 I/2\pi r_1$, and the integral of ds is $r_1 \theta_1$. In the second and fourth integrals, $\vec{B}$ is perpendicular to $\vec{\Delta s}$ at every point along the path, so $\theta = \frac{1}{2}\pi$, $\cos\theta = 0$, and the integrals vanish. In the third integral, $B = B_2 = \mu_0 I/2\pi r_2$, and the path length is $r_2\theta_2$. Hence

$$\oint \vec{B} \cdot \vec{ds} = (\mu_0 I/2\pi r_1)(r_1\theta_1) + (\mu_0 I/2\pi r_2)(r_2\theta_2)$$
$$= (\mu_0 I/2\pi)(\theta_1 + \theta_2).$$

But $\theta_1 + \theta_2$ is the full central angle, equal to 2π, so

$$\oint \vec{B} \cdot \vec{ds} = \mu_0 I,$$

as before.

Any closed path in a plane perpendicular to the wire can be approximated as closely as we please by a series of circular arcs and radial lines, so Ampère's law is valid for any such path. Any more general path, not necessarily planar, can be approximated by pieces of planar paths connected by straight lines parallel to the wire. Along each such straight line $\vec{\Delta s}$ is parallel to the wire and hence perpendicular to $\vec{B}$. Therefore, no additional contribution to the line integral results from making the path nonplanar. Crude approximations to two paths are sketched in Fig. 16.15; the reader should have no difficulty in seeing that these approximations may be improved by increasing the number of circular arcs and straight-line segments.

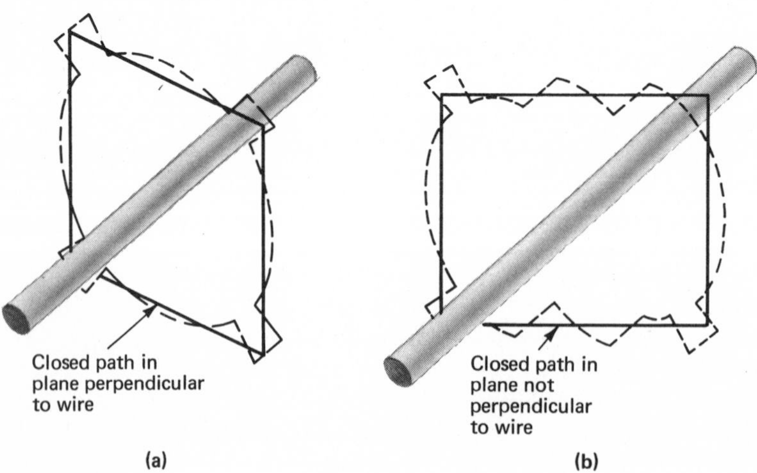

FIG. 16.15 The line integral of $\vec{B} \cdot \vec{ds}$ is the same for all closed paths surrounding the current.

Having shown that Ampère's law is valid for any closed path surrounding a long, straight current-carrying wire, we can generalize it even more. Suppose that the closed curve shown in Fig. 16.16 bounds a surface through which a number of wires, carrying currents I_1, I_2, I_3, etc., pass. We have seen that the line integral around the closed curve of that part of $\vec{B}$ due to any single current I_j is equal to $\mu_0 I_j$. Hence the line integral as a result of all the currents is

$$\oint_{\text{around}} \vec{B} \cdot \vec{ds} = \mu_0(I_1 + I_2 + I_3 + \cdots) = \mu_0 \sum_{\text{through}} I_j \tag{16.9-2}$$

where the summation includes *all* the currents passing through the surface. We have put the word "around" below the line integral to remind us that this integral is taken around a closed path, and the word "through" beneath the summation to indicate that this includes all the currents that pass through the surface.

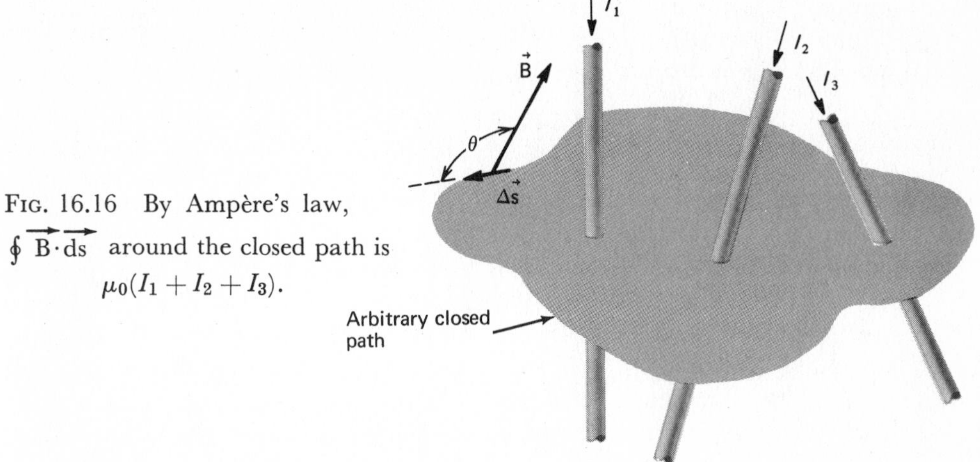

FIG. 16.16 By Ampère's law, $\oint \vec{B}\cdot\vec{ds}$ around the closed path is $\mu_0(I_1 + I_2 + I_3)$.

As a matter of fact, Ampère's law has even greater generality than we have shown. It holds even if the currents crossing the surface are not carried by long, straight wires. For example, it applies to the path shown in Fig. 16.17 if the summation on the right is taken as $I_1 + I_2 - I_3$.

To demonstrate that the wires need not be straight, consider the arrangement of Fig. 16.18. In part (a) of that figure, two long straight wires, PQ and RS, carry identical currents I. According to Ampère's law, the line integral of B around the closed path C must be equal to $2\mu_0 I$. Further, because of the symmetry of the arrangement, the two wires must contribute equally to this line integral, that is, each must make a contribution $\mu_0 I$. We may now note that the arrangement of (a) is not distinguishable from that of (b), in which a current I is present in the bent wire PS, and an equal current is present in the other bent wire RQ. Therefore, the line integral is still $2\mu_0 I$. Symmetry again demands that the two currents contribute equally, so the line integral that results from the current I in the wire PS of Fig. 16.18c must be $\mu_0 I$. The extension of the argument to a current-carrying wire of any shape is left as an exercise for the reader.

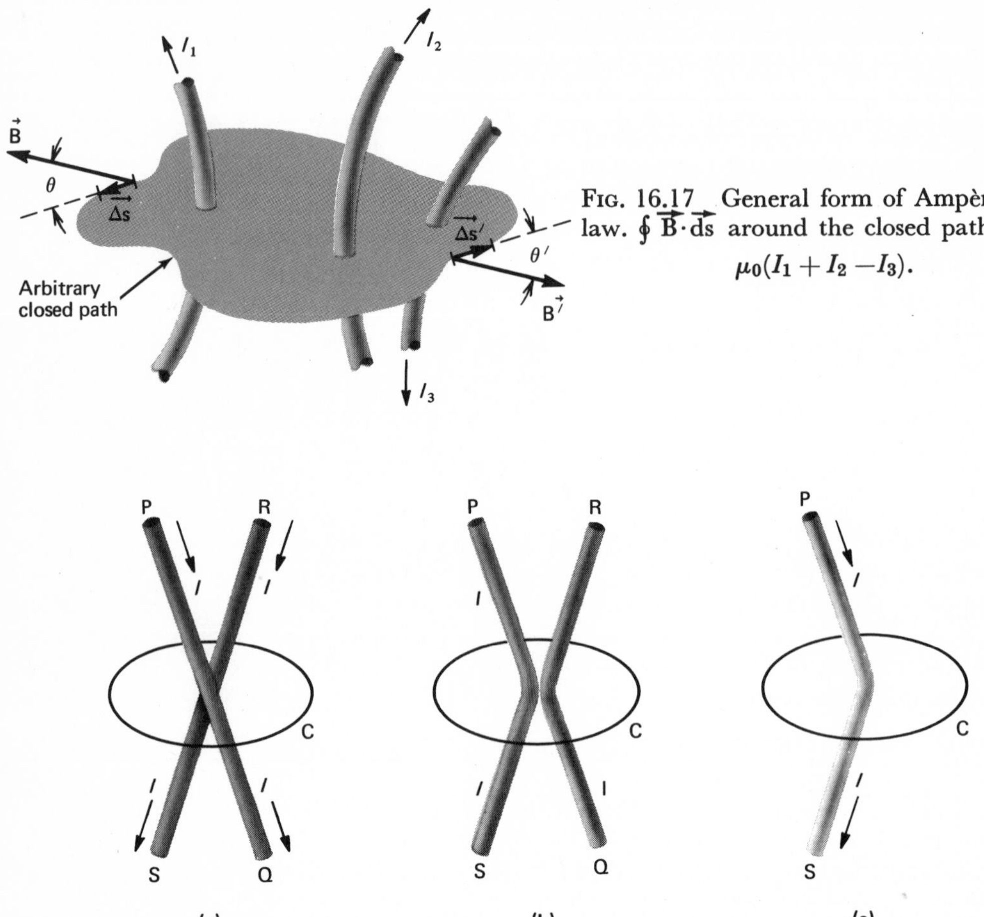

FIG. 16.17 General form of Ampère's law. $\oint \vec{B}\cdot\vec{ds}$ around the closed path is $\mu_0(I_1+I_2-I_3)$.

FIG. 16.18 Ampère's law holds for both bent and straight conductors.

16.10 The Magnetic Fields of Solenoids and Other Coils

One very useful device for the production of magnetic fields is the ***solenoid***, which is a helically wound coil of wire through which a current passes. The term is usually reserved to describe coils whose lengths are very much greater than their diameters. Figure 16.19 shows in cross section a portion of such a solenoid, which should be imagined as continuing far to the left and far to the right of the turns shown.

Suppose that the solenoid of Fig. 16.19 has N turns per unit length and that it carries a current I, flowing into the paper at the top of the turns and out of the paper at the bottom, as indicated by the arrow tails and heads. The right-hand rule tells us that the magnetic field *inside* the solenoid must be directed to the left as shown by $\vec{B}_i$ and that any field that exists *outside* must be directed to the right, as shown by $\vec{B}_o$.

To find more about the field, consider the line integrals of $\vec{B} \cdot \vec{ds}$ taken around various closed paths. First, let us follow the rectangular path ADFEA. This path encloses no current, so the line integral must be zero. If all the points on the path are very far from the ends of the solenoid, there are as many effective turns of the solenoid to the left of E as there are to the right.* According to the

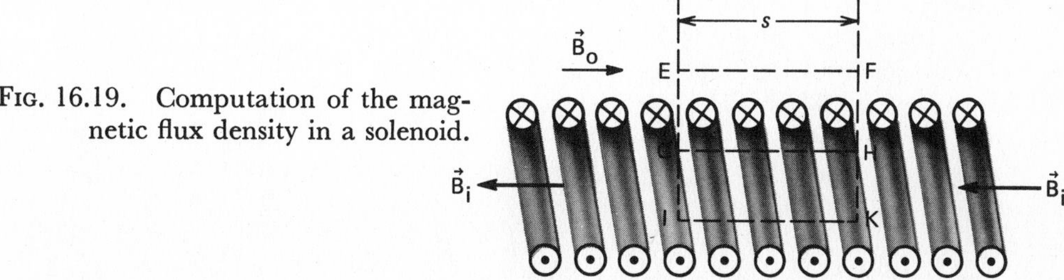

FIG. 16.19. Computation of the magnetic flux density in a solenoid.

right-hand rule, all turns to the left must produce a downward component of $\vec{B}$ along the line segment AE, and all those to the right produce an equal upward component. By symmetry, then, there can be no component of the flux density along AE (or FD), and hence these parts of the path contribute nothing to the line integral. The line integral is therefore the sum of the integrals over AD and FE and may be written

$$\oint \vec{B} \cdot \vec{ds} = B_{oA}\, s - B_{oE}\, s = (B_{oA} - B_{oE})s = 0,$$

which tells us that $B_{oA} = B_{oE}$. This is true independently of how far out from the solenoid AD is taken. But, if we go very far out, we are sure that the flux density must be zero. It follows that B_o is zero everywhere outside the solenoid.

Next consider the closed path GHKJG. By arguments similar to those used above, we can see that no contribution to the integral is given by HK and JG and that the field along JK must be equal to that along GH. Hence we find that the flux density ($\vec{B}_i$) inside the solenoid is uniform.

Finally, consider the closed path EFHGE. The segments FH and GE contribute nothing to the integral. The segment EF also contributes nothing, since the flux density everywhere along this line is zero. It follows that the line integral is

$$\oint \vec{B} \cdot \vec{ds} = B_i\, s.$$

* We are assuming here that turns far away from the point in question contribute less to the magnetic field than those near to it. We shall later justify this assumption, but we can temporarily accept it on the basis of experience—the magnetic field of any wire or coil certainly decreases rapidly as we move away from it.

This path, unlike the others that we have considered, encloses current. The wire crosses the rectangular surface Ns times, so the total current through the surface is NsI. We therefore have

$$\oint \overrightarrow{\mathrm{B}} \cdot \overrightarrow{\mathrm{ds}} = \mu_0 NsI = B_i s,$$

so that

$$B_i = \mu_0 NI. \tag{16.10-1}$$

We must remember that Eq. (16.10-1) was derived for a *long* solenoid and on the assumption that the flux density was computed in a region far from the ends. The equation will therefore not apply to a short coil or near the ends of a long solenoid (cf. Prob. 16.5).

Consider next the field somewhere on the axis of a thin coil, such as that shown in Fig. 16.20a. The symmetry of the coil and the right-hand rule indicate that the lines of magnetic induction must have, at least approximately, the

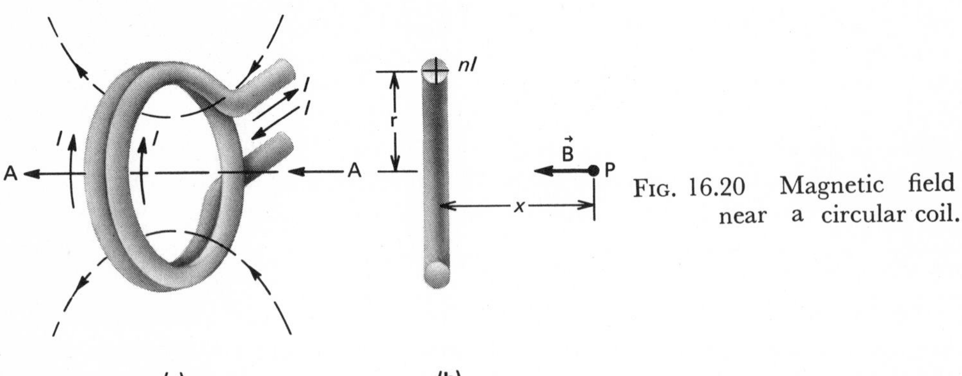

FIG. 16.20 Magnetic field near a circular coil.

shapes shown by the dashed lines. In particular, the magnetic flux density $\overrightarrow{\mathrm{B}}$ at any point on the axis A-A must be directed along the axis. The calculation of the magnitude of $\overrightarrow{\mathrm{B}}$ at any point near the coil is rather involved, but we can arrive without too much trouble at its value at any point on the axis.

Consider the point P, on the axis of the coil of radius r and at a distance x from the center of the coil, as shown in the cross-sectional view of Fig. 16.20b. In this figure we have shown only a single turn. This is equivalent to a coil of n turns carrying a current I if we let the current in the single turn coil be nI. We already know the direction of $\overrightarrow{\mathrm{B}}$ at P. We know the magnetic moment of the coil to be proportional to nI and to its area, and hence to r^2; we would expect the field at any point to be proportional to the same quantities. Hence we can write, for the magnitude of the flux density at P,

$$B = K' \mu_0 nIr^2,$$

where K' is an undetermined constant of proportionality. We can tell a little more about this constant if we notice that the dimensions of B are those $[mq^{-1}t^{-1}]$, while those of $\mu_0 Ir^2$ are $[m\ell^3 q^{-1} t^{-1}]$. Hence, K' must have the dimensions of an inverse length, cubed to make the equation dimensionally correct. The only lengths involved are r and x, so some combination of these must occur in K'. Among the possibilities are

$$K' = K/r^3,\ K/r^2x,\ K/rx^2,\ K/x^3,\ K/(r^2 + x^2)^{3/2},$$

where K is a new, dimensionless constant. The first of these can be ruled out because it would make B independent of x, which is clearly absurd. The next three are equally poor, because they would make B infinite at $x = 0$. The last guess is objectionable on none of these grounds, hence it is worth further investigation. If it is correct, we would have

$$B = K\mu_0 nIr^2/(r^2 + x^2)^{3/2}. \tag{16.10-2}$$

As a matter of fact, this expression for B on the axis of the coil is correct. One way of showing it to be true is to consider a solenoid to be equivalent to a series of parallel coils, all on the same axis and having a single turn, the distance between coils being $1/N$, where N is the number of turns per unit length of the solenoid. Using our expression for the field on the axis of a plane circular coil, one could sum the effects of all of these coils and compare the resulting expression with Eq. (16.10-1). We shall not go through the details here, but instead we shall say that such a treatment shows that Eq. (16.10-2) gives the correct result and that the comparison shows that $K = \frac{1}{2}$. We can therefore give the magnetic flux density at any point on the axis as

$$B = \mu_0 nIr^2/2(r^2 + x^2)^{3/2}. \tag{16.10-3}$$

When $x \gg r$, r^2 becomes negligible in the denominator and B varies as $1/x^3$. We thus see that the magnetic effect of a coil indeed decreases very rapidly as the distance from it increases. Hence the assumption that turns of the solenoid far from the point of observation made negligible contribution, used in the derivation of Eq. (16.10-1), is shown to be fully justified.

EXERCISES

16.10-1 A circular coil, pivoted to turn freely about a vertical axis through its center, is mounted at the magnetic equator of the earth. The coil consists of 100 turns of radius 10.0 cm and carries a current of 2.00 A. What will be its equilibrium position? If the coil is viewed from the south while in this position, will the current be flowing around it in a clockwise or a counterclockwise direction?

16.10-2 The coil of Ex. 16.10-1 is rotated until its north-seeking face is pointed to an angle of 45° east of the magnetic north. It is found that a torque of magnitude $17(10)^{-5}$ kg m^2/sec^2 is required to hold the coil in this position. According to this measurement, what is the magnitude of the horizontal component of the earth's magnetic flux density at the magnetic equator?

16.10-3 A small coil consisting of n turns of wire of radius a is mounted inside a solenoid of N turns and length l. The same current I flows through the coil and the solenoid. What torque will be required to hold the coil with its axis perpendicular to the axis of the solenoid?

16.10-4 Two thin coils have their centers at the same point. They carry equal currents. The radii of the two coils are 1.00 cm and 50.0 cm, respectively, and each coil consists of 200 turns of wire. The torque necessary to hold the small coil at an angle of 45.0° from its equilibrium position is found to be 4.10×10^{-5} kg m^2/sec^2. What current flows in the coils?

16.11 The Effect of the Medium

If we measure the magnetic flux density of a circular coil, or a straight wire, or a solenoid completely imbedded in a gas, liquid, or solid (rather than a vacuum), we find that the magnitude of $\vec{B}$ at the center of the coil or solenoid or near the straight wire still depends on the geometry of the situation as was indicated by Eqs. (16.7-1), (16.10-1), and (16.10-3), but a new constant μ must be used in place of μ_0. This constant μ varies from one substance to another and is called the ***permeability of the medium.*** It is often convenient to express μ in terms of μ_0, and we therefore write

$$\mu = \kappa_m \mu_0 \tag{16.11-1}$$

in which κ_m is called the ***relative permeability*** of the medium. It is clear that the units and dimensions of μ are the same as those of μ_0 and that κ_m is a dimensionless pure number.

Material substances are divided into three classes with regard to their magnetic properties. In the ***diamagnetic substances***, κ_m is less than unity and differs from unity by amounts which are of the order of a few parts in ten million. The ***paramagnetic substances*** have values of κ_m, greater than unity, which differ from unity by amounts of the order of one part in one hundred thousand. The small departures of κ_m for the paramagnetic and diamagnetic materials enable us to neglect their magnetic effects and to use for them the constant μ_0 except in measurements and calculations of the highest precision. This is, however, not true for the ***ferromagnetic substances***, which include iron, nickel, cobalt, and some of their compounds and alloys. The values of κ_m for nickel and cobalt are of the order of 40 or 50. The value of κ_m for soft iron may reach values of two or three thousand, whereas that for a substance called permalloy has reached values of over half a million! Note that the permeability of a ferromagnetic substance is not a constant, and that there is a maximum magnetization which can be produced in any ferromagnetic substance. We shall return to a discussion of ferromagnetic materials in Chapter 21.

16.12 Magnetic Field Strength

We notice from Sec. 16.11 that the magnetic flux density $\vec{B}$ due to any arrangement of current-carrying wires depends on the medium in which the wire is immersed. It is sometimes convenient to define a quantity that depends only on the arrangement of currents and not on the medium. Such a quantity is the vector $\vec{H}$ defined by

$$\vec{H} = \vec{B}/\mu. \tag{16.12-1}$$

This quantity is known as the ***magnetic field strength.*** It is easy to see from Eq. (16.10-1) that the unit in which H is measured is ***ampere turns per meter.***

We shall have little further use for this vector in the present text. It is introduced here for completeness and because of its importance in more advanced work in electromagnetic theory.

16.13 The Galvanometer

Measurement of the torque acting on a current-carrying coil, which has been discussed in the last few sections, furnishes the most commonly used means of measuring electric currents. The basic instrument for this purpose was invented by Arsène d'Arsonval (1851–1940) and is known as the ***d'Arsonval galvanometer***, shown schematically in Fig. 16.21. The current to be measured is passed

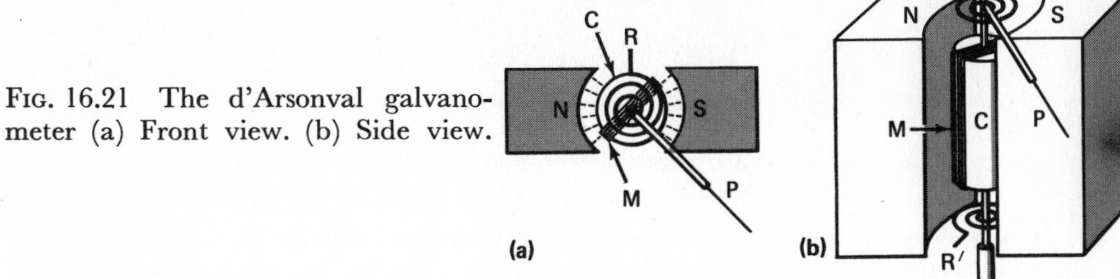

FIG. 16.21 The d'Arsonval galvanometer (a) Front view. (b) Side view.

through a coil of many turns, which is wound on a bobbin M. This coil is mounted on a shaft so that it can rotate about a vertical axis, and the electrical connections to it are made through the spiral springs R, R′. The coil is set between the poles N-S of a permanent magnet, and a stationary cylindrical core C of iron is usually mounted inside the coil. This core serves to concentrate the magnetic field, so that the lines of force are nearly radial to the axis of the coil, as shown by the dotted lines in Fig. 16.21a.

If there is no current in the coil, the spiral springs hold it in an equilibrium position, such as that shown in the figure. As soon as a current is passed through the coil, it becomes a magnetic dipole of moment NAI, where N is the number of turns, A is the area of the coil, and I is the current. It will therefore be subject to a torque of magnitude

$$T = -BNAI$$

in accordance with Eqs. (16.4-2) and (16.5-1). The $\sin\theta$ of that equation does not appear because the radial magnetic field insures that the magnetic flux in the neighborhood of the coil shall be in the plane of the coil in any position. B, of course, is the magnetic flux density in the gap between the magnet pole pieces and the core. Due to the torque acting on it, the coil will start to rotate. This rotation winds up the springs R, R′, and thus produces an elastic torque in these springs. Since the springs obey Hooke's law (Sec. 9.3), this elastic torque will be proportional to the angle θ through which the coil has turned. We may therefore write, for the torque of the spring,

$$T' = -k_T \theta,$$

where k_T is the elastic constant for the combined effect of the pair of springs R, R′. This torque will oppose the motion of the coil until, when $T = -T'$, the coil will be in equilibrium, i.e., it will come to rest. Equating the two torques, we find, for the angle through which the coil rotates due to the current,

$$\theta = BNAI/k_T. \tag{16.13-1}$$

We see from Eq. (16.13-1) that the angle through which the coil of a d'Arsonval galvanometer rotates is proportional to the current, since B, N, A, and k_T are all constants for a given instrument. In most portable galvanometers, a pointer (P in Fig. 16.21) is attached to the coil, and the rotation of the coil is read by noting the motion of the end of this pointer over a divided scale. Since the deflection of the pointer on this scale is proportional to the angle of rotation, we may write, for this deflection,

$$d = GI, \tag{16.13-2}$$

where G is known as the ***galvanometer sensitivity***. Since the scale is usually divided in divisions of rather arbitrary length (usually one to two millimeters), G is ordinarily expressed in divisions per ampere.

Good portable galvanometers, constructed on the lines of the one sketched in Fig. 16.21, ordinarily have sensitivities of about 10^5 divisions/A, so that a galvanometer with 50 divisions on its scale would give a full-scale deflection for 5×10^{-4} A. When extreme sensitivity is not required, instruments with fewer turns and stiffer springs may be used, so that full-scale deflections are obtained for currents of the order of 10^{-2} A. If much higher sensitivities are needed, the coil is wound with many turns of very fine wire and the spiral springs are replaced by long and fine straight wires, stretched along the axis of the coil. At the same time, the pointer is replaced by a mirror that can reflect a beam of light onto a scale at a distance of a meter or more from the galvanometer. These high-sensitivity instruments are not conveniently portable, but they make up for this disadvantage by yielding sensitivities of the order of 10^{10} divisions/A.

We shall find, as we continue our study of electricity, that the d'Arsonval galvanometer has a number of important applications and is, in fact, among the most useful of all electrical measuring devices.

16.14 Heating Effects of Currents and the Definition of Potential

Since the galvanometer provides a convenient device for the measurement of current, we can now study the heating effects of electric currents. In order to do this, we set up a circuit such as that shown in Fig. 16.22, in which current supplied by a battery B flows through a wire R and is measured by the galvanometer G. In order that a considerable length of wire may be included in R

and yet kept into a reasonable space, the wire is frequently wound on a spool or frame. The resultant device is known as a ***resistor.*** As we saw earlier, the flow of electricity in the wire produces heat. In order to measure the rate at which heat is produced, we immerse the resistor in a thermally insulated vessel filled with water. If the mass of the water and the thermal capacity of the container

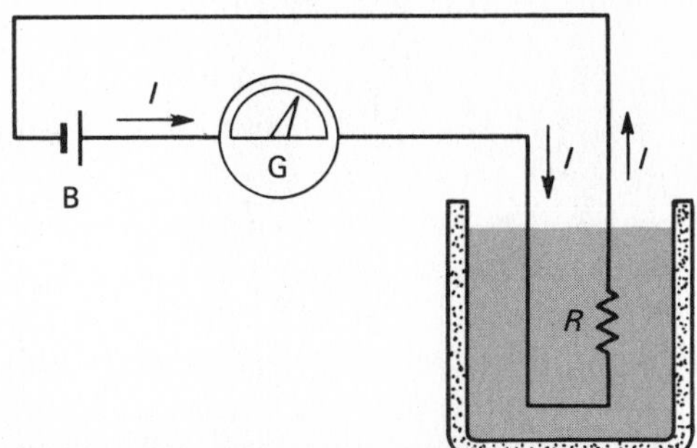

FIG. 16.22 Heat production by a current.

are known, the rate of heat production can be measured by the rate of temperature rise of the water. Such a water-filled container is known as a ***calorimeter*** and can be used to measure the power (e.g., in watts, Sec. 6.8) produced by the current in the wire (cf. Joule's experiment, Sec. 11.8).

We obtain additional insight into this heating effect by connecting three different resistors R_1, R_2, and R_3 in parallel and providing each resistor with its own galvanometer (G_1, G_2, G_3) and its own calorimeter (Fig. 16.23). In an experiment performed with this circuit, we can measure the currents I_1, I_2, and I_3 in each resistor, and we can also measure the energy per second—P_1, P_2, and P_3—developed by these currents in passing through the resistors. If we take care that the heat produced in the galvanometers and the connecting wires is small compared with that produced in the resistors immersed in the calorimeters, we find that

$$P_1/I_1 = P_2/I_2 = P_3/I_3 .$$

Thus, the energy per second produced by the current in each of the parallel resistors is proportional to the current which the resistor carries.

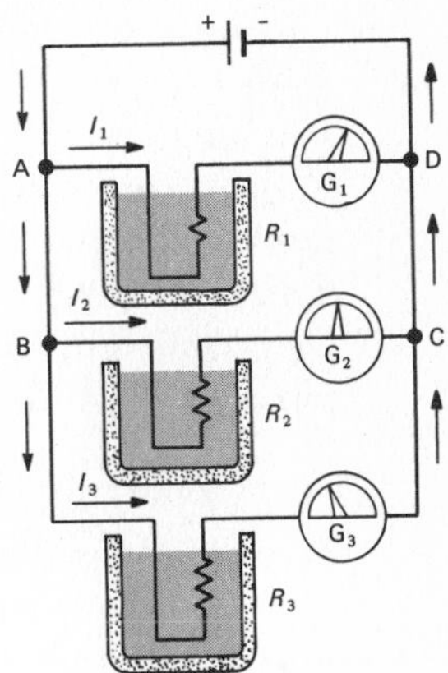

FIG. 16.23 Heating of parallel resistors.

Since the heat which is developed must result from a loss of energy of the electrical charges flowing in the circuit, this experiment allows us to arrive at the important notion that each unit of positive electric charge has a greater energy as it leaves the positive pole of the battery than it has when it reaches the negative pole. We can thus say that, if a charge Q possesses an energy of amount V_P per unit charge as it leaves the positive pole of the battery and an energy of amount V_N per unit charge as it arrives at the negative pole of the battery, it has done an amount of work $(V_P - V_N)Q$ in passing through the external circuit. Since I measures the charge passing per unit time and P measures the work per unit time, P/I measures the work per unit charge, and

$$V_P - V_N = P_1/I_1 = P_2/I_2 = P_3/I_3. \tag{16.14-1}$$

If a charge Q possesses an energy E_P, when it is at the positive pole of the battery, then we say that the potential at this pole is

$$V_P = E_P/Q. \tag{16.14-2}$$

Thus, the ***potential*** at any point in an electrical circuit is the potential energy per unit charge at that point in the circuit. Since there is an arbitrary additive constant in all measurements of potential energy (Sec. 6.10), there will also be an arbitrary additive constant in any expression for the potential.

In almost all circuit problems, we are concerned with the difference of potential or ***potential difference*** between two points in an electrical circuit. We can generalize the result of Eq. (16.14-2) by the statement that when a current I in a conductor, which connects two points A and B, produces power at a rate P in the conductor, then the potential difference V_{AB} between A and B is given by

$$V_{AB} = V_A - V_B = P/I. \tag{16.14-3}$$

We see that we can measure the potential difference between two points in a circuit by connecting a resistor and a galvanometer in series between the two points and measuring the ratio of the heat produced to the current in the resistor. Later we shall see that there are simpler methods of performing this measurement (Sec. 16.20).

It follows from Eq. (16.14-1) that *a common potential difference exists across any set of conductors connected in parallel.* We can reach this conclusion not only as a result of the experiment that led to Eq. (16.14-1), but also by considering the motion of charges through two parallel resistors. Suppose that a charge Q were were moved around the circuit ABCDA of Fig. 16.23. In moving from B to C, the charge would do an amount of work

$$w_1 = Q(V_B - V_C).$$

In going from D to A, the charge would be increasing its energy, and the amount of work which we would have to do on it to move it over this path would be

$$w_2 = Q(V_A - V_D).$$

Since the charge would have returned to its starting point, its total energy change would have been zero. We can therefore see that

$$w_1 - w_2 = Q[(V_B - V_C) - (V_A - V_D)] = 0,$$

or that

$$V_B - V_C = V_A - V_D. \tag{16.14-4}$$

The unit in which electrical potential is measured is J/Cb or W/A. This unit is given the name volt (V) after Alessandro Volta (1745–1827), an Italian physicist and physiologist who did pioneer work in electricity and in the biological effects of electricity. Thus the ***volt*** is defined by Eq. (16.14-3), and we can say that *there exists a potential difference of one volt between the terminals of a conductor when a current of one ampere flowing in the conductor produces heat at the rate of one watt.*

It is easy now to see that the batteries which we have used to send currents through conductors must be capable of accepting charge with low energy at their negative terminals and delivering charge at their positive terminals with a higher energy. In Sec. 18.16 we shall see that this process occurs as the result of a chemical reaction in the battery which provides the necessary energy.

16.15 Gravitational Potential

It is of help in understanding electrical potential to digress slightly and to return to the question of gravitational energy, considered in Sec. 4.18 and in Chapter 14. If we lift a mass m from the floor to a height h above the floor, we know that this mass has gained in ***gravitational potential***, i.e., in energy per unit mass, an amount $mgh/m = gh$. If this mass be allowed to fall freely from the height h to the floor, this energy per unit mass will of course reappear as kinetic energy per unit mass, i.e., $\frac{1}{2}v^2$, where v is the speed $(=\sqrt{2gh})$ with which the mass strikes the floor. If, however, this mass were allowed to fall very slowly through a viscous fluid or to slip on a slide on which the friction is very high, then the energy gh per unit mass would reappear, not as kinetic energy, but as heat in the viscous fluid or in the material of the slide that provided the friction (Sec. 11.6). We could, in fact, perform the experiments of Joule (Sec. 11.8) by raising a number of heavy bodies through a height h and allowing them to fall through that height in a vessel so arranged that their terminal velocity was very low; all their potential energy would be directly converted into heat. Then, the rate of production of heat in the vessel would be directly proportional to the rate of flow of massive bodies through the vessel. The reader should need no further prompting to see that this result is quite analogous to the electrical experiment described in the preceding section.

EXERCISES

16.15-1 The expression of the gravitational potential as gh is an approximate one, valid only if h is much less than the radius of the earth (R_E). Derive a better expression for the gravitational potential of a body that is raised to a height $(r - R_E)$ above the earth's surface. Express the potential in terms of r, R_E, and g_0, where g_0 is the value of the acceleration due to gravity at the earth's surface.

16.15-2 A cylindrical water tank has a cross section of 2.00 m². It is filled with water to a depth of 4.50 m. (a) What is the difference between the gravitational potential at the top of the water and at the bottom? (b) Show that the average gravitational potential of the water in the tank, relative to the bottom, is $\frac{1}{2}gh$.

16.16 Ohm's Law

In the present section, we shall assume that we have a number of different batteries, each capable of sending different currents through a given resistor R and a galvanometer G (Fig. 16.24). We measure the power dissipated in the resistor and find that with different batteries B_1, B_2, and B_3 we get different values P_1, P_2, and P_3, corresponding to different currents I_1, I_2, and I_3. As different batteries are connected by means of the switch, we find that different potential differences V_1, V_2, and V_3 exist across the ends of the resistor, since

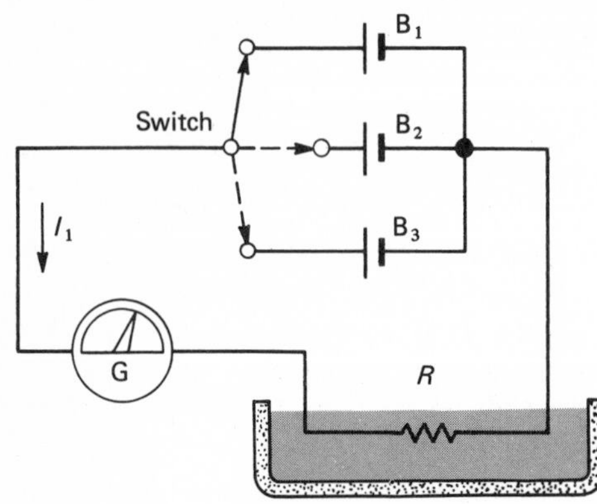

FIG. 16.24 Variation of heat production with different currents.

each battery is capable of imparting a different energy per unit charge to the electricity that flows through it. If we now compare the current I with the potential difference V to which it corresponds, we find approximately that

$$V_1/I_1 = V_2/I_2 = V_3/I_3 .$$

We call this ratio the ***resistance*** of the resistor, and we define the resistance R of any resistor by the equation

$$R = V/I, \tag{16.16-1}$$

where V is the potential difference between the terminals of the resistor and I is the current in it. The unit in which resistance is measured is volts per ampere. This unit is given the name ***ohm*** (abbreviated Ω) after George Simon Ohm (1787–1854), who discovered the proportionality between potential difference and current in 1827. The statement of this proportionality is known as ***Ohm's law*** and is represented by Eq. (16.16-1).

Ohm's law is obeyed quite closely by metallic conductors as long as the temperature of the conductor is kept constant. If the temperature changes, the resistance also changes, as we shall see below.

It is often useful to make use of the reciprocal of the resistance in calculations. This quantity is called the ***conductance*** S and is defined by

$$S = 1/R. \tag{16.16-2}$$

The unit of conductance is called the ***mho*** (abbreviated Ω^{-1} and pronounced "moe"). Using this new unit, we can write Ohm's law [Eq. (16.16-1)] in the two useful and equivalent forms

$$V = IR \tag{16.16-3A}$$

and

$$I = VS. \tag{16.16-3B}$$

Using these two expressions, we can obtain several equivalent relations for the power P dissipated in a resistor. Using Eq. (16.4-3), we have

$$P = VI = I^2R = V^2S. \tag{16.16-4}$$

In these equations, P will be in watts if V, I, and R are measured in volts, amperes, and ohms, respectively.

16.17. Combinations of Resistances

With the help of Ohm's law, it is easy to find the resistance of many combinations of resistors if the resistance of each is known. For example, in the series circuit of Fig. 16.25, let R_1 and R_2 be the resistances of the two resistors. Since

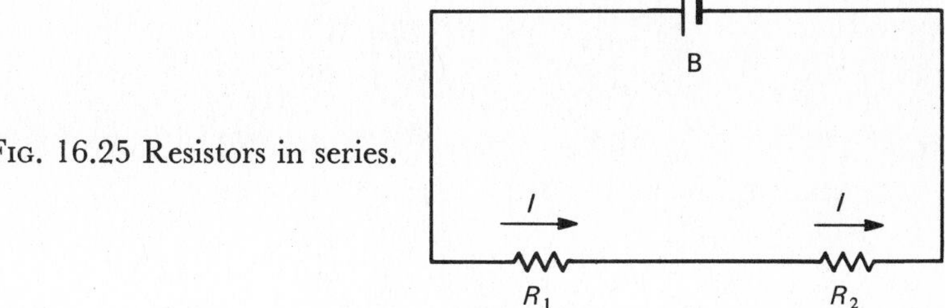

FIG. 16.25 Resistors in series.

the same current I passes through both resistors, the potential differences across them are

$$V_1 = IR_1 \qquad \text{and} \qquad V_2 = IR_2.$$

Since the work done in moving a charge successively through the two resistors is the work done in moving it through one plus that done in moving it through the other, the potential difference across the series combination is

$$V = V_1 + V_2.$$

The resistance of the combined resistors is therefore

$$R = V/I = V_1/I + V_2/I = R_1 + R_2. \tag{16.17-1}$$

Thus we can, if we wish, replace the two resistors R_1 and R_2 by the ***equivalent resistor*** $R = R_1 + R_2$ without affecting the current I drawn from the battery. Since our argument would be equally valid for any number of resistors in series, we conclude that *the resistance of any number of resistors in series is the sum of the individual resistances.*

We can now discuss the way in which the current divides itself between two unequal resistors connected in parallel (Sec. 16.2). In the circuit of Fig. 16.26, two resistors of resistance R_1 and R_2 are connected in parallel, their currents being I_1 and I_2 and the total current drawn by them both together from the

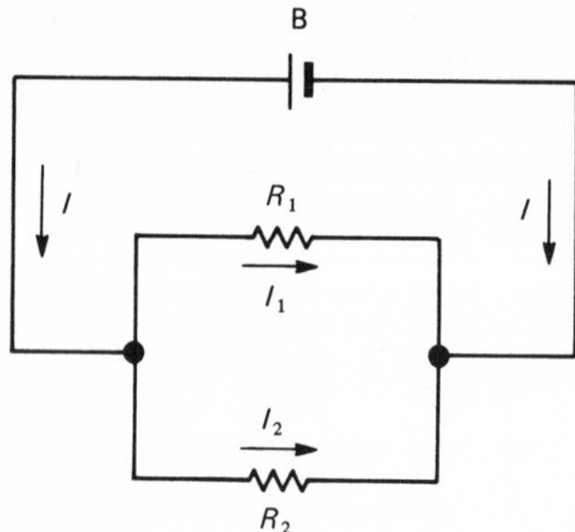

FIG. 16.26 Resistors in parallel.

battery being I. We have seen from the experiment of Fig. 16.23 [cf. Eqs. (16.14-1) and (16.14-4)] that the same potential difference V exists across all resistors connected in parallel. We may therefore write, using Eq. (16.16-3B),

$$I_1 = VS_1 \qquad \text{and} \qquad I_2 = VS_2 \tag{16.17-2}$$

and find that the current in two parallel resistors divides itself in proportion to the conductances of the two resistors, i.e.,

$$I_1/I_2 = S_1/S_2. \tag{16.17-3}$$

Suppose that we wish to replace the two resistors in parallel by a single resistor chosen so that the current I drawn by the single ***equivalent resistor*** will be the same as that drawn by both resistors together when they are connected in parallel. We know then that the equivalent resistor must have a conductance S that will satisfy the equation

$$I = SV. \tag{16.17-4}$$

However, we already know from Eq. (16.2-1) that

$$I = I_1 + I_2, \tag{16.2-1}$$

and it follows that

$$SV = S_1V + S_2V$$

and that

$$S = S_1 + S_2. \tag{16.17-5}$$

Thus, we must choose, as an equivalent resistor, one whose conductance S is the sum of the conductances of the two resistors connected in parallel. Again our argument is independent of the number of resistors connected in parallel, so we may conclude that *the conductance of any number of parallel resistors is the sum of the conductances of the individual resistors*. It is left as an exercise for the reader to calculate the equivalent resistance of two or more resistors connected in parallel (Ex. 16.17-5).

We often encounter electrical circuits in which the resistances are arranged in a more involved fashion than the simple series and parallel circuits of Figs. 16.25 and 16.26. For example, in Fig. 16.27, we have an arrangement in which two resistors R_1 and R_2 are connected in parallel, and a third resistor R_3 is in series with the combination. Suppose that the potential difference across the terminals of the battery is V and that we wish to find the currents I_1, I_2, and I_3 which are carried by the three resistors. We can, if we wish, derive formulas for these various currents in terms of the potential difference across the terminals of the battery and the values of the individual resistances. The nature of such

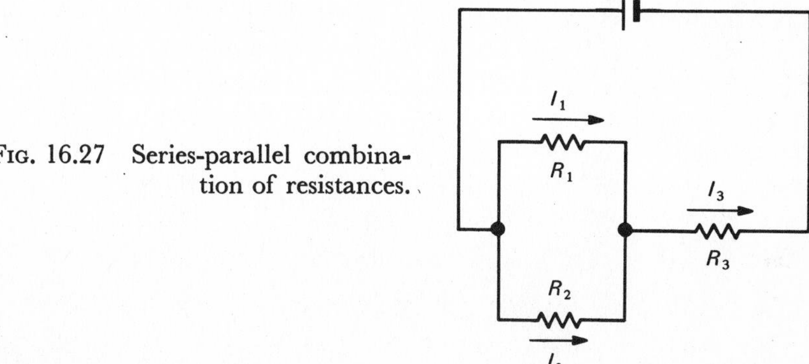

FIG. 16.27 Series-parallel combination of resistances.

formulas is indicated in Ex. 16.17-11. In a particular case, it is probably best to work out the problem numerically rather than to derive the detailed formulas. Suppose, in the circuit of Fig. 16.27, that a number of cells are used in the battery to give $V = 100$ V and that $R_1 = 100\ \Omega$, $R_2 = 300\ \Omega$, and $R_3 = 50.0\ \Omega$. The equivalent resistance R_{12} of the two resistances R_1 and R_2 in parallel is then given by Eq. (16.17-5) as

$$S_{12} = 1/R_{12} = S_1 + S_2 = 1/R_1 + 1/R_2 = (1/100 + 1/300)\ \Omega^{-1}$$
$$= (4/300)\ \Omega^{-1} = (1/75.0)\ \Omega^{-1}.$$

Thus, $R_{12} = 75.0\ \Omega$, and the total resistance connected in series with the battery is given by Eq. (16.17-1) as

$$R_{123} = R_{12} + R_3 = 75.0\ \Omega + 50.0\ \Omega = 125.0\ \Omega.$$

We can then use Eqs. (16.16-3) to obtain

$$I_{12} = I_3 = V/R_{123} = 100\ \text{V}/125.0\ \Omega = 0.800\ \text{A}.$$

Again using Eqs. (16.16-3), we get, for the potential drop across R_3,

$$V_3 = I_3 R_3 = 0.800\ \text{A} \times 50.0\ \Omega = 40.0\ \text{V},$$

and for the potential drop across the pair of resistances in parallel,

$$V_{12} = I_{12} R_{12} = 0.800\ \text{A} \times 75.0\ \Omega = 60.0\ \text{V},$$

in which we can verify

$$V = V_3 + V_{12} = 40.0\ \text{V} + 60.0\ \text{V} = 100.0\ \text{V}.$$

By further application of Ohm's law, we obtain the two currents

$$I_1 = V_{12}/R_1 = 60.0\ \text{V}/100\ \Omega = 0.600\ \text{A}$$

and

$$I_2 = V_{12}/R_2 = 60.0\ \text{V}/300\ \Omega = 0.200\ \text{A};$$

again we have the simple check that

$$I_{12} = I_1 + I_2 = 0.600\ \text{A} + 0.200\ \text{A} = 0.800\ \text{A}.$$

The problem solved in the preceding paragraph may seem to be one of only academic interest, but it is of the greatest technical importance. Resistors can, of course, be manufactured to have any specified value, but such special manufacture is very expensive. Resistors of a large number of values, not necessarily the ones needed, are available in every laboratory. It is often possible by a calculation of the type we have just sketched to choose, from the available resistors, a set whose combined resistance will have the required value (cf. Ex. 16.17-10).

EXERCISES

Illustrate the solutions of these exercises and of all subsequent problems in this chapter with circuit diagrams.

16.17-1 A lamp is rated to draw 100 W at 110 V. What current flows through it and what is its resistance?

16.17-2 Two lamps, one rated at 100 W and one at 60 W, are connected in parallel to a 110-V supply. What current is drawn from the supply line?

16.17-3 A 110-V household circuit contains a fuse which burns out when 20 A flow through it. What is the maximum number of 100-W lamps that can be connected to this circuit?

16.17-4 A heater coil connected to a 110-V line has a resistance of 82.5 Ω. How long will it take this coil to heat 1.00 kg of water from 20°C to 40°C?

16.17-5 Three resistances of values R_1, R_2, and R_3 are connected in parallel. Show that the resistance

$$R = \frac{R_1 R_2 R_3}{R_1 R_2 + R_2 R_3 + R_3 R_1}$$

is equivalent to them.

16.17-6 Three resistances, each 10.00 Ω, are connected in series. (a) What is their combined resistance? (b) What is their combined conductance? (c) What will be the current through them if they are connected across a machine whose terminals are maintained at a potential difference of 110 V?

16.17-7 The three resistances of Ex. 16.17-6 are connected in parallel across the terminals of the machine of that exercise. (a) What is their resistance? (b) What is their conductance? (c) What is the total current drawn from the machine? (d) What is the current in each of the three resistances?

16.17-8 Two resistors, of resistances 10.0 Ω and 15.0 Ω, respectively, are connected in series with a battery that maintains a potential difference of 15 V across its terminals. At what rate will heat be developed in each resistor?

16.17-9 Prove that the rates of heat production in each of two resistors connected in parallel are inversely proportional to the resistances.

16.17-10 Three resistances, of respective values 3.00 Ω, 4.00 Ω, and 5.00 Ω, are available. If these are connected together in all possible ways, singly, in pairs, and all three together, how many different values of their equivalent resistance can be obtained, and what are these values?

16.17-11 Show that the equivalent resistance of the three resistances of the circuit of Fig. 16.27 is

$$R_{123} = (R_1 R_3 + R_2 R_3 + R_1 R_2)/(R_1 + R_2)$$

nd hence that the current I_3 supplied by the battery is

$$I_3 = V(R_1 + R_2)/(R_1 R_3 + R_2 R_3 + R_1 R_2).$$

Hence show that

$$I_1 = VR_2/(R_1 R_3 + R_2 R_3 + R_1 R_2)$$

and that

$$I_2 = VR_1/(R_1 R_3 + R_2 R_3 + R_1 R_2).$$

Use these results to verify the numerical values for the currents obtained in the example worked out in Sec. 16.17.

16.18 Resistivity and Conductivity

It is easy to see that the resistance of a wire of uniform cross section is proportional to its length L, since we can consider any length of such a wire to be made up of a number of identical wires, each of unit length, all connected in series (Fig. 16.28a).

In a similar way, we can see that the conductances of a number of wires of a fixed length and variable cross section will be proportional to the area A of the

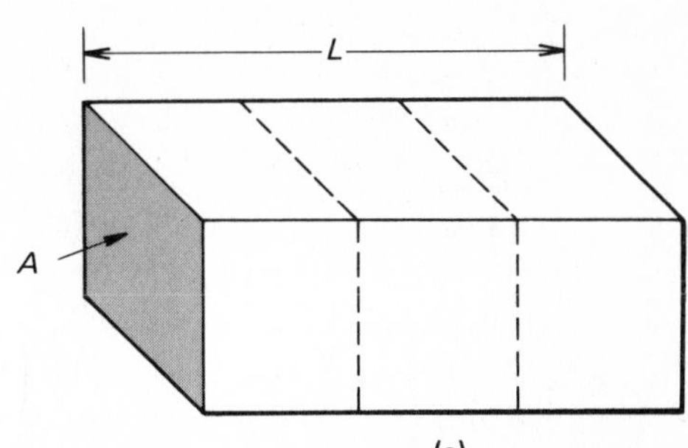

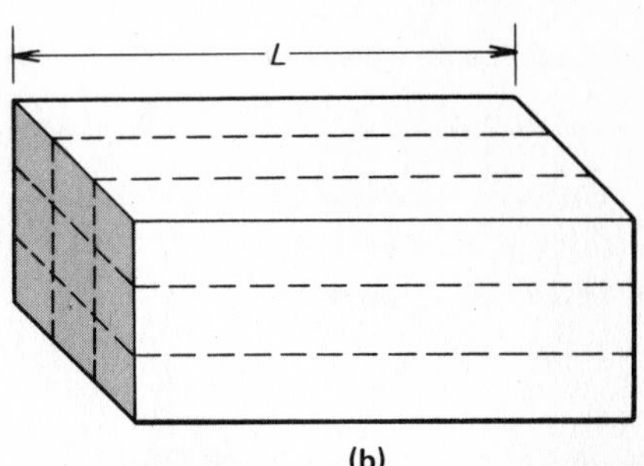

FIG. 16.28 (a) Resistance is proportional to length. (b) Conductance is proportional to area.

cross section, provided that the material is the same for all wires. We can consider any one such wire split up into a number of filaments of standard cross section (Fig. 16.28b). In the actual wire, these filaments are all in parallel, so the conductance of the wire will be proportional to the number of filaments—i.e., to the area of cross section. The resistance is thus inversely proportional to the area of the cross section, and we write

$$R = \rho L/A, \tag{16.18-1}$$

in which ρ is a constant for a given material at a given temperature. This constant is called the ***resistivity*** of the material. It is measured in ***ohm-meters*** (Ω m). The reciprocal of resistivity is ***conductivity***, σ. The conductance S of a wire is thus

$$S = \sigma A/L \tag{16.18-2}$$

and the conductivity is measured in units ***mhos per meter*** (Ω^{-1} m^{-1}).

The resistivity of a given material varies with the temperature of the material. The resistivity ρ_t at a temperature t (°C) can be obtained from the resistivity ρ_{20} (at 20°C) by a relation of the type

$$\rho_t = \rho_{20}[1 + \alpha(t - 20°\text{C})], \tag{16.18-3}$$

provided t does not differ to greatly from 20°C. Values of the resistivity ρ_{20} and of the ***temperature coefficient of resistivity*** α are given in Table 16.1.

Table 16.1 *Resistivities (20°C) and Temperature Coefficients*

Material	Resistivity ρ_{20} (Ω m)	Temperature Coefficient α (°C^{-1})
Aluminum	2.83×10^{-8}	0.0042
Graphite	400–1000	—0.001
Constantan	49	0.00003
Copper	1.724	0.0043
Iron (pure)	10	0.0050
Mercury	95.78	0.0009
Platinum	9.89	0.003
Tungsten (wolfram)	5.51	0.0045

EXERCISES

16.18-1 If the resistance of a given wire at 20°C is R_{20} and the wire is made of a material whose temperature coefficient of resistivity is α, show that the resistance R_t of the same wire at a temperature t (°C), not too far removed from 20°C, is given by

$$R_t = R_{20}[1 + \alpha(t - 20°\text{C})].$$

16.18-2 Calculate the resistance of a copper wire of cross-sectional area 1.00 mm^2 and length 1.000 m at a temperature of 20°C.

16.18-3 What will be the resistance of the wire of Ex. 16.18-2 at 10°C?

16.18-4 If the resistance of a uniform wire is R and its length is L, prove that the drop of potential V_x across a length x of the wire is given by

$$V_x = Vx/L,$$

where V is the potential drop across the whole wire.

16.18-5 Two wires, one of copper and one of aluminum, have identical dimensions. They are connected in parallel across the terminals of the same generator. Which wire carries the most current and what is the ratio of the two currents?

16.19 The Ammeter

We saw in Sec. 16.13 that the d'Arsonval galvanometer could be used as a current measuring instrument and that it gives a full-scale deflection for currents of the order of 10^{-3} A or less. When larger currents than this are to be measured, the ordinary galvanometer is far too sensitive. The device ordinarily used for measuring such currents is known as an ***ammeter*** and consists of a galvanometer connected in parallel with a low resistance, as shown in Fig. 16.29. The low resistance (R_s in the figure) is known as a ***shunt***, since it bypasses most of the current being measured around the galvanometer.

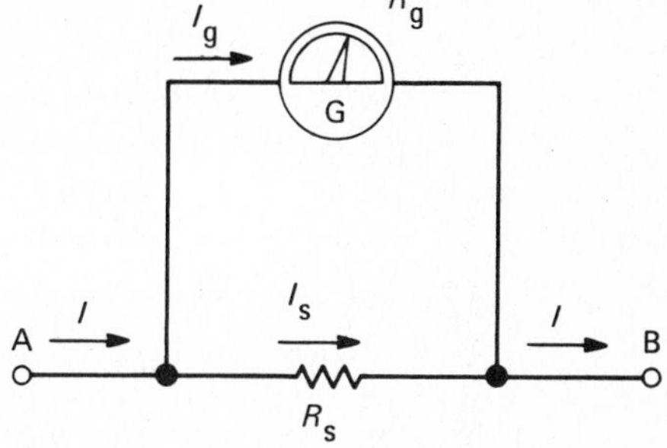

FIG. 16.29 Ammeter circuit.

Since the shunt and the galvanometer, whose resistance is R_g, are connected in parallel, the same potential difference exists across their terminals. Letting this be V, we see that the currents flowing in them are, respectively,

$$I_s = V/R_s \qquad \text{and} \qquad I_g = V/R_g.$$

Thus, the ratio of the current through the galvanometer to the total current, $I_g + I_s = I$, between the terminals A-B is

$$I_g/I = I_g/(I_s + I_g) = R_s/(R_s + R_g). \tag{16.19-1}$$

Hence, if the galvanometer sensitivity is G, the deflection d of the ammeter, for a given current I between its terminals, is given by Eq. (16.13-2) as

$$d = GI_g = GIR_s/(R_s + R_g). \tag{16.19-2}$$

By making R_s sufficiently small as compared with R_g, it is possible to reduce the ammeter sensitivity d/I to as small a value as we please and so to increase the current required to produce a full-scale deflection to a large value. The ammeter cannot, of course, be more sensitive than the galvanometer from which it is built. In most ammeters, the shunt is built into the case of the instrument, and the scale is calibrated to read directly in amperes.

An ammeter is calibrated by connecting it in series with a ***working standard ammeter*** in the laboratory where it is being used or in the factory where it is being built. In a laboratory calibration, a curve is plotted of the correction that must be applied to the meter to make it agree with the standard. In the factory, the scale of the meter is altered, or the values of R_s and R_g are altered until the reading of the ammeter agrees with the reading of the standard. The working standards in use throughout the world are compared with one of the ***national standard ammeters***, which are kept in the national standardizing laboratories of the principal countries of the world. The national standards, in turn, are compared with one another and are calibrated in terms of the absolute standard ampere by a measurement in terms of the definition given in Sec. 16.7. In this way, it is possible for current measurements made in any laboratory to be compared with those made in any other.

Aside from its decreased sensitivity, the ammeter has a second advantage over the galvanometer. In order to measure the current in a circuit or branch of a circuit, it is necessary that the ammeter carry the same current as the other conductors of the circuit. This can be insured (cf. Sec. 16.2) only if *the ammeter is connected in series with the circuit.* If the instrument has appreciable resistance, there will be an appreciable potential drop across it, and this will decrease the current which we are trying to measure. In order to minimize this disturbance, it is desirable that the resistance of the ammeter be as low as possible. The resistance of the galvanometer-shunt combination is easily found to be

$$R = R_s R_g/(R_s + R_g), \tag{16.19-3}$$

which takes on a very low value as R_s is decreased.

16.20 The Voltmeter

Although we have made considerable use of the concept of potential difference, the only way that we have had so far to measure this quantity involves the measurement of the power dissipation in a resistance. A much more convenient method employs the ***voltmeter***, which is a galvanometer connected in series with a high resistance known as a ***multiplier***. The voltmeter makes use of the fact that the current in a series of resistors is proportional to the potential difference between the ends of the series. A typical arrangement is shown in Fig. 16.30, in which the galvanometer G is used to measure the potential difference between the terminals A and B. If a potential difference V is applied to the terminals A-B of such an instrument, the current which the galvanometer will measure is given by Ohm's law as

$$I_g = V/(R_m + R_g).$$

Consequently, if the galvanometer sensitivity is G, the deflection in accordance with Eq. (16.13-2) is

$$d = GI_g = GV/(R_m + R_g). \tag{16.20-1}$$

By increasing R_m, we can make the voltmeter as insensitive as we please, so that we can use a galvanometer to measure quite large potential differences. In most voltmeters, the multiplier is included in the case of the instrument and the scale is calibrated directly in volts.

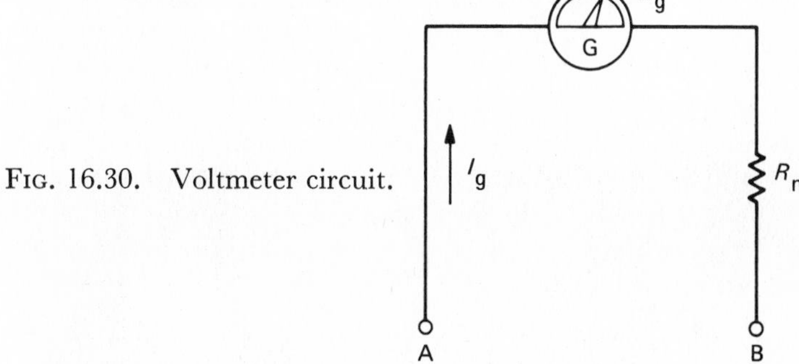

FIG. 16.30. Voltmeter circuit.

When the potential difference between two points is to be measured with a voltmeter, the instrument must obviously be connected *in parallel with any resistor connected between these two points.* If the voltmeter is of low resistance, it will draw appreciable current. This current must flow through any resistances which may be in series with the meter (e.g., R_3 in Fig. 16.27 if the meter is being used to measure the potential drop across R_1 and R_2). It will produce an increased potential drop across these resistances and so decrease the potential drop being measured. It is therefore desirable that a voltmeter have a high resistance in order that it may disturb as little as possible the potential difference being measured. The resistance between the terminals of a voltmeter is

$$R = R_m + R_g, \tag{16.20-2}$$

and this quantity can be made very large if a very sensitive galvanometer is used.

EXERCISES

16.20-1 A galvanometer has a resistance of 10.0 Ω and shows a full-scale deflection for 5.4×10^{-3} A. We wish to use this galvanometer in the construction of an ammeter that will give a full-scale deflection for 1.00 A. What resistance should be used for the shunt?

16.20-2 Calculate the value of the series resistance that should be used with the galvanometer of Ex. 16.20-1 to convert it to a voltmeter which will give a full-scale deflection for 10.0 V. For 125.0 V.

16.20-3 It is desired to measure the resistance of a piece of wire, which is known to be close to 1.5 Ω. Suppose that you have an ammeter with negligible resistance which gives a full-scale deflection for a current of 3.00 A; a voltmeter of very high resistance that gives a full-scale deflection for a potential difference of 2.50 V; and a battery that maintains a potential difference close to 2.0 V. Devise two circuits, either of which may be used to measure the resistance of the wire, and indicate in each case how you would combine the readings of the instruments to calculate this resistance.

16.20-4 The meters in Ex. 16.20-3 are replaced by an ammeter with a resistance of 0.10 Ω and a voltmeter of resistance 15 Ω. Will the resistance as calculated by the formulas derived in Ex. 16.20-3 be in error? If so, by how much will it be in error in each case? Suggest a method for correcting for these errors.

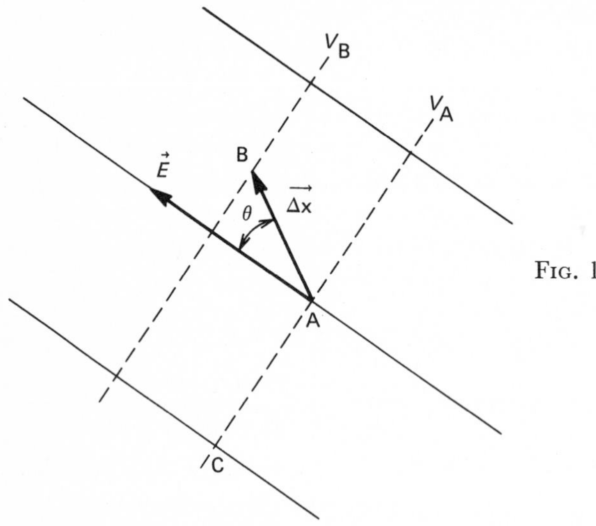

FIG. 16.31 Electrostatic potential.

16.21 *Electrostatic Potential*

The concept of potential has proved itself so useful in connection with electrical currents that it will be worth while to return, for a short time, to electrostatic phenomena and to apply the same idea in connection with them. If an electric field exists in any region of space, such as that shown in Fig. 16.31, a force

$$\vec{F} = \vec{E}q$$

will be exerted on a charge q at any point at which the field is $\vec{E}$ [cf. Eq. (15.7-1)]. Hence, in order to move the charge from point A to point B—i.e., to give it a displacement $\vec{\Delta s}$, one must exert a force $-F\cos\theta$ and do an amount of work [Eq. (6.6-2)]

$$\Delta w = -Eq\,\Delta s\cos\theta,$$

where θ is the angle between $\vec{E}$ and $\vec{\Delta s}$. Remembering our definition of potential difference as work per unit charge, we see that the potential difference between the neighboring points B and A is

$$V_B - V_A = \Delta V = \Delta w/q = -E\,\Delta s\cos\theta. \qquad (16.21\text{-}1)$$

Because of the occurence of cos θ in Eq. (16.21-1), the potential difference between two points, such as A and C in Fig. 16.31, which are on a line perpendicular to the direction of the electric field, is zero. This means that we can move a charge freely from one of the points to the other without doing any work.

Two interesting theorems of electrostatics can be derived immediately from the concept of potential. If the potential varies from point to point, Eq. (16.21-1) indicates that an electric field must be present. Were such a field present in the interior of a conductor, the charges that are free to move would be accelerated. They would therefore be in motion, and we would not have a static state of affairs. It follows at once that there can be no field inside a conductor in which no currents are flowing, and that *the entire volume of any conductor is an equipotential* under electrostatic conditions.

It is also true that *all of the net electrostatic charge carried by a conductor must reside on the surface of the conductor.* Were there charges of the same sign within a conductor, not compensated by equal amounts of charges of the opposite sign, they would repel each other and an electric field would exist. This would violate the equipotential condition, and it is therefore impossible.

Surfaces over which charges can be moved without any work being done are known as ***equipotential surfaces***, or ***equipotentials.*** They are perpendicular to the lines of force at every point. In Figs. 16.31 and 16.32 the equipotential

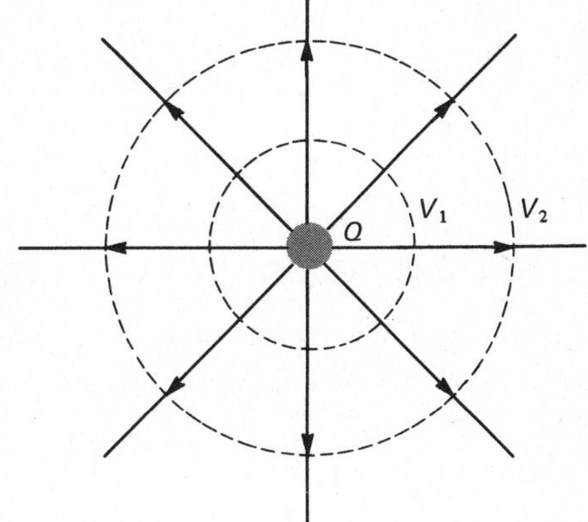

FIG. 16.32. Equipotentials about a point charge.

surfaces are indicated by dashed lines and the lines of force by solid lines. Figure 16.31 represents a very special case, in which the vector $\vec{E}$ has the same direction everywhere, so that the surfaces perpendicular to $\vec{E}$ are planes.

The equipotentials in the neighborhood of an isolated point charge Q are clearly spheres, as indicated in Fig. 16.32. It is easy to find the value of the potential on any sphere—i.e., at a given distance r from the charge.

Taking advantage of the fact that the zero of potential energy (and therefore of potential) may be chosen arbitrarily, we shall follow a common practice and make the potential at infinite distance equal to zero. The potential at a distance

r is then the work per unit charge needed to bring a test charge q from infinity to r. The work in going from $r+dr$ to r is $-qE\,dr$, so

$$V=(1/q)\int dw=-(1/q)\int_{\infty}^{r} qE\,dr=\int_{r}^{\infty} E\,dr.$$

Substituting $Q/4\pi\varepsilon_0 r^2$ for E, we have

$$V=-(Q/4\pi\varepsilon_0)\int_{\infty}^{r}(dr/r^2).$$

To evaluate the integral, we may note that it has the dimension of an inverse length. The only length in the problem is r, so V must be proportional to $(1/r)$. We may therefore write

$$V=(Q/4\pi\varepsilon_0)(k/r), \tag{16.21-2}$$

where k is a dimensionless constant. To find the value of k, note that the force on the charge due to the field is $-q(dV/dr)$, so the force needed to move the charge is the negative of this, or $q(dV/dr)$. The field is the force per unit charge, so

$$E=\frac{dV}{dr}=\frac{kQ}{4\pi\varepsilon_0}\frac{d(1/r)}{dr}. \tag{16.21-3}$$

We may now use the binomial theorem of Appendix H to show that

$$\begin{aligned}\frac{d(1/r)}{dr}&=\lim_{\Delta r\to 0}\frac{[1/(r+\Delta r)]-(1/r)}{\Delta r}\\&=\lim_{\Delta r\to 0}\left(\frac{1}{r}\right)\frac{[1+(\Delta r/r)]^{-1}-1}{\Delta r}\\&=\lim_{\Delta r\to 0}\frac{(1/r)\cdot(-\Delta r/r)+\cdots}{\Delta r}=-\frac{1}{r^2}.\end{aligned}$$

We therefore have, by substituting the value of E in Eq. (16.21-3),

$$\frac{Q}{4\pi\varepsilon_0 r^2}=-\frac{kQ}{4\pi\varepsilon_0}\frac{1}{r^2},$$

from which it follows that $k=-1$ and that the potential at a distance r from a charge Q is, from Eq. (16.21-2),

$$V=Q/4\pi\varepsilon_0 r. \tag{16.21-4}$$

We saw in Sec. 16.16 that the current between any two points of a conducting circuit is proportional to the difference of potential between those points. Since electrostatic phenomena are, by definition, those in which no current occurs, the current is everywhere zero in a conductor that is in electrostatic equilibrium. It follows immediately that the potential difference between any two points of such a conductor is zero, or that every conductor in electrostatic equilibrium is an equipotential. This result is very helpful in studying electrostatics, since it enables us at once to recognize the shape of some of the equipotentials involved and, hence, the directions of the lines of force near those equipotentials.

Since there is no potential difference between two points within a conductor, there can be no electric field inside a conductor. This follows directly from Eq. (16.21-1), both sides of which must be zero.

EXERCISES

16.21-1 Derive Eq. (16.21-4) by a shorter method that depends on the fact that $\int(dr/r^2) = -1/r$.

16.21-2 The electrostatic potential produced by a dipole at distances r, large compared with the dimensions of the dipole, is given by

$$V = \vec{p} \cdot \vec{r}/4\pi\varepsilon_0 r^3,$$

where $\vec{p}$ is the dipole moment and $\vec{r}$ is the radius vector from the dipole to the point where the potential is V. Starting from this expression, show that the field at any distant point on the axis of the dipole is of magnitude

$$E = p/2\pi\varepsilon_0 r^3,$$

in agreement with the result of Prob. 15.10(a).

16.22 The Plane Parallel Plate Capacitor—Capacitance*

One interesting electrostatic device, the consideration of which we have delayed until we had the concept of potential, is the capacitor.* A ***capacitor*** is an arrangement of two or more conductors, insulated from one another, so arranged that they can be used to store electrostatic charges. In its most common form, illustrated in Fig. 16.33, the capacitor consists of two plates, each of area A and separated from each other by a constant distance d.

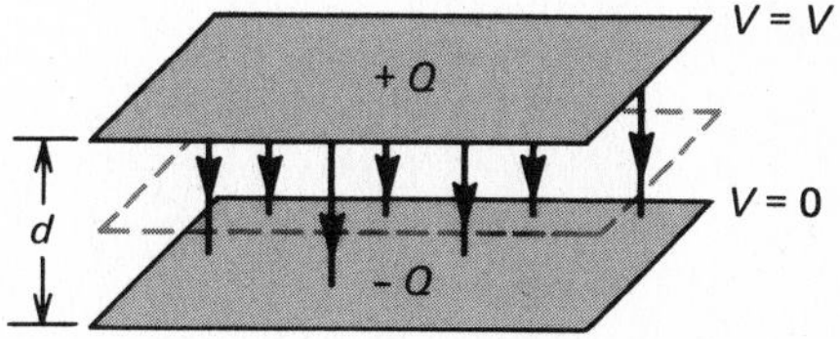

FIG. 16.33 The plane-parallel-plate capacitor.

Suppose that the two plates of the capacitor are connected to an electrical machine that maintains a potential difference V. Since each plate is necessarily an equipotential, and since the lines of force are perpendicular to equipotential surface (cf. Sec. 16.21), the electric field strength everywhere between the plates will have the direction shown by the arrows in Fig. 16.33. The potential difference can therefore be expressed, in accordance with Eq. (16.21-1), as

$$V = Ed, \tag{16.22-1}$$

where E is the magnitude of the electric field strength in the region between the plates.

* The capacitor is sometimes called a ***condenser***, but this term is becoming obsolete.

When the capacitor plates are connected to the electrical machine, charge will flow from the positive terminal of the machine to the upper plate and from the lower plate to the negative terminal. This flow of charge will continue until the plates carry just enough charge to remain at the potential difference of the machine. We can use Gauss' law to establish a simple relation between the charge on either plate and the field strength E in Eq. (16.22-1). Figure 16.34

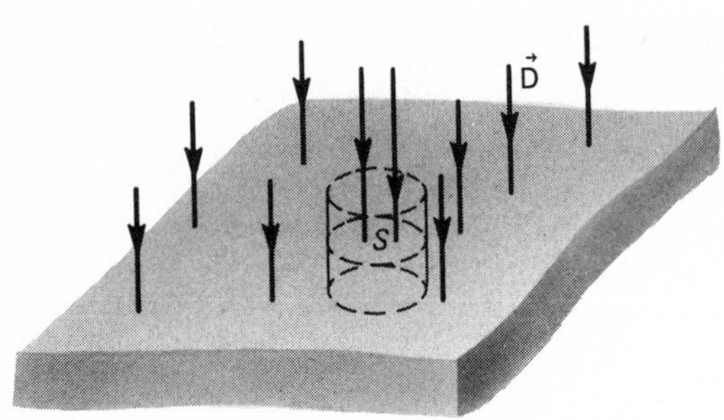

Fig. 16.34 Relationship between electric field and charge on a capacitor.

shows a portion of the lower plate of the capacitor so much enlarged that the thickness of the plate is apparent. Suppose that a pillbox-shaped Gaussian surface, shown by the dashed lines, is constructed partly inside and partly outside the plate, with the faces of the pillbox parallel to the surface of the plate and its sides perpendicular to that surface. If the total charge on the plate is Q, the charge per unit area is Q/A, and the charge within the pillbox is therefore QS/A, where S is the cross-sectional area of the box. Consequently, by Gauss' law (Sec. 15.8), the flux through the surface of the box is

$$\Psi = QS/A.$$

We have seen that there is no field within the conducting plate, hence, the electric displacement there is also zero, and there will be no flux through that part of the surface of the pillbox which is inside the plate. Those parts of the sides of the box which are outside the plate are parallel to $\vec{E}$ and $\vec{D}$; consequently, there is no flux through them. The entire flux, therefore, passes through the upper face of the pillbox, which has an area S, and is represented by

$$\Psi = DS,$$

where D is the magnitude of the displacement between the plates of the capacitor. Equating the two expressions for Ψ and remembering that $D = \varepsilon E$, where ε is the permittivity of the medium between the plates of the capacitor, we find that the field strength is

$$E = Q/\varepsilon A.$$

This value of E may be inserted in Eq. (16.22-1) to show that

$$Q = \varepsilon AV/d. \tag{16.22-2}$$

Since the same flux that leaves the upper plate goes to the lower plate (as indicated by the fact that the lines of force and tubes of displacement are perpendicular to the plates), the lower plate must carry a charge $-Q$ and the upper plate a charge $+Q$. We see from this analysis that the two plates of the capacitor acquire equal and opposite charges when a potential difference is applied to them. If the electrical machine is then disconnected, these charges will remain on the plates and may be released later by connecting a wire or other conductor between them. The capacitor can therefore be used to store electric charges.

The result of Eq. (16.22-2), that the charge acquired by the capacitor is proportional to the potential difference between its plates, can be shown to be true for any pair of conductors, regardless of their shape and separation. Because of this relationship, it is possible to define the ***capacitance*** of a capacitor as the ratio of the charge on the capacitor to the potential difference across it. Letting C be the capacitance, we therefore have

$$C = Q/V. \qquad (16.22\text{-}3)$$

By comparison of Eq. (16.22-3) with Eq. (16.22-2), we find that the capacitance of a plane parallel plate capacitor is

$$C = \varepsilon A/d, \qquad (16.22\text{-}4)$$

where A is the area of the plates, d is the thickness of the dielectric separating them, and ε is the permittivity of the material between the plates. The dimensions of capacitance are

$$[C] = [m^{-1}\ell^{-3}t^2q^2][\ell^2][\ell^{-1}] = [m^{-1}\ell^{-2}t^2q^2]. \qquad (16.22\text{-}5)$$

The unit of capacitance, i.e., the capacitance of a capacitor that acquires a charge of one coulomb when a potential difference of one volt is applied across it, is the ***farad*** (F), named after Michael Faraday (1791–1867), who contributed a great deal to the experimental foundations of modern electricity. A capacitor of one farad capacitance would be a very large one, and a more common measure for capacitors is the ***microfarad*** (μF), which is 10^{-6} F.

The equipotential surfaces between the plates of a parallel plate capacitor are clearly planes parallel to the plates. One such equipotential is indicated in Fig. 16.33 by the dotted lines.

EXERCISES

16.22-1 The potential difference between the two terminals of a high-voltage electrical machine is 1.00×10^6 V. How much work must be done to carry a charge of $+5.00 \times 10^{-3}$ Cb from the negative to the positive terminal? How much work would be required if the charge were -2.00×10^{-3} Cb?

16.22-2 Two parallel conducting plates, each of which has an area of 0.200 m^2, are placed 1.00 cm apart and a difference of potential of 100 V is applied between them. What is the difference of potential between the lower plate, which is connected to the negative terminal, and a point between the two plates and 1.00 mm from the upper plate?

16.22-3 What is the electric field strength at the point referred to in Ex. 16.22-2?

16.22-4 If the space between the plates of Ex. 16.22-2 is filled with paraffin, what will be the capacitance of the capacitor? What charge will each plate have if they are at a potential difference of 100 V?

16.22-5 The capacitor of Ex. 16.22-4 is disconnected from the electrical machine. The paraffin is then removed from between the plates, without disturbing the charge upon them. What will the difference of potential between the plates be when the paraffin is completely removed and there is only air between them?

16.23 Summary

The present chapter has been a continuation of the study of electrical phenomena. It has been found that an electric current produces both heating and magnetic effects. The former have been used to connect the electrical units of current and potential with the mechanical quantities that enter into the expression of energy; the latter were used to connect the electrical quantities with magnetic phenomena. The relations between electrostatics and electric currents have also been investigated. The most important results of our study have been the determination of the magnetic field of current-carrying coils, the establishment of Ohm s law, the design of instruments by which electrical quantities can be measured, and the calculation of the capacitance of a capacitor.

PROBLEMS

16.1 Suppose that the system of Prob. 15.5 has the dimensions $a = 10.0$ cm, $b = 15.0$ cm. The mass of the metal ball is 0.200 g. Each time the ball touches either sphere, it gives up any charge that it had previously. When it touches the inner sphere, it acquires a new charge equal to 1.00 percent of the charge on that sphere.

(a) If the ball comes into contact with the inner sphere when the charge on that sphere is 4.00×10^{-7} Cb, will it subsequently move to the outer sphere?

(b) What charge will remain on the outer sphere when the ball has just left it on its first trip upward? On its second trip? On its fourth trip?

(c) How many times will the ball touch the outer sphere?

16.2 A long, straight wire carrying a current of 20 A extends along the x-axis of a rectangular coordinate system, the current being in the direction of positive x. A second wire, carrying a current of 10 A, in the direction of positive y, is stretched along the y-axis. Sketch the system, with the $+x$-axis horizontal and to the right and with the $+y$-axis vertical and upward.

(a) Show that the magnetic field everywhere in the x-y plane is perpendicular to that plane. (b) Show that $\vec{B} = 0$ everywhere along the line $y = 2x$ in the x-y plane. (c) Locate those regions of the x-y plane in which $\vec{B}$ is directed out of the paper and those in which it is directed into the paper.

16.3 The line integral used in Sec. 16.9 was originally developed for the study of moving fluids, rather than of electricity and magnetism. Suppose that a round tank of water is rotating about its own vertical axis, so that all of the water has an angular velocity ω.

(a) Find the velocity $\vec{v}$ of the water at a distance r from the axis, and show that the line integral of $\vec{v}$ around a horizontal, circular path of constant r is

$$\oint \vec{v} \cdot \vec{ds} = 2\pi\omega r^2.$$

(b) Show that the line integral along a radial path

$$\int_{r=a}^{r=b} \vec{v} \cdot \vec{ds} = 0.$$

(c) Show that, for a closed path made up of two radial lines and two circular arcs, of radius a and b, respectively, $(b > a)$, that

$$\oint \vec{v} \cdot \vec{ds} = \omega(b^2 - a^2)\theta,$$

where θ is the angle between the two radial lines.

16.4 The magnetic flux density due to the earth's field has a magnitude of 5.0×10^{-5} Wb/m^2 in a given laboratory. It points downward and to the north, its angle with the horizontal being 45°. A circular coil whose diameter is 30 cm is to be designed to nullify the magnetic field of a small piece of apparatus positioned at the center of the coil.

(a) What should be the orientation of the axis of the coil? (b) Find the product of the number of turns (N) and the current (I) that they must carry. (c) What is the dipole moment of the coil? (d) What torque, if any, will be exerted on the coil by the earth's magnetic field?

16.5 A long solenoid has its axis in the x-direction and has one end in the plane $x = 0$. In answering the following questions compare this solenoid with a longer one, which extends on both sides of $x = 0$. Both solenoids carry the same current I and the same number of turns per unit length N.

(a) What is the magnetic flux density on the axis of the longer solenoid and at $x = 0$? (b) What fraction of this flux density is produced by that part of the solenoid that is on the $+x$ side of $x = 0$? (c) Show that the flux density on the axis of the shorter solenoid and in the plane of its end is

$$B = \tfrac{1}{2}NI.$$

16.6 The coil of a galvanometer is 2.0 cm wide and 8.0 cm long. It consists of 100 turns of fine wire and is in a magnetic field of flux density 0.20 Wb/m^2. The restoring torque constant of the suspensions is 10^{-6} N m/degree.

(a) What is the maximum current that can be measured by this galvanometer if the scale can accommodate a 45° deflection? (b) What is the smallest current that can be detected if a change of deflection of 0.10 degrees can just be noticed?

16.7 The galvanometer of Prob. 16.6 is to be used as part of a voltmeter that is to give full-scale deflection for 1.00 V. If the resistance of the coil is 70 Ω, what is the resistance of the series resistor that must be used?

16.8 The galvanometer of Probs. 16.6 and 16.7 is to be used as part of an ammeter that is to give full-scale deflection for a current of 1.00 mA. What is the resistance of the needed shunt?

16.9 The hydrogen atom of Prob. 15.7 consists of a proton (mass 1.66×10^{-27} kg, charge $= +1.60 \times 10^{-19}$ Cb) and an electron (mass $= 0.911 \times 10^{-30}$ kg, charge $= -1.60 \times 10^{-19}$ Cb). The electron was assumed to be in circular motion, of radius $r = (e^2/4\pi\varepsilon_0 m\omega^2)^{1/3}$ about the proton, where m is the mass of the electron.

(a) Show that the revolving electron is equivalent to a single turn loop of radius r, carrying a current

$$I = e\omega/2\pi$$

and find this current in amperes if one imposes the quantum condition

$$m\omega r^2 = h/2\pi,$$

where m is the electronic mass and h is Planck's constant. (See Secs. 12.21 and 24.4.)

(b) Show that the atom possesses a magnetic moment $p_m = \pi r^2 e\omega/2\pi$. Find the values of this moment in Am^2.

(c) Compute the ratio of the magnetic moment to the angular momentum.

16.10 Two incandescent lamps X and Y are connected individually to a source of electrical energy that maintains a potential difference of 125 V. It is found that each lamp glows brightly. The current in X is 0.20 A and that in Y is 0.82 A. The lamps are then connected in series, and the combination is connected to the same source. A high-resistance voltmeter is used to measure the potential difference across each lamp; these are, respectively, 122 V and 3 V.

(a) Do these observations violate Ohm's law? (b) Would you expect both lamps to glow brightly when they are in series? If not, which one would do so?

16.11 Two resistors, one having an unknown resistance and the other a resistance of $1.00 \times 10^3\ \Omega$, are connected in series across a dry cell. A voltmeter with a resistance of $1.00 \times 10^3\ \Omega$ is used to obtain the following potential differences:

Across known resistor, $V_1 = 0.300$ V.
Across unknown resistor, $V_2 = 0.600$ V.
Across series combination, $V_0 = 1.500$ V.

(a) Do these readings indicate a violation of Ohm's law?

(b) What is the resistance of the unknown resistor?

16.12 Many electrical circuits are difficult or impossible to analyze in terms of simple series or parallel combinations. One such circuit is shown in the figure. Suppose that steady currents are present in this circuit. Use the conservation laws for energy and charge to show that the following statements are true:

(a) At any ***junction point***, such as B, the sum of the currents approaching the point must be equal to the sum of the currents leaving it. Specifically, for B, $i_1 - i_2 - i_3 = 0$.

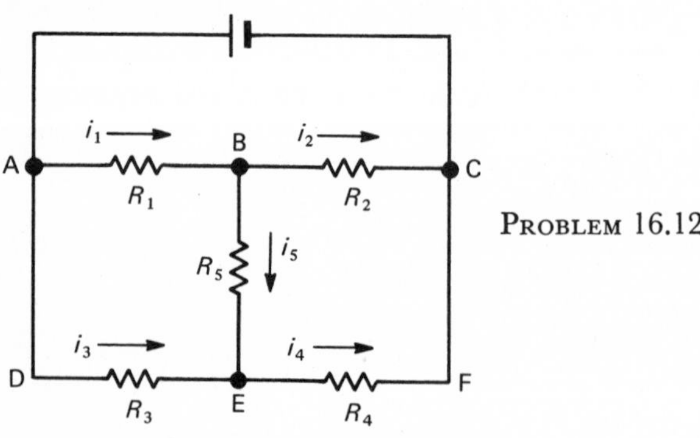

PROBLEM 16.12

(b) The sum of the potential differences around any ***closed loop*** that does not contain a source of electricity (e.g., ABED or BCFE) must be zero. Specifically, for the former loop, $V_{AB} + V_{BE} + V_{ED} + V_{DA} = 0$. (See Prob. 18.8 for an extension of these results to give ***Kirchhoff's laws***.)

16.13 The ***Wheatstone bridge***, used for the measurement of resistances, is identical with the circuit shown in Prob. 16.12, except that the resistor between points B and E is replaced by a galvanometer. Two or more of the resistances are varied until no current flows in the galvanometer. Show the following statements to be true under these circumstances:

(a) Points B and E are at the same potential.

(b) $i_1 = i_2$ and $i_3 = i_4$.

(c) $R_1 R_4 = R_2 R_3$.

16.14 (a) Compute the electric field E_1 at point P that results from the presence of the charges $+q$ and $-2q$ shown in the figure.

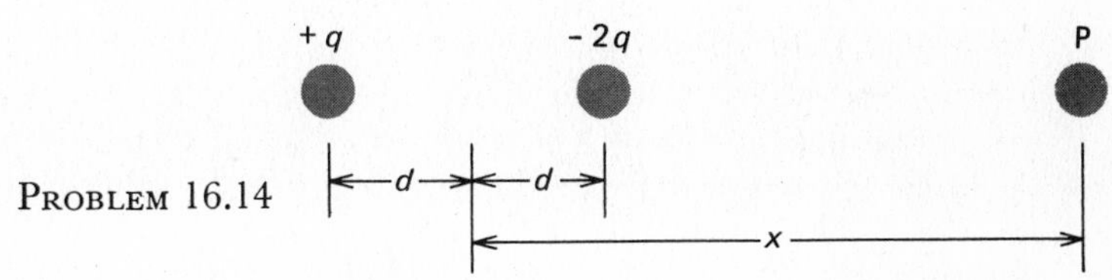

PROBLEM 16.14

(b) Compute the potential V at P as the sum of the potentials resulting from the two charges.

(c) Show that, for this simple geometry,

$$E = -dV/dx.$$

REFERENCES

16A Benjamin Franklin, *Experiments and Observations on Electricity* (I. B. Cohen, editor), Harvard, Cambridge, Mass., 1941.

16B William Francis Magie, *A Source Book in Physics*, Harvard, Cambridge, Mass., 1963. A good historical perspective may be achieved by consulting pp. 436–472.

16C Walter C. Michels, *Electrical Measurements and Their Applications*, Van Nostrand, Princeton, 1957. Theory and practice of the measurement of currents, resistances, and potential differences.

16D Morris Shamos, editor, *Great Experiments in Physics*, Holt, New York, 1960. Pages 121–127 deal with the definitive work of Hans Christian Oersted.

17 ➩ *Electromagnetic Induction*

17.1 Force on a Current-Carrying Wire

In Chapter 16 we saw that current-carrying coils produce magnetic fields in their neighborhoods and that such coils are subjected to torques when they are placed in a magnetic field. Since a torque can result only from forces acting on individual parts of the coil, we might suspect that any current-carrying wire in a magnetic field would be subject to forces. That this is indeed true may be demonstrated by observation of a loosely stretched wire in a fairly strong magnetic field. Such a field may be produced by a current I in one or more large coils as shown in Fig. 17.1. If the wire without current in it is hanging

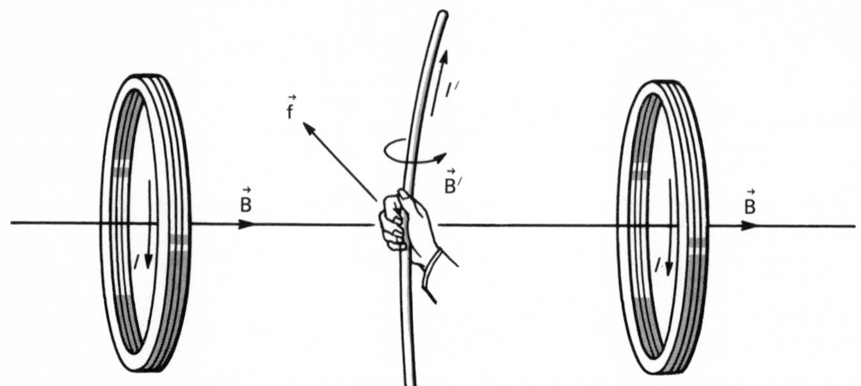

FIG. 17.1 Force on a current-carrying wire.

loosely in the field, it will be pulled into the taut arc shown as soon as the current I' starts to flow. The direction of motion, and therefore the force producing the motion, is always at right angles to the wire and also at right angles to the direction of the magnetic flux $\vec{B}$. Variations of the experiment of Fig. 17.1 show that the direction of the force depends both on the direction of the current and on that of the magnetic field. Thus, if the current in the wire were reversed, it would be found that the motion was toward the experimenter, instead of away. A reversal of the direction of $\vec{B}$, with the current still upward as shown, would also reverse the motion from that shown. Finally, a reversal of both I' and $\vec{B}$ would leave the direction of motion unchanged.

It is possible to predict the direction of the force on a current-carrying wire in all cases if we notice the relative directions of the magnetic field that produces the force and the magnetic field produced by the current in the wire. Thus, in Fig. 17.1 the right-hand rule of Sec. 16.3 tells us that the current I' produces a flux $\vec{B}'$, which circles the wire in the direction indicated just above the hand of the observer. In other words, the flux $\vec{B}'$ produced by the current in the wire is in the same direction as $\vec{B}$ in front of the wire, as viewed by us, and in the opposite direction behind it. This, in turn, means that the total flux density $(B + B')$ is higher on the front side of the wire than that $(B - B')$ on the rear side. In this case, then, it is found that the force on the wire is in such a direction that it pulls the wire *toward the weakest total magnetic field in its neighborhood.* Consideration of the other cases mentioned above, with $\vec{B}$, I', or both reversed, will convince the reader that this rule is a general one.

The relation between the force on a straight wire and the torque on a coil may be seen by the study of a rectangular coil, such as that shown in Fig. 17.2a. The coil is mounted on bearings, so that it is free to turn about a vertical line, and the

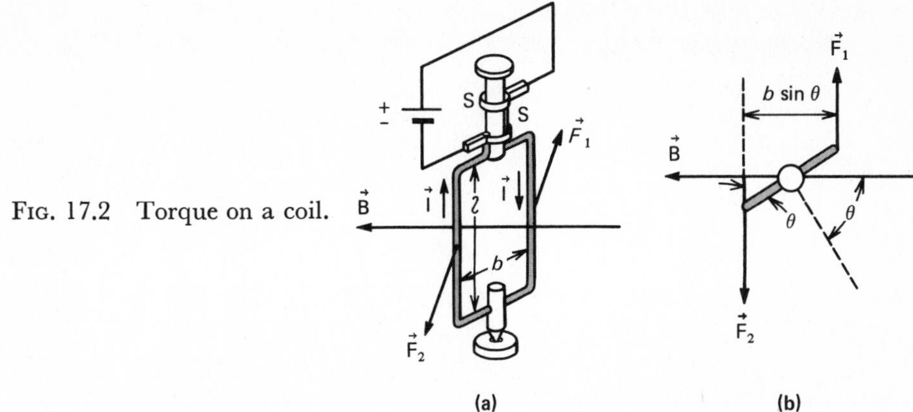

FIG. 17.2 Torque on a coil.

current is carried to it through the ***slip rings*** S–S. The whole assembly is in a horizontal magnetic field of flux density $\vec{B}$. Let us suppose that the coil is momentarily in the position shown in the top view of Fig. 17.2b, with its axis at an angle θ with $\vec{B}$. We know from Eq. (16.5-1) that there will be a torque tending to rotate the coil to its equilibrium position, for which $\theta = 0$. We wish to see whether the forces on the individual sides of the coil account for this torque.

Consider first the top and bottom wires of the coil, each of length b. Since both these wires and the magnetic field are horizontal, the forces on them must be vertical. Vertical forces, being parallel to the axle, will contribute nothing to a torque about the axle, so we can forget the existence of these forces as far as rotation is concerned. The vertical wires, each of length l, are perpendicular to the field; hence, the forces on them will be horizontal forces, as shown by $\vec{F}_1$ and $\vec{F}_2$. If $\vec{I}$ is in the direction shown, the rule given above for the direction of the forces shows that the right-hand side will be subject to a backward force

$\vec{F}_1$ and the left-hand side to a forward force $\vec{F}_2$. The symmetry of the arrangement insures that these forces will be equal in magnitude. It is easy to see that these two forces will result in a torque in the proper direction.

We can now use the same coil to determine the way in which the magnitude of the force on a current-carrying wire depends on the current and the magnetic field. We know from Eqs. (16.4-2) and (16.5-1) that the torque is of magnitude

$$T = BAI \sin\theta = BblI \sin\theta, \qquad (17.1\text{-}1)$$

where $A = bl$ is the area of the coil. As shown in Fig. 17.2, the forces act along lines separated by the distance $b \sin\theta$, so each force has a lever arm $\frac{1}{2}b \sin\theta$. If F denotes the common magnitude of the forces $\vec{F}_1$ and $\vec{F}_2$, the torque on the coil is

$$T = 2(\tfrac{1}{2}Fb \sin\theta) = Fb \sin\theta.$$

Comparing this equation with Eq. (17.1-1), we see that

$$F = BIl. \qquad (17.1\text{-}2)$$

In other words, *a current-carrying wire perpendicular to a magnetic field is subject to a force whose magnitude is proportional to the length of the wire, to the flux density, and to the current in the wire.*

We have now arrived at both the direction and the magnitude of the force exerted on a current-carrying wire by a magnetic field and may proceed to apply these results.

EXERCISE

17.1-1 (a) Show that the force per unit length acting on a current I can be expressed as

$$\vec{F}/l = \vec{I} \times \vec{B},$$

where $\vec{I}$ is a vector having the direction and magnitude of the current and B is the magnetic flux density,

(b) Explain why the equation:

$$\vec{F}/l = \vec{B} \times \vec{I}$$

is not correct.

17.2 Force on a Moving Charge

Throughout the preceding section we discussed the force on a wire in a magnetic field. Because this force results directly from the electric current in the wire, it would be more correct to speak of the force on a current in a magnetic field. Since a current consists of the motion of electric charges, or charged particles, it must be that any charged particle in motion in a magnetic field is subject to a force.

In order to deduce the nature of the force on a moving charge, we shall suppose that a stream of identical charges, each of magnitude q, are moving uniformly with a velocity $\vec{v}$, as shown in Fig. 17.3. If we wish to find the current resulting from this motion, we must find the total charge which passes any point, such as P, in unit time (cf. Sec. 16.1). We first notice that all the charges

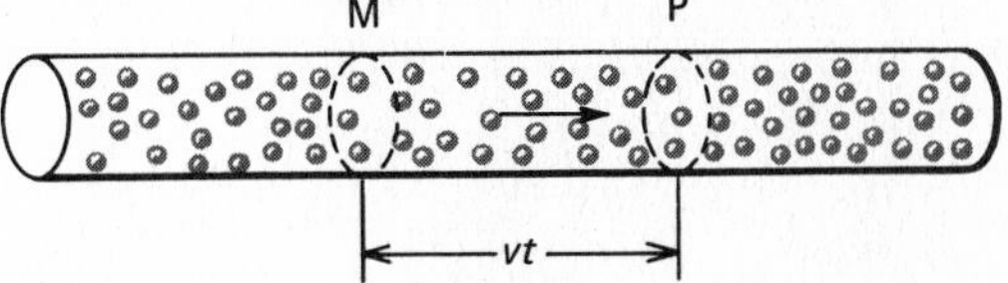

FIG. 17.3 Current due to motion of charges.

included in the cylinder between M and P, whose length is vt, will pass P in a time t. Therefore, the total charge that passes P during the time t is

$$Q = N_l qvt,$$

where N_l is the number of charges per unit length in the direction of motion. The current is therefore given by Eq. (16.1-1) as

$$I = Q/t = N_l qv. \tag{17.2-1}$$

Substitution of this value for I in Eq. (17.1-2) shows that the force per unit length on the current is

$$F/l = BI = BN_l vq,$$

where B is the magnitude of the magnetic flux density, supposed here to be perpendicular to the current. Since all the charges are identical, the force on each charge must be

$$= \frac{F/l}{N_l} = Bvq. \tag{17.2-2}$$

This force, of course, is perpendicular to both the magnetic field and the direction of motion of the charge. In applying the right-hand rule to find its direction, one must remember that the current has the same direction as the velocity of the charges if those charges are positive, and the opposite direction if the charges are negative.

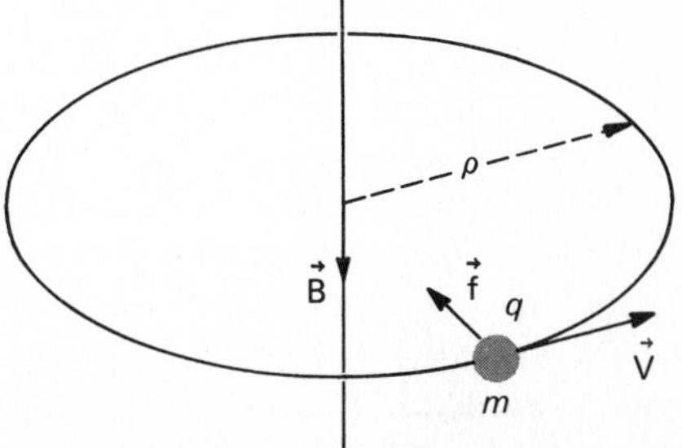

FIG. 17.4 Motion of a charged particle in a magnetic field.

An interesting consequence of Eq. (17.2-2) may be found if we consider that a particle of mass m, carrying a charge q, is moving with a velocity $\vec{v}$ at right angles to a magnetic field of flux density, $\vec{B}$, as shown in Fig. 17.4. The force $\vec{f}$

on the particle will have a magnitude given by Eq. (17.2-2) and will be perpendicular to $\vec{v}$. We have seen in Chapter 7 that a particle moving under the action of a force of constant magnitude which is always perpendicular to the velocity will move with constant speed in a circle. Hence, the particle we are considering will move in a circle as shown. We may find the radius ρ of this circle by equating the force as given by Eq. (17.2-2) to the centripetal force of Eq. (7.7-4). This shows that

$$Bvq = mv^2/\rho$$

or that

$$B\rho = mv/q. \tag{17.2-3}$$

As Eq. (17.2-3) shows, the radius of the circle in which a charged particle moves in a magnetic field depends on the speed v of the particle and the ratio q/m of its charge to its mass. It is therefore possible, by measurement of this radius in a known magnetic field, to determine the ratio of the charge of a particle to its mass if the particle is moving at a known speed, or to measure the speed of a particle of which the charge and mass are known. In particular, one can employ the method just described to determine the mass of the electron, the elementary charge of electricity, if the charge on the electron is known. We shall consider how this charge can be measured in Chapter 18.

Before we can go further to discuss methods for measuring q/m, we should describe a method by which streams of moving charges may be obtained.

EXERCISES

17.2-1 Show that Eq. (17.2-2) is consistent with the more general vector equation:

$$\mathrm{f} = q\vec{\mathrm{v}} \times \vec{\mathrm{B}}$$

17.2-2 Show that Eq. (17.2-3) is consistent with the more general vector equation:

$$\rho = -(q\rho^2/mv^2)(\vec{\mathrm{v}} \times \vec{\mathrm{B}}),$$

where ρ is the radius vector from the center of the circle to the particle at any instant.

17.3 Thermionic Emission

While working on the carbon filament electric lamps which he invented, Thomas Alva Edison (1847–1931) found that there is an electric current from the hot filament F to a second electrode P (Fig. 17.5) provided that this electrode is maintained at a positive potential with respect to the filament. There is no current if P is negative with respect to the filament. Since the current occurs when the bulb is evacuated, and only when the filament is heated, we can explain this effect if we suppose that the heated filament gives off charged particles, which we shall call ***electrons***. Since there is current only when P is positive, we must further suppose that the charges are negative, because only negative charges will be attracted by a positive electrode. The electrons apparently leave the filament, pass through the vacuum, and enter the metal electrode P. From P they flow through the galvanometer G to the positive pole of the battery B. Since no charge builds up on F even though the current flows for a long time, we must also suppose that electrons are supplied to F from the negative pole of the battery B. These can escape to P when the filament F is heated. It is thus clear that the electrons that we have postulated to account for the conduction between F and P have also the properties necessary to account for the conduction of electricity through metals (Chapters 15–16). The process of the emission of electrons by a hot filament is known as ***thermionic emission.***

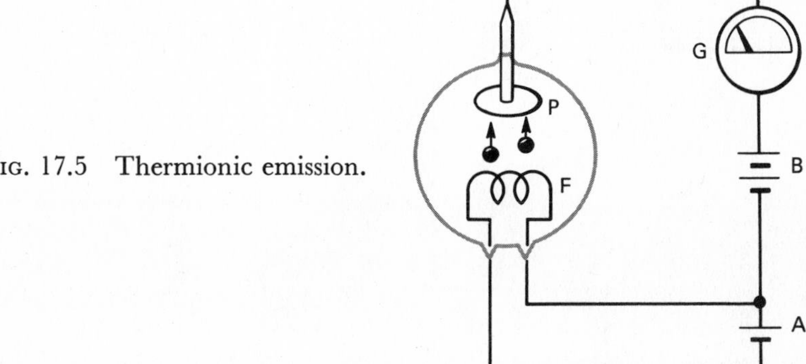

FIG. 17.5 Thermionic emission.

The positive electrode P to which the electrons flow is called the ***plate***, or ***anode***. The hot negative electrode that emits the electrons is known as the ***cathode***. The whole assembly of cathode, plate, and evacuated container is the simplest type of ***vacuum tube.***

If the plate P is maintained at a positive potential V with respect to the filament F, the electrons in moving from F to P will gain an amount of kinetic energy Ve, where e is the electronic charge. Consequently, if they start from the filament with negligibly small speeds, which may be shown to be true, their kinetic energy at the plate will be

$$\tfrac{1}{2}mv^2 = Ve.$$

They therefore arrive at P with the speed v given by

$$v = \sqrt{2Ve/m}, \tag{17.3-1}$$

where m is the mass of the electron.

17.4 The Electronic Mass

A rather simple experiment to measure the mass of the electron shows that all electrons (moving at speeds much less than the speed of light) have the same mass. In the apparatus shown in Fig. 17.6, electrons emitted by the hot filament F are accelerated by a potential difference V. Some of the electrons pass through the two slits S_1 and S_2, which serve to limit the width of the electron beam. In the same plane as S_2, and at a fixed distance 2ρ from it, there is a third slit

S_3. That part of the apparatus enclosed by the dashed line in the figure is inside a glass or metal case which is evacuated and placed in a magnetic field. This field, which bends the electrons in a semicircular path from S_2 to S_3, is parallel to these slits, as shown by the vector $\vec{B}$. Immediately in front of S_3 is a metal box T, which is connected to the battery through a galvanometer *G*. Any current passing through the final slit will be indicated by this galvanometer.

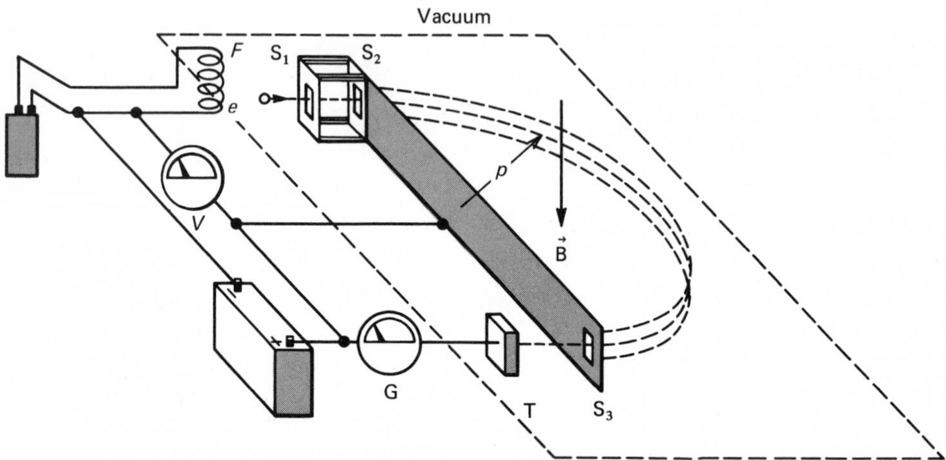

FIG. 17.6 The measurement of e/m.

If the apparatus is operated at an arbitrary potential V and with an arbitrary magnetic flux density B, little or no current will be read by the galvanometer. If V or B is adjusted, however, there will be found a condition under which a maximum current flows through S_3. Under these circumstances the electrons which pass through S_2 travel in a semicircular path of diameter 2ρ, as shown by the dotted line, in order to pass through S_3. In accordance with Eq. (17.2-3) the radius of this path is

$$\rho = mv/eB.$$

If we substitute the speed v of the electrons that emerge from S_2, as given by Eq. (17.3-1), we find that

$$\rho = (m/eB)\sqrt{2Ve/m} = (1/B)\sqrt{2mV/e}.$$

Solving this equation for e/m, we find that

$$e/m = 2V/B^2\rho^2. \tag{17.4-1}$$

When the value of e/m is obtained from Eq. (17.4-1), using values of V, B, and ρ, it is found that it has a constant value for reasonably small values of V. The best present value is

$$e/m = -1.759 \times 10^{11}\ \text{Cb/kg}. \tag{17.4-2}$$

The charge e itself is 1.602×10^{-19} Cb (Sec. 18.12), so we find from Eq. (17.4-2) that

$$m = 9.11 \times 10^{-31} \text{ kg} \tag{17.4-3}$$

If high-accelerating potentials V are used in this experiment, so that the speed of the electrons becomes comparable with the speed of light, it is found that the measured values of e/m are less than that given by Eq. (17.4-2). In fact, it is found that the measured ratio is that which would be predicted if the mass of the electrons were calculated according to the relativistic Eq. (8.9-5) and the electronic charge were supposed to be independent of the speed of the electron. We may therefore conclude that the charge of a particle is not affected by the motion of the particle relative to the observer.

EXERCISES

17.4-1 Two long parallel conductors carry equal currents in opposite directions. If the current in either conductor is I and the distance between them is d, find the magnetic flux density at one wire due to the current in the second. Find also the direction of this magnetic flux. Will the wires be pushed apart or pulled together by the electromagnetic forces acting on them? Find an expression for the magnitude of the force per unit length acting on each conductor.

17.4-2 The magnetic flux density in the apparatus of Fig. 17.6 is 1.58×10^{-3} Wb/m^2, and the distance between S_2 and S_3 is 10.00 cm. What potential difference must be used to accelerate the electrons if they are to pass through S_3?

17.4-3 If the potential difference between the filament and the slits of the apparatus discussed in Ex. 17.4-2 is 500 V, the magnetic field being unchanged, by how far will the electron beam miss the slit S_3?

17.4-4 An electron moving with a velocity $\vec{v}$ enters a region in which there is an electric field of strength $\vec{E}$, directed at right angles to $\vec{v}$, and a magnetic field of strength $\vec{H}$, which is perpendicular to both $\vec{v}$ and $\vec{E}$. Show that the electron will continue to move in a straight line if $v = E/\mu_0 H$. Draw a sketch showing the directions of $\vec{v}$, $\vec{E}$, and $\vec{H}$ necessary to accomplish this.

17.5 Electromagnetic Induction

We have thus far seen two effects that connect a current-carrying wire and a magnetic field: first, the production of a field by the wire and, second, a mechanical force on the wire due to the field. A third phenomenon, the production of an electrical potential difference in the wire when the magnetic field in its neighborhood changes, was discovered independently in the nineteenth century by Michael Faraday (1791–1867) in England and Joseph Henry (1797–1878) in the United States. This effect is known as ***electromagnetic induction.***

Electromagnetic induction may be demonstrated quite easily by an experiment of the type illustrated in Fig. 17.7. A coil of wire C, in the neighborhood of a magnet N–S, has its ends connected to a galvanometer G. If the magnet is suddenly turned end for end, the galvanometer will be deflected, showing that a current has passed through it. If the magnet is left undisturbed in its new position, the galvanometer soon returns to zero deflection, showing that the current persists only during the motion of the magnet. If one waits until the galvanometer has come to rest and then suddenly returns the magnet to its original position, a momentary deflection equal and opposite to the one initially observed is found.

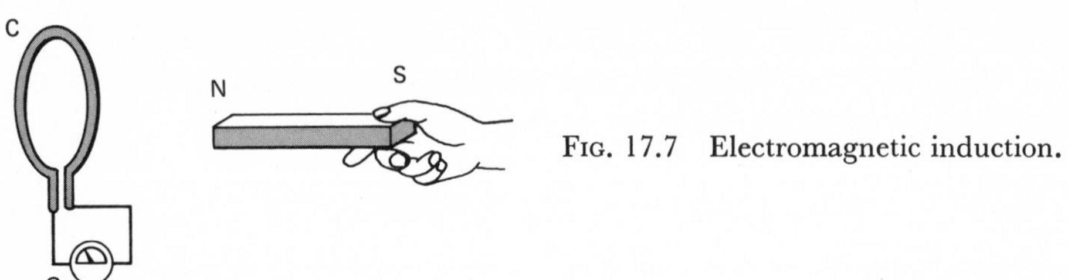

FIG. 17.7 Electromagnetic induction.

In the experiments just described, the turning of the magnet obviously reverses the direction of the magnetic flux which passes through the coil. Since the effect reverses when the flux *change* is reversed in sign, we may suspect that it is proportional to the amount by which the flux changes. This may be verified by a variation on the original experiment. If the magnet is suddenly removed from the neighborhood of the coil, the magnetic flux, instead of reversing, becomes zero. Since this represents half as much change as did the reversal, we expect that the galvanometer will deflect half as far. This is verified by test. Similarly, the sudden restoration of the magnet to its original position produces an effect equal and opposite to its removal.

A final experiment may be performed by replacing the single turn coil of Fig. 17.7 by a coil of the same diameter, but of N turns. If the resistance of this coil is small compared with that of the galvanometer, it is found that the deflection of the latter is N times as great as it was with the single turn coil, for any specified motion of the magnet.

17.6 Calculation of the Induced Electromotive Force

By a series of experiments of the type described in the preceding section, we could find the laws governing electromagnetic induction. It is simpler, however, to use our previous knowledge of the magnetic effects of currents to calculate the law of induction and then to test our deduction by experiment.

Suppose that a wire is bent into the form of an open-ended rectangle ACDF, as shown in Fig. 17.8, and that this loop is placed so that its plane is perpendicular to a magnetic field of flux density $\vec{B}$. Now let a straight wire MN be placed across the loop, parallel to the side CD, making contact with the loop at the points M and N. This wire completes a closed electric circuit around the path

CDNM. As long as the system is at rest, there is no potential difference around this circuit and no current in it. Suppose that the wire MN is now moved to the right with a speed V, in such a way that it always remains parallel to its original position. We know from our discussion in Chapters 15 and 16 that a conductor contains charges that are free to move, and we know from Sec. 17.2 that a

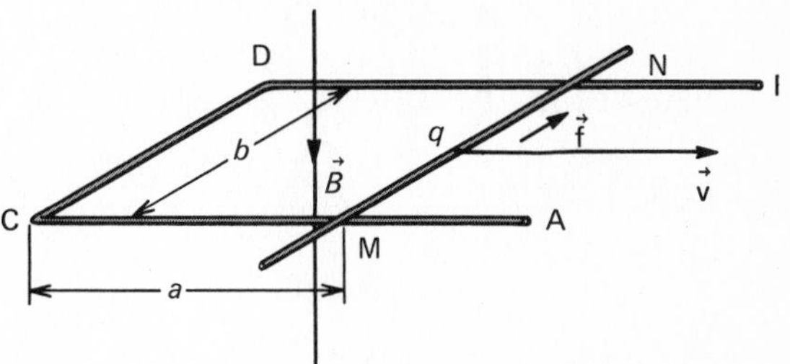

FIG. 17.8 Calculation of the induced emf due to a motion of a conductor in a magnetic field.

moving charge in a magnetic field is subject to a force at right angles to its motion. Suppose that one of the charges within the wire MN has a magnitude q. Equation (17.2-2) then tells us that a force

$$f = Bvq \tag{17.6-1}$$

will act on this charge because of its motion in the magnetic field. If the field is directed as shown by $\vec{B}$ in the figure, this force (for a positive q) will be along the wire in the direction shown by $\vec{f}$. Hence, the charge will move in this direction through the wire.

We saw in Chapter 16 that currents flow in conductors if an electric field is present in the conductor, i.e., if the potential varies within the conductor. We have now encountered a case in which there is no source of an electrostatic field and yet a current is produced. We can account for this if we suppose that the motion of the wire MN in the magnetic field produces an ***electromotive force**** in the loop MNDC. We define the magnitude of this electromotive force as the *amount of energy per unit charge that is supplied to any moveable charge each time that it traverses the complete* circuit. Electromotive force therefore has the same dimensions as does electrostatic potential difference; it is measured in volts. We shall customarily abbreviate electromotive force as ***emf*** and shall express it by the script symbol $\mathscr{E}$,

The charge of Eq. (17.6-1) has a force of magnitude f acting on it while it moves over the distance b, and no force acting on it around the rest of the circuit. Hence, the work done in moving this charge around the circuit is

$$w = fb = vqbB.$$

Equating this work to $\mathscr{E}q$, we find that

$$\mathscr{E} = vbB. \tag{17.6-2}$$

* The term "electromotive force" is somewhat unfortunate, as this quantity is not a force. The term has been so sanctified by history, however, that it can hardly be replaced by a more descriptive nomenclature.

Although Eq. (17.6-2) serves to predict the electromotive force induced in the apparatus of Fig. 17.8, it is not in a sufficiently general form for convenient application to other circuits. To put it into such a form, we notice that the magnetic flux which passes through the loop MNDC is

$$\Phi = abB.$$

During any time interval Δt, the wire MN moves a distance $v\ \Delta t$ to the right, so that the area of the coil increases during this time interval from ab to $(a + v\ \Delta t)b$. Hence, the flux through the loop at the end of the time Δt has increased to

$$\Phi + \Delta\Phi = (a + v\ \Delta t)bB,$$

and the change of flux during the time is

$$\Delta\Phi = vbB\ \Delta t.$$

Comparing this equation with Eq. (17.6-2), we see that the right side of the latter is equal to the time rate of change of flux $\Delta\Phi/\Delta t$. Making this substitution, we find that the induced emf is

$$\mathscr{E} = -\Delta\Phi/\Delta t. \tag{17.6-3}$$

The reason for the minus sign will be explained later. We therefore arrive at the law of electromagnetic induction: *The induced electromotive force in any closed loop is equal to the time rate of change of magnetic flux through that loop.*

The direction of the emf in Fig. 17.8 is, of course, the same as the direction of $\vec{f}$, and it leads to a current that flows in a counterclockwise direction, as viewed from above the loop. The mere fact that an emf exists tells us its direction, without reference to the detailed process which leads to the induction. For example, suppose that the induced emf sets up a current in the wire MN. This current is in a magnetic field and is therefore subject to a force perpendicular to both the current and the field. Were the current in the opposite direction from $\vec{f}$, i.e., from N to M, the right-hand rule of Fig. 16.9 tells us that the flux due to this current would aid the original field inside the loop and oppose it outside. The total field would therefore be a minimum on the side of the wire outside the loop, and the force on the wire would be outward, in accordance with the discussion of Sec. 17.1. This force would accelerate the wire in the direction in which it is already moving so the wire would move faster and faster outward. Not only do we fail to observe such an effect, but we recognize that it would violate the conservation law for energy. It follows that the induced current cannot be from N to M when the wire is moving outward. On the other hand, with the current from M to N, the force on the wire is inward, i.e., it opposes the motion of the wire. This leads to a stable situation instead of the completely unstable one imaged above.

We may also examine the situation of Fig. 17.8 in another way. According to Eq. (17.6-3), the induced emf is a result of a changing magnetic flux through the loop. Since the area of the loop is increasing, the flux through the loop is also increasing. We saw in the preceding paragraph that a current from N to M would give additional flux through the loop in the same direction as the original flux. Thus, the induced current due to an increase in flux would lead to a further increase, and the flux through the loop could be expected to increase without limit. This makes no more sense than did the continually accelerated wire considered above. It follows that the current must be in the direction of $\vec{f}$, i.e., in such a direction that it opposes the increase of flux.

Had we reversed the motion of the wire in Fig. 17.8, the flux through the loop would have been decreasing. The direction of the induced emf would also have reversed, and we would have found that the additional magnetic flux due to the induced current would have been in the same direction as the original flux; thus it would have opposed the decrease of flux.

The considerations of the preceding paragraphs lead to a general rule known as ***Lenz' law***: *The electromotive force induced by any change in physical conditions is always in such a direction that a current set up by the emf will oppose the change.* The law is named for Heinrich F. E. Lenz (1804–1865) who first enunciated it in a somewhat less general form. The use of the minus sign in Eq. (17.6-3) can now be explained in terms of the right-hand rule. We can choose quite arbitrarily the direction of magnetic flux which we call positive through the coil. The right-hand rule then determines a direction of current around the coil which we must call positive. This direction, of course, is the direction of a current that would produce positive flux. Since the induced current due to an increase in positive flux is in such a direction that it opposes the building up of the flux, this current must be negative; hence, the minus sign must appear in Eq. (17.6-3).

17.7 The General Law of Induction

The treatment in the preceding section led to a derivation of the magnitude and direction of the induced electromotive force in a particular case in which the magnetic flux through a closed loop of wire was changed by varying the area of the loop. In Sec. 17.5, we saw that currents were set up in closed circuits when the magnetic flux was varied in other ways, e.g., by the motion of a magnet. We may now ask whether the result expressed in Eq. (17.6-3) and derived for a special case applies to the more general circumstances in which the magnetic flux through the circuit is changed by any means. Since the final expression for $\mathscr{E}$ contains no reference to the mechanism by which the flux was changed, we suspect that it may be of general validity, but we must test this idea experimentally before coming to a final decision. Most of this chapter will be devoted to a consideration of various consequences of the law of induction; we shall find in each case that the law predicts correctly the observed effects.

Before proceeding to a demonstration of special cases, we note a few generalities about electromagnetic induction. One of these has already been hinted in Sec. 17.5, where we noticed that a coil of N turns produced an effect N times as great as one of a single turn. This is easily explained since the same magnetic flux passes through each of the turns. When a change $\Delta\Phi$ occurs in a time Δt, an emf $-\Delta\Phi/\Delta t$ will be included in each turn, and, since all the turns are in series, a total emf of

$$\mathscr{E} = -N\Delta\Phi/\Delta t \tag{17.7-1}$$

will be produced.

It is also worth note that the combination of the law of induction with Ohm's law can predict the amount of electricity which will be set into motion by a change of magnetic flux through a closed circuit. Suppose that a coil of N turns experiences a change of flux of $\Delta\Phi$ during a time Δt. If the coil is part of an electric circuit whose total resistance is R, the current passing in this circuit during the change will be

$$I = \mathcal{E}/R = -(N/R)\Delta\Phi/\Delta t. \tag{17.7-2}$$

Multiplying both sides of this expression by Δt and remembering that $I\,\Delta t$ is the charge Δq which passes during the time Δt [Eq. (16.1-1)], we see that

$$\Delta q = I\,\Delta t = -N\,\Delta\Phi/R. \tag{17.7-3}$$

Measurement of this charge offers a convenient method of measuring magnetic fields. For example, suppose that a coil of N turns and area A is placed perpendicular to a magnetic field of flux density B. The flux passing through the coil is then $\Phi = AB$. If the coil is suddenly removed from its location to a new point at which the magnetic field is zero, the change of flux will be $\Delta\Phi = -\Phi = -AB$, so that the charge set in motion by the movement will be

$$\Delta q = NAB/R,$$

where R is the resistance of the coil itself plus that of any instrument, such as a galvanometer, connected in series with it to measure the charge. A coil used in this manner to measure magnetic flux is known as a ***search coil.***

While most applications of the law of induction involve a closed electrical circuit, it is important to notice that the phenomenon of induction does not depend on the existence of such a circuit. For example, we notice that the expressions for $\mathcal{E}$ in Eqs. (17.6-3) and (17.7-1) do not involve the resistance of the circuit. If we replace the wires used in a coil by finer and finer wires, of the same length, the resistance will increase. The induced electromotive force $\mathcal{E}$ will remain constant. We may therefore suppose that in the limit of zero diameter wires, the induced electromotive force will be the same as with a wire of finite diameter. Since this limit corresponds to no wire at all we can see that *the electromotive force will exist even in the absence of a circuit.* Thus, we may conclude that an electromotive force $-\Delta\Phi/\Delta t$ will exist around any closed path through which the magnetic flux is changing at a rate $\Delta\Phi/\Delta t$, whether or not a wire is stretched around the path. This, in turn, means that an electric field exists in any region in which the magnetic flux is changing. We shall see in Chapter 23 that this is important in connection with the study of electromagnetic waves, such as those used in radio communication.

EXERCISES

17.7-1 The experiment of Sec. 17.6 is repeated three times in a magnetic field in which the flux density is 1.00×10^{-2} Wb/m^2, with a loop in which $b = 10.0$ cm. In each case a is initially 40.0 cm. The wire MN is moved in the following ways in the three experiments:

(a) Uniformly to the right with a velocity of 10.0 cm/sec for 3 sec. (b) Uniformly to the right with a velocity of 5.0 cm/sec for 6 sec. (c) Starting from rest with a positive acceleration (to the right) of 30 cm/sec^2 for 1.00 sec, then with a negative acceleration of the same magnitude for 1.00 sec.

Calculate the electromotive force which will be induced at any instant t during each experiment.

17.7-2 A search coil of 10 turns and of area 15.0 cm^2 is perpendicular to a magnetic field of flux density B. It is then removed to a location in which the flux density is zero. The coil has a resistance of 0.752 Ω and is connected to a galvanometer of resistance 3.25 Ω. If a charge of 0.0250 Cb passes through the galvanometer, what is the value of B?

17.7-3 Suppose that a search coil perpendicular to a magnetic field, instead of being removed from the field, is suddenly rotated about an axis in its own plane through an angle of 180°. Derive an expression for the charge that will pass through the coil as a result of the rotation. Take the resistance of the coil and its external series circuit as R, the flux density as B, the number of turns of the coil as N, and the area of the coil as A.

17.8 Induction in a Rotating Coil

Some of the most useful and interesting applications of electromagnetic induction can be illustrated by the behavior of a coil rotating about an axis in its own plane, the axis being perpendicular to a magnetic field. Such a coil is shown schematically in Fig. 17.9. As the coil rotates, the magnetic flux passing through it is a maximum when the plane of the coil is at right angles to the field, as shown in Fig. 17.9a, and is zero when the coil is parallel to the field. Since the flux through the coil is continually changing, there will be an emf induced in the coil. This emf, however, will not be constant in magnitude or direction, since the time rate of change of flux varies during each revolution.

In order to find the induced emf, we start by calculating the flux through the coil in any position. If the area of the coil is A and the coil is in a position making an angle θ with the perpendicular to the field, as shown in Fig. 17.9b, the flux

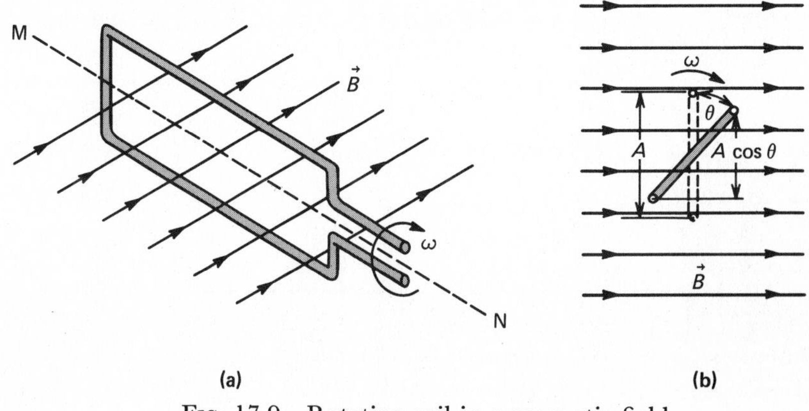

FIG. 17.9 Rotating coil in a magnetic field.

through it is obviously the same as that which would pass through a coil of area $A \cos \theta$, which was perpendicular to the field. Hence, the flux at this instant is

$$\Phi = BA \cos \theta = BA \cos \omega t, \tag{17.8-1}$$

where ω is the angular velocity of the coil and the time t is measured from the instant when the coil was perpendicular to the field. We now wish to find the time rate of change of flux $d\Phi/dt$. Using Eq. I.2 of Appendix I, we see that if

$$x = BA \cos \omega t,$$

$$dx/dt = -BA \sin \omega t \, d(\omega t)/dt = -\omega BA \sin \omega t.$$

Letting $x = \Phi$ in these equations, we see that the first is identical with Eq. (17.8-1). The second therefore tells us that

$$d\Phi/dt = -\omega BA \sin \omega t.$$

Substitution of this value of $d\Phi/dt$ into Eq. (17.6-3) shows that the instantaneous induced emf in the coil, and therefore the instantaneous potential difference between its terminals, is

$$V = \omega BA \sin \omega t = V_0 \sin \omega t, \tag{17.8-2}$$

where V_0 is the amplitude of the emf.

We therefore see that the voltage output of the coil is proportional to its angular velocity and varies with $\sin \theta$. Figure 17.10 shows the voltage output as

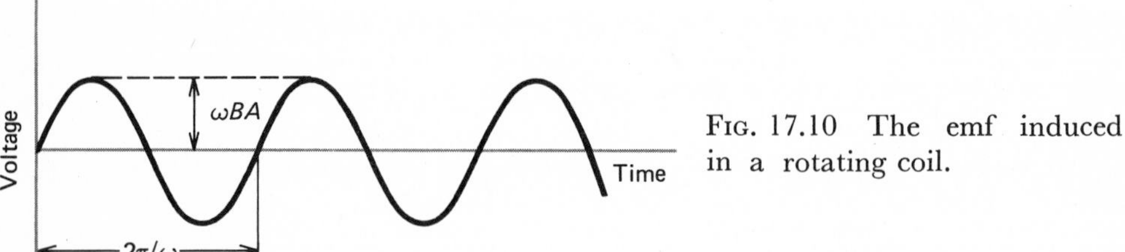

FIG. 17.10 The emf induced in a rotating coil.

it depends upon time. This production of an electromotive force by a rotating coil is the basis on which nearly all ***generators***, for the conversion of mechanical energy to electrical energy, are constructed. The simplest of all electromagnetic machines for the production of electricity is the ***alternator***, or ***alternating current generator***. This machine, in its most elementary form, is shown schematically in Fig. 17.11. The rectangular coil C rotates on a shaft between the poles N-S of a magnet. The two ends of the wire forming the coil are connected to a pair of cylindrical ***slip rings*** R-R. Connection to the terminals T-T is made through a pair of ***brushes*** B-B, which are merely blocks of metal or carbon which press against the slip rings. The rings, as they turn with the coil, slide over these brushes, maintaining continual electrical contact.

The major difference between a ***direct current generator*** and an alternator is in the manner in which the coil is connected to the external circuit. The ends of the coil in a simple version of the former, instead of being connected to slip rings, are connected to two semicylindrical conducting segments that rotate with the shaft. The brushes are fixed in position so that a given brush contacts one of the two segments during approximately half of a revolution and the other segment during the other half. The arrangement of segments that connect the coil to the brushes in this way is known as a ***commutator***. The purpose of the commutator is to keep switching the connection of the coil to the external circuit so that the lower half of the voltage curve in Fig. 17.10 will be flipped

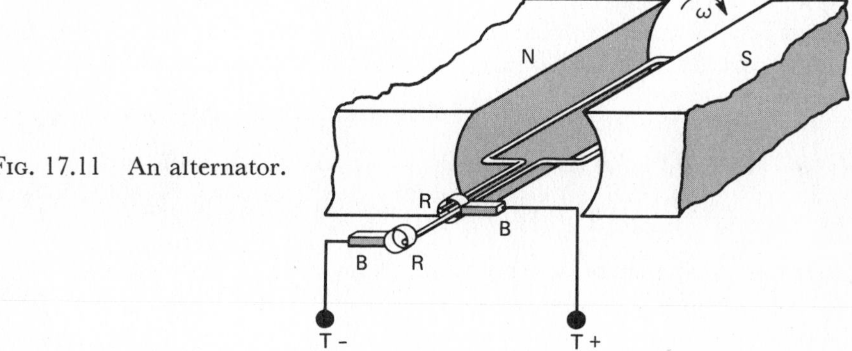

FIG. 17.11 An alternator.

over in such a way that it, too, lies above the axis. As seen by an external circuit, then, the voltage appears as a continuous series of arches—a variable voltage, to be sure, but always in the same direction. Since this voltage does not alter in direction, any current driven by it will not alter in direction; hence, such currents are known as ***direct currents*** in contrast to alternating currents (see Sec. 17.9).

For further details concerning the design and operation of generators, the reader is referred to textbooks of electrical engineering.

17.9 Power from Alternators

If an external resistance is connected between the terminals T-T of the alternator, a current will flow in this resistance. The current, of course, will vary sinusoidally with time. If the external resistance is R and the internal resistance of the alternator is R_i, the instantaneous current will be $V/(R+R_i)$. Substituting the value of V from Eq. (17.8-2), we find that the current is

$$I = V_0 \sin \omega t/(R+R_i) = I_0 \sin \omega t. \tag{17.9-1}$$

Here I_0 is the amplitude of the current and is related to the amplitude of the voltage V_0 by the equation

$$I_0 = V_0/(R+R_i). \tag{17.9-2}$$

Currents that vary with time in the manner indicated by Eq. (17.9-1) are called ***alternating currents***. In many applications of electricity, such alternating currents have advantages over direct currents, which always flow in the same direction.

It is clear from Eqs. (17.8-2) and (17.9-1) that at any instant the electric power expended by the alternator in the internal and external resistances is given by Eq. (16.16-4) in the form

$$P = VI = V_0^2 \sin^2 \omega t/(R + R_i). \tag{17.9-3}$$

From this equation, we see that the power expended by an alternator in resistances is always positive, though fluctuating, since the current and the voltage both change sign at the same time. By the methods of the calculus it can be shown that the average value of $\sin^2 \omega t$ is $\frac{1}{2}$ (see Prob. 17.9), so that we may write the average power in the form

$$\bar{P} = \tfrac{1}{2} V_0^2/(R + R_i). \tag{17.9-4}$$

If we define the ***effective voltage*** of an alternating voltage as

$$V_{eff} = V_0/\sqrt{2},$$

then Eq. (17.9-4) may be written

$$\bar{P} = V_{eff}^2/(R + R_i). \tag{17.9-5}$$

In a similar way, the ***effective current*** of an alternating current is defined as

$$I_{eff} = I_0/\sqrt{2}. \tag{17.9-6}$$

In these terms, Eq. (16.16-4) for the average power dissipated by an alternating current in a resistance can be rewritten as

$$\bar{P} = V_{eff}^2/R = V_{eff} I_{eff} = I_{eff}^2 R. \tag{17.9-7}$$

It is for this reason that alternating voltages and alternating currents are specified in terms of their effective values V_{eff} and I_{eff} rather than the amplitudes V_0 and I_0 of the voltage and current, respectively. Thus, a lamp or heater or other resistance device which will operate on a given direct current voltage will operate equally well on an alternating voltage of the same effective value. It will be clear later that this is true only for resistive devices and not for motors (c.f. Ex. 17.9-5) and not for inductive devices (Secs. 17.11–17.13).

EXERCISES

17.9-1 An alternator consists of a plane circular coil 10.0 cm in diameter and with 100 turns. This coil rotates 50 times per second about a diameter that is perpendicular to the earth's magnetic field, at a point where the flux density is 0.60×10^{-4} Wb/m^2. Calculate the maximum value of the voltage which will be developed by the rotating coil, and plot a curve of the voltage output vs. time for two complete revolutions of the coil.

17.9-2 The coil of Ex. 17.9-1 has a resistance of 2.5 Ω. The brushes are connected to an external resistance of 10.0 Ω. What is the maximum current that will flow in this resistance, and what is the maximum value of the voltage across its terminals?

17.9-3 The generator coil shown in the figure has a resistance R_i and an area A. It is rotating with a constant angular velocity ω in a constant magnetic field of flux density $\vec{B}$. At a particular instant, the plane of the coil is at an angle $\theta = \omega t$ with the

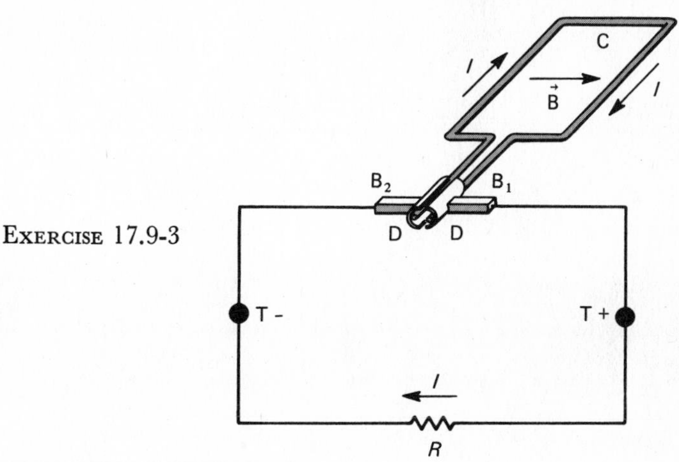

EXERCISE 17.9-3

perpendicular to $\vec{B}$ (cf. Fig. 17.9). Show that the current delivered to the external resistance at this instant is

$$I = \omega AB \sin \omega t/(R + R_i).$$

Hence, using Eqs. (17.9-1) and (16.5-2), show that there is a torque opposing the motion of the coil, of magnitude

$$T = I^2(R + R_i)/\omega.$$

17.9-4 Starting from the results of Ex. 17.9-3, show that the mechanical energy required to overcome the torque on the coil during a very short time Δt is

$$\Delta w_m = I^2(R + R_i)\Delta t.$$

Find the electrical energy Δw_e delivered to the external resistor during Δt, and show that the ratio $\Delta w_e/\Delta w_m = R/(R + R_i)$. Notice that this ratio does not depend on θ or the position of the coil.

17.9-5 The diagram shows the same machine illustrated in Ex. 17.9-3, except that the external lead has been replaced by a battery.

(a) Suppose that the battery maintains a potential difference $V_0 = \omega AB/\sqrt{2}$ across its terminals (T+ and T−). Show that the current will reverse twice during each half cycle ($0 < \omega t < \pi$) and that the electromagnetic torque on the coil will also reverse twice during each half cycle.

(b) Next suppose that the potential difference across the battery terminals is $V_0 > \omega AB$. Show that the electromagnetic torque is always in a direction to aid the motion of the coil and, therefore, that the turning coil can supply mechanical energy. (The generator under these circumstances is operating as a ***motor***.)

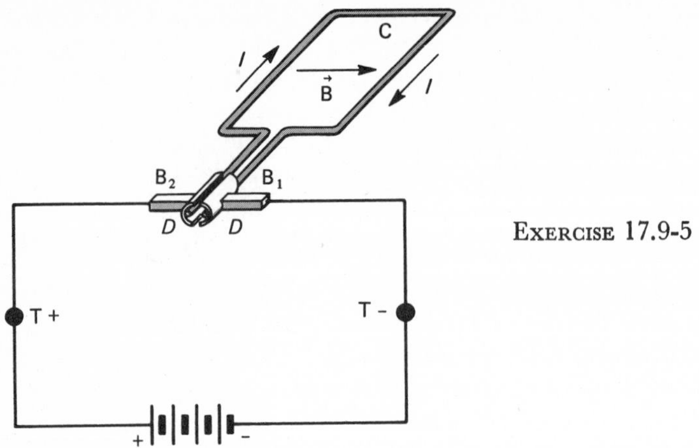

EXERCISE 17.9-5

17.9-6 The machine shown in the diagram for Ex. 17.9-5, when connected to a battery in the manner indicated, runs as a motor rotating in a counterclockwise direction as viewed from the front. Show that the machine will rotate in the opposite direction if the battery is reversed, i.e., if the positive terminal of the battery is connected to the T− and the negative terminal of the battery to T+.

17.10 Mutual Inductance

In generators, an electromotive force is induced in a coil due to the motion of the coil in a magnetic field. As we saw in Secs. 17.5 and 17.7, electromotive forces may also be induced when a coil remains stationary but the magnetic field in its neighborhood changes. If two coils of wire are placed close to each other and a current is passed through one, some of the magnetic flux due to this current will pass through the second coil. Thus, if the coils are arranged as in Fig. 17.12 and the switch S is closed, a magnetic field due to the current in coil C_1 will be established in the neighborhood of coil C_2. We have seen in Chapter 16 that the flux density at any point, due to a current I, is proportional to the current. It therefore follows that the flux Φ that passes through C_2 will also be proportional to I. Denoting the constant of proportionality by M, we have

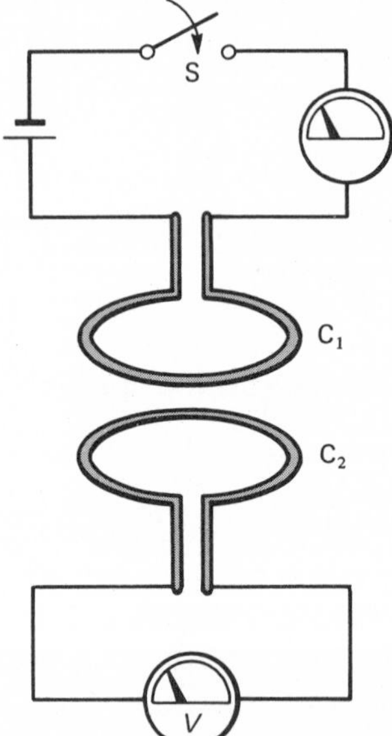

FIG. 17.12 Mutual inductance of two coils.

$$\Phi = MI. \qquad (17.10\text{-}1)$$

When the current is changing at a rate $\Delta I/\Delta t$, the flux through C_2 will be changing at a rate

$$\Delta\Phi/\Delta t = M(\Delta I/\Delta t). \qquad (17.10\text{-}2)$$

Therefore, an electromotive force will be induced in coil C_2 whenever the current in coil C_1 is changing. By combining Eq. (17.10-2) with the law of induction of Eq. (17.6-3), we see that the induced voltage will have the value

$$\mathscr{E} = -M(\Delta I/\Delta t). \tag{17.10-3}$$

The dimensions of the constant M are

$$[M] = [Vt/I] = [AB/I] = [m\ell^2 q^{-2}]. \tag{17.10-4}$$

The value of M which is characteristic of any pair of coils is called the ***mutual inductance*** of the two coils. The unit of mutual inductance is called the ***henry*** (H), after the American physicist Joseph Henry (Sec. 17.5). Two coils have a mutual inductance of *one henry when a current change in one coil at the rate of one ampere per second induces an* emf *of one volt in the other coil.*

As an example of two coils which have a calculable mutual inductance, consider two coplanar and concentric circular coils, having radii a and b and having n and N turns, respectively. Suppose that $a \ll b$ and that a current I flows in the larger coil. According to Eq. (16.10-3), the flux density due to this current at the center of the coil has a magnitude

$$B = \mu_0 NI/2b.$$

Since the other coil is very small, we can consider the flux density throughout its area to be equal to B and to be along the common axis, perpendicular to the coil. The flux passing through the coil is therefore

$$\Phi = \pi a^2 nB = \pi a^2 \mu_0 nNI/2b.$$

Comparing this equation with Eq. (17.10-1), we see that

$$M = \pi a^2 \mu_0 nN/2b. \tag{17.10-5}$$

17.11 Self-Inductance

When a current flows in any coil, the magnetic flux due to that current passes through the coil itself. Because of the proportionality of the flux density and the current, we can write

$$\Phi = LI, \tag{17.11-1}$$

where Φ is the flux, I is the current flowing in the coil, and L is a constant which is characteristic of the size and shape of the coil and, possibly, of the presence of any ferromagnetic materials in its neighborhood. This constant is known as the ***self-inductance*** of the coil.

Since the law of induction does not depend on the method by which the magnetic flux is changed, any change of current in the coil will be accompanied by an induced voltage in the coil. If the current is changing at the rate $\Delta I/\Delta t$, the induced voltage is

$$\mathscr{E} = -\Delta\Phi/\Delta t = -L\,\Delta I/\Delta t. \tag{17.11-2}$$

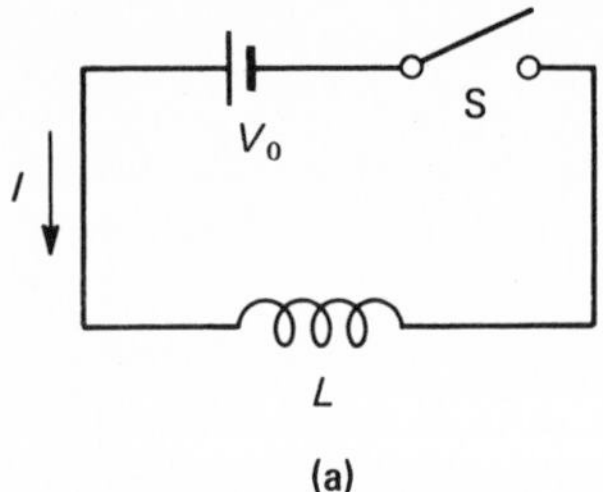

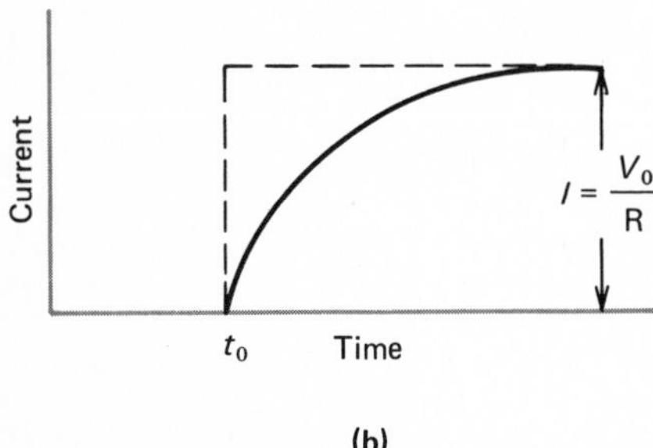

FIG. 17.13 The effect of self-inductance.

By comparison of Eq. (17.11-2) and Eq. (17.10-3), we see that self-inductance, like mutual inductance, may be measured in henries and that a coil has a self-inductance of one henry if an emf of one volt is induced in it when the current through it is changing at the rate of one ampere per second. Since every current produces a magnetic field, every electrical circuit possesses self-inductance.

One interesting consequence of self-inductance is that instantaneous changes of current are impossible. Suppose that the switch in the circuit of Fig. 17.13a is closed. Were it not for the self-inductance of the coil, the current would immediately reach the value V_0/R, where V_0 is the emf of the battery and R is the resistance of the circuit. Under these circumstances, the current would behave as shown in the dashed line of Fig. 17.13b, in which t_0 indicates the time at which the switch is closed. But this is impossible, since the time rate of change of current at t_0 would be infinite. If the current increases at a rate dI/dt, the induced electromotive force is

$$\mathscr{E} = -L\, dI/dt.$$

In accordance with Lenz' law, this electromotive force opposes the change of current. Hence, the net electromotive force in the circuit is $V_0 - \mathscr{E}$, and the current is

$$I = (V_0 - \mathscr{E})/R = V_0/R - (L/R)(dI/dt).$$

At the instant of closing the switch, I is zero, so the initial rate of change of current is

$$(dI/dt)_0 = V_0/L. \tag{17.11-3}$$

This is clearly the maximum rate at which the current can change. As I increases, its rate of change must decrease, finally becoming zero when $I = V_0/R$. Hence, the actual behavior of the current is that shown by the solid line in Fig. 17.13b. The time taken for the current to reach its full value becomes very great if the circuit has a large self-inductance.

A similar effect takes place when current flowing through a self-inductance is interrupted. For example, if the switch of Fig. 17.13a is opened after it has been closed for some time, the current decreases rapidly. This rapid change of current leads to an electromotive force $-LdI/dt$, in such a direction that it tends to maintain the current. If the change is sudden, as by the opening of a switch, the induced voltage may be many times that of the battery supplying the current. This large voltage may cause a spark to jump across the partially open switch and, if the initial current is large and the self-inductance high, this spark may be sufficient to melt some of the metal or do other damage.

EXERCISES

17.11-1 The two coils considered in the derivation of Eq. (17.10-5) are so mounted that the large coil can carry a current supplied by a battery, and the small coil is connected to a voltmeter of very high resistance. If the current in the large coil is being increased at the rate of 2.00 A/sec, what will be the reading of the voltmeter? Take these values as the constants of the coils:

$$a = 0.75\ \text{cm}; \qquad b = 10.0\ \text{cm}; \qquad N = 50; \qquad n = 200.$$

17.11-2 If the small coil in Ex. 17.11-1 has a resistance of 200 Ω and the voltmeter is replaced by one of 100 Ω resistance, what will the reading of the meter be, assuming all other conditions to be the same as in Ex. 17.11-1?

17.11-3 Show that the time taken for the current of Fig. 17.13 to reach its full value is greater than L/R.

17.11-4 Show that the total magnetic flux passing through a long solenoid is

$$\Phi = \pi a^2 \mu_0 NI/l,$$

where a is the radius of the solenoid, l is its length, N is the number of turns, and I is the current. Hence, show that the emf induced in the solenoid when the current is changing at a rate dI/dt is

$$V = -(\pi a^2 \mu_0 N^2/l)(dI/dt)$$

and that the self-inductance of the solenoid is

$$L = \pi a^2 \mu_0 N^2/l.$$

17.12 Inductances Carrying Alternating Currents

We saw in the preceding section that a changing current in any inductive circuit causes an emf that opposes the change. If a steady voltage is applied to such a circuit, the effect of the inductance is manifested only while the current is building up or decaying, and we have seen that the eventual steady value of the current depends only on the resistance of the circuit. If an alternating voltage such as that shown in Fig. 17.10 is applied, a very different state of affairs exists. Under these conditions the emf is continually changing, so the current will also be continually changing. Hence, the inductance will always affect the current.

Suppose that a coil, whose self-inductance is L and whose resistance is so small that its effect is negligible, carries an alternating current of instantaneous value I given by (cf. Eq. 17.9-1)

$$I = I_0 \sin \omega t. \tag{17.12-1}$$

Since this current is continually changing, an electromotive force $V = -LdI/dt$ will be induced in the coil. From Eq. (I.3) of Appendix I, we see that the time rate of change of the current is

$$(dI/dt) = \omega I_0 \cos \omega t.$$

Substitution of this value into the expression for V shows that

$$V = -\omega L I_0 \cos \omega t.$$

This equation gives the value of the emf induced in the coil. In order to maintain the current, an external voltage equal and opposite to this must be supplied by the alternator. Hence, the voltage that must be applied to the coil is

$$V' = -V = \omega L I_0 \cos \omega t. \tag{17.12-2}$$

In Fig. 17.14, the solid line shows the way in which the current through an inductance varies with time. The dotted line shows the variation of the voltage across the inductance. It is notable that the current and voltage do not pass

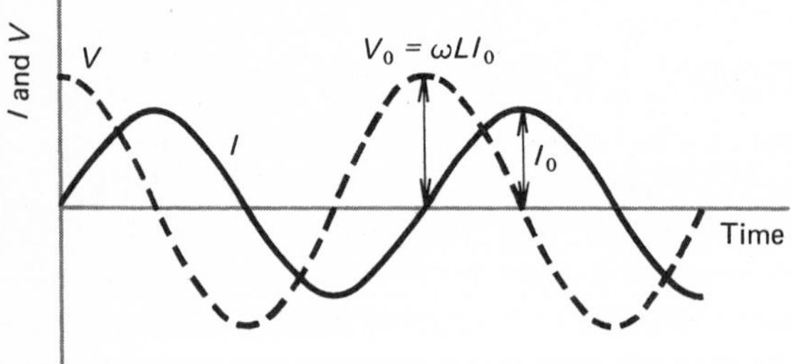

FIG. 17.14 Relation between the current in and the voltage across an inductance.

through their maxima at the same time, the maximum of the current occurring one quarter of a period later than the maximum of the voltage. We therefore say that the current through an inductance ***lags*** behind the voltage by 90° ($\pi/2$ radians). By comparison of Eqs. (17.12-1) and (17.12-2), we see that the ratio of the amplitudes of the voltage and current is

$$V_0'/I_0 = \omega L.$$

In the discussion above, we have not taken into account any resistance in the circuit. Had we done so, we should have recognized that an additional voltage

$$V'' = I_0 R \sin \omega t$$

would be required to overcome the potential drop across the resistance. For many inductances, however, ωL is so much larger than R that the effect of the latter may be neglected in a qualitative examination of the phenomena taking place, we shall temporarily limit ourselves to instances in which this condition is satisfied.

We shall return to the behavior of alternating current circuits that contain inductances and/or capacitances in Chapter 22, after we have laid the groundwork for a much more detailed discussion than we could use here.

17.13 The Transformer

One of the most useful applications of electromagnetic induction is the transformer. A simple ***transformer*** is shown schematically in Fig. 17.15. Two coils, each consisting of many turns of wire, are wound on a closed ***core*** of iron or

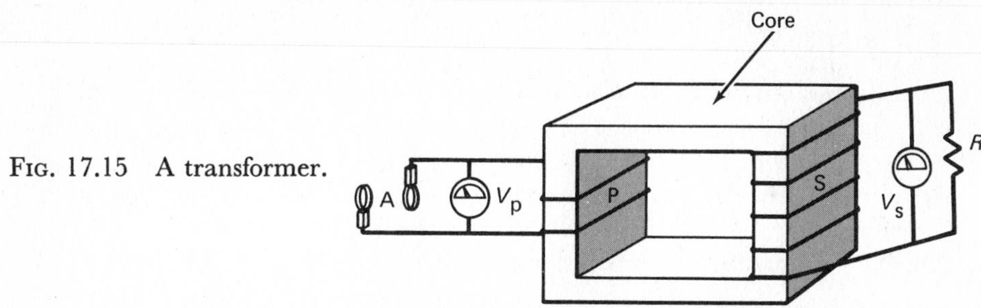

FIG. 17.15 A transformer.

other ferromagnetic material. One of these coils P, known as the ***primary***, is connected to a source of alternating current, such as the alternator A. The other coil S, called the ***secondary***, is connected to the resistance R or to any other electrical device to which an alternating current is to be supplied. When there is a sinusoidal alternating current in the primary, a sinusoidally varying magnetic flux is established in the core. Since the permeability of the core is much higher than that of the surroundings, practically no flux escapes from it, i.e., nearly all of the flux produced by the current in the primary passes through the secondary. Because this flux varies with time, an emf is induced in the secondary, and this emf may be used to pass a current through the ***load*** R.

There is a simple relation between the primary voltage V_p and the secondary voltage V_s. To show this, notice that the same flux links each coil. In accordance with Eq. (17.7-1), the emf induced in the primary by a time rate of change of flux $\Delta\Phi/\Delta t$ is

$$-V_p = -N_p \, \Delta\Phi/\Delta t,$$

where N_p is the number of turns in the primary. At the same time, the emf induced in the secondary is

$$V_s = -N_s \Delta\Phi/\Delta t,$$

where N_s is the number of turns in the secondary. In order that the current may be maintained in the primary, it is necessary that the alternator maintain a potential difference V_p equal and opposite to the emf induced in the primary. Hence, by comparison of the two induction equations, we find that

$$V_s/V_p = -N_s/N_p. \tag{17.13-1}$$

In this treatment, we have, of course, neglected the resistances of the two windings. To the extent that these resistances can be neglected, Eq. (17.13-1) shows that the voltage that appears across the secondary has at every moment a magnitude N_s/N_p times the voltage impressed on the primary. The ratio of these two voltages is known as the ***voltage ratio*** of the transformer.

The law of the conservation of energy tells us that the total energy delivered by the secondary of a transformer must be equal to or less than the energy supplied to the primary. We are therefore sure that the current in the secondary circuit must be lower than that in the primary if the voltage ratio of the transformer is greater than unity.

The transformer that we have discussed is a highly idealized one in which the flux linkage is perfect and the resistance of the coils negligible. In actual transformers these conditions are never perfectly satisfied, but in a well-designed transformer the error in Eq. (17.13-1) is small.

The availability of the transformer to change the voltage at which alternating current power is delivered allows great flexibility in alternating current circuits. The existence of this device is, in fact, the major reason for the wide use of alternating currents in preference to direct currents.

EXERCISES

17.13-1 The flux in the core of the transformer of Sec. 17.13 (Fig. 17.15) has the magnitude

$$\Phi = \Phi_0 \sin \omega t$$

at any time t. No current flows in the secondary. Show that the primary voltage V_p must be

$$V_p = N_p \omega \Phi_0 \cos \omega t,$$

where N_p is the number of primary turns. (Hint: Refer to Appendix I and to Sec. 17.12, and neglect the resistance of the primary winding.)

17.13-2 Let the self-inductance of the primary of the transformer of Ex. 17.13-1 be L_p. Using the result of that exercise, show that the current in the primary is

$$I_p = (N_p \Phi_0 / L_p) \sin \omega t.$$

Show also that the emf induced in the secondary is

$$V_s = -N_s \omega \Phi_0 \cos \omega t.$$

Finally, using the definition of mutual inductance and the results of Appendix I, show that the mutual inductance of the two coils is

$$M = L_p(N_s/N_p).$$

17.14 Summary

This chapter has been devoted to the interactions between electrical circuits and magnetic fields. Two basic effects have been studied. The first is the existence of a force on a current flowing in a magnetic field; the second is the production of an electromotive force in any circuit when the magnetic flux through that circuit changes. These two effects are important in the design of electrical machines such as the generator, the motor, and the transformer. Our study of some of these devices has led us into a preliminary discussion of the characteristics of alternating currents.

PROBLEMS

17.1 In a ***cathode ray tube*** (***CRT***) a beam of electrons, each moving with the same speed v_0, enters the region between two parallel plates of metal. The electrons are initially moving parallel to the plates, and the point at which they enter is halfway between the two plates. The length of the plates, in a direction parallel to the beam, is L. A potential difference V is applied between the two plates, which are separated by a distance w.

(a) Sketch the arrangement, showing the trajectory of the electrons. (b) Show that the electrons will strike the plate that is at positive potential if

$$L^2 > mv_0{}^2w/eV,$$

where e is the electronic charge and m is the electronic mass.

17.2 Suppose that the length of the plates in the CRT is less than that calculated in Prob. 17.1 (a) Show that the time taken by any electron in passing the plates is independent of V and is equal to L/v_0. (b) Show that the electron beam will leave the region between the plates moving in a direction at an angle θ with its original direction, such that

$$\tan\theta = eVL/mv_0{}^2 \approx \theta,$$

where the final approximate equality is obtained by setting $\tan\theta \approx \theta$ (see Appendix G.2).

17.3 A beam of electrons, each moving with a velocity $\vec{v}$, enters a region of space in which there is a magnetic field of flux density $\vec{B}$. The velocity makes an angle θ with $\vec{B}$. Show that the following statements are true.

(a) The electrons will follow a helical path, the radius of the helix being

$$r = mv\sin\theta/eB.$$

(b) The time taken to complete one turn of the helix is

$$t = 2\pi m/eB,$$

where e is the electronic charge and m is the electronic mass.

(c) The ***pitch*** of the helix, i.e., the distance along the helical axis between successive turns, is

$$d = 2\pi mv\cos\theta/eB = 2\pi m\vec{v}\cdot\vec{B}/eB^2.$$

17.4 A beam of electrons is produced by thermionic emission from a cathode. A positive metal plate near the cathode has a circular hole in it, so that the beam that emerges has the shape of a circular cylinder of radius R. The current is i.

(a) Show that the average number of electrons per unit volume within the beam is

$$n = i/\pi evR^2,$$

where v is the speed of the electrons.

(b) Find the direction and magnitude of the electric field at the outer surface of the beam.

(c) Show that the electrons will not remain in a circular beam of radius R. In particular, show that each electron at the surface of the cylinder is subject to an outward acceleration equal to $ei/2\pi Rvm\epsilon_0$.

17.5 Our treatment of the apparatus shown in Fig. 17.6 assumed that all electrons emerging from S_2 were moving in a direction perpendicular to the plate that contains S_2 and S_3. In practice, the electrons coming through S_2 will emerge at small angles to the normal to the plate. Consider three electrons, one moving along the normal and the others making angles $\pm\alpha$ with it. Draw a top view of the electron paths to scale, choosing ρ to have any convenient value. Take $\tan\alpha = 0.20$ ($\alpha \approx 12°$). By scaling your drawing, show that all three electrons will pass through S_3 if this slit has a width equal to 0.1ρ. (This phenomenon of ***electron focusing*** makes the e/m apparatus practical, because it insures that an appreciable fraction of the electron current through S_2 shall also pass through S_3 when ρ and B are properly adjusted.)

17.6 The apparatus shown in Fig. 17.6 is so adjusted that electrons are detected when $V = 1000$ V, $\rho = 2.50$ cm and $B = 4.26 \times 10^{-3}$ Wb/m^2. According to Eq. (17.4-1), a change to $V = 1.00 \times 10^5$ V should require that B be increased to 4.26×10^{-2} Wb/m^2.

(a) Show that relativistic effects will increase this value of B.

(b) Find the appropriate value of B when $V = 1.00 \times 10^5$ V.

17.7 In the discussion of search coils in Sec.17.7, it was suggested that a galvanometer could be used to measure the total charge moved by the change of magnetic field. A galvanometer used in this way is known as a ***ballistic galvanometer***. When a galvanometer is used ballistically, the entire charge q is passed through its coil in a very short time interval, so short that the coil does not have time to rotate appreciably until the current has dropped to zero. Hence there is no appreciable restoring torque during the passage of the charge. Under these circumstances, show that

(a) The coil will acquire an angular momentum

$$M\omega_0 = NABq,$$

while the charge passes. Here M is the moment of inertia. (Start from the equation for the torque, $T = NABI$, from Sec. 16.13.)

(b) The kinetic energy of the coil as it starts to move is $N^2A^2B^2q^2/2M$.

(c) When the coil has lost all its kinetic energy, the maximum deflection will be

$$\theta_m = NABq/\sqrt{Mk_T}.$$

17.8 Suppose that an electron is moving in a circular orbit of radius r with an angular velocity ω, as in Probs. 15.7 and 16.9. At time $t = 0$ a magnetic field is turned on, in a direction perpendicular to the orbit. The flux density is increased from zero to some value B during a short time, t. The sense of the field is opposite to that of the magnetic field produced by the revolving electron.

(a) Show that the induced emf around the electron orbit as the field is being built up is $\mathscr{E} = \pi r^2(dB/dt)$.

(b) Supposing r to change very little during this time, show that total energy of the electron changes from $-\frac{1}{2}mr^2\omega^2$ to

$$-\tfrac{1}{2}mr^2\omega^2 + \tfrac{1}{2}er^2\omega B$$

(c) Find the kinetic energy of the electron when the field has attained its full value.

(d) Show that the final angular velocity, Ω, is such that

$$\Omega^2 = \frac{r^2}{R^2}(\omega^2 - e\omega B/m),$$

where R is the new radius of the orbit.

17.9 In Sec. 17.9 we used the fact that the average value of $\sin^2\theta$ over a full cycle is $\frac{1}{2}$. (a) Starting from the definition

$$\overline{\sin^2\theta} = \frac{\int_0^{2\pi}\sin^2\theta\,d\theta}{\int_0^{2\pi}d\theta}$$

and remembering that

$$\cos 2\theta = \cos^2\theta - \sin^2\theta = 1 - 2\sin^2\theta,$$

show that $\overline{\sin^2\theta} = \frac{1}{2}$. (b) Obtain the same result without formal integration. First note that

$$\int_0^{2\pi}\sin^2\theta\,d\theta = \int_0^{2\pi}(1-\cos^2\theta)\,d\theta = 2\pi - \int_0^{2\pi}\cos^2\theta\,d\theta$$

and hence that

$$\int_0^{2\pi}\sin^2\theta\,d\theta + \int_0^{2\pi}\cos^2\theta\,d\theta = 2\pi.$$

Notice further that

$$\sin^2\theta + \cos^2\theta = 1$$

and therefore that $\overline{\sin^2\theta} = \frac{1}{2}$.

17.10 In Ex. 17.11-3 it was shown that the time taken for the current to rise to its final value in the inductive circuit of Fig. 17.13 is greater than L/R. A more exact description of the rise of current may be obtained as follows:

(a) From energy conservation, show that

$$-\frac{R\,dI}{V_0 - IR} = -\frac{R}{L}\,dt.$$

(b) Using the fact that

$$\int (dx/x) = \ln x,$$

where $\ln x$ is the natural logarithm of x, show that

$$\ln(V_0 - IR) = -(R/L)t + \ln V_0$$

and hence that

$$I = (V_0/R)(1 - e^{-Rt/L}),$$

where e is the base of natural logarithms ($e = 2.71828\ldots$).

(c) Compute I at various times between 0.00 sec and 2.00 sec for $V_0 = 10.0$ V, $R = 5.00\ \Omega$, and $L = 2.50$ H, and plot a curve of I vs. t.

17.11 (To be done after Prob. 17.10 has been completed.) Suppose that the switch S_2 of the curcuit shown in the figure is open and that the switch S_1 has been closed for a sufficiently long time so that a steady current I_0 $(=V_0/R_1)$ has been established. At $t=0$ the switch S_2 is closed. The coil labeled L, R may be considered to possess an inductance L in series with a resistance R.

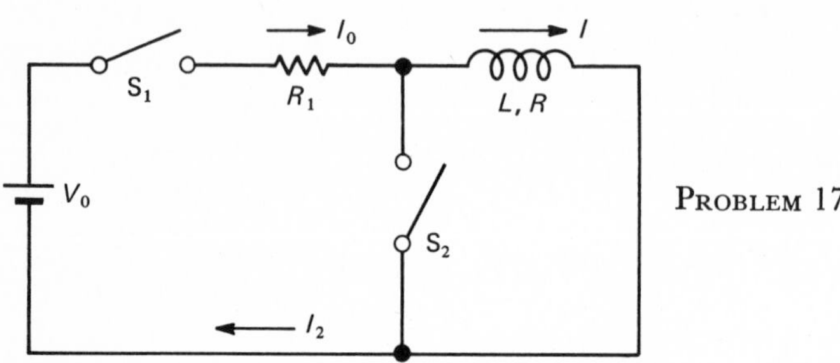

PROBLEM 17.11

(a) What is the current (I) in the coil immediately after S_2 is closed. (b) Show that $I = I_0 e^{-Rt/L}$. (c) What current (L_2) is present in the resistor R_1 after S_2 is closed? (d) What current is present in the switch S_2 at time t after the switch is closed?

17.12 A capacitor of capacitance C is connected to an alternator that maintains a potential difference

$$V = V_0 \sin \omega t$$

across its terminals. Starting from Eq. (16.22-3), (a) Find the magnitude of the charge Q on either plate of the capacitor as a function of time; (b) show that a current

$$I = \omega C V_0 \cos \omega t$$

will be supplied by the alternator.

17.13 (To be done after Probs. 17.10 and 17.12 have been completed.) A capacitor of capacitance C is connected in series with a battery that maintains a constant potential difference V_0 across its terminals, a switch, and a resistor of resistance R. Before time $t=0$, the switch is open and the capacitor carries no charge. At that time the switch is closed.

(a) Show that the charge (Q) on the capacitor varies with time in accordance with the relation

$$Q = CV_0(1 - e^{-t/RC}).$$

(b) Plot a curve of Q vs. t for the interval 0.00 sec to 0.50 sec if $C = 1.00\mu$ F, $R = 10^5\ \Omega$, and $V_0 = 1.60$ V.

17.14 (a) Express the current in the secondary of the idealized transformer of Fig. 17.15 in terms of V_s and R.

(b) At what instantaneous rate is energy being delivered to R?

(c) Neglecting all energy losses, express the current (I_p) in the primary in terms of N_p, N_s, R, and V_p.

(d) Show that the ***input resistance*** of the transformer, defined as V_p/I_p is

$$R_i = RN_p^2/N_s^2.$$

REFERENCES

17A David L. Anderson, *The Discovery of the Electron* (Momentum Book No. 3), Van Nostrand, Princeton, 1964. A good account of the birth of a major idea.

17B William Francis Magie, *A Source Book of Physics*, Harvard, Cambridge, Mass., 1963. Various aspects of the historical development are covered in pp. 436–460, 472–492, and 511–519.

17C Morris Shamos, editor, *Great Experiment in Physics*, Holt, New York, 1960. Pages 128–148 deal with the work of Michael Faraday.

17D Brian J. O'Brien, "Radiation Belts," *Scientific American*, May 1963, pp. 84–96. Effects of the earth's magnetic field on charged particles.

17E Forest I. Boley, *Plasmas—Laboratory and Cosmic* (Momentum Book No. 11), Van Nostrand, Princeton, 1966. The behavior of ionized gases in electric and magnetic fields.

17F Syun-Ichi Akasofu, "The Aurora," *Scientific American*, December 1965, pp. 28–36.

17G Noel C. Little, *Magnetohydrodynamics* (Momentum Book No. 18), Van Nostrand, Princeton, 1967. A different approach to the phenomena discussed in Reference 17E.

18 ⮕ *Molecules and Atoms*

18.1 Historical Background of Atomic Theories

We must now consider in some detail a question that occurred to early philosophers. If a material body were divided into smaller and smaller pieces, could the process be continued indefinitely or would there eventually be found a smallest particle that could not be divided—at least one that could not be divided without altering the characteristics of the substance? In the preceding chapters, we have been concerned mainly with the properties of matter in the bulk, and this question of ultimate particles has not been of interest. The behavior of planets, cars, balls, and metal rods, which we have studied, might be the same whether or not they could be continuously subdivided. The answer to our question about the constitution of matter can be found by appeal to experiments for which different results are predicted on the assumptions that matter can be continuously subdivided or that it is atomic in nature.

While the idea of atomicity is an ancient one, the first modern support is found in the work of the chemists of the eighteenth and nineteenth centuries. In our discussion, we shall depart considerably from the historical development of atomic theory, so we shall mention here those who contributed most to its growth—Robert Boyle (1627–1691), Joseph Priestley (1733–1804), Antoine Lavoisier (1743–1794), John Dalton (1766–1844), Amadeo Avogadro (1776–1856), Joseph Gay-Lussac (1778–1850), and Stanislaus Cannizzarro (1826–1910).

18.2 Homogeneity and Heterogeneity

If we examine a rock, a piece of wood, or the sand on an ocean beach, it is easy to see that those things each consist of a number of different materials. We say that anything that is made up of different materials is ***heterogeneous*** (Greek: *heteros*, different; *genos*, kind). On the other hand, in a glass of water, in the glass itself, in a diamond, or in a pail of fresh milk, every part is apparently quite the same as every other part. If every part of a material is the same as every other part, we say that the material is ***homogeneous*** (Greek: *homos*, same).

The term homogeneous is only applicable with reference to a particular method of observation. A drop of water on a microscope slide may appear to be perfectly homogeneous to the naked eye but heterogeneously teeming with microorganisms under the microscope. The heterogeneity of milk that has not been homogenized may be demonstrated by letting it stand; the cream will rise to the top.

But we can say that any heterogeneous system consists of a number of homogeneous parts, or ***phases.*** Since any heterogeneous system is more complicated than any one of its homogeneous phases, we must study the homogeneous phases to understand the simple substances of nature. Thus, we shall confine our attention to ***optically homogeneous materials***—those that appear to be homogeneous under the most powerful microscopes that we possess.

18.3 Fractionation Methods

Let us suppose that a homogeneous substance to be investigated is a liquid. We can cool it until some of the liquid solidifies and we can strain the solid which first forms from the remaining liquid. We can then warm the solid until it reliquifies and heat the two liquids to the same temperature. If we compare the two fractions into which the original liquid has been separated, we shall find that they possess either the same or different physical properties—melting points, boiling points, densities, color, etc. If the physical properties turn out to be different, we necessarily infer that the original liquid consisted of at least two components so intimately mixed that they could not be optically distinguished. This process of partial ***fractionation*** of the mixture into its separate components has been brought about by partial freezing or by ***fractional crystallization.***

We can also heat a liquid until it commences to boil, collecting and recondensing the first vapor which comes off; the distilled liquid and the residual liquid will again show different physical properties if the original liquid consisted of two components. A partial separation by this method is called ***fractional distillation.***

There are other methods for the fractional separation of two components of a liquid or a gas, but the foregoing examples will serve to illustrate the general idea.

18.4 Pure Substances

Some substances completely resist our attempts to separate them into parts by any of the fractionation methods which we have listed above. We assume that these substances consist of only one kind of material, but we make the reservation that different methods may show us that even these substances consist of more than one component.

Substances that cannot be separated into components by any known fractionation method are called ***pure substances.*** This definition has meaning only in terms of the fractionation methods. We shall now discuss the relation of pure substances to chemical reactions.

18.5 Chemical Reactions and the Law of Definite Proportions

Zinc and sulfur are pure substances in accordance with the definition of the preceding section. If small particles of these two substances are mixed in a test tube and the test tube is heated, a relatively violent reaction takes place. A new substance, which differs entirely from zinc and sulfur, appears. A considerable amount of sulfur mixed with a little zinc results in the new substance with some sulfur left over; or, alternatively, excess zinc and little sulfur will produce the new substance intermixed with unchanged zinc.

If we take zinc and sulfur in the proportion 2 : 1 by weight (more exactly, 65.38 : 32.06), the new substance will be very pure; in its formation both the zinc and the sulfur will have completely disappeared. We can say, therefore, that zinc and sulfur have combined to form zinc sulfide, a substance which is pure in accordance with the definition of the preceding section.

There are many other reactions of the type just described, in which two pure substances combine to form a third pure substance. Hydrogen and oxygen combine to form water, hydrogen and chlorine to form hydrochloric acid, and iron and oxygen to form ferric oxide (rust). Such combinations of two or more pure substances to form a new pure substance are ***chemical reactions***, and the resulting pure substance is a ***chemical compound***.

In all chemical reactions, the initial substances always combine in a definite proportion when they form a third pure substance. We can represent such a reaction by the scheme

$$A + B \longrightarrow C. \tag{18.5-1}$$

We observe that if A, B, and C are all pure substances and m_a, m_b, and m_c are the respective masses involved in the reaction, then m_a/m_b is always a constant ratio for the formation of a given C. Incidentally, we can also verify the law of conservation of mass for the reaction by weighing the substances; thus,

$$m_a + m_b = m_c. \tag{18.5-2}$$

It follows from Eq. (18.5-2) that m_a/m_c and m_b/m_c must also be in constant ratios for a given reaction.

There is another type of chemical reaction in which a single pure substance can be made to break up into two pure substances. Mercuric oxide is a pure substance and, if it is heated, it releases oxygen gas, a pure substance. The liquid metal mercury which is left behind is also a pure substance. This ***decomposition*** can be represented as

$$A \longrightarrow B + C. \tag{18.5-3}$$

As before, we find that m_b/m_c, m_a/m_b, and m_a/m_c are all constant for a given decomposition and that

$$m_a = m_b + m_c. \tag{18.5-4}$$

Of the many other types of chemical reactions, we shall consider only the one in which two pure substances react to form two different pure substances. For example, zinc and sulfuric acid combine to form hydrogen and zinc sulfate. The reaction scheme is

$$A + B \longrightarrow C + D \tag{18.5-5}$$

and the ratio of the mass of any one constituent of this reaction to that of any other is always the same in any instance when this reaction takes place. In our example, 65.38 g of zinc will combine with 98.08 g of sulfuric acid to make 2.02 g of hydrogen and 161.44 g of zinc sulfate. If we increase the proportion of zinc, some of it will be left over when the reaction is completed, or if we increase the proportion of sulfuric acid, some of it will be left over. Reactions represented by Eq. (18.5-5) are called ***displacement reactions.***

We can now state the ***law of definite proportions*** as an experimental result: *If one or more pure substances enter into a chemical reaction with the production of one or more pure substances, none of the original substances remaining, then the proportions by mass of all participants in the reaction have definite values that are characteristic of the reaction.*

18.6 Elements and Compounds

Of all pure substances there are those which contain only one constituent and those which contain more than one. Those substances that contain only one constituent are called ***elements***, and those pure substances that contain more than one are ***compounds.***

Iron, sulfur, zinc, copper, and mercury are some examples of elements. No chemical reaction has ever been found which will decompose these elements or any other element into simpler constituents. An element has only itself as a constituent. In Chapter 19 we shall see that by using very high energies it is possible to change or transmute one element into another. For the time being, we may take the foregoing definition of element as satisfactory; when we have studied transmutations, it will be easy to distinguish between them and chemical processes.

There are 92 elements that occur naturally on the earth, and these have all been identified beyond any reasonable doubt. These elements are tabulated in various arrangements in Table 21.1 and in Appendix J. In addition, as we shall see in Chapter 19, nuclear physics and technology have succeeded in making about a dozen other elements which are radioactive with short half-lives and which do not occur naturally at present on the earth. Some of them, however, have been detected in spectral studies of the light from novae (stars that greatly increase their energy output for a short time in what is apparently a stellar nuclear explosion), so it will not do to say that these other elements are strictly artificial.

Many thousands of compounds can be formed from the known elements. The detailed study of all possible compounds constitutes the science of chemistry.

18.7 The Law of Multiple Proportions

It is often found that two elements combine in several different ways. Carbon and oxygen unite under certain circumstances to form the poisonous gas carbon monoxide, whereas under other circumstances they form carbon dioxide. If we prepare pure samples of these two gases and analyze them, we find that the ratio of oxygen to carbon in carbon monoxide is 1.331 by weight, where as in carbon dioxide the ratio is 2.662, exactly twice that for carbon monoxide. Oxygen also forms two compounds with hydrogen. In water, the ratio of oxygen to hydrogen is found to be 7.94, and in hydrogen peroxide the ratio is 15.87, exactly twice that for water.

The compounds of nitrogen with oxygen are interesting. They are listed in Table 18.1 together with their oxygen-nitrogen ratios. All of these ratios are

Table 18.1 *The Oxides of Nitrogen*

Name	Ratio (m_{O}/m_{N})
Nitrous oxide	$0.57 = 1 \times 0.57$
Nitric oxide	$1.14 = 2 \times 0.57$
Nitrogen trioxide	$1.71 = 3 \times 0.57$
Nitrogen peroxide	$2.28 = 4 \times 0.57$
Nitrogen pentoxide	$2.85 = 5 \times 0.57$

simply related to one another. They are whole number or integral multiples of the ratio for nitrous oxide.

From these and many other similar results, we can enunciate the ***law of multiple proportions*** as follows: *If two elements* A *and* B *combine to form a number of different compounds, the ratio of the mass of* A *to that of* B *for any compound will always be simply related to the corresponding ratio for any other compound of the same two elements.* By a simple relation, we mean that one ratio will be a whole number multiple of the other, or a fractional multiple in which the fraction has small whole numbers as numerator and denominator. Thus, the oxygen-nitrogen ratio for nitrogen pentoxide is $\frac{5}{4}$ that for nitrogen peroxide, and $\frac{5}{3}$ that for nitrogen trioxide.

18.8 The Atomic Hypothesis

We can interpret the results of the last section by considering a simple example. Suppose we examine a number of cups of coffee. We find no sugar in some of them. In some, careful analysis shows us that a mass of 3.00 g is present; in others we find 6.00 g and 9.00 g, and in exceptional cases 15.00 or 18.00 g. In each case, we find a whole number multiple of 3.00 g. We must infer that the persons who put the sugar in the coffee used spoons which would hold exactly 3.00 g, or, more probably, that the sugar came in lumps each of mass 3.00 g.

It is reasonable to conclude then that elements occur in small indivisible units called atoms. We define an ***atom*** of an element as the smallest amount of that element which possesses all the properties of that element. We can then explain the law of multiple proportions in terms of an atomic theory by saying that *in the formation of any compound, a whole number of atoms of one element combines with a whole number of atoms of another element.* The entity formed by atoms of each of two or more elements, bound together to form a compound, is the smallest entity that possesses all the properties of the compound. We call this entity the ***molecule*** of the compound.

With the aid of the assumptions of the present section, we can determine the mass of the atom of one element in terms of the mass of another with which it combines. We arbitrarily define an ***atomic mass unit*** (amu) as exactly one-twelfth of the mass of an atom of the most common isotope of carbon, $_6C^{12}$ (cf. Sec. 19.4). We then define the ***atomic mass*** of an element as the mass of an atom of the element expressed in atomic mass units. In a similar way, the ***molecular mass*** may be defined and expressed in atomic mass units.*

Now examine the oxides of nitrogen and assume that each of the five molecules listed in Table 18.1 contains the same number of nitrogen atoms and that the first of these contains one atom of oxygen, the second two, etc., as indicated in Table 18.2. Using the values of the oxygen-nitrogen ratio from Table 18.1 for each of these five oxides, we predict the presence of 28.02 amu of nitrogen. A nitrogen atom must therefore have a mass of 28.02 amu or some integral submultiple of this quantity. We may also predict the molecular weights for these compounds as indicated in the sixth column of the table. These molecular masses can be measured by other methods, and the results are given in the seventh column of the table. We see that the predicted result for nitrous oxide is verified by experiment. That for nitric oxide is, however, twice too large. In a similar way, we find that the predicted value of the molecular mass for nitrogen peroxide is also twice too large, while those for nitrogen trioxide and nitrogen pentoxide check with the measured values.

Table 18.2 *Trial Formulas for the Oxides of Nitrogen*

Name	Oxygen		Ratio (m_O/m_N)	Nitrogen Mass (amu)	Molecular Mass (amu)	
	No. of Atoms	Mass (amu)			Predicted	Measured
Nitrous oxide	1	16.00	0.57	28.02	44.02	44.02
Nitric oxide	2	32.00	1.14	28.02	60.02	30.01
Nitrogen trioxide	3	48.00	1.71	28.02	76.02	76.02
Nitrogen peroxide	4	64.00	2.28	28.02	92.02	46.01
Nitrogen pentoxide	5	80.00	2.85	28.02	108.02	108.02

The failure of two of the predictions of Table 18.2 is typical of many troubles that were encountered in the early studies of the structure of chemical compounds and in the evaluation of the relative masses of atoms. It will readily be seen that these false predictions result from the assumption that each of the nitrogen oxides contains the same number of atoms of nitrogen. If we abandon this assumption, we can construct Table 18.3. The second and third columns of that table give the assumed number of oxygen and nitrogen atoms in a molecule. The fourth column represents these numbers in another way. If we represent an atom of oxygen by the symbol O and one of nitrogen by the symbol N, we may

* The more usual terms, atomic weight and molecular weight, are ambiguous, since weight refers to the gravitational force acting on a given mass.

use the symbol NO to represent a molecule containing one atom of each of these two elements. Similarly, we can represent a molecule which contains more than a single atom of a given element by using a subscript following the symbol for that element to denote the number of atoms of the element which enter into the molecule. Thus, N_2O represents a molecule which contains two atoms of nitrogen and one of oxygen, while N_2O_5 represents a molecule containing two nitrogen and five oxygen atoms. The fifth column of the table shows the predicted molecular mass of each of the nitrogen oxides, based on the new assumptions as to the number of atoms and on an atomic mass of 14.01 amu for N. The predicted molecular mass now checks with the measured mass in all cases.

Table 18.3 *Formulas for the Oxides of Nitrogen*

Name	No. of Atoms		Formula	Molecular Mass	
	Oxygen	Nitrogen		Predicted	Measured
Nitrous oxide	1	2	N_2O	44.02	44.02
Nitric oxide	1	1	NO	30.01	30.01
Nitrogen trioxide	3	2	N_2O_3	76.02	76.02
Nitrogen peroxide	2	1	NO_2	46.01	46.01
Nitrogen pentoxide	5	2	N_2O_5	108.02	108.02

In the compounds of carbon and oxygen referred to at the beginning of Sec. 18.7, the values of the molecular weights and of the oxygen-carbon ratios indicate that the atomic mass of carbon (C) must be 12.01 amu, with the formula CO for carbon monoxide and CO_2 for carbon dioxide (Ex. 18.9-1).

In a similar way, we can show that the atomic mass of hydrogen (H) must be 1.008 amu and that the formulas for water and hydrogen peroxide must be H_2O and H_2O_2, respectively.

By arguments such as those used above, it is possible to determine the atomic masses in mass units of all but a few of the known elements. The results of these determinations are given in Appendix J. The symbols by means of which the atoms of a given element are represented are also listed in this appendix.

In defining an atom we have said that it is the smallest particle that shows all the properties of a given element. The evidence considered thus far does not tell us whether all the atoms of a given element are identical in all respects—e.g., in mass. We shall find in Sec. 19.4 that atoms with identical chemical properties may indeed have different masses. Thus, there are three different known types of hydrogen atoms, with masses of approximately 1, 2, and 3 amu. The atomic masses found by the methods we have outlined are therefore average atomic masses. The fact that quite exact values may be found for these averages indicates that very large numbers of atoms enter into any chemical reaction which we may study by weighing the materials involved and that the relative numbers of atoms of different kinds remain constant for different samples. We shall see in Chapter 19 that the masses of the various types of individual atoms may be compared by means other than those of chemistry. The measurements made by these means confirm the conclusions reached in this section with regard to the average relative masses of the atoms of each element.

18.9 Some Chemical Equations

It is obviously impossible in a textbook of physics to give more than a very sketchy account of some of the closely related results of chemistry. There are a few facts, however, which we shall need in future discussion.

First, many of the elements do not occur normally as isolated atoms in pure form, but two or more of these atoms of the same kind are combined to form a molecule of the element. Thus, the molecule of hydrogen is H_2, that for oxygen is O_2, and the molecule of sulfur in the usual solid form is S_8.

Second, in some of the reactions we have discussed, more than one molecule of a kind takes part. For example, two molecules of hydrogen (H_2) combine with one of oxygen (O_2) to produce two molecules of water vapor (H_2O). In representing such a reaction in an equation, it is desirable that we indicate each atom in a kind of inventory. Thus, each atom of hydrogen that enters on the left should be accounted for in the products on the right, and so forth for all the kinds of atoms involved. Hence, we write

$$2H_2 + O_2 \rightarrow 2H_2O.$$

The first coefficient "2" shows that two molecules of hydrogen enter into combination with each molecule of oxygen; the coefficient of O_2 is "1." The second coefficient "2" states that two molecules of water vapor result. The coefficients and subscripts, then, indicate that four atoms of hydrogen, paired into two molecules of hydrogen, combine with two atoms of oxygen, paired as one molecule of oxygen, to produce a new grouping of the four hydrogen and two oxygen atoms—namely, two groups or molecules each composed of two atoms of hydrogen and one atom of oxygen.

Earlier, we mentioned the heating of zinc and sulfur in order to form zinc sulfide, and the combining of zinc and dilute sulfuric acid to produce hydrogen and zinc sulfate. Chemical equations to represent these reactions are:

$$8Zn + S_8 \rightarrow 8ZnS$$

and

$$Zn + H_2SO_4 \rightarrow H_2 + ZnSO_4.$$

The reader may verify that the atom inventory is balanced on the two sides of each equation.

EXERCISES

18.9-1 Using the information about the oxides of carbon given at the beginning of Sec. 18.7, and the fact that the molecular weights of carbon monoxide and carbon dioxide are approximately 28 and 44 amu, respectively, prepare a table (similar to

Table 18.3) which shows that the atomic weight of carbon is 12.01 amu and that the formulas for these substances are those given in the text.

18.9-2 In ammonia gas, the ratio of nitrogen to hydrogen is 4.63 by weight and the molecular mass is about 17 amu. What is the formula for the ammonia molecule?

18.9-3 In benzene, the ratio of carbon to hydrogen is 11.91 by weight and the molecular mass is about 78 amu. What is the formula for benzene?

18.9-4 Sodium sulfate is to be prepared according to the reaction:

$$H_2SO_4 + 2NaOH \rightarrow Na_2SO_4 + 2H_2O.$$

How much sulfuric acid (H_2SO_4) and how much sodium hydroxide (NaOH) will be needed to prepare 1.00 kg of sodium sulfate (Na_2SO_4)?

18.9-5 If 2.016 kg of hydrogen occupies a volume of 22.4 m^3 at 0°C and 760 mm pressure, how much zinc and how much sulfuric acid must be provided to prepare 10.0 m^3 of hydrogen at the same pressure and temperature?

18.10 An Electrochemical Reaction

Silver nitrate ($AgNO_3$) is formed when the metal silver (Ag) (Latin: *argentum*) is dissolved in nitric acid. This salt is readily soluble in water. If we pass an electric current through a solution of silver nitrate in water, we find that a remarkable chemical reaction takes place. The experiment is performed with

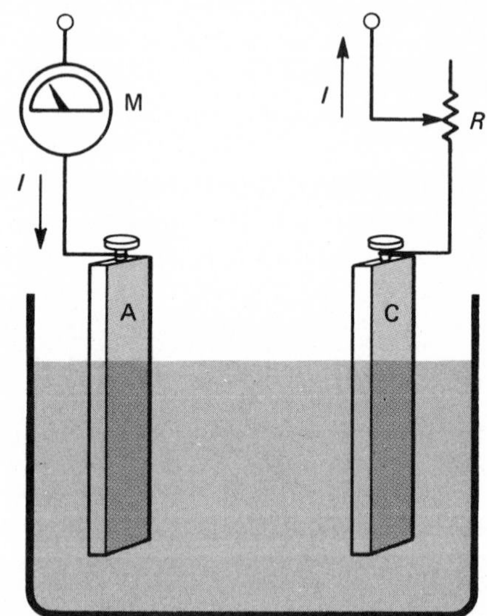

FIG. 18.1 Electrolysis of silver nitrate.

equipment such as that illustrated in Fig. 18.1. Two silver plates A and C, called ***electrodes***, are immersed in a dilute solution of silver nitrate. One of these (A), connected to the positive terminal (+) of an electric machine, is called the ***positive electrode***, or ***anode***. The other (C), connected to the negative terminal of the machine, is called the ***negative electrode***, or ***cathode***. An ammeter M is included in the circuit so that the current I in the circuit can be measured, and a variable resistance R is used to adjust the current to any predetermined value and to maintain it at that value. Suppose now that we carefully determine the masses of the silver electrodes A and C before they are immersed in the solution. We then connect them as shown in Fig. 18.1 and run a constant current I for a definite time t. We then dry the electrodes and redetermine their masses. We find that the mass of the anode has decreased and that the mass of the cathode has increased by exactly the same amount μ_{Ag}. If we repeat this experiment a number of times, changing the size of the electrodes A and C, and also changing I and t, we shall find that μ_{Ag} is independent of the size of the electrodes and depends only on the product of the current by the time; thus,

$$\mu_{Ag} = \varepsilon_{Ag} It, \tag{18.10-1}$$

where ε_{Ag} is a constant. If we repeat the series of experiments described above with electrodes of copper in a solution of copper sulfate, we shall again find proportionality of the mass μ_{Cu} deposited to quantity of electricity It, but the value of the constant ε_{Cu} will be different with copper electrodes from that obtained with silver.

Any chemical process accompanied by observable electrical effects is called an ***electrochemical process***, and in particular, a chemical reaction that is produced by the passage of an electric current through a liquid is called an ***electrolysis***, or an ***electrolytic process***.

There are many electrolytic processes in which two identical metal electrodes are immersed in a solution of a compound of the metal in question. In each of these, Eq. (18.10-1) holds with a value of ε that is typical of the metal in question. A somewhat different type of electrolysis takes place when an electric current is passed through a dilute solution of sulfuric acid (H_2SO_4) in water (H_2O). A three-armed glass tube, with two platinum electrodes (C and A, Fig. 18.2) is typically used in this experiment. When a current I is passed through the solution, with the ammeter M and the resistance R being used to measure and control the current, gases are evolved at the two electrodes. These gases collect in bubbles that rise to the top of each of the two outer tubes. The gas that is evolved at the cathode C and collected at C′ is found to be hydrogen, and the gas evolved at A and collected at A′ is oxygen. These gases can be examined by releasing them through the stopcocks at the top of each of the side tubes of the apparatus. Their masses can be determined by the methods to be discussed in Chapter 20.

It is found that the mass of the oxygen μ_O (evolved at A) and the mass of the hydrogen μ_H (evolved at C) are not equal to one another but that each of these masses is proportional to the quantity of electricity It which has passed through the apparatus. Thus, we have the two equations

$$\mu_H = \varepsilon_H It \qquad \text{and} \qquad \mu_O = \varepsilon_O It.$$

Many other kinds of electrolytic reactions can be carried out, but in all of them it is found that *the mass of any product of an electrochemical reaction is proportional to the total quantity of electricity which has passed through the reacting material.* This

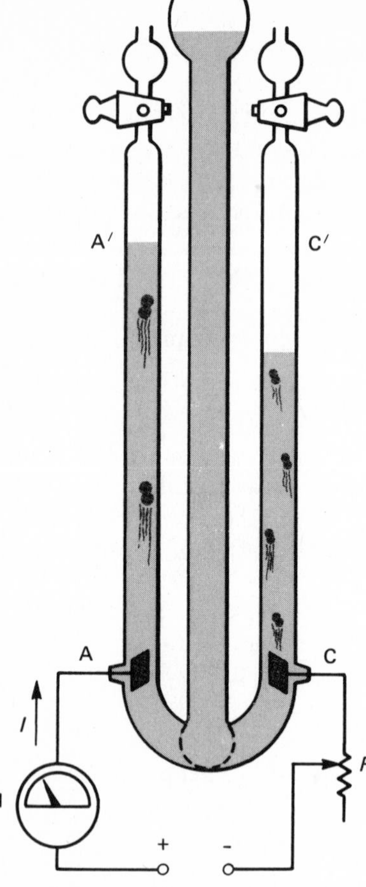

FIG. 18.2 Electrolysis of water.

result is known as ***Faraday's first law of electrolysis*** after Michael Faraday, who first established its validity. The general expression for this law is thus

$$\mu = \varepsilon It = \varepsilon Q, \qquad (18.10\text{-}2)$$

in which μ is now the mass of any product of electrolysis, and the constant ε is called the ***electrochemical equivalent*** of the product. The values of some electrochemical equivalents are given in Table 18.4.

Table 18.4 *Electrochemical Properties of Ions*

Ion	Electrochemical Equivalent (kg/Cb)	Kionic Mass i (kg/kion)	Charge/kion (Cb/kion)	Valence z
Ag^+	1.1180×10^6	107.88	96.5×10^6	+1
Cu^{2+}	0.3294	63.57	193.0	+2
H^+	0.0104	1.008	96.5	+1
$(NO_3)^-$	0.6427	62.01	96.5	−1
O^{2+}	0.0829	16.00	193.0	−2
$(SO_4)^{2-}$	0.4973	96.06	193.0	−2

The dimensions of the electrochemical equivalent are given by

$$[\varepsilon] = [mq^{-1}],$$

and Faraday's first law expresses the fact that a particular mass of any substance is always associated with a given charge. This result indicates that there is a law of definite proportions for electrochemistry and that every atom is associated with a definite charge of electricity.

Before we discuss the theory of electrolysis, there are two important applications worth consideration. Suppose that in the electrolytic cell of Fig. 18.1 we make the anode A of silver and, as the cathode C, we use a spoon or fork or other object made of a cheaper metal. If we pass a current through the cell, we can deposit a coating of silver on the metal object. In this way, we ***electroplate*** a thin coating of one metal on another.

Also, we can use an impure sample of a metal which we wish to refine as an anode. By a careful choice of the solution and of the potential difference between the anode and cathode, it is possible to arrange that only the pure metal is deposited on the cathode. This process is called ***electrolytic refining.*** Such refining can also be carried out in molten materials as well as in solutions in water.

18.11 The Ionic Theory of Solutions

We can account for the results of our experiments on electrolysis by means of the following simple theory. There is evidence that, when a salt such as $AgNO_3$ is dissolved in water, it splits up into two charged particles called ***ions.*** One of these consists of the metal atom (Ag) carrying a positive charge and the other consists of the remainder of the molecule (NO_3) carrying a negative charge. We thus represent the process of solution of silver nitrate by the reaction scheme

$$AgNO_3 \xrightarrow{\text{sol'n}} Ag^+ + (NO_3)^-,$$

in which the symbol Ag^+ represents the silver ion and the symbol $(NO_3)^-$ represents a group of atoms called the nitrate ion.* The charge on the silver ion Ag^+ must be equal and opposite to that on the $(NO_3)^-$ ion, since the molecule $AgNO_3$ is uncharged.

We explain the electrolysis of silver in the following manner. The Ag^+ ions in the solution are attracted by the negatively charged cathode (Fig. 18.3). They move toward the cathode and, on contacting it, they are discharged to form atoms of silver which adhere to the cathode plate. This removal of Ag^+ ions would leave an excess of $(NO_3)^-$ ions in the solution were it not for the fact that additional silver is continually dissolving at the anode. Since this electrode is

* In many cases, the ions may not be as simple as is indicated. Associated with each ion there may be one or more molecules of water. This "hydration" of ions does not affect the considerations of this chapter, so we shall continue to indicate the ions by the simple symbols used here.

maintained at a positive potential with respect to the solution, Ag^+ ions will be repelled from it; thus, the silver will dissolve, carrying a positive charge away at the same time. When everything is operating steadily, the rate of solution of silver at the anode will just equal the rate of deposition at the cathode. If the current is stopped by opening the external circuit, the process of solution and deposition will also stop, since there are no longer potential differences to attract the ions to the cathode or to repel them from the anode. Similar explanations account for the electrolysis of other metals.

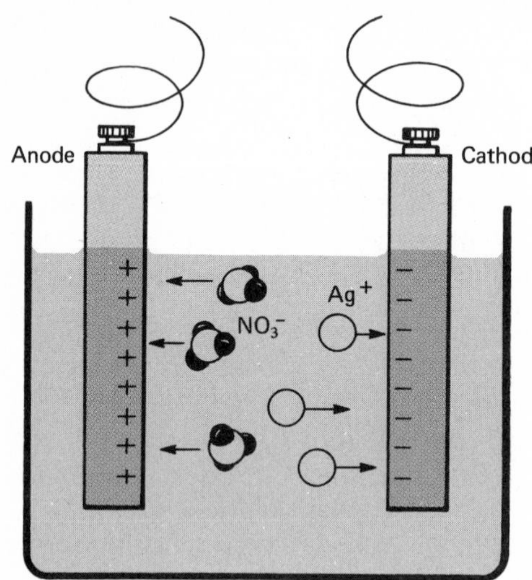

FIG. 18.3 Ionic theory of electrolysis of silver nitrate.

The electrolysis of water, discussed in the preceding section, can be explained in a like manner, but we must refer the reader to a textbook of chemistry for the details. In the solution, both water and sulfuric acid split into different types of ions, positive and negative, which migrate through the solution and carry the current as in the case of $AgNO_3$ solution. The net result of the flow of current is the splitting of two molecules of water into three molecules, two of hydrogen and one of oxygen; thus,

$$2H_2O \xrightarrow{\text{electrolysis}} 2H_2 + O_2 .$$

The hydrogen, which is carried by positive ions, is released at the negatively charged cathode, while the oxygen, carried by the negative ions, is released at the anode.

18.12 The Elementary Charge of Electricity

In Chapter 17 we described an experiment by which we could measure the ratio of charge to mass for an electron. We did not, at that point, consider how the charge on an electron might be measured. Also, in the preceding section, we spoke of charged atoms—ions—and we shall see later that such ions are atoms or groups of atoms which have lost or gained one or a few electrons. If electrons have been lost, the ion is positive, and if they have been gained, the ion is negative. It behoves us now to describe a beautiful experiment by Robert A. Millikan (1868–1953) which demonstrates that electrical charges occur only in integral multiples of a particular elementary charge, namely, the charge on the electron.

In Millikan's experiment, small oil droplets were introduced into the region between the parallel plates of a capacitor, through a small hole in the top plate, Fig. 18.4. If there was no electric field within the capacitor, these droplets fell

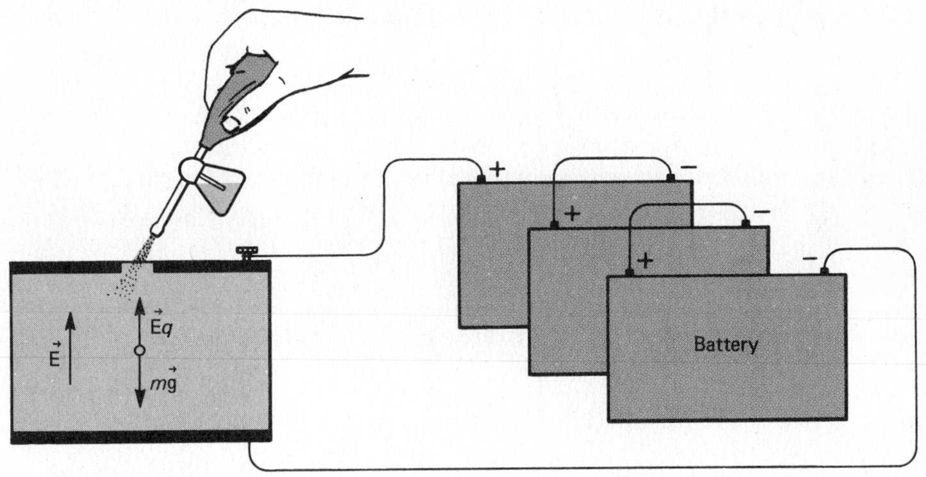

FIG. 18.4 Determination of electronic charge.

toward the bottom plate because of their weight. But since the droplets were very small, the air resistance to their motion was quite appreciable and they quickly reached a low terminal velocity. By a theoretical relation known as ***Stokes' law***, the terminal speed v of a spherical drop of radius a is given by

$$v = f/6\pi\eta a, \tag{18.12-1}$$

where f is the magnitude of the force acting on the droplet and η is the ***viscosity*** of the medium through which the droplet moves. For Millikan the medium was air at atmospheric pressure for which $\eta = 1.82 \times 10^{-5}$ N sec/m^2. Also, since the mass m of a spherical drop is $4\pi a^3\rho/3$, where ρ is the density of the liquid, the weight of the drop was

$$f_1 = 4\pi a^3\rho g/3 \tag{18.12-2}$$

and its terminal speed then was

$$v_1 = 2a^2\rho g/9\eta. \tag{18.12-3}$$

We have used the subscript 1 on f_1 and v_1 in Eqs. (18.12-2) and (18.12-3) because Millikan first let a droplet fall freely with no field between the plates of the capacitor. Through a microscope, he watched the fall of the droplet and measured its terminal speed v_1. Using Eq. (18.12-3), he calculated the radius a and by Eq. (18.12-2) he found the weight, mg, of the droplet.

Now if the same drop carries an electric charge q and if a field E is applied by charging the capacitor, an electric force Eq will act on the drop in addition to its weight. If the field is large enough and in the proper direction, the resultant force will be upward, so that the drop will rise instead of fall. Then, according to Eq. (18.12-1), the upward terminal velocity will be

$$v_2 = (Eq - mg)/6\pi\eta a. \tag{18.12-4}$$

In Eq. (18.12-4), the only quantity still unknown is q; thus, it can be calculated from this equation.

Millikan was able to raise and lower a single drop many times and find the charge on it with considerable precision. Although the charge varied from drop to drop—and the charge even changed on a single drop from time to time—he nonetheless found that the charge q was always an integral multiple of a certain elementary charge e. From Millikan's original experiments and from other similar ones performed since, we know that the value of this elementary charge is

$$e = (1.602 \pm 0.02) \times 10^{-19} \text{ Cb}. \tag{18.12-5}$$

This elementary charge is usually called the ***electronic charge.***

18.13 The Masses of Atoms

In the earlier sections of this chapter we saw that chemical evidence enables us to express the masses of atoms and molecules in terms of the atomic mass unit, defined as $\frac{1}{12}$ of the mass of the C^{12} atom, but we have obtained no evidence as to the actual value of these atomic masses in terms of the kilogram, the standard of mass which we have used for all our previous discussions.

In the preceding section we saw that the smallest unit of charge which can occur is the electronic charge

$$e = 1.602 \times 10^{-19} \text{ Cb},$$

and, in Sec. 18.11, we interpreted Faraday's first law of electrolysis as indicating that every ion is associated with a definite charge of electricity. It is therefore not unreasonable to assume, subject to later checks, that some ions are associated with one and only one charge e in electrolytic experiments, and that any ion is associated with a small whole number of such charges.

It is possible by chemical arguments to convince ourselves that ions such as H^+, Ag^+, and $(NO_3)^-$ each carry a charge whose magnitude is e ($+e$ in the two former cases, $-e$ in the latter). The ions $(SO_4)^{2-}$ and O^{2-} each carry twice this charge. We shall not enter into this argument here but shall assume the truth of its result. Later we shall see that there is more direct evidence for this assumption.

If we determine the electrochemical equivalent of silver experimentally, we find that $\varepsilon_{Ag} = 1.118 \times 10^{-6}$ kg/Cb—i.e., that 1.118×10^{-6} kg of silver is deposited by each coulomb of electricity which traverses the cell of Fig. 18.1. If we suppose that every atom of silver is associated with one electronic charge, it follows that the mass m_{Ag} of the silver atom is given by

$$m_{Ag} = \varepsilon_{Ag} \times e = 1.118 \times 10^{-6}\ (\text{kg/Cb}) \times 1.602 \times 10^{-19}\ \text{Cb}$$
$$= 1.791 \times 10^{-25}\ \text{kg}.$$

From studies of silver compounds, similar to those carried out in Sec. 18.7–18.8 for nitrogen compounds, we know that the mass of the silver atom is

$$m_{Ag} = 107.88\ \text{amu}.$$

Thus, we may write that 107.88 amu $= 1.791 \times 10^{-25}$ kg and, following our usual routines, we obtain the important conversion formulas:

$$1\ \text{kg} = 6.02 \times 10^{26}\ \text{amu} \qquad (18.13\text{-}1)$$

and

$$1\ \text{amu} = 1.66 \times 10^{-27}\ \text{kg}. \qquad (18.13\text{-}2)$$

With the aid of these conversion factors, we can express the mass in kilograms of any of the atoms whose mass we know in atomic mass units (Table 21.1).

18.14 Avogadro's Number

The equation $2H_2 + O_2 \rightarrow 2H_2O$ implies that two molecules of hydrogen combine with one molecule of oxygen to form two molecules of water. If we consider the masses of these reagents, we see that the mass of the hydrogen molecule (H_2) is 2.016 amu, that of the oxygen molecule (O_2) 32.00 amu, and that of water (H_2O) 18.016 amu. We then see that 2×2.016 amu $= 4.032$ amu of hydrogen combined with 32.000 amu of oxygen to form 2×18.016 amu $=$ 36.032 amu of water. Simple proportion tells us then that 4.032 kg of hydrogen will combine with 32.000 kg of oxygen to form 36.032 kg of water.

For convenience in handling calculations such as those discussed in the preceding paragraph, we define a ***kilogram atomic mass*** of an element as the mass in kilograms of the element which is numerically the same as the mass in atomic mass units of one atom of the element. This quantity of an element is frequently spoken of as a ***kiloatom*** of the element, and we shall abbreviate it as ***katom***. It is easy to see from Eq. (18.13-1) that there will be 6.02×10^{26} atoms in one katom of any element. This number is so important in chemistry and in physics that it is given a special name. It is called ***Avogadro's number***, or sometimes ***Loschmidt's number***, and it is represented by the symbol L. According to the most recent determinations, the best value of this number is*

$$L = (6.02486 \pm 0.00016) \times 10^{26}\ \text{atoms/katom}. \qquad (18.14\text{-}1)$$

* In the system of units based on the gram, which is commonly used in chemistry, the value of Avogadro's number is $L = 6.023 \times 10^{23}$ atoms/gram atom, and the gram atom and the gram mole are defined as the mass in grams of this number of atoms and molecules, respectively.

In a similar manner, we define a ***kilogram molecular mass*** (***kilomole***, abbreviated ***kmole***) of a compound as the mass in kilograms of a compound which is numerically equal to the mass in atomic mass units of one molecule of the compound. The number of molecules in one kmole is again L. The reader will easily see that we can express L in terms of either "atoms per katom" or "molecules per kmole," and that L is numerically equal to the number of atomic mass units in one kilogram.

It is perhaps worth while to emphasize that atoms are counted in terms of Avogadro's number just as eggs are counted in dozens. To aid in the counting process, we use a different mass "unit" in weighing out each element or compound, so that we can weigh out the same number of atoms or molecules of each. Thus, in the example used at the beginning of this section, a mass of 4.032 kg/kmole (2 kmoles) means that we have counted out $2L$ molecules of hydrogen. By taking 32.000 kg/kmole (1 kmole), we have counted out L molecules of oxygen. The resulting mass, 36.032 kg/kmole (2 kmoles), corresponds, of course, to $2L$ molecules of water

18.15 The Second Law of Electrolysis

We can immediately apply the discussion of the preceding section in a study of the experimental values of the electrochemical equivalents of the various ions. The experimentally determined values of some of these are listed in the second column of Table 18.4. We saw in Sec. 18.10 that the electrochemical equivalent ε of a substance is simply the mass of the substance set free by the passage of one coulomb of electricity. If we now introduce the notion of a ***kilogram ionic mass*** i (***kiloion***, abbreviated ***kion***) as the mass of Avogadro's number of ions, we can calculate the charge necessary to set free one kion of any type of ion. Thus, we have, as the charge per kion for silver,

$$i/\varepsilon = (107.88 \text{ kg/kion})/(1.1180 \times 10^{-6} \text{ kg/Cb}) = 9.650 \times 10^{7} \text{ Cb/kion}.$$

The results of similar calculations for other ions are shown in Table 18.4.

It is immediately apparent from the fourth column of the table that silver, hydrogen, and nitrate ions must all carry the same electrical charge, while copper, oxygen, and sulfate ions all carry twice this amount of charge. Thus, we obtain verification of the assumption of Sec. 18.12 that each ion carries a small integral multiple of the fixed charge e, the electronic charge determined by the methods of Sec. 18.12.

Of course, we could extend Table 18.4 to cover many other substances. In every case, we should find that a small whole number multiple of the quantity 9.65×10^{7} Cb is required for each kion of the substance which is released by electrolysis. The value of this small whole number z depends on the number of electronic charges (+ or −) carried by the ion that produces the given substance. The number z is called the ***ionic valence*** of the ion and is equal to the number of electronic charges carried by the ion. The valence is positive if the charge is positive, and negative if the charge is negative. The value of z for each ion is given in the last column of Table 18.4. Some of these ions are simple, being elementary atoms that have lost or gained one or more electrons. The ions $(SO_4)^{2-}$ and $(NO_3)^-$ are more complicated, a single ion being formed of a combination of several atoms.

We can now give a statement of ***Faraday's second law of electrolysis***, which will summarize all results of the type represented by Table 18.4: *The quantity of electricity required to release one kilogram ionic mass of a substance which appears in a solution as an ion of valence z is zQ_f*, where Q_f is a constant known as the ***faraday***. We have seen that the faraday has a value very close to 9.65×10^7 Cb/kion. This constant has been determined with considerable precision, and its more exact value is $(9.652 \pm 0.001) \times 10^7$ Cb/kion. It is now easy to see that the electrochemical equivalent [Eq. (18.10-1)] of a given ion is

$$\varepsilon = i/zQ_f, \tag{18.15-1}$$

in which i is the kilogram ionic mass, and z is the valence of the ion.

Faraday's laws of electrolysis were discovered long before the electronic charge was measured, and they provided one of the earliest evidences for the atomicity of electricity. These two laws imply that, if pure substances consist of atoms, the electric charge on a single ion must consist of a small whole number of an atomic unit of charge and that

$$Q_f = Le. \tag{18.15-2}$$

This is to say that the faraday is the charge on Avogadro's number of electrons, or the charge on a kion of electrons. One of the first determinations of the charge on the electron was made from the value of the faraday by the French physicist Jean Baptiste Perrin (1870–1920), who made a direct determination of L from the Brownian movement (Chapter 20). This determination was made a few years before Millikan's direct determination (Sec. 18.12).

EXERCISES

18.15-1 How many atoms are there in 1.00 g of gold?

18.15-2 Using data given in Ex. 18.9-5, calculate how long it will take the apparatus of Fig. 18.2 to produce 10.0 cm³ of hydrogen (at 0°C and 760 mm) if the current is 1.00 A.

18.15-3 The metallic element sodium is prepared by the electrolysis of molten sodium chloride. If $z = +1$ for sodium and $z = -1$ for chlorine, what quantity of electricity will be required per kilogram of sodium produced?

18.16 A Simple Primary Cell

We have seen in the preceding sections that it is possible to produce chemical reactions with the aid of electric currents. We shall now investigate the reverse process to study the way in which chemical reactions can produce electrical effects.

When a plate of zinc is dipped into a dilute solution of sulfuric acid, some of the zinc from the plate goes into solution as Zn^{2+}, leaving two electrons behind it on the zinc plate. This is so because the zinc ion is very strongly electropositive and has a much lower energy in solution as a positive ion in the acid than it does in the solid. As the zinc dissolves, the electrons left behind on the plate build up a negative charge on the plate. This negative charge will, of course, attract the Zn^{2+} ions and tend to prevent them from leaving the plate. The existence of this electric field due to the negative charge means that work must be done against electrostatic forces in order to carry a positive charge from the electrode to the solution. Hence, the electrode will have an electric potential lower than that of the surrounding solution.

If we now place a plate of copper in the same solution of dilute sulfuric acid, the copper will dissolve in the form of Cu^{2+} ions, and a process similar to that described for zinc will result. The copper plate will establish itself in equilibrium at a definite potential, which is negative with respect to the solution. The tendency of copper to dissolve, however, is very much less than that of zinc. Consequently, the potential necessary to prevent this solution taking place, i.e., the equilibrium potential of the copper with respect to the solution, will be very much less negative than that of zinc.

The plates of zinc and copper immersed in dilute sulfuric acid (Fig. 18.5) are thus at different potentials, since each is at a different potential with respect to the solution. In the diagram of Fig. 18.5b, the electrodes are respectively at potentials V_{Zn} and V_{Cu} below the potential of the solution, which is indicated by the horizontal line. Since the copper electrode is less negative with respect to the solution than is the zinc, it is easy to see that the copper is positive with respect to the zinc by an amount $\mathscr{E}_c$, as indicated in the diagram.

If the copper and zinc electrodes are connected by means of a resistance R, as indicated in Fig. 18.6, there will be an external electric current from the copper to the zinc. As soon as this charge flows, the zinc becomes less negative with respect to the solution, thereby permitting the solution of more Zn^{2+} ions. Thus, while positive charge flows from copper to zinc through the outside wire, the

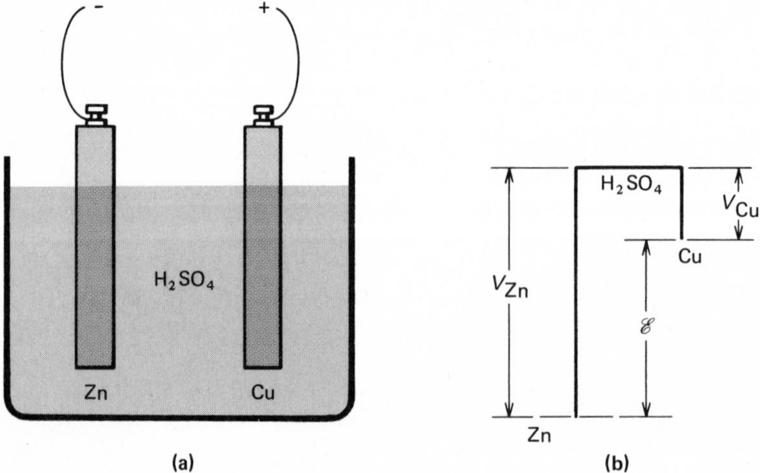

FIG. 18.5 Simple zinc-copper-sulfuric acid cell.

chemical process in the cell drives positive ions (Zn^{2+} and H^+) through the solution away from the zinc toward the copper. As long as the chemical reaction in the cell goes on, the current will continue to flow from copper to zinc through the outside wire, and a corresponding flow of positive ions will travel from zinc to copper through the solution. This type of cell is called a ***voltaic cell*** after its inventor, Alessandro Volta (1745–1827).

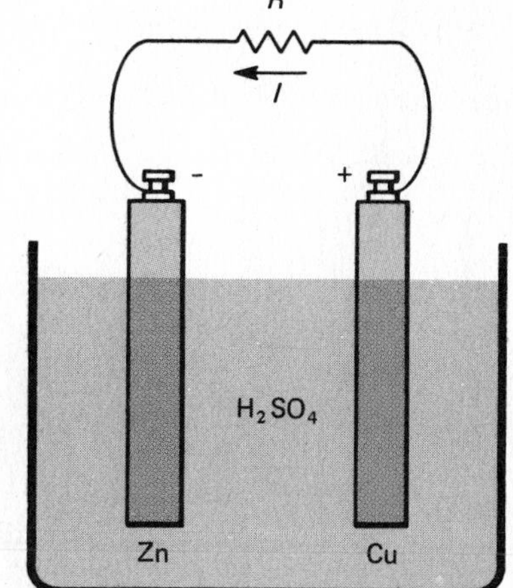

FIG. 18.6 Simple cell connected to a resistor.

If the Zn and Cu electrodes remain uncontaminated, the potentials V_{Zn} and V_{Cu} are kept constant, even while there is current, by the chemical reactions which take place. The difference between these potentials,

$$\mathscr{E} = V_{Zn} - V_{Cu}, \tag{18.16-1}$$

is called the ***electromotive force*** of the cell. This is the difference of potential between the terminals when there is no current. It is not always the difference of potential between the terminals, as we shall see in the next section.

18.17 Internal Resistance of Cells

We have just seen that, when a cell maintains a current I through an outside circuit, there must be an equal current inside it from the negative (Zn) to the positive (Cu) electrode. Thus, the energy expended by the chemical reaction is used up partly in sending a current through the solution of the cell and partly in sending it through the outside wire. The solution in the cell is itself a conductor, and it has a resistance called the ***internal resistance*** R_i of the cell; this resistance is in series with the resistance R of the external circuit. If we realize that the electromotive force $\mathscr{E}$ produced by the chemical reaction of the cell drives a current I through the two resistances R (external) and R_i (internal), we can see that

$$\mathscr{E} = I(R + R_i), \tag{18.17-1}$$

since these two resistances are in series in the circuit (Sec. 16.17).

We notice now that the ***terminal potential difference*** V for the cell—that is to say, the actual potential difference between the terminals of the cell when current is drawn from it—must be lower than the electromotive force $\mathscr{E}$ of the cell. The potential difference V which sends a current through an outside circuit is given by Ohm's law as

$$V = IR. \tag{18.17-2}$$

By combining Eqs. (18.17-1) and (18.17-2), we find that

$$V = \mathscr{E} - IR_i = IR. \tag{18.17-3}$$

Thus, the terminal potential difference of a cell, or any other electric machine, is equal to the electromotive force $\mathscr{E}$ of the machine less the drop of potential required to send the current I, drawn from the machine, through its internal resistance R_i.

The effect of internal resistance may perhaps be better understood by reference to Fig. 18.7. If the terminals Zn and Cu are now connected by a resistance R, the potential drop IR across this resistor must be equal to V, the potential difference across the cell. But the current in the cell will also cause a potential drop IR_i in the cell. A second potential diagram, in which the connection of the two points labeled A in Fig. 18.7a is indicated more clearly, is shown in Fig. 18.7b, which is obtained by wrapping the potential diagram of Fig. 18.7a around a cylinder. A circuit around the base of this cylinder corresponds to the complete electric circuit of Fig. 18.6.

The zinc-copper-sulfuric acid cell is one of a class known as ***primary*** cells. In all of these, the chemicals are gradually exhausted as the cell is used and must eventually simply be replaced. Another type of cell is the ***secondary cell.*** In

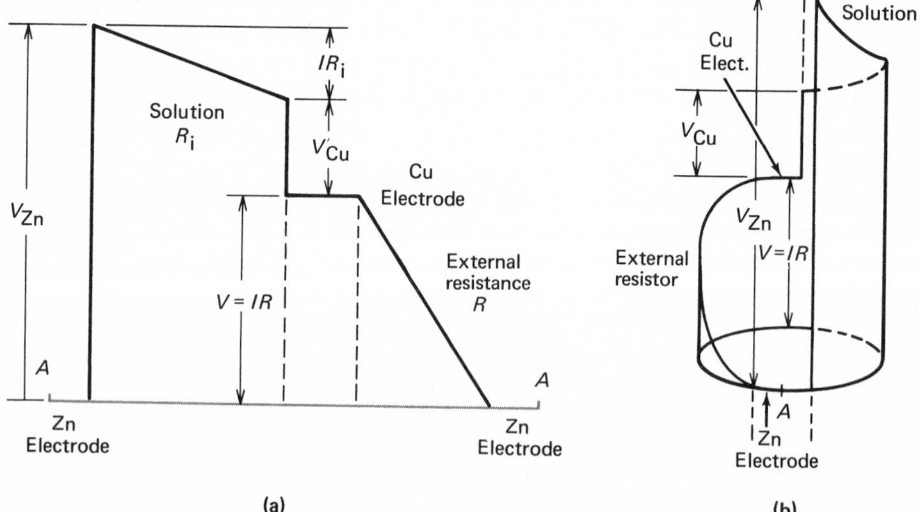

FIG. 18.7 Potential diagrams for a simple cell.

these, to be sure, there are chemical changes as the cell is used but, when the cell has "run down," it may be restored by passing a current in the reverse direction through the cell. The resulting electrolytic processes within the cell convert the chemicals back to their original chemical compounds and physical arrangement so that the cell is again ready for use. Thus, the secondary cell by its chemical processes "stores" electricity for later use; these cells are called ***storage cells.*** Storage cells most commonly encountered are the lead cells used in automobile batteries. The most common form of primary cell is the dry cell as used in flashlights and in batteries for portable radios.

The reader who might want to make a primary cell after the manner of Fig. 18.5 should be warned about ***polarization.*** The positive zinc and hydrogen ions migrate through the electrolyte to the copper anode. The hydrogen ions which accumulate at the copper are neutralized and form a layer of fine bubbles of hydrogen gas which effectively covers the surface of the copper. This not only changes the value of V_{Cu} but also increases the internal resistance R_i of the cell. Thus, the cell has become polarized and is useless after a short time. Commercial cells always have built-in provisions for avoiding polarization, but a discussion of such details would take us too far afield.

EXERCISES

18.17-1 A cell has an electromotive force of 1.326 V and an internal resistance of 0.100 Ω. (a) What current will be drawn from this cell by a resistance of 1.000×10^4 Ω connected across its terminals, and what will be the potential difference between the terminals when the current is flowing? (b) What will be the current and terminal potential difference if the external resistance is 1.000 Ω? (c) What will be the current and terminal potential difference if the external resistance is 0.100 Ω? (d) What is the maximum possible current that may be drawn from this cell, and what will be the terminal potential difference when this current is flowing? Draw potential diagrams similar to those of Fig. 18.7 for each of the four cases.

18.17-2 Plot a curve showing the variation of the current with the external resistance for the cell of Ex. 18.17-1. Plot a curve on the same paper showing the variation of the terminal potential difference with external resistance for the same cell.

18.17-3 A battery has an electromotive force of 8.072 V and an internal resistance of 0.001 Ω. Each of a number of lamps operates at 8.00 V and consumes 64.00 W. How many such lamps must be operated in parallel across this battery if they are all to operate at their rated voltage?

18.18 Cells in Series and in Parallel

In general, the electromotive force of a single cell lies in the range a fraction of a volt to three volts. It is often necessary to obtain much larger voltages than this. If we connect a number of cells in series (Fig. 18.8), connecting the positive of one to the negative of the next, we see that the emf of the ***battery***, as the series of cells is called, will be equal to the sum of the emfs of the individual cells. Similarly, the internal resistance of the series will be equal to the sum of the internal resistances of the individual cells. We can thus treat the battery as equivalent to a single cell of emf $\mathscr{E}$ given by

$$\mathscr{E} = \mathscr{E}_{c1} + \mathscr{E}_{c2} + \mathscr{E}_{c3} = \cdots$$

and internal resistance R_i given by

$$R_i = R_{i1} + R_{i2} + R_{i3} + \cdots,$$

where $\mathscr{E}_1, \mathscr{E}_2, \mathscr{E}_3$, and R_{i1}, R_{i2}, R_{i3}, are the emfs and internal resistances, respectively, of the individual cells. In this way, batteries can be built up to give as large a potential as we may need.

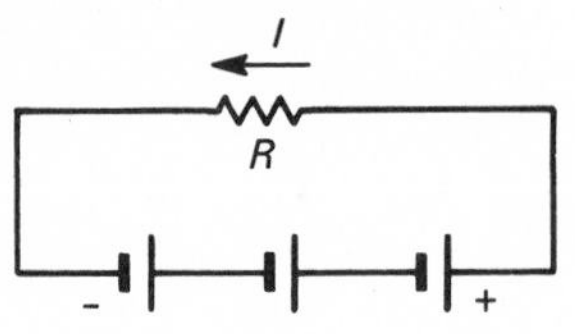

FIG. 18.8 Cells connected in series.

We saw in Sec. 18.17 that the terminal voltage V of any cell depends on the internal resistance R_i of the cell and on the current I drawn from it according to the relation

$$V = \mathscr{E} - IR_i. \tag{18.18-1}$$

Thus, if we wish to draw a large current from a cell, it should have as low an internal resistance as possible. This is usually done by making the electrodes large and the distance between them small. If an available type of cell has a larger internal resistance than is desirable for a given use, we may connect several such cells in parallel. This is done by joining all the positive terminals to

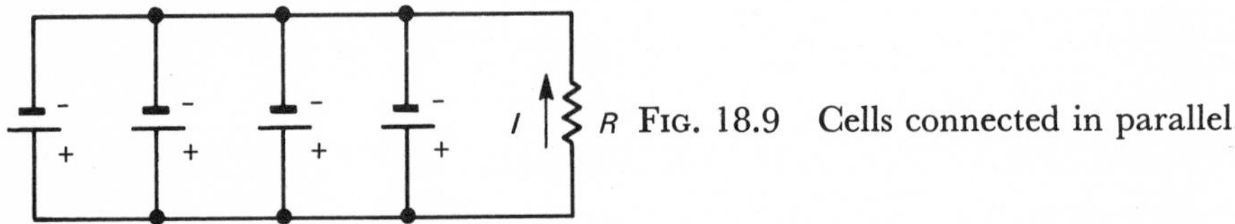

FIG. 18.9 Cells connected in parallel.

one conductor and all the negative terminals to another as shown in Fig. 18.9. If a total current I drawn from n identical cells in parallel, then each cell is required to deliver only $(1/n)$ of the current. Thus, the terminal potentials of the cells are

$$V = \mathscr{E}_c - IR_i/n, \tag{18.18-2}$$

and, since the terminal potential of the battery in parallel is the same as that of the individual cells, we can see that the battery behaves as a single cell with $(1/n)$ times the internal resistance of one of the components.

It is left as an exercise for the reader to consider the properties of a series-parallel connection such as that of Fig. 18.10 (Exs. 18.18-2 and 18.18-3).

It is important to note that it is inadvisable to connect in parallel two cells or sets of cells whose emfs are unequal. Consider the case in which two cells,

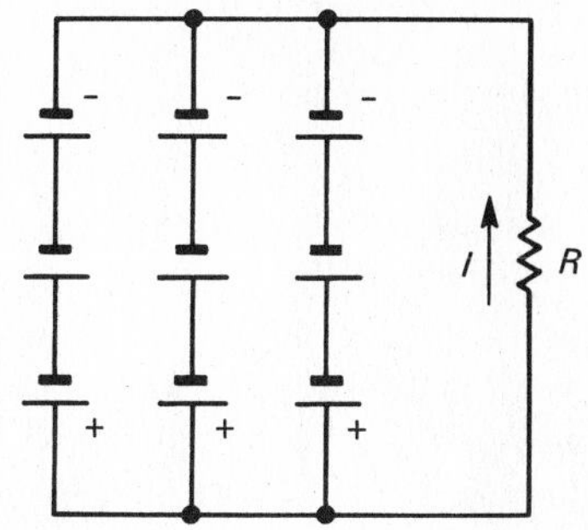

FIG. 18.10 Series-parallel connection.

($\mathscr{E}_1$, R_{i1}) and ($\mathscr{E}_2$, R_{i2}), are connected in parallel (Fig. 18.11), and suppose for the moment that no current is drawn from them. A closed circuit is formed through cell number 1 and back through cell number 2 and, if $\mathscr{E}_1$ is greater than $\mathscr{E}_2$, there is a current I_i in this circuit; the current is calculated by the relation

$$\mathscr{E}_1 - \mathscr{E}_2 = I_i(R_{i1} + R_{i2}).$$

This current does no useful work and simply heats the cells at the expense of the chemical energy stored in them. The current I_i is zero, of course, if the emfs of the cells are equal.

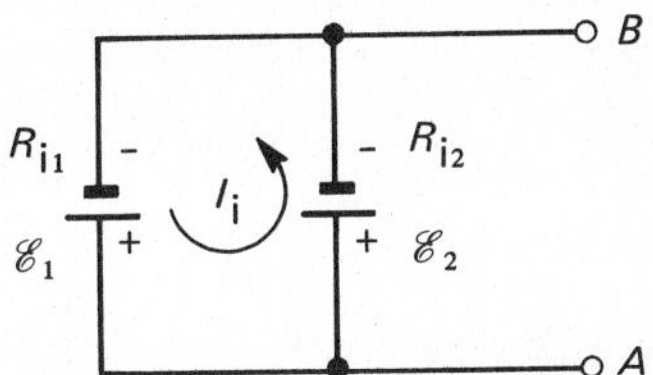

FIG. 18.11 Unequal cells in parallel.

EXERCISES

18.18-1 In each of a number of identical cells, the open circuit emf is 2.018 V and the internal resistance is 0.036 Ω. A certain lamp draws 2.00 A at 2.000 V. How many cells must be used to supply the lamp at its rated voltage, and how should they be connected?

18.18-2 Nine identical cells of the type described in Ex. 18.18-1 are connected as shown in Fig. 18.10. What is the electromotive force of the whole battery and what is its internal resistance? What is the maximum current which can be drawn from it?

18.18-3 A number of cells are divided into m equal groups of n cells each. In each group, the n cells are connected in series, and the m groups are connected in parallel (cf. Fig. 18.10). Calculate the electromotive force and the internal resistance of the battery as a whole in terms of V_c and R_i, the emf and resistance of a single cell.

18.18-4 Two cells, of equal open circuit emf ($\mathscr{E} = 1.50$ V) but of differing internal resistances ($R_{i1} = 0.050\ \Omega$ and $R_{i2} = 1.00\ \Omega$) are connected in parallel. An external resistance of 5.50 Ω is then connected to them. Find the currents in the external resistance and in each cell.

18.19 Summary

In this chapter, we have been concerned with the arguments which lead to the hypothesis that all matter is composed of ultimate small particles called atoms and molecules. In the course of this discussion, we have met the important laws of definite and of multiple proportions which are basic for all chemistry. We saw, too, that electric charge comes in indivisible small quantities, and we considered a method by which this natural quantity of charge can be measured. We then considered Faraday's two laws of electrochemistry and used them to determine Avogadro's number and the mass of any atom or molecule, and to introduce the important concept of valency.

We have discussed voltaic cells and have considered ways in which these cells are connected into electric circuits so that they can be used as sources of power.

PROBLEMS

18.1 The following table shows the boiling point of solutions of alcohol in water as a function of the fraction (by mass) of alcohol. It also gives the fraction of alcohol in the vapor phase that is in equilibrium with the liquid.

Fraction of Alcohol in Liquid	*Boiling Point* (°C)	*Fraction of Alcohol in Vapor*
0.50	81.2	0.80
0.40	82.1	0.79
0.30	83.5	0.77
0.20	86.0	0.72
0.10	90.2	0.60

A mixture of alcohol and water has a mass of 1.00 kg. It is boiled until the boiling point changes to 84.0°C. At that time, (a) how much mass remains in the liquid phase? (b) what mass of alcohol remains in the liquid phase? (c) what mass of alcohol has been evaporated?

18.2 It is known that there are three compounds that contain only phosphorus and oxygen. Their molecular masses are 110, 126, and 142, respectively. On the basis of this information and the fact that the atomic mass of oxygen is 16, find (a) the greatest possible atomic mass of phosphorus; (b) the chemical formulas for the three compounds if the one of lowest mass is $P_n O_m$.

18.3 Assume, as can be shown to be true, that both H_2O and CO_2 have the two like atoms of the molecule separated by the single atom of the other type. The water molecule is known to have an electric dipole moment of about 2×10^{-21} Cb m; the carbon dioxide molecule is known to have no dipole moment.

(a) Using symmetry arguments, show that the three atoms of CO_2 may lie on a straight line and that the three atoms of H_2O cannot lie on a straight line.

(b) Supposing each H atom of water to carry a charge $+e$, the resulting electrons to remain somewhere in the molecule, and the O atom to carry no charge, find the average distance of the electrons from the center of mass of the hydrogen ions. (This model is oversimplified but gives good order of magnitude estimates.)

18.4 When 2.00 katoms of hydrogen atoms combine to form 1.00 kmole of hydrogen molecules, energy in the amount of 2.17×10^8 J must be supplied. Using this fact and conservation laws, consider the collision of two hydrogen atoms, one of which is moving with a velocity $\vec{v}$ relative to the other. Suppose that they collide inelastically and form a molecule.

(a) Show that the molecule must be moving with a velocity $\vec{u}$ that has the same direction as $\vec{v}$.

(b) Show that the process is impossible unless $\frac{1}{2}mv^2 = 7.2 \times 10^{-22}$ J. (Combination of H atoms to form molecules occurs only at the walls of the container.)

18.5 The sodium chloride molecule consists of two ions (Na^+ and Cl^-), separated by a distance of 2.36 Å. (a) Assuming that the only forces between these ions are electrostatic, find the energy per molecule of NaCl required to accomplish the following reaction:

$$NaCl \rightarrow Na^+ + Cl^-$$

if the molecules form a very low-density gas. (b) Compute the energy required to carry out the same reaction if the molecules are in aqueous solution. (c) Comment on the fact that sodium chloride ionizes spontaneously in water solutions. Use the fact, anticipating Chapters 20 and 21, that molecules at room temperature have kinetic energies of about 6×10^{-21} J.

18.6 Many electrolytic solutions obey Ohm's law. Consider an electrolyte containing only two kinds of ions, one having a valence z_1 and the other a valence z_2. The respective numbers of ions per unit volume of solution are n_1 and n_2.

(a) Show that the validity of Ohm's law is consistent with a model of ionic conductivity in which ions of either type move through the solution with an average speed

$$v = \mu E,$$

where μ is a characteristic of the particular type of ion (use μ_1 and μ_2), known as the ***mobility***, and E is the electric field strength.

(b) Show that the conductivity of the electrolyte is

$$\sigma = e(n_1 \mu_1 z_1 + n_2 \mu_2 z_2).$$

(c) The conductivity of an aqueous solution containing 0.00365 g of HCl per liter is $3.79 \times 10^{-4}\ \Omega^{-1}\ \text{cm}^{-1}$ at 18°C. Find the quantity $(\mu_{H^+} + \mu_{Cl^-})$ at this temperature.

18.7 The result obtained in Prob. 16.12(b) may be generalized to apply to loops that include sources. The figure overleaf is similar to the one that accompanied Prob. 16.12, except that two sources of emf, $\mathscr{E}_1$ and $\mathscr{E}_2$, have been added.

(a) Using conservation of energy, show for the loop ABED that

$$i_1 R_1 - i_3 R_3 + i_5 R_5 = -\mathscr{E}_1.$$

(b) Generalize your result to state that *the algebraic sum of the iR drops around any closed loop in which steady currents are flowing is equal to the sum of the emfs included in the loop*. This statement is known as ***Kirchhoff's second law***.

(c) What sign conventions must be used in applying Kirchhoff's second law?

(d) Write the equation expressing the relation between iR drops and emfs in the loop BCFE.

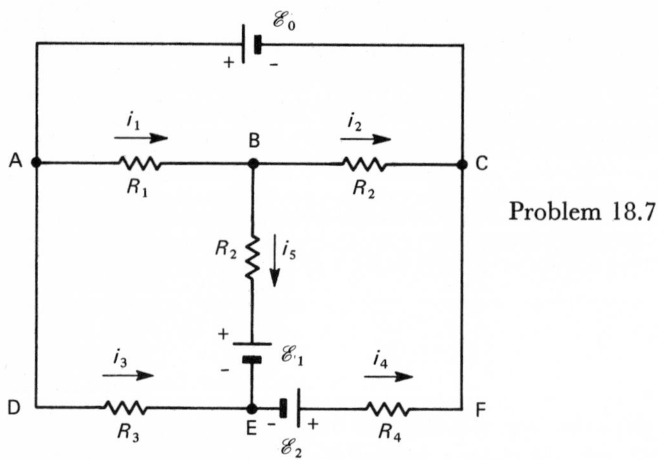

Problem 18.7

18.8 Use ***Kirchhoff's first law*** [Prob. 16.12(a)] and Kirchhoff's second law [Prob. 18.7] to find current in each resistor of the Wheatstone bridge (a) when $i_5 = 0$; (b) when i_5 is constant and is much less than any of the other currents. (Approximate by neglecting all terms that are of the order of $(i_5/i)^2$ or smaller, where i is the current in any resistor other than R_5. Set up six equations and solve simultaneously.)

18.9 A coin whose mass is 18.00 g is dropped into an aqueous solution of HNO_3, in which it dissolves completely. Hydrochloric acid (HCl) is then added to the solution. A fine white precipitate forms. After the liquid has been poured off and the precipitate has been dried, the mass of the precipitate is found to be 22.50 g. The liquid is tested for the presence of silver and is found to contain none of this element. (a) What compound probably forms the precipitate.? (b) What can you conclude about the solubility of this compound in water? (c) How much silver did the coin contain?

REFERENCES

18A David L. Anderson, *The Discovery of the Electron* (Momentum Book No. 3), Van Nostrand, Princeton, 1964. Especially see portions dealing with Robert A. Millikan's determination of *e*.

18B James B. Conant, editor, *Harvard Case Histories in Experimental Science*, Harvard, Cambridge, Mass., 1957. A useful approach to the work of Boyle, Priestly, Lavosier, Dalton, Gay-Lussac, Avogadro, and Cannizzarro.

18C Morris Shamos, editor, *Great Experiments in Physics*, Holt, New York, 1960. Pp. 146–157 reprint some of Faraday's works on electrolysis.

19 ⇨ *Atomic and Nuclear Structure*

19.1 Introdution

In Chapter 18 we saw how the chemical and electrochemical properties of matter can be explained on the assumption of an atomic theory, and in Chapter 20 we shall see that the same assumption will yield an adequate explanation of the properties of gases. In the present chapter, we shall consider physical researches, mostly of the 20th century, which give us some details of the structure of atoms. Later, in Chapter 25, we shall deal further with atomic structure. The investigations which we are about to recount differ from most of those of previous chapters in that we now deal largely with the behavior and properties of individual particles rather than with matter in the bulk.

19.2 Conduction of Electricity through Gases

The electrolytic experiments considered in Sec. 18.10 gave us some information as to the electrochemical properties of solutions. Experiments of a similar nature carried out in gases at low pressure give us additional information as to the nature of the atoms or molecules of the gas. Such experiments may be carried out with a ***gas discharge tube***, which is a closed glass tube (Fig. 19.1) containing gas at a pressure in the neighborhood of 10^{-2} mm of mercury and equipped with two metal electrodes (P and N), which are maintained at a potential difference V of several thousand volts.* If we introduce a sensitive meter M into the circuit, we can demonstrate that a current flows from P to N through the gas. Our experience with electrolysis leads us to believe that positively charged particles move through the tube from P to N and negatively charged particles in the opposite direction from N to P. We can verify this belief by drilling holes through the electrodes and observing the particles which come through these holes (Fig. 19.2). If the inside of the tube is coated with a fluorescent material, rapidly moving charged particles which strike this material cause it to glow, and bright spots appear at F and E, in line with the holes. We can easily demonstrate

* "Neon" advertising signs are discharge tubes of this sort, which usually contain neon, argon, mercury, or a mixture of these elements. The brilliant glow which appears in a discharge tube has a color which depends on the nature of the gas and on its pressure.

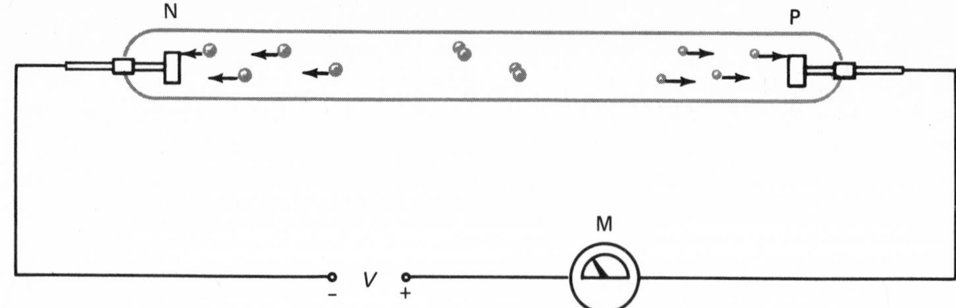

Fig. 91.1 Gas discharge tube.

that the particles that come from the space PN and go through the hole in the positive electrode P are negative in sign. This can be done by applying a magnetic field to the region just beyond P. When we do this, the particles are deflected at right angles to the magnetic flux density $\vec{B}$, indicated by the dashed line. Application of the right-hand rule (Secs 16.3 and 17.1) indicates then that these particles, moving to the right, must be negative. The particles coming through the hole in the negative electrode N are also deflected downward by a magnetic flux density $\vec{B}$ directed into the paper. Since these particles are moving to the left, the right-hand rule tells us that they must carry a positive charge.

We can explain the conduction which takes place in the tube of Fig. 19.1 by assuming that the molecules of the gas, initially uncharged, become charged in some manner. The mechanism of this process is simple. If a few electrons (Sec. 17.3) are set free within the discharge tube, they will be accelerated by the electric field between P and N, being attracted by P and repelled by N. These electrons can gain sufficient energy to knock out more electrons from the neutral molecules of the gas with which they collide. The molecules of the gas from which electrons have been removed are left positively charged and are attracted toward N by the electric field. There is thus a stream of electrons moving toward P and a stream of positively charged ions moving toward N through the gas. It is these two streams which constitute the current between P and N. Such a flow could not take place if all the molecules of the gas remained uncharged.

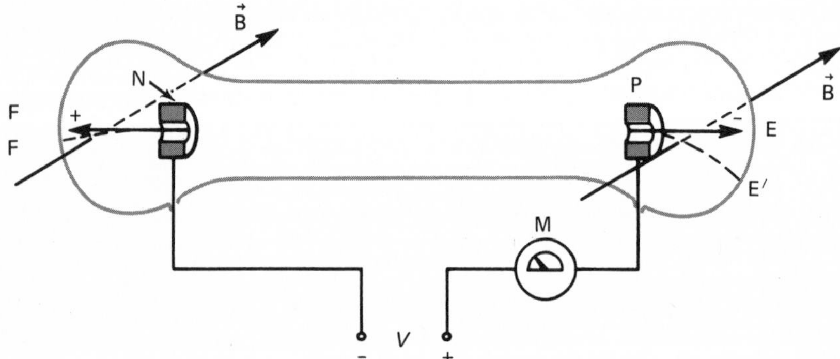

Fig. 19.2 Magnetic deflection of charged particles from a discharge.

A gas in which some of the molecules are charged is said to be ***ionized,*** and the positively charged molecules are called ***positive ions.*** This is a direct extension of the term "ion" which we have already used in connection with the discussion of electrolysis (Sec. 18.11). The negative ions in an ionized gas are usually electrons, but molecules which have acquired added electrons also act as ***negative ions.***

19.3 The Mass Spectrograph

We can determine the masses of the particles which come through the holes in the electrodes P and N by methods very similar to those described in Sec. 17.4, in which we discussed the determination of the electronic mass. The chief difficulty that arises in the direct application of such methods to the discharge tube, which we have just described, lies in the lack of an exact knowledge of the velocity of the particles that emerge from the holes. Many ingenious methods for avoiding this difficulty have been devised by such investigators as J. J. Thomson (1856–1940), F. W. Aston (1877–1945), A. J. Dempster (1886–1950), and others who have been interested in the determination of the mass of atoms, but we shall confine ourselves here to a simple device invented by K. T. Bainbridge (1904–   ), which is known as a ***velocity selector.*** In this device (Fig. 19.3), a beam of charged particles, originating in the discharge tube G, passes through the two slits S_1 and S_2 and then between the two parallel plates of a capacitor (Sec. 16.22). The whole apparatus is contained in a closed vessel, which is evacuated. If an upward electric field $\vec{E}$ is produced in the region between these plates, a force [Eq. (15.7-1)]

$$F_e = Eq$$

will act on a particle carrying a charge q. If a magnetic field of flux density $\vec{B}$ is directed outward as shown, the same particle will be subject to a downward force [Eq. (17.2-2)]

$$F_m = Bvq,$$

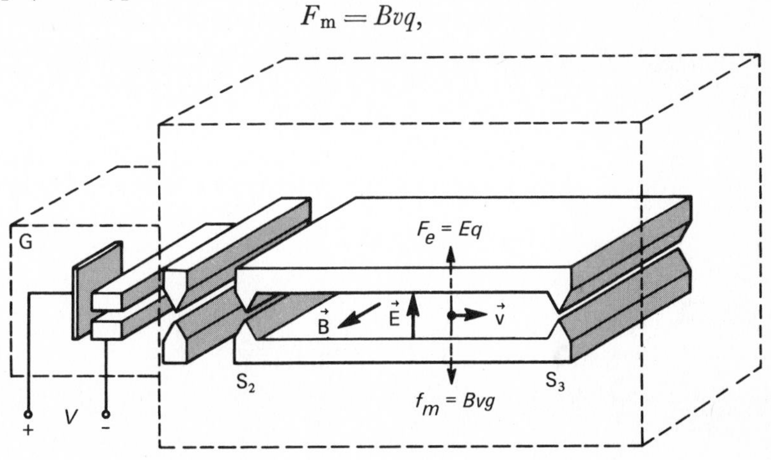

FIG. 19.3 Bainbridge's velocity selector.

where v is the speed of the particle. For a particle moving to the right along a line parallel to the capacitor plates, F_e and F_m will have opposite directions, and the particle will be subject to an upward force $F_e - F_m$. For a certain particle speed v_0, which satisfies the relation

$$Eq = Bv_0q,$$

the net force will be zero. Particles moving at the speed

$$v_0 = E/B \tag{19.3-1}$$

will therefore pass through the selector without deflection and will emerge through the slit S_3 (cf. Ex. 17.4-4). The particles traveling slower than v_0 strike the side of S_3 or the upper plate, while those traveling faster will be deflected downward. The velocity selector thus passes only those particles traveling with a velocity v_0 parallel to the axis of the selector, and it makes this selection irrespective of the mass and charge of the particles.

The velocity selector can now be combined in the same evacuated vessel with a magnetic deflector similar to that used for electrons (Fig. 17.6) as shown in Fig. 19.4. If the same magnetic field as is used in the velocity selector is used to deflect the particles which have passed through S_3, then particles of mass m and

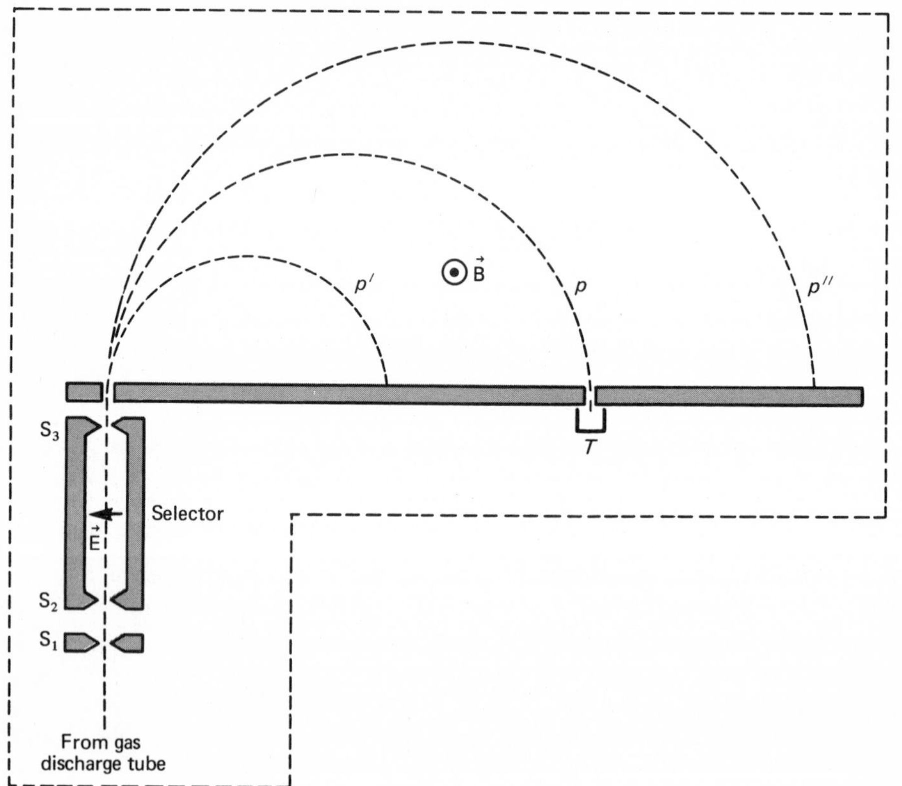

FIG. 19.4 Mass spectrograph.

charge q will be deflected into circles of radius ρ given by Eq. (17.2-3). Combining this equation with Eq. (19.3-1), we get

$$m/q = B\rho/v_0 = B^2\rho/E. \tag{19.3-2}$$

Thus, only those particles with a particular value for the ratio m/q will enter the slit near the trap T and be caught in T (cf. Sec. 17.4). Particles with other values for m/q will travel on circles of different radii and will not be collected with these values of B and E, but by changing the values of B and E, particles of any value of m/q within the range of the apparatus can be brought to the final slit and into T. The whole apparatus is, of course, enclosed in an evacuated chamber, as shown by the dashed lines in the figure.

The device which we have just described is called a ***mass spectrograph***, since we can use it to make a direct determination of the actual masses of atoms. We know that the charge q on any atom must be a whole number multiple of the electronic charge e (Sec. 18.12). Hence, we should expect that several values of the ***mass-to-charge ratio*** m/q might be found when a single type of atom is present in the stream of ions and that these would be

$$m/e, \quad m/2e, \quad m/3e, \text{ etc.}$$

This expectation is usually confirmed by the experimental results, and the largest value of the ratio can therefore be taken as m/e. Substitution of the value of the electronic charge for q in Eq. (19.3-2) therefore gives the mass of the atom in terms of the kilogram. The various ions, which contain one, two, etc. electronic charges are known as ***singly charged ions, doubly charged ions***, etc.

19.4 Isotopes

The results of mass spectrographic and other measurements for some of the lighter elements are given in Table 19.1. The ***atomic number*** Z in the first column of the table can be taken for the present simply as a numbering of the elements in their sequence of atomic masses. In Sec. 19.6 we shall see that this number has a deeper significance. The ***atomic mass*** A is the actual mass of an atom of a given element in atomic mass units (amu) as determined by the mass spectrograph, and the number M, called the ***mass number***, is the nearest whole number to the atomic mass A expressed in amu.

The results of mass spectrograph analysis verify the prediction of Frederick Soddy (1877–1956) that all the atoms of a given chemical element are not necessarily of the same mass, even though the chemical properties are the same for all such atoms. Thus, for example, there are three known kinds of hydrogen, with mass numbers 1, 2, and 3; and seven known kinds of argon, of mass numbers, 35, 36, 37, 38, 39, 40, and 41. Soddy gave the name ***isotopes*** to atoms of different masses which have the same chemical properties. Isotopes are therefore atoms of the same chemical element which have different masses. There are three isotopes of hydrogen, seven of argon, etc.

Table 19.1 *Masses of the Isotopes of Some of the Lighter Elements*

Z	Element	Mass Number M	Atomic Mass A (amu)	Abundance (percent)
1	Hydrogen (H)	1	1.007825	99.98
		2	2.014102	0.02
		3	3.016049	*
2	Helium (He)	3	3.016030	1.3×10^{-4}
		4	4.002604	100
3	Lithium (Li)	6	6.015126	7.4
		7	7.016005	92.6
		8	8.02241	*
4	Beryllium (Be)	7	7.016928	*
		8	8.005310	*
		9	9.012186	100
		10	10.013534	*
5	Boron (B)	8	8.006215	*
		10	10.012939	19.6
		11	11.009305	80.4
		12	12.01430	*
6	Carbon (C)	10	10.01334	*
		11	11.01143	*
		12	12.000000	98.9
		13	13.003354	1.1
		14	14.00324	*
7	Nitrogen (N)	13	13.00571	*
		14	14.003074	99.6
		15	15.000108	0.4
		16	16.00604	*
8	Oxygen (O)	14	14.00857	*
		15	15.003052	*
		16	15.994915	99.76
		17	16.999133	0.04
		18	17.999160	0.20
		19	19.00351	*
9	Fluorine (F)	17	17.002097	*
		18	18.000945	*
		19	18.998405	100
		20	20.000485	*

* Radioactive isotope.

Table 19.1 *Masses of the Isotopes of Some of the Lighter Elements (Continued)*

Z	Element	Mass Number M	Atomic Mass A (amu)	Abundance (percent)
10	Neon (Ne)	19	19.002885	*
		20	19.992440	90.9
		21	20.993849	0.3
		22	21.991384	8.8
		23	22.99447	*
		24	23.99358	*
11	Sodium (Na)	21	20.997619	*
		22	21.99442	*
		23	22.989773	100
		24	23.990955	*
		25	24.99012	*
12	Magnesium (Mg)	23	22.9941	*
		24	23.985045	78.7
		25	24.989840	10.2
		26	25.982591	11.1
		27	26.98432	*
		28	27.98385	*
13	Aluminum (Al)	24	24.00000	*
		25	24.99034	*
		26	25.98690	*
		27	26.981535	100
		28	27.98191	*
		29	28.98147	*
14	Silicon (Si)	27	26.9866	*
		28	27.976927	92.2
		29	28.976491	4.7
		30	29.973761	3.1
		31	30.975345	*
		32	31.9740	*
15	Phosphorus (P)	28	27.9917	*
		29	28.98182	*
		30	29.97832	*
		31	30.973763	100
		32	31.973900	*
		33	32.971727	*
		34	33.9734	*

* Radioactive isotope.

Table 19.1 *Masses of the Isotopes of Some of the Lighter Elements* (*Continued*)

Z	Element	Mass Number M	Atomic Mass A (amu)	Abundance (percent)
16	Sulfur (S)	31	30.97960	*
		32	31.972074	95.0
		33	32.971460	0.8
		34	33.967864	4.2
		35	34.969033	*
		36	35.967091	0.01
		37	36.9709	*
17	Chlorine (Cl)	32	31.9860	*
		33	32.9773	*
		34	33.97345	*
		35	34.968854	75.5
		36	35.9684	*
		37	36.965896	24.5
		38	37.97275	*
		39	38.98944	*
		40	39.970	*
18	Argon (A)	35	34.97525	*
		36	35.967548	0.34
		37	36.966769	*
		38	37.962724	0.06
		39	38.97674	*
		40	39.962384	99.6
		41	40.97750	*

* Radioactive isotope.

Some of the isotopes of the elements occur naturally, while others are made by radioactive processes and by transmutations which will be discussed later in the chapter. In the column headed *Abundance*, the relative percentages of the naturally occurring isotopes are given, and the elements that do not occur naturally are marked by asterisks.

For ease in referring to the more than four hundred isotopes of the 106 known elements, it is customary to combine as one symbol the atomic number, the chemical symbol, and the mass number. This is done by putting the atomic number Z *before* the chemical symbol as a subscript and the mass number M *after* it as a superscript. Thus ${}_1H^1$ refers to hydrogen, atomic number 1 and mass number 1, and ${}_{92}U^{235}$ refers to uranium, atomic number 92 and mass number 235.

The atomic mass of an element as determined by chemical means (Sec. 18.8) is clearly an average value for all naturally occurring isotopes of the element. Thus, chlorine has two natural isotopes, of masses 34.969 and 36.966 amu. In any sample of chlorine which can be used in a chemical experiment, the numbers of atoms of each mass will be proportional to the abundances, 75.5% and 24.5%, respectively (Table 19.1). Hence, the average mass of the chlorine atoms is

$$(34.969 \text{ amu} \times 0.755) + (36.966 \text{ amu} \times 0.245) = 35.458 \text{ amu}.$$

The average atomic mass as determined by chemists is 35.457 amu (Table 21.1).

Historically, before the development of mass spectroscopy, chemists based their atomic mass determinations on a unit which was $\frac{1}{16}$ of the average atomic mass of naturally occurring oxygen. When it was realized that there are three natural isotopes of oxygen—$_8O^{16}$, $_8O^{17}$, and $_8O^{18}$—mass spectroscopists developed their own scale whose unit was taken to be $\frac{1}{16}$ of the mass of the $_8O^{16}$ isotope of oxygen. However, the general practice in mass spectroscopy usually employs carbon and hydrocarbon compounds for calibration purposes. Therefore, a more convenient scale has been developed in which the unit is $\frac{1}{12}$ the mass of the $_6O^{12}$ isotope of carbon. In 1960 at Ottawa, the International Union of Pure and Applied Physics adopted the unit based on $_6C^{12}$ as the atomic mass unit. This amu is 1.660×10^{-27} kg.

Actually, the three units discussed in the preceding paragraph differ only slightly. In terms of the amu adopted in 1960, we can calculate that the mass unit based on $_8O^{16}$ is equal to 1.00032 amu, and the mass unit based on the *average* atomic mass of naturally occurring oxygen is equal to 1.00060 amu. The discrepancies among these three mass units are so small that they are unimportant except in the intercomparison of mass spectrographic data or in the most precise chemical measurements of atomic mass.

In Chapter 18 we saw that Avogadro's number, the number of atoms in a kilogram atomic mass of an element, is $(6.023 \pm 0.001) \times 10^{26}$. By definition, a kilogram atomic mass of $_6C^{12}$ is 6.023×10^{26} atoms having a total mass of 12.000 000 kilograms. Therefore, we find that

$$1.000 \text{ amu} = \frac{1}{12} \times \frac{12.000\,000}{6.023 \times 10^{26}} \text{ kg} = 1.660 \times 10^{-27} \text{ kg}.$$

The atomic mass unit defined in terms of $_6C^{12}$ has been officially adopted for universal use by both chemists and physicists. Most of the current wall charts and books show the atomic mass of a particular isotope as slightly different from that in a table published before 1960. Thus, the mass of the nitrogen atom $_7N^{14}$ is 14.003074 amu (new unit) as contrasted with 14.00754 amu (old unit).

19.5 The Discovery of Radioactivity

In 1896, Henri Becquerel (1852–1908) noticed that minerals containing uranium (atomic number $Z = 92$: Table 21.1) had the property of ionizing any gases which were in their neighborhood (cf. Sec. 19.2). His experimental arrangement consisted of an electroscope (Fig. 19.5, cf. Fig. 15.1) which was well insulated and thus capable of holding its charge for a long time. Becquerel found that whenever he brought a lump of uranium ore anywhere near the positively charged plate P of the electroscope, the gold leaves L immediately collapsed, indicating that the electroscope had lost its charge. Becquerel deduced that the uranium ore was sending out some sort of radiation which ionized the air around P. The negative ions from the air were attracted to P and their negative charges neutralized the positive charge on P.

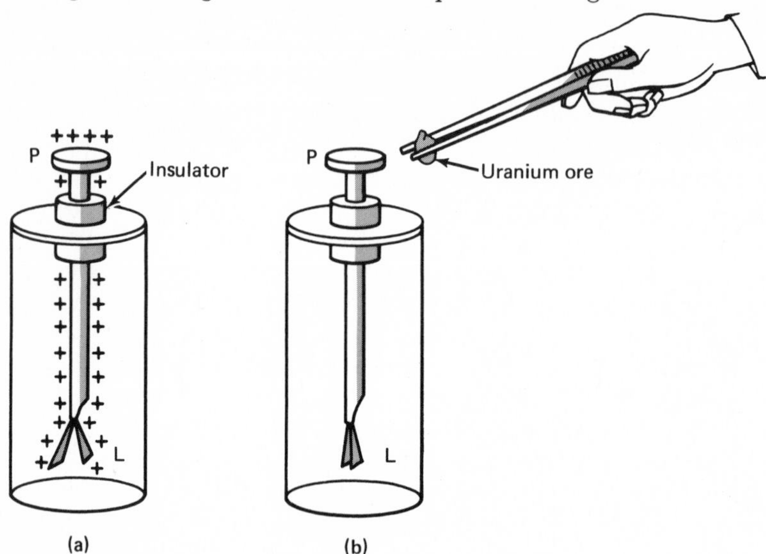

Fig. 19.5 Discharge of an electroscope by a radioactive material.

Marie Sklodowska Curie (1867–1934) and her husband, Pierre Curie (1859–1906), investigated this effect and found that the ore which contained uranium contained other elements that possessed the property of ionizing gases to a much greater extent than did the original uranium ore. The first of these is polonium ($Z = 84$: Table 21.1), named after Madame Curie's native land, Poland. The second is radium ($Z = 88$). Following the Curies and Becquerel, other investigators soon found more elements which could ionize gases. Such elements are said to be ***radioactive.***

In early studies of radioactive substances, it was found that three types of radiation are emitted. Becquerel recognized that at least some of the radiation from uranium could be deflected by a magnetic field. Experiments which in principle yielded mass spectrographic measurements proved that this component of the radiation consisted of high-speed electrons. These are known as ***β-rays*** or ***β-particles.*** Later, Ernest Rutherford (1871–1937) demonstrated that there is a second type of particle emitted by radioactive substances; this kind of particle, known as an ***α-particle***, has a mass of 4 amu and carries a positive charge $2e$. The α-particles as emitted from radioactive atoms constitute ***α-rays.*** Rutherford demonstrated also that there is a third type of radiation, ***γ-radiation***, which cannot be deflected by a magnetic or electric field. Later experiments in the diffraction of γ-rays proved that they were, in fact, photons of very high energy.

19.6 The Scattering of Alpha-Particles and the Rutherford Atom Model

At the time of the discovery of radioactivity, little was known about the internal structure of atoms. A number of phenomena, such as electric conduction, thermionic emission (Sec. 17.3), and the ionization of gases (Sec. 19.2), indicated that electrons were constituents of atoms. Since atoms are normally neutral, it followed that other constituents, at least some of which carried positive charges, must also be part of atoms, but neither the nature of these constituents nor their arrangement was known. It had been found, however, that atoms have radii of approximately 10^{-10} m (cf. Sec. 21.4).

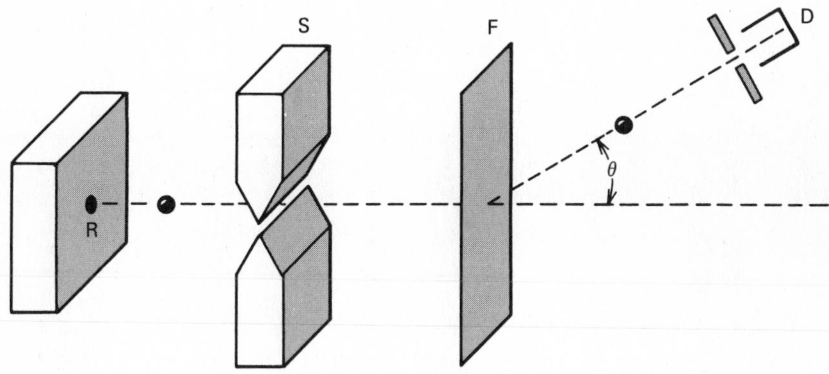

FIG. 19.6 Scattering of α-particles.

Rutherford discovered that the α-particles emitted by radioactive substances were valuable agents for investigating the structure of atoms. Since these α-particles carry an electric charge, they are subject to electrostatic forces whenever they are near other charged particles, such as those of which the atom is presumably composed. Moreover, they possess very great energies (equivalent to that of an electron which has fallen through a potential difference of about 4×10^6 V) (Sec. 17.3) and are therefore able to approach very close to other positively charged particles in spite of the force of repulsion.

An apparatus with which scattering experiments can be carried out is shown schematically in Fig. 19.6. A small amount of radioactive material R is located behind a slit S. This slit allows only a narrow beam of α-particles to fall on the thin foil F. A detector D, similar to that used for electrons (Fig. 17.6), measures the number of α-particles scattered through an angle θ from the direction of the incident beam. Measurements are made with the detector set for various values of θ.

An analysis of Rutherford's results showed that they were consistent with a very simple model of atomic structure. Suppose that an atom of atomic number Z consists of small central body, called the ***nucleus***, which carries a positive charge of magnitude Ze and is surrounded by a number of moving electrons. Then an α-particle approaching the nucleus (N in Fig. 19.7) along the path AB

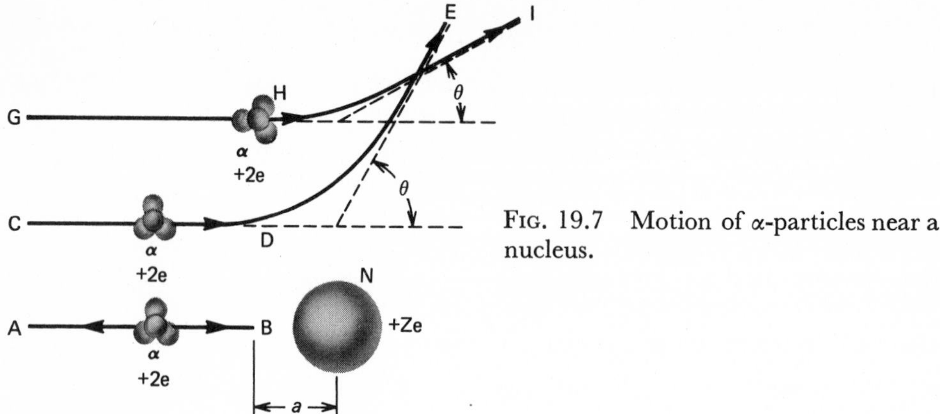

FIG. 19.7 Motion of α-particles near a nucleus.

will be subject to a retarding force due to the repulsion between the nuclear charge $+Ze$ and its own charge $+2e$. We can find the distance of closest approach a from considerations of energy. According to Sec. 16.21, the potential energy of a charge q, at a distance r from another charge Q, is

$$PE = qQ/4\pi\epsilon_0 r. \tag{19.6-1}$$

Replacing q in this equation by $2e$ and Q by Ze, we find that the potential energy at a distance a is

$$PE = 2Ze^2/4\pi\epsilon_0 a.$$

If the α-particle has a kinetic energy w before it comes near the atom, this kinetic energy will be converted to potential energy as it approaches, and the particle will be at rest—i.e., it will reverse its path—when $w = PE$. As was stated above, the α-particle kinetic energy is that of an electron which has fallen through a potential difference of about 4×10^6 V, so we have $w \approx eV$, where $V = 4 \times 10^6$ V. Equating this to the potential energy at distance a, we find that

$$a \approx Ze/2\pi\epsilon_0 V. \tag{19.6-2}$$

If the foil of Fig. 19.6 is made of silver, $Z = 47$, and a calculation from Eq. (19.6-2) yields the value $a \approx 3 \times 10^{-14}$ m.

The α-particle which we have been discussing was headed directly toward the nucleus; of course, that particle bounces back along the same path or, as we say, it is scattered through 180°. (See Prob. 19.2.) Another particle, incident along the path CD in Fig. 19.7, will be subject to forces deflecting it away from the nucleus and will be scattered through a smaller angle θ. Finally, one approaching along the path GH will never get near enough to the nucleus to have large forces acting upon it, and so it will be scattered by a still smaller angle θ.

In Rutherford's experiment, the foil F contained a very large number of identical atoms, each of which could act as a scatterer. Assuming that the nuclei are very small compared with the distance between them, the foil will appear, when seen from the point of view of the incoming α-particles, something like the sketch of Fig. 19.8, in which the dots represent the nuclei. If a beam of particles is moving toward this foil, the chance of one striking a nucleus head-on is very small, so scattering at 180° (AB in Fig. 19.7) is quite improbable.

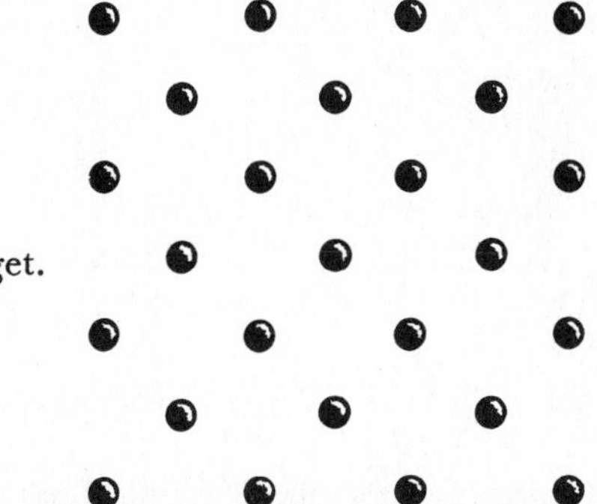

FIG. 19.8 Nuclei in the foil target.

Near misses are considerably less probable than far misses, so fewer atoms will be scattered through large angles (CDE in Fig. 19.7) than will be scattered through small angles (GHI in Fig. 19.7). The probabilities that α-particles will be scattered at various values of θ can be calculated by an extension of the arguments we have used. The experimental results which Rutherford obtained agreed with those calculated, on the assumption of very small nuclei and an inverse square law of force between the nuclei and the α-particles. This is exactly the behavior which is to be expected if the nuclei are positively charged as we have assumed. We have seen that the distance of closest approach, with the α-particles used by Rutherford, was about 10^{-14} m. Since the proposed structure leads to the correct result for all observed angles of scattering, the inverse square law holds for distances down to 10^{-14} m and the nucleus can be no larger than this.

The picture of atomic structure which we have discussed and which was proposed by Rutherford in 1911 as a result of his scattering experiments is known as the ***Rutherford atom model.*** According to this model, the atom consists of a nucleus of about 10^{-15} m radius with this nucleus is a charge $+Ze$; surrounded by Z moving electrons, each with a charge $-e$. Temporarily, at least, we can think of these electrons as traveling around the nucleus in much the same manner that planets travel about the sun. Their distance from the nucleus is about 10^{-10} m, about one hundred thousand times the nuclear radius. Since the mass of the electron is only about 1/1800 of an atomic mass unit, practically all of the mass of the atom resides in the nucleus. It is because of the small mass of the electrons that these particles do not cause appreciable scattering of the α-particles in experiments of the Rutherford type. (See Prob. 19.4.)

Rutherford concluded that the chemical properties of a given element would depend on its outer structure, i.e., on the number Z of electrons, but not on its mass. This number Z is the atomic number of Sec. 19.4. It is therefore possible to have nuclei of the same element with different masses but with the same charge, and these are the isotopes referred to in Sec. 19.4.

Thus, according to Rutherford, the hydrogen atom ${}_1H^1$ consists of a nucleus of mass number 1 and charge e with a single electron circulating around it. The helium atom ${}_2He^4$ has two electrons circulating around a nucleus of charge $2e$ and mass 4. In confirmation of this idea, Rutherford was able to prove that α-particles were actually helium nuclei without their accompanying electrons.

In Chapter 21 and again in Chapter 25, we shall return to a discussion of the outer electrons of atoms and of the way in which almost all of the chemical and physical properties of elements depend on these outer electrons. For the remainder of this chapter, we shall direct our entire attention to the atomic nuclei and to an examination of the way in which they are built up.

19.7 Natural Radioactivity

Among the many radioactive elements, discovered by the earliest investigators, some were found to give off their radiations quite steadily over a long period of time, while others radiated strongly at first but then died down rapidly. This fact was explained in 1903 by Rutherford and Soddy, who proposed the ***transformation theory of radioactivity***. According to this theory, an atom of a radioactive substance in emitting its radiation transforms itself into an atom of entirely different variety. For example, the isotope of radium ${}_{88}Ra^{226}$ emits an α-particle of mass number 4 and charge $2e$—i.e., a helium nucleus ${}^2He^4$. In this process the radium loses both charge and mass to become an isotope of radon ${}_{86}Rn^{222}$. We can represent this reaction by the scheme

$$ {}_{88}Ra^{226} \rightarrow {}_{86}Rn^{222} + {}_2He^4. $$

In another typical reaction, the isotope of lead ${}_{82}Pb^{210}$ emits a β-particle, that is to say, an electron of charge $-e$ and of very small mass. The loss of a negative charge will increase the positive charge on the nucleus and the isotope of lead ($Z = 82$) will transform into an isotope of bismuth ($Z = 83$) according to the scheme

$$ {}_{82}Pb^{210} \rightarrow {}_{83}Bi^{210} + {}_{-1}e^0, $$

where the final symbol indicates an electron of charge $-e$ (i.e., $Z = -1$) and of mass essentially zero. In a reaction of this type, the mass number does not change and the atomic number increases by one.

Rutherford and Soddy also suggested that *the number of atoms of any radioactive element which break down in a given time is proportional to the number of atoms of that element present.* Thus, if any amount of a radioactive substance, such as radium, is prepared at a given time, the amount available at any later time will steadily decrease. After a certain time has elapsed, half the original number of atoms will have transformed, and half will remain in the original form. This is known as the ***half-life*** of the radioactive substance. It is found that all samples of a given radioactive substance have the same half-life, which is unaffected by changes of temperature and pressure.

We can see that this transformation theory of Rutherford and Soddy implies that it is a matter of pure chance whether or not a certain atom of radioactive material breaks down. We can get a good picture of the process by considering an experiment in which several thousand dice are shaken up in a box and then thrown on a table. All those dice which show a six are removed and the remainder are shaken up a second time and spread on the table. This process is repeated many times. In the average throw, one-sixth of the dice thrown are removed. The arithmetically inclined reader can easily prove that the "half-life" of a die in this game is about four throws (Ex. 19.9-4). The reader can also easily see that, if the dice are replaced by pennies and all "tails" are removed, the "half-life" will be about one throw.

As a result of the transformation theory, it is possible to classify all naturally radioactive materials into families. One of these families, the ***uranium-radium family***, is exhibited in Fig. 19.9. The parent is the isotope of uranium $_{92}U^{238}$, which breaks down to $_{90}Th^{234}$ as the result of the emission of an α-particle. The half-life is 4.5×10^9 years as indicated in Fig. 19.9. The nucleus $_{90}Th^{234}$ breaks down in two ways, both with β-emission, to form two different forms of the nucleus $_{91}Pa^{234}$. These two forms, which have the same mass number and the same charge, but different half-lives, are said to be ***isomers*** of one another. It can be shown that these two isomers differ in their energy content and in the arrangement of the particles of which their nuclei are composed. Both of these

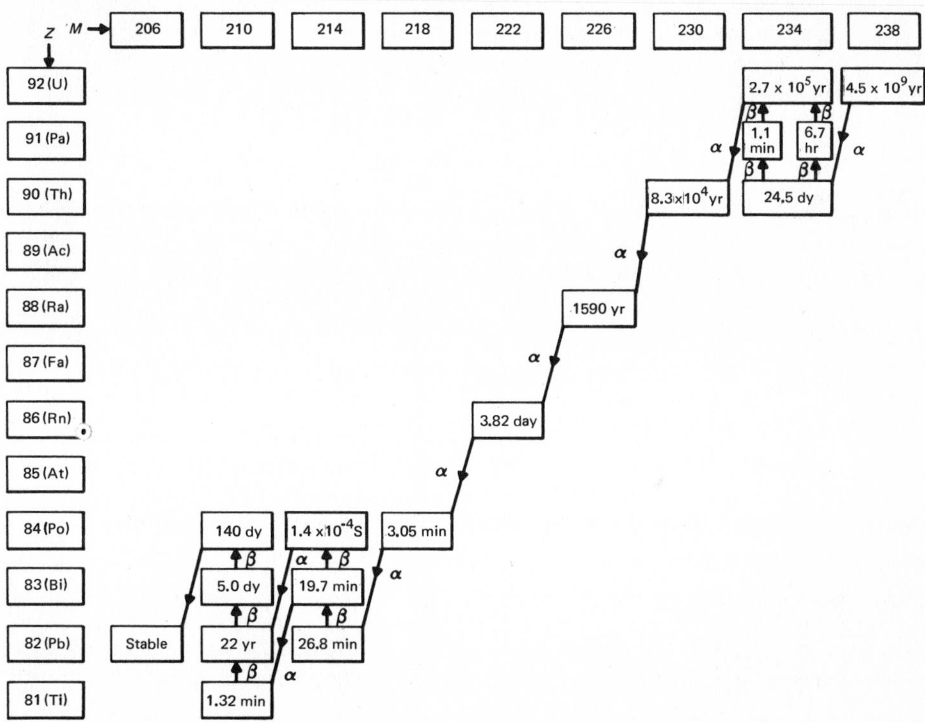

FIG. 19.9 Uranium-radium family of radioactive elements.

isomers break down to form $_{92}U^{234}$. A succession of α-emissions followed by a β-emission leads through the nuclei $_{90}Th^{230}$, $_{88}Ra^{226}$, $_{86}Rn^{222}$, $_{84}Po^{218}$, and $_{82}Pb^{214}$ to $_{83}Bi^{214}$. This nucleus transforms in two ways. In the one case, an α-emission is followed by a β-emission. In the other, a β-emission is followed by an α-emission. Both of these processes end in $_{82}Pb^{210}$, from which two β-emissions followed by an α-emission lead to the end product, $_{82}Pb^{206}$, one of the isotopes of lead, which is stable and shows no radioactivity.

There are two other important families of natural radioactive substances. One of these, the ***uranium-actinium family***,* starts with $_{94}Pu^{239}$ as parent and as a result of a series of α- and β-transformations ends with $_{82}Pb^{207}$. The ***thorium family**** starts with $_{90}Th^{232}$ and ends with $_{82}Pb^{208}$. Some other nuclei, including $_{19}K^{40}$ and $_{37}Rb^{87}$, are also radioactive as they occur in nature. In addition to the above naturally occurring radioactive elements, there are several hundred artificially produced radioactive nuclei. We shall discuss them again later.

19.8 Transmutation

To a certain extent, the transformations of the naturally radioactive elements have realised the hopes of the alchemists. These elements are "transmuting" themselves. Uranium changes by several stages into lead, and so on. But the realization is only partial, for it has been found impossible to alter, in any way available to man, the rate at which these transmutations are taking place.

The first controlled ***transmutation*** was performed by Rutherford in 1919. In the course of some experiments on the scattering of α-particles by nitrogen he noticed the presence of some high-speed particles which he later proved to be hydrogen nuclei $_1H^1$. These particles he called ***protons.*** He realized that he had succeeded, with the aid of an α-particle, in transmuting nitrogen into oxygen and hydrogen according to the scheme

$$_7N^{14} + {_2He^4} \rightarrow {_8O^{17}} + {_1H^1}. \tag{19.8-1}$$

This reaction was the first ***alpha-proton*** (α, p) ***reaction*** to be discovered. Such reactions can be represented by the general scheme

$$_ZX^M + {_2He^4} \rightarrow {_{Z+1}Y^{M+3}} + {_1H^1}. \tag{19.8-2}$$

According to this scheme, an element X of atomic number Z and mass number M is transformed by α-particle bombardment into an element Y of mass number $(M+3)$ and atomic number $(Z+1)$, plus a proton. Most of the elements of low atomic number can be transmuted by this reaction.

19.9 The Discovery of the Neutron

In 1930, the physicists Walther Bothe (1891–1957) and H. Becker observed that a very penetrating radiation was given off when the elements boron and beryllium were bombarded by α-particles. This radiation was not composed of

* See reference 19E at the end of the chapter for tables of these families.

protons, was not charged, and was at first thought to consist of γ-rays. Irène Joliot-Curie (1897–1956) (the daughter of the discoverers of radium) and her husband Frédéric Joliot (1900–1958) investigated this radiation and proved quite conclusively that it could not be γ-radiation. It remained for James Chadwick (1891–   ) to prove that this radiation consisted of neutral particles of zero charge and mass ≈ 1 amu. These particles are called ***neutrons.*** The transmutation scheme is

$$_4\mathrm{Be}^9 + {_2\mathrm{He}^4} \rightarrow {_6\mathrm{C}^{12}} + {_0\mathrm{n}^1}, \tag{19.9-1}$$

where the symbol $_0\mathrm{n}^1$ represents the neutron of zero atomic number and unit mass number. Chadwick realized that neutral particles would not of themselves produce ions in a gas, since they would exert no force on the charged particles in it. However, if the neutron were to strike the nucleus of an atom head-on, the nucleus would receive sufficient momentum to produce ionization as it moved through the gas. Therefore, Chadwick set up the experiment illustrated in Fig. 19.10. The radioactive material R produced α-particles, which fell on

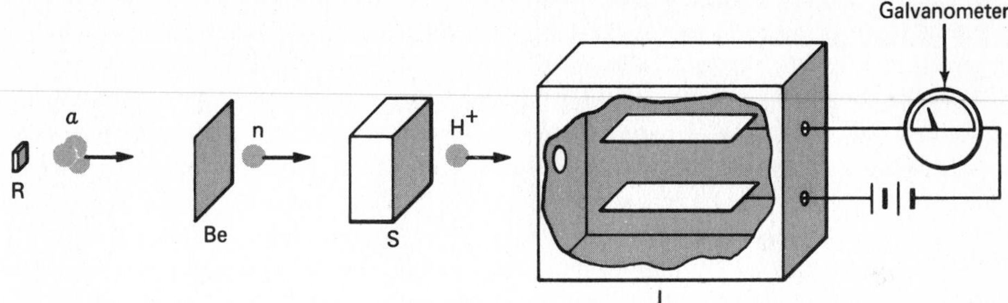

FIG. 19.10 Detection of neutrons

the beryllium plate Be. Neutrons (n) from the beryllium passed through a thin window W into an ionization chamber I. Under these circumstances only a few ions are produced, and these are ascribed to collisions between the neutrons and the nuclei of the walls of the chamber and of the gas in it. Chadwick found that if he introduced a screen S containing a large percentage of light atoms, such as hydrogen, the ionization in the chamber I increased markedly. For S in his experiments, Chadwick used a slab of paraffin. The fact that hydrogen proves to be the most effective atom to put in the screen S indicates that the mass of the neutron is as small or smaller than that of hydrogen (cf. Ex. 19.9-7). The method for the exact determination of the mass of the neutron is given in the next section.

There are many alpha-neutron (α, n) reactions other than that of beryllium. They are all represented by the scheme

$$_Z\mathrm{X}^M + {_2\mathrm{He}^4} \rightarrow {_{Z+2}\mathrm{Y}^{M+3}} + {_0\mathrm{n}^1} \tag{19.9-2}$$

These reactions are sometimes indicated in another way. The target nucleus is written first and is followed by a parenthetical expression that contains the bombarding particle and the light particle that is a product. The heavy product is written last. Thus the symbolism for the reaction is

$$_Z X^M (\alpha, n) _{Z+2} Y^{M+3}.$$

EXERCISES

19.9-1 A mass spectrograph of the type shown in Fig. 19.4 has its last two slits separated by a distance of 10.00 cm and is being used to determine the relative abundance of the two principal isotopes of neon. The magnetic flux density B has a magnitude 0.600 Wb/m^2. What must be the field strength E between the plates of the capacitor if singly charged ions of the isotope $_{10}Ne^{20}$ are to be collected?

19.9-2 The capacitor of the velocity selector in Ex. 19.9-1 has a separation of 1.500 cm between its plates. What voltage must be maintained across it if singly charged $_{10}Ne^{20}$ is to be collected? What voltage will be needed if singly charged $_{10}Ne^{22}$ is to be collected?

19.9-3 If the mass spectrograph of Ex. 19.9-1 and 19.9-2 is in a condition such that singly charged $_{10}Ne^{20}$ is being collected, by what distance will singly charged $_{10}Ne^{22}$ ions miss the final slit, and on which side of the slit will they fall?

19.9-4 Verify the statement made in Sec. 19.7 that the "half-life" of a die in the process described is about four throws. By plotting a curve of the number of dice left after each throw, assuming that you start with 1000 dice, show more exactly that the "half-life" is 3.8 throws. What meaning can you give to this nonintegral number of throws?

19.9-5 Suppose that a radioactive atom has a five percent chance of breaking down during any 1.0 sec. Assuming that N_0 atoms are present at some instant, find the number present 1.0 sec, 2.0 sec, 4.0 sec, 8.0 sec, and 16.0 sec later and so show that the half-life of this atom is between 8 sec and 16 sec.

19.9-6 Using the numbers found in Ex. 19.9-5, show that the half-life of the radioactive atom is approximately 13.5 sec.

19.9-7 Using Eq. (4.5-1) and the law of conservation of energy, prove that an atom of mass m_2, initially at rest and hit head-on by an atom of mass m_1, acquires a velocity

$$v_2 = 2m_1u/(m_1 + m_2)$$

where u is the velocity of the incident particle. Assume the collision to be perfectly elastic. Also find the kinetic energy acquired by m_2, and hence prove that the best material for the screen S of Fig. 19.10 will consist of atoms of the same mass as the neutrons.

19.9-8 Write down the reaction schemes for the (α, p) reactions on the elements $_5B^{10}$, $_9F^{19}$, $_{13}Al^{27}$, $_{14}Si^{28}$, and $_{16}S^{32}$, identifying the resulting product in each case.

19.9-9 Write down the reaction schemes for the (α, n) reactions on the elements $_3Li^7$, $_4Be^9$, $_9F^{19}$, and $_{15}P^{31}$, identifying the resulting product in each case.

19.9-10 In Ex. 19.9-4 after the first throw $\frac{5}{6}$ of the original number of dice will remain, on the average. After the second throw $\frac{5}{6}$ of the $\frac{5}{6}$ or $(\frac{5}{6})^2$ will remain, etc. In order to determine the half-life of a die, use logarithms to find n in the equation $(\frac{5}{6})^n = 1/2$.

19.10 *The Energy of Transmutation*

It is particularly interesting for us to examine the conservation of mass and energy in (α, p) and (α, n) reactions of the type which we have considered in the preceding section. Consider, for example, the (α, p) reaction on nitrogen. We notice first that the masses of the initial particles and of the final particles are as follows (cf. Table 19.1):

Initial Particles		*Final Particles*	
${}_7N^{14}$	14.003074 amu	${}_8O^{17}$	16.999133 amu
${}_2He^4$	4.002604 amu	${}_1H^1$	1.007825 amu
	18.005678 amu		18.006958 amu

There is thus an increase of mass of the final particles over that of the initial particles of amount $\Delta m = 0.00128$ amu. Our experience with the Einstein mass-energy relation tells us that this must be accounted for by the difference of the kinetic energy of the initial α-particle and that of the final proton and oxygen nucleus combined. We must therefore rewrite Eq. (19.8-1) in the form

$$ {}_7N^{14} + {}_2He^4 + E_N + E_{He} = {}_8O^{17} + {}_1H^1 + E_O + E_H, \qquad (19.10\text{-}1) $$

where the symbols E_N and E_{He} represent the kinetic energies of the nitrogen atom and the α-particle before the reaction and E_O and E_H the kinetic energies of the oxygen atom and the proton after the reaction. All of these kinetic energies can be measured, and it is found that the combined energies of the final particles are less than those of the initial particles by an amount very close to 1.8×10^{-13} J. We now use the mass-energy relation to compute

$$ \begin{aligned} c^2\Delta m &= 1.28 \times 10^{-3}\ (\text{amu}) \times 9 \times 10^{16}\ (\text{m}^2/\text{sec}^2) \times 1.66 \times 10^{-27}\ (\text{kg/amu}) \\ &= 1.9 \times 10^{-13}\ \text{J}, \end{aligned} $$

and find that the gain in mass is just equivalent to the loss of kinetic energy. Thus, we are able to connect our measurements of the masses of atoms and of their energies with the prediction of the relativity theory, which requires that mass and energy be related by the Einstein equation (Eq. 8.12-1).

Consequently, the Einstein mass-energy relation receives confirmation from all the nuclear reactions in which the masses and kinetic energies of all the particles taking part in the reaction are known. If the mass of only one of the particles is unknown, then this mass can be determined by means of the Einstein equation.

A transmutation of particular interest from the point of view of mass-energy is that of the isotope of hydrogen ${}_1H^2$ (often called ***deuterium***) into hydrogen ${}_1H^1$ and a neutron. This transmutation is produced with the aid of energy alone in the form of γ-radiation. The equation for this reaction is

$$ {}_1H^2 + E_\gamma = {}_1H^1 + {}_0n^1 + E_H + E_n, \qquad (19.10\text{-}1) $$

in which the kinetic energy of the deuterium atom is not included because it is so small that it can be neglected. If the γ-ray energy is reduced, the energy E_H, which can be measured, will decrease. From the law of conservation of momentum, we know that the energy of the neutron E_n will be proportional to E_H. If, therefore, we plot a curve of E_H against E_γ we can determine the value of E_γ for which E_H and E_n will be zero. This ***threshold*** value $(E_\gamma)_0$ then satisfies the equation

$$_1H^2 + (E_\gamma)_0 = {_1H^1} + {_0n^1}. \qquad (19.10\text{-}2)$$

The experimentally determined value of $(E_\gamma)_0$ is 0.000 237 0 amu, and we have (Table 19.1)

$$\begin{array}{rlrl} _1H^2 = & 2.014\,102 \text{ amu} & & 2.016\,472 \text{ amu} \\ (E_\gamma)_0 = & \underline{0.002\,370} & _1H^1 = & \underline{1.007\,825} \\ & 2.016\,472 & _0n^1 = & 1.008\,647 \end{array}$$

Thus, the mass of the neutron is found to be $(1.008\,647 \pm 0.000\,001)$ amu.

19.11 Energy Units

In discussion of nuclear problems, several units of energy are used. We are already familiar with the ***joule*** and the ***kilogram*** as units in which energy can be measured. In the preceding section we have made use of the ***atomic mass unit*** for this purpose. Another unit used very often in nuclear physics is the ***electron volt*** (eV), which is defined as the energy gained by a charge e in falling through a potential drop of 1 volt. The abbreviations MeV and GeV are used for one million (10^6) and one billion (10^9) electron volts, respectively. Finally, it is sometimes convenient to express energies in terms of the electronic mass, m_e. Table 19.2 will prove convenient in converting from one of these units to another.

Table 19.2 *Equivalent Energies in Various Units*

	kg	J	amu	MeV	m_e
1 kg =	1	8.99×10^{16}	6.02×10^{26}	5.61×10^{29}	1.11×10^{30}
1 J =	1.11×10^{-17}	1	6.71×10^{9}	6.24×10^{12}	1.22×10^{13}
1 amu =	1.66×10^{-27}	1.49×10^{-10}	1	9.31×10^{2}	1847
1 MeV =	1.78×10^{-30}	1.60×10^{-13}	1.07×10^{-3}	1	1.93
m_e =	0.911×10^{-30}	8.20×10^{-14}	5.41×10^{-4}	0.512	1

19.12 Electrostatic Accelerators

The success of Rutherford, both in studying atomic structure and in producing transmutations with α-particles, pointed to the desirability of accelerating the nuclei of the light elements to high speeds. It soon became apparent that higher-energy projectiles than those available from radioactive sources were necessary if the particles were to penetrate the nucleus itself or were even to get much closer than 10^{-14} m of its center. Since 1930, a number of ***accelerators,*** or machines for producing energies of several million electron volts or more in charged particles, have been constructed and have been used to produce high-energy electrons, protons ($_1H^1$), deuterons ($_1H^2$), and helium nuclei ($_2He^4$).

The simplest means of accelerating such particles is the ***accelerating tube,*** which is represented schematically in Fig. 19.11. Ions of the appropriate gas

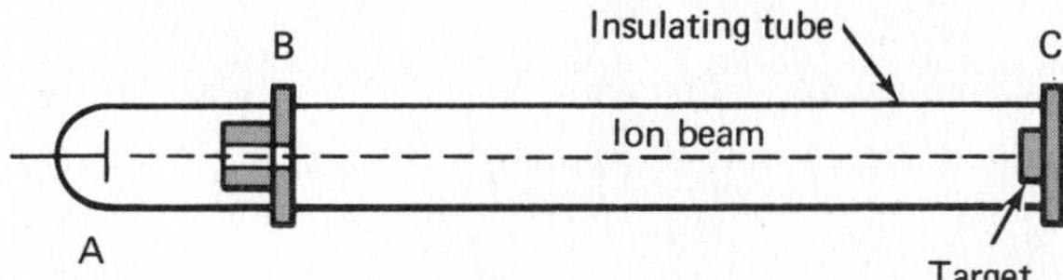

FIG. 19.11 Accelerating tube for high-speed particles.

are produced in the ***ion source*** A, which is essentially a discharge tube like that of Fig. 19.1, and enter the accelerating tube BC through a hole in the electrode B. This electrode is maintained at a high positive potential V with respect to the electrode C on which a target of the material to be bombarded is mounted. The energy of the particles hitting the target is thus

$$E = zeV,$$

where ze is the charge carried by the ion which is accelerated. With such machines, particles of energies of several million electron volts may be obtained. The great advantage of these machines is the accuracy with which the voltage of the accelerated particles can be controlled and measured, but their upper

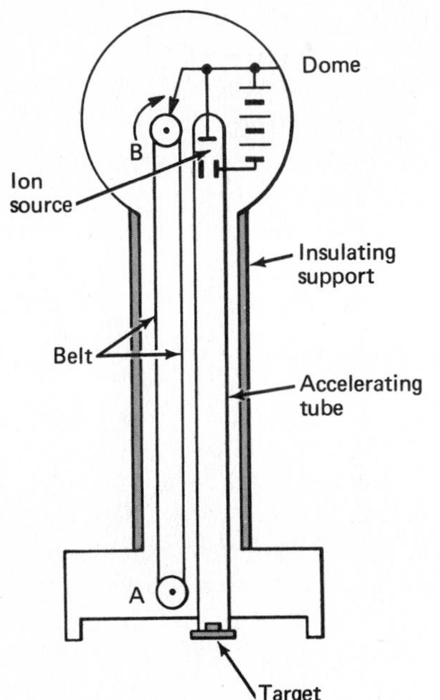

FIG. 19.12 Schematic diagram of a Van de Graaff generator.

Fig. 19.13 Tandem Van de Graaff Accelerator. The accelerator proper is in the large metal chamber extending into the background. This chamber contains a Van de Graaff electrostatic machine and an accelerating tube. Negative ions are introduced at a grounded negative terminal and are accelerated to the positive terminal, which may be maintained at a potential of as much as 3 MV with respect to ground. Near the positive terminal these ions are stripped of two or more electrons, so that they become positive ions. They are then accelerated toward a second negative terminal, acquiring a total energy up to 6 MeV if the ions are singly charged and more if they carry multiple charges. After emerging from the accelerator, the ion beams are bent as they pass between the poles of the magnet in the center of the picture, thus being directed into one of a number of experimental chambers, two of which are shown in the foreground. (Courtesy of High Voltage Engineering.)

limit of energy is probably about 10 MeV because of the difficulty of providing insulation which will stand the very high voltages needed.

One of the best ways of supplying electric power at high voltage to an accelerating tube is by the use of a ***Van de Graaff electrostatic generator,*** which was developed by Robert J. Van de Graaff (1900–1967). This machine is identical in principle with the electrophorus and other machines of Sec. 15.4. As shown schematically in Fig. 19.12, this generator uses a motor-driven insulating belt that runs over two pulleys, one at ground potential and the other inside a large conducting dome, which is insulated from the ground. An electric charge is placed on the belt at A. This charge is then carried by the belt until it reaches the dome, where it flows off through the contact B and collects on the dome. As the potential of the dome increases, extra mechanical work must be done to bring the charges to it—i.e., to drive the belt—and this work is the source of the energy delivered by the machine. A discharge tube similar to that shown in Fig. 19.11 may be connected between the dome and ground, in which case the ion source is mounted inside the dome. Some idea of the scale and construction of a practical Van de Graaff machine may be gained from Fig. 19.13.

19.13 The Cyclotron

Many accelerators are based on the principle of the cyclotron, which was invented by Ernest O. Lawrence (1901–1958). In this device, the ions to be accelerated move in a circular path in a strong magnetic field. As we know, the radius R of such a path will be given by Eq. (17.2-3) as

$$R = mv/Bze, \tag{19.13-1}$$

where m is the mass, v is the speed, ze is the charge of the ion, and B is the magnetic flux density in which the ions describe a circular path. In Lawrence's machine the ions are released and travel in their circular tracks within a hollow

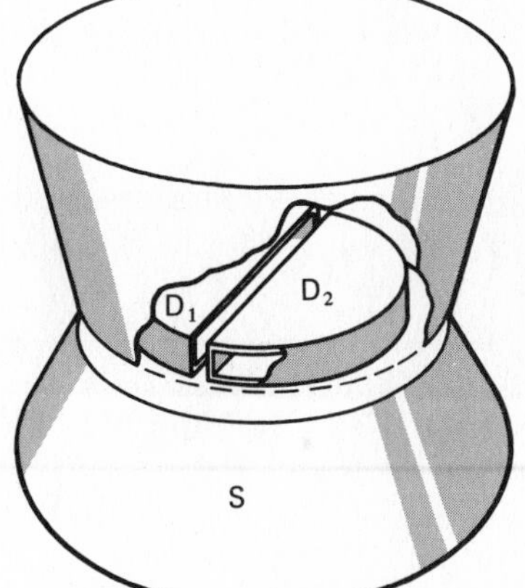

Fig. 19.14 Cyclotron dees between the poles of an electromagnet.

metal box, Figs. 19.14 and 19.15, which is shaped like a pillbox. This box is cut in half along a diameter in order to make two dee-shaped boxes, D_1, and D_2, which are insulated from one another and are called ***dees***. The dees lie between the poles of a large electromagnet so that there is a uniform magnetic flux density B inside the dees. A group of ions from the ion source I in Fig. 19.15a

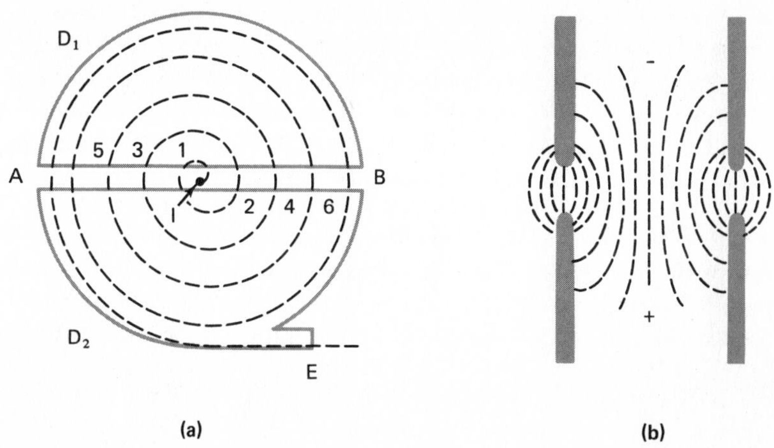

Fig. 19.15 Acceleration of particles by the cyclotron.

is released near the center of the dees at a time when D_2 is at a positive potential V with respect to D_1. These ions are then accelerated by the electric field between D_1 and D_2 (Fig. 19.15b) to a speed v_1 such that

$$Vze = \tfrac{1}{2}mv_1^2.$$

Because of the magnetic field, the ion paths are bent into a circle of radius R_1 given by

$$R_1 = mv_1/Bze.$$

The potential difference across the gap between the dees is supplied by an oscillator operating at such a frequency that, by the time the ions have again reached the diameter AB, the electric field will have reversed and the same ions will again be accelerated by a potential difference V. The ions will thus enter D_2 with a speed such that

$$2Vze = \tfrac{1}{2}mv_2^2,$$

the energy Vze having been accumulated twice. While the ions are in D_2, they travel a path with the radius R_2 given by

$$R_2 = mv_2/Bze,$$

and R_2 is greater than R_1, since v_2 is greater than v_1. This process is repeated many times, and after n passages across the gap the energy will be

$$nVze = \tfrac{1}{2}mv_n^2, \tag{19.13-2}$$

and the radius will be

$$R_n = mv_n/Bze. \tag{19.13-3}$$

We can see that the time τ taken by an ion to traverse any one of the semicircles is the same as that required for it to travel the nth semicircle:

$$\tau = \pi R_n/v_n = \pi m/Bze. \tag{19.13-4}$$

Hence, the time is independent of v and of its corresponding R. Therefore, when D_1 is positive with respect to D_2, the potential difference V can accelerate positive ions at any of the points 1, 3, 5, ... in Fig. 19.15a; $\tau = \pi R_2/v_2 = \pi R_4/v_4 = \cdots$ later these ions will be at points 2, 4, 6, ..., respectively. By this time, if the field is reversed so that D_2 is positive with respect to D_1, the ions can again be accelerated through a potential difference V. If the field is reversed with a frequency $1/\tau$, then it can simultaneously accelerate ions at various stages of their outward spiral. The reader should easily perceive that the ions will emerge at E in bunches, at intervals of 2τ. At any instant within the dees, the ions are traveling in groups along the spiral path, each group being separated from its nearest neighboring groups by one complete turn of the spiral.

The field in the gap between the dees is reversed at intervals of τ by applying a potential difference

$$V = V_0 \cos 2\pi\nu t,$$

where the frequency of the alternation is $\nu = 1/2\tau$; thus, the period of the oscillation is $T = 2\tau$.

From Newtonian mechanics, we would calculate that the maximum kinetic energy which could be imparted to an ion by a cyclotron would be

$$w_n = \tfrac{1}{2}mv_n^2 = (BzeR_n)^2/2m, \tag{19.13-5}$$

limited only by the radius of the dees and the magnitude of B. However, when the ions reach speeds which are an appreciable fraction of the speed of light, Eq. (19.13-5) no longer works and relativistic dynamics must be used. For protons, this breakdown of Newtonian mechanics occurs at about 10 MeV. The cyclotron can be made to give more massive ions a somewhat greater energy; for example, the 60-inch-diameter cyclotron at Berkeley, California, has produced 25 MeV deuterons.

19.14 The Problem of Synchronization

Let us consider one of the groups of ions being accelerated in a cyclotron, say, those at point 5 in Fig. 19.15a. Some of the ions in the group will arrive at the gap a little earlier, and some a little later, than the majority of the ions. A more detailed analysis than that which we employ here (see Prob. 19.11) will show that those which arrive early at point 5 will take a little longer than τ (Eq. 19.13-4) to arrive at point 6; similarly, those which arrive late will take a little less than τ. Thus, both leaders and stragglers tend to be pulled into the center of the group. In this way, as long as the speeds do not become too great, the successive arrivals of the ions at the gap remain synchronized with the field alternations.

However, when the kinetic energy of the ions has become so great that their speed is an appreciable fraction of the speed of light, the observed mass of the ions increases as their speed increases [cf. Eq. (8.9-5)]. This is equivalent to saying that the ions are harder to accelerate; their speed increment will not be enough to make them arrive at the gap at the correct time for their next acceleration. It is this fact, based on relativistic dynamics, that limits the production of higher-energy particles by cyclotrons.

The problem of adapting the cyclotron to the production of higher energies than those at which Newtonian mechanics apply was solved independently by V. I. Veksler (1908–) in Russia and Edwin M. McMillan (1907–) in the United States in 1945. They realized that the condition expressed by Eq. (19.13-4) could be satisfied even for very high-energy particles if either the frequency of the alternating potential ($\nu = 1/2\tau$) or the magnetic flux density (B), or both, were changed in the proper way while the particles were being accelerated. We need not concern ourselves either with the details of the calculations or with the way in which the changes are brought about, except to say that acceleration of light nuclei to speeds approaching that of light has been found entirely possible, by holding the radius R_n (Eq. 19.13-3) essentially constant and changing both B and v (see Prob. 19.9). Adaptations of the cyclotron in which v and B are changed are variously called the frequency-modulated cyclotron, the synchro-cyclotron, the sychrotron, the alternating gradient cyclotron—depending on particulars of design.

Typical machines of the synchro-cyclotron or frequency-modulated type have magnetic pole pieces about 14 ft in diameter. The potential difference for providing the acceleration is 10 to 30 kv. The radiofrequency oscillator is controlled by a motor-driven variable capacitor, so that the frequency of the accelerating field varies from about 28 megahertz (megacycles per second) to 17 megahertz at a repetition rate of 60/sec. Such frequency-modulated cyclotrons will produce 450 MeV protons.

With some modification, primarily of the ion source, in the University of Chicago synchrocyclotron, heavier ions have been accelerated. The most massive of these were stripped carbon nuclei (C^{6+}) which had energies ranging up to 1.1 GeV.

19.15 The Betatron

The relativistic effects which limit the cyclotron are even more serious when electrons are being accelerated, since these very light particles acquire speeds comparable with that of light at much lower energies than do protons or deuterons. Another type of accelerator, called the betatron, has been developed by Donald William Kerst (1911–). This device capitalizes on the fact that very-high-speed particles have a speed ($\approx c$) which changes little with increasing energy. It follows from this fact that the frequency of revolution of high energy electrons in a magnetic field that is properly arranged so that the circular orbit is of constant radius (see Prob. 19.8) is itself very nearly constant. The electrons are made to circulate in a doughnut-shaped vacuum tube under the influence of a magnetic field. Such electrons are then equivalent to a current in a circular coil, and if the magnetic flux through the coil is changed [Eq. (17.7-1)] they will be accelerated by the induced emf in their path.

Modern betratrons produce electrons with energies ranging up to 300 MeV. The varying magnetic field is provided by energizing the large electromagnet with current drawn from a 60-hertz AC source. Although the flux change for providing the emf to accelerate the electrons has the proper sign for a half-cycle, we also require that the direction of the field be correct for curving the electron path into the proper orbit—that is, the field must direct electrons around a path in the interior of the doughnut-shaped vacuum tube. These two requirements are both met during only one-fourth of each cycle, for $\frac{1}{240}$ sec. In typical betatrons the energy acquired by an electron in each revolution is 400 eV. Thus, if the maximum energy is 100 MeV, each electron must travel through 2.5×10^5 revolutions while being accelerated to maximum energy.

Electrons can be kicked out of orbit and into the target by suddenly diminishing the magnetic field. This is accomplished by installing a separate coil of a few turns which lie adjacent to the main magnetizing coil. At the proper instant a capacitor bank is discharged through this coil so that the total field is suddenly weakened. During this weakening, the electrons will spiral outward to strike a suitably placed target. The electrons are not generally used directly to produce transmutations, but they can be made to produce γ-rays which, in turn, will produce transmutations.

We shall mention three other modifications of the betatron design which have made it possible to produce machines of greater utility. First, in the larger orbit machines, it is neither feasible nor necessary to fill the entire area enclosed by the orbit with magnetic flux. The centripetal force for curving the electron path can be provided by suitably designed electromagnets placed along the entire extent of the doughnut-shaped tube. Moreover, the establishment of the field provides a $d\phi/dt$ through the area and, although this is not uniformly distributed over the area, it will nonetheless provide an accelerating emf. With such design features, it becomes possible to build machines wherein the diameter of the ion path is of the order of 1000 ft.

A second kind of modification capitalizes on the fact that electrons having very small mass acquire speeds close to that of light at relatively small energies. For example, electrons whose kinetic energy is two MeV are moving with $v = 0.98c$. The change in ω, the angular velocity with which the electrons revolve, is therefore insignificant and any further change of energy will show up mainly in the observed mass of the electrons (cf. Secs. 8.9–8.11). It is possible then to place two cylindrical shells in tandem within the evacuated doughnut-shaped tube, as in Fig. 19.16, and to apply a radiofrequency potential

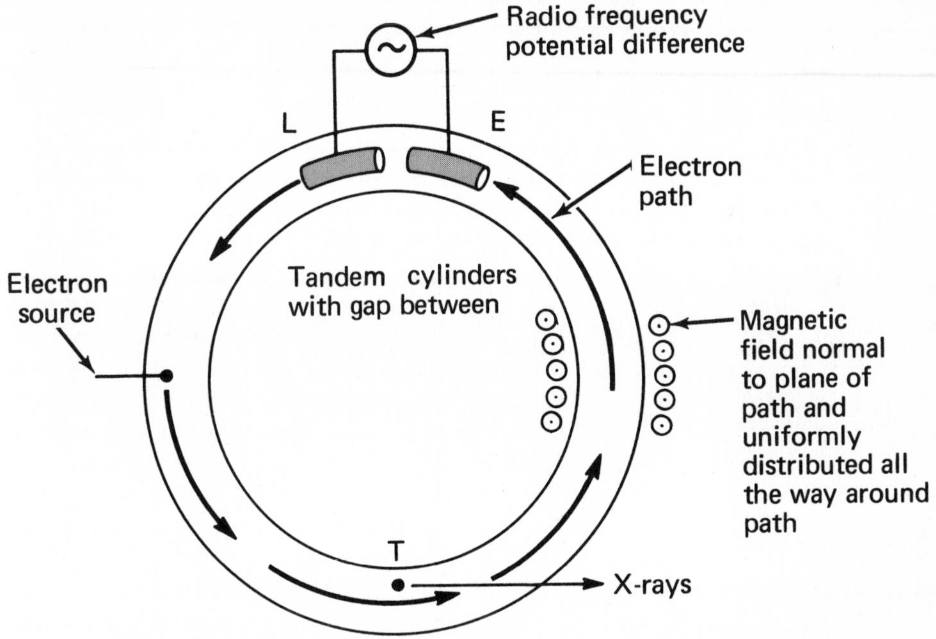

FIG. 19.16 Schematic diagram of a betatron-synchrotron.

difference across the gap between the cylinders so that it can impart still higher energies to the electrons. On each revolution, the electrons traveling with nearly constant ω will arrive in synchronism with an applied V so that they are given an additional energy $\Delta E = Ve$. It is important, of course, that the

Fig. 19.17 The 28 GeV proton synchrotron at CERN (Organisation Européene pour la Recherche Nucléaire, located near Geneva, Switzerland). The upper photograph is an aerial view of the installation. The acceleration of the ions takes place in a vacuum tube with a radius of 100 meters. This tube is placed in an underground tunnel—it lies beneath the slightly raised circle that shows in the center of the picture. The lower photograph shows part of the inside of the tunnel, including several of the large electromagnets that bend the beam into its circular path. (Courtesy of CERN.)

length of the cylinders be so planned that the field is zero as the electrons enter the first cylinder at E or leave the second at I; otherwise, the energy would be diminished.

Devices which incorporate the two modifications described above are called electron synchrotrons. Energies up to a few hundred MeV are possible. But the electrons undergo strong centripetal accelerations as they are directed along the circular path at speeds near to c. Accelerated charges radiate electromagnetic waves, or rather, photons. Hence, there is a point of diminishing returns at which any attempted increase in energy is balanced by the loss of energy radiated as photons.

The third modification in betatron design is simply to adapt the equipment to particles of greater mass. There is no fundamental difference in principle between the proton synchrotron and the electron synchrotron. Figure 19.17 shows one of the largest existing proton accelerators. Protons are injected into the track by another accelerator, a Van de Graaff accelerator, with energies of about 10 MeV. These are then accelerated to energies up to 30 GeV. Higher energies, 10 to 20 times those produced by present machines, are contemplated.

EXERCISES

19.15-1 Calculate the speed of a 30 GeV proton. What will be its observed mass?

19.15-2 For a betatron which draws its energy from 60 hertz AC, sketch curves for ϕ and $d\phi/dt$ on the same time axis. Then assume that the electron path requires the magnetic induction to be directed upward. State what direction the current must flow in the coils, and on your graphs identify the quarter cycle during which the system will operate.

19.16 Linear Accelerators

In Sec. 19.12 we described a single-stage linear accelerator, an electrostatic accelerator in which a Van der Graaff generator provided the accelerating potential difference. One might think of connecting several such machines in series in order to create a multistage linear accelerator, but insulation and corona discharge problems would soon limit the employment of such methods for obtaining high energies. During the earlier development of accelerators, devices such as the cyclotron and the betatron, which recycled the particles through the same potential differences, offered much more promise of success. As we mentioned in Sec. 19.15, however, the centripetal acceleration of charged particles and the accompanying photonic radiation imposes certain limits on recycling accelerators, particularly on those which use electrons as the particles to receive the energy. A way to avoid such radiation involves new approaches to linear acceleration.

One type of linear accelerator is the drift-tube proton accelerator, Fig. 19.18. A copper tank about 12 m long and 1 m in diameter serves as a resonant cavity or wave guide for radio frequency waves of about 200 megahertz (cf. Chapter 23). As these electromagnetic (e-m) waves travel down the guide at approximately the speed of light, the electric field along the axis of the guide

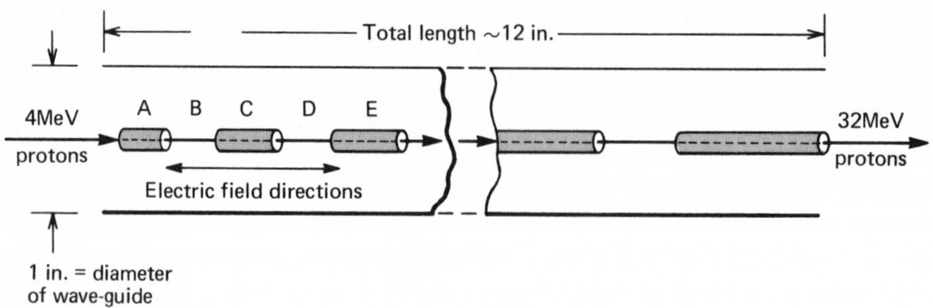

FIG. 19.18 Schematic diagram of a drift-tube proton accelerator.

at any given point, such as B, oscillates from the forward to backward direction 2×10^8 times/sec. If protons are in region B when the electric field is in the forward direction, they will experience an acceleration in that direction, to the right in Fig. 19.18. However, since the protons are not moving with the speed of light, the region of the e-m wave where the field is in the forward direction will leave them behind and they will be overtaken by a region of the e-m wave where the electric field is in the reverse direction; they would, thus, be immediately decelerated, and our purpose to provide high-energy protons would be defeated. Since the protons are traveling to the right, let us suppose that the reversed or decelerating electric field would overtake them at C. At this point, they can be shielded from the reverse field by arranging that they drift through

FIG. 19.19 The Stanford Linear Accelerator. This machine, designed to accelerate electrons to an energy of 20 GeV, was first operated in 1966. The long, narrow building extending into the distant background houses the oscillators that supply the accelerating voltages and the pumps that maintain the necessary vacuum. It has a length of two miles. The tube through which the electrons are accelerated runs under this building. An underground electromagnet can deflect the beam, at a "switching yard," to either of the two large buildings in the foreground. These buildings contain the target on which the beam impinges and the analyzing and detecting devices that are needed to study the products of the nuclear reactions which take place when the electrons strike the targets. The target buildings are backed by a hill (in the immediate foreground) which acts as a shield for the scattered radiation that may be produced. (Photograph by Roland Quintero.)

a section of a conducting cylinder inside of which the field will be zero, except for slight effects at the open ends of the cylinder. By the time the protons have drifted at constant velocity through the shielding tube at region C and have arrived at region D, the next e-m wave crest with the electric field in the forward direction will have arrived at D; the protons will be accelerated again into region E, where they are again shielded from the reverse electric field. This process of alternate acceleration and shielding can be repeated many times. The tube sections A, C, E, ... are known as drift-tubes, and, since the velocity of the protons is increasing, the lengths of both the drift tubes and the gaps must be increased progressively along the path followed by the protons.

In the drift-tube accelerator designed by Luis Alvarez (1911–) and built at Berkeley, 4 MeV protons from a Van de Graaff accelerator are injected at the input end. These protons are accelerated in the gaps separating a line of 46 drift-tubes to emerge with 32 MeV of energy.

Electrons may also be accelerated by an e-m wave which travels along a wave guide. In this case, however, the drift-tubes are not necessary. By microwave techniques, the crest of the electric field in an e-m wave can be made to travel along a wave guide at speeds somewhat less than c. If electrons at about the same velocity are injected into this crest, they will be moving with a field that can accelerate them, provided of course that the field is in the right direction at the instant of injection. Since 4 MeV electrons, which move with speeds of $0.9935c$, can be injected, a wave that moves at about this speed can provide acceleration of the electrons throughout the length of the wave guide.

A linear accelerator based on the principles just described has been designed at Stanford University. When fully operational, the wave guide will be about 3 km long, and the energy of the emergent electrons will be about 45 GeV. The machine will be pulsed 360 times per second for a time of 1.7 μ sec. The average current output will be 60μA.

EXERCISES

19.16-1 Show that 4.000 MeV electrons travel with 0.9935 c. Then compute the speed of 45 GeV electrons.

19.16-2 How many electrons per pulse can be provided by the Stanford linear accelerator?

19.17 Cosmic Radiation

Despite the size of the largest accelerators, by far the most energetic of particles are to be found in cosmic radiation. The early investigators who studied radioactivity found that electroscopes set up on the surface of the earth continued to lose charge even though all possible sources of radioactivity had been removed from their neighborhood. All attempts—by improvement of construction, change of materials, better insulation, etc.—to reduce this loss of charge to zero failed. There seemed to be a ***residual ionization*** in the air surrounding the electroscope below which one could not go. In an effort to get away from the source of this residual ionization, experimenters began to carry electroscopes aloft in manned balloons. They soon discovered that the rate of loss of charge decreased during the first several meters of ascent but then, as greater heights were reached, the electroscopes lost charge at markedly increased rates. The discovery of the heretofore unsuspected radiation that caused this ionization opened up a whole new field for investigation. As new instrumentation and new investigative techniques were developed, the radiation was explored by unmanned balloons to heights of 12 miles or more and in deep mines, as well as under water.

We cannot go into detail concerning the fascinating history of the study of this radiation which occupies the entire first half of the twentieth century. We shall limit our remarks to a few pertinent facts. Since the radiation impinges on the earth from all directions in space, it is called ***cosmic radiation.*** It consists primarily of high-speed protons, and, as one might surmise, these charged particles follow curved paths in the magnetic field of the earth; hence there are latitude effects as well as altitude variations. Although some of the protons evidently come from the sun and there are variations associated with solar activity—solar flares and prominences—many other protons apparently come from other stars. Protons of energies ranging up to 1000 GeV have been found. Other particles, including γ-ray photons, also impinge on the upper atmosphere from outer space.

When the cosmic radiation hits the oxygen and nitrogen atoms in the earth's upper atmosphere, many secondary effects occur. Radioactive ${}_6C^{14}$ is produced, as are many of the elementary particles listed in Sec. 19.19. Also, there are bands of ionized molecules of oxygen and nitrogen which surround the earth as broad belts roughly over the tropics. These belts are known as ***Van Allen belts*** after their discoverer, James A. Van Allen (1914–   ).

While cosmic radiation provides a natural source of high-energy particles—indeed, including particles of much higher energy than man has yet been able to produce—the intensity of the radiation for probing the nature of the nucleus is not great. Transmutations which can be readily carried out in a short time in an accelerator not uncommonly would occur once a year, on the average, if the source of particles were only cosmic radiation and if the same target were used. Hence, man's growing knowledge of the nucleus depends heavily on accelerator technology. At the same time, of course, we can regard ourselves as most fortunate that cosmic radiation is relatively weak; life as we know it could not exist under constant bombardment by high-energy particles.

19.18 Types of Transmutations

In Sec. 19.8 we discussed transmutations that involve (α, p) reactions in which the α-particles were provided by naturally radioactive elements. The development of particle accelerators that we have described in the preceding sections has provided new sources of particles for inducing transmuting reactions. The range of energies, the numbers of kinds of particles, and rates of production of the particles have all been vastly increased. By means of these tools, nuclear physicists have studied a great number of transmutation reactions. In Table 19.3 some of the more important types of transmutations are summarized. The table assumes that there is a general target nucleus $_ZX^M$. When this target is struck by a high-speed particle, the Z and/or the M are increased or diminished,

Table 19.3 *Transmutation Reactions*

Notation: Target nucleus is denoted by $_ZX^M$

$\alpha = \alpha$-particle $_2He^4$
p = proton $_1H^1$
d = deutron $_1H^2$
n = neutron $_0n^1$
$\gamma = \gamma$-ray photon $_0\gamma^0$

Reaction	Product	Example
n, γ	$_ZX^{M+1}$	$_{53}Xe^{132} + {_0n^1} \rightarrow {_{53}Xe^{133}} + {_0\gamma^0}$
n, p	$_{Z-1}Y^M$	$_7N^{14} + {_0n^1} \rightarrow {_6C^{14}} + {_1H^1}$
n, α	$_{Z-2}Y^{M-3}$	$_5B^{10} + {_0n^1} \rightarrow {_3Li^7} + {_2He^4}$
n, 2n	$_ZX^{M-1}$	$_{55}Cs^{133} + {_0n^1} \rightarrow {_{55}Cs^{132}} + {_0n^1} + {_0n^1}$
p, γ	$_{Z+1}Y^{M+1}$	$_5B^{10} + {_1H^1} \rightarrow {_6C^{11}} + {_0\gamma^0}$
p, n	$_{Z+1}Y^M$	$_8O^{18} + {_1H^1} \rightarrow {_9F^{18}} + {_0n^1}$
p, d	$_ZX^{M-1}$	$_1H^3 + {_1H^1} \rightarrow {_1H^2} + {_1H^2}$
p, α	$_{Z-1}Y^{M-3}$	$_9F^{19} + {_1H^1} \rightarrow {_8O^{16}} + {_2He^4}$
d, p	$_ZX^{M+1}$	$_{11}Na^{23} + {_1H^2} \rightarrow {_{11}Na^{24}} + {_1H^1}$
d, n	$_{Z+1}Y^{M+1}$	$_6C^{12} + {_1H^2} \rightarrow {_7N^{13}} + {_0n^1}$
d, 2n	$_{Z+1}Y^M$	$_{29}Cu^{65} + {_1H^2} \rightarrow {_{30}Zn^{65}} + {_0n^1} + {_0n^1}$
d, α	$_{Z-1}Y^{M-2}$	$_{12}Mg^{26} + {_1H^2} \rightarrow {_{11}Na^{24}} + {_2He^4}$
d, 2α	$_{Z-3}Y^{M-6}$	$_{33}As^{75} + {_1H^2} \rightarrow {_{30}Zn^{69}} + {_2He^4} + {_2He^4}$
α, n	$_{Z+2}Y^{M+3}$	$_{47}Ag^{107} + {_2He^4} \rightarrow {_{49}In^{110}} + {_0n^1}$
α, p	$_{Z+1}Y^{M+3}$	$_{12}Mg^{25} + {_2He^4} \rightarrow {_{13}Al^{28}} + {_1H^1}$
α, 2n	$_{Z+2}Y^{M+2}$	$_{82}Pb^{208} + {_2He^4} \rightarrow {_{84}Po^{210}} + {_0n^1} + {_0n^1}$
γ, n	$_ZX^{M-1}$	$_{20}Ca^{40} + {_0\gamma^0} \rightarrow {_{20}Ca^{39}} + {_0n^1}$
γ, p	$_{Z-1}Y^{M-1}$	$_{12}Mg^{25} + {_0\gamma^0} \rightarrow {_{11}Na^{24}} + {_1H^1}$

giving a different nucleus as a product of the reaction. Column 1 of the table indicates the kind of reaction, and Column 2 characterizes the nucleus that results; column 3 gives a typical example, and in most cases there are many other similar reactions. Table 19.3 lists only the more important types of reactions, and it is by no means exhaustive. For more details on transmutation reactions, the interested reader should consult the references at the end of this chapter.

We should make two general remarks about Table 19.3. First, the equations give only the grosser features of the reactions. On the left, for example, there is nothing to indicate the kinetic energy of the reacting particles. The atoms $_5B^{10}$ and $_1H^1$, the (p, γ) example, will not react unless the proton strikes the boron nucleus with a sufficient amount of kinetic energy. Likewise, the total energy on the right is not accounted for, since the resulting particles possess kinetic energy. Second, while several of the product atoms are stable, some are radioactive. Thus, the (n, p) example yields $_6C^{14}$, which is radioactive, and, since it is produced in the atmosphere, it becomes the basis for radiocarbon dating of the remains of organic matter.

19.19 *Artificial Radioactivity*

Many transmuting reactions result in stable nuclei, but some do not; rather, they produce radioactive nuclei which may have half-lives ranging from the very short to the very long. In fact, one way of looking at a transmutation is to regard the original nucleus and the bombarding particle as first forming a compound nucleus. A theory involving compound nuclei was developed by Bohr. Thus, in the (d, α) example of Table 19.3, the reaction would be written

$$_{12}Mg^{26} + {}_1H^2 \rightarrow ({}_{13}Al^{28}) \rightarrow {}_{11}Na^{24} + {}_2He^4,$$

where $({}_{13}Al^{28})$ represents the compound nucleus. But $_{13}Al^{28}$ does not occur in nature (cf. Table 19.1) and, since it decomposes by emitting a proton, it is said to be artificially radioactive. In Table 19.4 we list several types of artificial radioactivity with examples.

Table 19.4 *Decay of Artificially Produced Radioactive Nuclei: Typical Processes*

Proton emission	$_9F^{18} \rightarrow {}_8O^{17} + {}_1H^1$
Neutron emission	$_6C^{13} \rightarrow {}_6C^{12} + {}_0n^1$
Positron emission	$_7N^{13} \rightarrow {}_6C^{13} + \beta^+$
Electron emission	$_6C^{14} \rightarrow {}_7N^{14} + \beta^-$
Alpha emission	$_4Be^8 \rightarrow {}_2He^4 + {}_2He^4$
	$_4Be^7 \rightarrow {}_2He^4 + {}_2He^3$
	$_{94}Pu^{239} \rightarrow {}_{92}U^{235} + {}_2He^4$
Gamma emission	$({}_5B^{11}) \rightarrow {}_5B^{11} + \gamma$
	$({}_{22}Ti^{49}) \rightarrow {}_{22}Ti^{49} + \gamma$

In Table 19.4 we have given an example of positron emission. The ***positron*** is a *positive* electron, and we shall discuss it further in Sec. 19.20. Also, under alpha emission, the nucleus $_2He^3$ appears; this, of course, is the nucleus of an isotope of helium and as such may be regarded as a "light alpha particle."

Under gamma emission, we have shown reactions as starting with compound nuclei: $({}_5B^{11})$ and $({}_{22}Ti^{49})$. As was mentioned above, we might regard all of the sample reactions as starting with compound nuclei. But the difference between say, ${}_5B^{11}$ and ${}_9F^{18}$ is that the former does occur naturally as a stable nucleus, while the latter exists only as an artificially produced radioactive isotope. The reason for writing $({}_5B^{11})$ is that this nucleus can be artificially produced as an *excited* nucleus—that is, as a nucleus, it contains an excess of energy. It then emits a γ-ray in order to rid itself of the excess energy.

We give two examples of the production of excited nuclei. The first is known as ***α-capture*** wherein all of the nucleons—protons and neutrons—are incorporated into the product nucleus. Thus, if ${}_3Li^7$ is bombarded with α-particles, we may get

$$ {}_3Li^7 + {}_2He^4 \rightarrow ({}_5B^{11}). $$

Since the γ-ray is soon emitted, this reaction is sometimes simply written as

$$ {}_3Li^7 + {}_2He^4 \rightarrow {}_5B^{11} + \gamma. $$

In the other example, an artificially produced isotope of vanadium ${}_{23}V^{49}$ captures one of its own inner electrons. This electron comes from the shell closest to the nucleus, the K-shell (cf. Chapter 25), so the process is known as ***K-capture.*** The reaction may be written

$$ {}_{23}V^{49} + {}_{-1}e^0 \rightarrow ({}_{22}Ti^{49}). $$

Again, since the compound nucleus is short-lived, the equation is sometimes simplified to say

$$ {}_{23}V^{49} + {}_{-1}e^0 \rightarrow {}_{22}Ti^{49} + \gamma $$

Much more about artificial radioactivity will be found in the references at the end of the chapter.

19.20 Elementary Particles

Two particles encountered thus far stand out distinctly from such things as atoms, molecules, or even atomic nuclei. The proton and the electron give no evidence of having structure, i.e., of being made up of simpler particles. Entities of this sort are known as ***elementary particles.**** A considerable number of elementary particles have been discovered since 1930. A full discussion of these particles and of their properties would take us well beyond the scope of this book, but some introduction to them is of interest.

In 1928, P. A. M. Dirac (1902–) published a theory in which he investigated the consequences of making the quantum mechanics (cf. Chapters 24–25) consistent with the theory of special relativity. One of the results of his treatment was the prediction that there should exist a particle having the same mass as the electron, but having a charge of $+e$, rather than the $-e$ of the electron. Such particles would be expected to be rare, since the theory indicates that any

* The photon is also elementary in this sense.

one of them and an electron would, upon encounter, be mutually annihilated. Because electrons are present in great quantities in matter, such encounters can be expected to insure the annihilation of any of the positive particles, which we call ***positrons,*** in a short time. The conservation of mass-energy and of momentum demands that the annihilation be accompanied by the emission of two photons, having a combined energy of at least $2m_ec^2$, where m_e is the mass of the electron. Conversely, an electron-positron ***pair*** can be ***created*** by the disappearance of a photon of energy equal to or greater than $2m_ec^2$, provided that the event takes place in the neighborhood of matter that can absorb a small part of the total energy and so insure the conservation of momentum.

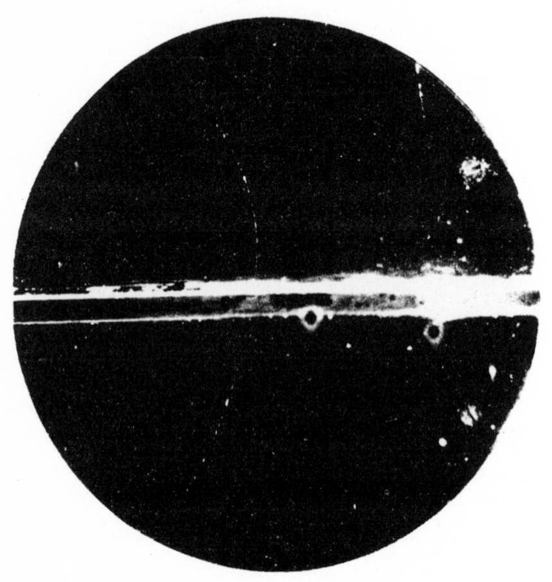

FIG. 19.20 Track of a positron in a cloud chamber. A magnetic field was present, directed into the plane of the paper, hence the curvature of the tracks indicates that the particle was either a positive charge moving upward or a negative charge moving downward. That the former is true is shown by the further fact that the radius of curvature is less above the 6 mm lead plate than it is below. The particle lost part of its kinetic energy in traversing the lead. (Courtesy and permission of Carl D. Anderson.)

Within a short time after Dirac's publication, Carl D. Anderson (1905–) in the United States and P. M. S. Blackett (1897–) in England found that the predicted particles did occur when cosmic rays interacted with matter. Figure 19.20 shows the path of one of Anderson's early positrons, traveling upward in a cloud chamber in a magnetic field and passing through a metal plate. The electron and the positron thus became the first known examples of particles that could be created in a process of ***pair production*** and that could annihilate each other with the production of ***annihilation radiation.*** The positron is known as the ***antiparticle*** of the electron.

As we shall see later, every known elementary particle possesses an antiparticle. The whole set of antiparticles is said to constitute ***antimatter***. The use of the prefix "anti" is perhaps unfortunate. There are reasons to believe that portions of the universe may have as their constituents antiparticles and that the things that make up matter for us (such as electrons) may there be rare.

A quite different type of elementary particle was predicted in 1935 by Hideki Yukawa (1907–). In attempting to explain the fact that nuclei hold together in spite of the mutual electrostatic repulsion of the protons within them (cf. Sec. 19.21), Yukawa invoked an analogy with electrostatic forces. We have discussed such forces in terms of an electric field, but they can be viewed in another way. We shall see in Chapter 23 that light can be described as an electromagnetic wave; hence, the photon can be considered to be an electromagnetic particle. It is possible to describe the forces of electrostatic attraction between a positive and negative charge as being the result of the creation and annihilation of photons. We shall not attempt to justify this statement but shall ask the reader to accept it provisionally. Yukawa argued that the forces that hold nuclei together might be the result of the creation and annihilation of a new particle. Knowing that the forces are effective only over very short distances (Sec. 20.21) and invoking the Heisenberg uncertainty principle, which we will encounter further in Chapter 24, he was able to calculate the approximate mass of such particles to be about 200 m_e.

In 1936, Anderson and S. H. Neddermeyer (1907–) found particles of the mass predicted by Yukawa, during their studies of cosmic rays. These particles came to be called ***μ*-mesons***; it was found that they can carry either positive or negative charge, but that the magnitude of this charge is always e. As might be expected, the μ-meson with positive charge is the antiparticle of that with negative charge.

It is ironic that the μ-meson, as has been revealed by later experiments, cannot account for the binding of nuclei, on the basis of which its existence was predicted. Another set of mesons, discovered later and having masses of about 270 m_e, are now believed to be responsible for the stability of nuclei. They are known as ***π*-mesons**. Three such mesons, carrying charges of $+e$, 0, and $-e$, are known. The negative π-meson is the antiparticle of the positive one; two neutral π-mesons may annihilate each other, so this particle is its own antiparticle.

The existence of a very illusive particle, the ***neutrino*** was first postulated in 1934. When radioactive substances decay by β-emission, it is found that the energies of the ejected electrons vary over a wide range. How can it be that two atoms, identical in all respects, including mass, can emit electrons of different energies and yet end up as identical atoms? Such a possibility seems to violate the conservation of mass-energy. Wolfgang Pauli (1900–1958) suggested a way out of this difficulty by supposing that a very light, uncharged particle is emitted at the same time as the electron and that the sum of the energies of the two particles is a constant for a given type of radioactive decay. The low mass and the lack of charge would allow the particle to travel through great thicknesses of matter, accounting for the fact that it had not been detected. The particle that is emitted at the same time as an electron was originally called a neutrino ("the little one without charge"). It has since been renamed as the ***antineutrino***, and the name ***neutrino*** has been given to the neutral particle

* The term "meson," meaning "intermediate," is applied to elementary particles having masses greater than that of the electron but less than that of the proton.

Table 19.5 *The Elementary Particles*

[From *Elementary Particles*, by David H. Frisch and Alan M. Thorndike (Reference 19B)

Particle	Symbol	Rest Mass (units of m_e)	Charge	Spin*	Mean Life (seconds)	Antiparticle
Leptons						
Neutrino	ν	0	0	$\frac{1}{2}$	stable	$\bar{\nu}$ (Antieutrino)
Electron	e^-	1	$-e$	$\frac{1}{2}$	stable	e^+ (Positron)
Mu minus	μ^-	206.77 ± 0.02	$-e$	$\frac{1}{2}$	$(2.212 \pm 0.001) \times 10^{-6}$	μ^+ (Mu plus)
Mesons						
Pi zero	π^0	264 ± 0.1	0	0	$(2.2 \pm 0.8) \times 10^{-16}$	π^0 itself
Pi plus	π^+	273.2 ± 0.1	$+e$	0	$(2.55 \pm 0.03) \times 10^{-8}$	π^- (Pi minus)
K plus	K^+	966.6 ± 0.4	$+e$	0	$(1.224 \pm 0.013) \times 10^{-8}$	K^- (K minus)
K zero	K^0	974 ± 1	0	0	$K_1{}^0$:$(1.00 \pm 0.04) \times 10^{-10}$ $K_2{}^0$:$(6.1 \pm 1\ .4) \times 10^{-8}$	$\overline{K^0}$ (K zero-bar)
Baryons						
Proton	p	1836.12 ± 0.02	$+e$	$\frac{1}{2}$	Stable	$\bar{p}$ (Antiproton)
Neutron	n	1836.65 ± 0.02	0	$\frac{1}{2}$	$(1.01 \pm 0.03) \times 10^3$	$\bar{n}$ (Antineutron)
Lamba	Λ^0	2182.8 ± 0.3	0	$\frac{1}{2}$	$(2.51 \pm 0.09) \times 10^{-10}$	$\bar{\Lambda}^0$ (Antilambda)
Sigma plus	Σ^+	2327.7 ± 0.4	$+e$	$\frac{1}{2}$	$(0.81 \pm 0.06) \times 10^{-10}$	$\bar{\Sigma}^-$ (Antisigma minus)
Sigma zero	Σ^0	2331.8 ± 1.0	0	$\frac{1}{2}$	less than 10^{-11}	$\bar{\Sigma}^0$ (Antisigma zero)
Sigma minus	Σ^-	2340.5 ± 0.6	$-e$	$\frac{1}{2}$	$(1.61 \pm 0.10) \times 10^{-10}$	$\bar{\Sigma}^+$ (Antisigma plus)
Xi zero	Ξ^0	2565 ± 8	0	$\frac{1}{2}$	approximately 10^{-10}	$\bar{\Xi}^0$ (Antixi zero)
Xi minus	Ξ^-	2580 ± 2	$-e$	$\frac{1}{2}$	$(1.3 \pm 0.4) \times 10^{-10}$	$\bar{\Xi}^+$ (Antixi plus)

* The spin is in units of $h/2\pi$, where h is Planck's constant (cf. Sec. 25.11).

emitted at the same time as a positron (cf. Sec. 19.19). Both the neutrino and the antineutrino possess angular momentum, as do many other elementary particles. The two differ only in that the neutrino's angular momentum corresponds to a spin in the sense of a left-handed screw advancing along the line of motion, while the antineutrino's angular momentum corresponds to a spin in the sense of a right-handed screw. There seems to be clear evidence that the neutrino, like the photon, has *zero rest mass.*

As accelerators have been developed to give greater and greater kinetic energies to ions, new and more massive elementary particles have been produced by pair production. The presently known elementary particles are listed in Table 19.5, together with their antiparticles. These particles are divided into three classes: the ***leptons*** (light particles), the ***mesons*** (intermediate mass), and the ***baryons*** (heavy particles). The reasons for the inclusion of the μ-meson among the leptons have to do with the fact that its properties, except for mass, are much more like those of the electron than those of the π^- or K^- mesons.

As is implied by the sixth column of the table, most of the elementary particles are unstable. They decay, generally with very short lifetimes, giving rise to different elementary particles. For example the Σ^+ baryon decays either into a proton and a π^0 meson or into a neutron and a π^+ meson.

For the full and exciting story of the search for elementary particles and the study of their properties we refer the interested reader to the references at the end of the chapter. We shall have to content ourselves here with the indication that the paths of the short-lived particles can be studied by the use of Geiger counters, scintillation counters, Wilson cloud chambers, hydrogen bubble chambers, spark chambers, and the like; that the momenta of charged particles can be determined by deflecting them in magnetic fields; and that many of their properties are found by the application of the various conservation laws we have studied. As a matter of fact, a whole new set of conservation laws (for lepton number, baryon number, parity, strangeness, etc.) have been found to apply to the creation and decay of elementary particles. It is certain that the story of such particles is not yet complete.

EXERCISES

19.20-1 Pi plus mesons may be created by the reaction:

$$\mathrm{p} + \mathrm{p} \rightarrow \mathrm{p} + \mathrm{n} + \pi^+.$$

(a) What is the least kinetic energy of the two protons, in their center of mass system, needed for this reaction? (b) If one of the two protons is initially at rest in the laboratory system, what is the lowest energy of the other proton needed for the reaction?

19.20-2 A μ^- meson is moving at right angles to a magnetic field, of flux density 0.50 Wb/m^2, at a speed of 1.00×10^7 m/sec. Find the radius of curvature of its path.

19.20-3 Suppose that a π^+ meson at rest decays according to the scheme

$$\pi^+ \rightarrow \mu^+ + \nu.$$

Apply the conservation of mass-energy and the conservation of momentum to this process, treating the μ^+ as a classical (Newtonian) particle and the neutrino relativistically.

(a) Hence show that the μ^+ will be moving at a speed of 0.84×10^8 m/sec. (b) Show that the neutrino carries away about seven times as much kinetic energy as does the μ^+.

19.21 Nuclear Structure

In Sec. 19.6 we saw how Rutherford concluded that nearly all of the mass of an atom is concentrated in its nucleus. Thus, while the atom itself has a diameter of the order of 10^{-10} m, that of the nucleus is about 10^{-15} m. Furthermore, in Sec. 19.4 we observed that the atoms of a given element are not all alike but occur as isotopes which exhibit the same chemical behavior but have different masses. In Chapter 18 we recounted the grosser aspects of the chemical behavior of matter, including its involvement of electric charge. In Chapter 25 we shall see that the outer structure of the atom—the structure *outside* of the nucleus—is composed entirely of electrons. It is this outer structure that defines the chemical behavior and the optical spectra of an element. The chemical and optical activities of different isotopes of the same element are so nearly the same that for our purposes we can ignore them entirely.

With this background, then, we are prompted to ask how the nucleus of one isotope differs from that of another isotope of the same element. What is the structure of the nucleus? The best that we can do in answer to this question is to describe three different models of nuclear structure. None of these models accounts for all of the observed properties, and each exhibits some strengths it does not share with the others.

According to present-day ideas, an atomic nucleus of mass number M contains a total of M particles in which there are Z protons and $M-Z$ neutrons. Thus, if any nucleus may be represented as ${}_Z\mathrm{X}^M$, following the symbolism introduced in Sec. 19.8, the hydrogen nucleus (${}_1\mathrm{H}^1$) has $Z=1$ proton, $M=1$ particle, and $M-Z=0$ neutrons, while the deuterium nucleus (${}_1\mathrm{H}^2$) has $Z=1$ proton, $M=2$ particles, and $M-Z=1$ neutron. The two types of particles, protons and neutrons, which make up the nucleus are commonly called ***nucleons.***

Table 19.1 suggests that, with the exception of the very rare isotope ${}_2\mathrm{He}^3$, all stable—that is, all nonradioactive—isotopes have at least as many neutrons as protons. Indeed, a more complete table would show that this is true. As the atomic number increases, the excess of neutrons over protons increases until in the heaviest known stable isotope, ${}_{83}\mathrm{Bi}^{209}$, the excess of neutrons over protons is 43. Thus, we see that the forces which hold neutrons and protons together within the nucleus are such that some combinations are stable while others are unstable. As examples, we note that ${}_8\mathrm{O}^{16}$ with 8 protons and 8 neutrons is stable, whereas ${}_{92}\mathrm{U}^{234}$ with 92 protons and 142 neutrons is radioactive. Furthermore, the number of excess neutrons in the stable isotopes of a given element varies within a small range. Thus, stable oxygen isotopes have 8, 9, or 10 neutrons, and tin, with $Z = 50$, has ten different stable isotopes: $M - Z = 62$, 64, 65, 66, 67, 68, 69, 70, 72, and 74. We conclude that, for each element, when the number of neutrons in the nucleus falls outside the small range, the nucleus will be unstable; it will be radioactive.

There are several other facts about nuclei that we should want our models or theories of nuclear structure to explain. For example, in Sec. 19.22 we shall define specific binding energy ε_B of a nucleus as the average energy per nucleon required to break that nucleus down completely into separated protons and neutrons. We shall see there that the measured specific binding energies for $_2He^4$ and $_6C^{12}$ lie considerably above the smooth curve plotting ε_B vs. M, and that $_4Be^8$ and $_8O^{16}$ also have higher ε_B than do isotopes of adjoining mass numbers.

Then, in Fig. 19.9, we saw that $_{92}U^{238}$, which is naturally radioactive, undergoes a series of α-particle emissions interspersed with some β-emissions before ending the decay series with the stable lead isotope $_{82}Pb^{206}$. The same propensity for emitting α-particles is shared by $_{90}Th^{232}$, which starts a decay series that ends in $_{82}Pb^{208}$, a stable isotope, and by $_{92}U^{235}$, which ends in $_{82}Pb^{207}$. The same observation can be made concerning $_{93}Np^{237}$, which ends its decay series in stable $_{83}Bi^{209}$.

Another fact at which our models must aim is that very few of the stable isotopes are composed of an odd number of protons combined with an odd number of neutrons. Most odd-odd combinations are radioactive, and by emitting an electron or a positron they change a neutron to a proton [Eq. (19.21-3)] or a proton to a neutron [Eq. (19.21-2)], respectively; either change results in an even-even combination which is more stable.

Furthermore, certain nuclei that are particularly stable are characterized by even numbers of protons or even numbers of neutrons. The stability is determined at the low end of the periodic table by measuring the specific binding energy; we have already referred to this above. But for $Z > 20$, other evidence for stability must be used. For example, if a given nucleus were particularly stable, we should expect it to be relatively abundant in the matter of the universe. Or, if there are several nuclei with the same number of neutrons or the same number of protons, we can assume that that number is particularly stable. When all of these criteria are used, it is found that the preferred numbers for high stability are 2, 8, 20, 28, 50, 82, and 126.

Still other experimental facts, which we can merely mention here, are the details of scattering and absorption experiments. Beams of neutrons or protons or electrons of appropriate energies can be aimed at targets composed of the nuclei being investigated. The angular distribution of the scattered particles as a function of particle energy should also be accounted for by satisfactory models of the nucleus. Moreover, if neutrons of certain energies are absorbed, this fact too should be explained.

As a first task for a nuclear model, let us consider how nucleons are held together in the nucleus. Enormous forces must act not only between neutral particles (neutron-neutron) and between neutral and charged particles (neutron-proton), but they must also act between particles of like charge (proton-proton) and be strong enough to counteract the electrostatic forces of repulsion. These forces must be very much stronger than either electrostatic or gravitational forces at distances of 10^{-15} m or less, yet they are shown by scattering experiments to be much weaker than the electrostatic forces at distances appreciably greater than this. They are therefore called ***strong forces*** and ***short range forces.*** One of the most important problems of the present time is the study and understanding of intranuclear forces.

We saw in Sec. 19.20 that Yukawa made a start toward this understanding by postulating the creation and annihilation of mesons. Because the mesons can transfer charge, this is equivalent to an exchange of charge between two nucleons A and B, thus:

$$({}_1p^1)_A + ({}_0n^1)_B \rightleftarrows ({}_0n^1)_A + ({}_1p^1)_B, \qquad (19.21\text{-}1)$$

where the double arrows indicate that the reaction can proceed equally well in the two directions. According to this scheme, particle A is a proton on the left side of the equation but on the right it is a neutron; particle B plays the opposite role. The charge goes from A to B to A to B and so on. We shall see in Sec. 25.18 that such processes, involving an interchange of properties between two particles, lead to attractive forces.

It now seems well established that exchange forces as suggested by Eq. (19.21-1) are responsible for the cohesion of the nucleus.

Regardless of the nature of nuclear forces, it is clear that they are *short-range* forces—i.e., they decrease very rapidly with increasing distance between the particles. This is a requirement, since the Rutherford scattering experiments show no sign of forces other than electrostatic ones at distances of 10^{-14} m, whereas the nuclear forces dominate the electrostatic ones at distances of 10^{-15} m, within the dimensions of the nucleus. This distance, 10^{-15} m, has become quite important in the study of nuclear forces, so it has been adopted as a unit, the ***fermi***, named in honor of Enrico Fermi.

While we have supposed these forces to act within the nucleus, there is good evidence that they act between nucleons which are not both in a nucleus. Thus, when beams of high-energy neutrons are shot through hydrogen targets, the neutron scattering which occurs indicates that there are very strong interactions when the distance of closest approach is about one fermi. Moreover, at approach distances less than about 0.5 fermi, the interaction between the nucleons becomes strongly repulsive, while for distances greater than 0.7 fermi, the force becomes strongly attractive. As the distance increases still more, however, the short-range force between the nucleons soon becomes negligible.

Consistent with the notion of nuclear exchange forces which involve pions, we can build several models which will account qualitatively for some of the observations recounted at the beginning of this section. For example, we can explain the α-particle emission of the naturally radioactive substances quite easily if we suppose that groups consisting of 2 protons and 2 neutrons occur preferentially within the nucleus. Alpha-emission then consists simply of the escape of one of these groups from the nucleus. In Sec. 19.22, we shall see that there is very good reason to postulate the existence of such groups. Gamma-radiation can also be easily explained if we suppose that in some nuclei the particles possess more than a normal amount of kinetic energy, which is later released from the nucleus in the form of photon radiation.

The emission of electrons and positrons from the nucleus seems difficult to explain at first, since we have postulated no electrons or positrons within the nucleus. But we have already alluded above to mechanisms by which this emission can occur. Thus, we have

$$_1p^1 \rightarrow {}_1e^0 + {}_0n^1 \tag{19.21-2}$$

and

$$_0n^1 \rightarrow {}_{-1}e^0 + {}_1p^1. \tag{19.21-3}$$

Therefore, it is possible for a proton to transmute into a positron and a neutron and, likewise, for a neutron to transmute into an electron and a proton. We then see that an electron emission (β^-) will occur when the number of neutrons in any atom is in excess of that required for stability, and a positron emission (β^+) will occur when there is an excess of protons. We can account for K-electron capture by adding the reaction

$$_{-1}e^0 + {}_1p^1 \rightarrow {}_0n^1. \tag{19.21-4}$$

Neutron emission apparently occurs only when the excess of neutrons over protons is very large.

We can make use of the picture which we have set up for the structure of the nucleus to account for the radioactivity of the uranium-radium series (Fig. 19.9). We have seen above that the neutron excess decreases in general as the atomic number decreases. The emission of an α-particle by ${}_{92}U^{238}$ reduces the number of protons and the number of neutrons equally by two units, and the result is ${}_{90}Th^{234}$, which has a neutron excess greater than normal. Two successive β-emissions reduce the neutron excess, and the isotope ${}_{92}U^{234}$ is reached. This is relatively stable (half-life, 2.7×10^5 yr) and it leads to a succession of α-emissions which produce a series of nuclei of relatively stable neutron-proton ratio. When ${}_{82}Pb^{214}$ is reached, there is again a large neutron excess, which is corrected by β-emissions. This alternation of α-emissions and β-emissions goes on until the stable end product ${}_{82}Pb^{206}$ is reached. Our accounting for the radioactivity of the uranium-radium series is thus quite plausible if we can account for the emission of α-particles by nuclei of large atomic number. A succession of such α-emissions must always lead to a neutron excess and consequently to β-emission. The fact that the α-particle is emitted in so many natural radioactive decay processes and in so many transmutations indicates that the combination of forces which bind together a pair of neutrons and a pair of protons must be particularly strong. One model then assumes that the α-particle exists as a "building block" within nuclei, and that as many neutrons and protons as can combine to form α-particles will do so. The nucleus will then consist of a number of α-particles plus single protons or neutrons. On this basis, a nucleus ${}_ZX^M$ would contain $Z/2$ α-particles and $(M - 2Z)$ neutrons if Z is even, or $(Z - 1)/2$ α-particles, one proton, and $(M - 2Z - 1)$ neutrons if Z is odd.

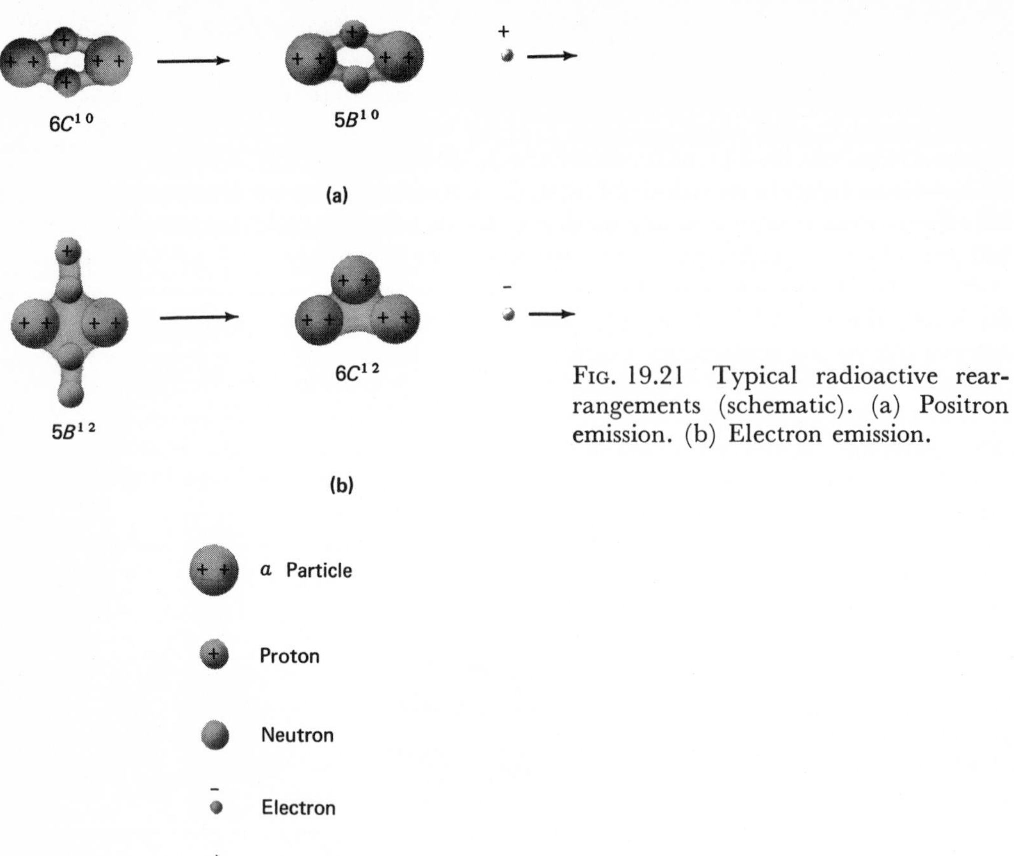

FIG. 19.21 Typical radioactive rearrangements (schematic). (a) Positron emission. (b) Electron emission.

Figure 19.21 shows, in a very schematic fashion, the arrangements of several nuclei according to this concept. Figure 19.21a represents the (β^+)-decay of ${}_6C^{10}$. Figure 19.21b illustrates the (β^-)-decay of ${}_5B^{12}$. Diagrams of this sort must not be taken literally; the arrangements of the nucleons shown are purely imaginative, since we do not suppose the nucleus to exist in a static arrangement.

In the large nuclei with large neutron excess, this model would predict a large number of α-particles. For example, in ${}_{92}U^{235}$ there could be 46 α-particles and 51 neutrons. In such a nucleus, we can assume, following Niels Bohr (1885–1962) and John A. Wheeler (1911–   ), that the particles within the nucleus are clustered together in a roughly spherical mass. This cluster of particles will behave very much like a liquid drop, and calculations based on this simple assumption as to the behavior of the larger nuclei have been successfully made by Bohr and Wheeler and by many others. We cannot follow these calculations in detail, but we can use this model to obtain a qualitative picture of the process of α-emission.

We know that the α-particles and neutrons within any nucleus will possess kinetic energy. In the ***liquid drop model***, we can imagine that within a large nucleus some particles will have more energy than others and that the particles will be changing their arrangement and colliding with one another, just as do the particles in a gas or in an ordinary liquid. In all this nuclear rearrangement, the charges on the α-particles will be repelling one another with an inverse square law force, so that every α-particle in the nucleus will be exerting a strong repulsive force on every other α-particle in the nucleus. The attractive exchange forces between the particles, though very strong for small distances, will fall off very rapidly with distance, so that a given particle (α-particle or neutron) will attract and be attracted by its immediate neighbors only.

As long as the nucleus is roughly spherical in shape, every α-particle will have many neighbors which will attract it and hold it in the cluster. This situation is represented very schematically in Fig. 19.22a. However, if one α-particle, by chance, moves out of the spherical arrangement as indicated in Fig. 19.22b, it will be attracted by only one or two neighbors, while it will still be repelled electrostatically by all the other charged particles in the nucleus. The α-particle thus leaves the nucleus and receives an added amount of kinetic energy due to the electrostatic repulsion of the nucleus it has left.

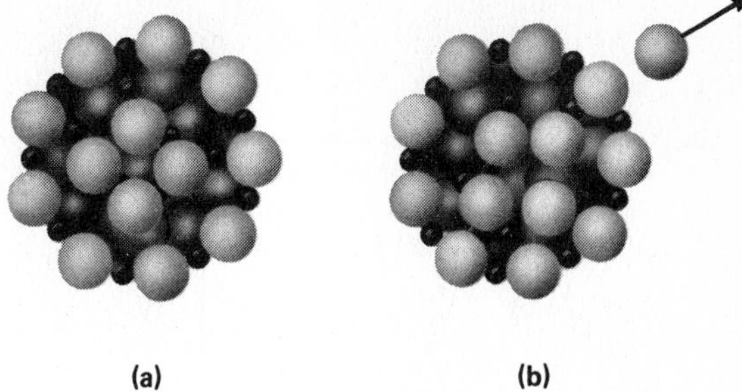

FIG. 19.22 Emission of an α-particle. (a) All particles tightly bound. (b) Escape of α-particle.

The liquid drop model also furnishes a nice qualitative picture of nuclear fission (cf. Sec. 19.24). When a neutron enters a heavy nuclear drop, the kinetic energy of the neutron distorts the drop and causes it to oscillate into dumbbell shapes. If such oscillations are violent enough, the dumbbell may break in two at its handle and thereby become two nuclear drops whose mass numbers cluster in the neighborhood of $M/2$, where M is the atomic mass number of the nucleus before fission. One is usually a little more massive than $M/2$, the other a little less massive.

There are many other observations, however, for which the liquid drop model cannot account. It does not account, for example, for the numbers of neutrons or protons associated with particularly high stability—2, 8, 20, 28, 50, 82, and 126—as mentioned earlier. The ***shell model*** of the nucleus, brought to its present stage of development by Maria G. Mayer (1906–) succeeds in accounting for the magic numbers. The shell model employs the ***Pauli exclusion principle*** to determine the number of electrons that can occupy each shell. The Pauli exclusion principle was first advanced by Wolfgang Pauli, and it was applied very successfully to the determination of the number of electrons in each shell of an atom (cf. Sec. 25.9). The principle as modified for the nucleus states that within a nucleus *no two identical nucleons can occupy exactly the same* *quantum state*. The quantum state is determined by a set of quantum numbers based on Z, $M - Z$, the spins of the nucleons, and the angular momenta of their orbital motions, When all of these quantities are properly taken into account, they predict successfully the numbers above which are associated with high nuclear stability.

The shell model can also explain the existence of long-lived excited states in nuclei and can aid in accounting for the details of β-emission in decay processes.

A model that takes a quite different approach to nuclear structure is the ***optical model.*** We saw in Sec. 12.21 that every moving material particle has a de Broglie wave associated with it. If we direct a beam of nucleons at a nucleus, then, each nucleon will carry a de Broglie wave with it. The scattering of nucleons by a nucleus could then be regarded as the refraction of the waves in a light beam as the beam passes through a glass ball. Using this model, one can determine an index of refraction of nuclear matter for the de Broglie wave that belongs to nucleons of different energies. Such models have enjoyed some success in accounting for the observed scattering of nucleons by nuclei of various kinds.

Moreover, the optical model has a built-in possibility to account for the absorption of nucleons of certain energies. Since there will be a de Broglie wavelength *within the nucleus* for a nucleon which is traveling through the nucleus, we can consider absorption as occurring when the internal wave exists as a standing wave within the nucleus. Since standing waves do not transfer energy through the medium, the energy of the impinging nucleon will not pass through the nucleus. We therefore regard the nucleon as trapped or absorbed. This optical model which refracts some wavelengths and absorbs others has been called the "cloudy crystal ball."

We have not been able to be very complete in our descriptions of these nuclear models, but perhaps the reader has gained some notion of the nature of research in nuclear physics. The development of a universal model for the structure of the nucleus is far from complete. There are a half dozen or so models that have some currency, but none is complete and none is useless. The ultimate model of the nucleus may or may not be a composite of the present day fruits of nuclear research, but it will have to accomplish all of the tasks that are presently accomplished in a piecemeal fashion.

19.22 Nuclear Energy

The discussion of the preceding sections has indicated that large forces between nucleons are necessary if nuclei are to be held together against the electrostatic repulsion of the protons. We can obtain a more quantitative notion of the magnitude of such forces by a study of the energy that would be necessary to separate a nucleus into its parts or, conversely, the energy which would be released when such a nucleus is formed. In doing this, we use the Einstein mass-energy relationship and consider the masses of various atoms in relation to the sum of the masses of the nucleons of which they are composed.

From Table 19.1 and Sec. 19.10 we can write

$$(\text{mass of H atom}) + (\text{mass of } {}_0n^1) - (\text{mass of } {}_1H^2)\ \Delta = m;$$
$$1.00783 \text{ amu} + 1.00866 \text{ amu} - 2.01410 \text{ amu} = 0.00239 \text{ amu}.$$

This is to say that an amount of energy equivalent to 2.39×10^{-3} amu or, by Table 19.2, 2.22 MeV, will be released whenever a proton and a neutron, nucleus combine to form a deuterium nucleus.

Similarly, when two hydrogen atoms combine with two neutrons to form a helium atom, there is a loss of mass equal to

$$2 \times 1.00783 \text{ amu} + 2 \times 1.00866 \text{ amu} - 4.00260 \text{ amu}$$
$$0.03038 \text{ amu} = 28.3 \text{ MeV}.$$

Corresponding amounts of energy must be supplied, of course, whenever deuterium or helium atoms are separated into their constituent neutrons, protons, and electrons.

The amounts of energy involved in the building up and breaking down of atoms are tremendous. Thus, the energy which would be released if a kilogram mole of helium (4.00 kg) could be made from neutrons, protons, and electrons is 3.038×10^{-2} amu/molecule $\times\ 6.025 \times 10^{26}$ molecules/kg mole $\times\ 1.49 \times 10^{-10}$ J/amu $= 2.73 \times 10^{15}$ J $= 7.6 \times 10^{9}$ kW-hr. This is enough energy to provide electric power for a city the size of Philadelphia for about two years! A reaction which involves a number of intermediate nuclei, but which has as an end result the synthesis of helium from protons and neutrons, has been proposed by H. Bethe (1906–   ) as the source of the energy of the stars. We shall return to a consideration of helium synthesis in Sec. 19.26.

We can now find a method for expressing the energy of any nucleus in terms of the number of neutrons and protons which build it up. The mass of these protons and neutrons before they combine is clearly

$$Zm_p + (M - Z)m_n,$$

where m_p and m_n are the masses of a neutron and a proton, respectively. Since the mass of the nucleus is A, an amount of mass

$$Zm_p + (M - Z)m_n - A$$

has been released as a result of the formation of the nucleus. This mass is equivalent to an energy E_B, which depends on the relative arrangement of the nucleons and is known as the ***binding energy***:

$$E_B = [Zm_p + (M - Z)m_n - A]c^2. \qquad (19.22\text{-}1)$$

The binding energy is obviously the energy required to separate the nucleus into its component nucleons. It is frequently useful to refer to the ***specific binding energy*** ε_B, which is defined as the binding energy per nucleon. We therefore have

$$\varepsilon_B = [Zm_p + (M - Z)m_n - A]c^2/M. \qquad (19.22\text{-}2)$$

The specific binding energies may be calculated from tables of atomic masses similar to Table 19.1.* When the values obtained in this way are plotted against the mass number M, it is found that they do not lie exactly on a smooth curve. They do, however, lie quite close to the curve shown in Fig. 19.23. Figure 19.24 is a magnified portion of a part of Fig. 19.23, with some of

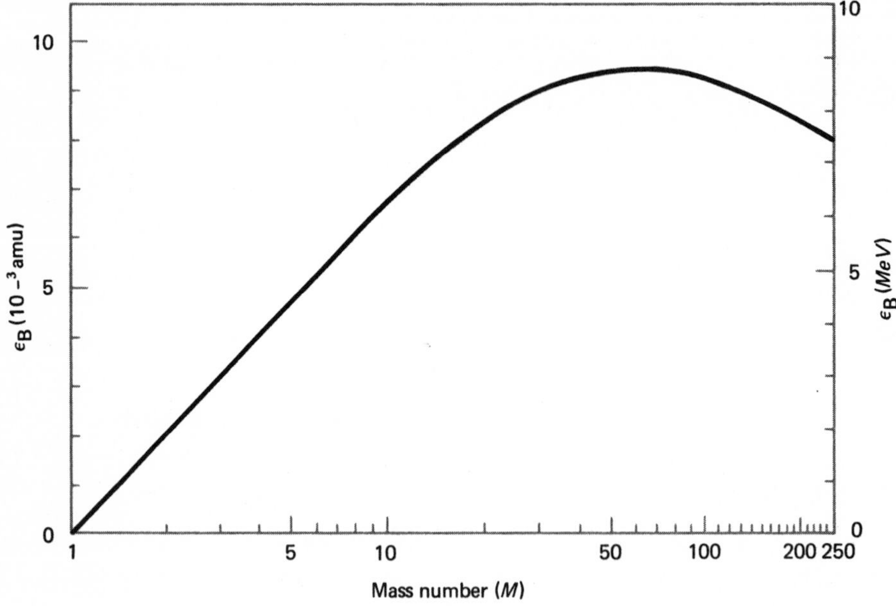

FIG. 19.23 Variation of specific binding energy with mass number.

the experimentally determined specific binding energies shown, to indicate the extent of the departures from the smooth curve. It is noticeable in this figure that those nuclei that may be considered to consist of α-particles only ($_2He^4$, $_6C^{12}$, $_8O^{16}$) are more tightly bound than are neighboring nuclei, in agreement with the assumption of Sec. 19.21.

Returning to Fig. 19.24, we notice that the specific binding energy is zero for $_1H^1$ and that it rises quite rapidly up to $M \approx 16$, after which it rises more slowly to a flat maximum in the neighborhood of $M = 60$, above which it decreases steadily with increasing atomic mass. We therefore judge that elements in the middle of the periodic table are most tightly bound, or most stable. Extra energy is required either to break these atoms into parts or to combine two of them into a heavier atom. On the other hand, energy is released if an atom of high atomic mass breaks into elements of medium mass, or if very light atoms combine to form elements of intermediate mass. We shall return to a consideration of such processes in Secs. 19.25 and 19.26.

* To consider or not to consider the mass of the electrons for most atoms makes a difference of less than 0.03 percent. It may therefore be disregarded.

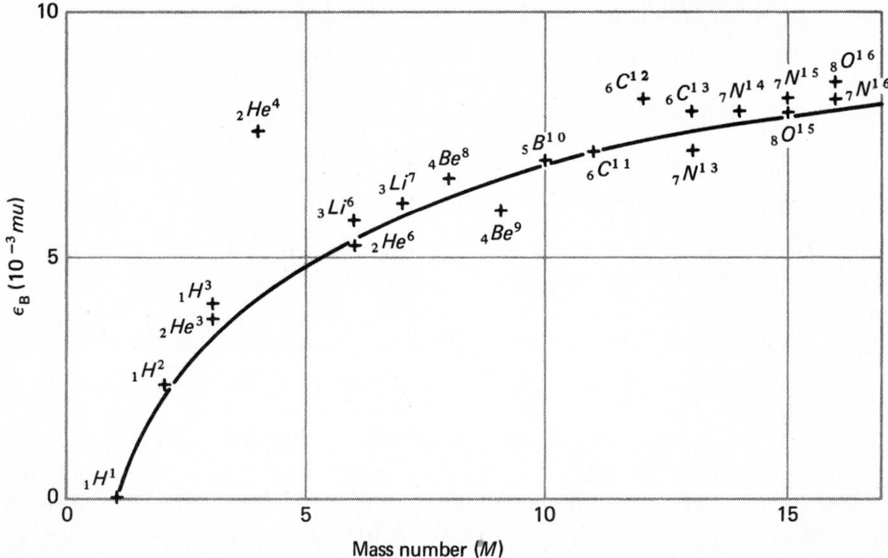

FIG. 19.24 Specific binding energy for atoms of low mass number.

19.23 The Transuranic Elements

Before we go on to the more detailed consideration of the questions of energy production referred to in the last section, it is well to consider the methods by which the elements of higher atomic number than uranium ($Z = 92$) have been produced. The first indication of the presence of these elements was obtained by Enrico Fermi (1901–1954), who bombarded uranium with neutrons. He observed a number of products which were β-emitters and inferred that they must lead to elements of atomic number 93 or greater. He assumed the reactions

$$_{92}U^{M} + _{0}n^{1} \rightarrow _{92}U^{M+1} + _{0}\gamma^{0}$$

and

$$_{92}U^{M+1} \rightarrow _{93}?^{M+1} + _{-1}e^{0}.$$

Later Otto Hahn (1879–   ) and his co-workers demonstrated that many of the β-active products were fission products of much lower atomic number. Therefore, Fermi cannot be credited with the discovery of the transuranic elements, although the reaction which he suggested is now known to take place.

In 1940, E. MacMillan and P. Abelson isolated element 93 from the products of the deuteron bombardment of uranium. Later it was demonstrated that the reaction was

$$_{92}U^{238} + _{1}H^{2} \rightarrow _{93}Np^{238} + _{0}n^{1} + _{0}n^{1}. \qquad (19.23\text{-}1)$$

The neptunium isotope is radioactive and gives rise to plutonium by β-emission according to the reaction

$$_{93}Np^{238} \rightarrow _{94}Pu^{238} + _{-1}e^{0}. \qquad (19.23\text{-}2)$$

Since then the isotopes of neptunium and plutonium of mass 239 have been formed by the reactions

$$_{92}U^{238} + {_0}n^1 \rightarrow {_{92}}U^{239} + {_0}\gamma^0 \qquad (19.23\text{-}3)$$

$$_{92}U^{239} \rightarrow {_{93}}Np^{239} + {_{-1}}e^0 \qquad (19.23\text{-}4)$$

$$_{93}Np^{239} \rightarrow {_{94}}Pu^{239} + {_{-1}}e^0. \qquad (19.23\text{-}5)$$

This series of reactions is of the greatest importance in the operation of the atomic pile and in the production of atomic energy (Sec. 19.25). It is the series originally suggested by Fermi as producing transuranic elements.

Two isotopes of the element americium were produced by G. T. Seaborg (1912–) and his coworkers. The lighter of these, $_{95}Am^{241}$, results from the β-decay of $_{94}Pu^{241}$; the heavier $_{95}Am^{242}$ is the product of an (n, γ) reaction involving $_{95}Am^{241}$. The same experiment showed that the bombardment of $_{94}Pu^{239}$ by fast α-particles results both in an (α, 3n) reaction yielding a curium isotope, $_{96}Cm^{240}$, and an (α, n) reaction ending in $_{96}Cm^{242}$. More recently, groups of experimenters working with the largest accelerators have announced the production of isotopes of berkelium ($Z = 97$), californium (98), einsteinium (99), fermium (100), mendelevium (101), and nobelium (102).

19.24 Nuclear Fission and Atomic Energy

The original experiments of Fermi on the bombardment of uranium by neutrons were explained by Otto Hahn and F. Strassmann as a splitting of the uranium nucleus into two more or less equal fragments. This process is called ***fission.*** Their explanation followed from the identification of barium ($Z = 56$), cerium ($Z = 57$), lanthanum ($Z = 58$), and krypton ($Z = 36$) among the many substances produced when uranium was bombarded by slow neutrons. Since then at least one or two isotopes of every element in the atomic number range from 30 (Zn) to 64 (Gd) have been identified as products of fission, and in some cases as many as fifteen isotopes of a single element occur.

A mass spectrograph separation of the isotopes of uranium carried out by A. O. Nier (1911–) enabled J. R. Dunning (1907–) and his coworkers to prove that $_{92}U^{235}$ underwent fission when it was bombarded by slow neutrons (0.04 eV); on the other hand, it required neutrons of energy about 1.5 MeV to produce fission in $_{92}U^{238}$. It was also demonstrated that the energy produced when the fission of $_{92}U^{235}$ took place was about 185 MeV. An examination of the specific binding energy curve (Fig. 19.23) shows a value of about 7.5 MeV for uranium and about 8.5 MeV for elements of half the uranium mass ($M \approx 120$). Hence, we should predict an energy release of 235 (8.5 MeV $-$ 7.5 MeV) $= 2.4 \times 10^2$ MeV by the fission of $_{92}U^{235}$ into two approximately equal fragments. The difference between this value and that determined experimentally is due to the production of some neutrons, which have a very low binding energy.

Shortly after the discovery of uranium fission, the fission of thorium $_{90}Th^{232}$ and the fission of protactinium $_{91}Pa^{231}$ were demonstrated respectively by

Nishina in Tokyo and by Dunning in New York. It has been demonstrated subsequently that many of the elements of atomic number greater than 90 can be split by the addition of a neutron of appropriate energy. Many of these atoms can also be split by the addition of energy alone in the form of γ-radiation. This latter process is called ***photofission.***

If a neutron is added to $_{92}U^{235}$, the unstable isotope $_{92}U^{236}$ is formed. If this were to split into two equal parts, an isotope of palladium $_{46}Pd^{118}$ would result. The heaviest stable isotope of palladium is $_{46}Pd^{110}$, so that the product of equal fission would have 8 extra neutrons. Actually, fission into exactly equal parts does not seem to occur very often, but however the fission occurs, there must be about 16 extra neutrons above the number required to form two stable isotopes near the middle of the atomic number scale. It is found that this excess of neutrons can be accounted for by three processes as follows:

1. A few neutrons are set free during the original fission.
2. Some of the products of fission are neutron-radioactive, emitting the so-called "delayed" neutrons within times varying from a small fraction of a second to about one minute after fission.
3. All the other products of fission are β-radioactive, indicating that they have an excess of neutrons which they convert into protons.

The neutrons produced by the fission of $_{92}U^{236}$ have energies of the order of 1 MeV. These neutrons have much too high an energy to produce efficient fission of $_{92}U^{235}$, and much too low an energy to produce fission of $_{92}U^{238}$, which, as we have said, requires about 1.5 MeV neutrons.

It was recognized soon after the discovery of uranium fission that, if each of the neutrons from a single fission of $_{92}U^{235}$ could be used to produce a new fission, an explosive process would take place. Each splitting uranium atom would give rise to a large amount of energy and to a few neutrons. Each of these neutrons would produce a new fission and consequently more energy and more neutrons. The process would repeat indefinitely resulting in a tremendous release of energy in the material in which the fission process was taking place. This large energy production would vaporize the fission products and heat them to a high temperature. A violent explosion would then result. This ***chain process*** can be produced in a large mass of the pure isotope $_{92}U^{235}$, and it is this process that was used in the first atomic bomb which was dropped on Hiroshima. In the second atomic bomb, used on Nagasaki, and in the bombs tested at Bikini, the element $_{94}Pu^{239}$ was used, the fission process being very similar to that of $_{92}U^{235}$.

19.25 The Controlled Release of Nuclear Energy

In general, whenever any isotope absorbs a neutron to produce a compound nucleus which then undergoes fission, more than one neutron is emitted in the fission process. These emitted neutrons may then be absorbed by other nuclei of the same isotope, and more fission results. A nuclear reaction in which one of the products is a necessary ingredient for more nuclear reactions of the same kind is known as a ***chain reaction.****

Let us suppose that each fission produces five neutrons and that *on the average* only one of these neutrons is absorbed to trigger a new fission. In this case, the chain reaction will simply sustain itself and will release energy at a controlled rate. A controlled chain reaction which would produce 10^6 W of power from the fission of $_{92}U^{235}$ would thus require that fissions occur at the rate of 3.37×10^{16} fissions/sec. (1.85×10^2 Mev/fission $\times$ 3.37×10^{16} fissions/sec = 6.24×10^{18} MeV/sec.) But since there are 6.24×10^{12} MeV/J, we can express this power as 10^6 J/sec, or 10^6 W. In one kilogram of $_{92}U^{235}$ there are 2.56×10^{24} atoms. Thus, a kilogram of $_{92}U^{235}$, *if it could all be caused to fission,* could provide the "fuel" to produce 10^6 W of power for 7×10^7 sec or more than two years. Actually, of course, the fission products would remain within the material and, as these accumulate, further operation would be impeded.

On the other hand, if each fission produces five neutrons, and if three of these are absorbed to produce a "second generation" of fissions, the rate of energy production will go up very rapidly. Thus, the fission of one atom begets three, which beget nine, twenty-seven, etc. The fission rate goes entirely out of control, and an explosion results.

There are several different isotopes which can be used in controlled nuclear fission reactors—$_{94}Pu^{239}$, $_{92}U^{235}$, $_{92}U^{238}$, for example. We can profitably consider what must be done to employ one of these isotopes, say $_{92}U^{235}$, in a controlled reaction. The development of this chain reaction depends on the following facts:

(1) The fission of $_{92}U^{235}$ is most efficient for very low energy neutrons (< 1 eV).
(2) This fission produces several high-energy neutrons (1 MeV).
(3) Neutrons in the range from 0 to 1000 eV are absorbed by $_{92}U^{238}$ to produce plutonium by the reaction of Eqs. (19.23-2) to (19.23-4), but this reaction takes place most violently for certain definite energies within this range.

The problem, then, is to slow down the neutrons produced by fission (2) so that at least one neutron per fission will produce a new fission (1) without having been absorbed in the production of plutonium (3).

Enough fission neutrons from $_{92}U^{235}$ to maintain the reaction must be allowed to escape into a region where they can meet no $_{92}U^{238}$ atom. There they must be slowed down below the speed at which they are most critically absorbed by $_{92}U^{238}$ (i.e., below 1 eV). Then they must be allowed to meet uranium again so that they can produce a new fission in $_{92}U^{235}$. To satisfy

* Although it is not a *nuclear* reaction, any combustion process may be regarded as a chain reaction. The carbon in coal does not combine spontaneously with oxygen in the air, but when the atoms are sufficiently agitated—that is, when the temperature is raised enough—a combination occurs. One of the products of the reaction is enough thermal energy to assure that more carbon and oxygen will combine. In this way, the reaction sustains itself until the coal or oxygen supply is interrupted.

these conditions, small quantities of uranium are imbedded in a material, called a ***moderator,*** in which the neutrons can be slowed down by collision. This material must not absorb neutrons. Various low Z materials could be used for slowing the neutrons, but carbon in the form of graphite works well and is readily available. Hydrogen cannot be used as a moderator because it absorbs neutrons to produce deuterium.

Since each fission produces several neutrons and only one from each is needed to sustain the chain reaction, the extra neutrons may be used for producing other reactions. For example, ${}_6C^{14}$ can be produced from ${}_7N^{14}$ or ${}_{94}Pu^{239}$ from ${}_{92}U^{238}$.

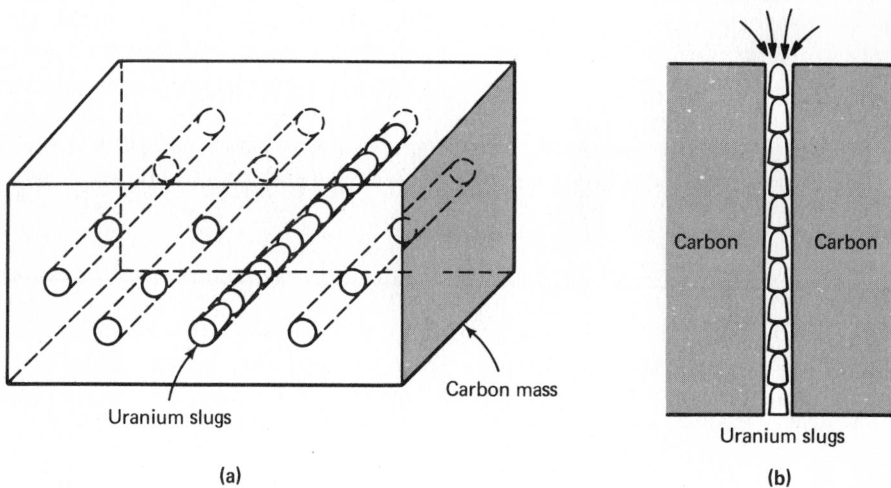

FIG. 19.25 Diagram of an atomic reactor.

The atomic ***pile***, or ***reactor***, used for the production of plutonium and other new isotopes is constructed on the general plan of Fig. 19.25. A number of tubes pass parallel to one another through a large mass of carbon. Slugs of uranium metal surrounded by water for cooling fill these tubes. If a fission takes place in one of these slugs, there is a large probability that the neutrons produced will escape from the slug into the carbon moderator. There they are slowed down to an energy well below the critical energy for capture by ${}_{92}U^{238}$ so that, when they meet a second uranium slug, they will have a high probability of producing a new fission of ${}_{92}U^{235}$.

It is easy to see that if the number of new fissions produced by each new fission is greater than one, the rate at which fission takes place will increase rapidly, or, if the number falls below one, the reaction will die down. It is therefore necessary to provide a means of controlling the rate of operation of the pile. This is done by inserting cadmium rods into some of the holes in the carbon pile. Cadmium is a very good absorber of neutrons, and by adjusting the length of cadmium rod within the pile, it is possible to maintain at a constant level the number of fissions per second taking place in the pile.

Some of the neutrons produced by the fission of $_{92}U^{235}$ are captured by $_{92}U^{238}$ before they can enter the moderator. These result in the production of Np and Pu according to the reactions of Eqs. (19.23-3) to (19.23-5). After the uranium slugs have been in the pile for some time, they will contain unchanged uranium, neptunium, plutonium, and all the products of fission of these elements. Or, if the pile has been charged with other suitable nuclei, say, $_7N^{14}$, there will also be $_6C^{14}$ present. These materials may be separated chemically and put to various technological and scientific uses.

19.26 Nuclear Fusion

In the preceding sections, we have been considering the release of energy when nuclei of large mass number break into those of intermediate mass number. As we pointed out in Sec. 19.22, energy is also available from the ***fusion*** of light nuclei to form more tightly bound nuclei. The most effective reactions for this purpose probably involve the transmutation of deuterons by deuterons. It has been shown that two processes occur with approximately equal probability:

$$_1H^2 + {}_1H^2 \rightarrow {}_1H^3 + {}_1H^1 + 3.97 \text{ MeV} \qquad (19.26\text{-}1)$$

$$_1H^2 + {}_1H^2 \rightarrow {}_2He^3 + {}_0n^1 + 3.22 \text{ MeV}. \qquad (19.26\text{-}2)$$

In order to carry out these reactions, it is necessary that the two positively charged hydrogen nuclei be brought close enough to interact strongly, i.e., within about 10^{-15} m. As is shown by Eq. (16.21-4) the energy necessary to do this is

$$eV = e^2/4\pi\epsilon_0 r,$$

where $r = 10^{-15}$ m. Substitution of magnitudes into this equation shows the necessary energy to be about 10^6 eV, or about 10^{-13} J. Such energies can be imparted to deuterons by accelerators, but the carrying out of the reaction on a large scale demands a simpler and more compact device. We shall see in Sec. 20.8 that the average kinetic energy of a molecule in a gas is $\frac{3}{2}kT$, where k is Boltzmann's constant and T is the Kelvin temperature. Hence, if the temperature of a mass containing deuterium could be raised to a temperature of about

$$T = (2/3k)(10^{-13}\text{ J}) = (2 \times 10^{-13}\text{ J})/(3 \times 1.38 \times 10^{-23}\text{ J/deg})$$
$$= 5 \times 10^9\ ^\circ\text{K},$$

nearly any pair of deuterons would come close enough to each other to react without any energy being supplied from outside. Actually, it is not necessary to reach a temperature as high as this, since some of the deuterons will have sufficient energy at much lower temperatures, and collisions between atoms are so frequent at high temperatures that only a small fraction of the collisions need to be effective. It follows that temperatures of the order of 10^7 °K are sufficient to insure that the reactions of Eqs. (19.26-1) and (19.26-2) will proceed with rapidity.

After a mass of deuterium has been raised to this high temperature, the temperature can be maintained by the energy released in the fusion process. In the ***hydrogen bomb***, or ***fusion bomb***, a fission bomb acts as the trigger to bring the surrounding material, which has a high concentration of deuterium, to the temperature at which a chain-fusion reaction is initiated. Since the energy per nucleon is so much higher than for the fission process, and since there seems to be no theoretical limit to the mass of deuterium that can be used, the fusion bomb is a weapon of great destructive power. It may well be unfortunate that mankind has succeeded in constructing such a device.

19.27 Applications of Artificial Radioactivity

It would be unduly pessimistic to close this chapter on the dismal note of the preceding section without mentioning some of the effects of the development of atomic energy which are beneficial to mankind and not focused on man's destruction. The atomic reactor, with a tremendous number of neutrons wandering about within it, is an excellent device for producing the neutron-induced transmutations listed in Table 19.3. Many of the nuclei thus formed are radioactive, with various types of emission and with various half-lives. As a result, there are available a large number of radioisotopes of elements which are not radioactive in their naturally occurring forms.

One of the most important applications of these artificially radioactive elements lies in the field which has been called ***tracer chemistry***. It is apparent that any radioactive isotope can be recognized by its radiations. Thus, if a sugar is made containing radioactive carbon ${}_6C^{14}$ and this sugar is fed to an animal, its progress into the various tissues of the animal can be followed in great detail.

Also, radioactive radiations cause marked changes in the nature of materials which are radiated by them. In intense doses these radiations are lethal to living systems. In small doses, changes can be produced in the genetics of organisms. Studies of these lethal and genetic effects led to great advances in the knowledge of biological systems, and these effects are also applied directly to the treatment of disease.

EXERCISES

19.27-1 An electron-pair is produced by a 2.00 MeV γ-ray. Show that the observed mass of each particle produced is 1.96 times the rest mass of an electron. Then find the speed with which each particle is moving just after the pair formation.

19.27-2 Show that the artificial production of a π-meson-pair requires a particle with an energy of at least 0.306 GeV.

19.27-3 Find the energy (in MeV) produced per helium nucleus formed in accordance with the fusion reaction of Eq. (19.26-2). What is the energy (in kW-hr) if 4.00 kg of helium is produced in this way?

19.27-4 Suppose that all of the energy produced by the formation of 4.00 kg of helium by the process of Ex. 19.27-3 could be utilized to heat a body of water. How great would be the mass of the water if its temperature were to be raised from 20°C to the boiling point?

19.27-5 In the use of radioactive tracers, the disposal of the final products often offers difficulty, since they may be highly radioactive. Suppose that $_{11}Na^{22}$, which has a half-life of 3.0 yr, were used as a tracer. How long would it be before the activity of this material would decay to (1/512) of its original value? What is the corresponding figure for $_{11}Na^{24}$, which has a half-life of 14.8 hr?

19.28 Summary

In this chapter a discussion of the subject of nuclear physics has been presented. It begins with the discovery of radioactivity and of x-rays at the end of the nineteenth century, and ends with the modern problems of cosmic rays and of atomic energy. Its major steps involve the suggestion of the nuclear atom by Rutherford, the discovery of isotopes, the direct measurement of atomic masses by mass spectrograph, and the application of the mass-energy relation to nuclear processes. These steps were followed by the discoveries of transmutation and of artificial radioactivity and the consequent discovery of many new particles. We have also discussed the development of accelerators for controlled bombardment of atoms and the detailed knowledge of the energy relations among nuclei which they have given. Finally, the discovery of fission has given us the ability to tap the tremendous resources of atomic energy.

PROBLEMS

19.1 The chemical atomic mass of helium is given in Table 21.1 as 4.0026. The helium for which this has been determined is that obtained from mineral deposits. This helium consists almost entirely of $_2He^4$, formed by radioactive decay. Atmospheric helium, on the other hand, contains the fraction of $_2He^3$ shown in Table 19.1, formed by cosmic ray bombardment. Find the chemical atomic mass of atmospheric helium.

19.2 The path of an α-particle near a heavy nucleus of atomic number Z must be similar to that shown by the heavy line in the figure. To see that this is so, we need only notice that the force on the α-particle, when it is far from the nucleus, becomes vanishingly small. Hence the α-particle must move along a straight line at constant speed when r is large.

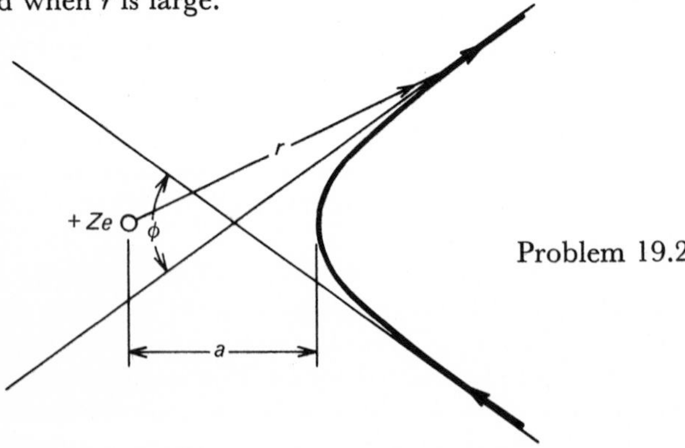

Problem 19.2

(a) Show that the speed of the α-particle v_a, when it is at its closest approach to the nucleus, is $v_a = v_0 b/a$, where v_0 is the speed at large distances and b is the ***impact parameter***, i.e., the perpendicular distance from the nucleus to the original direction of travel.

(b) Show that

$$a^2 = b^2 + aZe^2/2\pi\varepsilon_0 m v_0{}^2.$$

(c) Check Eq. (19.6-2) against the more general result obtained in (b).

19.3 Equation (19.6-2) was derived on the assumption that the target nucleus was so massive that its motion could be neglected. The equation could be written:

$$a = Ze^2/\pi\varepsilon_0 m v_0{}^2,$$

where m is the mass of the α-particle and v_0 is the speed of this particle when it is a long distance from the nucleus.

(a) By considering the scattering in the center of mass system, show that the equation above may be turned into a better approximation if m is replaced by the reduced mass, $mM/(m+M)$, where M is the mass of the target nucleus. (b) What percentage error is made in computing a from Eq. (19.6-2) if the target is ${}_{18}A^{40}$?

19.4 (a) Using the reduced mass (cf. Prob. 19.3) instead of m in the result of Prob. 19.2(b), consider the scattering of an α-particle by an electron. Show that the α-particle and the electron never get closer to each other than

$$e^2/\pi\varepsilon_0 m_e v_0{}^2.$$

(b) Compute the distance of closest approach for an electron and an α-particle of 4.0 MeV energy. (c) Explain why Rutherford scattering is not appreciably affected by the electrons that surround the targer nucleus.

19.5 According to Sec. 19.7, the number of radioactive nuclei remaining from an initial number N_0, after a time equal to one half-life, is $\frac{1}{2}N_0$; after two half-lives it is $\frac{1}{4}N_0$; after 3 half-lives it is $\frac{1}{8}N_0$, etc.

(a) Show that these numbers are consistent with the statement that the number remaining after a time t is

$$N = N_0(2)^{-t/\tau},$$

where N_0 is the number at $t=0$ and τ is the half-life.

(b) Show that log N is a linear function of time, i.e.,

$$\log N = \log N_0 - (t/\tau)\log 2.$$

(c) Given that the derivative

$$(d/dx)(\ln x) = 1/x,$$

where $\ln x$ denotes the logarithm of x to the natural base e, show that the rate at which the number of radioactive nuclei is changing with time is

$$dN/dt = -(N/\tau)(\ln 2).$$

19.6 Suppose that a nucleus X undergoes radioactive decay to a nucleus Y, the half-life being τ_1. The nucleus Y then decays to a new, stable nucleus Z with a half-. life τ_2. Suppose further that $\tau_1 \gg \tau_2$. At time $t=0$, only nuclei of type X are present

Use qualitative reasoning only to show (a) that the number of nuclei of type Y will increase at times $t < \tau_2$; (b) that the number of nuclei of type Y will reach a maximum and will then decrease slowly.

19.7 Figure 19.15b shows the lines of force near the gap in a cyclotron. Suppose that positive ions approach the gap from the bottom of the figure and that a particular ion is following a path to the right of the line of force marked + and −.

(a) Show that the ion will be accelerated to the left as it approaches the gap. (b) Suppose that the ion does not reach the central plane before crossing the gap. Show that it will be accelerated to the right after passing the gap, but that, because of its increased speed, the velocity component it gains to the right will have less magnitude than had the velocity component it gained to the left earlier. (c) Suppose that the ion crossed the central plane before it crossed the gap. Show that it will be accelerated to the right after crossing. (This phenomenon of ***focusing*** ion beams makes the cyclotron practical, since it insures that the ions will travel near the central plane and not strike the metal of the dees.)

19.8 An electron is in a betatron orbit of radius R. The magnetic flux density depends on R, the distance from the center of the doughnut. The *average* flux density inside R is increasing at the rate $d\bar{B}/dt$.

(a) Show that the electron is subject to a tangential force equal to $\frac{1}{2}eR(d\bar{B}/dt)$. (b) Show that the radius of the orbit (R) is connected with the momentum of the electron (mv) by the relation:

$$R = mv/eB,$$

where B is the instantaneous magnitude of the flux density at the radius of the orbit. (c) Show that the electron will continue in an orbit of constant radius if the average field ($\bar{B}$) is $\frac{1}{2}B$.

19.9 Protons of rest mass m_0 and with a kinetic energy of E_0 are injected into a synchrocyclotron, on a path of radius R. They are accelerated across a gap, with an increase of energy ΔE, once during each revolution.

(a) What must be the flux density (B_1) at the time of injection?

(b) What must be the frequency of the alternating field across the gap at the time of injection?

(c) Show that the flux density when the protons have achieved a kinetic energy E must be

$$B = [E(E + m_0c^2)]^{1/2}/ecR,$$

(d) Show that the frequency of the alternating field at the time when the protons have achieved the same energy must be

$$\nu = [(E + m_0c^2)/E]^{1/2}.$$

(e) Find B and ν at the time that the kinetic energy of the protons is 100 MeV.

19.10 In the drift-tube linear accelerator described in Sec. 19.16, the ions move in field-free space over most of their paths, being accelerated only as they cross the gaps between drift tubes. Suppose that ions of mass m and charge q are being accelerated, that they come to the first gap with essentially zero energy, and that the potential difference across any gap at time t is

$$V = V_0 \sin \omega t,$$

where V_0 and ω are constants. Assume that the time spent in crossing each gap is negligibly small and that a group of ions crosses the first gap at time t_1. It is desired that this group cross the nth gap at a time $t_1 + 2\pi n/\omega$.

(a) Supposing the ions to be moving so slowly that Newtonian mechanics apply, show that the length of the nth drift tube must be

$$l_n = \frac{2\pi}{\omega}\left(\frac{2nqV_0 \sin \omega t_1}{m}\right)^{1/2}.$$

(b) Removing the restriction to low speeds, show that the length of the nth drift tube must be

$$l_n = \frac{2\pi c}{\omega}\left[1 - \left(1 - \frac{nqV_0 \sin \omega t_1}{m_0 c^2}\right)^2\right]^{1/2}.$$

(c) Show that the result found in (b) reduces to that found in (a) if $nqV_0 \sin \omega t_1 \ll m_0c^2$.

19.11 Demonstrate qualitatively that "bunching" of ions, similar to that described in the first paragraph of Sec. 19.14, will occur in the linear accelerator of Prob. 19.9 if $t_1 < \pi/2\omega$.

19.12 Consider the reaction

$${}_2\text{He}^4 + {}_2\text{He}^4 \rightarrow {}_4\text{Be}^8.$$

In answering the following questions, use Newtonian mechanics

(a) Show that the reaction requires that an amount of internal energy, $\Delta E =$ 0.0945 MeV, must be supplied to form the beryllium nucleus.

(b) Suppose that a helium nucleus having a kinetic energy E_1 strikes, head-on, a second helium nucleus that is initially at rest, and that a ${}_4\text{Be}^8$ nucleus is formed. Show that the newly formed nucleus will have a kinetic energy $E_2 = \frac{1}{2}E_1$.

(c) Hence, demonstrate that the lowest possible kinetic energy of the moving helium nucleus is $E_1 = 2\Delta E$.

(d) Compute the lowest possible kinetic energy of the helium nuclei in the center of mass system and show that it is equal to ΔE.

19.13 The reaction

$${}_3\text{Li}^7\ (p, \alpha)\ {}_2\text{He}^4$$

can be brought about by bombarding stationary lithium nuclei with energetic protons. Suppose that the reaction can occur only if the proton approaches the center of the lithium nucleus within a distance of 10^{-15} m or closer. Use Newtonian mechanics

(a) Find the electrostatic potential energy when the nuclei are separated by 10^{-15} m.

(b) Show that the kinetic energy of the compound ${}_4\text{Be}^8$ nucleus after the collision is $E_H/14$, where E_H is the kinetic energy of the moving proton.

(c) Show that the kinetic energy of the proton must, in the laboratory system of coordinates, be at least 5.84×10^{-13} J to bring about the reaction.

(d) Show that the kinetic energy of the proton in the center of mass system need by only 5.42×10^{-13} J.

(e) The compound ${}_4\text{Be}^8$ breaks into a two α-particles. One of these is found to be moving in the direction of motion of the original proton. What is the kinetic energy of this particle? What are direction of motion and the energy of the other α-particle?

19.14 Problems 19.12–19.13 indicate that the full kinetic energy of the bombarding particle, as measured in the center of mass system, is available to produce the nuclear reaction. In ***ring storage accelerators*** two beams of ions are accelerated in opposite directions about circular orbits in a synchrotron and are then allowed to impinge on each other. Demonstrate that such a machine can produce nuclear reactions requiring four times as much energy than those that could be produced if either beam alone impinged on a stationary target.

REFERENCES

19A C. Sharp Cook, *Structure of Atomic Nuclei* (Momentum Book No. 9), Van Nostrand, Princeton, 1964.

19B David H. Frisch and Alan M. Thorndike, *Elementary Particles* (Momentum Book No. 1), Van Nostrand, Princeton, 1964. A readable account of elementary particle physics.

19C Kenneth W. Ford, *The World of Elementary Particles*, Blaisdell, New York, 1963. Another good account of elementary particles.

19D Robert Hofstadter, "The Atomic Nucleus," *Scientific American*, July, 1956. (Reprint No. 217, W. H. Freeman.) An account of the probing of nuclei with beams of high-energy electrons.

19E Wilfrid B. Mann and S. B. Garfinkel, *Radioactivity and Its Measurement* (Momentum Book No. 10), Van Nostrand, Princeton, 1966. An account of the theory, as well as the practice, of the subject.

19F Maria G. Mayer, "The Structure of the Nucleus," *Scientific American*, March 1951. (Reprint No. 228, W. H. Freeman.) A useful and understandable introduction to the shell model of the nucleus.

19G Franklin Miller, *Radioactive Decay* and *Scintillation Spectrometry*. (Nos. 80-200 and 80-201, The Ealing Corp., Cambridge, Mass.) Useful short film loops.

19H R. E. Peierls, "Models of the Nucleus," *Scientific American*, January 1959. (Reprint No. 235, W. H. Freeman.) A comparison of the liquid drop, optical, and shell models of the nucleus.

19I Carl D. Anderson, "Early Work on the Positron and Muon," *American Journal of Physics*, vol. 29, pp. 825–830, 1961. Personal history of two significant discoveries.

19J William B. Fowler and Nicholas P. Samios, "The Omega-Minus Experiment," *Scientific American*, October 1964, pp. 36–45. The story of a new fundamental particle.

19K G. K. O'Neill, "Particle Storage Rings," *Scientific American*, November 1966, pp. 107–116. Plans for high-energy accelerators.

19L Gerald Feinberg and Maurice Goldhaber, "The Conservation Laws of Physics," *Scientific American*, October 1963, pp. 36–45. Are conservation laws universally valid?

19M Geoffrey Burbidge, "The Origin of Cosmic Rays," *Scientific American*, August 1966, pp. 32–38.

20 ⇨ *The Behavior and Theory of Gases*

20.1 Boyle's Law

In Chapter 18, we considered evidence which led us to believe that material bodies are made up of molecules and atoms and so laid the foundations for an atomic theory of matter. Modern physics, however, is not satisfied with as qualitative a picture as we have thus far constructed; it demands of an atomic theory that it predict, on the basis of deduced or measured properties of the atoms and molecules, the behavior of matter in bulk. Many of the ensuing pages will be devoted to the methods by which such predictions are made. Since it is found that the connection between atomic and large-scale behavior is simpler in gases than in solids or liquids, we shall start with a consideration of the gaseous state of matter.

Before we attempt any theory of the behavior of gases, it will be worth while to consider some of the experimental observations which have been made. We shall first discuss a variation on the experiment performed by Robert Boyle (1627–1691), which we referred to in Sec. 1.4. A small volume of air is enclosed in a glass tube B (Fig. 20.1) above a column of mercury. The mercury is contained in a flexible tube, at the opposite end of which there is a second glass tube A which is open to the atmosphere at one end. Since atmospheric pressure acts on the mercury column at A, the pressure at B is

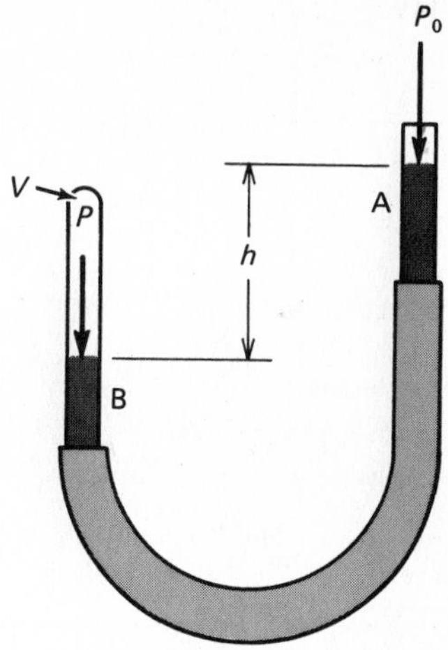

FIG. 20.1 Boyle's law apparatus.

$$p = p_0 + \rho g h,$$

where p_0 is the pressure of the atmosphere and ρ is the density of mercury. If the tube at A is raised, the pressure on the gas in B will increase. Boyle found that this increase in pressure resulted in a decrease in the volume V of the enclosed gas. Careful measurements of the volume and of the pressure showed him that, if the temperature remained constant, then, for a given amount of enclosed gas, the product of the pressure by the volume is a constant; thus,

$$pV = C, \qquad (20.1\text{-}1)$$

where C is a constant depending upon the mass and kind of gas enclosed and on the temperature. We may rewrite Eq. (20.1-1) as

$$V = C/p, \tag{20.2-2}$$

which is read as follows: *At a given temperature, the volume of a given quantity of gas varies inversely as the pressure.* This statement is known as ***Boyle's law.***

Boyle did his original experiments with air. They have since been repeated for many other gases. While Boyle's law is obeyed very closely for permanent gases such as oxygen, nitrogen, hydrogen, and helium, the easily liquefied vapors, such as water vapor, ammonia, or carbon dioxide, show appreciable departures from the law, particularly at high pressures. As a matter of fact, even relatively small admixtures of these vapors will cause departures from the law. Figure 20.2 shows plots of V against p for dry air and for air containing water vapor.

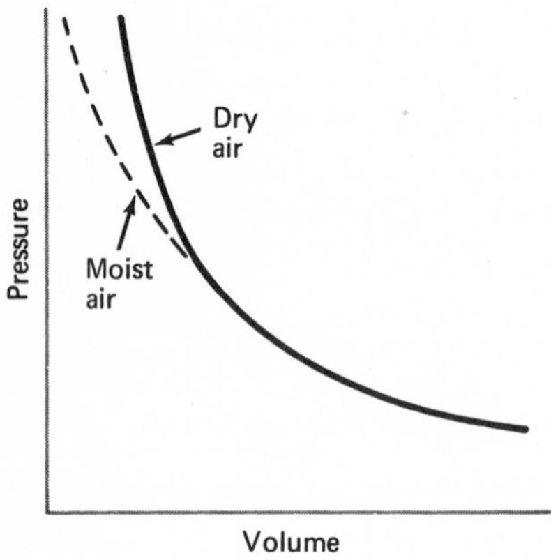

FIG. 20.2 Behavior of moist and dry air.

If experiments of the type that we have outlined above are carried out with varying masses of the same gas, it is found that the constant C is proportional to the mass of gas present. Furthermore, if the same masses of different pure gases are used, it is found that the constant is inversely proportional to the molecular weight of the gas. But the number of kmoles of gas (Sec. 18.14) in a given mass is also inversely proportional to the molecular weight, so we can sum up the dependency of C on the constitution and mass of the gas by saying that C is proportional to the number of kmoles of gas present. We may therefore write

$$C = nK,$$

where n is the number of kmoles of gas present and K depends only on the temperature. Making this substitution in Eq. (20.1-1), we have, as a form of Boyle's law which may be applied to any mass of any pure permanent gas,

$$pV = nK. \tag{20.1-3}$$

We finally wish to investigate the behavior of a mixture of two or more gases, each of which individually obeys Boyle's law. It is found experimentally that such a mixture also obeys the law, and that the total volume of the gas is just equal to the sum of the volumes which the component gases would occupy at the same temperature and pressure. This result is stated as the ***law of partial pressures***: *When a mixture of two or more gases is present, each gas behaves as if the others were not present.* We may use the law of partial pressures to rewrite Eq. (20.1-3), for a mixture of permanent gases, as

$$pV = K\sum_{1}^{n} n_j, \tag{20.1-4}$$

where n_j is the number of kmoles of the jth gas and there are n different gases present. (For the meaning of $\sum$ see Appendix C.5.)

EXERCISES

20.1-1 At 0°C and at 760 mm Hg pressure* (cf. Sec. 9.6) it is found that 1.00 kmole of hydrogen (H_2) occupies 22.4 m^3. What volume will this mass of gas occupy if the pressure is (a) 1.00 mm Hg, (b) 1520 mm Hg?

20.1-2 Using the data of Ex. 20.1-1, calculate the volume occupied at 0°C and 760 mm Hg by (a) 1.00 kg of hydrogen (H_2), (b) 1.00 kg of oxygen (O_2), (c) 1.00 kg of helium (He).

20.1-3 If 1.00 g of solid carbon dioxide (CO_2) is allowed to evaporate, what volume will it occupy at 0°C and 760 torr?

20.1-4 If 1.00 g of solid carbon dioxide is allowed to evaporate in a closed vessel (kept at 0°C) whose volume is 5.00 cm^3, what will be the pressure of the gas in atmospheres?

20.2 The Thermal Expansion of Gases

In Secs. 11.1 and 11.4, we saw that most solids and liquids expand upon heating. With such substances, the change of the volume with change of pressure was so small that it was not important when thermal expansions were being measured. With gases, however, such is not the case and, if we wish to investigate thermal expansion of gases, we shall need to hold the pressure constant. This may be done by an arrangement such as that shown in Fig. 20.3. Here the gas is enclosed in a bulb B and is separated from the atmosphere by the mercury column M–N. The bulb may be surrounded by a bath of water or some other liquid that can be maintained at a given temperature. If M and N are at the same height at a given temperature of the bath, we know that the pressure on the gas at M is equal to that of the atmosphere. If the bath temperature is now

* The rather clumsy unit "millimeters of mercury" or "mm Hg" is being replaced by the term ***torr***, named in honor of Evangelista Torricelli (Sec. 9.7). It is abbreviated as T. We shall use the two terms interchangeably.

increased, the gas will expand, forcing the mercury level at M downward and that at N upward. By lowering the right-hand tube, the two mercury surfaces may again be brought to the same level and the pressure restored to atmospheric. This constitutes a still further expansion of the gas, and the left-hand mercury surface will now stand, say, at M′. The change in volume of the gas, at constant pressure, will now be the volume ΔV, between M and M′.

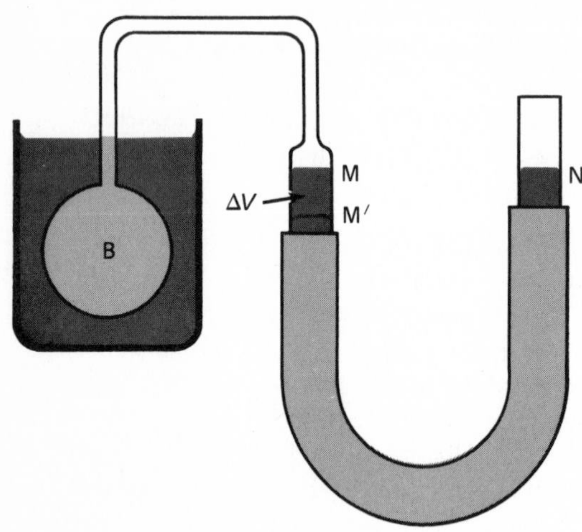

FIG. 20.3 Constant pressure gas thermometer.

If we study the expansion of any of the permanent gases in this way, we obtain a very interesting result. If the volume of the gas at a temperature t_0 (in °C) is V_0, we find that the volume V_t at any other temperature t is

$$V_t = V_0[1 + b(t - t_0)], \tag{20.2-1}$$

provided the pressure is kept constant [cf. Eq. (11.3-3)]. We thus see that gases follow the same general law of expansion as solids or liquids. The surprising result, found originally by Jacques Charles (1746–1823) and Joseph Gay-Lussac early in the nineteenth century, is that the ***coefficient of volume expansion*** *b has the same value for all permanent gases, provided only that the initial temperature is the same.* Further, the value of b for these gases is found to be

$$b = 1/(273°\text{C} + t_0) \tag{20.2-2}$$

where t_0 is the initial temperature in °C. If we substitute this value into Eq. (20.2-1), we find the extremely simple law for the expansion of gases at constant pressure:

$$\frac{V_t}{V_0} = \frac{273°\text{C} + t}{273°\text{C} + t_0}. \tag{20.2-3}$$

The statement of Eq. (20.2-3) is known as ***Gay-Lussac's law.***

20.3 The Kelvin Temperature Scale

Gay-Lussac's law suggests an interesting possibility. Suppose that a permanent gas is cooled to —273°C. Then we should expect its volume, in accordance with Eq. (20.2-3), to decrease to zero. Such behavior is not actually observed for two reasons:

1. It is found experimentally that cooling becomes more and more difficult as we approach the temperature —273°C.* There are reasons to believe that this temperature can be approached as closely as we please but can never be reached.
2. No gas justifies the name "permanent" at these very low temperatures. All gases can be liquefied at temperatures appreciably above —273°C.

In spite of the fact that we cannot carry the temperature of gases as low as —273°C, the occurrence of this temperature in the expression for the expansion of all permanent gases suggests that it has a peculiar significance. This suggestion is given added weight by the fact that as this temperature is approached the specific heats of many substances become zero (Sec. 11.12).

Guided by the facts just stated, as well as by many others, we are led to believe that the temperature —273°C is the lowest temperature that can be reached—i.e., it is the ***absolute zero of temperature.*** It is logical to use this natural zero as the zero of our temperature scale rather than the arbitrarily chosen ice point, which is defined as 0°C. For this reason, the ***Kelvin temperature scale,*** named for Lord Kelvin (William Thompson, 1824–1907), is very commonly used in physics and chemistry. Each degree on this scale has the same size as a degree on the Celsius scale, but the zero is taken as the absolute zero. We shall speak of temperatures on this scale as measured in ***degrees Kelvin*** (°K). It will be obvious from the definition that, if the temperature of a body on the Kelvin scale is T and its temperature on the Celsius scale is t, the two are related by the equation:

$$T = 273°\text{K} + t.$$

We shall use the Kelvin scale almost entirely through the rest of this text, and it must be understood that all temperatures hereafter are on this scale, unless otherwise specified.

If Gay-Lussac's law is written using Kelvin temperatures, it takes the particularly simple form

$$V/V_0 = T/T_0. \qquad (20.3\text{-}1)$$

20.4 The Ideal Gas Law

We have seen, in the last few sections, that Boyle's and Gay-Lussac's laws express the behavior of gases quite closely at sufficiently high temperatures but

* Wherever the temperature —273°C is used in the following discussion, the more accurate value —273.16°C is implied. The approximate value is sufficiently accurate for most of our purposes.

that no gas obeys them at low temperatures. In order to have a term for discussion purposes, we define an ***ideal gas*** as one which obeys these laws at all temperatures and pressures. An ideal gas, then does not exist in nature, but permanent gases approximate an ideal gas more or less closely. Helium in particular is very close to an ideal gas. If we discuss the laws of an ideal gas, we can then apply these laws to real gases, with the mental reservation that they become inaccurate at low temperatures or high pressures.

If we have a definite amount of gas of known composition, *the condition of that gas is completely specified if we know any two of three quantities: the pressure, the temperature, and the volume.* From the two preceding sections, we know that these three quantities are not independently variable for an ideal gas but are connected by Boyle's and Gay-Lussac's laws. If we combine these laws into a single equation, that equation tells how any one of the three quantities, p ,T, and V, will change when one or both of the others are changed. Such an equation for a substance is known as the ***equation of state*** of the substance. Our problem now is to derive the equation of state for an ideal gas.

In order to combine Boyle's law and Gay-Lussac's law, we now notice that K in Eq. (20.1-3) depends upon the temperature. In order to study this dependence, we may multiply and divide the left-hand side of Eq. (20.3-1) by p, the pressure of the gas, to obtain

$$pV/pV_0 = T/T_0.$$

We now notice that $pV = nK$ and that $pV_0 = nK_0$, where n is the number of kmoles of the gas present and K and K_0 are the Boyle's law constants for the two temperatures T and T_0, respectively. Hence, we have

$$T/T_0 = K/K_0.$$

This equation tells us that K is proportional to the Kelvin temperature. Letting the constant of proportionality be R, we have

$$K = RT$$

as an equation valid for all ideal gases. Finally, substituting this value into Eq. (20.1-3), we arrive at the ***equation of state of an ideal gas:***

$$pV/T = nR. \tag{20.4-1}$$

The quantity R is obviously a very important one, since it is a constant for any ideal gas. We see that, for one kmole of the gas,

$$pV/T = R. \tag{20.4-2}$$

Further, the dimensions of R are

$$[R] = [m\ell^{-1}t^{-2}][\ell^3][\text{kmole}^{-1}\text{ deg K}^{-1}] = [m\ell^2t^{-2}(\text{kmole deg K})^{-1}].$$

We may therefore write R in joules per kmole degree. To evaluate this ***general gas constant,*** we need merely to measure the mass of a sample of gas of which we know the pressure, volume, and temperature. If this mass is M and the molecular weight of the gas is m, then the number of kmoles in the sample is $n = M/m$, and the general gas constant is given by

$$R = pVm/MT. \tag{20.4-3}$$

Measurements made on the permanent gases under nearly ideal conditions, i.e., at high temperatures and low pressures, indicate that the value of the constant is

$$R = 8.314 \times 10^3 \text{ J/kmole deg.} \tag{20.4-4}$$

EXERCISES

20.4-1 Using the results of Eqs. (20.4-3) and (20.4-4), verify the statement made at the beginning of Ex. 20.1-1 that the volume occupied by 2.016 kg of hydrogen (H_2), at 0°C and 1.013×10^5 N/m^2 pressure, is 22.4 m^3.

20.4-2 The stratosphere balloon "Explorer II" was originally filled with 6.37×10^3 m^3 of helium at a pressure of 660 mm and a temperature of 6°C. At the top of the flight (2.15×10^3 m) the pressure was 30.0 mm and the gas temperature was −21°C. What volume was occupied by the gas at this time?

20.4-3 Before the balloon of Ex. 20.4-2 began to descend, the gas temperature rose to 0°C, while the pressure remained constant. What was then the volume of the gas?

20.4-4 What mass of helium was used to fill the balloon of Ex. 20.4-2?

20.4-5 In an experiment on the electrolysis of water (cf. Fig. 18.2), 10.3 cm^3 of hydrogen are collected at a temperature of 20°C and a pressure of 764 mm. What quantity of electricity has passed through the apparatus?

20.5 The Gas Thermometer

The reader will remember that one of the difficulties in establishing a thermometric scale was due to the fact that different substances have different coefficients of expansion and that these coefficients depend upon the temperature. Since the coefficients of all of the permanent gases approach so closely to the inverse of the Kelvin temperature, these materials suggest themselves as very nearly ideal thermometric substances. A second advantage of gases for this purpose is that their coefficients of expansion are so large compared with those of solids that the expansion of the container necessitates only a very small correction. The ordinary ***gas thermometer*** is a device very similar to that shown in Fig. 20.3, and either nitrogen or helium is used as the gas. There are two ways in which the thermometer may be used:

1. In the ***constant pressure thermometer,*** the height of the mercury column at N is adjusted to the same level as the surface at M′. The change of volume of the gas is then read on a scale along the tube at M–M′, and the temperature is computed by Gay-Lussac's law (Eq. 20.3-1).
2. In the ***constant volume thermometer,*** the height of the mercury column at N is adjusted so that the surface at M is kept at a constant level. The

difference of the levels N and M then indicates the change in pressure, and the pressure and temperature are related by the equation

$$p/p_0 = T/T_0, \tag{20.5-1}$$

which may be deduced from Eq. (20.4-1) if V is constant.

20.6 The Molar Heats of Gases

When we discussed the measurement of the specific heats of solids and liquids in Sec. 11.12, we saw that these quantities could be determined by adding known amounts of thermal energy to a known mass of the material and then measuring the temperature rise. If we attempt the same type of measurement with gases, an obvious difficulty arises. Since gases expand so much with changing temperature, we must allow either the pressure or the volume of the gas, or both, to increase during the measurement. For purposes of simplicity, one of these quantities is usually held constant. Thus the ***specific heat*** is usually measured either ***at constant volume***, by heating the gas in a fixed container

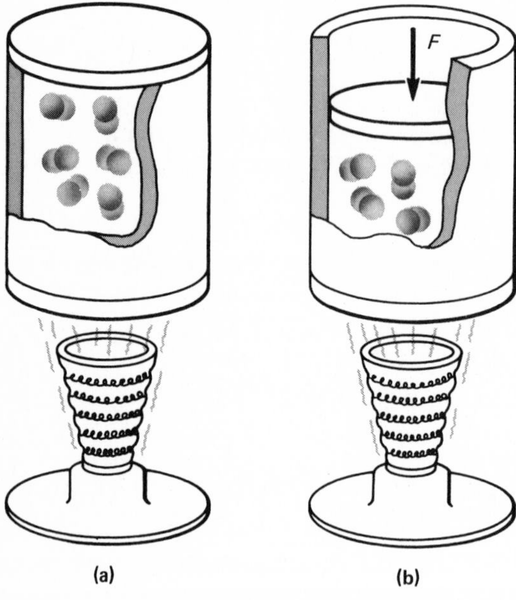

Fig. 20.4 The two specific heats of gases.

such as that shown in Fig. 20.4a, or ***at constant pressure***, by heating the gas in a cylinder with a movable piston, as in Fig. 20.4b. The two specific heats thus determined are found to be different for every gas, and the thermal capacity at constant pressure is always larger than that at constant volume. It is further found that each of the specific heats is practically independent of pressure and temperature, unless the temperature is far below room temperature. Finally, both specific heats, when measured for various gases, are found to decrease, in general, as the molecular weight of the gas increases.

The last mentioned fact suggests a method for correlating the data on the specific heats of gases. If we use, instead of the kilogram, the kilogram molecular weight of the gas as the unit of mass, we express the specific heat in terms of joules (or calories) per kmole degree. This quantity is usually called the ***molar heat*** of the gas. Table 20.1 gives the measured values of the molar heats of a number of ordinary gases at constant volume (C_v) and at constant pressure (C_p).

Table 20.1 *Molar Heats of Gases at Room Temperature*

Gas	Molar Heat (10^3 J/kmole deg)	
	C_v	C_p
Argon (A)	12.6	21.0
Helium (He)	12.6	20.9
Hydrogen (H_2)	20.1	28.3
Carbon monoxide (CO)	20.7	29.0
Nitrogen (N_2)	20.7	29.0
Oxygen (O_2)	20.9	29.2
Carbon dioxide (CO_2)	28.3	36.8
Water vapor (H_2O)	27.9	37.1
Ammonia (NH_3)	28.4	37.2

A glance at this table will convince one of a marked regularity in the molar heats of gases. Both of the given monatomic gases have values of C_v equal to 12.6×10^3 J/kmole deg, the diatomic gases all have values close to 21×10^3 J/kmole deg, and the polyatomic gases all have values close to 28×10^3 J/kmole deg. Similarly, the values of C_p group together for each of the three types of gas. A still more striking result is found when we express the molar heats in terms of the gas constant R, which was evaluated in Eq. (20.4-4). If we do this we find that the values given in Table 20.2 represent quite closely the molar

Table 20.2 *Molar Heats of Gases at Room Temperature*

Type of Gas	Molar Heat ($R = 8.314 \times 10^3$ J/kmole deg)	
	C_v	C_p
Monatomic	$3R/2$	$5R/2$
Diatomic	$5R/2$	$7R/2$
Polyatomic	$(6–7)R/2$	$(8–9)R/2$

heats of all the gases listed in Table 20.1. This table shows that there must be a close relation between the gas constant and molar heats, for not only are the molar heats for monatomic and diatomic gases representable by a whole number times $R/2$, but also the difference between C_p and C_v for any gas is very close to R.

We may explain the constant difference between C_p and C_v by the use of the conservation law for energy. Suppose that one kmole of a gas is enclosed in the cylinder of Fig. 20.5. Let the gas be first heated with the piston held rigidly

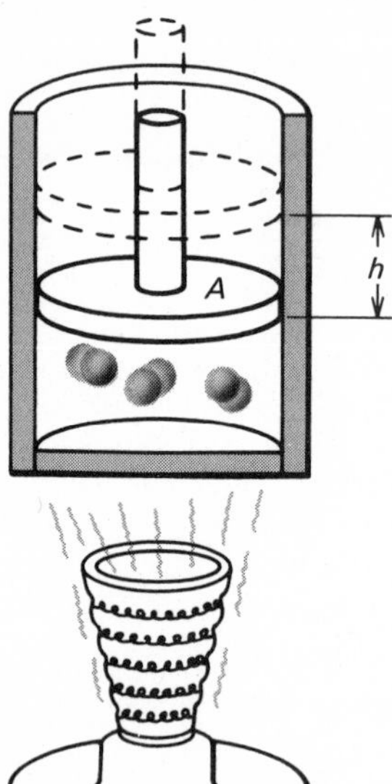

FIG. 20.5 The difference of the molar heats.

in place. If the temperature rise of the gas is ΔT and the amount of heat supplied to it is Q_v, these two quantities will be related by the equation

$$Q_v = C_v \, \Delta T. \qquad (20.6\text{-}1)$$

If the gas is restored to its original condition and then heated again with the piston free to move, the quantity of heat required for a temperature rise ΔT will be

$$Q_p = C_p \, \Delta T. \qquad (20.6\text{-}2)$$

During this second heating, the piston will have risen through some distance h. Since the force on the piston is pA, where p is the pressure of the gas and A is the area of the piston, the amount of work done is

$$\Delta w = pAh = p \, \Delta V,$$

where ΔV is the change of volume of the gas. Since the expansion of the gas takes place at constant pressure, we apply Gay-Lussac's law to find ΔV. If V is the initial volume and $V + \Delta V$ is the final volume, Eq. (20.3-1) tells us that

$$(V + \Delta V)/V = (T + \Delta T)/T,$$

where T is the initial temperature. Hence,

$$\Delta V = (V/T)\Delta T,$$

and

$$\Delta w = (pV/T)\Delta T = R\,\Delta T \tag{20.6-3}$$

from Eq. (20.4-2).

If we assume that the internal energy of an ideal gas depends only upon its temperature, then the internal energies at the ends of the two heating processes are the same, and the extra energy which was necessary to heat the gas at constant pressure must be just sufficient to account for the work done in this process. Hence, we have

$$Q_p = Q_v + \Delta w.$$

Substitution from Eqs. (20.6-1) to (20.6-3) shows that

$$C_p = C_v + R \tag{20.6-4}$$

so that *the difference between the two molar heats for an ideal gas is R.*

The fact that the relation between the two molar heats does satisfy Eq. (20.6-4) justifies the assumption which we made that the internal energy of an ideal gas depends only on the temperature. We shall see in Sec. 20.9 that this is equivalent to the assumption that no forces act between the molecules of a gas except during collisions. The argument leading to Eq. (20.6-4) was used as evidence for the law of the conservation of energy by Julius von Mayer (1814–1878) before the experiments of Joule (cf. 11.8). Mayer's assumption with regard to the internal energy of a perfect gas was later justified by an ingenious experiment, also due to Joule. Suppose that two bulbs are connected by a stopcock, as in Fig. 20.6, and that one of them is filled with gas at a pressure

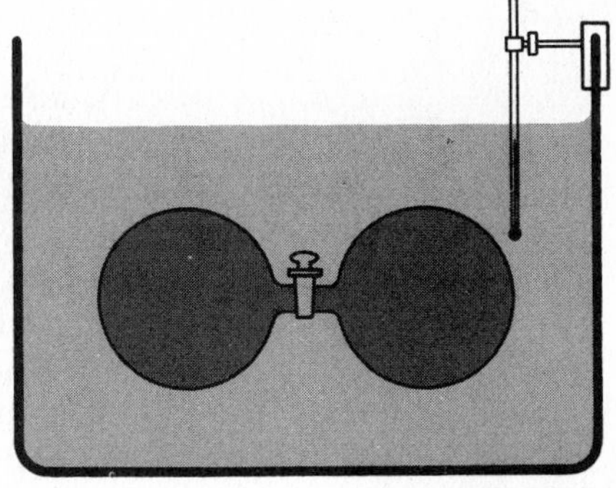

FIG. 20.6 Joule's experiment on the internal energy of a gas.

p, while the other is evacuated. Then let the entire system be placed in a water bath and the stopcock be opened. The gas will expand to fill the volume of the two bulbs. If the internal energy of a gas increases with increasing volume, this expansion will require energy, and this energy must come from the water bath. The assumption of a dependence of energy on volume would therefore lead to a prediction of a change of temperature of the water bath. Actually, Joule found no such change, and he concluded that the internal energy of a gas depends only upon the temperature. Later, more precise experiments by Joule and Kelvin showed a small effect for real gases, and this effect may be used as an indication of their departures from ideal gases.

20.7 The Elastic Moduli of Gases

We can easily apply the methods of Sec. 9.5 to determine the bulk modulus of a gas at constant temperature. Suppose that the initial pressure of the gas in a container such as that of Fig. 20.7 is $p_0 = F/A$, where F is the force on the piston of area A. Then an increase in the force F of amount ΔF will produce an increase in pressure of amount $\Delta p = \Delta F/A$ and this increase in pressure will produce a decrease in volume of amount ΔV. In agreement with the definitions of Secs. 9.3 and 9.5, we can define the bulk modulus [cf. Eq. (9.5-1)] for a gas by the relation

$$M_B = V\Delta p/\Delta V, \qquad (20.7\text{-}1)$$

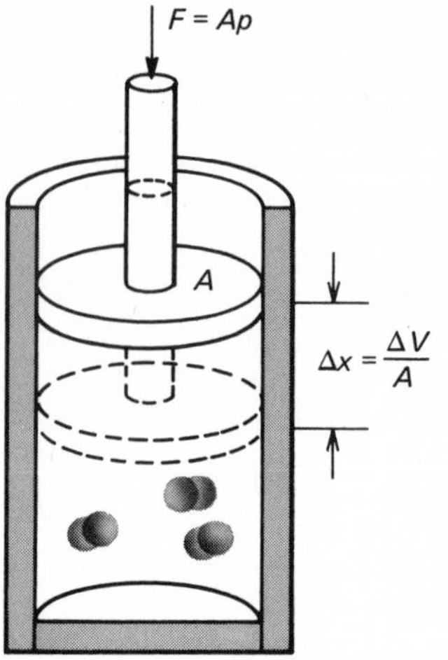

FIG. 20.7 Elastic moduli of a gas.

since the stress Δp has produced a strain $\Delta V/V$.

If the temperature is kept constant, we know from Eq. (20.1-1) that

$$\begin{aligned} p_0 V &= (p_0 + \Delta p)(V - \Delta V) \\ &= p_0 V + V\Delta p - p_0\,\Delta V - \Delta p\,\Delta V. \end{aligned}$$

If we neglect the product $\Delta p\,\Delta V$ of two small quantities with respect to the other terms in this expression, we may write

$$V\,\Delta p = p_0\,\Delta V.$$

It then follows [from Eq. (20.7-1)] that the bulk modulus of a gas at constant temperature or the ***isothermal bulk modulus*** is given by

$$M_i = V\,\Delta p/\Delta V = p_0. \qquad (20.7\text{-}2)$$

The fact expressed by this equation is vividly illustrated by the elastic properties of the air in an automobile tire. When the pressure is low, the tire is soft; its elastic modulus is low. The tire gets harder and the elastic modulus larger as the pressure is increased.

In the discussion of the isothermal compression of a gas, one important point has been glossed over in the statement that the temperature is to remain constant. When any gas is compressed, work is done in compressing the gas and the energy supplied to the gas will result in an increase in the temperature of the gas. This increase in temperature will result in a larger increase in pressure than that given by Eq. (20.1-3) for a given change in volume. Let us see if we can calculate this increase in pressure under ***adiabatic conditions*** (Greek: *adiabatos*—not passable) i.e., under conditions in which no heat escapes from the gas during the compression process.

If we decrease the volume of a kmole gas by an amount ΔV against a pressure p_0, we must move a piston of area A (Fig. 20.7) through a distance Δx such that $\Delta V = A\,\Delta x$ and, in doing so, the force F applied to the piston is given by $F/A = p$. The work done in compressing the gas is thus

$$\Delta w = F\,\Delta x = pA(\Delta V/A) = p\,\Delta V.$$

This will produce a rise in temperature ΔT without further change in volume, so we must have

$$\Delta w = p_0\,\Delta V = C_v\,\Delta T. \tag{20.7-3}$$

We now consider that all the quantities p, V, and T change by the small amounts Δp, ΔV, and ΔT. Using Eq. (20.4-2), we have initially

$$p_0 V = RT \tag{20.7-4}$$

and finally

$$(p_0 + \Delta p)(V - \Delta V) = R(T + \Delta T),$$

which may be multiplied out into the form

$$p_0 V + V\,\Delta p - p_0\,\Delta V - \Delta p\,\Delta V = RT + R\,\Delta T.$$

Again neglecting the product $\Delta p\,\Delta V$, we have

$$V\,\Delta p - p_0\,\Delta V = R\,\Delta T$$

or

$$\begin{aligned} V\,\Delta p/\Delta V &= p_0 + R\,\Delta T/\Delta V \\ &= p_0 + Rp_0/C_v, \end{aligned}$$

using Eq. (20.7-3). Thus, the ***adiabatic bulk modulus*** for a gas may be written in the form

$$M_a = p_0(C_v + R)/C_v.$$

Since, however, $C_p = C_v + R$ [Eq. (20.6-4)], this expression may be written in the form

$$M_a = \gamma p_0, \tag{20.7-5}$$

in which $\gamma = C_p/C_v$ is the ***ratio of the molar heats*** of the gas.

The value for the speed of sound in a gas, which we gave as an empirical result for air in Sec. 10.8, can now be derived from the properties of the gas. Since sound consists of compressional waves, Eq. (10.4-5) is applicable. Sound waves involve extremely rapid fluctuations in the pressure of the gas. Thus, very little heat conduction can take place between one part of the gas and another and the processes of compression and rarefaction can be taken as adiabatic. We therefore write Eq. (10.4-5) in the form

$$W = \sqrt{M_a/\rho} = \sqrt{\gamma p_0/\rho}. \tag{20.7-6}$$

With the aid of Eq. (20.4-3), we may write

$$\rho = M/V = p_0 m/RT,$$

so that

$$W = \sqrt{\gamma RT/m}. \tag{20.7-7}$$

Thus, the speed of sound depends only on the molecular properties of the gas and the temperature, but not on the pressure. It is left as an exercise (Ex. 20.7-4) to show that Eq. (10.8-1) results from Eq. (20.7-7).

Equations (20.7-6) and (20.7-7) have been of great importance historically in the study of the rare gases of the zero column of the periodic table (Table 21.1) and of the diatomic gases. The density of a gas and the speed of sound in it can be determined when only very small quantities are available. In this way, both the molecular weight and the value of γ can be determined. The results of Sec. 20.6 then enable one to decide whether the gas is monatomic, diatomic, or polyatomic.

In modern aviation practice, the speed of a fast airplane is expressed in terms of its ***Mach number,*** which is defined as the ratio of the speed of the plane to the speed of sound. Thus, a high Mach number corresponds to a lower speed at high altitudes than it does at low altitudes, because of the lower temperature of the air, rather than the lower pressure. However, the aerodynamic problem of reaching these high speeds depends both on the pressure and the temperature in a way which cannot be discussed here.

EXERCISES

20.7-1 Calculate the heat in joules required to produce the rise in temperature of the gas referred to in Ex. 20.4-3. How much heat would have been required if the volume had been kept constant?

20.7-2 The ratio of the specific heats (γ) for a particular gas is found to be 1.67. What can you say about the nature of this gas? If the ratio is 1.40, what can you then say?

20.7-3 Calculate the adiabatic and isothermal bulk moduli for (a) hydrogen, (b) oxygen, and (c) carbon dioxide at a pressure of 760 mm Hg and at 0°C.

20.7-4 Since air at the surface of the earth consists of $\frac{1}{5}$ oxygen and $\frac{4}{5}$ nitrogen with only a small percentage of other gases, the "average" molecular mass may be taken as $[32 + (4 \times 28)]/5$. Using this result and other necessary information, verify that Eq. (10.8-1) is consistent with the results of the present section.

20.7-5 A plane is said to have a speed of Mach 1.5 at an altitude of 40,000 ft where the pressure is 152 mm Hg and the air temperature is −51°C. What is the speed of the plane in km/sec?

20.8 *The Kinetic Theory of Gases*

Let us now see if we can account for the large-scale behavior of gases by a theory which supposes that gases are made up of a large number of molecules. We know that gases expand indefinitely as the pressure is decreased. We might try to account for this expansion by assuming that the molecules repel each other, were it not that the experiment of Joule and the agreement of the molar heats with the conservation of energy indicate that forces of repulsion do not exist. Consequently, we assume instead that the molecules of the gas are in constant motion and that this motion accounts for the expansion of the gas. Because of this assumption, the theory which we are about to develop is known as the ***kinetic theory of gases.*** In developing the kinetic theory, we shall make a number of assumptions. They are about the simplest that we can make and still obtain agreement with the general experimental facts. In order that we may see exactly what we assume, we shall list these assumptions below:

1. A gas consists of a number of molecules, which are in continual random motion.
2. There are no forces acting between these molecules except during collisions.
3. Collisions of the molecules with each other or with the walls of the containing vessel are perfectly elastic; there is no loss of energy during the collisions.
4. The forces which act between the molecules, or between the molecules and the walls, are negligible except during the collision processes.
5. The volume occupied by the molecules themselves is negligible compared with the volume of the container.

Now let us suppose that we have a gas, consisting of N identical molecules, each of mass m. Suppose also that the container is in the form of a cube, of length a on a side. Temporarily, we shall concentrate our attention on a single molecule, which we shall call the jth molecule, supposing that the molecules can all be identified and numbered from 1 to N. Suppose that this molecule, in accordance with assumption 1, has a velocity $\vec{v}_j$. This velocity may be broken up into components along the three axes parallel to the sides of the cube (Fig. 20.8), so that

$$\vec{v}_j = \vec{v}_{jx} + \vec{v}_{jy} + \vec{v}_{jz}. \qquad (20.8\text{-}1)$$

Because of assumption 5, collisions between molecules will be infrequent, and we can therefore consider this molecule to be moving around entirely by itself. If it collides with a wall perpendicular to the x-axis, any forces acting upon it will be perpendicular to the wall, and assumption 3 tells us that the x-component of the velocity will be reversed in sign and will not be changed in magnitude as a result of the collision. Hence, this collision will result in a change Δp_{jx} of the component of the momentum of the molecule perpendicular to the wall. This is given in magnitude by

$$\Delta p_{jx} = mv_{jx} - (-mv_{jx}) = 2mv_{jx}.$$

An equal and opposite change of momentum is, of course, given to the wall. Further, since the molecule moves with a uniform speed in the x-direction, it will take a time equal to a/v_{jx} to travel from one side of the box to the other, or a time $2a/v_{jx}$ for a round trip. Hence, the time between collisions of the jth

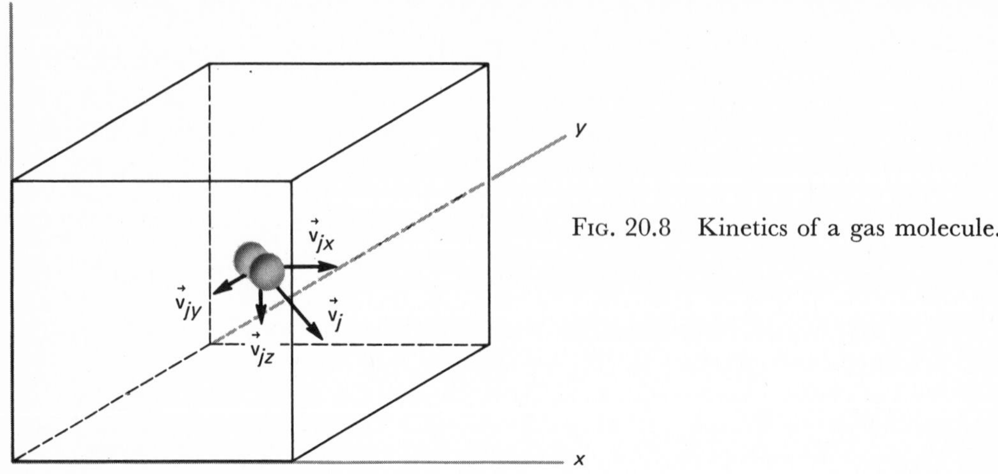

FIG. 20.8 Kinetics of a gas molecule.

molecule with a given wall, perpendicular to x, will be $2a/v_{jx}$, and the number of collisions made with this wall in unit time will be $v_{jx}/2a$. Therefore, the total momentum transferred to the wall in unit time by this molecule is

$$\Delta p_{jx}/\Delta t = (v_{jx}/2a)(2mv_{jx}) = mv_{jx}^2/a. \tag{20.8-2}$$

We now remember that the jth molecule is but one of many that are continually colliding with the wall. The total momentum transferred to the wall by all of these is obviously the sum of the individual momentum changes, so we have for the momentum given to the wall per unit time

$$\Delta p_x/\Delta t = \sum_{j=1}^{N} \Delta p_{jx}/\Delta t = \sum_{j=1}^{N} mv_{jx}^2/a = (m/a) \sum_{j=1}^{N} v_{jx}^2. \tag{20.8-3}$$

We can get rid of this rather cumbersome expression, if we replace the summation by an average value for the velocity component. To do this we notice that the average of a number of quantities is obtained when we add the quantities together and divide by the number. Thus, if we want the average value of the x-component, or the mean x-component, of the velocities for all of the molecules of the gas, we could write

$$(v_x)_{\text{av}} = \left(\sum_{j=1}^{N} v_{jx}\right)/N.$$

Since we have assumed that the motions of the molecules are completely random, there will be as many negative as positive values of the velocity components in this expression, so $(v_x)_{\text{av}}$ will be zero. The average of the square of the velocity components, however, will involve only positive quantities, so we should not expect this average to vanish. For it we may write the quantity

$$(v_x^2)_{\text{av}} = \left(\sum_{j=1}^{N} v_{jx}^2\right)/N,$$

from which we may find that

$$\sum_{j=1}^{N} v_{jx}^2 = N(v_x^2)_{\text{av}}. \tag{20.8-4}$$

We define $(v_x^2)_{\text{av}}$ as the ***mean square*** of the x-components of the molecular velocities. Notice that the mean square is not equal to the square of the mean x-component, since the latter quantity is zero. If we insert the mean square value into Eq. (20.8-3) by the use of Eq. (20.8-4), we obtain

$$\Delta p_x/\Delta t = Nm(v_x^2)_{\text{av}}/a. \tag{20.8-5}$$

Each impact of a gas molecule on the wall will be a sharp blow. If these blows were delivered infrequently, the wall would bounce in and out, being held in place by the elastic forces of the solid of which it is composed. Since each of many billions of molecules is striking the wall many thousand times a second, however, the wall will not have time to recover from one impact before another takes place close to the location of the first, and the net effect will be the same as if a steady force pushed against the wall. To find the magnitude of this force, we remember that force is the time rate of change of momentum. Since Eq. (20.8-5) gives the time rate at which momentum is given to the wall, the total force on the wall is equal to $\Delta p_x/\Delta t$. Because of the random nature of the impacts, this force is uniformly distributed over the wall and so results in a uniform pressure. From the definition of pressure (Sec. 9.5), we find that the pressure is

$$p_x = (\Delta p_x/\Delta t)/A = Nm(v_x^2)_{\text{av}}/a^3, \tag{20.8-6}$$

since the area A of the wall is a^2.

Since assumptions 1 and 4 tell us that all directions in the container are equivalent, we see that the same pressure must be exerted on all the walls. We can completely remove the reference, in Eq. (20.8-6), to the x-direction by a very simple argument. By means of Eq. (20.8-1) and the Pythagorean theorem, we see that

$$v_j^2 = v_{jx}^2 + v_{jy}^2 + v_{jz}^2.$$

Since this equation holds for any molecule in the gas, it also holds on the average, and we may write

$$(v^2)_{\text{av}} = (v_x^2)_{\text{av}} + (v_y^2)_{\text{av}} + (v_z^2)_{\text{av}}.$$

Further, since the velocities are oriented at random, the mean square component in any direction will be equal to the mean square component in any other. Therefore,

$$(v_x^2)_{\text{av}} = (v_y^2)_{\text{av}} = (v_z^2)_{\text{av}},$$

and

$$(v^2)_{\text{av}} = 3(v_x^2)_{\text{av}}. \tag{20.8-7}$$

Substitution of this result into Eq. (20.8-6) gives for the pressure

$$p = Nm(v^2)_{\text{av}}/3a^3.$$

Finally, since $a^3 = V$, the volume of the container, we have

$$pV = Nm(v^2)_{av}/3. \tag{20.8-8}$$

If we compare Eq. (20.8-8) with the experimentally determined equation of state for an ideal gas, Eq. (20.4-1), we notice a marked similarity of form. The similarity becomes even more pronounced if we recognize that the total number of molecules in a gas is the product of the number of kmoles n and Avogadro's number L. Hence, $nL = N$, and Eq. (20.4-1) becomes

$$pV = NRT/L.$$

We may now introduce a new constant $k = R/L$. Since R is the gas constant per kmole, the new quantity, known as the ***Boltzmann constant***, is the *gas constant per molecule.* The constant is named for Ludwig Boltzmann (1844–1906), an Austrian physicist who contributed greatly to the development of thermodynamics. With the substitution of k for R/L, the equation of state is

$$pV = NkT. \tag{20.8-9}$$

The numerical value of the Boltzmann constant is given by

$$\begin{aligned} k &= R/L = (8.314 \times 10^3 \text{ J/kmole deg})/(6.023 \times 10^{26} \text{ molecules/kmole}) \\ &= 1.380 \times 10^{-23} \text{ J/molecule deg.} \end{aligned} \tag{20.8-10}$$

Comparison of the theoretically derived Eq. (20.8-8) and the experimentally determined Eq. (20.8-9) shows that our theory is at least partially successful in predicting the experimental behavior of a gas. The two equations, in fact, can be made identical if we make one more assumption. We first notice that kT is an energy, since k is measured in J/deg. We also observe that the average translational kinetic energy of a molecule of the gas is

$$E_t = m(v^2)_{av}/2. \tag{20.8-11}$$

If we now assume that

$$E_t = 3kT/2, \tag{20.8-12}$$

we find that

$$m(v^2)_{av}/3 = 2E_t/3 = kT. \tag{20.8-13}$$

Substitution of this value into Eq. (20.8-8) leads to Eq. (20.8-9) and thus to exact agreement between experiment and theory. We have needed, of course, to force this agreement to some extent by the introduction of the assumption of Eq. (20.8-12). Before we can be completely satisfied, we must independently justify this assumption, but we shall see in the next section that this can be done by a consideration of the molar heats of gases.

The importance of what we have here accomplished can hardly be exaggerated. Using six simple assumptions, the first five of which seem inherently reasonable, and going through a very simple logical argument, based on our mechanical definitions and principles, we have arrived at a prediction which agrees very nicely with experimental results. We have been guided in our development by the known experimental facts and the crucial test of the kinetic theory will now be determined by how well we can answer two questions:

(a) Does the theory enable us to make predictions of the behavior of gases beyond those characteristics which we used in connection with the derivation?
(b) Can the theory be modified, by reasonable changes in the assumptions, to include not only the ideal gas law but also the departures from that law which are observed with real gases?

Most of the remainder of this chapter will be devoted to a consideration of these two questions, and we shall find that we can obtain very satisfactory answers to them.

20.9 The Theory of Molar Heats of Gases

One of the first successes of our theory is that it can predict the molar heats of an ideal gas. Let us first consider one kmole of the monatomic ideal gas. In accordance with Eq. (20.8-12), we expect each molecule of the gas to possess a kinetic energy of translation equal to $3kT/2$, and, since there are L molecules present, the total internal energy of translation at the temperature T is

$$E = 3LkT/2.$$

Moreover, since there are no forces acting between molecules, there can be no potential energy in the gas; thus, we should expect E to be the total internal energy. If we now heat the gas at constant volume to a temperature $T + \Delta T$, the new energy will be

$$E' = 3Lk(T + \Delta T)/2.$$

Since no external work was done in this process, the energy Q_v which was added to the gas in order to bring about the increased temperature must be equal to $E' - E$, the change in the internal energy of the gas. Hence,

$$Q_v = 3Lk\Delta T/2,$$

or, since $Lk = R$ and $C_v = Q_v/\Delta T$ [cf. Eq. (20.6-1)],

$$C_v = 3R/2. \tag{20.9-1}$$

This result is in complete agreement with the result of Table 20.2 for monatomic gases.

If we wish to consider polyatomic gases, we must introduce a new concept. Since a monatomic gas molecule may move along any one of three independent axes (x, y, z), we see that three coordinates are necessary to describe its position. We say that such a molecule has three ***degrees of freedom***. In general, *a body has as many degrees of freedom as the number of coordinates necessary to describe its position and orientation.* It is possible to prove, by mathematical methods beyond the scope of this text, that the assumption of Eq. (20.8-12) is equivalent to a more general statement, known as ***the law of the equipartition of energy***. This law states that the mean kinetic energy of any molecule is given by $fkT/2$, where f is the number of degrees of freedom of the molecule. We can easily see that $f = 3$ for a monatomic gas, and that the equipartition law agrees completely with our development. If we suppose, as a rather crude approximation, that an atom is similar to a hard elastic sphere, then a diatomic molecule must appear somewhat like the dumbbell figure of Fig. 20.9. If we take a temporary z-axis as the axis of the dumbbell, we see that rotation of the molecule about this axis will not change the positions of the two atoms, but that rotation about the x- or y-axes will change these positions. Hence, in order to specify the position of the molecule in addition to the x-, y-, and z-coordinates of its center of mass, we must give the angles which its axis makes with two of the coordinate axes. A diatomic molecule, therefore, has two degrees of rotational freedom, or five degrees of freedom in all. Hence, the mean kinetic energy of a molecule of a diatomic gas at temperature T is

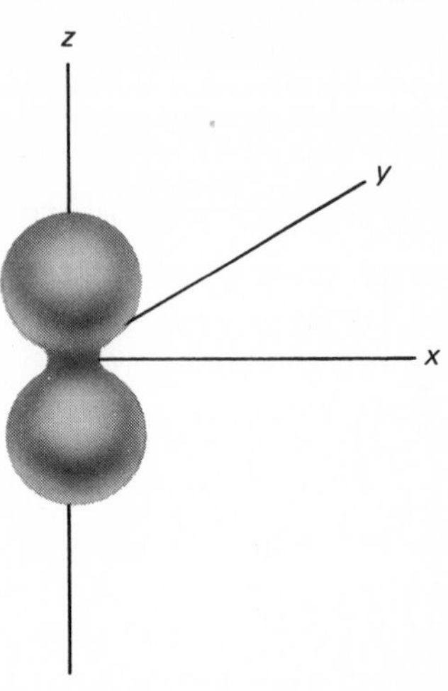

FIG. 20.9 Diatomic molecule

$$5kT/2,$$

and an argument exactly similar to that given above for a monatomic gas shows that the molar heat of a diatomic gas is

$$Cv = 5R/2. \qquad (20.9\text{-}2)$$

In most of the polyatomic gases internal vibrations of the molecules contribute to the energy, so the molar heats are somewhat higher than the $3R$ value which we would predict from their six degrees of freedom.

Although the treatment above gives good agreement with experimental data taken at or near room temperature, it cannot be considered entirely satisfactory if measurements at other temperatures are taken into account. For example the molar heat of hydrogen drops to about $1.5R$ at low temperatures ($<50°K$) and rises to about $3.0R$ at temperatures of a few hundred degrees Celsius. Even at room temperature we had to suppose that vibrations within diatomic gas molecules did not contribute to the specific heat and that rotation about the axis of the molecule does not count as an additional degree of freedom. These difficulties arise because of quantum phenomena, which we shall discuss further in Chapters 23 and 24. We shall find there that the ascribing of an average energy of $\frac{1}{2}kT$ per degree of freedom is valid only at high temperatures.

20.10 Diffusion

We know that two gases, when placed in a container, diffuse into each other, so that both gases are soon distributed throughout the container. The continual motion assumed in our kinetic theory would lead to this qualitative result. If we wish to study the process of diffusion more closely, it is worth while considering the way in which gas escapes through a small hole in one of the walls of the vessel. Suppose that the vessel D of Fig. 20.10 is initially filled with a mixture containing equal numbers of molecules of each of two gases. The vessel C is initially empty, and a small hole in the wall between the two vessels permits gas to diffuse from D to C. We have seen in Sec. 20.8 that the number of times

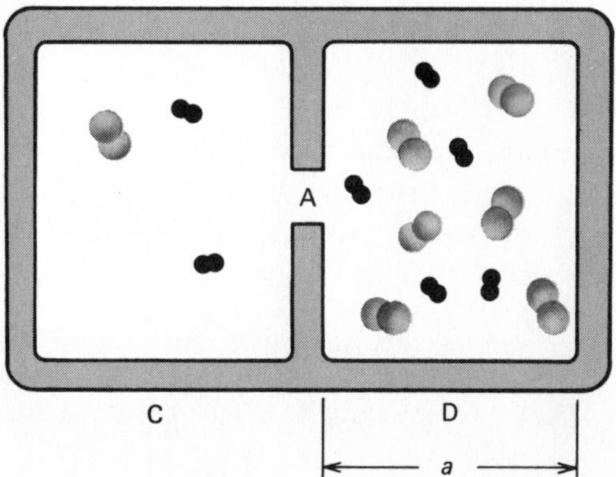

FIG. 20.10 Diffusion of gases through a small hole.

a given molecule strikes one wall of the vessel is proportional to the velocity of that molecule perpendicular to the wall; for the jth molecule this number is $v_{jx}/2a$, where a is the length of the vessel. Since this molecule also has components parallel to the wall, it is a matter of pure chance where the molecule strikes on the wall W. The chance of the molecule hitting the hole is thus A/W, the ratio of the area A of the hole to the area W of the wall. Hence, the number of times per second a molecule will hit the hole is on the average $(v_{jx}/2a)(A/W)$. Thus, the number of molecules which escape will be proportional to the total number of molecules in the vessel, to the speed of the molecules, and to the area of the hole in the wall. From Eq. (20.8-13), the average value of the square of the speed is given by

$$(v^2)_{\text{av}} = 3kT/m. \tag{20.10-1}$$

We now define the ***root-mean-square speed*** (v_{rms}) by the expression

$$v_{\text{rms}} = (v^2)_{\text{av}}{}^{1/2} \tag{20.10-2}$$

and it follows that

$$v_{\text{rms}} = (3kT/m)^{1/2}. \tag{20.10-3}$$

The result which we have just obtained is of the greatest importance to us in the separation of individual gases from a mixture of two or more gases. If two gases of molecular masses m_1 and m_2 are mixed in equal numbers in the vessel D of Fig. 20.10, then the ratio of the numbers n_1 and n_2 which escape into C during a time interval so short that n_1 and n_2 do not change appreciably will be given by

$$n_1/n_2 = (m_2/m_1)^{1/2} \tag{20.10-4}$$

according to the result just obtained. Thus, if 1 kmole of H_2 ($m_H = 2$ amu) and 1 kmole of O_2 ($m_O = 32$ amu) are mixed in D, the relative numbers which escape into C during a short time will be given by

$$n_H/n_O = (m_O/m_H)^{1/2}$$
$$= (32/2)^{1/2} = 4.$$

Thus hydrogen will escape through the hole four times as fast as does oxygen.

EXERCISES

20.10-1 Calculate the value of the root-mean-square velocity of the hydrogen molecule at 0°C and 760 mm Hg. What will be the value of this velocity at 0°C and 1520 mm Hg pressure?

20.10-2 What is the value of the rms velocity (cf. Ex. 20.10-1) of a helium atom at −200°C and 10^{-6} mm pressure?

20.11 Measurement of Molecular Speeds

Equation (20.10-3) enables us to predict the actual speeds of molecules. Thus for hydrogen at room temperature, $T = 293$°K and $m = 2.02$ amu/6.02×10^{26} amu/kg $= 3.36 \times 10^{-27}$ kg, so

$$v_{rms} = \left[\frac{3(1.38 \times 10^{-23}\ \text{J/deg})(293\ \text{deg})}{(3.36 \times 10^{-27}\ \text{kg})}\right]^{1/2}$$
$$= 19.2 \times 10^3\ \text{m/sec}.$$

This speed is considerably above that of a high-speed rifle bullet, and attempts to measure molecular velocities directly offer considerable experimental difficulty. These difficulties have been overcome in a device invented by I. F. Zartman (1899–), very similar in principle to that used by Fizeau for his speed of light determinations. In this apparatus, which is shown schematically in Fig. 20.11, a beam of molecules is emitted from a furnace F, which may be maintained at any desired temperature. A continuous beam of molecules

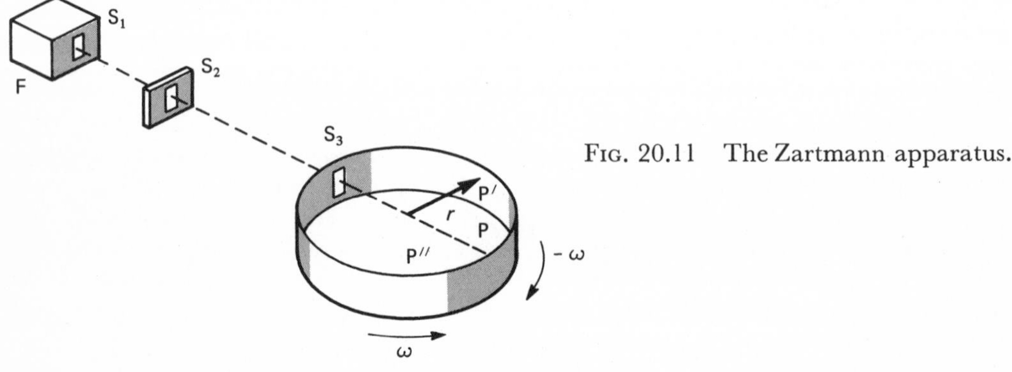

FIG. 20.11 The Zartmann apparatus.

is obtained by using a solid substance, such as iodine or tin, in the furnace, and by evaporating the molecules from it. The molecules then pass through a series of slits, S_1, S_2, S_3, which eliminate all molecules except those traveling in nearly parallel paths. Finally, they enter a drum-shaped chamber, which may be rotated about its own axis. The entire apparatus is evacuated, of course, to prevent collisions between molecules of the vapor and molecules of air, which would scatter the beam from its parallel path. Were the drum at rest, the molecules would impinge on the drum at P, where they would condense to form a solid. The point P is diametrically opposite to the entry slit S_3. If the drum is rotating with an angular velocity ω, the drum will rotate through an angle $2r\omega/v$, where v is the molecular velocity, in the time $t = 2r/v$ during which the molecules travel across the diameter $2r$. Hence, the point P″ at which the molecules strike is located at a distance $2r^2\omega/v$ from P. The effect is doubled by allowing some of the molecules to collect while the drum is rotating in one direction and some while it is rotating in the opposite direction, with the same angular speed. Hence, the deposits P′ and P″ are separated by a distance $4r^2\omega/v$. The Zartman experiments not only confirm the fact that the molecular velocities are of the order of magnitude predicted by Eq. (20.10-3), but also show that the velocities vary somewhat about this value. The most probable speed of the molecules is slightly less than v_{rms}, and the number of molecules having a given speed becomes less as the speed departs from the most probable speed in either direction. It is interesting that the exact distribution of speeds found experimentally agrees with a theoretical prediction that may be made by an extension of the methods used in this chapter.

20.12 Brownian Motion

A body at rest in a gas generally experiences equal pressures on all sides, due to the random nature of the molecular velocities. We can easily see that the assumptions of our kinetic theory lead to this result, on the average, for any large body, but the random nature of the impacts of the molecules must itself lead to small ***fluctuations*** in the pressure. Thus, if a very small body is immersed in a gas, at one instant the bombardment of the molecules on one side of it may be greater than on the other. Instantaneously, then, this body will be subject to a force which will start it into motion. At some later instant, the force may be in a different direction. Hence, we should expect such a small body to go through an irregular motion. Since a large surface, due to the high frequency of impacts upon it, will not be subject to as great relative fluctuations of pressure as a small surface, we should further expect the motion to be appreciable only for bodies of microscopic size.

The exact phenomenon which we have predicted was observed in the nineteenth century by the botanist Robert Brown (1773–1858) and is known as ***Brownian motion***. In studying biological preparations under the microscope, he noticed a random motion of small particles. For a long time this motion remained unexplained, and attempts were made to account for it by assuming life in the particles. When it was shown that such materials as brick dust exhibited Brownian motion, this explanation had to be abandoned. The only satisfactory theory follows the ideas that we have just presented.

The calculation of the velocities which can be expected as a result of the pressure fluctuations is quite difficult if we attempt to carry it out directly by a consideration of molecular bombardment. Einstein, however, found a far simpler way to attack the problem. He reasoned that a small particle suspended in a gas is in no essential way different from a gas molecule. If we accept this hypothesis, we must expect that the law of the equipartition of energy will also apply to such a particle, and that its average kinetic energy of translation will be

$$E_t = 3kT/2. \tag{20.12-1}$$

The root-mean-square velocity of the particle will be inversely proportional to the square root of the mass, so only very small particles will have observable speeds.

Equation (20.12-1) may be used to give a quantitative check on the theory of Brownian movement. A small particle is observed in a gas, and its positions at short time intervals are observed. The root-mean-square speed may be calculated from these observations. The particle will also settle downward under the action of gravitational forces, and its mass may be calculated from the rate of settling by Stokes' law (Sec. 18.12). From these data, the average kinetic energy may be obtained and compared with that predicted by Eq. (20.12-1). As a matter of fact, values of k calculated from Brownian motion observations and Einstein's result check within experimental accuracy with those obtained by other means.

20.13 Real Gases

While the behavior of real gases closely approaches that of an ideal gas under some conditions, there are many circumstances for which the ideal gas law does not fit the experimental facts. In particular, real gases at high pressures or low temperatures depart radically from the ideal. It is not difficult, if we examine the assumptions of the kinetic theory closely, to see where the breakdown occurs. As gases become more and more dense, the size of the molecules becomes more nearly comparable to the volume of the container, and assumption 5 of Sec. 20.8 must be abandoned. Also, as the average distance between the molecules decreases, the effect of any small forces of attraction or repulsion will increase. Assumption 2 must also be given up, since we know that attractive forces do exist, as is indicated by the cohesion of the liquid which is formed as a result of the compression and cooling of a gas.

Various attempts have been made to deal with the problem of a real gas. One of the most successful is due to Johannes van der Waals (1837–1923), who showed that, if assumptions 2 and 5 are dropped, a treatment very similar to that of Sec. 20.8 leads to an equation of state:

$$(p + n^2a/V^2)(V - nb) = nRT, \tag{20.13-1}$$

where p is the pressure, T the Kelvin temperature, n the number of kmoles enclosed in the volume V, and R is the gas constant. The two quantities a and b are constants for a given gas. The term n^2a/V^2 is an added pressure due to the attractive forces between the molecules, while $V - nb$ represents the volume in which the molecules are free to move, after the space taken up by the molecules themselves is taken into account.

The ***van der Waals equation of state*** is not in complete agreement with the experimental data, but it represents a real advance over the ideal gas law. Somewhat better agreements with experiment may be obtained by the introduction of more constants, but attempts in this direction have not clarified our theoretical picture to any great extent, so we shall not discuss them here.

20.14 The Second Law of Thermodynamics

In the present chapter, we have discussed the consequences that follow when we assume a gas to be made up of molecules which are in continual random motion. We shall later see that this kinetic theory can be extended to include solids and liquids, as well as gases. In fact, we can arrive at a new idea of the term temperature, as being a measure of the average kinetic energy of the molecules of a substance. For all except the very low temperatures, the equipartition law holds for the molecules of any substance, and at low temperatures it is replaced by a more general law which is derived on the basis of the quantum theory.

The one characteristic thing about the kinetic theory is that it assumes a random, or *completely disordered*, motion of the molecules. We can define a completely disordered state of affairs by saying that it is one in which individual molecules or individual regions of space have no distinguishing characteristics by which we can tell them apart. Conversely, the ***degree of order*** of a state is measured by the number of characteristics that allow us to distinguish between different molecules or different regions. As a simple example, suppose that we have a box divided into two equal volumes by a partition down the middle, and that one side contains hydrogen at a given pressure and the other contains oxygen at the same pressure. These two sides are easily distinguishable, by chemical or physical tests, and a certain degree of order exists in the box. If we remove the partition, we know that the two gases will diffuse into each other. As soon as this process is finished, the two sides will contain equal amounts of oxygen and hydrogen and the state of the box will be more disordered than before. A second example is a container of a gas into which a jet is projecting more gas, as shown in Fig. 20.12. All of the molecules, including those already in the container and those being projected into it, will have random velocities, but those coming from the jet will have, in addition, a velocity component directed as shown by the arrows. This implies a certain degree of order, as these molecules are distinguished from their neighbors by this velocity component. As soon as they strike other molecules of the gas, however, their forward motion is disturbed, their extra energy is transferred to other molecules, and their subsequent motion is completely random. The result is an increase in the disorder of the system. The energy of the incoming molecules, of course, has been distributed to increase the average kinetic energy of all the other molecules, so that the temperature within the container has been increased.

In both of the examples cited above, the processes which we knew could take place have resulted in greater disorder of the system. Long studies of a large number of processes have indicated that this tendency toward disorder seems to be a general rule, as long as we deal with large enough samples of matter so that more than a few molecules are involved. Because no exceptions to the rule have been found, it has been generalized as the ***second law of thermodynamics.***

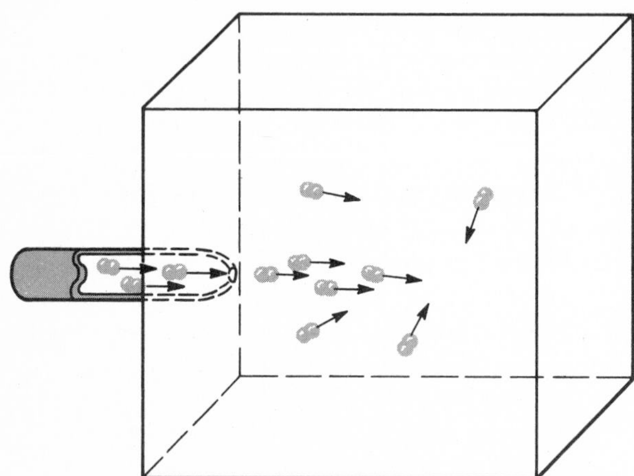

Fig. 20.12 Molecules issuing from a jet.

This law may be stated in the form: *In any isolated system, no processes that increase the order of the system will take place, and processes that decrease the order are preferred to processes that leave the order unchanged.*

As one of the most important applications of the second law, let us suppose that two bodies at different temperatures are brought into contact. In accordance with the equipartition law, their molecules will have different average kinetic energies and will be distinguishable. If we apply the first law (conservation of energy, Sec. 11.11) to the system, we see that any one of three things might happen:

1. The bodies might remain at their original temperatures, with no energy exchange taking place.
2. The cooler body might become cooler than before, giving up energy to the hotter body. This would require that the hotter body grow still hotter.
3. The hotter body might give up energy to the cooler body, causing the two temperatures to approach each other.

Of these three processes, we see that the first would result in no change in the disorder of the system; the second would result in increased distinction, and therefore increased order; the third would result in increased disorder. Hence, the second law tells us that the last process is the one which will take place, as we know it to do in practice. As a result of this argument, we see that the second law states that heat will not flow from a cooler to a hotter body, without changes in other bodies. The last qualification is necessary because, if a third body were present, the increased disorder in it might more than compensate for the increased order in the two original bodies. This, in fact, is exactly what happens in any mechanical refrigerator, in which heat is transferred from the cool refrigerator to the warm room around it. In order for this to be accomplished, work must be done by a compressor or similar device, and this work results in increased disorder of the system as a whole.

A less trivial example is the conversion of mechanical energy to heat by friction. If we slide a block of wood across a table, all of the molecules of the block have a component of velocity in the direction of motion, in addition to their random motions. Hence, the mechanical motion of the block represents an ordered state of affairs. Due to friction the block is slowed down, its mechanical energy is converted into heat, and this results in an increased energy of agitation of the molecules of the block and the table, both of which increase their temperatures. Here again, the process which actually takes place results in an increase of disorder. As far as the first law is concerned, it would be equally possible for the table and block to cool suddenly and for the energy thus released to start the previously resting block into motion. But since this process would result in increased order, the second law tells us that it will not take place. It will be obvious from the above case that mechanical energy is characteristic of a highly ordered state of affairs (i.e., large groups of molecules moving together), whereas heat energy is characterized by a completely disordered condition. Hence, we can see from the second law that mechanical energy may always be converted into heat, but that heat cannot be converted into the mechanical energy of a body without changes in other bodies. An example of this is furnished by the expansion of a gas under constant pressure, as discussed in Sec. 20.6. In that case, an amount of thermal energy $Q_p = C_p \, \Delta R$ was supplied to a kmole of the gas, and only $R \, \Delta T$ of this appeared as mechanical energy of the piston and weight. The balance of the energy, $C_v \, \Delta T$, was used to produce a change in the gas.

The second law of thermodynamics has very important consequences. It seems to tell in what direction the energy of the universe is moving. Since thermal energy represents a more disordered state than mechanical energy, we may say that thermal energy is less available than mechanical energy. By this we mean that mechanical energy can be completely converted into thermal, but that, if we have a given amount of thermal energy available, only part of it can be converted into mechanical energy. The result of all of the conversions which actually take place, then, must be a net change of mechanical into thermal energy. Hence, we must predict from the second law that the total energy of the universe will be less and less at our control, as time goes on; until, in an equilibrium state, the universe will be completely disordered, and all of its energy will be thermal. Under these circumstances everything would be at the same temperature, and all of the matter in the universe would be scattered uniformly and thinly through space. The picture proposed by the second law is rather cheerless, but at present there seems to be no escape from it.

20.15 *Summary*

In this chapter we have made an important application of the atomic theory of matter developed in Chapter 18. We have been able to account quite completely for the properties of gases on the assumption that they are made up of a large number of molecules in rapid motion. We have seen that an increase in the thermal energy of the gas, and a consequent increase in its temperature, corresponds to an increase in the kinetic energy of the random motions of the molecules.

In discussing the properties of gases we have set up the equation of state for an ideal gas, based on the experimental laws of Boyle and of Gay-Lussac. We have seen how this concept of an ideal gas gives us a new method of thermometry and enables us to establish the Kelvin temperature scale.

It was then possible to show that the empirical equation of state for a gas is quite accurately explained in terms of the kinetic theory and that the same theory gives a quantitative account of the molar heats of a gas. A qualitative discussion was also given of several other properties of gases which can be explained on this theory.

PROBLEMS

20.1 (a) Suppose that a container having a volume of 500 cm^3 contains oxygen gas, at a temperature of 23°C and a pressure of 100 atmospheres, and solid carbon, of mass 12.0 g. The carbon is heated until it ignites and burns completely to form CO_2. The system is then cooled to its original temperature. What is the resulting pressure in the container? (The volume occupied by the original carbon may be neglected in comparison with the volume of the container.)

(b) If you performed a lengthy numerical calculation to arrive at a result in (a), does your answer suggest that there was an easier way to solve the problem?

20.2 The following data have been obtained for a sample of pure neon gas at a temperature of 20°C:

Pressure (P) (atmospheres)	*Volume* (V) (cm^3)
20.00	54.18
25.00	43.41
30.00	36.29
35.00	31.16
40.00	27.44
45.00	24.34
50.00	21.96

(a) Make a plot of the product PV as a function of the pressure. Does neon obey Boyle's law over this pressure range?

(b) By extrapolating your plot to $P = 0$, estimate the number of kmoles of neon in the sample.

(c) Over what range of pressures, at this temperature, is Boyle's law correct within 1.0 percent for neon?

20.3 Equation (20.4-2) is often called the ***equation of state*** of an ideal gas. Equations of state for real gases, solids, and liquids connect the pressure, temperature and volume of such materials. An approximate equation of state for a liquid or solid, valid over a limited range, may be written

$$V_0 + \Delta V = V_0[1 + A(T - T_0) - B(P - P_0)],$$

where ΔV is the change in volume that takes place when the temperature changes from T_0 to T and the pressure from P_0 to P. Express A and B in this equation in terms of coefficients or moduli that we have previously encountered in this book.

20.4 In Eq. (20.6-3), we saw that the work done as a gas was heated at constant pressure was $R\,\Delta T$ per mole. Suppose that a gas expands isothermally, at a temperature T, from a volume V_1 to a volume V_2.

(a) Show that the work per mole done during a small part of the expansion, from V to $V + \Delta V$, is

$$\Delta w \approx (RT/V)\Delta V.$$

(b) By passing to the limit and then integrating, show that the total work done is

$$w = RT \ln (V_2/V_1),$$

where ln denotes the logarithm to the base e.

20.5 Consider the adiabatic expansion of an ideal gas. The conservation of energy demands that the change of internal energy during any part of the expansion must be the negative of the work done, i.e.,

$$C_v dT = -PdV.$$

(a) Starting from this equation and the ideal gas law, show that

$$\frac{dP}{dV} = \frac{C_v + R}{C_v} \cdot \frac{P}{V} = \frac{\gamma P}{V}.$$

(b) By integration, show that

$$P_1 V_1^{\gamma} = P_2 V_2^{\gamma}$$

during the adiabatic expansion from a pressure P_1 and a volume V_1 to a pressure P_2 and a volume V_2.

20.6 A glass tube of length 0.800 m is closed at both ends and is filled with an ideal gas at a temperature of 20.0°C. A small loud speaker at its center may be driven at various frequencies. It is found that the sound issuing from the tube shows maxima at frequencies of 68, 114, 159, and 204 cycles per second.

(a) What is the speed of sound in the gas? (b) An approximate determination of the molecular mass of the gas shows this quantity to be less than 35. What is the probably nature of the gas?

20.7 Suppose that a particular gas showed a decrease in temperature in the Joule experiment of Fig. 20.6. What could be concluded about the dependence of the internal energy of this gas on its volume?

20.8 Equation (9.6-1) was derived for an incompressible fluid and was modified slightly to allow for compression in Probs. 9.1 and 9.9. A rigorous expression for the dependence of the pressure on height in the atmosphere, known as the ***law of isothermal atmospheres,*** may be obtained easily if we consider the temperature to be constant and the air to be an ideal gas containing no water vapor.

(a) Show that, as the height above the earth's surface changes from z to $z + \Delta z$, the pressure changes by

$$\Delta p \approx -\rho g \, \Delta z,$$

where ρ is the density at height z. Then pass to the limit to show that

$$\frac{dp}{dz} = -\left(\frac{Mg}{RT}\right) p,$$

where M is the molecular mass.

(b) By integrating, show that

$$p = p_0 e^{-Mgz/RT},$$

where e is the base of natural logarithms and p_0 is the pressure at the earth's surface.

20.9 We have seen that the root-mean-square velocity of molecules of mass m is $(3kT/m)^{1/2}$ and that the root-mean-square of any velocity component is $(kT/m)^{1/2}$. Supposing that the molecules are not all traveling at the same speed, show that the mean speed of the molecules must be less than $(3kT/m)^{1/2}$.

20.10 A bird, whose mass is 3.0 ounces, is in a cage, whose mass is 3.00 lb. The cage is weighed on an equal arm balance. (a) What mass will be required to balance the system if the bird is standing on the floor of the cage? (b) What mass will be required if the bird is flying about in the cage? (c) Does the answer to (b) depend on the nature and construction of the cage?

20.11 An alternative method to that described in Sec. 20.11 for the determination of molecular speeds involves the fall of molecules under the action of gravity. Suppose that a furnace containing caesium has slits at one side so that a beam of caesium atoms can leave in exactly a horizontal direction. This furnace is mounted at one end of a long, well-evacuated tube. The level at which the atoms strike at the other end is determined by allowing them to impinge on a fine hot wire, where they are ionized, so that a current proportional to the rate of arrival of atoms is produced. In such an apparatus the temperature of the furnace is 100°C and the distance from it to the hot wire is 3.00 m. The hot wire receives atoms at the greatest rate when it is (0.17 ± 0.02) cm below the level at which the atomic beam leaves the furnace. Is this result consistent with the estimates of molecular speeds that we have found in this chapter?

20.12 (a) What is the average number of molecules per cubic meter in the atmosphere at 20°C and normal atmospheric pressure?

(b) Estimate the average volume per molecule.

(c) If each molecule can be approximated as a sphere of 10^{-10} m radius, what fraction of the total volume is occupied by the molecules themselves?

(d) Estimate the average distance between two neighboring molecules. (It may help if you imagine the molecules to be arranged at the corners of little cubes.)

REFERENCES

20A Max Born, *Atomic Physics*, 7th edition, Hafner, New York, 1962. Pages 1–23 are relevant.

20B T. G. Cowling, *Molecules in Motion*, Harper Torchbook (TB 516), Harper, New York, 1960. The first three chapters are historical in orientation, and the rest of the book presents physics in readable mathematical terms.

20C Peter Fong, *Foundations of Thermodynamics*, Oxford, New York, 1963. Chapter 3 deals with the second law of thermodynamics.

20D Morris Shamos, editor, *Great Experiments in Physics*, Holt, New York, 1960. Chapter 3 presents Boyle's account of his work on "the spring of the air."

20E Mark W. Zemansky, *Temperatures Very Low and Very High* (Momentum Book No. 6), Van Nostrand, Princeton, 1964. The second law of thermodynamics is the central theme of Chapter 2.

20F John King, *The Size of Atoms from an Atomic Beam Experiment*, produced by Educational Services Incorporated (No. 0455, The Ealing Corp., Cambridge, Mass.). A filmed demonstration showing the effects of collisions between atoms.

21 ⇨ *The Behavior and Theory of Liquids and Solids*

21.1 Gases, Solids, and Liquids

In Chapter 19 we studied in some detail some of the characteristics of the atoms of matter, whose existence was postulated in Chapter 18. We saw that each of these atoms consists of a positively charged nucleus in which most of the mass resides and which is surrounded by a cloud of electrons. The number of electrons is just sufficient to make the atom as a whole electrically neutral.

One of the problems of physics is to explain the bulk behavior of matter in terms of the properties of the individual atoms. We have already made a start on this problem in Chapter 20, where we found that the properties of gases could be explained by supposing that the atoms or molecules of which the gas is composed are in continual chaotic motion. The successes of the kinetic theory of gases may lead us to hope that we can also connect the properties of solids and liquids with the behavior of atoms and molecules.

We have already encountered many of the properties of matter which must be treated in our discussion. We have seen that all materials can be solidified at sufficiently low temperatures, and that solids can be characterized by elastic resistance to changes of shape or size (Chapter 9) and by relatively low coefficients of thermal expansion (Chapter 11). In addition, certain solids can conduct electric currents, and a few exhibit the interesting property of ferromagnetism (Chapter 15). As the temperature is increased, most solids can be melted by the addition of energy (Sec. 11.13) and so pass to the liquid state. The liquids thus formed exhibit elastic resistance to changes of volume (but not of shape) (Chapter 11) and have temperature coefficients of expansion intermediate between those of solids and those of gases (Chapter 11). Finally, at higher temperatures, liquids may be vaporized into gases (Chapter 11). Liquids and gases share the property of transmitting equally in all directions pressures which are applied to them (Chapter 9).

In our discussion of gases in Chapter 20 we supposed that the molecules occupied only a very small part of the total space taken up by the gas, or, put in another way, that the distances between molecules were very large compared with the dimensions of the molecules themselves. Since the condensation of a gas to a liquid is always accompanied by an increase in density, and since the freezing of a liquid to a solid is almost always accompanied by a similar change, we must believe that the molecules are packed together much more closely in solids and liquids than they are in gases. Under such circumstances the forces between adjacent atoms or molecules, which were found to be very small in gases, may become appreciable, and we might reasonably expect these forces to play a dominant role in determining the properties of solids and liquids. We shall therefore start our study of these condensed states of matter by investigating the forces between atoms.

21.2 Forces between Atoms

If we ask ourselves what types of forces exist between neighboring atoms, we might suspect that gravitational, electric, or magnetic forces would exist. In most cases it can be shown that the gravitational and magnetic forces are so small compared with electrical forces that they may be neglected. We shall therefore limit our first discussion of interatomic forces to those which are electrical in nature.

When an atom is far remote from any other atom, the negative charge is spherically distributed about the nucleus, and there is clearly no electric field outside the atom. When two atoms approach one another, the first effect is one of repulsion between the electrons of one atom and those of another, as indicated in Fig. 21.1a. In this figure the spheres of negative charge ($-Ze$) are

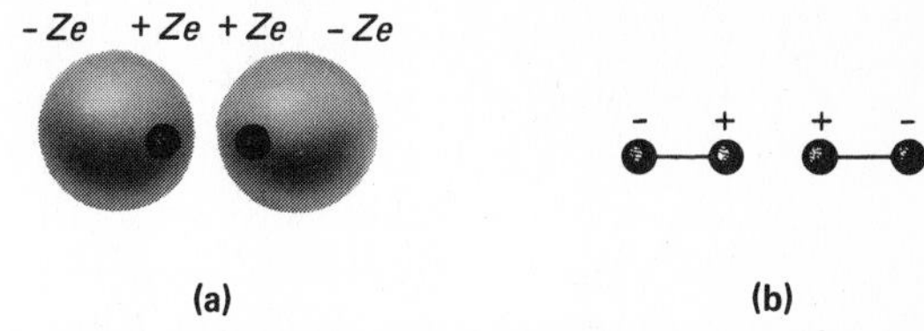

FIG. 21.1. Van der Waals forces due to polarization of atoms.

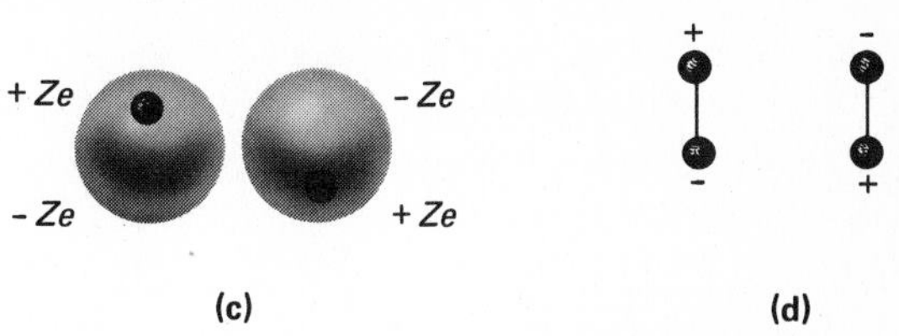

shown (in a rather exaggerated manner) to be displaced outward with respect to the two nuclei ($+Ze$). In this condition the two atoms are said to be ***polarized***, since they approximate two electric dipoles (Sec. 15.9) oriented as in Fig. 21.1b. In this position the two dipoles will repel, but only as long as they are in line. If either is slightly displaced out of line, the action of one dipole on the other will force both dipoles to rotate into an orientation such as Fig. 21.1d, with the polarization of the two atoms oriented as in Fig. 21.1c. In this position the dipoles attract one another. Thus the repulsive position of Fig. 21.1a and b is quite unstable, but the attractive position of Fig. 21.1c and d is quite stable. The electric field due to each dipole atom is in the right direction to increase the polarization of the other. The mutual polarization therefore increases as the atoms move closer to one another, increasing the attractive force. (The repulsive forces that limit the approach of two atoms will be discussed below.) The forces between atoms or molecules which result from polarization are called ***van der Waals forces.*** They explain the departures of real gases from the perfect gas law (Sec. 20.13), and in many liquids and solids these forces are solely responsible for cohesion. Van der Waals forces fall off very rapidly as the distance between the attracting bodies increases (inversely as the sixth power of the distance), and for this reason almost all vapors approximate perfect gases at low pressures.

If the external electrons are secured tightly to the nucleus as they are in the ***noble gases*** (helium, neon, argon, etc., the elements in the zero column of Table 21.1), the van der Waals forces are quite small and are the only important ones. Such elements are therefore gases at ordinary temperatures and pressures. It is only at very low temperatures, when the kinetic energy of the atoms is low, that the attractive forces will be great enough to hold the atoms in the close proximity necessary for the formation of liquids or solids. Helium, at atmospheric pressure, boils at $-268.9°C$, i.e., $4.2°K$. Under a pressure of 25 atm it has been frozen at $1°K$, and for this gas the van der Waals constant a (Sec. 20.13) is extremely small.

The electron arrangement that occurs in the noble gases has great significance in atomic structure. To illustrate this point we consider the elements such as lithium, sodium, potassium, etc., located in column I of the periodic table (Table 21.1). In discussing these elements we shall anticipate some results which we shall obtain in Chapter 25. In each of the elements in column I there is one electron that can be very readily removed, whereas it is very much more difficult to remove the second and third electrons. In the elements of column II, such as beryllium, magnesium, sodium, etc., two electrons can readily be removed, and the third and fourth are again more tightly bound. We are thus led to believe that the first 10 electrons of sodium (for example) form a neon-like structure which we call a ***closed shell.*** The eleventh electron circulates outside this shell as indicated schematically in Fig. 21.2a. Since the closed shell contains a sodium nucleus of charge $+11e$ and 10 electrons of total charge $-10e$, the outer electron is circulating in a relatively weak field due to a charge $+e$ on the neon-like shell, and it is therefore readily detached, leaving a positive ion. In a similar way, the two extra electrons of magnesium circulate outside a

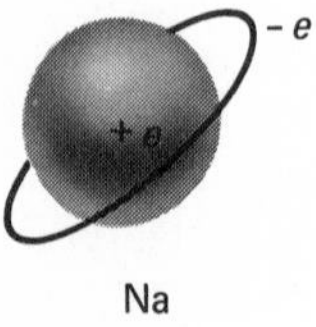

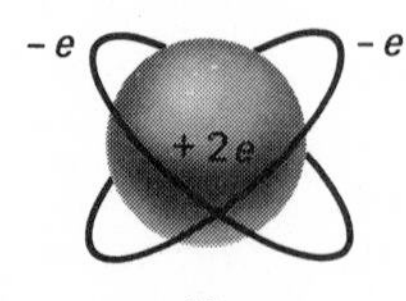

FIG. 21.2 Electrons outside of a closed shell. (The orbits of the outer electrons should not be taken too literally; cf. Chapters 24 and 25.)

Table 21.1 Periodic Table of the Elements

	I	II	III	IV	V	VI	VII	VIII		
	1 H 1.00797									
2 He 4.0026	3 Li 6.939	4 Be 9.0122	5 B 10.811	6 C 12.011	7 N 14.0067	8 O 15.9994	9 F 18.9984			
10 Ne 20.183	11 Na 22.9898	12 Mg 24.312	13 Al 26.9815	14 Si 28.086	15 P 30.9738	16 S 32.064	17 Cl 35.453			
18 A 39.948	19 K 39.102 29 Cu 63.54	20 Ca 40.08 30 Zn 65.37	21 Sc 44.956 31 Ga 69.72	22 Ti 47.90 32 Ge 72.59	23 V 50.942 33 As 74.9216	24 Cr 51.996 34 Se 78.96	25 Mn 54.9380 35 Br 79.909	26 Fe 55.847	27 Co 58.9332	28 Ni 58.71
36 Kr 83.80	37 Rb 85.47 47 Ag 107.870	38 Sr 87.62 48 Cd 112.40	39 Y 88.905 49 In 114.82	40 Zr 91.22 50 Sn 118.69	41 Nb 92.906 51 Sb 121.75	42 Mo 95.94 52 Te 127.60	43 Tc (99) 53 I 126.9044	44 Ru 101.07	45 Rh 102.905	46 Pd 106.4
54 Xe 131.30	55 Cs 132.905 79 Au 196.967	56 Ba 137.34 80 Hg 200.59	* 81 Tl 204.37	72 Hf 178.49 82 Pb 207.19	73 Ta 180.948 83 Bi 208.980	74 W 183.85 84 Po (210)	75 Re 186.2 85 At (210)	76 Os 190.2	77 Ir 192.2	78 Pt 195.09
86 Rn (222)	87 Fr (223)	88 Ra 226.05	**							

The following rare earth elements have properties which would place them in the table where indicated by * and **.

*57La 138.91	58 Ce 140.12	59 Pr 140.907	60 Nd 144.24	61 Pm (147)	62 Sm 150.35	63 Eu 151.96	64 Gd 157.25	65 Tb 158.924	66 Dy 162.50	67 Ho 164.930	68 Er 167.26	69 Tm 168.934	70 Yb 173.04	71 Lu 174.97
**89 Ac (227)	90 Th 222.038	91 Pa (231)	92 U 238.03	93 Np (237)	94 Pu (242)	95 Am (243)	96 Cm (247)	97 Bk (247)	98 Cf (249)	99 Es (254)	100 Fm (253)	101 Md (256)	102 No (253)	103 Lw (257)

The chemical atomic masses given are those recommended by the International Union of Pure and Applied Chemistry in 1961. They are based on the mass of C^{12} being exactly 12 atomic mass units. Figures in parentheses are the atomic mass numbers of the most common isotope in the case of naturally occurring nonradioactive elements and of the isotope that has been produced by nuclear reactions or by radioactive decay for other elements.

closed neon shell which has a charge $+2e$ (Fig. 21.2b). These ideas are confirmed by the fact that all the elements of column I form positive ions of valence 1 in solution, while the elements of column II form positive ions of valence 2. In each case there is a closed shell of electrons with the configuration of the preceding noble gas, and one or two electrons that can readily be removed.

We can obtain further support for the idea of a closed shell by considering the elements of column VII of the periodic table, which lack one electron of a rare gas shell. Thus fluorine has one electron less than neon, and chlorine has one electron less than argon. These elements all form negative ions of valence 1 in solution and thus must acquire from somewhere else in the solution the one extra electron they need to complete a closed shell. Although the behavior of the elements of column VI of the periodic table is not simple in water solutions of their compounds, there is clear evidence that they do accept two electrons and form a closed shell of structure similar to the nearest noble gas.

The ***electropositive elements***, which can readily lose one or more electrons, and the ***electronegative elements***, which gain extra electrons whenever they are available, form an interesting series of solid and liquid compounds in which the forces holding the atoms together are almost entirely electrostatic. Thus in NaCl (common salt), a sodium atom gives up its extra electron to a chlorine atom, forming respectively a sodium ion Na^+ and a chlorine ion Cl^-. The sodium ions thus attract the chlorine ions with powerful electrostatic forces, and we call this type of attraction ***ionic bonding***. Because of the large forces involved, substances in which ionic bonding is important usually have high melting points. Compounds of this type are classed as ***salts***, and LiF, KCl, $CaCl_2$, $SrBr_2$ are typical examples. In this paragraph we have discussed only the elements that lie near the noble gases. The elements more remote from the closed shell configurations can also form ionic bonds. Although the discussion of such bonds depends on notions similar to those which have been used here, the detailed treatment must be left to textbooks of chemistry or of solid state physics.

We have seen that, for the elements we have just discussed, the polarization which was initially the cause of van der Waals attraction goes to such an extreme that the transfer of weakly bound electrons takes place. If two identical atoms of an element such as hydrogen approach one another, there is no reason for one or the other to acquire an electron permanently. The bonding that results in the formation of the ***hydrogen molecule*** H_2 can be explained by a sharing of electrons. Each hydrogen atom initially has one electron, and the atoms initially attract one another by van der Waals forces. When two atoms come close together, each of the two electrons is subject to forces from both nuclei. Under these circumstances, we say that the electrons are shared between the two atoms. We shall see in Chapter 25 that this electron sharing leads to a force of attraction. This type of bonding is called ***covalent bonding***, or ***shared-electron-pair bonding***. Although the sharing of electrons has been worked out quantitatively only for the hydrogen molecule, the idea of electron sharing has been used very successfully in the understanding of the bonding in many complicated molecules. In some cases more than one pair of electrons may be shared between two atoms of a molecule. The electron which an atom can contribute to a pair is called a ***valence electron.*** An atom that shares one pair is said to be ***monovalent***; one that shares two pairs, ***divalent***; three, ***trivalent***; etc.

We have discussed the three types of attractive forces, ionic, covalent, and van der Waals, as if only one were important at a time. Actually, the basic differences among them depend on the ease with which the exterior electrons of the atoms are displaced or removed. In many materials, two or even three types of attraction may exist at once.

Thus far we have considered only attractive forces between atoms. When two atoms are brought close enough together, ***repulsive forces*** also come into play. We see the reason for this if we consider two noble gas atoms drawn together by van der Waals forces, such as those shown in Fig. 21.3. As the atoms come very close to each other, the tightly bound electron clouds of the two will begin to interpenetrate, and large repulsive forces will be set up between these like charges. These forces increase so rapidly, at close distances, that the nuclei remain at almost constant distance, regardless of the forces attracting them. In practice, of course, this distance is not quite constant but depends somewhat on the magnitude of the attractive forces. It will be clear that the equilibrium distance between two atoms will be that at which the repulsive forces are equal in magnitude to the attractive forces.

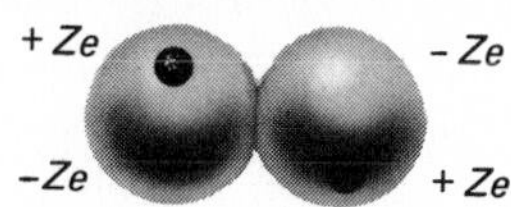

FIG. 21.3 Repulsive forces due to interpenetration of electron clouds.

21.3 The Packing of Atoms

Because of the rapid increase of the repulsive forces at small distances, atoms behave very much like hard billiard balls of fixed radius. This radius, of course, will be different for atoms with different numbers of electrons. In view of the discussion of the preceding section, we might expect any group of atoms, if they are once brought close enough together for the attractive forces to come into play, to draw themselves as closely together as possible. We shall see later that this expectation is not always fulfilled, but it is satisfied in a sufficient number of cases to be worth detailed consideration.

One method of packing spherical atoms together to form an elementary solid is that which we would adopt in packing spherical balls, all of the same radius, into a cubical box. We assume that the inside dimension of the box is $8r$, where r is the radius of a single ball, so that the bottom layer will be the square array (4 balls $\times$ 4 balls) of Fig. 21.4a, and four such layers will fill the box (Fig. 21.4b). In this manner we can pack $4 \times 4 \times 4 = 64$ balls into a box of volume $8r \times 8r \times 8r = 512r^3$. Thus the volume occupied by a single ball is $512r^3/64 = 8r^3$, or we may say that each ball occupies a cube $2r$ on a side, as indicated at C in Fig. 21.4b. In Fig. 21.5 the same $2r \times 2r \times 2r$ cube is indicated with atoms at each of its eight corners. Each of these atoms is shared with the

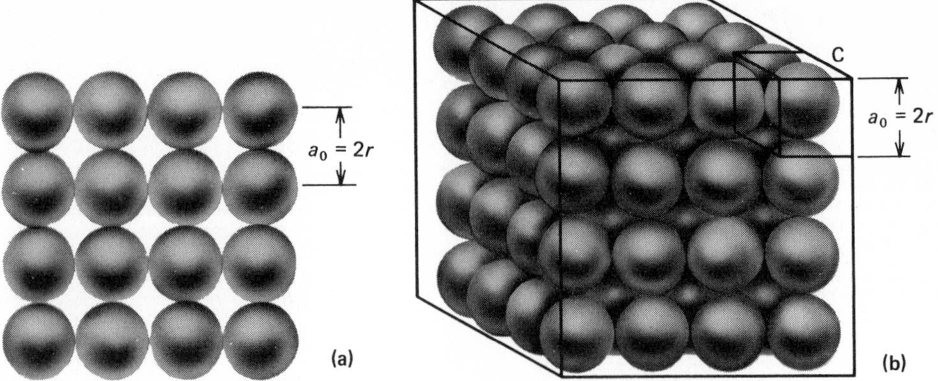

FIG. 21.4 Simple cubic packing: The unit cell ($a_0 = 2r$) contains one atom.

seven cubes that touch this cube at each of its eight corners, so that $\frac{1}{8}$ of each atom lies within the $2r \times 2r \times 2r$ cell. Since each of eight atoms contributes $\frac{1}{8}$ of an atom to the cell, again we see that there is one atom in the cell of edge $2r$. The type of packing of atoms described here is called ***simple cubic packing.*** The cell outlined in Figs. 21.4b and 21.5 is called the ***unit cell.*** The length of the cell edge is called the ***cell translation*** a_0, and in the case of simple cubic packing, $a_0 = 2r$, where r is the radius of the ball (or atom). No element is known to pack in this manner, since there are denser ways in which elements can pack, but in some salts (e.g., cesium chloride, Fig. 21.6) the negative ions (Cl^-) pack in simple cubic packing, held together by the positive ions (Cs^+).

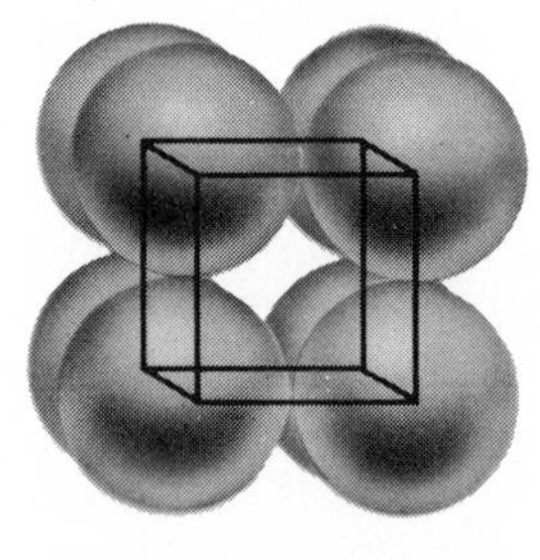

FIG. 21.5 The unit cell in simple cubic packing, taken with its corners at the centers of atoms.

FIG. 21.6 Cesium chloride: The chlorine ions (Cl^- large spheres) are in simple cubic packing, held together by the cesium ions (Cs^+) which are also in a simple cubic arrangement.

The second type of packing of spheres of identical radii also starts from a square array (Fig. 21.4a), but now, instead of setting the second layer vertically above the first, the balls of the second layer are allowed to drop into the depressions in the first. Thus each ball of the second layer rests on four balls of the first layer. Similarly, the third layer is placed in the depressions of the second, and so on. This type of packing (Fig. 21.7) will be familiar to the reader as that used in piling ornamental cannon balls in parks and on courthouse lawns.

FIG. 21.7 Close packed pyramid.

It will be clear from Fig. 21.8a that this type of packing also results in a unit cell that is cubic, but now the length of the cell edge a_0 is longer than it was for simple cubic packing, and the cell contains more atoms. The unit cell outlined in Fig. 21.8a is looked at from a different point of view in Fig. 21.8b and is shown in plan in Fig. 21.8c. From the latter figure it is seen that $a_0^2 = (2r)^2 + (2r)^2$ and that $a_0 = (2\sqrt{2})r$. To count the number of atoms in a cell, note first that in the cube of Fig. 21.8b there are eight atoms at the cube corners, and that

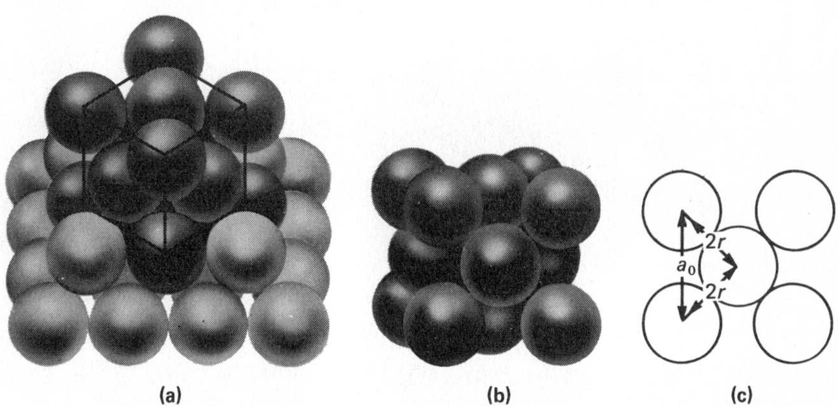

FIG. 21.8 Cubic closest packing (face-centered cubic).

each of these is shared among eight adjacent cubes. Thus each of the eight corner atoms contributes $\frac{1}{8}$ atom, i.e., together they contribute one atom. There are in addition six atoms, one in the center of each face, each of which contributes one half an atom to the cell, i.e., $\frac{1}{2} \times 6 = 3$ atoms. There are thus $\frac{1}{8} \times 8 + \frac{1}{2} \times 6 = 1 + 3 = 4$ atoms in each cell of edge $a_0 = (2\sqrt{2})r$. Thus the volume occupied by each atom of radius r is $a_0^3/4 = (16\sqrt{2})r^3/4 = (4\sqrt{2})r^3$, a volume less by a factor $1/\sqrt{2} = 0.71$ than that occupied by an atom in simple cubic packing. This type of packing is known as ***face-centered cubic packing*** from the fact that there is an atom at the center of each of the faces of the cube of Fig. 21.8b. It will be noted that each atom in this type of packing is in contact with twelve other atoms: four in the same layer, and four in each of the layers above and below it. It is possible to convince oneself quite easily by experiment (and with only a little more difficulty by geometrical methods) that twelve is the largest number of balls that can be made to contact one ball of the same radius. For this reason, face-centered cubic packing is also called ***cubic closest packing***, since there is no way of packing balls of the same radius with greater density, although there are other ways of achieving the same density (Ex. 21.5-3).

Our discussion of binding would indicate that cubic closest packing, since it brings the atoms so closely together, would be the form in which the atoms would pack in any solid made up of a single kind of atom. We shall see in Sec. 21.5 that there are ways of determining the actual arrangement of atoms in a solid, with the help of x-rays. X-ray studies show that many of the elementary solids do pack in cubic closest packing or in other closed packed structures. In other cases in which the bonding between atoms is wholly or partially covalent, other types of packing occur, and a study of the type of packing gives us important information as to the nature of this bonding. The packing of some salts is based on closest packing, NaCl for example (Fig. 21.9), in which the chlorine ions are

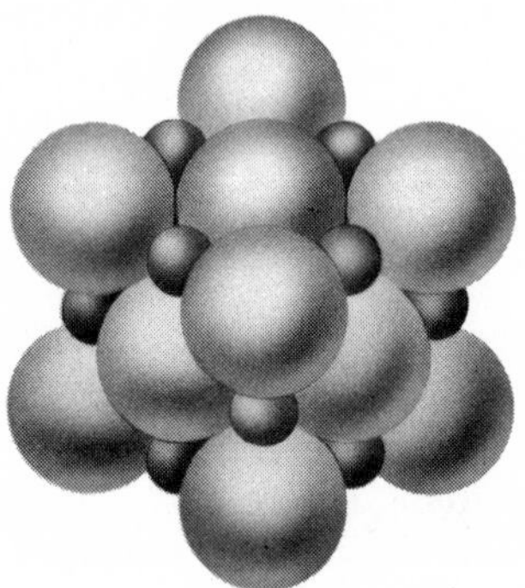

FIG. 21.9 Sodium chloride: The chlorine ions (Cl^- large spheres) are in cubic closest packing, held together by the sodium ions (Na^+) which are also in cubic close packed arrangement.

close packed while the smaller sodium ions fill the holes between the chlorine ions. The packing of the more complicated salts and of molecules into solids is varied and interesting, but cannot be discussed further here. For further details the reader is referred to books on crystallography.

21.4 The Size of Atoms

We saw in Chapter 19 that the nucleus of the atom has a radius of about 10^{-15} m, but we have thus far encountered no evidence of the dimensions of the cloud of external electrons. We saw in Sec. 21.3, however, that the diameter of this cloud will be very nearly the same as the distance between the closest adjacent atoms in a solid. It is therefore possible to estimate the size of the atom from measurements of the density of an elementary solid if we know the way in which the atoms of the solid are packed.

From x-ray measurements, it is shown that a number of metals, of which gold, silver, and copper are examples, have their atoms arranged in cubic closest packing. As an example of the determination of ***atomic radii***, we shall use copper. Since a cube that is $(2\sqrt{2})r$ on a side will contain 4 atoms in cubic closest packing, the density of the solid is

$$\rho = 4m/(2\sqrt{2})^3 r^3 = m/(4\sqrt{2})r^3, \tag{21.4-1}$$

where m is the mass of a single atom. Noting that the mass of the copper atom (Table 21.1) is 63.54 amu, converting this to kilograms with the help of Eq. (18.13-2), and taking the density of copper from Table 9.1, we see that

$$\begin{aligned} r^3 &= m/(4\sqrt{2})\rho = (63.54 \times 1.66 \times 10^{-27}\text{ kg})/(4 \times 1.414 \times 8.9 \times 10^3\text{ kg m}^{-3}) \\ &= 2.10 \times 10^{-30}\text{ m}^3 \end{aligned}$$

and

$$r = 1.3 \times 10^{-10}\text{ m}.$$

Hence the radius of the copper atom is found to be slightly greater than 10^{-10} m (one angstrom unit). Determinations of the radii of other atoms shows that they are of the same order of magnitude. We thus see that the outer radius of the atom is about one hundred thousand times as great as the radius of the nucleus (cf. Sec. 19.6).

21.5 X-ray Diffraction from Crystals

We saw in Sec. 12.15 that a wave which falls on a grating of regularly spaced lines is diffracted. The diffraction pattern is most pronounced when the number of lines is large and when their spacing is somewhat greater than, but of the same order of magnitude as, the wavelength. Notice that the regular arrangement of atoms in a solid, which we have been discussing, results in a regular pattern within the solid. If, therefore, we have available a type of radiation which can penetrate solids and which has a wavelength of the order of one angstrom unit, we might expect a diffraction pattern to be produced when this radiation falls on solids. Fortunately, such radiation is available in the form of x-rays.

The diffraction of x-rays by solids was first observed by Max von Laue (1879–1960) and was applied to the detailed investigation of the structure of solids by William Henry Bragg (1862–1942) and his son William Lawrence Bragg (1890–). In order to see how x-rays may be used for this purpose, we first notice that there are certain parallel planes in the solid in which large numbers of atoms are located. Typical sets of planes are the successive layers of Fig. 21.4–21.9. Because of the dense packing of the atoms in these planes, x-rays falling upon them will be reflected from them. Suppose that a beam of parallel x-rays is falling on the crystal along the direction AB, which makes an angle θ with a set of these parallel planes, the separation between successive planes being d, as shown in Fig. 21.10. The ray AB is reflected by the top plane in the direction Bf. The ray A′B′ is reflected by the second plane along the direction B′f′. From the results of Sec. 12.14, we see that the two reflected rays

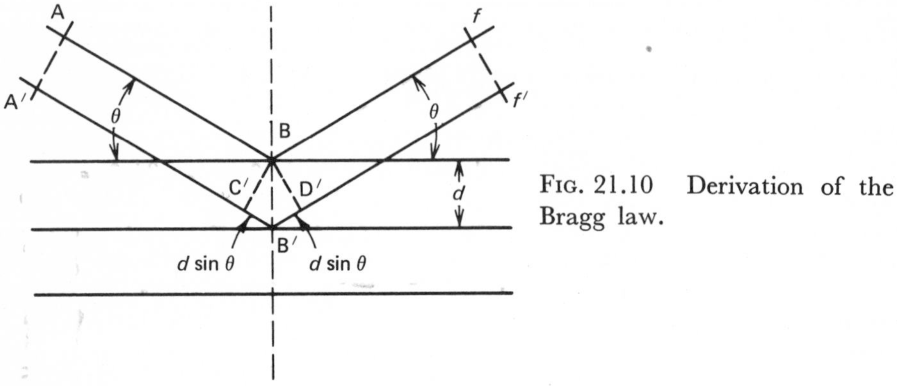

Fig. 21.10 Derivation of the Bragg law.

Bf and B′f′ will interfere constructively, i.e., will give a maximum of intensity, if the distances ABf and A′B′f′ differ by a whole number of wavelengths. Since AB = A′C′ and Bf = D′f′, the difference in the two paths is C′B′ + B′D′ = $2d \sin\theta$. The condition that the two rays intefere constructively, therefore, is

$$n\lambda = 2d \sin\theta, \tag{21.5-1}$$

where λ is the wavelength of the x-rays and n is an integer. If this relation is satisfied, it is clear that the rays reflected from all the planes below the second will also intefere constructively, so that a strong maximum of intensity will be observed in the direction Bf. Equation (21.5-1) is known as the ***Bragg law of x-ray diffraction.***

In some solids the atoms are arranged regularly throughout the entire body. Such bodies are known as ***single crystals.*** More commonly, the body as a whole is made up of a number of small single crystals, in each of which the atoms are regularly arranged, but which have their planes of atoms in different directions. Such solids are said to be ***polycrystalline.***

If a beam of parallel x-rays of known wavelength is allowed to fall on a single crystal in an arbitrary direction, Eq. (21.5-1) will ordinarily not be satisfied, and no strong diffraction will be observed. If, however, the crystal is rotated, so that θ is changed, certain orientations of the crystal will result in maxima of the diffracted rays. The directions of these maxima can be observed. It will be noted from Fig. 21.10 that the direction of the planes that are responsible for a given maximum lies on the bisector of the angle between the incident and the diffracted beams. Further, the separation between adjacent planes, according to Eq. (21.5-1), is

$$d = n\lambda/2 \sin\theta.$$

The ***x-ray diffraction pattern*** can therefore be used to determine both the directions and the spacings of the planes in which atoms are densely packed. From these directions and spacings and from the intensity of the diffracted x-rays, the nature of the packing and the density with which the atoms are packed into the crystal planes can be determined. In this way the details of the simple packing arrangements which we have illustrated, as well as those of many hundreds of much more complex solid structures, have been worked out.

EXERCISES

21.5-1 The atoms of gold, like those of copper, are arranged in a cubic closest packed structure. What is the radius of the gold atom in the metal?

21.5-2 Rock salt (NaCl) at 20°C has a density 2.165×10^3 kg/m^3. If we assume that its crystal structure is that of Fig. 21.9, what is the length of the edge of the cube in that figure? What is the maximum possible radius of the chlorine ion? If the chlorine ion has this maximum radius, then what is the maximum possible radius of the sodium ion?

21.5-3 Consider six balls of the same radius, all in contact with a seventh, on a table or other flat surface. Convince yourself that there are two ways in which three balls can be placed above this layer so that all three touch the central ball. Hence, by considering the two layers one above and one below that on the table, show that there are at least two types of closest packing. Make sketches illustrating the relationship between the balls in the three layers, illustrating in each case the 12 nearest neighbors of the central ball.

21.5-4 In body-centered cubic packing, spheres are packed so that one is at each of the eight corners of a cubic cell and one is in the center of the diagonal of the cell. Show that there are two atoms in this cell. If spheres packed in this manner are in contact, prove that the cell translation is given by $a_0 = 4r/\sqrt{3}$, and hence that the densities of simple cubic body-centered cubic, and face-centered cubic are in the proportion 1 : 1.29 : 1.41 for the same spheres.

21.6 Elastic Properties of Solids

It is possible now to see how the model we have set up for the structure of solids will explain the elastic properties discussed in Sec. 9.3. When we pull on the two ends of a solid rod, all the atoms in the structure are separated slightly, so that their distance apart is slightly greater than the equilibrium distance r. This increase in separation will, of course, be very small since it will be the same fraction of r as ΔL is of L. In a similar way, a compression will produce a small decrease in r.

We know that Hooke's law (Sec. 9.3) holds only for small extensions. If large forces are applied, the material stretches and does not return to its original length after the stress is released. The wire or other material is then said to have passed the ***elastic limit***, and the permanent stretch is called the ***permanent set***. In such cases, the change from r has been great enough for the atoms to repack in a form which has a lower energy. The energy thus gained is no longer available to return the wire to its original length, and it appears as heat.

In Sec. 9.3 we saw that solids resist tension and compression. There is a third type of distortion to which solids offer resistance. This distortion is best illustrated by considering a pack of cards, shown schematically in Fig. 21.11a. We take these cards in our hands and distort them into the form illustrated in Fig. 21.11b. This is obviously a type of strain, and it is called ***shear***. We can

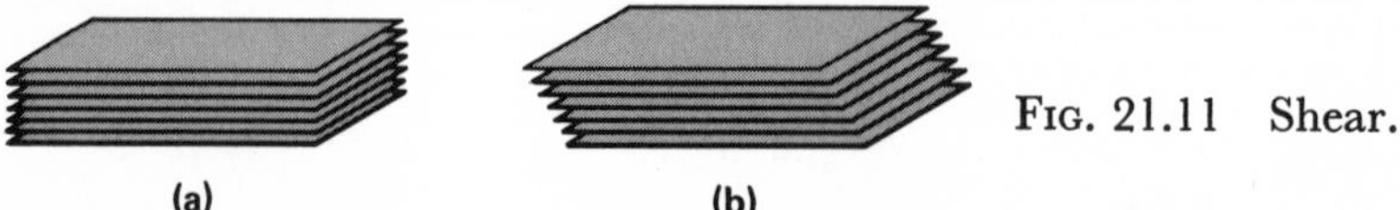

FIG. 21.11 Shear.

account for the fact that solids offer resistance to shear by the following simple picture. If we attempt to apply shear to two lines of atoms that are close-packed (Fig. 21.12a) it is necessary for the two lines to pass through the configuration of Fig. 21.12b, before they can shift with respect to one another. In this process, it is obvious that atoms such as A and B have been separated, and work must have been done in producing this separation. To produce such a shear, we must apply a torque as indicated by the equal and opposite forces $\vec{F}$ and $\vec{F}'$ of Fig. 21.12b.

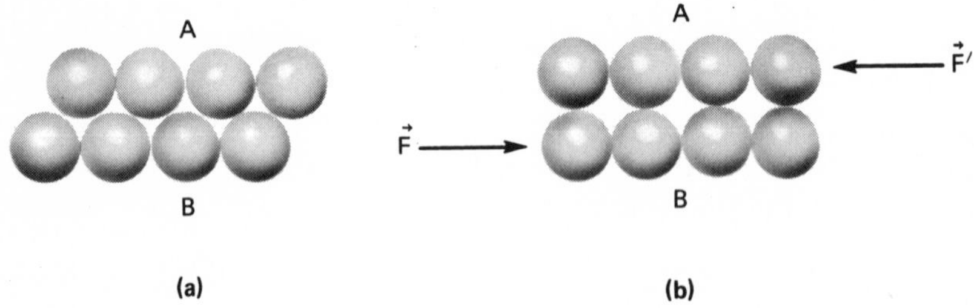

FIG. 21.12 Torque necessary to produce shear.

We cannot concern ourselves here with the connection between the shear modulus and Young's modulus, although we have perhaps said enough to indicate that such a connection must exist. We shall simply make use of the idea that a solid substance (i.e., one in which the atoms and molecules are of low energy and are closely packed), will resist a shearing strain.

21.7 Thermal Effects in Solids

So far we have treated the atoms of a solid as if they were in contact with each other and at rest. We have seen in Chapter 20 that the atoms of a gas are in continual chaotic motion, with an average translational kinetic energy $3kT/2$, and there is no reason to suppose that this thermal agitation of the atoms will be stopped by their mutual attractions. Actually, the atoms of a solid, like those of a gas, are in continual motion about the positions that they would occupy if they were packed under the action of their mutual attractive and repulsive forces. Their average separation while in motion is not the same as it would be if they were at rest, because the repulsive forces change more rapidly with distance than do the attractive forces. As a result, the net force between two adjacent atoms varies with distance, as shown by the dashed line of Fig. 21.13. The potential energy of the two atoms varies according to the solid line of that figure.

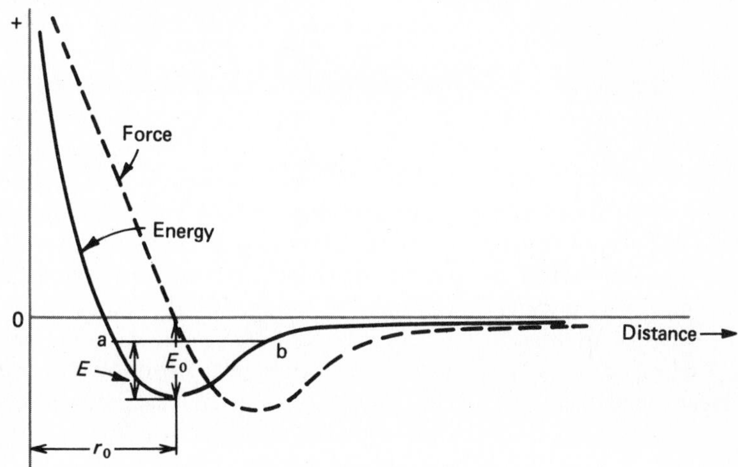

FIG. 21.13 Forces between atoms.

If the atoms were at rest, they would be separated by the distance r_0, at which the net force is zero and the potential energy is a minimum. When they are in motion with additional energy E, however, they can "climb" the potential energy "hills" on both sides of this equilibrium position (cf. Fig. 6.16). For example, an atom with extra energy E would oscillate between the positions a and b in Fig. 21.13. Since these positions are not symmetrical with respect to r_0, the two atoms will spend more time at separations greater than r_0 than they do at distances less than r_0. This means that the average distance between any two atoms will be increased by the thermal agitation, and the solid will therefore be larger than it would be without this agitation. Since the kinetic energy increases with increasing temperature, the solid can also be expected to increase in size with increasing temperature. We have therefore accounted for the thermal expansion of solids, which was discussed in Secs. 11.1–11.3.

The thermal conductivity of nonmetallic solids (Sec. 11.19) is also due to the thermal agitation of the atoms. Since the atoms are in close proximity and are subject to mutual forces, the motion of any atom will be communicated to its neighbors. If the atoms in all parts of a solid are moving with the same average energy (i.e., if all parts of the solid are at the same temperature), there will be a continual exchange of energy among the individual atoms, but the average exchange will be zero. On the other hand, if the temperature varies, the atoms in the region of higher temperature will continually transfer energy to their neighbors. Energy will therefore be passed from atom to atom, from any region of high temperature to regions at lower temperatures, and this, of course, accounts for thermal conductivity.

In certain materials, particularly the metals, the thermal conductivity is much greater than in others. We shall see in the following section that this is due to the part which electrons, detached from individual atoms, play in transferring energy.

21.8 Electrical Conduction

It can be understood now why some solid materials conduct electricity and some do not. In those materials which are held together by van der Waals forces, by covalent bonds, or by ionic bonds, the charges are rigidly bound to the atoms and molecules. Such materials are therefore nonconductors, or very poor conductors, of electricity. No large motion of charge can take place without corresponding motion of ions through the solid. In some materials conduction can take place as a result of the motion of ions, and such materials are called ***ionic conductors***. Their conductivity, however, is very small.

In the class of materials known as metals, however, an extreme case of covalent bonding occurs. In these materials, the electrons detached from an atom by the forces of adjacent atoms are shared to such an extent that no one of them can be considered to be associated with any particular atom. In a metal, therefore, we have a structure consisting of an array of positive ions, with a large number of electrons moving among them. These electrons are known as ***free electrons***. The negative free electrons between the positive metal ions attract these ions and provide the necessary forces to hold the metal together. This type of bonding is known as ***metallic bonding*** and should be distinguished from ionic bonding, in which positive ions are held together by negative ions between them, rather than by free electrons. As soon as an electric field is applied to a metal, the positively charged atom centers tend to move in the direction of the field, but they cannot do so, since they are packed closely together. Some of the electrons, on the other hand, are free to move and are constantly accelerated, and they travel through the metal in a direction opposite to that of the field. The carriers of the current in a metal are thus the electrons, but a flow of negative charge in a direction opposite to the field is equivalent to a flow of positive charge in the direction of the field.

As the electrons move through the field they gain kinetic energy. An electron cannot, however, move very far without a collision with an atom of the lattice. In this interaction, energy is given up by the electron to the atom, with a consequent increase in the average kinetic energy of the atoms of the lattice. The metal is thus heated by the flow of electrons through it. A further discussion of the electron theory of metallic conduction is beyond the scope of this book. We can understand, however, that the fact that the resistivity of a metal increases with the temperature is explained by saying that probability of a collision between an electron and an atom is increased when the thermal motion of the atoms increases. When the atoms are at rest, the electrons can travel through considerable distances in the lattice without interaction. The resistivity is therefore small. When the atoms are in violent motion, there is continual interaction between the electrons and the atoms, and the resistivity is large.

The increase of resistance with temperature is characteristic of ***metallic conduction.*** In ***ionic conduction***, in which the charge is carried by the wandering of ions through the lattice, the process of conduction is facilitated by an increase of temperature. Most ionic solids are insulators at low temperatures but become conductors at high temperatures.

There exists another class of conducting materials, known as ***semiconductors***, of which germanium and silicon are prime examples, especially when they contain very small amounts of certain impurities. In these materials, the number of free electrons per unit volume is much less than the number of atoms per unit volume, in contrast to the metals, in which the numbers are of the same order of magnitude. The conductivity of semiconductors is therefore much less than that of metals. Further, the density of free electrons in semiconductors increases with rising temperature, so their conductivity does also. In this respect they behave like ionic conductors.

We cannot at this point discuss the theory of semiconductors in detail, but we can at least see the basis of their behavior. Suppose that a single crystal of silicon (atomic number 14) contains a few atoms of phosphorus (atomic number 15). If the relative number of impurity atoms is small, the crystal structure will not be seriously disturbed—it will be essentially that of silicon. The atoms are held together by shared valence electrons, each silicon atom contributing the four electrons outside its closed shell, which is like that of neon (see Sec. 21.2). The four electrons are shared with each of four nearest neighbors, so that there are two valence of electrons for each pair of silicon atoms. Each phosphorus atom present, however, has five electrons outside a closed shell, as indicated by the place of P (phosphorus) in column V of Table 21.1. Only four are needed to bond the atom to its silicon neighbors. Either of two things may happen. The extra electron may remain attached to the phosphorus atom, in which case this atom, containing one extra electron, will repel its neighbors more strongly than they repel each other. On the other hand, the extra electron may wander away from the phosphorus atom, becoming a free electron like those characteristic of metals. Then this atom, containing more negative charge than its neighbors, will be surrounded by an electric field that distorts the crystal structure in its neighborhood. It turns out that a small amount of energy is required to remove the electron; hence, the proportion of free electrons to phosphorus atoms depends on the temperature, increasing as the average energy per atom increases. Each impurity atom that may lose an electron is known as a ***donor.***

A somewhat different state of affairs exists if the impurity atoms are those of aluminum, i.e., of they are in column III of the periodic table. In this case one extra electron is required in the neighborhood of the aluminum atom if the covalent bonding pattern is to be left undisturbed. There is very little difference in energy between this condition and one in which the aluminum atom and its neighboring silicon atoms have a full complement of valence electrons but some neighboring pair of silicon atoms is one electron short. The impurity atoms therefore become ***acceptors*** of electrons from their neighbors. The absence of an electron in the bonds between two silicon atoms is called a ***hole.*** Wherever such a hole exists, it may, in turn, be filled by an electron from a neighboring bond.

As this electron moves in, the hole moves in the opposite direction to it. If no electrical field is present, the average motion of the electrons will be zero; in the presence of an electric field, more of the *negative* electrons will be moving in a direction opposite to that of the field. The situation is somewhat analogous to that which exists in a freshly poured glass of a carbonated beverage. The small gas bubbles that exist throughout its volume correspond to the holes in the semiconductor. They may be observed to rise in the liquid, but what is happening can be described equally well by saying that some of the liquid is moving downward, flowing around the bubbles and pushing them up. Which description we use is a matter of convenience and of choice.

Because the number of holes in a semiconductor of this second type is much smaller than the number of valence electrons, it is easier to concentrate one's attention on them. Because they move in the direction of the electric field, they behave like *positive* charges. They are therefore treated as if they were entities carrying a charge +e, where e is the magnitude of the electronic charge.

In the relatively simple case of silicon ***doped*** with an impurity, we have two different mechanisms for conduction, depending on what atoms constitute the impurity. Those semiconductors that contain a few free electrons are known as ***n-type*** (n for negative); those characterized by holes are known as ***p-type*** (p for positive). In many semiconductors both free electrons and holes exist simultaneously, but usually they exist in unequal numbers.

It is found that the metals, which are good electrical conductors, are also good thermal conductors (cf. Table 11.10). This is so because the free electrons also possess thermal energy and pass it from electron to electron (usually through the atoms as intermediaries). Since the free electrons can move for relatively great distances between collisions, they are particularly effective in carrying energy from a point at high temperature to one at low temperature.

21.9 Superconductors

As the temperature of most metallic conductors approaches 0°K, the resistivity decreases continuously, approaching zero for pure metals and a constant small value for those with impurities. There are some exceptions to this rule, however. The first exception was discovered by Kamerlingh Onnes (1853–1926) in 1911, when he observed that the resistivity of mercury became *zero* as the temperature was lowered through 4.2°K and that it remained zero at all lower temperatures. Materials showing this property of the complete vanishing of resistivity below some critical temperature are known as ***superconductors***. Among the elementary metals that have since been found to exhibit superconductivity are aluminum, cadmium, gallium, indium, lead, osmium, thorium, tin, titanium, and zirconium. The critical temperatures of these materials (in the absence of a magnetic field, which lowers the value) vary from about 7°K for lead to less than 1°K for zirconium.

That the resistivity of superconductors is truly zero, rather than some small value, is shown by a very ingenious experiment. A closed ring or a short circuited coil of superconducting metal is cooled to below the critical temperature in the presence of a magnetic field. The field is then removed, and the induced emf in the ring establishes a current. The coil is then kept a temperature below critical for hours, days, or even months. At the end of that time the magnetic field near the coil is measured and so the current in the superconductor is measured. In no case has the magnitude of the current been found to depend on the length of time that charge has been flowing around the coil.

Naturally, when the resistance vanishes, so does any Joule heating—no energy is dissipated as a result of current in a superconductor.

Superconductivity is a quantum mechanical effect that cannot be explained in terms of classical physics. We have called attention to the phenomenon only because the peculiar classes of material that exhibit this strange and interesting behavior deserve at least a mention of their existence.

21.10 Ferromagnetism

Another property of solids, which is intimately connected with the existence of electrons within the solid, is ferromagnetism. There is good evidence that electrons are continually spinning, in somewhat the same way that a top spins on its axis. Since the electron is an electrical charge (Secs. 17.4 and 18.12), this ***spin*** results in the movement of a charge around a circular path, and so it is equivalent to a current flowing in a circular coil. Each electron, therefore, has a magnetic moment [cf. Prob. 16.9], and behaves like a small magnet, oriented along the axis of spin.

The full treatment of ferromagnetism is somewhat complicated, but we are in a position to consider the general features of this phenomenon. In most materials, the spinning electrons line up in such a way that equal numbers of them have their spins exactly opposite in direction. The net magnetic effect of the electrons is therefore zero. In a few substances (iron, cobalt, and nickel, the elements in the fourth row of column VIII of Table 21.1, are the prime examples) the forces between the electrons are such that a few of the electrons in neighboring atoms spin in the same direction. The magnetic moments of these electrons all add up and result in the magnetization of that part of the material in which the spins are parallel. These magnetized regions, in the absence of an external magnetic field, may be as large as a tenth of a millimeter on a side. Within each of these ***ferromagnetic domains*** the electrons that contribute magnetic moment are all lined up parallel to each other and to one of several directions determined by the crystal structure. These are known as ***directions of easy magnetization.*** In iron they are parallel to the cube edges of the unit cells (see Fig. 21.4); in nickel they are parallel to the body diagonals of these cells. Any single domain may have its magnetic moment parallel to one of the directions of easy magnetization, and a neighboring domain has its moment aligned antiparallel (i.e., along a parallel line but directed in an opposite sense). Other pairs of neighboring domains within a single crystal may have moments parallel or antiparallel to a different direction of easy magnetization. In the absence of an external magnetic field, the number of spinning electrons in the whole crystal having one direction of spin will be equal to the number having the opposite direction of spin.

Although each domain is magnetized as strongly as it may be, the sample as a whole possesses no magnetic moment.

If a small magnetizing field is applied, those domains whose magnetic moments are most nearly parallel to the direction of the field are not affected, but the magnetization of other domains changes to the direction of easy magnetization that is most nearly that of the field. As a result, the properly aligned domains grow in volume, at the expense of their neighbors. This process continues as the magnetizing field is increased, until most of the sample is a single domain, with a magnetic moment in the direction of easy magnetization that is closest to that of the field. It takes a great deal of energy to magnetize a sample in a direction that is not one of easy magnetization; if the applied field is not along a direction of easy magnetization, shifting of the magnetic moment from such a direction toward the direction of the field occurs only at very high fields.

The existence of domains and their change under the influence of a magnetic field is beautifully demonstrated under the microscope by the method originally suggested by Francis Bitter (1902–1967). A suspension of very small ferromagnetic

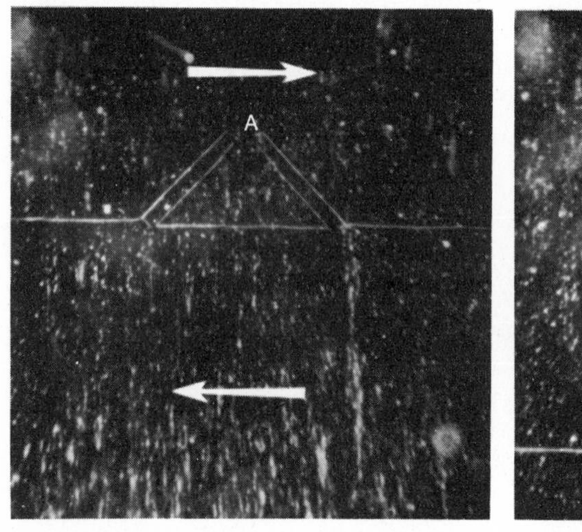

(a)

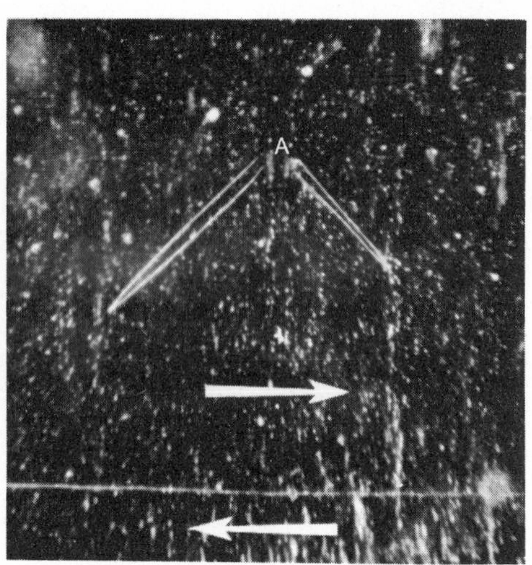

(b)

FIG. 21.14 Motion of a domain boundary during magnetization. (By permission of E. A. Nesbitt, Bell Telephone Laboratories.) These enlarged photographs show the motion of the boundary between two large ferromagnetic domains as a single crystal of iron is magnetized. The boundary is shown by the white horizontal line. In (a) the crystal is not magnetized, and the two domains are of almost equal size, their magnetizations being in the directions shown by the arrows. In (b) a magnetic field has been applied, with $\vec{B}$ to the right. As a result, the lower domain has grown at the expense of the upper domain. At A there is a small region containing impurities. This irregularity in the crystal leads to the formation of the two small spikelike domains which are not magnetized in the same direction as the large domain in which they are imbedded. In the crystal, these "spikes" are less than a millimeter in length.

particles is placed on top of a magnetic specimen. The magnetic particles are concentrated at the boundaries between the domains, since it is there that the magnetic field will be the strongest. The migration of the domain boundaries under the influence of the field is then clearly indicated as in Fig. 21.14.

In some materials the interaction between electrons is such that an atom has a net electron spin that is antiparallel to that of its nearest neighbors. Under these circumstances the domains do not possess magnetic moment in the absence of a field. Such materials are called ***antiferromagnetic.*** Finally, some compounds have the property that neighboring antiparallel spins are favored but all the spins do not have the same magnitude. Their effects, therefore, do not cancel completely, and the material behaves somewhat like a ferromagnetic one. These substances are called ***ferrimagnetic.*** The existence of antiparallel spins has been verified experimentally by the use of neutron diffraction. We shall see in Chapter 24 that material particles can be diffracted in a manner closely analogous to that in which light and x-rays are refracted. When an experiment similar to that described in Sec. 21.5 is performed with neutrons instead of x-rays, the fact that the neutrons themselves possess magnetic moment allows a distinction to be made between different directions of electron spin.

21.11 Surface Energy

Recall from Secs. 21.3 and 21.4 that the atoms of a solid are arranged in regular arrays and that this packing is due to the forces between atoms. If we break a solid in two pieces, as shown along the lines A-A and B-B in Fig. 21.15, we must exert a force equal and opposite to the attractive force which previously held the atoms together. Since this force must be exerted over some distance, work must be done. We are therefore forced to conclude that the broken solid possesses more energy than it possessed in the single piece.

Since the increase of energy of a solid as a result of ***cleavage*** accompanies the formation of new surfaces, we speak of the increased energy as ***surface energy.*** We can see that the amount of surface energy involved in cleavage depends on direction of the cleavage relative to the planes in which the atoms are arranged in the crystal. For example, if the cleavage is accomplished in the direction A-A through the close-packed crystal of Fig. 21.15a, each atom must be pulled away from four immediate neighbors. Two of these (b and c as neighbors of a) are shown in the cross section of the figure. The other two are above and below the plane of the paper. On the other hand, when the solid is cleaved along the plane B-B, as in Fig. 21.15b, each atom is separated from only one neighbor which has been at the closest possible distance from it (e.g., d from e). The force between neighboring atoms in the latter case is along the direction of motion, while in the former case it was at a considerable angle with that direction. The exact calculation of the work necessary to cleave the surface is somewhat complicated, since it depends both on the number of neighbors and on the strength and direction of the forces between them, but the example given should convince us that it will, in general, depend on the direction of cleavage.

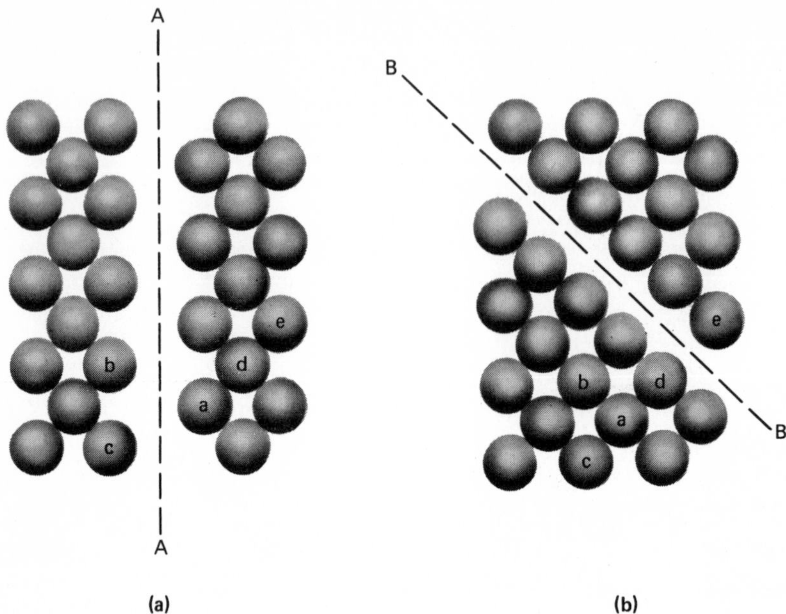

FIG. 21.15 Cleavage of a solid to produce a new surface.

It is because of the differences in the surface energies involved in different directions of cleavage that natural crystals are found in somewhat regular shapes. When a crystal is formed, or when a large crystal is broken, those faces that involve a minimum amount of surface energy are favored. Each facet of a cut diamond, for example, is a preferred cleavage plane of the crystal. Most solids do not break in this regular manner because they are made up of large numbers of small crystals, each of which is composed of regularly arranged atoms, but whose atomic planes are not parallel to each other.

If we limit ourselves to the consideration of single crystals and to the formation of surfaces along a particular direction, we see that *the amount of surface energy involved in forming any new surface is proportional to the area of the surface*. This follows from the fact that the work necessary to remove any one atom from its neighbors on one side is the same as that required to remove any other atom. Since the number of atoms so separated is proportional to the area of the surface, the proportionality of energy with surface follows.

21.12 The Structure of Liquids

The resistance of a solid to change of shape is due to the regular arrangement of atoms within the solid, and the thermal agitation of the atoms (Sec. 21.7) keeps them in oscillation about the average positions that they would occupy if they were at rest. When a solid is heated, the average distance between atoms is usually increased, with a result that the forces restraining the atoms to fixed positions are decreased. Each atom, therefore, has a little more volume in which to move, and slight irregularities in arrangement begin to appear. This process can be understood by reference to Fig. 21.16, which shows a solid that at low temperatures has its atoms packed closely together, as indicated in Fig. 21.16a.

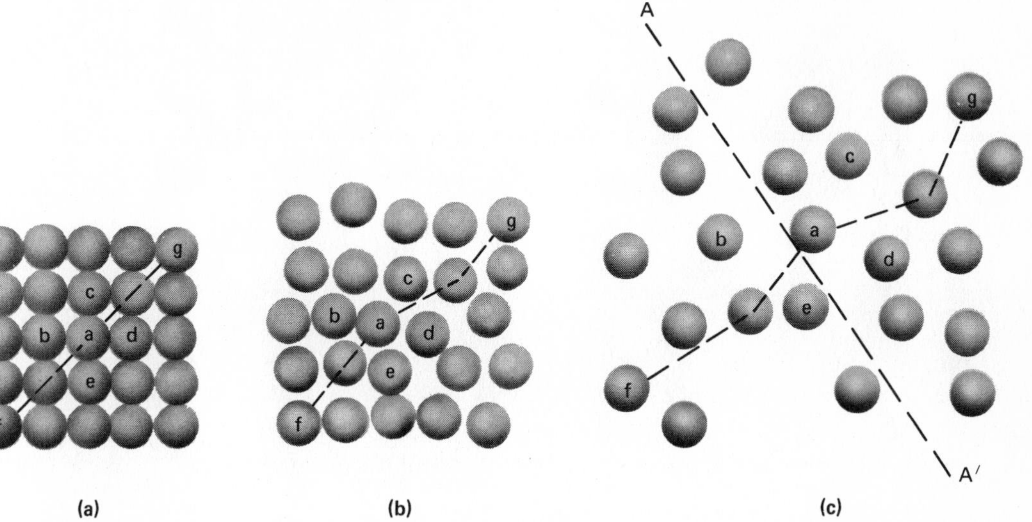

FIG. 21.16 Change in order on melting.

As the temperature is increased, the arrangement becomes more like that of Fig. 21.16b. It will be noticed that the relation of any particular atom to its near neighbors (e.g., a to b, c, d, e) is not far different from what it was at low temperatures, but that the cumulative effect of the small changes is to disrupt greatly the relation of an atom to its more distant neighbors (e.g., notice the dashed line connecting the atoms f-a-g). We say that a solid near the melting point possesses ***short range order*** and that it does not possess ***long range order.***

As the temperature rises above the melting point, the situation approaches that shown in Fig. 21.16c. Here there is still a considerable measure of short range order, since each atom is surrounded by three or four near neighbors at almost constant distances as it was below the melting point, but there is no long range order. With the disappearance of long range order, the distinct cleavage planes, which characterized a solid, have also disappeared. Since the atoms are still close enough together for appreciable attractive forces to exist, a separation of the liquid into two parts, with an increase in surface, will still require the addition of surface energy, but the amount of energy required will no longer depend on the direction of the surface.

A second consequence of the disappearance of long range order is that *a liquid does not resist shear.* If, for example, that part of the liquid above and to the right of the dotted line A-A′ in Fig. 21.16 is displaced in the direction A-A′, the distance between atoms will not be affected, on the average. Comparing

Fig. 21.16c with Fig. 21.12, we see that the interatomic forces that resulted in resistance to shear in solids do not come into play in the liquid state. The inability to resist shear which our model predicts for a liquid is subject to a simple experimental verification. Consider a small layer of a liquid, located at the surface, such as v in Fig. 21.17a, and suppose that a force $\vec{f}$ is acting

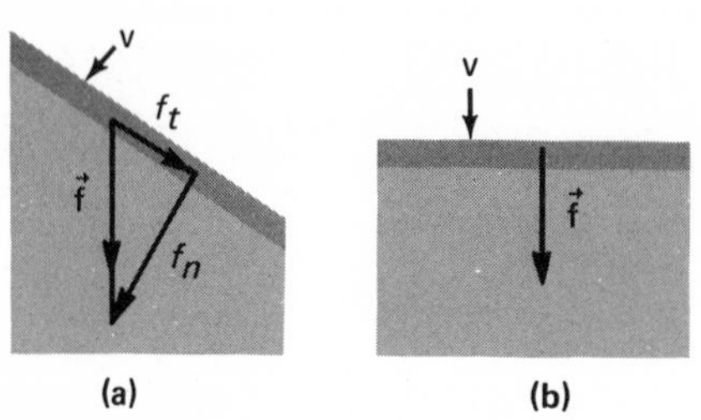

FIG. 21.17 Forces at the surface of a liquid.

on this layer. This force may be broken into the components f_t and f_n, which are, respectively, tangential and normal to the surface. The normal component pulls the layer toward the rest of the liquid, and therefore sets up a compression, which the liquid can resist. The tangential component, however, tends to cause the layer to slide along the surface. Since the liquid cannot resist shear, this motion will be unopposed, and the layer will move. The motion will continue until the surface takes a position in which the tangential component of force on it is zero. We may therefore conclude that the free surface of a liquid under the action of gravitational forces only will be perpendicular to those forces, i.e., will be horizontal. This, of course, is verified by experience. The small departure of a free liquid surface from the horizontal near the edges of the container is due to forces other than gravitation which act between the liquid and the material of the container, and this will be discussed more fully in Sec. 21.13.

The reader will recognize that the heat of fusion discussed in Sec. 11.13 is merely the energy required to separate the atoms sufficiently to destroy the long range order and is therefore a measure of the interatomic forces.

EXERCISES

21.12-1 Use the results of Sec. 21.12 and of Chapter 14 to account for the shape of the surface of a calm lake or ocean.

21.12-2 A large circular tank of water is arranged to be rotated about a vertical axis through its center with an angular velocity ω. By considering the forces acting on a small mass of water at the surface, show that the surface will take such a shape that it is inclined to the horizontal at an angle θ, which depends on the horizontal distance r from the axis of rotation in accordance with the relation

$$\tan \theta = \omega^2 r/g,$$

where g is the acceleration due to gravity.

21.13 Surface Tension

Since the absence of long-range order in a liquid insures that the surface energy of the liquid depends only on the exposed area, this energy will be proportional to the exposed area and will be a minimum when that surface is a minimum. A liquid surface therefore behaves as if it were under tension, trying to shrink to a minimum area. It is well known (although not easy to prove) that a sphere has the smallest surface of all solids of equal volume. In the absence of external forces, we should therefore expect that a liquid would collect into spherical drops, and this is the form taken by freely falling raindrops.

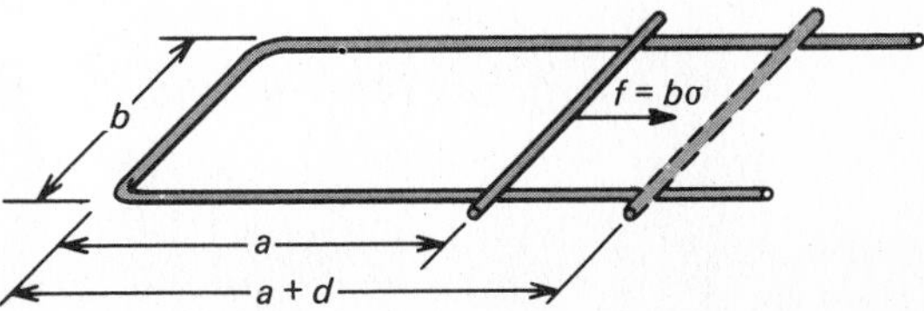

Fig. 21.18 Relation between surface energy and surface tension.

The concept of tension in a liquid surface is a useful one, and it leads to a simple approximate expression of the surface energy. Suppose that the liquid surface of area ab, shown in Fig. 21.18, is to be stretched to the area $b(a+d)$, as shown by the dotted lines. If the surface energy per unit area is σ, the stretching will involve an increase of energy of $[b(a+d)-ba]\sigma = bd\sigma$. We notice that this increase in energy is exactly equal to the work that would be done if a force $b\sigma$ produced a displacement d, i.e., if a force of magnitude σ were needed per unit length of the line b is being displaced. Hence the ***surface tension*** of a liquid is the force per unit length needed to stretch the surface of a liquid. This surface tension is equal to the surface energy per unit area, or, denoting the surface tension by γ,

$$\gamma = \sigma. \tag{21.13-1}$$

In using the concept of surface tension, we must be careful not to ascribe too much reality to it, but rather to consider it as a convenient measure of the surface energy.

The effect of surface tension is clearly demonstrated in soap bubbles and in soap films stretched over wire frames. If a frame is dipped into a soap solution that wets the wires, a film of liquid will generally be left on the frame when it is lifted. If this film is a very thin one (which is usually demonstrated by the appearance of colors produced by the interference of light reflected from the two faces), its weight will be small compared with the forces of surface tension, and the latter may be considered to be the only forces acting. Since the film behaves as if it were under tension, we can expect that it will take such a shape that it will have the minimum possible area. Some of the cases which may arise are illustrated in Fig. 21.19. For example, in a square or a circular frame (Figs. 21.19a and b) the film will lie in the same plane as the frame. If the frame is not planar, as in the distorted frame of Fig. 21.19c, the film will take up the surface of minimum area and will have the saddle-like appearance of the figure.

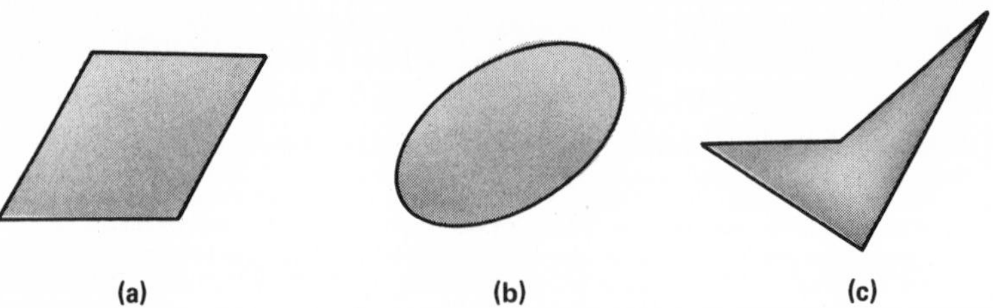

FIG. 21.19 Soap films on wires.

21.14 Interfacial Tensions and the Wetting of Surfaces

Thus far we have discussed surface energies and surface tension only for surfaces of solids or liquids in contact with a vacuum. Such surfaces are generally called free surfaces. (In practice, for most substances, the results are almost the same in air.) Since attractions exist between molecules of different kinds, as well as between like molecules, the energy per unit area of a surface between two substances may be quite different from the energy per unit area of the free surface of either of the substances. This is illustrated by Table 21.2, which gives the observed surface tensions of a number of liquid-air and liquid-liquid surfaces.

Table 21.2 *Interfacial Surface Tensions (Measured at* 20°C)

Substances	Surface Tension γ (N/m)
Water-Air	73×10^{-3}
Ethyl Alcohol-Air	22
Mercury-Air	465
Benzene-Air	29
Soap Solution-Air	28
Water-Benzene	35
Water-Mercury	375
Benzene-Mercury	357

Table 21.2 gives no values for solid-gas or solid-liquid surfaces. The surface energies of such interfaces are very difficult to measure and are generally not available. We can deduce some qualitative results regarding these energies, however, from the behavior of systems that involve two liquids and a solid, or a liquid, a solid, and a gas. For example, suppose that a small amount of liquid is spilled over a flat horizontal surface, as shown in Fig. 21.20. If the only energies involved were gravitational, the liquid would spread out uniformly over the surface, in order to lower its center of mass as far as possible. In some instances, such as water on clean glass, this actually happens, and a

condition like that shown in Fig. 21.20a results. In other cases, such as water on greasy glass, the liquid collects in droplets, as shown in Fig. 21.20b.

When the liquid collects in drops, its center of mass is obviously higher than when it is in a thin film. Energy is required to raise the center of mass, and this energy must come from a decrease in surface energy as the drops are formed.

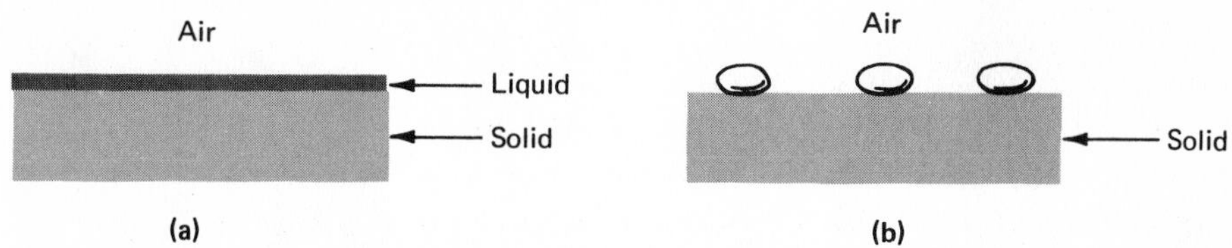

FIG. 21.20 Solid-liquid-gas system. (a) Wetted surface. (b) Drop formation.

It is also obvious that the arrangement of Fig. 21.20b has less liquid-air surface and less liquid-solid surface than that shown in Fig. 21.20a. On the other hand, the amount of solid-air surface is greater. We can therefore conclude that the energy per unit area of either the liquid-air or the liquid-solid interface, or both, is so high that the decrease of the area of these faces more than makes up for the energy necessary to raise the center of mass and to expose the solid-air interface. Since water collects in droplets on a greasy surface, whereas it wets a clean surface, we know that the surface tension of a water-grease interface must be very high.

The energy balance among the various interfacial surface tensions also accounts for the shape of the liquid surface near the edges of a container. We know that such a surface seldom has the shape shown in Fig. 21.21a. If the

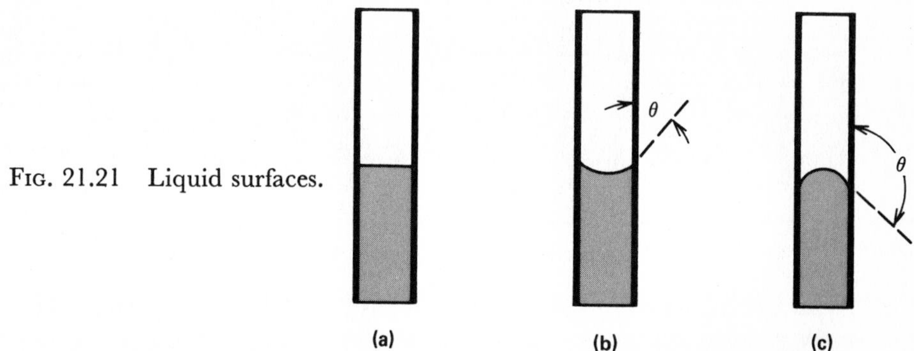

FIG. 21.21 Liquid surfaces.

liquid wets the container (e.g., water in clean glass), the surface curls up at the edges as shown in (b); if it does not wet the container (e.g., mercury in glass), the surface curls downward, as in (c). This behavior is exactly what we should expect from the discussion of the preceding paragraph, since the arrangement of Fig. 21.21b maximizes the liquid-solid surface, while that of Fig. 21.21c minimizes the surface of the liquid-solid interface.

It is found that the surface of a given liquid in a particular type of container always meets a vertical side of the container at the same angle, as shown as θ in Fig. 21.21. This angle is known as the ***angle of contact.***

21.15 Capillary Attraction

We have seen that the decrease in surface energy resulting from the formation of droplets can be sufficient to raise the center of mass of a liquid. A similar phenomenon takes place when a liquid is contained in a ***capillary tube***, which is any tube of small internal diameter. If such a tube dips into a container of liquid, as shown in Fig. 21.22, and the liquid wets the material of the tube, it is found that the level of the liquid in the tube is higher than that in the large container. Since energy is gained by forming an additional area of the liquid-solid interface at the expense of the solid-air interface, some of this energy can be used to raise the water in the capillary.

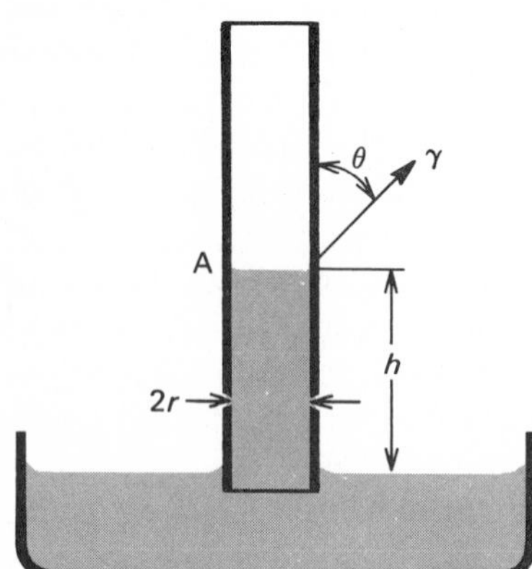

FIG. 21.22 The rise of a liquid in a capillary.

In order to find the height to which the liquid will rise, notice that the part of the liquid which is raised above the level of the surface outside the tube must by supported by the surface tension. This tension acts around the inside of the tube at A. If γ is the surface tension, a force of γ per unit length must act around the circumference of the tube. The vertical component of this force, which is the only component that can support the liquid against gravity, is $\gamma \cos \theta$, and, since the circumference is $2\pi r$, the total upward force is

$$f = 2\pi r\gamma \cos \theta.$$

The volume of the liquid supported by this force is $\pi r^2 h$, where h is the amount of capillary rise. Consequently, the weight is

$$w = \pi r^2 h \rho g,$$

where ρ is the density of the liquid and g is the acceleration due to gravity. Equilibrium will be established when the upward force just equals the weight, or when

$$h = 2\gamma \cos \theta / r\rho g. \tag{21.15-1}$$

EXERCISES

21.15-1 A wire frame with one movable side, such as that shown in Fig. 17.8, is dipped into a soap solution and removed with a film spread over the rectangle and attached to the wires. The frame is then held in a horizontal plane. What will be the equilibrium position of the movable wire MN? If $a = 15$ cm and $b = 10$ cm, what force will be required to hold MN in position?

21.15-2 Given a sensitive equal arm balance and a ring of wire, which may be suspended beneath one of the pans of the balance, devise a method of measuring the surface tension of a liquid. Illustrate your method with a diagram and derive an equation for the surface tension in terms of measurable quantities.

21.15-3 A glass " U " tube is constructed asymmetrically, so that one of its vertical arms has an inside diameter of 2.00 mm and the other has an inside diameter of 5.00 mm. If ethyl alcohol is poured into the tube and both ends are left open, what will be the difference in height between the surfaces of the liquid in the two arms, and which surface will be higher? Take the angle of contact between alcohol and glass as 45°.

21.15-4 The sap of a tree is lifted from the roots by capillary action. Supposing that the sap may be considered equivalent to pure water in its mechanical properties and that the angle of contact is 35°, find the maximum radius of the capillary tubes if capillarity is responsible for lifting the sap in a tree which is 30 m high.

21.15-5 Liquids such as mercury, which do not wet glass, show a capillary depression instead of a capillary rise, i.e., the level of the liquid inside a small tube is lower than that in a surrounding large container. Explain this and derive an equation for the amount of depression that will be observed in a tube of inside radius r if it contains a liquid of density ρ and surface tension γ, with an angle of contact of θ with the material of the tube.

21.15-6 The following perpetual motion machine was proposed in the seventeenth century. "A small capillary tube is placed with its axis vertical in a container of liquid. The liquid rises to a height h in the tube, due to capillary action. The tube is then cut off at a height $h/2$ above the surface of the surrounding liquid, and the water will spray from the open top, as from a fountain." Discuss in detail why this device will not work.

21.16 Vaporization and Sublimation

The melting of a solid is a process in which the long-range order between atoms disappears, and the heat required to melt the solid is a measure of the energy necessary to rearrange the atoms (Sec. 21.12). The resulting liquid possesses surface energy, which is somewhat different from that of the solid before melting. If the temperature of the liquid is further increased, the thermal motion of the molecules will also increase. Some of the molecules near the surface may be moving fast enough to break away from the attraction of their neighbors, and they may escape completely. This process, of course, is identical with the vaporization process discussed in less detail in Sec. 11.15. We can now see why energy is required to vaporize a liquid, for each molecule that escapes must be supplied with sufficient energy to climb the potential energy hill due to the attraction of its neighbors (cf. Fig. 21.13). Hence the heat of vaporization and the surface tension of a liquid are intimately related quantities.

It can be shown why a liquid is warmed by the condensation of a vapor on its surface. Each molecule that is captured from the vapor is attracted by the surface molecules and is speeded up. This brings additional kinetic energy into the liquid and so warms it.

Since the molecules of a solid or liquid do not all have the same kinetic energies (cf. Sec. 20.11), only the faster molecules will have sufficient energy to pass outward to the vapor. The number of molecules with sufficiently high speeds to do so will increase rapidly with temperature, which is the reason for the shape of vapor pressure curves, such as that shown in Fig. 11.9. Because of the spread of molecular speeds, a few molecules may have sufficient energies to escape even at temperatures below the melting point. It is such molecules that account for the sublimation of a solid (Sec. 11.18).

EXERCISES

21.16-1 From the data of Table 11.7, show that the surface tension of water must decrease with increasing temperature in the range from 0°C to 100°C.

21.16-2 Show that the heat of sublimation of a crystalline solid may have several different values, depending on the crystal face from which the sublimation takes place.

21.17 Thermionic Emission

Section 17.3 described the thermionic emission of electrons from heated metals. In view of our knowledge of the structure of metals (Sec. 21.8) and of our study of vaporization, we are now able to understand the process of electron emission in some detail. The free electrons in a metal, although they may move through the metal, are ordinarily prevented from escaping by electrical forces. If an electron does break through the surface, the presence of this negative charge outside and near the metal induces a positive charge on the surface (Sec. 15.4). The attraction between this positive charge and the electron pulls the electron back toward the metal. Therefore, the free electrons in a metal are bound to the solid in much the same way that the atoms of the solid are bound together. Hence a metal has extra surface energy, which is associated with the free electrons.

Just as the faster atoms within a solid may have enough kinetic energy to escape in spite of the surface energy, so the faster electrons may have sufficiently high energies to break away from the metal. Thermionic emission is therefore equivalent to a vaporization process for electrons. Corresponding to the heat of vaporization, a certain amount of energy is required for each electron removed. This energy is known as the ***work function*** of the metal, and it is of the order of 10^{-18} J per electron (Sec. 24.2).

A liquid in a closed container will evaporate until sufficient vapor pressure is built up over the liquid so that the rate at which molecules are returning to the liquid equals the rate at which they are escaping from it (Sec. 11.15). Similarly, a hot metal plate or wire will build up an ***electron gas*** in the region around it.

If the emitted electrons are kept near the wire, some of them will strike the metal surface from time to time and will be recaptured by the metal. As a result, the net rate of electron emission from the metal (i.e., the difference of the emission and recapture rates) will drop to zero. On the other hand, if the electrons are removed from around the wire as fast as they are emitted, the net rate of emission will reach a maximum value, which depends upon the temperature of the metal.

It is fortunate that the electrons near the metal can be either held in that region or removed from it by the application of an electric field in the region. In the vacuum tubes used in radio communication and in similar devices, a hot metal cathode is surrounded by one or more other electrodes which are maintained at positive or negative potentials with respect to it. Changes in the potentials of these electrodes sweep electrons away from the cathode or hold them close to it. Such changes therefore allow the control of the rate of electron emission, and it is this control which is the basis of most electronic devices. The applications of electronic emission will be discussed in greater detail in Chapter 22.

EXERCISES

21.17-1 The work function of silver is 76×10^{-20} J per electron. Express this work function in electron volts (Sec. 19.11).

21.17-2 Using the information of Ex. 21.17-1, the experimental fact that the heat of sublimation of silver is 2.6×10^6 J/K, and the information concerning atomic masses given in Table 21.1, find the ratio of the energy required to remove one electron from a piece of silver to that required to remove one atom from it.

21.18 Summary

This chapter has attempted to connect the major properties of bulk matter, in the solid, liquid, and vapor states, with the known properties of the atoms of which such matter is composed. It has been shown that solids are made up of orderly arrangements of atoms and that these atoms are held together by electrical forces. The elastic properties of solids, the electrical and thermal conductivities of metals and semiconductors, and the magnetic permeabilities of ferromagnetic, antiferromagnetic, and ferrimagnetic materials can be satisfactorily correlated with this structure.

Liquids have a less orderly arrangement of the atoms than do solids, since the process of melting removes the long-range order. The disappearance of the long-range order accounts for the greatest difference between a solid and a liquid, the inability of the latter to resist shear.

Considerable attention has been given to the idea of surface energy, i.e., the energy involved in the formation of a solid or liquid surface. Among the phenomena connected with surface energy are the formation of crystal faces, the formation of liquid drops, the capillary rise (or depression) of liquids in small tubes, the processes of vaporization and sublimation, and the thermionic emission of electrons.

PROBLEMS

21.1 The electrostatic energy of a system of a single Na^+ ion and a Cl^- ion, with centers a distance r apart, is $-e^2/4\pi\varepsilon_0 r$, where e is the electronic charge.

(a) Consider a system of two Na^+ ions and two Cl^- ions, arranged at the corners of a square with sides of length r, with the Na^+ ions at diagonally opposite corners. Calculate the electrostatic energy of this system.

(b) Consider a system of four Na^+ ions and four Cl^- ions, arranged at the corners of a cube in such a way that each Na^+ ion has only Cl^- ions as its nearest neighbors. Calculate the electrostatic energy involved.

(c) Calculate the electrostatic energy *per ion pair* for one, two, and four pairs of ions.

(d) Can you *suggest* a way of computing the energy needed to break an NaCl crystal that contains N ions ($\frac{1}{2}N$ of each type) into its constituent ions? Would you expect, on the basis of the results of (c) above, that this energy would be greater or less than

$$Ne^2/8\pi\varepsilon_0 r,$$

where r is the distance between nearest neighbors in the crystal?

21.2 Imagine a "one-dimensional crystal" of NaCl made up of a long "chain" of Na^+ and Cl^- ions and arranged alternately on a straight line, with a separation of r between nearest neighbors.

(a) Concentrate your attentions on any one particular Na^+ ion. Show that the electrostatic energy contributed to the system by the interaction of *all* of the other ions with this one may be expressed as

$$U_1 = \frac{e^2}{4\pi\varepsilon_0}\left(-\frac{2}{r}+\frac{2}{2r}-\frac{2}{3r}+\frac{2}{4r}-\cdots\right)=\frac{e^2}{2\pi\varepsilon_0 r}\left(-1+\frac{1}{2}-\frac{1}{3}+\frac{1}{4}-\cdots\right).$$

(b) Given the series expansion for the natural logarithm of $(1+x)$, which is good for all x that satisfy the condition $0 \le x \le 1$,

$$\ln(1+x) = x - x^2/2 + x^3/3 - x^4/4 + \cdots$$

show that

$$U_1 = -\frac{e^2}{2\pi\varepsilon_0 r}(\ln 2)$$

(c) Show that the electrostatic energy for a chain containing N ions ($\frac{1}{2}N$ of each type) is

$$U_N = -\frac{Ne^2}{4\pi\varepsilon_0 r}(\ln 2) = -\frac{0.0550e^2N}{\varepsilon_0 r}.$$

21.3 Suppose that the free electrons in a metal behave like the molecules of an ideal gas. By considerations similar to those used in Chapter 20, show that a metal might be expected to have a specific heat greater than a nonmetal by an amount $3kTn/2\rho$, where k is the Boltzmann constant, T is the absolute temperature, n is the number of electrons per unit volume, and ρ is the density of the metal. The fact that the specific heats of metals do not greatly exceed those of nonmetals of about the same average molecular mass (e.g., the measured values of 0.21 Cal/kg deg for aluminum and 0.20 Cal/kg deg for sodium chloride, both at room temperature) shows that there is something wrong with this assumption about the "electron gas."

21.4 The mechanism by which the free electrons in a metal or semiconductor contribute to electrical conduction may be understood in terms of a very simple model. It is assumed that the conductor contains n electrons per unit volume and that these electrons, in the absence of an electric field, are moving in completely random directions with the same speed V. If an electric field $\vec{E}$ is applied, these electrons will acquire a drift velocity. It is supposed that each electron, after collision with an atom, is accelerated by the field while it travels a distance λ, after which it collides with another atom and its direction of motion again becomes randomized. The *average* excess velocity acquired by the electron between collisions is called the ***drift velocity***, v_d. In the following computations, assume that $v_d \ll V$.

(a) Show that $v_d \approx -eE\lambda/2mV$, where m is the mass of an electron. (Hint: The time between collisions is λ/V.)

(b) Show that the current density (current per unit area) is $j = -nev_d = ne^2E\lambda/2mV$. (Hint: See Sec. 17.2.)

(c) Consider a little cube of volume a^3, having four of its edges parallel to $\vec{E}$. Find the ratio of the potential difference across the cube to the current in it. Is your result consistent with Ohm's law? Find the resistivity of the metal in terms of n, λ, e/m, and V.

(d) Supposing λ to be of the order of the interatomic distance (say 2 angstrom units) and n to be about equal to the number of copper atoms per unit volume of the solid, find what value of V is necessary to give the observed resistivity of copper. Is this value consistent with the assumption made in Prob. 21.3?

21.5 The unit cell shown in Fig. 21.8 is known to have sides of length 3.608 Å in a copper crystal. Suppose that an x-ray beam, each of whose photons has an energy of 1.5×10^4 eV, impinges on a crystal of copper.

(a) Find the wavelength of the x-rays.

(b) If a first-order ($n = 1$) diffraction maximum is to be produced by the layers of atoms whose centers lie on two parallel faces of the unit cube, what must be the angle between the x-ray beam and an edge of the cube perpendicular to these faces?

(c) Repeat the computation of (b) for the second-order ($n = 2$) diffraction maximum instead of the first.

(d) Suppose that the x-ray beam has the direction found in (c). What layers of atoms will also produce a diffraction maximum in the same direction as the one considered there?

21.6 The magnetic moment of an electron as a result of its spin is known to be

$$p = eh/4\pi m,$$

where e is the charge on the electron, m is its mass, and h is Planck's constant. It has been found experimentally that a single crystal of iron "saturates," i.e., reaches the maximal value of its magnetic dipole moment per unit volume, $\vec{P} = \vec{B} - \mu_0\vec{H}$, when

$$|\vec{B} - \mu_0\vec{H}| = 0.163 \text{ Wb/m}^2.$$

(a) Find the magnetic moment of a small, cubic iron crystal, of volume a^3, when it is magnetized to saturation. (Hint: The problem is similar to that of the plane-parallel-plate capacitor of Sec. 16.22.)

(b) How many spinning electrons per copper atom in the crystal contribute to the ferromagnetism of the crystal?

REFERENCES

21A T. A. Buchhold, "Applications of Superconductivity," *Scientific American*, March 1960. (Reprint No. 270, W. H. Freeman.)

21B C. V. Boys, *Soap Bubbles and the Forces Which Mould Them* (Science Study Series No. S3), Doubleday, Garden City, 1959. An excellent and seldom equalled set of three popular demonstration lectures originally given about 1890.

21C F. B. Cuff, Jr., and L. M. Schetky, "Dislocations in Metals," *Scientific American*, July 1955. (Reprint No. 204, W. H. Freeman.)

21D J. E. Kunzler and M. Tanenbaum, "Superconducting Magnets," *Scientific American*, June 1962. (Reprint No. 279, W. H. Freeman.)

21E Leon F. Phillips, *Electronics for Experimenters*, Wiley, New York, 1966. A strictly descriptive treatment of semiconductor devices in Chapter 3, together with a useful bibliography for further study.

21F R. L. Sproul, "The Conduction of Heat in Solids," *Scientific American*, December 1962. (Reprint No. 249, W. H. Freeman.)

21G Elizabeth A. Wood, *Crystals and Light* (Momentum Book No. 5), Van Nostrand, Princeton, 1964.

21H G. H. Wannier, "The Nature of Solids," *Scientific American*, December 1962. (Reprint No. 249, W. H. Freeman.)

21I L. K. Runnels, "Ice," *Scientific American*, December 1966, pp. 118–126.

21J Gerald L. Pollack, "Solid Noble Gases," *Scientific American*, October 1966, pp. 64–72.

21K Charles Knight, *The Freezing of Supercooled Liquids* (Momentum Book No. 14), Van Nostrand, Princeton, 1967. Interesting phenomena involved in transitions from the liquid to the solid phase.

22 ➾ *Oscillations*

22.1 Simple Harmonic Motion

At various places in earlier chapters we have encountered to-and-fro oscillations and have found that many of them could be approximated quite closely by a displacement that varies sinusoidally with time, i.e.,

$$x = X_1 \sin (2\pi t/\tau), \tag{22.1-1}$$

$$x = X_2 \cos (2\pi t/\tau), \tag{22.1-2}$$

or some combination of these two expressions. In both expressions x is the instantaneous value of the displacement, X_0 is the ***amplitude***, and τ is the ***period.*** A general expression that combines Eqs. (22.1-1) and (22.1-2) is

$$x = X_0 \sin\left(\frac{2\pi t}{\tau} + \phi\right) = X_0 \sin (\omega_0 t + \varphi), \tag{22.1-3}$$

where ϕ is called the ***phase angle*** and ω_0 is the ***radian frequency***, equal to $2\pi/\tau$. It may be shown that Eq. (22.1-3) can be written as a sum of two expressions as given by the earlier equations, the two having different amplitudes (see Exs. 22.1-2 and 22.1-3). Among the examples of such oscillations are the motion of a mass suspended by a spring (Secs. 2.19 and 3.5), the to-and-fro motions of particles in elastic bodies (Chapter 10), the vibrations of atoms about their equilibrium positions in solids (Sec. 21.7), and the oscillation of electric charges in alternating currents (Secs. 17.8 and 17.12).

If ***simple harmonic motion*** (SHM) is defined as any motion described by Eq. (22.1-3), it is not difficult to find the physical conditions necessary to produce the motion. The instantaneous velocity of the moving body is obtained by using the result of Appendix I for the derivative of the sine of an angle:

$$v = dx/dt = \omega_0 X_0 \cos (\omega_0 t + \phi). \tag{22.1-4}$$

Taking the mass of the oscillating body as m, we therefore have its kinetic energy at an instant as

$$\tfrac{1}{2}mv^2 = \tfrac{1}{2}m\omega_0{}^2X_0{}^2 \cos^2 (\omega_0 t + \phi). \tag{22.1-5}$$

We may now apply the law of the conservation of energy. Let us suppose that the total energy of the oscillating mass is a constant E. Then the potential energy must be

$$U = E - \tfrac{1}{2}m\omega_0{}^2X_0{}^2 \cos^2 (\omega_0 t + \phi).$$

This expression gives an easy way of finding how the potential energy varies with time. We first rearrange the equation:

$$\frac{2U}{m\omega_0{}^2X_0{}^2} + \cos^2(\omega_0 t + \phi) = \frac{2E}{m\omega_0{}^2X_0{}^2}.$$

The relation of Eq. (E.6) of Appendix E, $\sin^2 A + \cos^2 A = 1$, then tells us that

$$\frac{2U}{m\omega_0{}^2X_0{}^2} = \sin^2(\omega_0 t + \phi)$$

and

$$\frac{2E}{m\omega_0{}^2X_0{}^2} = 1. \qquad (22.1\text{-}6)$$

Solving the first of these equations for U, we find

$$U = \tfrac{1}{2}m\omega_0{}^2X_0{}^2 \sin^2(\omega_0 t + \phi),$$

which, with the help of Eq. (22.1-3), may be rewritten as

$$U = \tfrac{1}{2}m\omega_0{}^2x^2 = \tfrac{1}{2}kx^2. \qquad (22.1\text{-}7)$$

Here the constant k is

$$k = m\omega_0{}^2. \qquad (22.1\text{-}8)$$

Equation (22.1-7) specifies the physical condition that a body oscillate with simple harmonic motion—its potential energy must be proportional to the square of its displacement from its equilibrium position ($x = 0$), at which the potential energy is taken as zero. Another way of stating this is found if we remember that the force acting on a body can be expressed as the negative of the derivative of the potential energy with respect to distance, so that this force is

$$f = -\,dU/dX = -kX. \qquad (22.1\text{-}9)$$

It follows at once that a body will oscillate in simple harmonic motion if it is subject to a ***restoring force*** proportional to its displacement. The term "restoring force" is used because the force always has a direction opposite to the displacement, i.e., the force always tends to restore the body to its equilibrium position.

Our treatment tells us more than this, for we can use Eq. (22.1-8) to find the radian frequency of the motion in terms of the constant k. We have

$$\omega_0 = (k/m)^{1/2}. \qquad (22.1\text{-}10)$$

EXERCISES

22.1-1 A simple harmonic motion in which the oscillating body has zero displacement at time $t = 0$ is described by Eq. (22.1-1). Show that Eq. (22.1-2) describes the motion equally well if the origin of time is changed in such a way that the body has zero displacement at $t = -\tau/4$, where τ is the period of the oscillation.

22.1-2 By using the trigonometric addition formula

$$\sin (A + B) = \sin A \cos B + \cos A \sin B, \tag{22.1-11}$$

show that Eq. (22.1-3) is equivalent to

$$x = X_1 \sin (\omega_0 t) + X_2 \cos (\omega_0 t),$$

where

$$X_1 = X_0 \cos \phi \qquad \text{and} \qquad X_2 = X_0 \sin \phi.$$

22.1-3 Using the trigonometric addition formula

$$\cos (A + B) = \cos A \cos B - \sin A \sin B, \tag{22.1-12}$$

show that the equation

$$x = X_1 \sin (\omega_0 t) + X_2 \cos (\omega_0 t)$$

is equivalent to

$$x = X_0 \cos (\omega_0 t + \phi),$$

where

$$X_0 = (X_1{}^2 + X_2{}^2)^{1/2} \qquad \text{and} \qquad \tan \phi = -X_1/X_2 .$$

22.1-4 (a) Show that the acceleration of a body in simple harmonic motion is equal to $-\omega^2 x$, i.e., that it is proportional and opposite in direction to the displacement at any instant.

(b) At what times in the simple harmonic motion $x = X_0 \sin (\omega_0 t)$ is the acceleration zero? At what times does it have its greatest magnitude?

(c) What is the velocity when the acceleration is zero?

22.1-5 At $t = 0$, the coordinate x of a particle executing simple harmonic motion has a value x_0, and the velocity v_x has a value of v_0. Prove that the motion is described by the equations

$$x = x_0 \cos \omega_0 t + (v_0/\omega_0) \sin \omega_0 t,$$

$$v_x = -\omega_0 x_0 \sin \omega_0 t + v_0 \cos \omega_0 t,$$

$$a_x = -\omega_0{}^2 x_0 \cos \omega_0 t - \omega_0 v_0 \sin \omega_0 t.$$

22.1-6 A periodic oscillatory motion that is not simple harmonic may be represented as the sum of two or more simple harmonic motions. Suppose, for example, that a body moves in such a way that its displacement is

$$x = X_1 \sin (\omega t) + \tfrac{1}{2} X_1 \cos (2\omega t).$$

Calculate the displacement at various times between $t = 0$ and $t = 2\tau = 4\pi/\omega$ and plot the displacement as a function of time. Is the motion periodic in the sense that it repeats itself regularly (cf. Sec. 2.15)? What is the period?

22.2 *The Oscillation of a Mass on a Spring*

Let us return to the problem of a body suspended by a spring, which was encountered in Secs. 2.19 and 9.4, as shown in Fig. 22.1. If the mass of the body is m and the spring obeys Hooke's law, the force constant being k, the spring will be stretched by an amount $x_0 = mg/k$ when the system has come to equilibrium

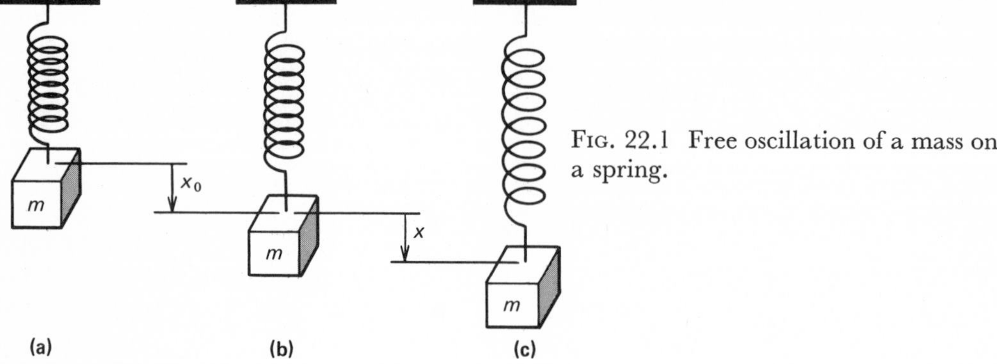

FIG. 22.1 Free oscillation of a mass on a spring.

(Fig. 21.1b). Let us suppose that the mass is farther displaced by a distance x, as shown in Fig. 21.1c. The potential energy, taken relative to the unstretched spring, is then

$$-mg(x_0 + x) + \tfrac{1}{2}k(x_0 + x)^2.$$

When we expand the parentheses and substitute mg/k for x_0, we find this potential energy to be

$$-\frac{1}{2}\frac{m^2g^2}{k} + \frac{1}{2}kx^2.$$

We know that we can take the origin of potential energy at any point by the addition of an appropriate constant. Let us therefore take the potential energy to be zero at the position shown in Fig. 22.1b (i.e., add the constant $\frac{1}{2}m^2g^2/k$) and write the potential energy as

$$U = \tfrac{1}{2}kx^2. \tag{22.2-1}$$

This expression is identical with Eq. (22.1-7), so we can conclude at once that the mass, if displaced in a vertical direction from its equilibrium position, will execute simple harmonic motion. The radian frequency of the motion is given by Eq. (22.1-10) as

$$\omega_0 = (k/m)^{1/2} \tag{22.2-2}$$

so that the period is

$$\tau = 2\pi/\omega_0 = 2\pi(m/k)^{1/2}. \tag{22.2-3}$$

Illustrative Example

A force of 1.00 N stretches a given spring 1.00 cm. A mass of 1.62 kg is hung on this spring. (a) Calculate the time of oscillation of this mass on the spring. (b) Write down the equations of motion of the mass on the spring if the displacement at $t = 0$ is -2.00 cm and the velocity is zero. (c) Plot the graphs of the displacement, the velocity, and the acceleration for this mass.

Solution. (a) By Eq. (9.3-1) the spring constant $k = 1.00$ N/1.00×10^{-2} m $= 100$ N/m. By Eqs. (22.2-2) and (22.2-3),

$$\begin{aligned}\tau &= 2\pi/\omega_0 = 2\pi(m/k)^{1/2}\\ &= 2\pi(1.62 \text{ kg}/100 \text{ N/m})^{1/2} = (\pi/5)(1.62)^{1/2} \text{ sec}\\ &= 0.80 \text{ sec.}\end{aligned}$$

For part (b) we also need

$$\begin{aligned}\omega_0 &= (k/m)^{1/2} = (100/1.62)^{1/2} \text{ rad/sec}\\ &= 7.86 \text{ rad/sec.}\end{aligned}$$

(b) The equations of motion (from Ex. 22.1-4) are

$$\begin{aligned}x &= -(2.00 \text{ cm}) \cos (2\pi t/0.80 \text{ sec}),\\ v_x &= (15.7 \text{ cm/sec}) \sin (2\pi t/0.80 \text{ sec}),\\ a_x &= (123 \text{ cm/sec}^2) \cos (2\pi t/0.80 \text{ sec}).\end{aligned}$$

(c) The graph of x vs. t is that plotted in Fig. 2.13. The preparation of simliar plots for the range $t = 0$ to $t = 0.80$ sec for v_x and a_x is left to the reader. Hint: Calculate points for intervals of t either 0.80 sec/12 or 0.80 sec/24.

EXERCISES

22.2-1 A mass m is hung on the end of a wire of original length L_0 and performs vertical oscillations. If the cross-sectional area of the wire has area S and the material of the wire has a Young's modulus Y, prove that the time of oscillation τ is given by

$$\tau = 2\pi(mL_0/SY)^{1/2}.$$

22.2-2 What is the time of oscillation of the mass of Ex. 9.3-3 on the wire of that exercise?

22.2-3 A long straight wire is stretched horizontally between two buildings. It is found that if a succession of masses are hung from the mid-point of this wire, the depression of the mid-point is proportional to the mass for small masses. A mass of 500 g produces a depression of 10.00 cm. If this mass is set in motion vertically as it hangs on the wire, what will be the time of a single oscillation?

22.2-4 Given a known mass and a watch, but no method of measuring a length, how would you determine the stiffness constant of a spring? (Cf. Ex. 22.2-1).

22.2-5 When an unknown mass is loaded onto a spring of unknown stiffness constant, the extension is 0.49 cm. What is the time of oscillation of the mass on the spring?

22.2-6 Imagine a straight tunnel to be dug through the center of the earth, and a ball of mass of 1000 kg allowed to fall into this tunnel from the surface of the earth. Calculate the time taken by such a ball to reach the center of the earth from the surface. (Cf. Exs. 14.11-4 and 14.11-5.)

22.3 *Rotational Oscillations*

Because of the analogy between linear and rotational mechanics (Table 7.2), it is possible to apply our considerations of SHM to ***rotational oscillations.*** Suppose that a rigid body of moment of inertia I is subject to a torque

$$T = -k_T\theta, \tag{22.3-1}$$

where k_T is a constant and θ is the angle by which the body is displaced from its equilibrium position. Its angular acceleration will then be given by Eq. (7.9-5) as

$$\alpha = T/I = -(k_T/I)\theta. \tag{22.3-2}$$

The analogy between Eq. (22.3-1) and Eq. (22.1-9) leads us to expect that the body may vibrate in SHM of rotation. To check this, we suppose that

$$\theta = \theta_0 \cos \omega_0 t,$$

where θ_0 is the maximum angular displacement of the body. Exact repetition of the discussion of Sec. 22.1 then shows that the angular velocity at any time t is

$$\Omega = -\omega_0\theta_0 \sin \omega_0 t,$$

where Ω has been used to denote the angular velocity to avoid confusion with ω_0, the radian frequency. The angular acceleration is

$$\alpha = -\omega_0^2\theta_0 \cos \omega_0 t = -\omega_0^2\theta.$$

Comparison of this expression with Eq. (22.3-2) shows that our assumption of SHM is completely justified and that

$$\omega_0^2 = k_T/I. \tag{22.3-3}$$

22.4 *The Simple Pendulum*

There are a number of important types of physical oscillations that are not exactly SHM but which are approximated very closely thereby. A typical example is the pendulum which is an essential part of many clocks. Let us first consider a so-called ***simple pendulum*** which consists (Fig. 22.2) of a body of mass M hung from a point O by a rod of negligible weight and of length L. When undisturbed, the mass M will hang vertically below O. If the rod is displaced through an angle θ from the vertical, the torque T tending to return it to the vertical position will be

$$T = -MgL \sin \theta$$

and the angular acceleration α will be

$$\alpha = T/I = -(MgL/ML^2) \sin \theta = -(g/L) \sin \theta,$$

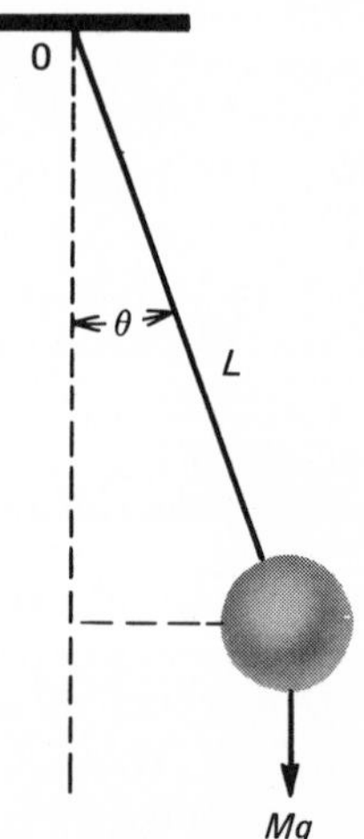

FIG. 22.2 The simple pendulum.

since the moment of inertia (in radian units) of a small particle of mass M at a distance L from the axis O is ML^2 [Eq. (7.6-1)]. Comparison of this equation with Eq. (22.3-2) shows that the motion is not strictly SHM, but if we remember the fact (Eq. G.12) that

$$\sin \theta \approx \theta$$

for small θ (θ in dimensionless radians), we can write the expression for the angular acceleration in the form

$$\alpha \approx -(g/L)\theta.$$

Hence the motion of the pendulum is approximated by SHM for which

$$\omega_0^2 = g/L, \tag{22.4-1}$$

in accordance with Eq. (22.3-3). A number of other motions which approximate in a similar way to simple harmonic motions are discussed in the following exercises and in the problems at the end of the chapter.

EXERCISES

22.4-1 Calculate the length of the pendulum for which the period τ will have the value 2.000 sec in a location in which g has the value 9.800 m/sec^2.

22.4-2 Given two pendulums and a means of rapid communication, such as a radio, describe a method for comparing the value of g at two different locations on the surface of the earth.

22.4-3 A wire hangs in a tall dark tower, the lower end of the wire being visible but the upper end being invisible and inaccessible. How would you determine the length of the wire? Note: This problem was proposed and solved by Galileo.

22.4-4 A rigid body is hung so that it is free to rotate about a horizontal axis. The center of mass of the body is located at a distance L from the axis, the moment of inertia of the body about the axis is I, and its mass is M. What is the equilibrium position? Prove that the period τ of a small oscillation about the equilibrium position is given by

$$\tau = 2\pi(I/M\,Lg)^{1/2}.$$

Show that this is the same as the period of a simple pendulum of length I/ML.

22.5 *The Effect of Friction on a Harmonic Oscillator*

In the oscillations so far considered, we have assumed that the only forces acting are those connected with potential energy of some sort (gravitational, elastic, etc.). Under such circumstances mechanical energy is conserved, as was assumed in Sec. 22.1. Were this true with real oscillating systems, the motion could be simple harmonic and, once started, would go on forever. We know that pendula, masses hanging from springs, etc. do not behave in quite this way. After they are started in oscillation, they move with decreasing amplitude and finally come to rest at equilibrium. One difference between real oscillators and simple harmonic oscillators is that the former are subject to friction or to other dissipative forces that convert mechanical energy into heat. The oscillation is said to be ***damped*** by the dissipative force.

It is found experimentally that the frictional force on many moving bodies can be approximated closely as being directly proportional, and in the opposite direction, to the velocity. Let us assume for the present that this statement is true for a body executing approximate SHM, and write for the frictional force

$$F = -R_m v, \tag{22.5-1}$$

where R_m is a constant with the name ***mechanical resistance.*** The rate at which work is done against the frictional force is the force times the velocity, so the energy of the moving body changes at a rate

$$dE/dt = Fv = -R_m v^2. \tag{22.5-2}$$

Let us now suppose further that the friction is so small that the change of the mechanical energy during any one period of the oscillation is a small fraction of the energy at the beginning of the period. Then the motion will not be far different from SHM, and we can substitute the value of v from Eq. (22.1-4) in Eq. (22.5-2) to find

$$dE/dt = -\omega_0^2 R_m X_0^2 \cos^2(\omega_0 t + \phi).$$

During a full cycle, from $t = 0$ to $t = \tau$, the amount of energy dissipated is

$$\Delta E = \omega_0^2 R_m \int_0^\tau X_0^2 \cos^2(\omega_0 t + \phi)\, dt.$$

Consistent with our assumption that the effect of damping is small, we can consider X_0 to be essentially constant during any particular cycle and so move it outside the integral. At the same time, let us substitute θ for $(\omega_0 t + \phi)$ and, therefore, $d\theta/\omega_0$ for dt. At $t = \tau$, $\theta = (2\pi + \phi)$, and we have for the change in the energy

$$-\Delta E = -\omega_0 R_m X_0^2 \int_\phi^{2\pi+\phi} \cos^2\theta\, d\theta.$$

The integral here may be evaluated simply if we think of it as the area under the curve of $\cos^2\theta$ vs. θ. In Fig. 22.3 we plot both $\sin^2\theta$ and $\cos^2\theta$. Clearly, the

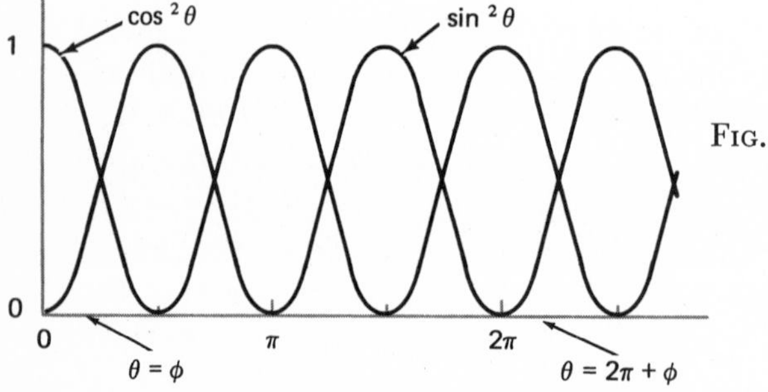

FIG. 22.3 $\int_0^{2\pi} \sin^2\theta\, d\theta = \int_0^{2\pi} \cos^2\theta\, d\theta = \pi.$

area under the $\sin^2\theta$ curve over any complete cycle (say from $\theta=\phi$ to $\theta=2\pi+\phi$) is equal to the area under the $\cos^2\theta$ curve over the same cycle. Hence,

$$\int_\phi^{2\pi+\phi}\sin^2\theta\,d\theta=\int_\phi^{2\pi+\phi}\cos^2\theta\,d\theta.$$

If we now remember that $\sin^2\theta=1-\cos^2\theta$ for all θ [Eq. (E.6) of Appendix E] we can write

$$\int_\phi^{2\pi+\phi}\cos^2\theta\,d\theta=\int_\phi^{2\pi+\phi}d\theta-\int_\phi^{2\pi+\phi}\cos^2\theta\,d\theta.$$

The integral of $d\theta$ over the full period is just 2π, so we have

$$\int_\phi^{2\pi+\phi}\cos^2\theta\,d\theta=2\pi/2=\pi. \tag{22.5-3}$$

We thus have a simple expression for the energy change per cycle:

$$-\Delta E=-\pi\omega_0 R_m X_0^2. \tag{22.5-4}$$

We now ask by how much the amplitude X_0 decreases in one period. Remembering that all of the energy of the oscillator is potential when $x=X_0$, we can write, for the energy,

$$E=\tfrac{1}{2}kX_0^2.$$

Differentiating both sides of this expression and then integrating over a full cycle, we obtain

$$-\Delta E=\int_0^\tau\frac{dE}{dt}\,dt=kX_0\int_0^\tau\frac{dX_0}{dt}\,dt=kX_0\,\Delta X_0,$$

where ΔX_0 is the (small) change of amplitude during the time interval τ. Equating of the two expressions for ΔE then leads to

$$\frac{\Delta X_0}{X_0}=-\frac{\pi\omega_0 R_m}{k}=\frac{\pi R_m}{\omega_0 m}, \tag{22.5-5}$$

where the final equality is obtained by substituting $\omega_0{}^2m$ for k.

We define the ***decrement*** δ as the fractional decrease in the amplitude per cycle. Then

$$\delta=-\frac{\pi R_m}{\omega_0 m}=-\frac{\pi}{Q_0}, \tag{22.5-6}$$

where the quantity Q_0 is often used to measure the extent to which the oscillator is free of friction. This quantity is called the ***quality factor*** or simply Q_0 (***cue zero***). It is infinite for an oscillator that is completely free of dissipation and is small for one with large frictional forces. It is necessary to keep in mind that all the equations derived in this section are valid only for Q_0 much greater than

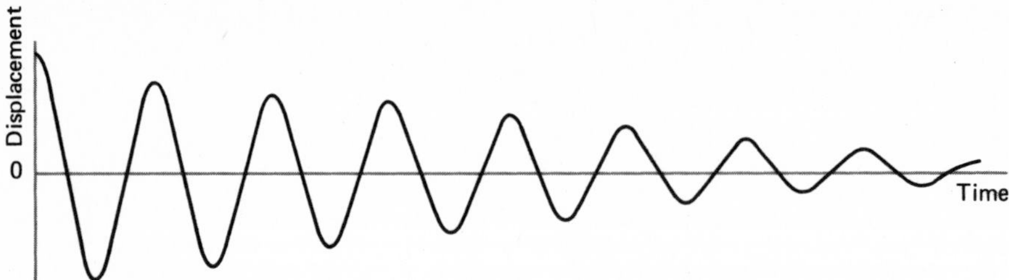

FIG. 22.4 Displacement vs. time for a damped oscillator ($Q_0 \approx 10$).

unity. Figure 22.4 shows the way that a damped oscillator with $Q_0 \approx 10$ behaves. Notice that the second equality of Eq. (22.5-6) gives Q_0 in terms of the mechanical resistance, the mass, and the natural radian frequency:

$$Q_0 = \omega_0 m / R_{\mathrm{m}}. \tag{22.5-7}$$

22.6 Forced Motion of a Damped Oscillator

We have thus far discussed oscillations in which only the restoring force is acting and those in which a dissipative force is present in addition to the restoring force. There is another type of oscillation that is of great importance. Suppose that a periodic force is exerted on the suspended mass of Fig. 22.5. We know that we can set the mass into motion, even if the period of the driving force is different from the natural period of oscillation ($\tau = 2\pi/\omega_0$). When we first start applying the periodic force, the motion may be rather complicated but, if we continue the application for many periods, the mass will come to a state of steady oscillation, with the same frequency as that of the driving force.

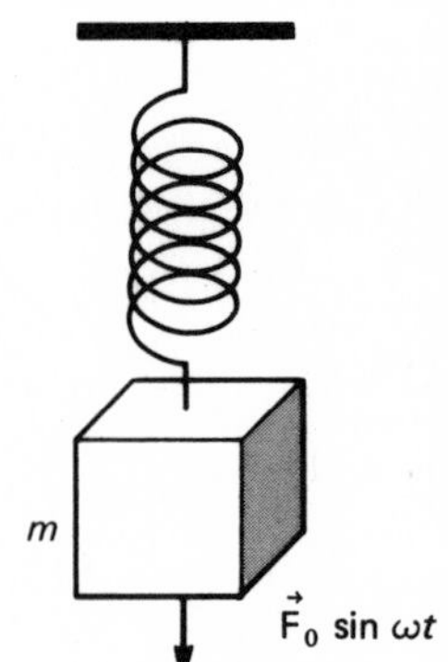

FIG. 22.5 Forced oscillation.

As was done in Secs. 22.1 and 22.5, we shall try to arrive at an understanding of this situation by examining the energy exchanges and the work done.

Let us suppose that the equation for the displacement is

$$x = X \sin \omega t, \tag{22.6-1}$$

so that the velocity is

$$v = dx/dt = \omega X \cos \omega t = V \cos \omega t, \tag{22.6-2}$$

where V is the ***velocity amplitude***, equal to ωX. Note here that the zero subscripts have been dropped because ω is not necessarily equal to ω_0, the natural radian frequency. The driving force must do two things. First, it must balance the frictional force in order to maintain constant amplitude. Second, it must combine with the restoring force, $-kx$, to accelerate and decelerate the mass.

For convenience, let us write the force as the sum of two components:

$$f = f_r + f_a,$$

both of which must vary sinusoidally with radian frequency ω, but which may differ in phase. If f_r is to balance the frictional force, it must be equal to it in magnitude and opposite in sign at every instant. Using Eqs. (22.5-1) and (22.6-1), we can therefore say that

$$f_r = R_m v = R_m V \cos \omega t. \tag{22.6-3}$$

The component f_r is in phase with the velocity (zero phase angle) and *does work on the system* continuously. On the other hand, f_a only changes the kinetic and potential energies of the system. Sometimes it is doing work on the system, and sometimes the system is *doing work on it.* To find f_a, first note that the total energy of the system at any time is

$$\begin{aligned} E &= \tfrac{1}{2}kx^2 + \tfrac{1}{2}mv^2 \\ &= \tfrac{1}{2}kX^2 \sin^2 \omega t + \tfrac{1}{2}m\omega^2 X^2 \cos^2 \omega t. \end{aligned}$$

The rate at which the energy is changing at any instant is found by differentiating the expression for the energy:

$$\begin{aligned} dE/dt &= \omega k X^2 \sin \omega t \cos \omega t - m\omega^3 X^2 \sin \omega t \cos \omega t \\ &= \omega(k - m\omega^2) X^2 \sin \omega t \cos \omega t. \end{aligned}$$

This change of energy must be brought about by f_a, which is doing work at the rate $f_a v$. We therefore have

$$\omega f_a X \cos \omega t = \omega(k - m\omega^2) X^2 \sin \omega t \cos \omega t,$$

from which it follows that

$$f_a = (k - m\omega^2) X \sin \omega t = V(k/\omega - m\omega) \sin \omega t. \tag{22.6-4}$$

Before going further, note that the net work done per cycle by f_a is

$$\int_0^{2\pi/\omega} f_a v \, dt = VX(k - m\omega^2) \int_0^{2\pi/\omega} \sin \omega t \cos \omega t \, dt.$$

Figure 22.6 shows a plot of $\sin \theta \cos \theta$ vs. θ. The area below the horizontal axis in the full period from 0 to 2π is equal to that above the axis; hence the integral of ($\sin \omega t \cos \omega t \, dt$) over a full cycle is zero. The component f_a does *no net work.* We could have predicted this in advance from the fact that this component does not work against dissiptative forces. Conservation of energy therefore demands that it do no net work.

Combining Eqs. (22.6-3) and (22.6-4), we find that the force necessary to maintain the oscillation at frequency ω is

$$f = R_m V \cos \omega t + (V/\omega)(k - m\omega^2) \sin \omega t.$$

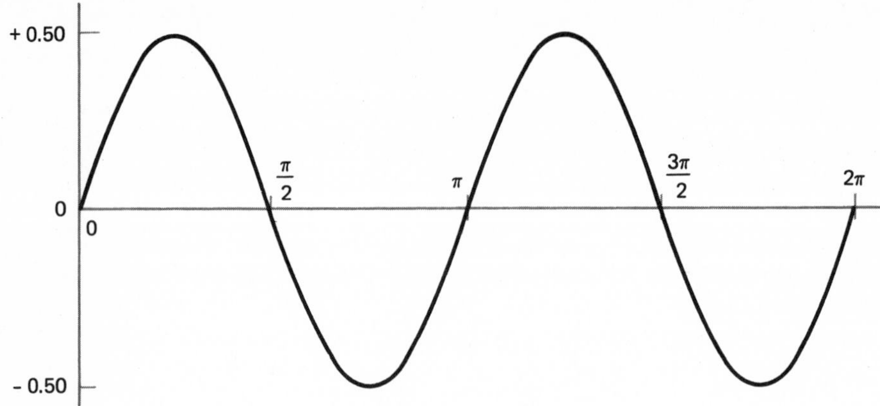

FIG. 22.6 Plot of $\sin\theta \cos\theta$ vs. θ.

This equation is identical in form with that given in Ex. 22.1-3. Hence we can use the results of that exercise to show that

$$f = F_0 \cos(\omega t + \phi), \tag{22.6-5A}$$

where

$$F_0 = V[R_{\mathrm{m}}{}^2 + (k/\omega - m\omega)^2]^{1/2} \tag{22.6-5B}$$

and

$$\tan\phi = \frac{m\omega - k/\omega}{R_{\mathrm{m}}}. \tag{22.6-5C}$$

The ratio F_0/V is known as the mechanical ***impedance***, Z, of the oscillator (cf. Probs. 10.2–10.3). We have, from Eq. (22.5B),

$$Z = [R_{\mathrm{m}}{}^2 + (m\omega - k/\omega)^2]^{1/2}. \tag{22.6-6}$$

It is often convenient to choose the origin of time so that we can write the force without a phase angle. When this choice is made, and when Eqs. (22.6-5) are simplified with the help of Eq. (22.6-6), the former become

$$f = F_0 \cos\omega t, \tag{22.6-7A}$$

$$v = V\cos(\omega t - \alpha) = (F_0/Z)\cos(\omega t - \alpha), \tag{22.6-7B}$$

$$\tan\alpha = \frac{m\omega - k/\omega}{R_{\mathrm{m}}}. \tag{22.6-7C}$$

We can see from Eqs. (22.6-7) that the response of an oscillator to a sinusoidally varying force of amplitude F_0 and radian frequency ω depends on the values of Z and α for that oscillator and therefore on ω. We shall not go through a full discussion here, but leave the work to the interested reader (see Exs. 23.6-1 to 23.6-8). We can however, deduce a member of interesting qualitative results by inspection of Eqs. (22.6-6), (22.7B), and (22.7C).

We first consider an oscillator with fixed m, k, and R_m and investigate how the velocity amplitude varies with the frequency of an applied force, $f = F_0 \cos \omega t$, as the frequency is changed. The maximal response clearly occurs when Z is minimal, i.e., when $m\omega = k/\omega$. This equality is satisfied when $\omega = \omega_0$ [see Eq. (22.1-10)], i.e., when the frequency of the applied force is the natural frequency of the oscillator. At this frequency the velocity amplitude is F_0/R_m. It is then said that the oscillator is ***in resonance*** with the force, and $f_0 = \omega_0/2\pi$ is known as the ***resonant frequency***. Everyone has noticed how certain parts of a car vibrate strongly at a certain speed. In such cases we can be sure that a varying force due to engine vibration is in resonance with the vibrating part.

When the oscillator is driven at its resonant frequency, α in Eq. (22.6-7C) is zero. The force and the velocity are then said to be ***in phase***. When $\omega > \omega_0$, $\tan \alpha$, and hence α, is negative. Hence $\cos (\omega t - \alpha)$ reaches its maximum at a later time (t) than does $\cos \omega t$, and the velocity goes through its maximum in each cycle after the force does. The velocity is therefore said to ***lag*** behind the force when $\omega > \cdot_0\, \omega$ Conversely, when $\omega < \omega_0$, α is positive, and the velocity ***leads*** the force.

Once the variation of velocity with time is known for a given oscillator under the influence of a given periodic driving force, we can find how the displacement x and the acceleration a of the mass vary with time, by using the relations

$$x = \int_{V_0}^{t} v \, dt \tag{22.6-8}$$

and

$$a = dv/dt. \tag{22.6-9}$$

In the first of these equations, the lower limit of integration is determined by the fact that the displacement is zero and increasing when the velocity has a maximal value. Curves showing how the force, velocity, displacement, and acceleration vary with time, for various values of ω/ω_0, are shown in Fig. 22.7.

EXERCISES

22.6-1 A sinusoidally varying force whose maximum value is 0.10 N is applied to the oscillating mass of the worked example of Sec. 22.2. If the periodic time for this force is 1.00 sec and friction can be neglected, what is the amplitude of the resultant oscillation?

22.6-2 In Ex. 22.6-1 assume that the oscillating mass is subject to a frictional force whose mechanical resistance is 1.50 N sec/m^2, and calculate the amplitude of the response.

22.6-3 Using the data of Exs. 22.6-1 and 22.6-2 except for the the period of the applied force, which is now to be taken as 2.00 sec, calculate the amplitude of the oscillation and also the maximum velocity.

22.6-4 What are the dimensions of each of the quantities Z, R, m, and k/ω?

22.6-5 What are the dimensions of Q_0 in Eq. (22.5-6)?

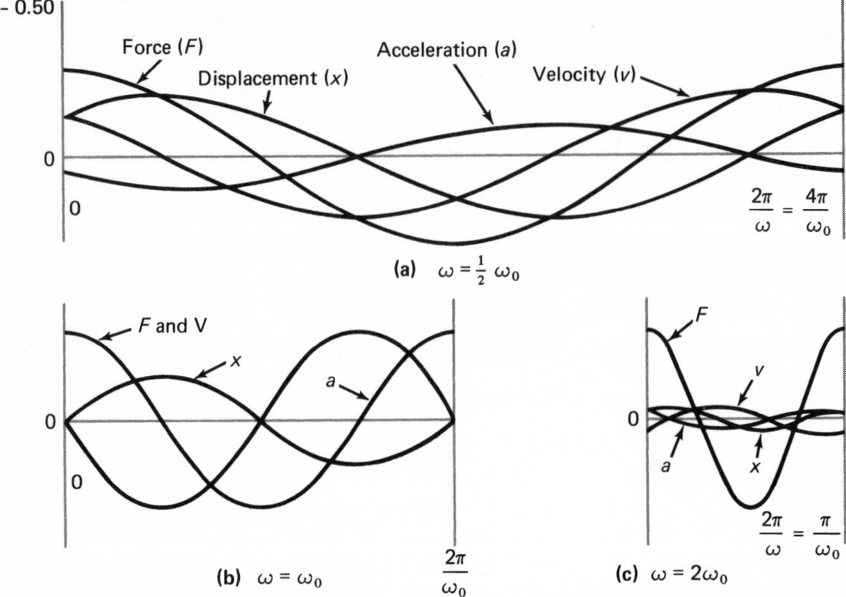

FIG. 22.7 Response of an oscillator to a sinusoidal force of fixed amplitude, $F = F_0 \cos \omega t$. In (a), $\omega = \frac{1}{2}\omega_0$, the natural radian frequency; in (b) $\omega = \omega_0$; in (c), $\omega = 2\omega_0$. The curves have been calculated for an oscillator with $Q_0 = 2$, and the amplitude of the force is $F_0 = \omega_0 R$. The scales of F, x, v, and a remain unchanged among the three parts of the figure.

22.6-6 Writing $\Omega = \omega/\omega_0$, prove that Eqs. (22.6-5C) and (22.6-6) can be written in the form

$$\tan \phi = Q_0(\Omega - 1/\Omega)$$

and

$$Z = R_m[1 + Q_0{}^2(\Omega - 1/\Omega)^2]^{1/2} = R_m[1 + \tan^2 \phi]^{1/2}.$$

22.6-7 From the results of Ex. 22.6-6 prove that Z has its smallest value and that $\phi = 0$ when $\omega = \omega_0$, and that consequently the maximum velocity response for a given maximum force occurs for this frequency.

22.6-8 Sketch curves of the variation of Z/R_m against frequency (Ω in Ex. 22.6-6) for $Q_0 = 10, 1.0, 0.1$. (Hint: Calculate values for $\Omega = 0.1, 0.5, 0.9, 1.0, 1.1, 2, 10$, and for any other values which then seem interesting.)

22.7 *The Elements of an Oscillator*

We can recapitulate our discussion of the forced oscillations of mechanical oscillators by considering three things that the applied force must do. First, one component of the force (f_r) must overcome the resistance due to friction, and we have its value from Eq. (22.6-3):

$$f_r = R_m v. \tag{22.7-1}$$

It will be convenient to break the other component (f_a) into two parts. The first of these, which we may call f_k, is required to extend or compress the spring. It is

$$f_k = kx. \tag{22.7-2}$$

Finally, the last part of the force is required to accelerate the mass. It is written as

$$f_m = ma = m(dv/dt). \tag{22.7-3}$$

The total force is the sum of the three, so

$$\begin{aligned} F &= f_m + f_r + f_k \\ &= ma + R_m v + kx. \end{aligned} \tag{22.7-4}$$

Equation (22.7-4) must hold at every instant. The individual components of the force cannot do so independently of one another, because a and v are related by the two equations:

$$a = dv/dt \qquad \text{and} \qquad v = dx/dt,$$

the definitions of velocity and acceleration. For this reason, all three components are determined as soon as F is determined. We have carried out this determination in Sec. 22.6 and have found that the amplitude of the needed periodic force is the product of the velocity amplitude and the mechanical impedance, while the tangent of its phase angle is the ratio of $(m\omega - k/\omega)$ to the mechanical resistance.

EXERCISES

22.7-1 An oscillator, whose natural radian frequency is ω_0 and which is without friction, is being driven in a forced oscillation of radian frequency ω. Find the force acting on the oscillating particle of mass m, and show that this force satisfies Eq. (22.7-4).

22.7-2 An oscillator, whose mechanical resistance is R_m, is being driven at its natural radian frequency ω_0. Find the force acting on the oscillating particle of mass m, and show that this force satisfies Eq. (22.7-4).

22.8 The Analogy Between Electrical and Mechanical Quantities

At various stages in our study of physics we have found that the repetition of detailed derivations and discussions can be avoided by the development of a complete mathematical analogy between two sets of quantities which have quite different physical significance (cf. Secs. 9.4 and 7.12). We can now proceed to another important analogy, that which exists between the mechanical oscillator and the electrical oscillator. We do this by consideration of the three types of components of an electric curcuit which we have discussed in the earlier chapters: resistances, capacitances, and inductances.

As far as resistance is concerned, the important law is Ohm's law [cf. Eq. (16.16-1)].

$$V_R = RI = R\,dq/dt. \tag{22.8-1}$$

According to this law, the current I through a resistor is proportional to the potential drop V_R across the resistance, measured so that the potential is decreasing in the direction of current (Fig. 22.8a). We know also that a current I corresponds to a flow of charge at a rate $I = dq/dt$ [Eq. (16.1-2)]. This is the

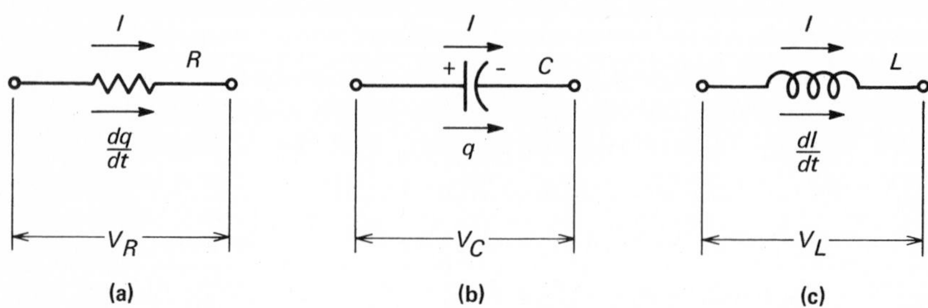

Fig. 22.8 Elements of an electrical circuit: (a) resistance, (b) capacitance, (c) inductance.

beginning of our analogy. As far as the two equations (22.7-1) and (22.8-1) are concerned, we have the analogy expressed by the first four entries of Table 22.1, and we can now look for the remaining analogies of the table.

Table 23.2
Electromechanical Analogues

Mechanical	Electrical
F	V
R_m	R
x	q
$v = dx/dt$	$I = dq/dt$
$a = dv/dt$	dI/dt
k	I/C
m	L

In a search for an analogy to Eq. (22.7-2), we have already made V analogous to F and q to x. We must therefore search for an equation expressing a proportionality between V and q. We soon find Eq. (16.22-3), which expresses the charge q on a capacitor of capacitance C in terms of the potential difference V_C between its terminals. This equation is rewritten in the form

$$V_C = (1/C)q, \tag{22.8-2}$$

and we see that the analogy of Table 22.1 is pursued, provided we consider the quantity $1/C$ as analogous to the stiffness constant k of the oscillator spring.

The analogy to Eq. (22.7-3) is found in Eq. (17.11-2) for self-inductance, which is rewritten as

$$V_L = L\, dI/dt \tag{22.8-3}$$

in which L is the coefficient of self inductance of a coil, dI/dt is the rate at which the current is increasing in the coil, and V_L is the electromotive force which must be applied across the terminals of the coil to produce an increase of current at that rate.* In Eq. (22.8-3), L is analogous to m and dI/dt is analogous to the acceleration $a = dv/dt$, thus maintaining the analogy between I and v already indicated. We now can complete the analogy with the oscillator by connecting

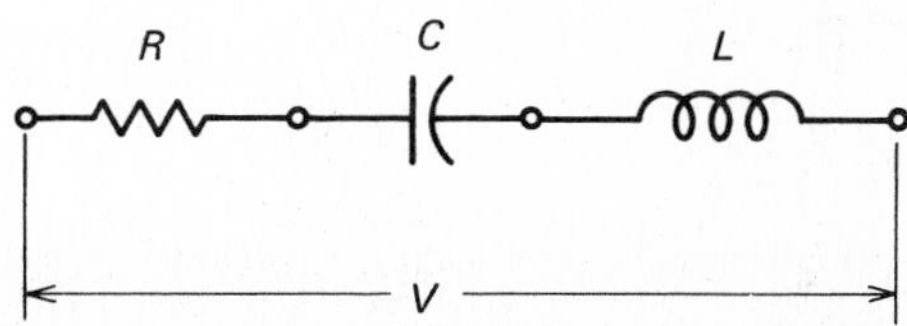

FIG. 22.9 *L-C-R* circuit.

the three elements of Fig. 22.8 in series into the circuit of Fig. 22.9. In such a circuit the potential drop V between the ends must be equal to the sum of the individual potential drops and we must have

$$\begin{aligned} V &= V_L + V_R + V_C \\ &= L(dI/dt) + RI + (1/C)q, \end{aligned} \tag{22.8-4}$$

which, of course, completes the analogy between the electrical and the mechanical system, as will be seen by comparison with Eq. (22.7-4).

We can now consider the case of the free electrical oscillator. Suppose that three electrical elements (C, L, and R) are connected in series as shown in Fig. 22.10. If there is no charge on the capacitor and no current flowing in the other elements, the system will be stable, just as an undisturbed mass hanging on a spring is stable. If a charge is placed on the capacitor, say by the temporary connection of the terminals of a battery across it, the effect will be analogous to the stretching of the spring. After the battery is disconnected, the charge left on the capacitor will produce a current I through the resistance and the inductance such that the sum of the voltages across the three elements is zero, there being no applied voltage. The individual voltages will not, in general, be separately equal to zero, and, as we shall later see, will each fluctuate at least approximately sinusoidally, giving an ***electrical oscillation.***

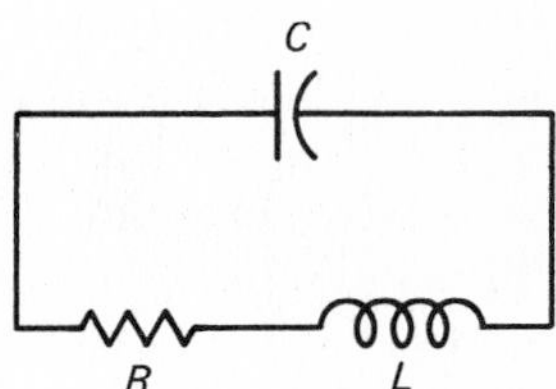

FIG. 22.10 Free electrical oscillator.

* Notice the change of sign between Eq. (17.11-2) and Eq. (22.8-3). In the former the voltage is induced by the changing current, whereas that expressed in the second is needed to produce the change of current.

So far we have developed our analogy, as we should always develop such analogies, on the basis of the mathematical relations that exist between the variable quantities. It is a help, however, to obtain a more physical picture of the analogy if possible. To do this we press the mathematical side of the analogy a little further and use it to calculate some of the energy relations of the electrical circuit. We know that the energy of a compressed spring is given by $E = \frac{1}{2}kx^2$ [Eq. (22.2-1)]. We leave it as an exercise for the reader (if he wishes) to rewrite the argument given in Sec. 9.4, using the analogous electrical quantities, to prove that the energy E_C of a capacitor which carries a charge q is given by

$$E_C = \tfrac{1}{2}q^2/C. \tag{22.8-5}$$

In a similar way the analogy between an inductance carrying a current and a mass moving with a speed v enables us to write for the energy E_L stored up in an inductance the expression

$$E_L = \tfrac{1}{2}LI^2, \tag{22.8-6}$$

in analogy to the familiar $\frac{1}{2}mv^2$ for the kinetic energy of a moving body. The reader (from Missouri) can, if he wishes, substitute the analogous electrical quantities in the argument of Sec. 4.11 to obtain Eq. (22.8-6).

The energy stored in the capacitor in the circuits of Figs. 22.9 and 22.10 is thus entirely analogous to the potential energy stored in the spring. This energy is stored by virtue of the displacement of charges from one plate of the condenser to the other, just as the energy is stored in the spring by virtue of the displacement of one end of the spring with respect to the other. The energy stored in the inductance provides the analogy to the kinetic energy of the moving oscillator. When a current is started in an inductance, work is done in building up the magnetic field within it. This current will continue unless work is done to stop it, i.e., unless energy is expended in heating a resistance, or unless an emf is applied to oppose the current. This is entirely analogous to the work done in accelerating a mass—work that gives the mass kinetic energy. The mass continues to move in the same straight line unless it is slowed down by friction or by an opposing force.

We return to a discussion of the behavior of the circuit of Fig. 22.10 which is redrawn in Fig. 22.11. Suppose that, when the circuit is first completed, the current is zero and the capacitor is charged with a charge q_0, the left-hand plate being positive with respect to the right, as indicated in Fig. 22.11a. This situation is analogous to the oscillator of Figs. 2.12 and 2.13, whose mass is initially displaced from its equilibrium position and then released. As soon as the circuit is completed, a current I will start to flow through R and L (Fig. 22.11b), and the charge q on the condenser will decrease. In the inductance L, the passage of a current I will result in the building up of a magnetic field. This corresponds to the acceleration of the mass m by the spring. Some energy will be dissipated in the resistance R, corresponding to the energy dissipated in the mechanical system in overcoming the friction. The current I through the inductance will continue to build up as long as there is a potential difference across the plates of the capacitor. This current will reach its maximum value when the charge on the capacitor has reduced to zero (Fig. 22.11c). At this point the energy, originally stored up in the capacitor, has now been transferred to the inductance, which now contains an amount of energy $\frac{1}{2}LI^2$ since it is carrying a current I. This amount of energy will, of course, be less than $\frac{1}{2}q_0^2/C$ (the original energy of the capacitor) by the energy lost in heating the resistance R. The energy now stored in the inductance will tend to maintain the current I, and as a result the capacitor will begin to receive a charge opposite in sign to its original charge (Fig. 22.11d). This

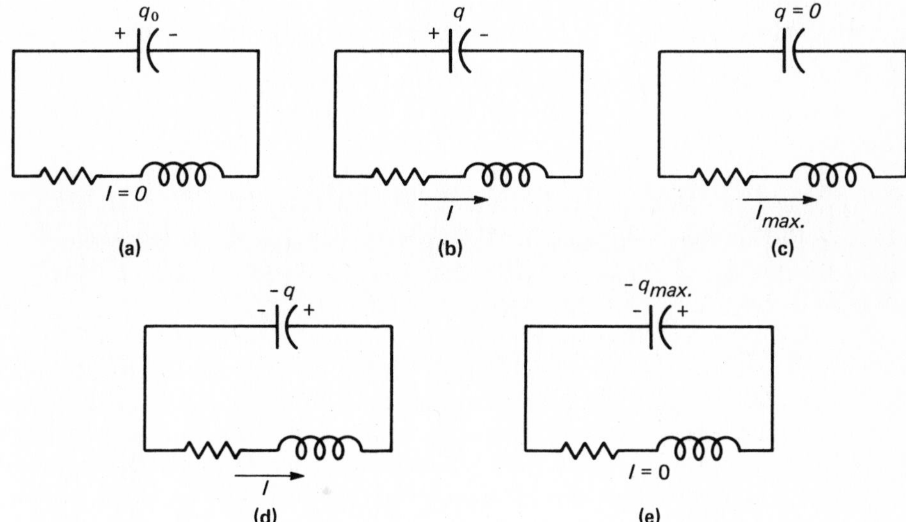

FIG. 22.11 Forced oscillations in an *L-C-R* circuit.

building up of reverse charge will go on until there is no more current through the inductance (Fig. 22.11e). This situation is exactly the reverse of that in Fig. 22.11a; a reverse current I will start and the system will continue to oscillate until it has dissipated all its energy by heating the resistance R.

The analogy can now be used to obtain the radian frequency for the oscillation (R small). Eq. (22.2-2) takes the form

$$\omega_0^2 = 1/LC, \tag{22.8-7}$$

and the damping of the oscillator is accounted for by the quantity Q_0, which by analogy with Eq. (22.5-7) can be written

$$Q_0 = \omega_0 L/R = 1/\omega_0 RC. \tag{22.8-8}$$

By analogy with the argument of Sec. 22.6, we can immediately obtain equations for the behavior of the circuit of Fig. 22.9 when a sinusoidal votage

$$V = V_0 \cos \omega t \tag{22.8-9A}$$

is applied to it. The current I is then given [cf. Eq. (22.6-7B)] by

$$I = (V_0/Z) \cos (\omega t - \alpha) \tag{22.8-9B}$$

in which the ***electrical impedance*** Z is defined [cf. Eq. (22.6-6)] by

$$Z = [R^2 + (\omega L - 1/\omega C)^2]^{1/2} \tag{22.8-9C}$$

and the ***phase angle*** α [cf. Eq. (22.6-7C)] by

$$\tan \alpha = \frac{(\omega L - 1/\omega C)}{R}. \tag{22.8-9D}$$

In a similar way, the charge on the capacitor at any time t is given [cf. Eq. (22.6-8)] by

$$q = \int_{I_0}^{t} I\, dt = (V_0/\omega Z) \sin (\omega t + \alpha). \tag{22.8-9E}$$

We see that, for a given voltage maximum, the maximum current will be drawn when Z is as small as possible, i.e., when $\omega = \omega_0$, the condition for resonance.

Many other interesting deductions can be made from these equations. Suggestions that will lead to a few of the most important are included in the exercises which follow and in the problems at the end of the chapter.

EXERCISES

22.8-1 By simultaneously setting $R = 0$ and $C = \infty$ in the results of this section, obtain results equivalent to those of Sec. 17.12.

22.8-2 Comment on the physics of the fact implied by Ex. 22.8-1, that an infinite capacitance is equivalent to a wire of zero resistance.

22.8-3 By setting $R = 0$ and $L = 0$ in the results of Sec. 22.8, prove that for a given current the voltage drop across a capacitor varies inversely as the frequency, and hence that a capacitor in a line will block low-frequency currents and pass high-frequency currents.

22.8-4 An alternator that maintains an emf $V = V_0 \cos \omega t$ is connected to the terminals of a series combination consisting of a coil of inductance 1.00 H and resistance 5.0 Ω and a capacitor of capacitance 100 μF. If ω can be changed while V_0 is held contant at 100 V, at what frequency will the alternator deliver maximum current to the circuit? What will be the amplitude of this current?

22.8-5 What is the current delivered by the alternator of Ex. 22.8-4 if the frequency is 5 sec^{-1}? If it is 30 sec^{-1}?

22.8-6 It is desired to use the coil of Ex. 22.8-4 in series with a different capacitor, so chosen that the circuit will draw maximum current when connected to the 110-V_{eff} (cf. Sec. 17.9), 60-cps/sec lines. A capacitor of what rating should be used, and what is the effective value of the current?

22.8-7 (a) Show that the energy delivered to a capacitor, whose capacitance is C, during the time interval Δt, during which its potential is changed from V to $V + \Delta V$, is

$$\Delta E_C \approx V \,\Delta q = q\, \Delta q/C,$$

where q is the charge on the capacitor. (b) By letting $\Delta t \to 0$ and $\Delta q \to 0$ and integrating, prove that Eq. (22.8-5) is correct.

22.9 The Parallel Resonant Circuit

The circuit of Fig. 22.10 will oscillate freely (as long as $R \ll \omega_0 L$), but the amplitude of each succeeding oscillation will be smaller, since energy is continually being dissipated in the resistance. If a way can be found to deliver energy to the oscillating circuit at just the proper rate to compensate for this dissipation, the oscillations can be maintained indefinitely at constant amplitude. We shall see that this is possible in the electrical case, just as it was in the mechanical oscillator.

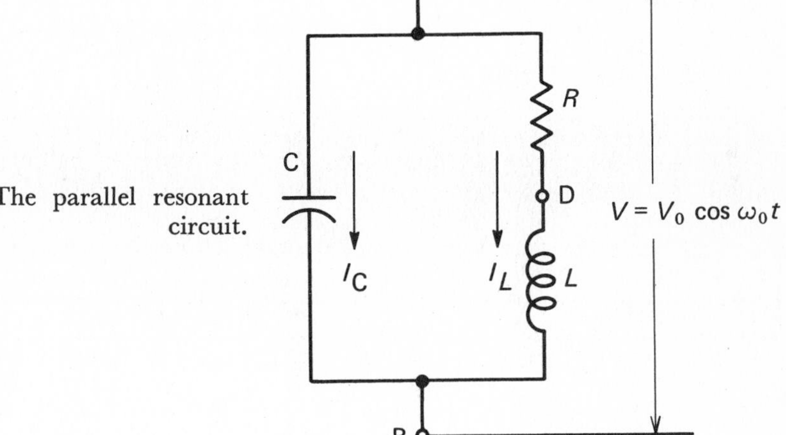

FIG. 22.12 The parallel resonant circuit.

Consider the ***parallel resonant circuit*** of Fig. 22.12, which differs from that of Fig. 22.10 by the inclusion of an external, periodic emf connected to terminals A and B. The name of the circuit results from the fact that the branch containing C and the branch containing R and L are in parallel, across the external source whose potential difference at any instant is

$$V = V_0 \cos \omega t.$$

To analyze the behavior of the system, let us first ask what would happen if R were equal to zero. The potential difference across the capacitor at any instant is equal to V, regardless of the value of R. The impedance of the capacitor is $1/\omega C$, and the phase angle, relative to V is given by Eq. (22.8-9D), with the R of that equation equal to zero. We see that $\tan \alpha = -\infty$. Hence we have $\alpha = -90° = -\frac{1}{2}\pi$ radians, and

$$I_C = \omega C V_0 \cos (\omega t + \tfrac{1}{2}\pi) = -\omega C V_0 \sin \omega t. \qquad (22.9\text{-}1)$$

Were R equal to zero, the impedance of the branch containing L would be ωL, and $\tan \alpha = +\omega L/R = +\infty$. Hence $\alpha = +\frac{1}{2}\pi$, and the current in the inductance would be

$$I_L = (V_0/\omega L) \cos (\omega t - \tfrac{1}{2}\pi) = (V_0/\omega L) \sin \omega t. \qquad (22.9\text{-}2)$$

Rather than giving the full analysis, we shall discuss a case of special importance, that for which $\omega = \omega_0$, the natural radian frequency of the resonant circuit. Replacing ω by ω_0 in Eqs. (22.9-1) and (22.9-2), and recognizing that Eq. (22.8-7) shows that $\omega_0 C = 1/\omega_0 L$, we see that $I_C = -I_L$. Under the conditions of no dissipation, then, there would be a current

$$I = I_0 \sin \omega_0 t = -\omega_0 C V_0 \sin \omega_0 t = -(V_0/\omega_0 L) \sin \omega_0 t$$

around the C-L loop when

$$V = V_0 \cos \omega_0 t. \tag{22.9-3}$$

Because the same current goes away from terminal A towards C as is going toward A from R, the current i supplied by the external source would be zero in the ideal, nonresistive case.

We now return to the real curcuit, with $R \neq 0$. If $R \ll \omega_0 L$, the currents will not be very far different from those given by Eqs. (22.9-1) and (22.9-2). There will be one very important difference, however, because the current I_L passes through R and dissipates energy at a rate P, given by the Joule law of heating:

$$P \approx I_L{}^2 R = R(V_0/\omega L)^2 \sin^2 \omega_0 t.$$

If the steady state of oscillation is to be maintained, this power must be delivered to the oscillating circuit by the external source. The power can be supplied only if a current i flows from the external source, as shown in the figure. Then we must no longer have $I_C = -I_L$ at every instant. Instead,

$$I_L = -I_C + i.$$

The amplitude of the current in C must be a little greater than that of the current in L. This is certainly reasonable since, as we have seen in our analysis of the ideal circuit (with $R = 0$), the potential difference between points D and A would be zero if the two currents were the same. The extra voltage drop across R means that the amplitude of the voltage across C must be greater than that across L. It follows that the amplitude of the current I_C must be greater than that of I_L.

To arrive at a quantitative relation, we return to Eqs. (22.9-1) and (22.9-2). We first find

$$I_C = -\omega_0 C V_0 \sin \omega_0 t;$$

then, remembering that the voltage across L is $V_0 \cos \omega_0 t - I_L R$, instead of $V_0 \cos \omega_0 t$, we get, if $R \ll \omega_0 L$,

$$I_L = \frac{V_0 \sin \omega_0 t - I_L R}{\omega_0 L}.$$

This equation can be solved for I_L:

$$I_L = \frac{V_0 \sin \omega_0 t}{\omega_0 L + R} = \frac{V_0}{\omega_0 L}\left(1 + \frac{R}{\omega_0 L}\right)^{-1} \sin \omega_0 t.$$

We then use the binomial theorem of Appendix H to show that

$$I_L \approx \frac{V_0 \sin \omega_0 t}{\omega_0 L}\left(1 - \frac{R}{\omega_0 L}\right) = \left(\frac{V_0}{\omega_0 L} - \frac{V_0 R}{\omega_0{}^2 L^2}\right) \sin \omega_0 t.$$

Finally we set

$$i = I_L + I_C \approx \left(\frac{V_0}{\omega_0 L} - \frac{V_0 R}{\omega_0{}^2 L^2} - \omega_0 C V\right) \sin \omega_0 t.$$

Because $\omega_0 C = 1/\omega_0 L$, the first and third terms in the parenthesis add to zero, and

$$i \approx -\frac{V_0 R}{\omega_0{}^2 L^2} \sin \omega_0 t.$$

We thus find that the amplitude of the current supplied by external source is

$$i_0 \approx -\frac{V_0 R}{\omega_0{}^2 L^2} = -\frac{V_0}{R Q_0{}^2}, \tag{22.9-4}$$

where we have used the Q_0 of Sec. 22.5.

It is interesting to compare i_0 with the amplitude of the current in the *C-L-R* loop, which can be taken as approximately equal to the amplitude of I_C if R is small. This ratio is

$$\frac{i_0}{I_0} = \frac{V_0 R}{\omega_0{}^2 L^2} \cdot \frac{1}{\omega_0 C V_0} = \frac{R}{\omega_0 L} = \frac{1}{Q_0}. \tag{22.9-5}$$

If the Q_0 of the parallel resonant circuit is large, i_0 becomes a very small fraction of I_0, and the external source need supply very little current or power to maintain an oscillation of large amplitude.

The process we have been considering is closely analogous to the pushing of a child on a swing. If the force is applied periodically, at the natural frequency of the swing, a very small push during each oscillation can build up a very large amplitude of motion.

Before discussing some very important applications of the ways in which the necessary driving energy can be supplied to the parallel resonant circuit, we shall have to digress from our main line of argument to consider the electronic amplifiers that play so large a part in modern science and technology.

22.10 The Electronic Diode Vacuum Tube

Sec. 17.3 we discussed the thermionic emission of electrons from a hot wire in a vacuum and have seen how a current will pass between a hot cathode and a plate contained in such a tube (Fig. 17.5) when the plate is made positive with respect to the cathode. If the plate is made negative, there will be little or no current, since the electrons emitted by the hot wire are repelled by the negative plate. Such a tube is called a ***diode*** (Greek: *di*, two; *hodos*, path). A diode tube is able to carry current in one direction only, and for this reason it is often used to change alternating current into direct current. This property of a vacuum tube is called ***rectification*** and was discovered by Thomas A. Edison (1847–1931) in 1880.

A simple rectifier circuit is indicated in Fig. 22.13a. A ***cathode*** K is raised to a high temperature by an electrical ***heater*** H. The cathode emits thermionic electrons. Suppose that an alternating voltage, $V = V_0 \sin \omega t$, is applied to terminals T_1 and T_2. To a first approximation, electrons from the cathode are drawn to the plate P only when the latter is positive with respect to K. To this approximation there is no current in the tube, and hence none through the resistance R, during the half of the cycle when P is negative with respect to K.

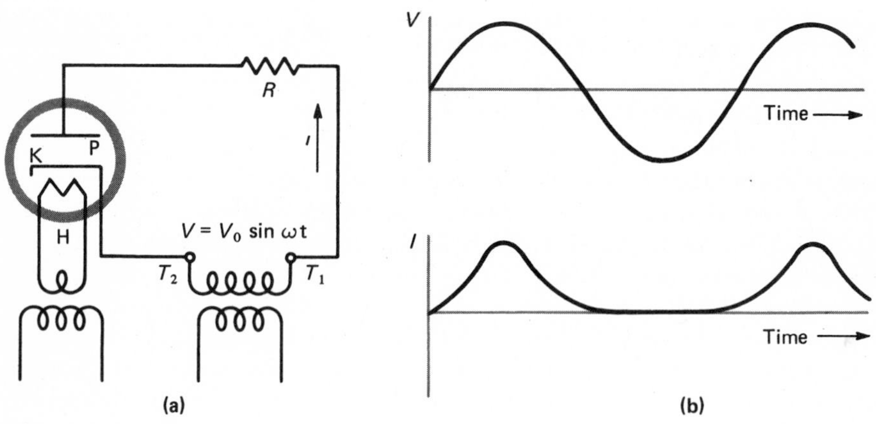

FIG. 22.13 Simple rectifier: (a) circuit diagram, (b) voltage and current vs. time.

The statement that there is *no* current when P is negative is not quite true. We saw in Sec. 21.16 that the process of thermionic emission is analogous to that of vaporization. In the latter process, some of the molecules of a liquid may have more than enough energy to escape, and they will emerge from the liquid with kinetic energy. The same is true of electrons escaping from a heated cathode. If the plate is slightly negative, the faster electrons may have sufficient energy to reach it in spite of the retarding force of the electric field. Therefore, small currents are present when the plate is negative, but they are of much lower magnitude than those that occur when the plate is positive.

Plots of the voltage, $V = V_0 \sin \omega t$, and of the current, I, through the simple rectifier circuit, both as functions of time, are shown in Fig. 22.13b. The exact shape of the current curve depends on the design of the diode, on the magnitude of V_0, and on the value of R. More complicated rectifier circuits, which produce essentially steady currrents, have been devised. The details of such circuits can be found in some of the books referred to at the end of the chapter.

22.11 The Triode Vacuum Tube

Although the rectifying properties of the diode vacuum tube are of tremendous industrial and scientific importance, the introduction of a third electrode, called a ***grid***, increases the versatility of the vacuum tube very greatly. The grid G (Fig. 22.14) is inserted between the plate P and the cathode K so that it completely surrounds the latter and shields it from the plate. The grid, however, is made of wire netting, or it is simply a single wire spiraled around the cathode, so that it is possible for electrons from the cathode to pass through the openings in the grid and thus reach the plate. The introduction of the third electrode to make the ***three-electrode tube*** or ***triode*** (Greek: *tri*, three; *hodos*, path) was due to the American inventor Lee de Forest (1873–1961), who invented it in 1906.

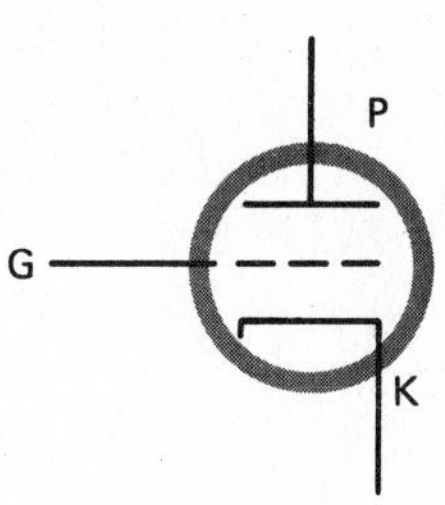

FIG. 22.14 Schematic drawing of a triode vacuum tube.

To understand the operation of the triode, consider the schematic diagram of Fig. 22.14. (It is conventional to omit the heater from such diagrams as is done here, but we must remember that it must be present in real tubes.) Let us first assume that the grid and the cathode are at the same potential. Then the region between K and G becomes filled with the "electron gas" mentioned in Sec. 21.16. This is a flowing gas, as electrons are continually escaping into it from the cathode and are continually escaping from it through the openings in the grid. The rate at which electrons pass the grid is determined by the density of the electron gas. Each new electron emerging from the cathode must do work against the repulsion of the electrons already present. Some of the electrons will have sufficient energy to pass the grid. If the plate P is kept at a positive potential with respect to K and G, all of these electrons that diffuse through the grid will be accelerated toward the plate. On the other hand, the less energetic electrons near the cathode will be unable to reach G. They will have their motions reversed and will return to the cathode. The *net* electron flow, i.e., the difference between the rate at which electrons are emitted by the cathode and the rate at which they return to it, must be equal to the rate at which electrons pass through the grid and on to the plate.

Now suppose that the grid is maintained at a potential V_0, negative with respect to the cathode. Electrons emitted from K must then not only do work against the repulsion of the electron gas, they must also do it against the repulsion of the negatively charged grid. It follows that the net electron flow will be decreased, and so the current in the tube becomes less as V_0 is made more negative. Finally, if the grid is made sufficiently negative, essentially all of the electrons will be confined to the neighborhood of the cathode, and the net current will be essentially zero. The grid voltage at which this happens is known as the ***cut-off voltage***. Because the grid is an open structure and the field due to the charge on the plate can penetrate somewhat into the region between cathode and grid, the cut-off voltage depends somewhat on the potential of the plate.

The action just discussed is illustrated by a series of experiments that can be carried out with the circuit of Fig. 22.15. The battery B keeps the plate at a positive potential V_p with respect to the cathode, and the battery C is arranged so that it can make the grid positive or negative with respect to the cathode. The

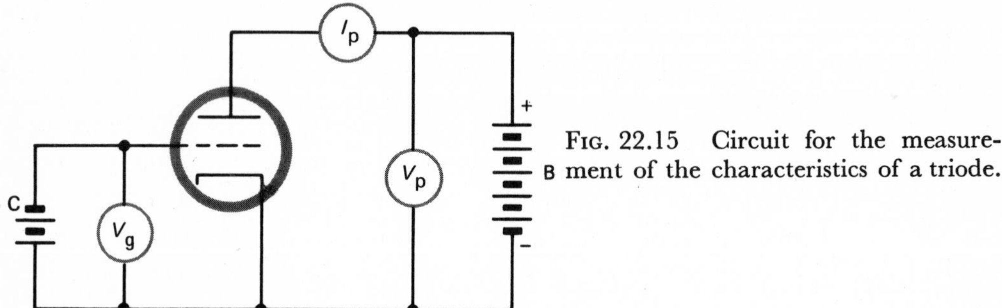

FIG. 22.15 Circuit for the measurement of the characteristics of a triode.

voltmeters V_g and V_p measure the grid and plate potentials, respectively, and the ammeter I_p measures the current to the plate. Our series of experiments now consists of choosing a succession of values for V_p and for each of these values determining the variation of the plate current I_p for various values of the grid voltage V_g. The results of a typical experiment of this type are shown in Fig. 22.16, in which the plate current I_p (in milliamperes) is plotted against V_g

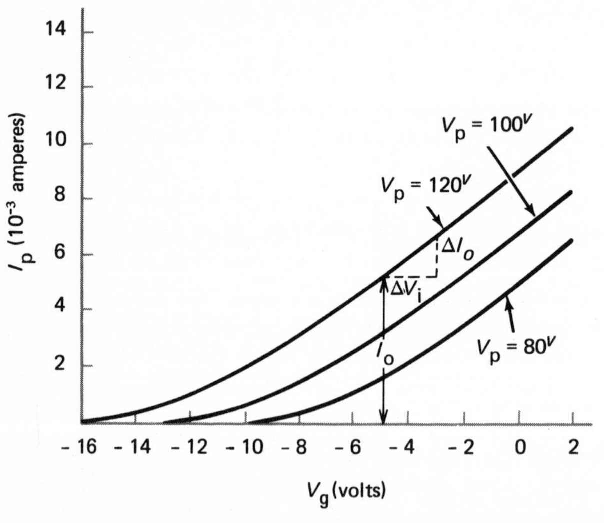

FIG. 22.16 Characteristic curves for a triode.

(in volts) for three different values of V_p (in volts). Examining the curve for $V_p =$ 120 V, we see that I_p is zero when V_g is below about -15.6 V. As V_g is raised above this value (i.e., as the grid becomes less negative with respect to the cathode), the current I_p increases steadily. The voltage V_g at which I_p just ceases is the grid cut-off voltage for the given value of V_p and is -15.6 V in the case we have just discussed. For $V_p = 100$ V and $V_p = 80$ V the same sort of variation takes place, I_p increases as V_g increases, but we notice that the grid cut-off voltage increases (i.e., becomes less negative) as V_p decreases, and that for a given V_g, the plate current I_p increases as V_p increases.

The curves of Fig. 22.16 are the result of an experiment on one particular type of tube. A different type of tube will give different cut-off values and curves of different shape and slope, but the general features will be the same. One of the problems of tube design involves the appropriate choice of cathode, grid shape, and plate shape so that the resulting tube will have characteristics suitable for the application which the designer has in mind.

When V_g is negative, the grid will repel electrons so that none will strike it and no current will flow in the grid circuit. Consequently, all that the battery C will be required to do is to keep the grid G at a given potential, without supplying it with any current. This, of course, is essentially an expression of the rectifying property of the diode. For this reason, we need only a very small current to make a large change in the potential V_g of the grid, and this can produce a large change in the plate current I_p. This current is supplied by the battery B, and the triode can therefore be used in such a way that small amounts of power supplied to the grid can control large amounts of power from the battery. This leads us to one of the most important applications of the triode, which will be discussed in Sec. 22.14.

22.12 Solid State Rectifiers

When a metal and a semiconductor, or two semiconductors with different properties, are brought into contact, it is often found that the system behaves differently for currents in opposite directions. In many cases the resistance to currents in one direction is a thousand times as great as that to currents in the other. Hence such junctions can be used as rectifiers, in much the same way that the vacuum tube diode of Sec. 22.10 is used.

Because nearly all solid state rectifiers operate on similar principles, our discussion will be limited to a single type, known as a ***p-n junction***. Such a junction is made by the use of two semiconductors such as those discussed in Sec. 21.8, one being p-type (hole conduction) and the other an n-type (electron conduction). Such units can be made of a single piece of silicon or germanium if different impurities are introduced from the two ends.

A schematic diagram of a p-n junction is shown in Fig. 22.17a. The n-type material has some free electrons, whereas the p-type material has a deficiency of electrons and so exhibits hole conduction. What happens when the two are brought in contact? We might expect some or all of the conduction electrons in the n-material to spill over into the p-material, supplying the deficiency there, i.e., filling the holes. This indeed happens, but it stops short of complete spill-over because the flow of the first electrons from n to p makes the former electrically positive and the latter negative. Each subsequent electron must move against the electrostatic forces of the resulting field, and only the most energetic electrons in n will be able to move to p. The equilibrium state of affairs is shown by the solid curve (I) in Fig. 22.17b, where the potential energy of an electron

$(-eV)$ is shown as a function of position. When this condition has been reached, only electrons with energies greater than E_0 can move across the boundary. The entire change of potential takes place in a very thin layer near the interface of the two materials, because charges can reside only on the surface of a conducting material (Sec. 16.21).* A few electrons will have energy enough to

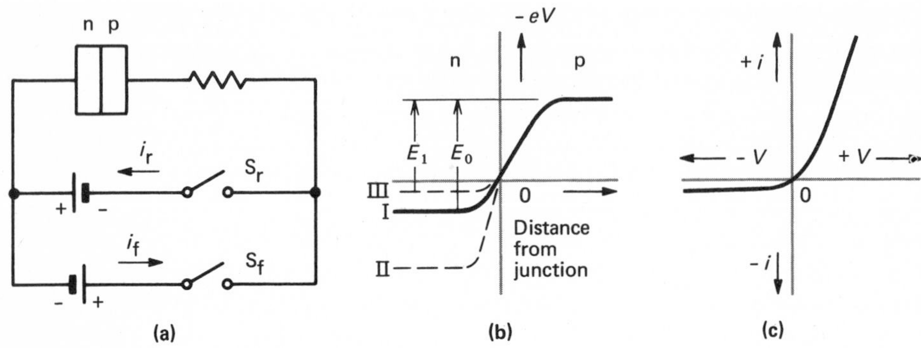

FIG. 22.17 The n-p junction rectifier: (a) circuit diagram, (b) potential energy curves for electrons, (c) current-voltage curve.

climb the potential hill and get across, but the p material has some free electrons as well as holes, so there will be a small reverse current of electrons. When the two currents are equal—when the potential hill holds back most of the electrons from the densely populated n-region and helps those from the rarely populated p region—equilibrium will be established and there will be no net flow. The situation is very much like that discussed in connection with vaporization (Secs. 11.15 and 21.16).

Suppose that the switch S_r in Fig. 22.17a is closed, so that the battery raises the potential of n. The situation is then that shown by the dashed curve (II) in Fig. 22.17b. The movement of electrons from n to p is further inhibited, but that from p to n is unaffected, because every electron that approaches the junction from the p side gets carried across by the field, as it did before. We remember that this current is small, because of the paucity of electrons in p. Hence a small reverse current, i_r, will flow when the junction is connected like this.

Now suppose that S_r is open and S_f is closed so that n is made more negative with respect to p than it was with the switch open. The situation is then that shown by the dotted curve (III). Electrons having kinetic energy greater than E_1 can now move across the junction from n to p. Because there are many such electrons, the ***forward current***, i_f, will be much greater than was the backward current i_r. The current will continue, since the battery supplies electrons to n as

* The "surface" of a material is not a mathematical surface of zero thickness. It extends many atomic distances into the material, just as in a liquid in which the asymmetrical forces that cause surface tension are apparent for molecules slightly below the surface.

fast as they spill over to p. We thus see that the p-n junction has rectifying properties. A typical curve of current through the junction vs. potential difference across it is shown in Fig. 22.17c, where the positive directions of i and V are those that exist when S_f is closed and S_r is open.

22.13 The Transistor

The p-n junction acts very much like the vacuum tube diode. We might therefore wonder if a combination of such junctions might behave somewhat like the vacuum tubes discussed in Sec. 22.11. This is indeed true. Many combinations, in fact, are possible. The resulting devices are called ***transistors.*** Transistors were invented by three American physicists, John Bardeen (1908–), Walter Brattain (1902–), and William Shockley (1910–). We shall consider only a single kind, the **n-p-n** ***transistor.***

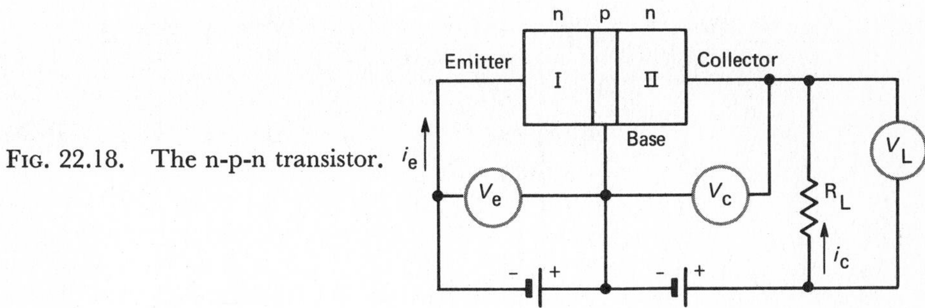

FIG. 22.18. The n-p-n transistor.

Consider the block of semiconducting material shown in Fig. 22.18. It consists of a thin layer of p-type material sandwiched between two layers of n-type. Three metal electrodes are connected to the semiconductor. One of these, connected to p is called the ***base***, the others, each connected to one of the two samples of n, are known as the ***emitter*** and the ***collector***. The emitter is maintained at a voltage, relative to the base, that is in the forward direction; the collector is maintained at a voltage, again relative to the base, in the reverse direction. Therefore, a change in the voltage of the emitter will have a much larger effect on the current through the emitter than the same change in the voltage of the collector will have on the current through the collector.

In a well designed n-p-n transistor, the p-type material is doped much less heavily than the n-type. It therefore has a relatively high resistivity. Hence, when a change ΔV_e is made in the emitter voltage, the additional emitter current $-\Delta i_e$ passes almost entirely across the thin p section and across boundary II, instead of over the long path from boundary I to the base. One of the most important characteristics is the ***current multiplication factor***,

$$\alpha = -\frac{di_c}{di_e}. \qquad (22.13\text{-}1)$$

This factor is always less than unity, but for a good transistor, operated at the proper voltages, it is very close to one.

The behavior of a transistor is similar to that of a vacuum tube; the emitter, like the cathode, supplies electrons (or holes); the base, like the grid, determines what fraction of these electrons pass on; and the collector, like the plate, acts as a receiver of the charged particles. It follows that transistors and vacuum tubes may be used for the same purposes, some of which are taken up in the next section.

There are many types of transistors other than the n-p-n that we have discussed. For example, a **p-n-p** ***transistor*** has a thin layer of n-type semiconductor sandwiched between two layers of p-type. In ***point contact transistors*** a single kind of semiconductor is used. The emitter in this case is a metallic wire that contacts the semiconductor, as is the collector. Details of these and other transistors cannot be given here but the foregoing discussion should enable the reader to follow the growing literature on transistors. Transistors are shown in circuit diagrams by the symbol shown in Fig. 22.19.

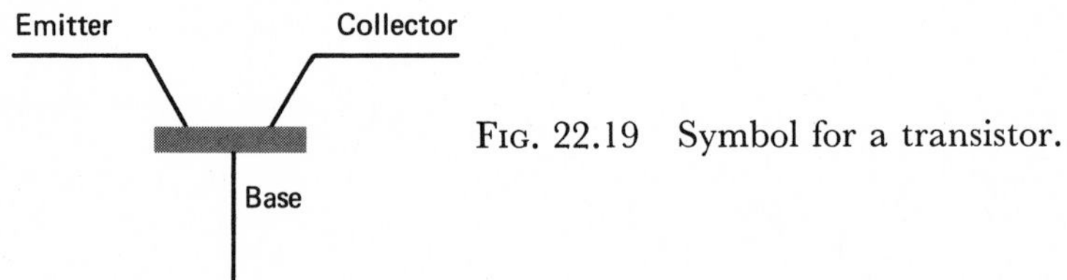

FIG. 22.19 Symbol for a transistor.

22.14 Amplifiers

The last few sections have described two devices, the triode vacuum tube and the transistor, that have common characteristics. (1) Each has three terminals. (2) An electrical signal applied across two of these terminals causes a change in the various currents. (3) In both cases the signal requires very little power: in the vacuum tube the negative potential of the grid prevents almost all electrons from reaching it; hence there is very little current between the cathode and the grid; in the transistor the resistance between the emitter and the base is low, so little voltage is required. (4) The current between the cathode and the plate, or between the base and the collector, is supplied by a battery that can deliver power. Hence the low power signal applied to the other pair of terminals can be used to control a larger amount of power delivered by the battery. The behavior of either device may be compared to that of an automobile, in which the signal is the movement of the accelerator pedal, which requires very little power but that produces large changes in the power output from the engine. Here the gasoline tank corresponds to the battery that furnishes the power in the plate or collector circuit.

Either of these devices (or variants of them, such as vacuum tubes containing more than three electrodes) may be used in the construction of an ***amplifier***. The simplest electronic amplifier circuits are shown in Fig. 22.20a and b. The applied signal, identified as V_i, is called the ***input***. The current produced through

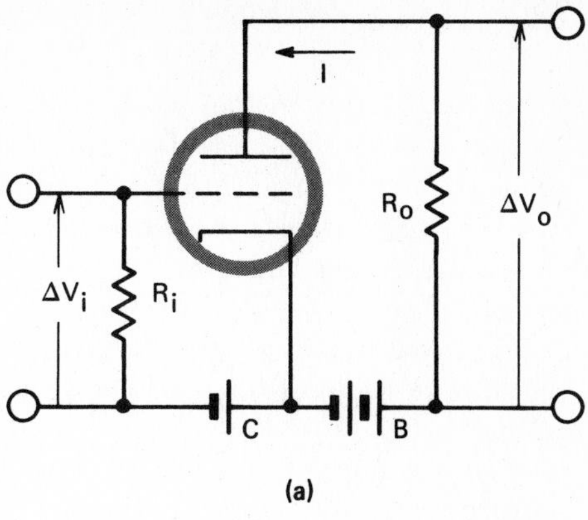

Fig. 22.20 Simple amplifiers.

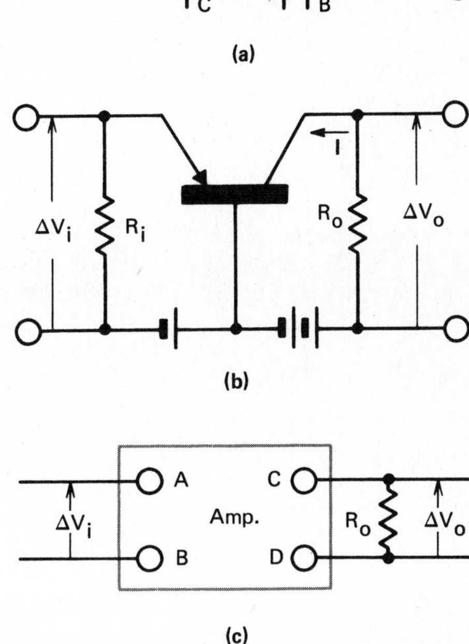

some ***load***, which may be a resistor connected in series with the battery and the plate or collector, produces a change in potential difference V_0, across the load. This change is called the ***output voltage***.

If we have chosen the grid potential relative to the cathode in Fig. 22.20a properly, it is possible to have the tube operating on the portion of its characteristic that is essentially a straight line (see Fig. 22.16). Then the change in the current through the load, ΔI, is proportional to V_i and

$$V_o = R_o \, \Delta I = k_v V_i, \tag{22.14-1}$$

where k_v is a constant for a given choice of the tube, the grid and plate potentials, and the magnitude of the lead resistance. This constant is called the ***voltage gain*** of the amplifier.

Similarly, if we have chosen the emitter and collector potentials properly, Eq. (22.14-1) will apply equally well to the circuit of Fig. 22.20b.

Because we need not interest ourselves at this time in the details of amplifier circuits, we shall consider the amplifier to consist of a "black box" having four terminals, as shown in Fig. 22.20c. The input signal is applied across A and B, and the load is connected to C and D. Inside the box there are the tube(s) or transistor(s), the source of output power, the input resistor, and any other components of the amplifier circuit other than R_0. In the simple amplifiers shown in Fig. 22.20a and b, terminals B and D are electrically connected, but this is not necessarily true for all amplifiers. For example, A and B might be connected to the primary of a transformer in an amplifier intended only for alternating current use, the secondary of the transformer connecting the cathode and grid, or the base and emitter.

We may notice that the grid and plate voltages in Fig. 22.20a are

$$V_g = V_c + V_i \qquad \text{and} \qquad V_p = V_B - R_o I, \tag{22.14-2}$$

respectively, where V_c is the ***quiescent*** grid voltage (the value of V_g when no signal is applied) and V_p is the potential difference maintained by the battery B. Similarly, the emitter and collector voltages in Fig. 22.20b are

$$V_e = V_E + V_i \qquad \text{and} \qquad V_c = V_B - R_o I, \tag{22.14-3}$$

respectively, where V_E is the quiescent emitter voltage and V_B has the same meaning as in Eq. (22.14-2). (See Prob. 22.10.)

22.15 The Electronic Oscillator

The fact that an amplifier can deliver appreciable power to a load as a result of an input signal of low power provides just what is needed to maintain oscillations of constant amplitude and predetermined frequency to the parallel resonant circuit of Sec. 22.9. Consider the circuit of Fig. 22.21. The load of the

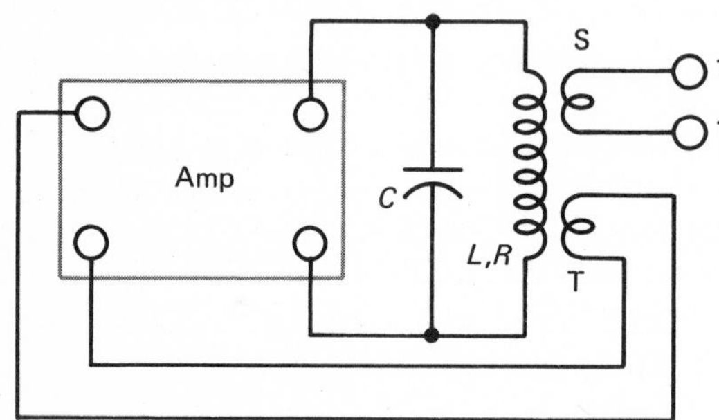

FIG. 22.21 An oscillator circuit.

amplifier here consists of a parallel resonant circuit made up of the inductance L, R and the capacitance C. We have labeled the inductance L, R (rather than L) because any inductance we can make will have a resistance. We try, however, to keep this as small as possible. Oscillations of large magnitude can be maintained in a parallel circuit by a small input voltage applied to its terminals (Sec. 22.9). Suppose that any disturbance, such as that produced by the initial connection of the batteries, starts an oscillation in the parallel circuit, which is called the ***tank circuit***. Were it not for the rest of the oscillator circuit, this oscillation would die down rapidly due to the loss of energy in R. In the arrangement shown in the figure, a small ***tickler coil*** T is placed near (L, R) so that it becomes the secondary of a transformer of which (L, R) is the primary. The oscillations, which have the natural radian frequency $\omega_0 = 1/\sqrt{LC}$, therefore induce voltages of the same frequency in T, and these voltages are applied to the grid of the vacuum tube. They are amplified by the tube, and the resulting larger oscillations in the plate voltage are applied to the tank circuit. By appropriate electrical and mechanical arrangements, it is possible to insure that the varying voltage impressed on the grid has the proper phase so that it reinforces the original oscillation that started the process. The vacuum tube therefore acts like the escapement of a pendulum clock, since it supplies energy (from the power source within Amp) to the tank circuit to keep that circuit oscillating, while the frequency of oscillation is determined by the constants of the tank circuit.

In order to use this oscillator as a source of alternating current, we can introduce a second coil S into the field of (L, R) to form another transformer secondary. The alternating emf induced in S can then be used directly to produce an alternating current, but more frequently this emf is fed into an amplifier such as one of those of Fig. 22.20, and the output of the amplifier is then used as a source of alternating current.

The chief advantages of the electronic oscillators described here results from the fact that the frequency can be adjusted over a very wide range by appropriate choice of L and C [cf. Eq. (22.8-7)]. This type of oscillator can be made to produce frequencies from a few hundred cycles to several million cycles per second. Other types of electron tube oscillators can produce frequencies as low as one or two cycles per minute and as high as 100 or 200 billion ($1\text{–}2 \times 10^{11}$) cycles per second.

The oscillators that we have just been discussing are of the greatest importance in modern scientific work and in modern technology. We shall see in the next chapter that they have many applications in radio and in television transmission. In addition there are many scientific applications. For example, the cyclotron and synchrotron of Chapter 19 could not be operated without oscillators, which provide the rapid alternations of potential necessary to provide the field reversals for the dees.

22.16 Summary

This chapter has dealt with a large number of systems, both mechanical and electrical, that have the common characteristic that they will continue to oscillate, with a motion that is at least approximately periodic, after they are disturbed. All such systems involve the storage of energy in two forms, and the oscillation results from an exchange between these two forms. In mechanical oscillators the energy can be *kinetic* or *potential*; in electrical oscillators the forms are *electric* and *magnetic*. Electric oscillators involve the flow of current through an inductor, and magnetic oscillators use the storage of charge on a capacitor.

A consideration of the energy exchange has enabled us to determine the frequency of oscillation of the free oscillator, to account for the damping of the oscillations as a result of dissipation of energy by friction or Joule heating, and to predict the behavior of systems that are acted upon by periodic forces at frequencies other than the natural frequency. We have dealt first with idealized systems but have later seen that many real systems approximate these idealized ones very closely.

Finally, after a digression on vacuum tubes, transistors, and electronic amplifiers, we have come upon ways in which electrical oscillations of predetermined frequency can be maintained in electrical circuits.

PROBLEMS

22.1 Suppose that a straight tunnel were bored through the earth between two points, both at latitude $90° - \theta$ and with longitudes differing by 180°. Neglect temperature effects and friction. A mass m is dropped into one end of the hole.

(a) Find the component of force on m that is in the direction of the hole when the mass is at a distance x from the axis of the earth.

(b) Show that the mass will undergo SHM and find the period of the oscillation. (Hint: See Ex. 22.2-6.)

22.2 In a simple apparatus such as that illustrated in Fig. 9.6, assume that the piston has a mass m and an area S exposed to a liquid with volume V. Calculate the period of oscillation of this piston in terms of the bulk modulus of the liquid.

22.3 Suppose that an open-ended U-tube of the type shown in Fig. 9.11 is filled with a single homogeneous liquid. Suppose also that the liquid is temporarily depressed on one side, say by a piston, so that the liquid stands at different levels in the two sides, as in Fig. 9.11. There will then be an unbalanced force [$(h_B - h_A) \cdot A\rho g$, where ρ is the density of the liquid and A is the cross-sectional area of the tube]. Show that, when the piston is removed, the level of the liquid in either side will oscillate with a period $\pi\sqrt{2L/g}$, where L is the total length of the liquid in the tube. Hint: Set $x = (h_B - h_A)$ as a variable, and consider the potential energy of the liquid column.

22.4 It was shown in Sec. 22.6 that the maximal velocity amplitude of a forced oscillator occurs at resonance, i.e., when $\omega = \omega_0$.

(a) At what value of ω does maximal displacement amplitude (X) occur? (b) How does X vary with ω (for a given force amplitude F_0) when $\omega \gg \omega_0$? (c) What is the value of X/F_0 when $\omega \approx 0$? (d) How does X vary with ω (for a given F_0) when ω is such that $\omega_0 \gg \omega > 0$?

22.5 You wish to find the moment of inertia of a body that has an axis of symmetry, but otherwise does not have a mass distribution that is convenient for calculation. The body is suspended from a rigid support by a wire in line with its axis of symmetry and is set into torsional oscillation. The period of oscillation is found to be τ_0. The body is then replaced by a uniform cylinder of mass m, radius r, and length L, and the period of oscillation is found to be τ_1. What is the moment of inertia of the body?

22.6 A ***bifilar pendulum*** is constructed in the following manner: Two strings hang vertically from a horizontal ceiling. They are separated by a distance D and they support a uniform rod of length $L(L > D)$, and mass M at a level H below the ceiling. The system is set into oscillation by rotating the rod about a vertical axis through its center of mass, through an angle θ_0. At $t = 0$ the rod is released from the rest.

(a) Show that the rod will oscillate with rotary SHM. (b) Show that the natural radian frequency of the oscillation is $(D/L)(g/H)^{1/2}$, where g is the acceleration due to gravity.

22.7 A galvanometer of the type shown in Fig. 16.21 has a rectangular coil of N turns. The mass of the coil is m, its width is a, its height is b, and its resistance is R_c. The sensitivity of the galvanometer is G. When the galvanometer is disturbed, the coil oscillates with a period τ and with very little damping.

(a) What is the magnitude of the magnetic flux density in the neighborhood of the coil?

(b) What is the torsional constant of the suspension?

(c) When the instantaneous angular velocity of the coil about the vertical axis is Ω, what emf is induced in the coil?

(d) A resistance R is now connected across the terminals of the galvanometer. It is found that the period of oscillation is essentially the same as it was when the galvanometer was on open circuit, but the motion is now damped so that the amplitude of any swing is 0.90 of that of the previous swing. Explain and calculate the value of R in terms of the quantities given above.

22.8 Comment on the following three statements:

(a) When ω is very small compared with ω_0, a series *L-C-R* circuit is ***capacitance controlled.***

(b) When ω is very close to ω_0, the circuit is ***resistance controlled.***

(c) When ω is very much greater than ω_0, the circuit is ***inductance controlled.***

22.9 Consider an idealized circuit of the type shown in Fig. 22.9, with $R=0$. The circuit is connected in series with an oscillator that maintains a periodic potential difference, $V = V_0 \cos \omega t$, across its terminals. Here V_0 and ω are constants. The natural radian frequency of the L-C circuit is ω_0.

(a) Show that the current in the circuit lags the voltage by $\pi/2$ if $\omega > \omega_0$.

(b) Show that the current in the circuit leads the voltage by $\pi/2$ if $\omega < \omega_0$.

22.10 Suppose that the amplifier of Fig. 22.20a contains a triode such that the plate current can be expressed as

$$I = \sigma(V_g + V_p/\mu),$$

where σ and μ are constants, over some range of the grid voltage V_g and the plate voltage V_p. (σ is called the ***transconductance*** of the tube, and μ is the ***amplification factor.***) In the following calculations, suppose that V_g and V_p always remain in the range in which the expression for I is valid. Suppose that a signal ΔV_i is applied to the amplifier so that the grid voltage changes from V_g to $(V_g + \Delta V_i)$. As a result, the plate current changes to $I + \Delta I$.

(a) Show that $V_p = V_B - (I + \Delta I)R_o$, where V_B is the potential difference across the battery B.

(b) Find ΔI as a function of σ, μ, and R_o.

(c) Show that the voltage gain, $-\Delta V_o/\Delta V_i$, of the amplifier is $\mu\sigma R_o/(1+\sigma R_o)$.

(d) Show that the change in the power delivered to the load as a result of the signal being applied is approximately $2I\,\Delta I\,R_o$, if $\Delta I \ll I$.

(e) Show that the maximal power is delivered to the load for a given ΔV_i if $R_o = \mu/\sigma$.

22.11 By considering the energy delivered to an inductance L while the current through it is changing from I to $I + \Delta I$, verify Eq. (22.8-6).

REFERENCES

22A R. M. Kerchner and G. F. Corcoran, *Alternating Current Circuits*, 4th edition, Wiley, New York, 1960. An extensive treatment of the subject.

22B William Francis Magie, *A Source Book of Physics*, Harvard, Cambridge, Mass., 1963. Pages 1–22 recount Galileo's work with pendulums.

22C Harry Ferdinand Olson, *Dynamical Analogies*, 2nd edition, Van Nostrand, Princeton, 1958. Particularly relevant to Sec. 22.8.

22D Leon F. Phillips, *Electronics for Experimenters*, Wiley, New York, 1966. A descriptive treatment of vacuum tubes, transistors, and electronic circuits.

22E Bernhard Kurrelmeyer and Walter H. Mais, *Electricity and Magnetism*, Van Nostrand, Princeton, 1967. Chapters 14 and 15 extend the treatment of alternating current circuits.

23 ⇒ *Electromagnetic Waves*

23.1 The Conditions Necessary for Wave Propagation

In Chapter 10 we investigated the behavior of both transverse and longitudinal waves in elastic materials. The mechanism by which such waves are propagated involves the elastic forces set up in the matter by the motion of its particles. These forces accelerate adjacent particles, and the strain thus set up in the matter results in the further spread of the elastic forces. Thus a disturbance started at one point spreads to neighboring points, causing the phenomenon of wave motion.

Although the detailed picture of elastic forces and accelerations is a convenient one, it is also possible to describe a wave in terms of the energy considerations involved. From this point of view the motion of the material particles involves kinetic energy, and the elastic strains involve potential energy (cf. Secs. 22.1 and 22.8 for discussions of oscillators on this basis). It was, in fact, this energetic approach that we used in Secs. 10.3 and 10.4 to derive an expression for the speed of propagation of a longitudinal wave. This line of argument might lead us to expect that waves can travel in any medium in which both potential and kinetic energies can be stored simultaneously.

In the present chapter, we shall show that the electrical analogues of potential and kinetic energies, i.e., electrostatic and electromagnetic energies, can exist in dielectric materials or even in free space. An interplay between these two types of energy, similar to that between potential and kinetic energies in an elastic medium, may take place. Consequently, electromagnetic waves may be set up and may travel through dielectric materials or through empty space. We shall be able to deduce some of the properties of these waves and to show their applications. Among other things, we shall demonstrate that the light and heat waves discussed in Chapter 12 are identical with these electromagnetic waves.

23.2 The Localization of Electric Energy

The charging of a capacitor represents the storage of potential energy (Sec. 22.8). We may now ask where this energy is located when the capacitor is charged. For simplicity, we shall limit our discussion to a plane parallel plate capacitor (Sec. 16.22). Suppose that the capacitor shown in Fig. 23.1 carries a charge Q, that each plate has an area A, that the distance between the plates is d, and that the space between the plates is filled with a material of permittivity

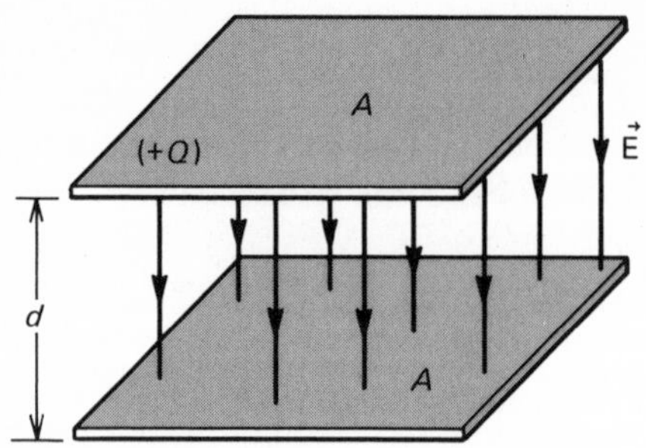

FIG. 23.1 Energy density in a parallel-plate capacitor.

ε. We know from Eq. (22.8-5) that the electric energy associated with the charge is

$$U_e = \tfrac{1}{2}Q^2/C, \tag{23.2-1}$$

where C is the capacitance of the capacitor. This expression can be put into a more convenient form if we remember from Sec. 16.22 that the capacitance is

$$C = \varepsilon A/d \tag{23.2-2}$$

and that the electric field strength between the plates is

$$E = V/d = Q/Cd = Q/\varepsilon A \tag{23.2-3}$$

or that

$$Q = \varepsilon AE.$$

If the values of C and Q are substituted into Eq. (23.2-1), it is found that the electric energy may be expressed as

$$U_e = \tfrac{1}{2}\varepsilon AdE^2.$$

This evaluation of the energy becomes particularly meaningful if we notice that the product Ad is exactly the volume v between the plates of the capacitor. The electric field strength E is uniform throughout the volume between the plates (Sec. 16.22). If we now suppose that the energy is stored in the electric field itself, we come to the conclusion that the energy of the capacitor is distributed uniformly over the volume v, and that the ***electric energy density*** is

$$u_e = U_e/v = \tfrac{1}{2}\varepsilon E^2. \tag{23.2-4}$$

Since the whole field of an ideal parallel plate capacitor is localized between the plates, the acceptance of Eq. (23.2-4) as a general expression for the electric energy density is completely consistent with Eq. (23.2-1), which has summarized our previous knowledge of the energy of a charged capacitor. It is true that we have considered only the relatively simple case of a plane parallel plate capacitor, but more general calculations, with a slightly greater degree of complexity than we have used here, show that Eqs. (23.2-1) and (23.2-4) are completely consistent for all types of capacitor.

The idea suggested by Eq. (23.2-4) is one that we shall find to be extremely useful. According to it, energy is stored throughout any space in which an electric field exists, the density of the energy at any point being that given by the equation. The reader may find it helpful to compare this idea with that of the storage of energy in a compressed piece of elastic matter. When a force is applied to compress the material, work is done. This work is transformed to potential energy (cf. Sec. 9.4). Since the elastic strain exists throughout the volume of the material, we can say that the energy is also distributed throughout the volume, and that it will remain there as long as the matter is compressed. Similarly, the charging of a capacitor, which requires work, leads to the creation of an electric field, with which energy is associated, and this energy will remain spread throughout the volume over which the field exists as long as the capacitor is charged. One difference between the two cases is that empty space, as well as matter, can store electrical energy. Had a vacuum existed between the plates of this capacitor, the treatment would have been unchanged except for the use of the particular value ε_0 for the permittivity of free space. Hence the energy density in free space is

$$u_e = U_e/v = \tfrac{1}{2}\varepsilon_0 E^2. \qquad (23.2\text{-}5)$$

23.3 The Localization of Magnetic Energy

The rather neat picture which we obtained for the location of the electric energy in the region of the electric field suggests that a similar concept may hold for magnetic energy. We learned in Sec. 22.8 that a current I flowing in an inductance L possesses a magnetic energy [cf. Eq. (22.8-6) and Prob. 22.11].

$$U_m = \tfrac{1}{2}LI^2. \qquad (23.3\text{-}1)$$

A case which involves magnetic energy, in about as simple a way as the plane parallel plate capacitor involves electric energy, is that of the long solenoid discussed in Sec. 16.10. We know that the flux of such a solenoid is concentrated within the solenoid, that the flux density inside is uniform, and that it has the magnitude [cf. Eq. (16.10-1)]

$$B = \mu NI/l, \qquad (23.3\text{-}2)$$

where μ is the permeability of the medium, N is the number of turns, I is the current flowing, and l is the length of the solenoid.

It was shown in Chapter 17, Ex. (17.11-4), that the self-inductance of this solenoid is

$$L = \mu N^2 A/l, \qquad (23.3\text{-}3)$$

where $A(=\pi r^2)$ is the cross-sectional area of the solenoid and μ has been substituted for μ_0 to allow the possibility of a magnetic medium inside the solenoid. We now write Eq. (23.3-2) in the form $I = lB/\mu N$ and substitute this value for the current in Eq. (23.3-1), together with the value of L from Eq. (23.3-3). We then obtain

$$U_m = \tfrac{1}{2}(\mu N^2 A/l)(lB/\mu N)^2 = \tfrac{1}{2}AlB^2/\mu. \qquad (23.3\text{-}4)$$

Since the volume within the solenoid, and therefore the volume v within which the uniform field is concentrated, is Al, the magnetic energy may be considered to be spread over this volume, the ***magnetic energy density*** at any point being given by

$$u_m = U_m/v = \tfrac{1}{2}B^2/\mu. \qquad (23.3\text{-}5)$$

In particular, if the magnetic field exists in a vacuum, the magnetic inductive capacity is μ_0 and the energy density is

$$u_m = U_m/v = \tfrac{1}{2}B^2/\mu_0. \qquad (23.3\text{-}6)$$

We thus see that magnetic energy, like electric energy, can be considered to be spread over the space in which a magnetic field exists. Detailed treatments of more complicated cases than that of the solenoid confirm this conclusion, but we cannot enter into them here.

23.4 The Interaction of Electric and Magnetic Fields

Having established the existence of energy in the electric and magnetic fields, we now ask whether the two types of energy interact like the potential and kinetic energies in an elastic wave. If so, a magnetic disturbance must lead to the creation of an electric field.

The creation of an electric field by a magnetic disturbance has already been treated in some detail in Chapter 17, particularly in Secs. 17.5–17.7. We saw there that any change in a magnetic field always leads to an induced electromotive force, whether or not a closed conducting circuit exists at the location of the change. Two of the conclusions which we reached in Chapter 17 will be of particular value to us here:

1. The electric field is always at right angles to the direction in which the magnetic field is changing.
2. The magnitude of the electric field is proportional to the time rate of change of the magnetic flux density.

In order to find whether the analogous effect, the creation of a magnetic field by an electrical disturbance, takes place, we shall have to repeat an argument due to James Clark Maxwell (1831–1879). Consider the circuit shown in Fig. 23.2. With the switch open, as shown, no charge resides on the capacitor and

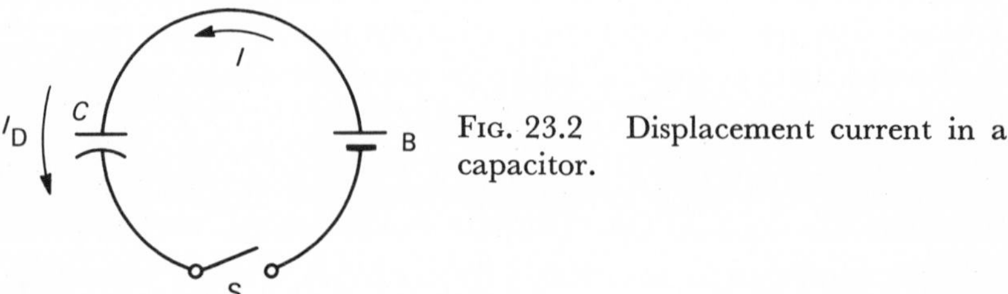

FIG. 23.2 Displacement current in a capacitor.

there is no current in the circuit. If the switch S is now closed, the capacitor C will begin to acquire a charge and will continue to do so until the potential difference across it exactly balances the emf of the battery B. During this charging process, there is a current in the battery and in the wires connecting it to the capacitor. If the magnitude of this current at any instant is I, the law of the conservation of electricity tells us that the rate at which charge is building up and on the capacitor is

$$dQ/dt = I. \tag{23.4-1}$$

It occurred to Maxwell that the process of the charging of a capacitor could be visualized in another way. According to this concept, the conservation law is satisfied by a ***displacement current*** between the plates of the capacitor, this displacement current being exactly equal to the current flowing in the wires connected to the capacitor. While the capacitor is charging, the electric field between the plates is building up, and the displacement current is intimately related to the rate at which this field changes. To establish the relationship, we first notice that the field, at a time when the charge on the capacitor is Q, is given by Eq. (23.2-3) as

$$E = Q/\varepsilon A,$$

where ε is the permittivity and A is the area of the plates. It follows at once that the electric displacement (Sec. 15.7) in the region is

$$D = \varepsilon E = Q/A,$$

and that the time rate of change of the displacement is

$$dD/dt = (dQ/dt)/A.$$

Multiplying both sides of the equation by A and recollecting Eq. (23.4-1), we find that the electric flux Ψ is changing at a rate

$$\Delta\Psi/\Delta t = A(dD/dt) = dQ/dt = I, \tag{23.4-2}$$

so that the current to the capacitor is equal to the time rate of change of electric flux within the capacitor.

We have now shown that the current which flows during the charging of a capacitor can be expressed in terms of the rate at which the electric flux is changing within the condenser. We can satisfy the conservation law by saying that the circuit of Fig. 23.2 is equivalent to a circuit composed entirely of conductors carrying a uniform current I. This would be equivalent to saying that the displacement current I_D within the capacitor, equal to $A\ (dD/dt)$, has all the properties of a real current, in which charges are moving. If this is true, a circuit of the type shown in Fig. 23.2 should produce the same magnetic field as a circuit with the same geometry but with a wire replacing the capacitor, provided that the currents are identical. This prediction is indeed verified experimentally, indicating that Maxwell's idea has physical meaning and that it expresses more than just a mathematical accident.

After he arrived at an expression equivalent to Eq. (23.4-2), Maxwell carried the argument forward by another step. Since the field within the plane parallel plate capacitor is uniform, we can also express this idea by saying that the displacement current per unit area, or the ***displacement current density,*** everywhere between the plates is

$$i_D = I_D/A = dD/dt. \tag{23.4-3}$$

Maxwell supposed that such a displacement current occurred not only within a capacitor, but at any time and place characterized by a change in the electric flux density. Following his reasoning, we may take Eq. (23.4-3) as a general expression for the displacement current density, thereby removing all connection with the plane parallel plate capacitor, which we have used merely as a convenience in the derivation.

As soon as we accept the idea of displacement currents, we see that *any change in an electric field must produce a magnetic field in the neighborhood.* In Sec. 16.10 we investigated the magnetic fields that resulted from various configurations of currents. A reexamination of that section will show that, in every case investigated, two general rules were followed:

1. In the immediate neighborhood of a current the magnetic field is at right angles to the direction of current flow.
2. The magnitude of the magnetic flux density, and therefore of the magnetic field, is proportional to the current.

Now suppose that the electric field at some point of space is changing in strength. The electric displacement will also be changing and, according to the idea of displacement current, the effect will be identical with that of a current in the direction in which the change is taking place. Consequently the two rules just stated can be rephrased to read as follows:

1. In the immediate neighborhood of a changing electric field, there is set up a magnetic field at right angles to the direction in which the electric field is changing.
2. The magnetic field strength is proportional to the time rate of change of the electric displacement and therefore to the time rate of change of the electric field.

The similarity of these two statements to the rules given at the beginning of this section for the production of an electric field by a changing magnetic field is obvious. We may therefore conclude that the interaction between electric and magnetic fields is a quite symmetrical one.

EXERCISES

23.4-1 A capacitor of capacitance C carries a charge Q. Its terminals are then connected by a resistance, allowing the charge to leak off. State qualitatively what becomes of the energy that was stored in the charged capacitor.

23.4-2 A plane parallel plate capacitor with air for a dielectric has plates of area A and separation d. It is connected to a battery that maintains a potential difference V across its terminals until it is fully charged, after which the battery is disconnected. Find the charge on the capacitor, and the energy stored. The plates of the capacitor are then separated to a new distance d', the charge remaining constant. Calculate the new potential difference across the capacitor and the amount of energy present.

23.4-3 What is the source of the additional energy added to the capacitor of 23.4-2 by the separation of the plates? What can you deduce about the force between the plates of a charged capacitor? Is this deduction consistent with your knowledge of electrostatics?

23.4-4 A plane parallel plate capacitor of capacitance C carries a charge Q. A resistance R is connected across its terminals. By applying Ohm's law to the resistance, show that the instantaneous current in it is Q/RC.

23.4-5 Suppose that the current found in Ex. 23.4-4 flows for a very short time dt. By calculating the magnitude of the electric displacement between the capacitor plates before and after the current flow, find the displacement current density during this time and show that the total displacement current during discharge is identical with the external current.

23.5 Maxwell's Equations

Before going on with our discussion of the electromagnetic wave, it will be worth while to recapitulate the relations between electric and magnetic fields and their relation to their sources, i.e., to the charges and currents that produce them.

We may start with Gauss' law (Sec. 15.8), which we have seen to be a consequence of Coulomb's law. We shall *sketch* the derivation of a more general expression of Gauss' law than those used earlier. The total charge within any

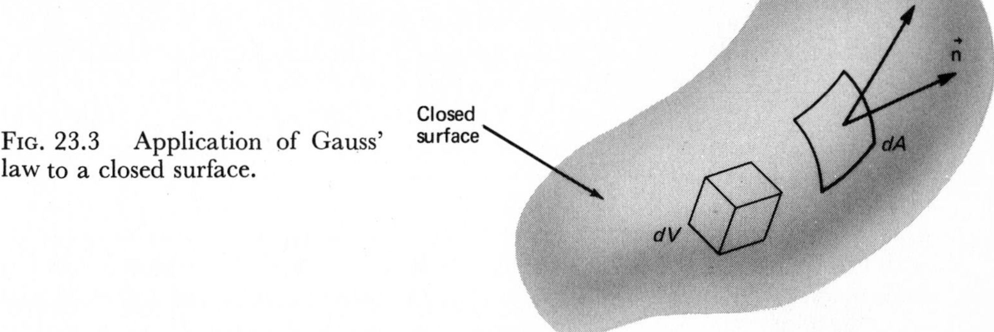

FIG. 23.3 Application of Gauss' law to a closed surface.

closed surface, such as that shown in Fig. 23.3, can be found by dividing the entire volume enclosed by the surface into small elements such as dV and assigning to each element a charge $dq = \rho\, dV$, where ρ is the charge density. The total charge within the surface can then be expressed as the integral of $\rho\, dV$, taken over the enclosed volume. Similarly, the total electric flux Ψ through the surface can be expressed as the sum of the fluxes through elements of area such as dA. The flux through this element is $\varepsilon E \cos \theta \, dA$, where ε is the permittivity of the medium in which the surface is imbedded and θ is the angle between the electric field $\vec{E}$ and the outwardly directed normal to the surface, shown as $\vec{n}$ in the figure. The total flux through the closed surface is obtained as an integral:

$$\varepsilon \int_{\text{C.S.}} E \cos \theta \, dA = \int_V \rho \, dV, \tag{23.5-1}$$

where the letters C.S. indicate that the first integral is taken over the entire closed surface, and V indicates that the second integral is taken over all of the volume enclosed by the surface.

The integrals in Eq. (23.5-1) may be easy or hard to evaluate in general, depending on the geometry, but it is often possible to use the equation by employing surfaces that are chosen for convenience.

Because the behavior of the magnetic field is so like that of the electric field (Secs. 15.11–15.13), we can write the analog of Eq. (23.5-1) by inspection. We have to remember, however, that magnets exist only as dipoles, with equal magnitudes of positive and negative "magnetic charge," so that the magnetic analog of electric charge density is everywhere zero. Hence we have

$$\int_{\text{C.S.}} B \cos \theta \, dA = 0, \tag{23.5-2}$$

where B is the magnitude of the magnetic flux density at any point on the surface and θ is the angle between $\vec{B}$ and the normal to the surface.

A third equation, which expresses the relation between the magnetic field and the currents that produce it, is based on Eq. (16.9-2):

$$\int_{\text{Around}} \vec{B} \cdot \vec{ds} = \mu I_{\text{Total through}}.$$

Here we have written μ, instead of μ_0, so that we are not restricted to empty space. We can modify this equation by expressing the current through the closed loop as the sum of currents through little elements of area, such as dA in Fig. 23.4. If the current density, i.e., the current per unit area of a surface

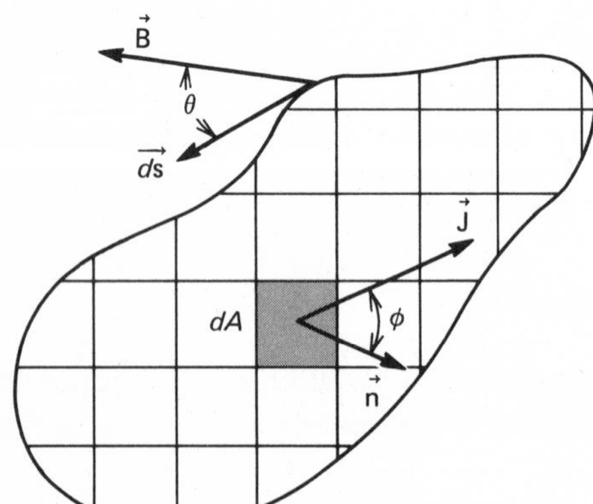

FIG. 23.4 Application of Ampère's law to a closed loop.

normal to the direction of current, is represented by $\vec{J}$, the current through dA is $J \cos \phi\, dA$, where ϕ is the angle between $\vec{J}$ and the normal to dA. The total currents through the closed loop is the integral of $J \cos \phi\, dA$, so Eq. (16.9-2) becomes

$$\int_{\text{Around}} \vec{B} \cdot \vec{ds} = \mu \int_S J \cos \phi\, dA,$$

where the letter S indicates that the integral on the right must be taken over the entire surface enclosed by the loop. Finally, we must include the displacement current density, $\vec{J}_D = \varepsilon\, d\vec{E}/dt$, because displacement currents produce magnetic fields, just as real currents do (Sec. 23.4). At the same time, we shall express the scalar product $\vec{B} \cdot \vec{ds}$ explicitly:

$$\begin{aligned} \int_{\text{Around}} B \cos \theta\, ds &= \mu \int_S (J \cos \phi\, dA + J_D \cos \chi\, dA) \\ &= \mu \int_S J \cos \phi\, dA + \mu\varepsilon(d/dt) \int_S E \cos \chi\, dA, \end{aligned} \qquad (23.5\text{-}3)$$

where χ is the angle between $\vec{E}$ and the normal to dA. We have put the derivative in front of the integral because displacement current can result from variation of area or direction, as well as of $\vec{E}$.

The last required equation comes directly from Sec. 17.7. We saw there that the emf induced in any closed loop is equal to the negative of the time rate of change of magnetic flux through the loop. We can write the emf around the

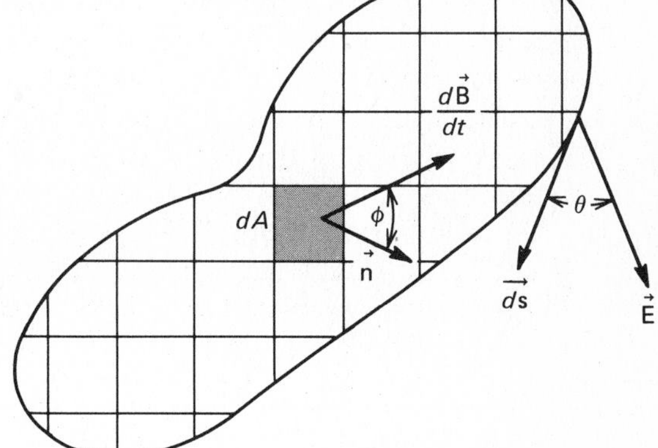

FIG. 23.5 Application of Faraday's law of induction to a closed loop.

closed loop of Fig. 23.5 as the integral of $\vec{E} \cdot \vec{ds} = E \cos \theta\, ds$, taken all the way around the loop. By the same process used in connection with Fig. 23.4, we can also express the flux through the loop as an integral, over the surface enclosed by the loop of $B \cos \phi\, dA$; so we have

$$\int_{\text{Around}} E \cos \theta\, ds = -(d/dt) \int_S B \cos \phi\, dA. \qquad (23.5\text{-}4)$$

In dealing with Eqs. (23.5-3) and (23.5-4), we must take account of the fact that the latter has a minus sign on the right and the former does not. These signs must be interpreted in terms of the right-hand rule. Suppose that we count $\vec{J}$, $d\vec{E}/dt$, and $d\vec{B}/dt$ positive when they are directed out of the paper (upward) through the loops of Figs. 23.4 and 23.5. According to the right-hand rule, then, the flux density $\vec{B}$ resulting from a positive $\vec{J}$ must be in a counter-clockwise direction at any point in the loop. The integral on the right of Eq. (23.5-3) must then be taken by going in a counter-clockwise direction around the closed loop. Put in another way, one must go around the loop keeping the inside on his left. The minus sign in Eq. (23.5-4) then indicates that $\vec{E}$ is in a direction such that any current resulting from this electric field must *oppose* the $d\vec{B}/dt$ that causes it. If we follow the rule given above, $\vec{E}$ is positive if it is in such direction that we move with it when we go around the loop counter-clockwise when we count $d\vec{B}/dt$ as positive out of the paper (upward). Hence the negative sign on the right of Eq. (23.5-4) means that we must perform the integral on the left by going around the loop clockwise, that is, by keeping the inside on our *right.*

The four equations (23.5-1) to (23.5-4) are equivalent to a set of equations obtained by James C. Maxwell in 1873. They are known as ***Maxwell's equations.*** They pack a tremendous amount of information into very little space, since, coupled with the expression for the force on a charge [Eq. (17.2-2)] and Ohm's law [Eq. (16.16-1)], they summarize almost everything known about electrical and magnetic fields.

23.6 The Mechanism of Energy Exchange

Maxwell's superb combination of logic and imagination led him to many triumphal discoveries. Among the greatest of these was his prediction that any electrical or magnetic disturbance in empty space would result in the propagation of a transverse electromagnetic wave that would travel with the speed of light. We shall now attempt to show that this prediction follows from Maxwell's equations.

Let us first write Eqs. (23.5-1) to (23.5-4) in the form that they take in empty space, i.e., in a region of permittivity ε_0 and permeability μ_0 that contains no charge and no currents. The equations then become

$$\varepsilon_0 \int_{\text{C.S.}} E \cos\theta \, dA = 0. \tag{23.6-1}$$

$$\int_{\text{C.S.}} B \cos\theta \, dA = 0. \tag{23.6-2}$$

$$\int_{\text{Around}} B \cos\theta \, ds = \varepsilon_0 \mu_0 (d/dt) \int_S E \cos\chi \, dA. \tag{23.6-3}$$

$$\int_{\text{Around}} E \cos\theta \, ds = -(d/dt) \int_S B \cos\phi \, dA. \tag{23.6-4}$$

To show that Maxwell's equations lead to interaction between the electric and magnetic fields and hence to the energy exchange mentioned in Sec. 23.1, we examine the situation indicated in Fig. 23.6. Suppose that an electric vector exists in some region of space. We may choose a coordinate system x, y, z with its x-axis parallel to $\vec{E}$. Suppose also that the magnitude of $\vec{E}$ is increasing with time, so that dE_x/dt is positive, as shown in the figure. There will then be an upward displacement current through the rectangle of width w and length l, labeled I. Equation (23.6-3) then tells us that the integral of $B \cos \theta \, ds$ around the perimeter of that rectangle cannot be zero. The magnetic flux density $\vec{B}$ therefore cannot be zero in the neighborhood; it must have either a nonvanishing y-component, a nonvanishing z-component, or both. Hence the presence of changing electric field requires the existence of a magnetic field. Further, its magnitude is proportional to dE_x/dt. Unless this derivative remains constant, $\vec{B}$ must also depend on time, and $dB_y/dt \neq 0$.

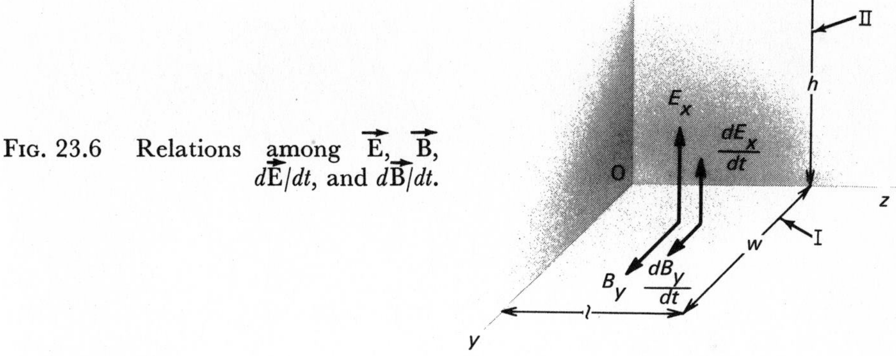

FIG. 23.6 Relations among $\vec{E}$, $\vec{B}$, $d\vec{E}/dt$, and $d\vec{B}/dt$.

We have not yet specified the direction of the y-axis. Suppose that we have chosen it, as we can do, parallel to the $\vec{B}$ that we know to be present. Then $\vec{B}$ has only one component, B_y. The fact that dB_y/dt is not zero tells us that the integral on the right-hand side of Eq. (23.6-4), taken around the rectangle, is not zero. Hence the integral on the left is not zero, and either the x-component of $\vec{E}$ or its z-component (or both) must exist. Since we have already postulated the existence of E_x, this condition has been satisfied.

Note that our first step, the production of B_y as a result of the existence of dE_x/dt, showed that a changing electric field is a *sufficient* condition for the existence of a magnetic field at right angles to it. Our second step, the production of E_x as a result of the existence of dB_y/dt, shows that the existence of the electric field is also a *necessary* condition for the existence of B_y. By interchanging the two steps, we could show that the existence of dB_y/dt is a necessary and sufficient condition for the existence of E_x.

We have not yet shown that any disturbance in the electromagnetic field will be propagated as a wave. We have merely demonstrated that there is an interaction between $\vec{E}$ and $\vec{B}$ that can result in energy being transferred from the electric field to the magnetic field, or vice-versa.

23.7 The Speed of Propagation of Electromagnetic Waves

We may show that the electromagnetic disturbance will be propagated and find the speed of propagation by an approach very similar to that used to find the speed of a longitudinal elastic wave, in Secs. 10.2–10.4. We suppose that some disturbance to the left of the *x-y* plane in Fig. 23.7 has created fields of the type shown in Fig. 23.6, with E_x and B_y the only components present. We further suppose that the disturbance at some particular instant has reached as far to the right as z_0, so that the fields everywhere to the left of that plane have constant magnitudes E_x and B_y. Everywhere to the right of z_0 they are still zero.

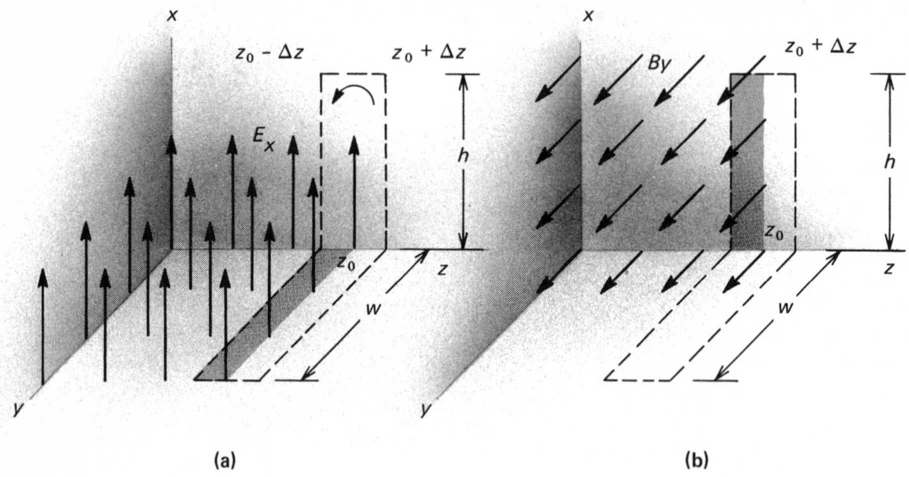

FIG. 23.7 Relations between $\vec{E}$ and $\vec{B}$.

We now consider a little rectangle, of width $2\Delta z$ along the *z*-axis and of height *h* parallel to the *x*-axis. If we consider the integral on the left side of Eq. (23.6-4), we see that the top and bottom of the rectangle make no contribution because they are perpendicular to $\vec{E}$ ($\theta = 90°$, $\cos\theta = 0$). There is no contribution from the right-hand side of the rectangle because $\vec{E}$ is zero there. Hence the integral reduces to $-E_x h$, where the minus sign results from the rule of Sec. 23.5, that we go around the rectangle in a counter-clockwise direction, i.e., in a direction opposite to $\vec{E}$ along the left-hand side of the rectangle. In evaluating the integral on the right-hand side of Eq. (23.6-4), we may note that $\vec{B}$ is nonzero only in that part of the rectangle that is shaded in Fig. 23.7b, and that it is there of constant magnitude and perpendicular to the surface ($\phi = 0$, $\cos\phi = 1$). Hence the integral over the surface is just $B_y h\,\Delta z$. Equating the two integrals, we find that

$$-E_x h = -(d/dt)(B_y h\,\Delta z).$$

The only way in which the time derivative by $B_y h\,\Delta z$ can be nonzero, since B_y and h are constants, is for Δz to be changing. Suppose that the wave moves to the right with a speed of propagation W. Then $d(\Delta z/dt) = W$, and the derivative is $B_y hW$. We therefore have

$$E_x = WB_y. \tag{23.7-1}$$

We now transfer our attention to the rectangle shown in the y-z plane, which has a length $2\Delta z$ along the z-axis and a width w parallel to the y-axis. By considerations exactly similar to those used above, except that we start with the integral of $B_y \cos\theta\, ds$ in Eq. (23.6-3), we find that

$$B_y w = \varepsilon_0\mu_0(d/dt)(E_x w\,\Delta z)$$

and that

$$B_y = \varepsilon_0\mu_0 WE_x. \tag{23.7-2}$$

We eliminate W from Eqs. (23.7-1) and (23.7-2) to find that

$$E_x/B_y = (\varepsilon_0\mu_0)^{-1/2}. \tag{23.7-3}$$

The substitution of this ratio into Eq. (23.7-1) shows that

$$W = (\varepsilon_0\mu_0)^{-1/2}. \tag{23.7-4}$$

We have now shown that the disturbance, once having reached z_0, must move to the right in order to satisfy Maxwell's equations. Further, we have found the speed of propagation, W. The magnitude of this speed raises an interesting possibility. If we use the values of ε_0 and μ_0 as given in Sec. 16.8 to compute W, we find

$$W = 2.998 \times 10^8 \text{ m/sec}. \tag{23.7-5}$$

The fact that this coincides exactly with the speed of light in empty space suggests a connection between electricity and magnetism on one hand and light on the other. The value of μ_0 has been chosen arbitrarily, but that of ε_0 has been determined by electrical measurements that have nothing to do with the speed of light. The exact equality of W and c indicated to Maxwell that light could be interpreted as an electromagnetic wave of very high frequency. As we shall see later, other predictions from Maxwell's equations support this conclusion. By accepting it, we shall have improved the wave model of light developed in Chapter 12. We now can say what vibrates in the waves—it is the electromagnetic field. We also see how light can be propagated in empty space, because electromagnetic fields do not require a material medium.

EXERCISES

23.7-1 Show that the speed of propagation of an electromagnetic wave in an uncharged, nonconducting material of permittivity ε and permeability μ_0 is $(1/\varepsilon\mu_0)^{-1/2}$.

23.7-2 Equation (23.7-3) shows that the ratio of the electric field strength to the magnetic flux density in a wave propagated in free space is a constant.

(a) Find the dimensions of E/B. (b) Find the dimensions of E/H, where H is the magnetic field strength, B/μ_0. (c) The ratio E/H for a wave traveling in a vacuum is called the ***impedance of free space***. Calculate its value to three significant figures.

23.7-3 An advancing wave such as that discussed in Secs. 23.6–23.7 is characterized by an electric field of magnitude 0.80 $\mu V/\text{m}$. What is the magnitude of the magnetic field strength?

23.7-4 Repeat the arguments of Sec. 23.6 except that it is assumed that the coordinate system is so chosen that $\vec{E}$ has its only component in the $+y$-direction. Find the direction of the magnetic field.

23.7-5 (a) Show that the energy density in the wave of Secs. 23.6–23.7 has the value $\varepsilon_0 E_x^2$ everywhere to the left of z_0 and zero everywhere to the right.

(b) Show further that the power carried by the wave across any unit area perpendicular to z is $E_x^2(\varepsilon_0/\mu_0)^{1/2}$.

23.7-6 (a) Show that the direction of propagation of the wave of Sec. 23.7 is that of the vector product, $\vec{E} \times \vec{B}$.

(b) Using the result of Ex. 23.7-5(b), show that the energy flow in the wave may be represented by a vector,

$$\vec{P} = (\vec{E} \times \vec{H}). \tag{23.7-6}$$

This vector is called the ***Poynting vector*** in honor of its discoverer, John Henry Poynting (1852–1914).

23.8 The Transverse Nature of Electromagnetic Waves

The existence of a changing E_x in Sec. 23.6 was a necessary and sufficient condition that B_y exist, and vice-versa. Now we ask whether any other component of $\vec{B}$, B_x or B_z, also accompanies E_x.

A repetition of the argument of Sec. 23.6, assuming that $B_x \neq 0$ shows that $E_y \neq 0$ (Ex. 23.7-4). But the coordinate system of Fig. 23.6 was chosen in such a way that E_y was zero. Therefore there can be no component of $\vec{B}$ parallel to $\vec{E}$, i.e., $B_x = 0$.

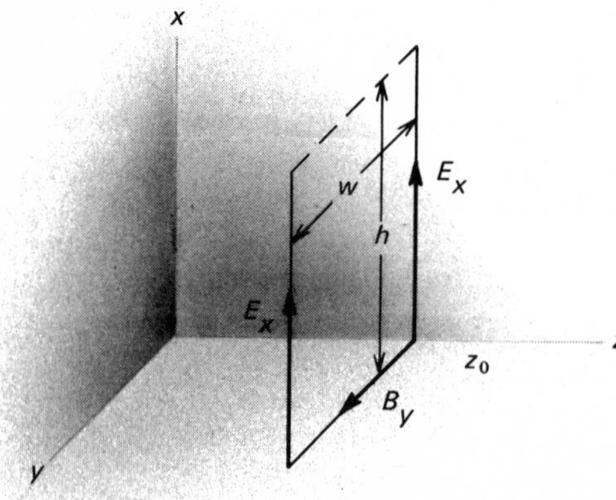

FIG. 23.8 $\vec{E}$ and $\vec{B}$ are perpendicular to each other and to the direction of propagation.

To find out about the possible existence of B_z, consider Fig. 23.8. The surface over and around which we shall apply Eqs. (23.6-1) to (23.6-4) is here chosen to be parallel to the x-y plane, i.e., perpendicular to the direction of propagation.

If the surface is to the right of z_0, both $\vec{E}$ and $\vec{B}$ are zero in its neighborhood—all of the integrals in Maxwell's equations vanish. If it is to the left of z_0,

$$\int_{\text{Around}} E \cos \theta \, ds = 0,$$

since $\cos \theta = 0$ for the top and bottom of the loop, and since we move with $\vec{E}$ as we go up the back side of the loop and against it as we go down the front side. It follows at once from Eq. (23.6-4) that

$$(d/dt) \int_S B \cos \phi \, dA = 0.$$

Here $B \cos \phi$ is just B_z. Because the loop has constant area, the only way in which the integral over the surface can vanish is that $(dB_z/dt) = 0$.

We have not shown that B_z is zero, but only that any z component of the magnetic field must be unchanging with time. Such a constant field has nothing to do with a wave. It is perfectly true that an electromagnetic wave can move in the direction of a static magnetic field that results from sources other than the wave, e.g., a radio wave may be propagated in the direction of the earth's magnetic field at any point. We may therefore dissociate any constant magnetic field from the wave and say that only the y-component of $\vec{B}$ exists if only the x-component of $\vec{E}$ is present in the wave.

We can summarize these results by saying that the electric and magnetic fields in an electromagnetic wave in free space are perpendicular to each other and that both are perpendicular to the direction of propagation. The second statement is equivalent to saying that the electromagnetic wave is a transverse wave (cf. Sec. 10.12). The vibrations of $\vec{E}$ and $\vec{H}$ take place in directions perpendicular to that in which the wave progresses.

23.9 The Radiation of Periodic Waves

Up to this point considerable attention has been given to the electromagnetic wave without any mention about how it originates. Suppose that an ***antenna*** consists of a vertical conductor, as shown in Fig. 23.9, and that one end of it is connected to one terminal of an oscillator, the other terminal of which is connected to the ground. The potential of the antenna will fluctuate periodically, at the frequency of the oscillator. The antenna may be considered to be one conductor of a capacitor, ground being the other conductor. This is true because an electric field must exist in the neighborhood of the antenna. During that part of the cycle during which the antenna carries positive charge, and a current is flowing upward in it, the lines of electric force will be approximately as shown by the dotted lines, while the lines of magnetic force are in the directions shown by the arrow heads and tails, i.e., they are approximately circles about the current flowing in the antenna. Since the wave is propagated in a direction perpendicular both to $\vec{E}$ and to $\vec{H}$, the wave will be sent out approximately in the directions shown by the vectors labeled $\vec{W}$.

In the preceding paragraph it was tacitly assumed that the antenna is short enough so that it is, at any particular time, at constant potential. This will be true only if the antenna is short compared with the wavelength of the wave that it sends out. Otherwise, the time taken for charge to reach the end of the antenna will be greater than the time between reversals of the oscillator. Under these circumstances the whole antenna will not be at the same potential, and the lines of force around it will have a more complicated pattern than that shown in Fig. 23.9. Antennae that have lengths comparable with the wavelength are very useful, but we shall at present content ourselves with the discussion of the ***short antenna,*** whose length is much less than a wavelength.

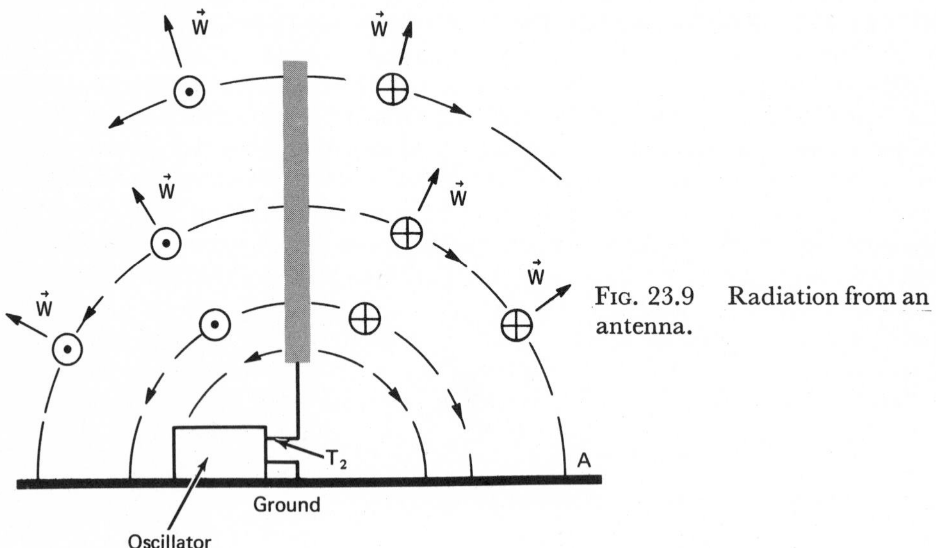

FIG. 23.9 Radiation from an antenna.

We shall later have occasion to devote particular attention to the radiation which may be observed at considerable distance from an antenna, in a direction approximately at right angles to the antenna. A point that satisfies these conditions is point A in Fig. 23.9. At such a point the radiation from a vertical antenna is traveling approximately horizontally, the electric vector being vertical and the magnetic vector being horizontal.

The existence of time-varying electric and magnetic fields at a point such as A in Fig. 23.9 does not insure that an electromagnetic wave will carry energy outward from the antenna. To see this, we remember that the maximal current flows to a capacitor when a minimal potential difference exists across its terminals i.e., the current to the antenna is approximately 90° out of phase with the voltage (cf. Sec. 22.8). Consideration of the directions of $\vec{E}$, $\vec{B}$, and $\vec{W}$ in Fig. 23.9 then shows that energy is flowing inward, toward the antenna, as often as it is flowing outward. The net energy flow would appear to be zero. Yet the existence of radio and television shows that energy can be radiated!

The flaw in this reasoning is that we have not used the fact that the wave moves at finite speed. As a result, the fields at a point such as A at any instant will not be those corresponding to the voltage of the antenna and the current in it at that instant. They depend, rather, on the values of these variables at a time t earlier, where $t = r/c$, r being the distance from the antenna to A and c being the speed of light. We shall not go through the full details of the treatment here, but merely state that a consideration of the fields shows that the electric lines of force at distances greater than $(\pi c/2\omega)$ from the antenna no longer extend back to the antenna. Rather, they form closed loops. Similarly, the magnetic lines of force no longer surround the antenna. They also form closed loops that do not surround it. At first, these statements seem to contradict our earlier beliefs that lines of electric force always begin and end on charges (Gauss' law) and that magnetic lines of force always form closed loops surrounding currents (Ampere's circuital law). The contradiction is only apparent, however, for these beliefs grew from experience with *static* fields. When the fields are changing, the displacement current and electromagnetic induction come into play [Eqs. (23.6-3) and (23.6-4)]. The vertical loop marked **E** in Fig. 23.10 has a changing magnetic flux through it, and the horizontal loop marked **B** has a displacement current through it if the magnetic and electric fields vary with time.

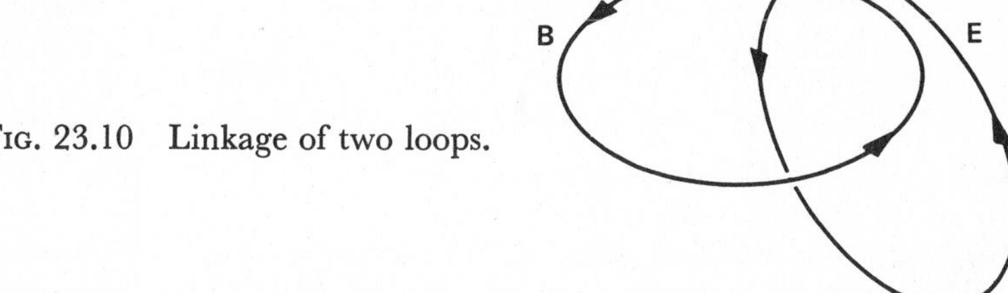

FIG. 23.10 Linkage of two loops.

The full treatment mentioned above shows that an antenna does radiate, with a continual outward net flow of energy. One point is especially worth mention. If the antenna sends energy into the wave, the conservation law demands that the oscillator supply the antenna at the same rate. This means that the current and the voltage cannot be 90° out of phase, as they would be if the antenna and ground formed a perfect capacitor (cf. Sec. 22.6 and Fig. 22.6). The antenna therefore must behave as if it were a capacitor in series with a resistance. The power radiated is then the product of the mean square current by this ***radiation resistance***.

23.10 The Detection of Electromagnetic Radiation

In order to study and use electromagnetic waves, it is necessary to have a method of setting them up and some device for detecting their presence and measuring their strength. One of the simplest schemes for the study of electromagnetic radiation is illustrated in Fig. 23.11. It consists of a short horizontal antenna A, a tuned antiresonant circuit *L-C*, an amplifier B, a detector D, and a galvanometer G. If an electromagnetic wave with the electric field vertical is present in the neighborhood of the antenna, a varying potential difference will be set up between the antenna and the ground. In a practical case, the maximum amplitude of this potential difference may be of the order of microvolts (10^{-6} V) and the period during which it goes through a complete cycle may be less than a microsecond (10^{-6} sec). The amount of power delivered to the antenna is generally much too small to allow direct measurement, so it is necessary to

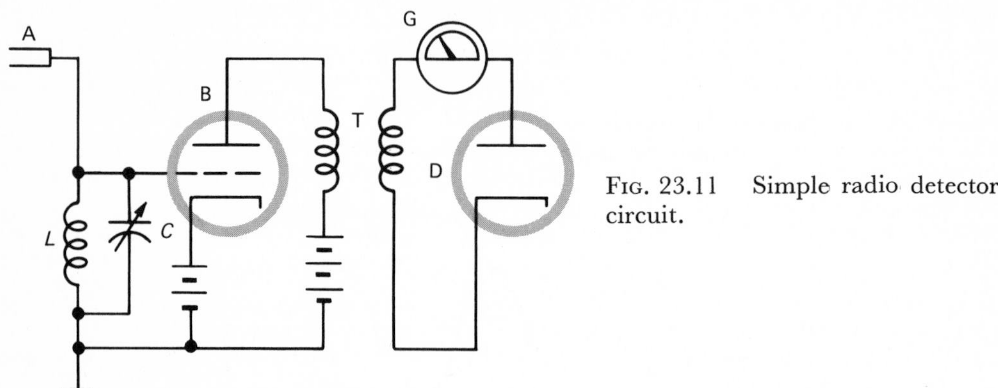

FIG. 23.11 Simple radio detector circuit.

amplify it in some way. As a first step in this amplification process the potential is applied to a parallel resonant circuit. Such a circuit offers a large impedance to an alternating source of radian frequency $\omega = 1/(LC)^{1/2}$, but it can be maintained in oscillation at this frequency with the supply of very little energy. In order that the circuit may be adjusted to the same frequency as the incoming wave, the capacitance C is adjustable, as indicated by the arrow drawn across it. The high-frequency voltage across this capacitor is applied to the grid of the amplifier B (cf. Sec. 22.11), which produces a varying current in the primary of the transformer T. Were a galvanometer connected directly across the secondary of this transformer, it would not be effective, since the current through it would reverse much faster than the galvanometer could follow. It is therefore necessary that a ***detector*** be used. In one of its simplest forms, such a detector consists merely of a rectifier (cf. Secs. 22.10 and 22.12) as shown at D in Fig. 23.11. Since this rectifier allows a current to flow only during that part of the time when the plate is positive, a rapidly varying but undirectional current will flow through the galvanometer G. Since the variations in this current are much too fast for the instrument to follow, it will merely read the average value of the current through it. This average value is a measure of the strength of the incoming electromagnetic wave.

The action of the system just discussed may be clarified somewhat by the diagrams of Fig. 23.12, which show the way in which the voltage between the antenna and ground, the voltage delivered by the transformer, and the current through the galvanometer vary with time. The dotted line of Fig. 23.12b shows the deflection of the galvanometer. Since this instrument cannot move rapidly enough to follow the variations in current, it will hold an almost steady deflection which is proportional to the average current flowing.

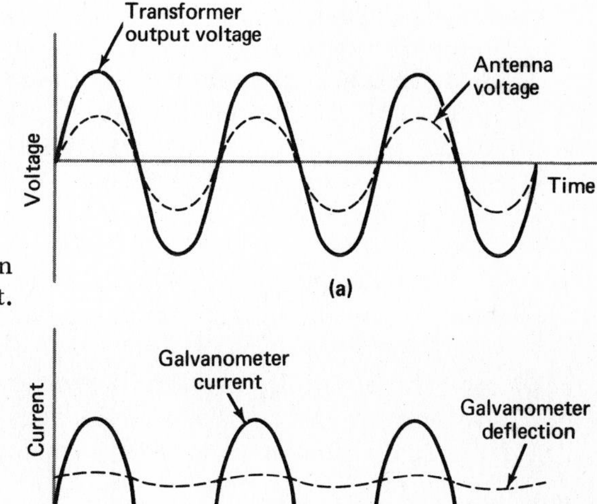

FIG. 23.12 Voltages and currents in detector circuit.

In the device just described the electric field of the incoming wave sets up a potential difference between the antenna and ground. It is equally possible to use the magnetic field of the wave to supply energy to a detector. This may be accomplished by the use of a coil of wire, or a ***loop antenna,*** such as that shown schematically in Fig. 23.13. If the magnetic field of the wave passes through such a coil, its rapid changes will induce an emf in the coil and these may be amplified and detected in exactly the same manner as was the emf picked up by the antenna of Fig. 23.11.

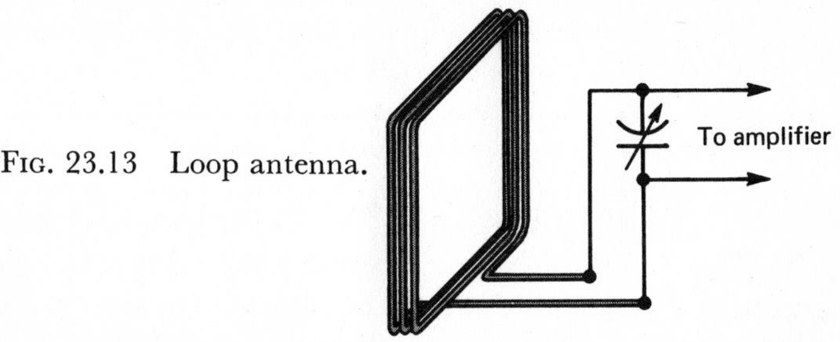

FIG. 23.13 Loop antenna.

23.11 Reflection and Interference

It is quite possible to build oscillators, similar to those described in Sec. 22.15, which have natural frequencies ($\nu_0 = \omega_0/2\pi$) of the order of 3×10^9 per sec. In accordance with the basic equation for waves [Eq. (10.5-3)], the wavelength of the waves set up by such an oscillator will be of the order of

$$\lambda = c/\nu = 3(10)^8 \text{ m sec}^{-1}/3(10)^9 \text{ sec}^{-1} = 0.1 \text{ m}.$$

Such waves, although very long compared with light waves, have wavelengths of the same order as those of sound waves, and oscillators of this frequency range may be used to demonstrate the properties of electromagnetic radiation.

In the use of such oscillators, the short antenna described in Sec. 23.9 would not be of much use, since an antenna that was short compared with $\frac{1}{10}$ meter would not produce a field over a large enough region of space to be an effective radiator. A much more effective antenna, shown in Fig. 23.14, is the ***dipole antenna***. It consists of two conducting rods, each a quarter of a wavelength long, with the terminals of the oscillator connected to their adjoining ends. Standing waves are set up in it in a manner very similar to the way in which standing acoustic waves are set up in musical instruments (cf. Secs. 10.13–10.15).

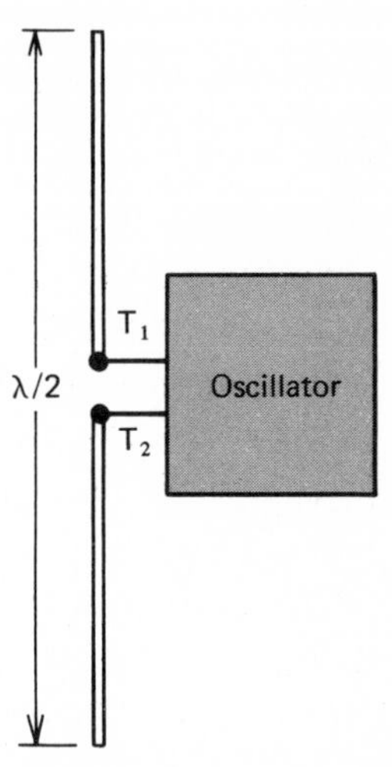

FIG. 23.14 Transmitter with dipole antenna.

If a dipole antenna is excited by an appropriate oscillator at a frequency of about $3(10)^9$/sec, the waves emitted from it may be detected at considerable distances by a very simple system. This consists of another dipole antenna, identical with the first, but with a detector similar to that shown in Fig. 23.11, connected between the two rods, in place of an oscillator. We shall speak of the antenna-oscillator system as a ***transmitter*** and of the antenna-amplifier-detector system as a ***receiver***.

If the receiver is tuned to pick up radiation from the antenna at some distance, and then a sheet of metal (at least a meter or two on a side) is introduced

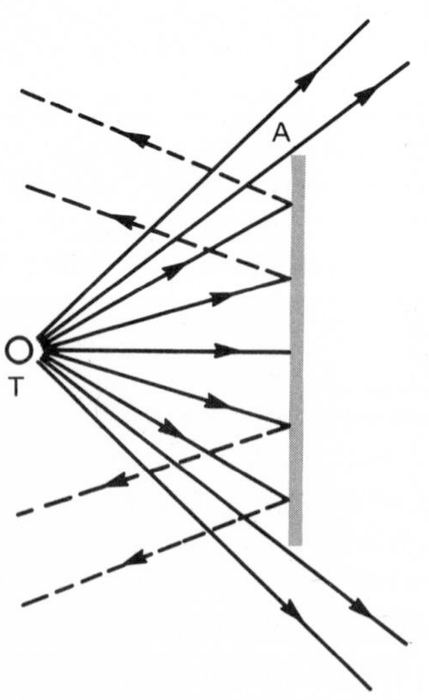

FIG. 23.15 Shadow effect for electromagnetic waves.

between the two (A, Fig. 23.15), it is found that the radiation from the transmitter T is in general prevented from reaching the receiver R. We thus see that electromagnetic waves can be shadowed in a manner similar to light.

A more effective demonstration is provided if a second sheet of metal (B in Fig. 23.16) is put into place, leaving the first sheet of metal where it was. In this

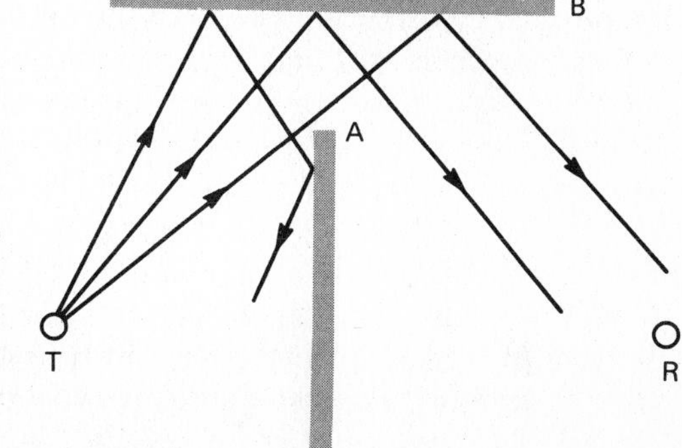

FIG. 23.16 Reflection of electromagnetic waves.

figure the antenna of the transmitter and the receiver are perpendicular to the plane of the paper. It is found that the signal, which had been cut out by the insertion of A, is restored by the insertion of B, indicating that the electromagnetic wave is reflected by the second sheet of metal. If the metal sheet is rotated, the reflection decreases in intensity, indicating that the same law of reflection that holds for light (Sec. 12.3) also holds for electromagnetic waves.

If sheet B is now left in place and sheet A is removed, as shown in Fig. 23.17,

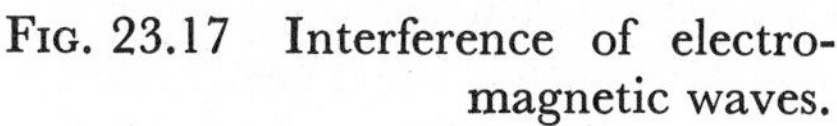

FIG. 23.17 Interference of electromagnetic waves.

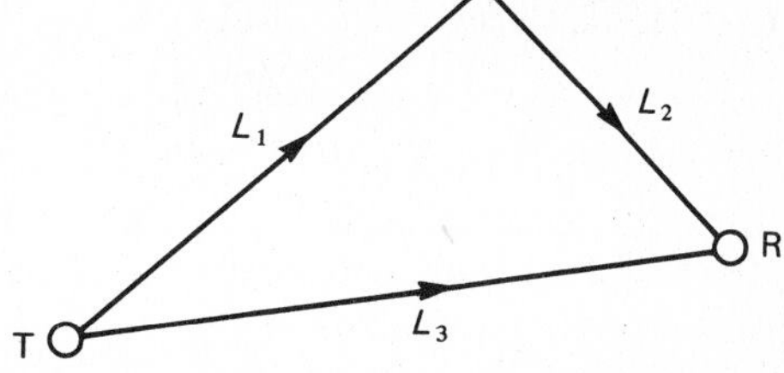

it is found that the strength of the signal received is very sensitive to the position of the receiver antenna. As the antenna is moved about (always being kept parallel to the transmitter antenna) it is found that there are positions of maximum and positions of minimum intensity, as indicated by the deflection of the detector galvanometer. Measurement of these positions shows that the maxima occur when the difference of the paths traveled by the direct and reflected rays, i.e., $L_1 + L_2 - L_3$ in Fig. 23.17, is equal to an integral number of wavelengths, and the minima occur when this difference is an odd number of half wavelengths. The phenomena observed in this experiment are clearly identical with those discussed in Sec. 12.14, so another parallelism between electromagnetic waves and light waves has been demonstrated.

The experiments just described are identical in principle with those performed by Heinrich Hertz (1857–1894) in 1888. Hertz, working without the advantages of the vacuum tube oscillator and detector, which now make such demonstrations easy ones, had set out to check on the possibility of producing the electromagnetic waves that had been predicted by Maxwell fifteen years earlier. This pioneer work of Hertz formed the basis for the later development of wireless telegraphy and hence of modern radio communication.

EXERCISES

23.11-1 The electromagnetic waves used in ordinary (AM) broadcasting have frequencies which vary between 550 kilocycles per second and 1500 kilocycles per second. What are the maximum and minimum wavelengths involved?

23.11-2 A radio detector of the type sketched in Fig. 23.11 is to be used to measure the intensity of radio broadcast waves (cf. Ex. 23.11-1). The inductance L has a value of 0.40×10^{-3} H. What are the maximum and minimum values between which the capacitance of the capacitor C must be adjustable?

23.11-3 Radio waves are reflected quite well from an ionized layer, known as the ***ionosphere,*** which is about 100 km above the earth's surface. Show that you would expect poor radio reception at points whose distance from the transmitting antenna is D, where D satisfies the relation:

$$2(h^2 + D^2/4)^{1/2} - D = (n + 1)\lambda/2,$$

where h is the height of the ionosphere, λ is the wavelength of the radio wave, and n is any integer. Assume a flat earth.

23.12 Polarization

There is one type of phenomena, characteristic of all transverse waves, which we have not discussed either in Chapter 10 or in Chapter 12. It is easily demonstrable with electromagnetic waves of about one meter wavelength or less. Suppose that a dipole transmitting antenna is used as a source of waves and that a dipole receiving antenna of the same length as the transmitter antenna is used to detect them. Let the center of the receiving antenna be fixed, but suppose that the antenna can be rotated about an axis perpendicular to its own length, i.e., about the direction in which the wave is traveling. It is found that the signal received has maximum strength when the two antennae are parallel (Fig. 23.18), and that its strength goes to zero when the receiving antenna (dotted line, Fig. 23.18) has been rotated 90° from this position. It is clear from this experiment that the properties of the electromagnetic wave depend on the direction in the plane perpendicular to the line of propagation. Any wave with a variation of this sort is a ***polarized wave.***

It is easy to see why the electromagnetic wave from a straight antenna is polarized. The electric field in the wave is parallel to the direction of the transmitting antenna, and a receiving antenna perpendicular to this direction has no component of the electric field along its length; hence it cannot acquire different potentials along its length.

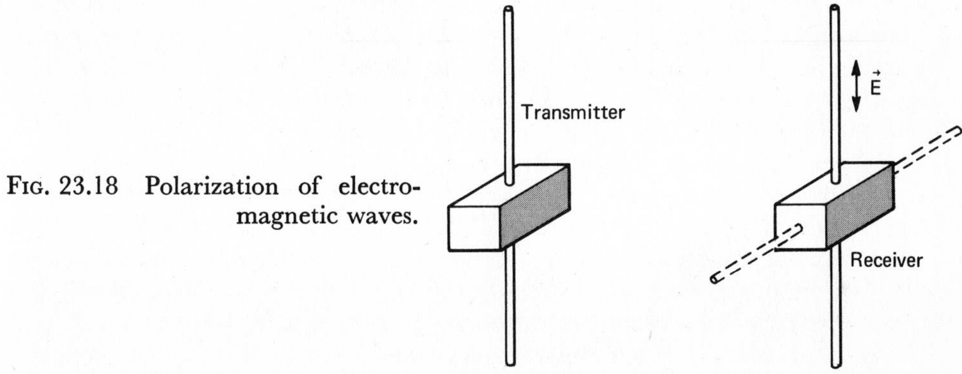

FIG. 23.18 Polarization of electromagnetic waves.

The polarization of the magnetic field of the electromagnetic wave can also be demonstrated with the help of a loop antenna. The magnetic field is at right angles to both the electric field and the direction of propagation (Sec. 23.8). The loop antenna should give a maximum response when its plane is perpendicular to the magnetic flux, i.e., when the transmitting dipole antenna lies in

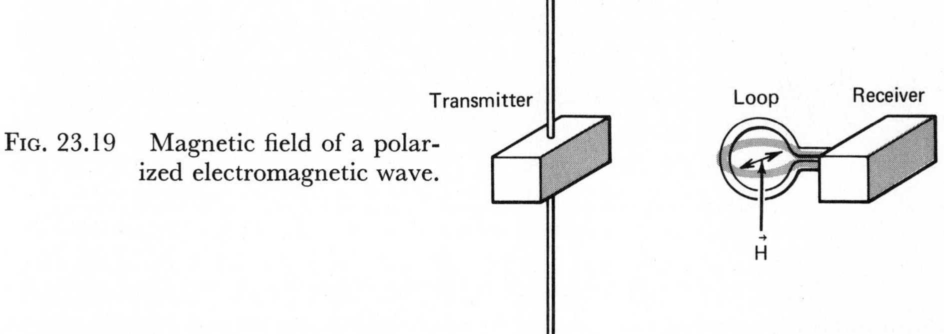

FIG. 23.19 Magnetic field of a polarized electromagnetic wave.

the plane of the loop (Fig. 23.19). The minimum response should occur when the perpendicular to the plane of the loop is parallel to the dipole antenna of the transmitter (dotted loop, Fig. 23.19). Both predictions are indeed verified, confirming the conclusions reached in Sec. 23.8 concerning the relative directions of the electric and magnetic fields.

23.13 Polarization of Light Waves

Since the electromagnetic and the optical waves are identical in speed, in their behavior at reflecting surfaces, and in their ability to exhibit interference phenomena, we may finally convince ourselves of their identity if we can show that light waves are transverse waves which can be polarized. The methods used for radio waves would hardly be appropriate for light waves, since we know the wavelength of visible light to be of the order of 5×10^{-7} m, and the apparatus for detecting and measuring light waves by the use of antennae and amplifiers would need to be absurdly small. There are, however, a number of ways of testing the ***polarization of light.*** Some of these involve the use of substances in which light beams with different direction of polarization travel with different speeds, others make use of the fact that the reflection of light depends to some extent on the direction of polarization.

For simplicity, we shall confine our discussion to one method of polarizing light. The material sold commercially under the name of ***Polaroid*** has the rather remarkable property of transmitting light which is polarized in one direction and absorbing light polarized at right angles to this direction. To demonstrate this, and to show that light is polarizable, we merely need a source of light and two sheets of Polaroid. If the light source S is examined through

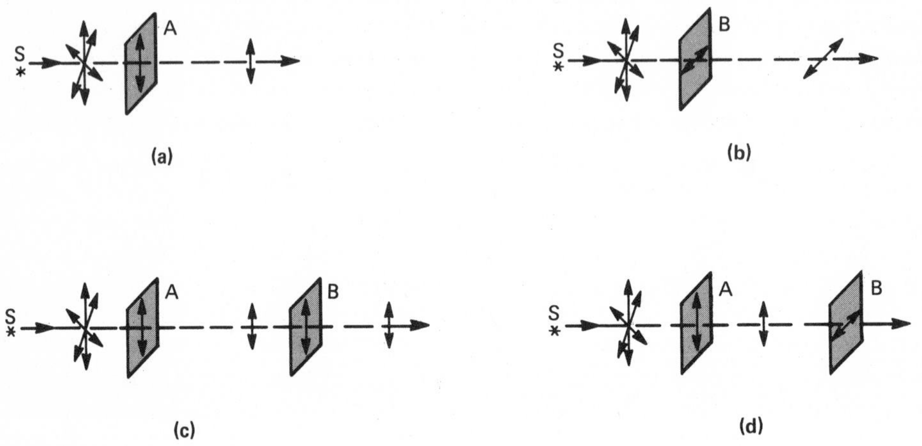

FIG. 23.20 Polarization of light.

a single sheet, A in Fig. 23.20, it is found that its intensity is reduced to about half of the value it had when viewed directly. If the Polaroid sheet is rotated about an axis along the line of sight, no change in the intensity takes place. Examination of the source through the second sheet of Polaroid, B in Fig. 23.20b, yields similar results. If both sheets are inserted parallel to each other and perpendicular to the line of sight, as shown in Fig. 23.20c, the behavior is very different. If the first sheet is left fixed and the second rotated about the line of sight, it is found that the intensity of the transmitted light varies from a maximum value in one position of the second sheet to a minimum when the sheet has been rotated through 90°, back to a maximum for 180° rotation, and to another minimum for 270° rotation.

The phenomena observed with the two Polaroid sheets are consistent with the following idea. Ordinary light is not polarized, for reasons to be discussed later, but it can be polarized by passage through a Polaroid sheet. If the Polaroid allows only light with the electric field in the direction shown by the double-headed arrow at A in Fig. 23.20c to pass through it, the light beyond this sheet will be polarized with the electric field in the direction shown by the arrow. If the second sheet is so oriented that it also allows light with the same polarization to pass, as in Fig. 23.20c, the light examined through it will be about as bright as that seen through a single sheet. On the other hand, if the second sheet is rotated through 90°, it will only pass light with its electric vector in the direction shown by the double-headed arrow at B in Fig. 23.20d. Light polarized in this way has been completely removed by the first Polaroid sheet, so no light will be observed through the second sheet.

The experiment just described verifies both the polarizability of light and the fact that Polaroid will transmit light of only one polarization, but it does not explain why the light from the source is ***unpolarized*** while the electromagnetic waves from an antenna are polarized. The reason for this is that the light from the source S consists of the radiations from very many independent small sources, each of which has an arbitrary direction of polarization. We shall later see that these sources are the individual atoms or molecules of the emitting source. *The light from any single atom or molecule is polarized, but the combined effect of a large number of atoms or molecules each producing light of a different polarization leads to unpolarized light,* as indicated by the multiple arrows shown between the source and the first Polaroid sheet in Fig. 23.20. The Polaroid sheet sorts out from all these radiations those which have vector components in the particular direction which it will transmit, and so gives us ***polarized light.***

The intensity with which light is reflected from a surface of water, glass, or other nonmetal depends to some extent on whether the electric field is in the plane of incidence (i.e., the plane containing the incident direction and the perpendicular to the surface) or in the plane of the surface. Light reflected from a lake or a road is therefore partially polarized. It is this fact which makes Polaroid sunglasses preferable to ordinary absorbing glasses of the same optical quality. If the Polaroid is so oriented in the frames that it cuts out the light which is polarized by reflection, it will reduce the "glare" more than it will reduce the general intensity of illumination.

The statement that light from a source is not polarized is generally true but not universally so. For example, the blue light of the sky, which is scattered sun light, is partially polarized. Light from gaseous sources may be partially polarized if magnetic fields are present. Finally, light sources known as ***lasers*** can be so constructed that they emit polarized light. (See reference 23B at the end of this chapter.)

23.14 Additional Evidence for the Identity of Light and Electromagnetic Waves

The idea of light as an electromagnetic wave, originated by Maxwell, has been a very profitable one in the field of atomic theory. Atomic phenomena, in turn, have been helpful in further verifying the identity. One of the most helpful things about the concept is that it accounts, at least in part, for the fact that gases in a discharge tube can emit light. Chapter 19 gave evidence that an atom consists of a positively charged nucleus surrounded by a group of more or less tightly held electrons. As these electrons move toward or away from the nucleus, the electric field in the neighborhood of the atom must change, giving rise to an electromagnetic wave. It would be convenient to believe, as most physicists did during the last half of the nineteenth century, that the frequency of the emitted light is identical with the frequency of oscillation of the electron, but we shall see in Chapter 25 that this notion is not in general tenable.

Other phenomena that support the identity of light and electromagnetic waves are the photoelectric and Compton effects, which will be discussed in the next chapter. Both of these effects show that light can exert forces on electrons, and it is hard to see how this could happen if electric and magnetic fields were, not involved in the propagation of light.

Throughout the last few sections, the wave nature of light has been emphasized. The concept of light as an electromagnetic wave is so satisfactory in many ways that we might be tempted at this stage to discard the photon description considered at length in Chapter 12. The following chapters will show, however, that the electromagnetic wave description by itself is not sufficient, and we shall be obliged to continue with a dual description of optical phenomena.

23.15 The Modulation of Radio Waves

The electromagnetic wave, because of its ability to travel through space without great losses of energy, forms an excellent means for long-distance communication. The frequencies suitable for this purpose lie in a broad band from about 10^5 cycles per second to about 3×10^7 cycles per second. Frequencies below the lower limit are excluded by the fact that it is difficult to design low-frequency antennae which will radiate enough energy to be useful, and frequencies above the upper limit are useful only for short distance communication.

Electromagnetic waves in the proper frequency range are useful as ***carriers*** for communication purposes, but they are not sufficient by themselves. This is true because intelligence can be conveyed from one point to another only by changes that can be recognized at the receiving end. The simplest way of using radio waves if by ***pulsing*** or ***keying*** the oscillator, i.e., by turning it on and off. This demands that some sort of prearranged code be used, and the usual one is the "dot-dash" code used in telegraphy. A short excitation of the transmitter is called a dot and a longer one a dash. Fixed combinations of dots and dashes represent letters, and any message that can be spelled can be sent. At the receiver, a detector similar to that shown in Fig. 23.11 can be used if the galvanometer has a short enough period of vibration to allow it to respond to a "dot" and to return to its zero before the next symbol is received. The type of wave sent out in telegraphy of this sort is shown in Fig. 23.21, which shows the combination for the letter B in Morse code (— · · ·). For purposes of simplicity, the figure has been distorted so that it shows only six oscillations of the radio

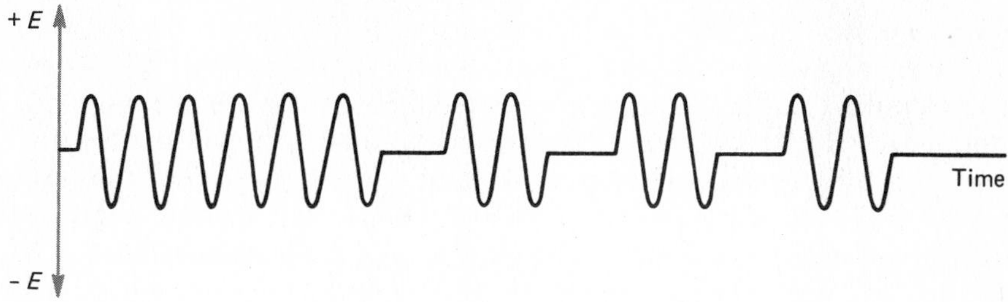

FIG. 23.21 Keyed radio wave.

wave for a dash and two for a dot. Actually, a dash may correspond to a keying of the oscillator for an appreciable fraction of a second and hence to thousands or even millions of oscillations of the radio wave.

The flexibility of the communication of intelligence by radio waves can be increased greatly if the wave is continually controlled by an audio-frequency wave. Such a process is called the ***modulation*** of the radio-frequency wave by the audio-frequency wave. In the older form of modulation, known as ***amplitude modulation*** (AM), the radio wave sent out from the transmitter is controlled in such a way that its intensity varies with the audio frequency.

Figure 23.22 shows a simple scheme for modulating a radio frequency with an audio frequency. At the left of the diagram is a radio-frequency oscillator,

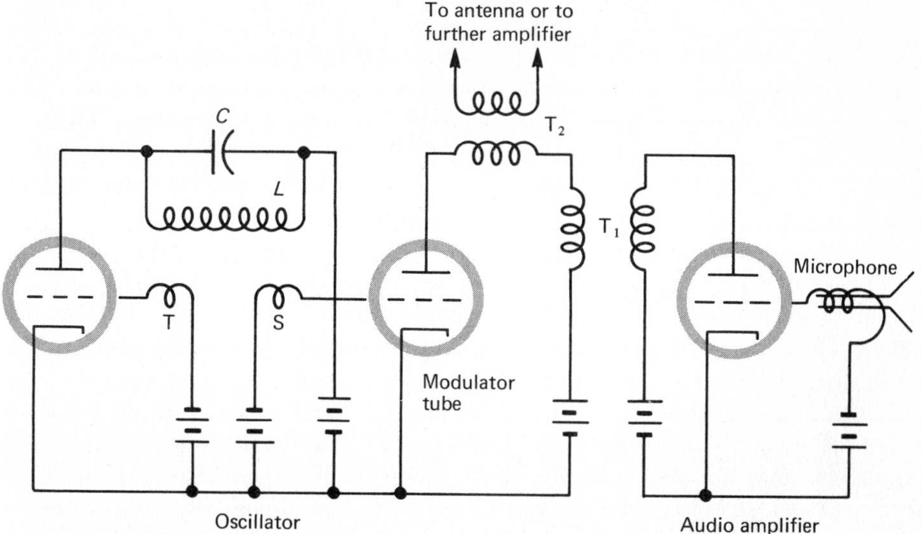

FIG. 23.22 Amplitude modulator for radio waves.

similar to that of Fig. 22.21. The tank circuit is *L-C*, T is a tickler coil that maintains the oscillations by feeding a signal back to the grid of the tube, and S is the secondary of a transformer of which *L* is the primary. This transformer serves to impress a voltage varying at radio frequency on the grid of the modulator tube. Any sounds that reach the microphone at the right of the diagram result in the generation of an emf which varies with the audio frequency of the sound. This emf is impressed on the grid of the audio-frequency amplifier tube, and the amplified emf is applied to the plate of the ***modulator tube*** through the transformer T_1. The current in this tube will be dependent on both the radio-frequency amplitude applied to the grid and the audio-frequency amplitude applied to the plate. If the plate and grid potentials are properly adjusted, the current in the tube will have a form similar to that shown in Fig. 23.23.

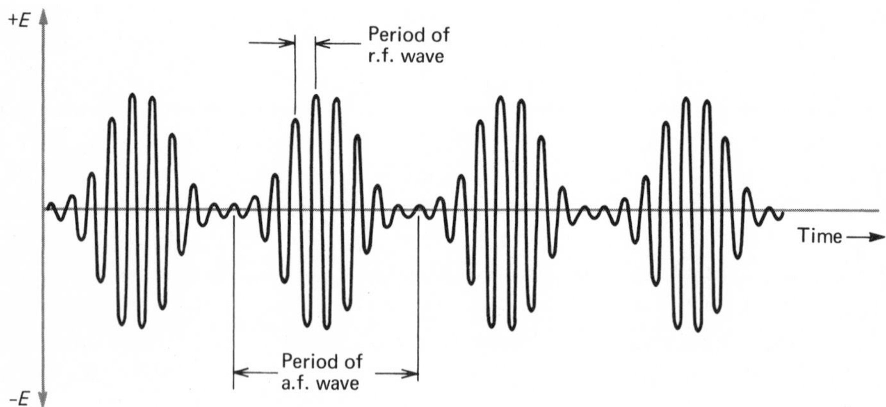

FIG. 23.23 Amplitude modulation of a wave.

The radio-frequency variation will take place with fixed frequency, but its amplitude will vary with the magnitude of the audio-frequency signal. (In this figure, as in Fig. 23.21, the radio frequency is shown lower than in actual practice.) The modulated radio-frequency current produces a similar voltage wave in the secondary of the transformer T_2, and this is applied to the antenna either directly or, if more power is needed, through a further amplifier.

23.16 Radio Receivers—Demodulation

When a radio wave causes the potential of the antenna of a radio receiver to fluctuate in the manner shown in Fig. 23.23, the receiver has to sort out from the complex wave pattern the audio-frequency wave that carries the intelligence supplied to the radio-frequency wave by the microphone and modulator. About the simplest practical receiver which will do this is shown schematically in Fig. 23.24. The parallel-resonant circuit *L-C*, the transformer T_1, and the detector play the same roles as did those shown in Fig. 23.11. Because of the rectifying properties of the detector tube, the wave form of the current in the transformer T_2 will be approximately that shown in Fig. 23.25. When a signal of this sort is applied to the coil of the loud speaker of Fig. 23.24 (after amplification by the audio-frequency amplifier), the fluctuations of the radio frequency will be much faster than the coil and cone of the speaker can follow. These parts,

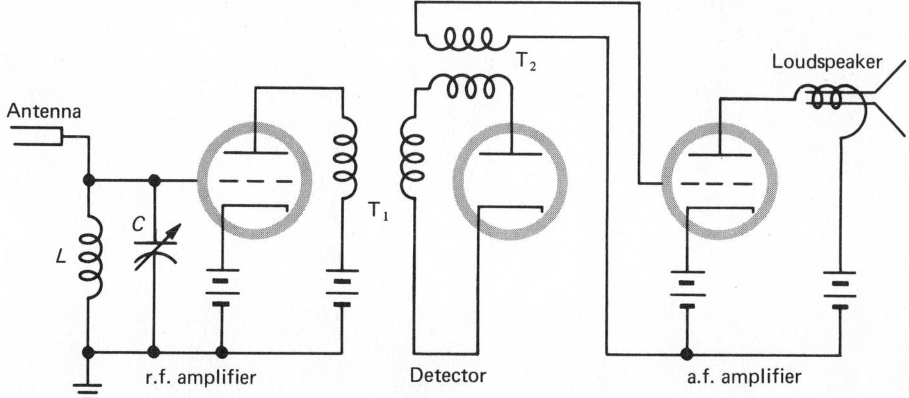

FIG. 23.24 Radio receiver for an amplitude-modulated wave.

however, can respond to the slower audio-frequency changes, and the speaker will therefore move as if the current supplied to it varied along the dotted curve of the figure. Since this curve reproduces closely the original audio-frequency impulse from the microphone, the speaker will reproduce the sounds which reached the microphone.

Since a detector serves to separate out the audio-frequency component of the complex incoming wave, it is often called a ***demodulator.*** The process it performs is known as ***detection,*** or ***demodulation.***

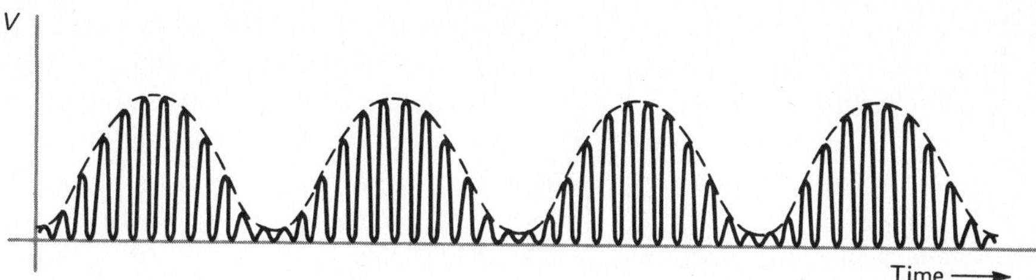

FIG. 23.25 Demodulated wave.

23.17 Frequency Modulation

In amplitude modulation the amplitude of the radio frequency wave was modulated by the audio-frequency signal while its frequency stayed constant. It is equally possible to arrange that the amplitude be kept constant and that the frequency be changed by the audio-frequency signal. When this is done, the outgoing radio wave has a form of the type shown in Fig. 23.26. The change in the frequency, from the minimum value shown at A to the maximum value shown at B, is proportional to the amplitude of the audio frequency, while the number of times that the frequency changes per second is equal to the audio frequency. This type of modulation is called ***frequency modulation*** (FM).

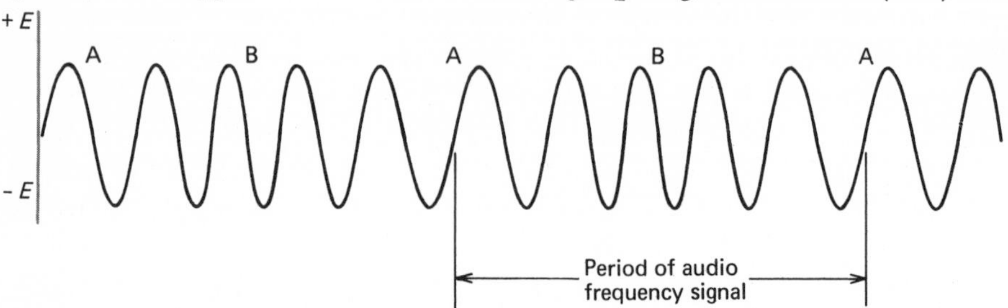

FIG. 23.26 Frequency modulation of a radio wave.

The apparatus for frequency modulation and demodulation is somewhat more complicated than that required for amplitude modulation. We shall therefore omit its discussion here, and the interested reader is referred to texts devoted specifically to electronics.

The great advantage of frequency modulation over amplitude modulation is that it is less subject to disturbances. These disturbances may be either natural, such as lightning, or artificial, such as electric motors, In either case, they generally lead to the creation of amplitude modulated waves that produce "static" in AM receivers. The receivers designed to demodulate frequency modulated signals do not respond to such amplitude modulated disturbances.

In order that FM waves can carry speech and music with high fidelity, it is necessary that the frequency vary over a wide range, about 20 kilocycles above and below that of the radio carrier frequency (see Prob. 23.9). For this to be accomplished without the variations being appreciable with respect to the carrier frequency itself, which would cause trouble in tuning receivers, FM broadcasting stations operate on much higher frequencies than AM stations. The frequencies assigned to the FM stations by the Federal Communications Commission are of the order of 10^8 cycles per second. Waves of such frequencies travel in straight lines, are not readily bent around obstructions, and are not well reflected from the ionosphere (cf. Ex. 23.11-3). For these reasons, FM broadcasting cannot extend over as large an area as can AM broadcasting.

23.18 Summary

The known properties of electric and magnetic fields, particularly their storage of energy, lead to the prediction of the existence of electromagnetic waves that can be propagated through dielectric materials or through empty space. These waves are characterized by a varying electric field and by a varying magnetic field at right angles to it, both fields being perpendicular to the direction of propagation. Evidence has been given that light waves, discussed in Chapter 12, are in fact electromagnetic waves of this type. A number of the properties and applications of electromagnetic waves in the field of communications have been investigated. In particular, the new concept of polarized transverse waves has been presented, and it was shown experimentally that all electromagnetic waves, including light waves, can be polarized.

In summary, the full range of the observed electromagnetic spectrum is outlined in Table 23.1.

Table 23.1 *The Electromagnetic Spectrum*

Frequency Range (cps)	Wavelength Range (m)	Classification
0–60	$>5 \times 10^6$	†Commercial frequencies
$60–2 \times 10^4$	$5 \times 10^6—1.5 \times 10^4$	†Audio frequencies
$2 \times 10^4–1 \times 10^5$	$1.5 \times 10^4–3 \times 10^3$	†Ultrasonic frequencies
$1 \times 10^5–5.5 \times 10^5$	$3 \times 10^3–5.5 \times 10^2$	Low radio frequencies
$5.5 \times 10^5–1.5 \times 10^6$	$5.5 \times 10^2–2 \times 10^2$	Broadcasting frequencies
$1.5 \times 10^6–3 \times 10^7$	$2 \times 10^2–10$	High radio frequencies (short wave)
$3 \times 10^7–3 \times 10^8$	10–1	Ultra-high frequencies
$3 \times 10^8–6 \times 10^{19}$	$1–5 \times 10^{-3}$	Microwaves (radar)
$6 \times 10^{10}–4 \times 10^{14}$	$5 \times 10^{-3}–7.5 \times 10^{-7}$	Thermal radiation
$4 \times 10^{14}–6 \times 10^{14}$	$7.5 \times 10^{-7}–5 \times 10^{-7}$	Visible radiation
$6 \times 10^{14}–3 \times 10^{16}$	$5 \times 10^{-7}–10^{-8}$	Ultraviolet radiation
$3 \times 10^{16}–3 \times 10^{18}$	$10^{-8}–10^{-10}$	X-rays
$>3 \times 10^{18}$	$<10^{-10}$	*X-rays and γ-rays

† Electromagnetic waves of frequency less than 10^5 cps are difficult to produce in free space. When they are radiated they are propagated only over very short distances. Alternating currents of these frequencies are, however, very commonly used. The currents which actuate the loud speaker of a radio set and produce sound are in the audio-frequency range.

* The distinction between x-rays and γ-rays is not very clearly defined. Perhaps the best way to distinguish them is to limit the term γ-rays to those radiations arising from nuclei and to group all other radiations in this range as x-rays.

PROBLEMS

23.1 Equation (23.2-4) can be derived in a more general way than was used in Sec. 23.2. In the figure, A and A' represent the areas of portions of two equipotential surfaces which are not necessarily flat. Their four corners are so located that lines joining adjacent corners, such as MN, are perpendicular to both A and A', even though this requires curvature of these lines. The electric field $\vec{E}$ is everywhere perpendicular to the surfaces (Sec. 16.22), and its magnitude is σ/ε, where σ is the magnitude of the charge density on the surfaces; ε is the permittivity.

(a) Demonstrate that A and A' approach plain surfaces as the figure is shrunk to small size and that lines such as MN approach straight lines.

(b) Prove that no change in the field will be produced if A and A' are replaced by thin metal sheets.

(c) Show that, in the limit, the figure becomes a small plane parallel plate capacitor of capacitance $\varepsilon A/d$, and hence that the energy stored in it is $\frac{1}{2}Q^2 d/\varepsilon A = (\frac{1}{2}E^2/\varepsilon)(Ad)$.

(d) Prove that the expression for the energy density holds for any region of space in which there is an electric field.

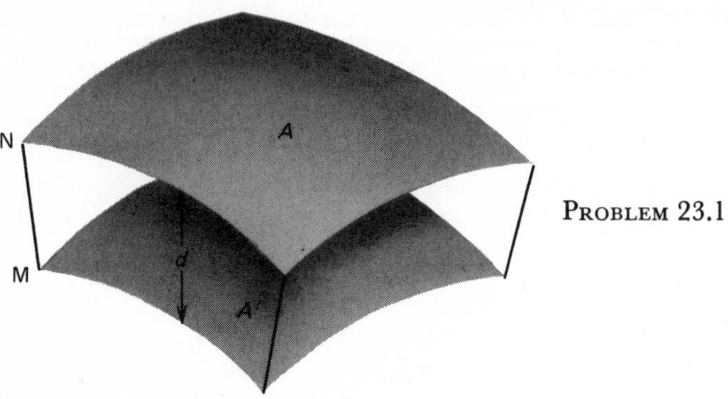

PROBLEM 23.1

23.2 A cylinder of material of radius a, length L, and Young's modulus Y is compressed by a force of magnitude F. Show that elastic energy is stored in the cylinder with a uniform density

$$u = \tfrac{1}{2}T^2/Y,$$

where $T = F/\pi a^2$, in strict analogy with Eq. (23.2-4).

23.3 A ***spherical capacitor*** consists of two concentric metal spherical shells, the inner one having an outer radius a and the outer one an inner radius b. They carry charges of $+Q$ and $-Q$, respectively.

(a) Find the electric field $\vec{E}$ as a function of r, the distance from the common center.

(b) Show that the energy stored in a spherical shell that extends from r to $r + \Delta r$ $(a < r;\ b > r + \Delta r)$ is

$$\Delta U = Q^2\,\Delta r/8\pi\varepsilon r^2,$$

if terms proportional to $(\Delta r)^2$ are neglected.

(c) Passing to the limit $\Delta r \to 0$ and integrating, find the total energy stored in the capacitor.

(d) Show that the capacitance of the capacitor is $C = 4\pi\varepsilon ab/(b - a)$.

23.4 A ***coaxial cable*** consists of an inner conductor of radius a surrounded by a coaxial, conducting cylindrical shell of inner radius b, the region between being filled with a material of permittivity ε and permeability μ. There are equal and opposite currents in the two conductors. Suppose that the currents are steady and that each is of magnitude I.

(a) Find the magnitude of the magnetic flux density at any point distant r from the axis.

(b) Show that the energy stored in an angular ring between r and $r + \Delta r$ and of length L along the cable is such that

$$\Delta U \approx \frac{\mu_0 I^2 L\,\Delta r}{4\pi r}.$$

(c) By approaching the limit ($\Delta r \to 0$) and integrating, show that the total magnetic energy stored per unit length of cable is

$$U_L = \frac{\mu_0 I^2}{4\pi} \ln \frac{b}{a}.$$

(d) Find the inductance of the cable per unit length.

23.5 (a) By applying Ohm's law to a small cube of conducting material of conductivity σ, show that the field strength and the current density are related by

$$\vec{J} = \sigma \vec{E}.$$

(b) Using the results of (a), write Maxwell's equations in the form appropriate to a conducting medium in which the charge density is everywhere zero. (Take ε and μ as ε_0 and μ_0.)

(c) By arguments similar to those of Sec. 22.7, show that an electromagnetic wave advancing in the $+z$-direction in a conducting medium must have the magnitudes of $\vec{E}$ and $\vec{B}$ decrease as z increases. Such a wave is said to be ***attenuated***.

23.6 The Poynting vector gives a satisfactory measure of power flow, even for conditions very different from those under which it was derived. Consider a long, straight wire of radius a and conductivity σ, which carries a current I distributed uniformly over its cross section.

(a) Find the current density ($\vec{J}$) and hence the electric field ($\vec{E}$) within the wire (cf. Prob. 23.5). The electric field at the surface is equal to that inside.

(b) Find the direction and magnitude of the magnetic flux density ($\vec{B}$) at the surface of the wire.

(c) Show that the directions of $\vec{E}$ and $\vec{B}$ at the surface are such that the Poynting vector is directed radially inward at every point on the surface of the wire.

(d) By applying Eq. (23.7-6) and integrating over the surface of a piece of the wire of length L, showing that the power delivered to this piece of wire is just sufficient to provide for the Joule heating within the piece.

23.7 A dipole antenna may be considered as an electric dipole of variable moment. When it is driven at a radian frequency ω, the dipole moment may be written as

$$p = P \sin \omega t,$$

where P is a constant. Complete analysis of the radiation from such a dipole shows that the power radiated is proportional to $P^2\omega^4\varepsilon_0^{1/2}\mu_0^{3/2}$. Show that this quantity is dimensionally correct and that no other quantity that is a product of powers of P, ω, ε_0, and μ_0 (the only quantities on which the power could reasonably depend) could be correct. (Hint: Write the power as $KP^a\omega^b\varepsilon_0{}^c\mu_0{}^d$, where K is dimensionless, and equate exponents of $\mathscr{m}$, ℓ, $\mathscr{t}$, and $\mathscr{Q}$ on two sides of the resulting equation. This is an example of ***dimensional reasoning***.)

23.8 An antenna of the type shown in Fig. 23.14 has a length L from end to end. (a) Will the ends of the antenna be nodes of voltage? Of current? Explain your answer. (b) At what frequencies can standing waves be set up on this antenna? Suppose the speed of propagation of the wave along the antenna to be the speed of light.

23.9 A modulated wave of the type shown in Fig. 22.23 may be represented by the equation

$$E = E_0 \sin \omega_r t \sin \omega_a t,$$

where ω_r and ω_a are the radian frequencies of the radio frequency carrier wave and the audio frequency modulation.

(a) Starting from Eq. (E.9) of Appendix E and taking both positive and negative values of β, show that

$$\sin\alpha \sin\beta = \tfrac{1}{2}\cos(\alpha-\beta) - \tfrac{1}{2}\cos(\alpha+\beta).$$

(b) Letting $\alpha = \omega_r t$ and $\beta = \omega_a t$ in the result obtained in (a), show that the modulated wave may be represented by the equation

$$E = \tfrac{1}{2}E_0\cos(\omega_r-\omega_a)t - \tfrac{1}{2}E_0(\omega_r+\omega_a)t.$$

The two radian frequencies, $(\omega_r-\omega_a)$ and $(\omega_r+\omega_a)$, are present in the radiation from the antenna. They are known as ***side bands.***

23.10 A ***circularly polarized*** electromagnetic wave is one in which the electric vector $\vec{E}$ is constant in magnitude but varies in direction.

(a) If θ is the angle between $\vec{E}$ and some arbitrary x-axis, perpendicular to the direction of propagation (z), show that the components of $\vec{E}$ in such a wave can be written as

$$E_x = A\sin\omega t + B\cos\omega t \qquad \text{and} \qquad E_y = C\sin\omega t + D\cos\omega t,$$

where A, B, C, and D are constants.

(b) Show that $A = \pm D$ and $B = \pm C$, where either the upper or the lower signs are used together.

(c) Finally, demonstrate that the two choices of signs in (b) depend on whether $\vec{E}$ rotates in the sense of a right-handed or a left-handed screw as it moves along the direction of propagation.

23.11 Demonstrate that one cannot distinguish between unpolarized light and circularly polarized light (cf. Prob. 23.10) by interposing a sheet of Polaroid between the source and the observer.

REFERENCES

23A Morris Shamos, editor, *Great Experiments in Physics*, Holt, New York, 1960. Appendix 1 presents excerpts from Maxwell's work on electromagnetic waves; Chapter 13 reprints Hertz' report of his production and detection of such waves.

23B William A. Shurcliff and Stanley S. Ballard, *Polarized Light* (Momentum Book No. 7), Van Nostrand, Princeton, 1964. An extensive and readable presentation.

23C Hugh H. Skilling, *Fundamentals of Electric Waves*, 2nd edition, Wiley, New York, 1948. A good introduction to electric waves from a vector point of view.

23D Raymond Bowers, "A Solid-State Source of Microwaves," *Scientific American*, August 1966, pp. 22–31.

23E Klaus Dranfeld, "Kilomegacycle Ultrasonics," *Scientific American*, June 1963, pp. 60–68.

23F Charles Luther Andrews, *Optics of the Electromagnetic Spectrum*, Prentice-Hall, Englewood Cliffs, N.J., 1960.

24 ⇨ *Waves and Particles*

24.1 Theories of Light

Many properties of light can be explained either by assuming that light consists of particles (photons) or in terms of a wave theory (Chapter 12). Historically, these two theories have run side-by-side since the earliest beginnings of an understanding of the nature of light.

Newton was led by his experiments to the assumption that light consisted of particles, and he made use of the theory of attractions, which he had developed to account for gravitation, in explaining the reflection and refraction of light. The discovery of the diffraction of light led to the discard of the particle theory, and this discard was made almost complete by the electromagnetic wave theory of Maxwell (Chapter 23). In the last two decades of the nineteenth century any mention of a particle theory was extremely unpopular, and it was only at the beginning of the present century that new evidence for such a theory began to accumulate.

24.2 The Quantum Theory and the Photoelectric Effect

The first experiments of importance in these developments were carried out in 1899 by Otto Lummer (1860–1925) and Ernst Pringsheim (1859–1917), who measured the distribution in energy of the spectrum of a hot body. They used a spectroscope (Sec. 13.15) to spread out into a spectrum the light coming from a small opening in a hot oven, operating at a known temperature. They were then able to measure the way in which the total energy emitted by the furnace was distributed over the range of wavelengths. They found that for a particular temperature the distribution curve was of the type shown in Fig. 24.1.

At the shortest wavelengths little energy was emitted. As the wavelength increased the intensity rose until it reached a maximum at a wavelength λ_{max} determined by the temperature, after which it fell off to zero again as the wavelength increased. If the temperature of the oven was increased, the position of the intensity maximum moved toward shorter wavelengths, but the general shape of the curve remained the same.

We cannot here go through the very energetic discussion which took place in an attempt to explain these measurements.* It is a matter for mechanics and

* A good account in reasonably simple terms is given in the books by Reiche and Simon referred to at the end of the chapter.

electric theory to explain how the thermal motion of molecules in the wall of the furnace gives rise to the light which is emitted by the furnace, and no discussion in terms of the Newtonian mechanics was able to give this explanation.

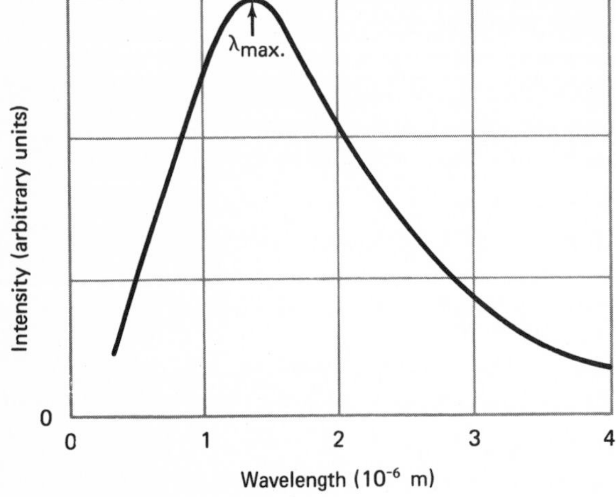

FIG. 24.1 Intensity distribution of light from a furnace.

In the process of attempting an explanation, Max Planck (1858–1947) was led in 1899 to the assumption that emission from the walls of the furnace could only take place in bundles of energy or ***quanta*** (cf. Sec. 12.21) of amount

$$E = h\nu, \tag{24.2-1}$$

in which ν is the frequency of the light emitted and h is Planck's constant. Planck obtained an approximate value for h. Later, more precise methods have shown it to have the value

$$h = 6.624 \times 10^{-34} \text{ J sec.} \tag{24.2-2}$$

The idea that energy is continuous is quite fundamental in Newtonian mechanics. If, for example, a frictionless simple pendulum is swinging with a given amplitude A, Newtonian mechanics imply that a slight disturbance could change A, and hence the energy, by any arbitrarily small amount (cf. Secs. 22.1–22.5). If Planck's explanation of the emission curves is correct, the energy increases in definite small steps, equal to h times the pendulum frequency $\nu = (1/2\pi)\sqrt{g/L}$, L being the length of the pendulum (cf. Exs. 24.5-1–24.5-2). Calculation of the size of these steps for a real pendulum shows that they are so small that they cannot be detected by reasonable physical measurements; hence the energy of a laboratory pendulum is continuous for all practical purposes. It is only in systems of very low energy, such as individual atoms or molecules, that the distinction between a continuous and discontinuous energy distribution becomes important, but the success of Planck's hypothesis shows that Newtonian mechanics must be basically at fault in this respect.

In 1905 Einstein made use of Planck's quantum theory to explain the ***photoelectric effect.*** Heinrich Hertz in 1887 had noticed that the air surrounding a metal plate became conducting when the plate was illuminated. Wilhelm Hallwachs (1859–1922) and Philipp Lenard (1862–1941) proved that electrons were emitted by such a plate and that the energy of such electrons was independent of the intensity of the light falling on the plate, and depended only on the frequency of the light. In extension of Planck's ideas, Einstein proposed the ***photon hypothesis.*** Planck had suggested that light was emitted in bundles of energy $h\nu$. Einstein went one stage further and suggested that not only is light emitted and absorbed in quanta $h\nu$ but that it travels through space in such bundles. He predicted, by an argument which we shall summarize below, that if light of frequency ν falls on a metal plate, then the energy of the electrons emitted will be given by

$$\tfrac{1}{2}mv^2 = h\nu - W_A, \tag{24.2-3}$$

where W_A is the energy required to remove the electron from the metal A, that is to say the ***work function*** of the metal (Sec. 21.17).

Equation (24.2-3), which is ***Einstein's photoelectric equation,*** was verified with high precision by Millikan, who used the apparatus shown schematically in Fig. 24.2. The two metal plates A and B are located in an evacuated chamber.

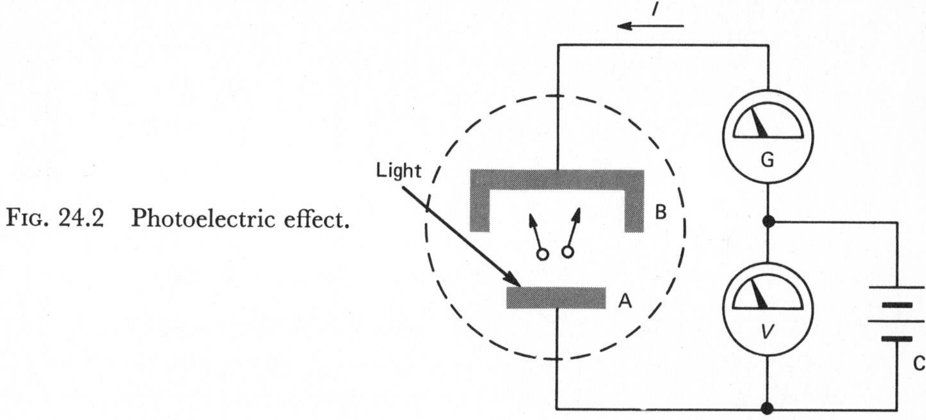

FIG. 24.2 Photoelectric effect.

Plate A is illuminated by light of known frequency ν. Plate B is located so that any photoelectrons emitted from A strike it and produce a current I in the galvanometer G. The battery C maintains between the two plates a potential difference that can be adjusted at will and is measured by the voltmeter V. If light of a constant intensity J falls on the plate A and the applied potential V is varied, the current I changes as indicated in Fig. 24.3. If a positive voltage V is applied, the current increases until a maximum current I_m passes through the galvanometer. This means that all the photoelectrons emitted from plate A are being collected by B. The value of this saturation current depends in a complicated way on the nature of the metal A, the frequency of the light, and the construction of the tube. But for a given tube and a given light frequency, the current I_m is directly proportional to the intensity J of the light falling on A.

The current I_m consists solely of the photoelectrons emitted, so that the number of photoelectrons emitted in a given time is proportional to the total energy falling on A in that time. That is to say, the number of electrons emitted is proportional to the number of photons absorbed. The second important feature

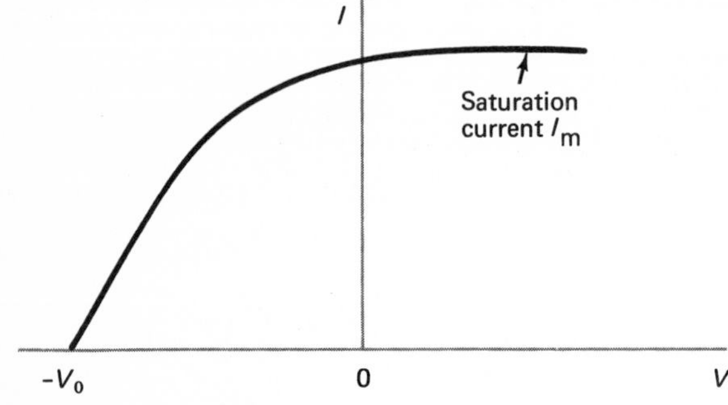

FIG. 24.3 Current-voltage curve for the photoelectric effect.

of the curve of Fig. 24.3 is the fact that, when a negative potential is applied to V, the current decreases until at a particular value $-V_0$, the current ceases, i.e., no electrons reach the plate B. Suppose now an electron starts out inside plate A with a kinetic energy $h\nu$. It loses an amount W_A in leaving the metal A, and then a further amount $V_0 e$ by the repulsion of the negative charge due to a potential $-V_0$ on B. If the electron just fails to reach plate B, we then have

$$h\nu - W_A - V_0 e = 0,$$

which may be written

$$V_0 e = h\nu - W_A. \tag{24.2-4}$$

In this expression we can measure V_0 with the apparatus of Fig. 24.2, and we can measure ν by a diffraction grating (Sec. 12.16). The electronic charge e is already known, so that it remains for us to determine h and W_A. Actually we shall not concern ourselves with the latter quantity here but shall eliminate it from our argument.

If we perform an experiment with the apparatus of Fig. 24.2 in which we vary ν and measure $-V_0$ (the cut-off voltage of Fig. 24.3) corresponding to each ν, we get the straight-line relationship of Fig. 24.4. In this figure, the crosses represent experimental points and the straight line the prediction of Eq. (24.2-4). Such a curve at one time verifies the result that Einstein obtained and demonstrates, incidentally, the technically very important result that the work function of a metal does not depend on the speed of the electrons being removed from it.

If now we determine the value of V_0 corresponding to one frequency ν and the value of V_0' corresponding to a second frequency ν' we have the two equations

$$V_0 e = h\nu - W_A$$

$$V_0' e = h\nu' - W_A.$$

Subtracting the first from the second, we get

$$e(V'_0 - V_0) = h(\nu' - \nu),$$

and it follows that

$$h = e(V'_0 - V_0)/(\nu' - \nu). \tag{24.2-5}$$

From such an experiment the value of h can be determined.

It was a great triumph for the quantum theory to find that the value of h obtained from the photoelectric effect agreed quite closely with that obtained originally by Planck in his interpretation of the experiments on the radiation from a hot oven.

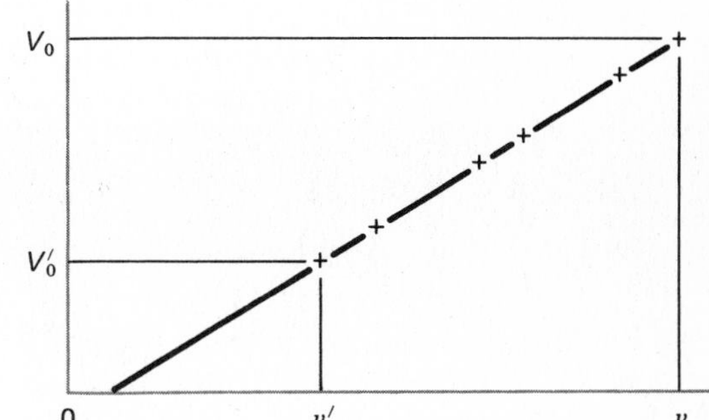

FIG. 24.4 Determination of Planck's constant from the photoelectric effect.

A moment's consideration of the experiments on the photoelectric effect indicates their strong support for a particle theory. Suppose that light falls uniformly over a large area of metal plate. On the basis of a wave theory, or of any other theory in which energy is continuously subdivided, one would expect that the energy falling on the plate, regardless of its frequency, would be absorbed by the electrons until they acquired sufficient energy to escape. Hence the electrons would be ejected from the metal with small energies, independent of frequency, and light of any frequency would cause the photoemission of electrons. Contrary to this expectation, the experimental facts are that the energies of the electrons vary with frequency, and that light of frequency less than W_A/h cannot cause any emission of electrons, as is seen from Eq. (24.2-3). (Such electrons would be emitted with negative energies, which is absurd.) The observed phenomena, therefore, support strongly the assumption that light of frequency ν carries energy in bundles $h\nu$ and that each of these bundles gives up its energy to a single electron.

24.3 The Compton Effect

Many observers working with x-rays had noticed that, when x-rays were scattered from a solid body (Fig. 24.5), the scattered x-rays had a lower frequency than that of the incident rays. Arthur Holley Compton (1892–1962) was the first to make accurate measurements of this effect and to give an explanation of this process on the photon theory. Compton correctly assumed that an x-ray photon was scattered by a collision with an electron within the scatterer. He then realized that this process was a simple collision between two particles of the type discussed in Chapters 4 and 6 (cf. Fig. 6.2). Before the

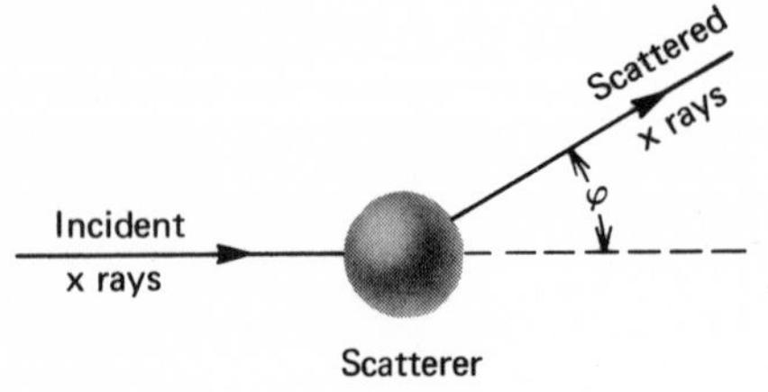

FIG. 24.5 Scattering of x rays.

collision, the photon could be considered as possessing a momentum $\vec{p}_0$, and the electron could be considered at rest ($\vec{p}_1 = 0$, Fig. 24.6a). After the collision (Fig. 24.6b), the photon could be considered as having a momentum $\vec{p}'_0$ in a direction making an angle ϕ with its original direction, while the electron would have a momentum $\vec{p}'_1$ in a direction χ with the original direction of the photon.

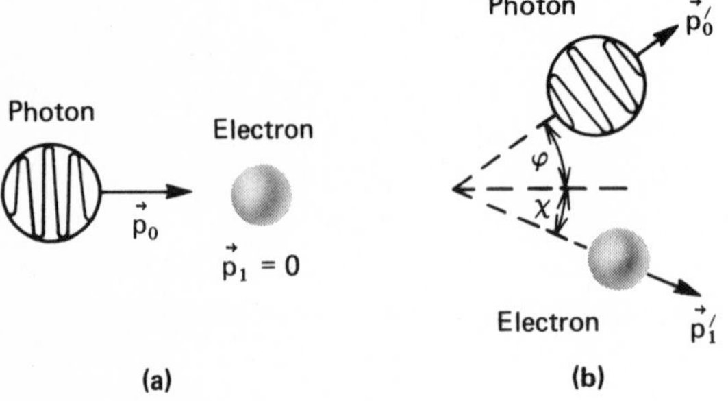

FIG. 24.6 Conservation of momentum in the Compton effect (a) before collision and (b) after collision.

Compton realized that both energy and momentum must be conserved in such a collision, and he could write

$$E_0 + E_1 = E_0' + E'_1, \tag{24.3-1}$$

where E_0 and E_0' were the energies of the photon before and after the collision and E_1 and E_1' the energies of the electron before and after the collision. From conservation of the momentum component parallel to the original direction of the photon, he could write

$$p_0 = p'_0 \cos \phi + p'_1 \cos \chi, \tag{24.3-2}$$

and from conservation of the momentum component perpendicular to this direction,

$$0 = p'_0 \sin \phi - p'_1 \sin \chi. \tag{24.3-3}$$

Compton combined Eqs. (24.3-1) and (24.3-2) to eliminate the energies and momentum of the electron and to find how the energy and momentum of the photon depended on the angle ϕ through which it was scattered. Since some of the energy of the photon is transferred to the electron in the process, it follows that the frequency ν' of the scattered photon will be less than the frequency ν of the incident photon ($E_0 = h\nu$ and $E_0{}' = h\nu'$). We shall not repeat the rather involved algebra necessary to obtain Compton's final result but shall discuss the case in which the largest possible transfer of momentum takes place. This will occur when the direction of motion of the photon is reversed and the electron is accelerated in the original direction of the photon, i.e., when $\phi = 180°$ and $\chi = 0°$. In this case, Eq. (24.3-3) is satisfied automatically, and the treatment is very similar to that carried out in Sec. 4.14. If the electron is initially at rest, and after the collision has a velocity $\vec{v}$, we can write Eq. (24.3-1) in the form

$$h\nu + m_0c^2 = h\nu' + m_0c^2/\gamma, \tag{24.3-4}$$

where m_0 is the rest mass of the electron, c is the speed of light, and [cf. Eq. (8.11-4)]

$$\gamma = \sqrt{1 - v^2/c^2}. \tag{24.3-5}$$

Using Eqs. (12.21-3) and (12.21-4) and inserting the values of ϕ and χ, we may then write Eq. (24.3-2) in the form

$$h\nu/c = -h\nu'/c + m_0v/\gamma. \tag{24.3-6}$$

To simplify the algebra, it is convenient to express all energies as fractions of the rest energy of the electron (m_0c^2). Thus we write $\alpha = h\nu/m_0c^2$ and $\alpha' = h\nu'/m_0c^2$, and we express the decrease in energy of the photon by

$$\Delta\alpha = \alpha - \alpha' = h(\nu - \nu')/m_0c^2. \tag{24.3-7}$$

With this notation, Eq. (24.3-4) becomes

$$\Delta\alpha = \alpha - \alpha' = (1/\gamma) - 1, \tag{24.3-8}$$

after dividing through by m_0c^2 and rearranging. If we divide Eq. (24.3-6) by m_0c and rearrange, we obtain

$$\alpha + \alpha' = 2\alpha - \Delta\alpha = v/c\gamma. \tag{24.3-9}$$

From Eq. (24.3-5) we have $v^2/c^2 = 1 - \gamma^2$, so that by squaring Eq. (24.3-9) we can write

$$(2\alpha - \Delta\alpha)^2 = v^2/c^2\gamma^2 = (1 - \gamma^2)/\gamma^2 = (1/\gamma^2) - 1.$$

Using Eq. (24.3-8), we then obtain

$$(2\alpha - \Delta\alpha)^2 = (1 + \Delta\alpha)^2 - 1,$$

which may be multiplied out in the form

$$4\alpha^2 - 4\alpha\,\Delta\alpha + (\Delta\alpha)^2 = 1 + 2\Delta\,\alpha + (\Delta\alpha)^2 - 1.$$

Canceling where necessary and rearranging, we then have

$$\Delta\alpha(1 + 2\alpha) = 2\alpha^2$$

or

$$\Delta\alpha/\alpha = 2\alpha/(1 + 2\alpha). \tag{24.3-10}$$

Thus for low-energy photons ($\alpha \ll 1$), the change of energy of the photon caused by Compton scattering is small, and the energy transferred to the electron is also the same small fraction of the photon energy. If, however, the energy of the photon is large ($\alpha \gg 1$), almost all its energy will be transferred to the electron in a head-on collision (cf. Exs. 24.5-7 and 24.5-8).

In obtaining Eq. (24.3-10), we have solved Eqs. (24.3-1) to (24.3-3) for the special case of a head-on collision ($\phi = 180°$, $\chi = 0$). In his general solution of these equations, Compton was able to obtain an expression for the variation of $\Delta\alpha/\alpha$ with the angle ϕ:

$$\frac{\Delta\alpha}{\alpha} = \frac{2\alpha \sin^2(\phi/2)}{[1 + 2\alpha \sin^2(\phi/2)]}. \tag{24.3-11}$$

Figure 24.7 shows a plot of the fractional change in the energy of the photon ($\Delta\alpha/\alpha$) as it depends on the angle of scattering ϕ, for x-rays of $\lambda = 0.50$ Å, for which $\alpha = 0.049$. Compton's measurements of the observed changes of frequency checked excellently with the predictions, and this verified the fact that x-ray photons were scattered by electrons according to the laws predicted for the scattering by considering it to be a simple collision between two particles.

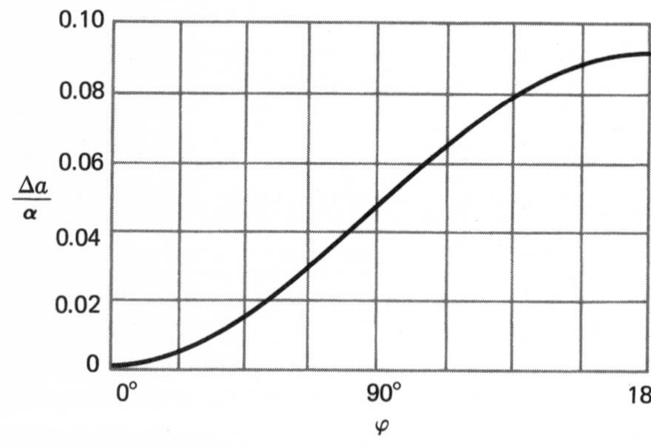

FIG. 24.7 Fractional change of energy as a function of the scattering angle of a photon in the Compton effect.

24.4 The de Broglie Hypothesis

The next step in the development, after Planck's work, was made by Einstein, who found that he could account for the variations of the specific heats of solids with temperature if he supposed that the oscillations of the atoms about the mean positions could take place only with certain discrete energies. We shall not discuss his work here, but shall pass on directly to a very important step taken by the French physicist Louis de Broglie in 1925.

The concept that light can be described in terms either of waves or of particles (photons) (Chapter 12) has been given additional support in the last few sections. When the wave description is used, the light is characterized by a wavelength λ and a frequency ν, connected by Eq. (12.21-4):

$$\nu\lambda = c,$$

where c is the speed of light, i.e., the wave speed. When the particle description is used, the photon is characterized by a momentum p and an energy ε, connected by Eq. (12.11-3):

$$p = mc = \varepsilon/c,$$

where m is the observed mass of the photon. As we saw in Sec. 12.21, the quantities involved in the two descriptions are connected by the two equations [cf. Eqs. (12.21-1) and (12.21-3)]:

$$\nu = \varepsilon/h \tag{24.4-1}$$

$$\lambda = h/p \tag{24.4-2}$$

De Broglie extended this dual description of light to material particles. He made the hypothesis that *every particle has associated with it a wave of frequency given by Eq. (24.4-1) and of wavelength given by Eq. (24.4-2)*. Using the Einstein equations for the energy [Eq. (8.12-1)] and the momentum of a particle of observed mass m, moving at a speed v, we find that the frequency and wavelength of the ***de Broglie wave*** are

$$\nu = mc^2/h \tag{24.4-3}$$

and

$$\lambda = h/mv. \tag{24.4-4}$$

Hence, in accordance with Eq. (10.5-3), the wave speed W is

$$W = \nu\lambda = mc^2/mv = c^2/v. \tag{24.4-5}$$

Thus the wave speed W associated with a particle whose speed is $v(<c)$ is always greater than the speed of light. This does not contradict the theory of relativity, since no signal can be sent by means of this wave. (For further discussion of the point see Sec. 24.10.)

These hypotheses are rather astonishing until we consider in some detail what they mean. Consider first a ball of mass 1.0 kg traveling with a speed of 1.0 m/sec. According to Eq. (24.4-4), it will have associated with it a wavelength λ given by

$$\lambda = 6.6 \times 10^{-34}\text{ J sec}/1.0\text{ kg} \times 1.0\text{ m/sec} = 6.6 \times 10^{-34}\text{ m}.$$

This wavelength is so small that no experiment which we now know about or can imagine could measure it.

On the other hand, consider an electron accelerated by a potential difference V (cf. Sec. 17.3). Its speed v will be given by the relation

$$Ve = \tfrac{1}{2}mv^2,$$

and its momentum p will be

$$p = mv = m(2Ve/m)^{1/2} = (2\ Vem)^{1/2}.$$

Its wavelength will then be given by

$$\lambda = h/(2\ Vem)^{1/2}. \tag{24.4-6}$$

An electron that has fallen through a potential difference of 100 V will therefore have a wavelength

$$\lambda = 6.624 \times 10^{-34}\,\text{J sec}/(2 \times 100\,\text{V} \times 16.02 \times 10^{-20}\,\text{Cb} \times 0.9107 \times 10^{-30}\,\text{kg})^{1/2}$$
$$= 1.23 \times 10^{-10}\ \text{m}.$$

This wavelength is of just the right order of magnitude to be diffracted by crystals (cf. Secs. 21.4 and 21.5) and is therefore susceptible of experimental determination.

24.5 *The Davisson-Germer Experiment*

The prediction made by de Broglie was verified completely by the experiment of Clinton J. Davisson (1881–1958) and Lester H. Germer (1896–) working in the Bell Telephone Laboratories in New York in 1927. They reflected electrons from the surface of a nickel crystal, in just the same sort of arrangement that the Braggs had used (Sec. 21.5) for x-rays, and found that the wavelength of the electrons corresponded exactly to that predicted by de Broglie's equation. The British physicist George Paget Thomson (1892–) published similar results, obtained independently, soon after Davisson and Germer's report of their experiments.

Since the work of Davisson, Germer, and Thomson, the de Broglie relation has been verified for protons by Otto Stern (1888–) and by Thomas Johnson (1899–), and for neutrons by a large number of workers.

These results have left us with the conclusion that *all particles, material particles as well as photons, possess a wave character as well as a particle character.*

The wave character of the material objects such as suns and planets and baseballs is not recognizable owing to the shortness of the wavelength. It is only when we consider the smallest particles, electrons, protons, neutrons, etc. that the wave character becomes important.

One may be tempted to ask whether an electron is *really* a particle or is *really* a wave. Similarly, is light *really* an electromagnetic wave or is it *really* a stream of photons? A reply to both questions can be given at once: physics cannot answer the question of the *real* nature of entities, it can only find ways to describe their behavior. What we have found is that an electron cannot be completely described as being like a billiard ball or as being like a sound wave. The electron has some of the characteristics of both, and both particle behavior and wave behavior must be considered in our attempting to deal with it.

EXERCISES

24.5-1 Show that the energy of oscillation of a simple pendulum of length L and with a bob of mass m is $mgA^2/2L$, where A is the amplitude and g is the acceleration due to gravity. Show that the increase of amplitude ΔA which corresponds to a minimum change of energy, according to Planck's hypothesis, is

$$\Delta A \approx (h/2\pi mA)\sqrt{L/g},$$

neglecting terms in ΔA as compared with A. Calculate ΔA, according to Planck's hypothesis, for a pendulum with $L = 1.00$ m, $m = 500$ gr, and $A = 3.50$ cm. Also calculate the relative change in amplitude, i.e., $\Delta A/A$.

24.5-2 Using the results of Ex. 24.5-1, calculate the size of the minimum amplitude change for a hypothetical pendulum of atomic dimensions, i.e., for $L = 2.00 \times 10^{-10}$ m, $m = 1.00 \times 10^{-25}$ kg, and $A = 3.68 \times 10^{-9}$ m. Compare $\Delta A/A$ as obtained here with that found in Ex. 24.5-1.

24.5-3 By consideration of the Compton scattering of a photon with $\phi = 0$ (Fig. 24.6), show that the frequency of the x-ray is unchanged by the scattering, and hence that scattering through 0° is equivalent to no scattering at all.

24.5-4 An x-ray beam of wavelength 1.00 Å is scattered in an experimental study of the Compton effect. Find the fractional change of frequency for 180° scattering, i.e., $\Delta\alpha/\alpha = (\nu - \nu')/\nu$.

24.5-5 Find the speed of the electron which has scattered the photon referred to in Ex. 24.5-4.

24.5-6 Why are electrons, rather than nuclei, important in the Compton scattering of x-rays?

24.5-7 What is the maximum change in energy of a cosmic ray photon which has been produced by electron pair annihilation (Sec. 19.20) when this photon undergoes Compton scattering? Calculate the speed of the electron (initially at rest) which has produced such scattering.

24.5-8 What is the energy of the scattered photon of Ex. 24.5-7 after scattering?

24.5-9 Compute the de Broglie wavelengths associated with each of the following particles:

(a) An automobile of mass 1500 kg, traveling at a speed of 100 km/hr. (b) A helium atom traveling at a velocity equal to the mean square velocity at 300°K (cf. Chapter 20). (c) An α-particle of 4.00×10^6 eV energy (cf. Chapter 19).

24.5-10 Show that the longest wavelength of light which can eject electrons photoelectrically from a metal of work function W_A is ch/W_A. What is the highest work function that a metal can have if it is to exhibit the photoelectric effect under the action of visible light?

24.6 The Heisenberg Uncertainty Principle

De Broglie's hypothesis and the discovery that particles had wave properties was a direct indication that the Newtonian and Einsteinian mechanics could only be approximations valid for large particles. Werner Heisenberg (1901–) in 1925 made the first step toward recognition of the nature of the difficulty. His first papers led to the formulation of a new mechanics called ***quantum mechanics*** in which the classical mechanics of Newton and Einstein appeared as an approximation valid for large particles. His mathematics were formidable except for one very simple and elegant idea which was fundamental for all his work.

He reasoned as follows. Suppose we try to locate a small particle by means of a microscope. If we are to see the particle, we must allow light to fall on it, and this light must be scattered by the particle. Unless the light is scattered, we have no way of knowing that the particle is present. If we want to distinguish between two particles at a distance Δx apart, we must use a wavelength λ short enough so that we can see the diffraction pattern from the two particles.

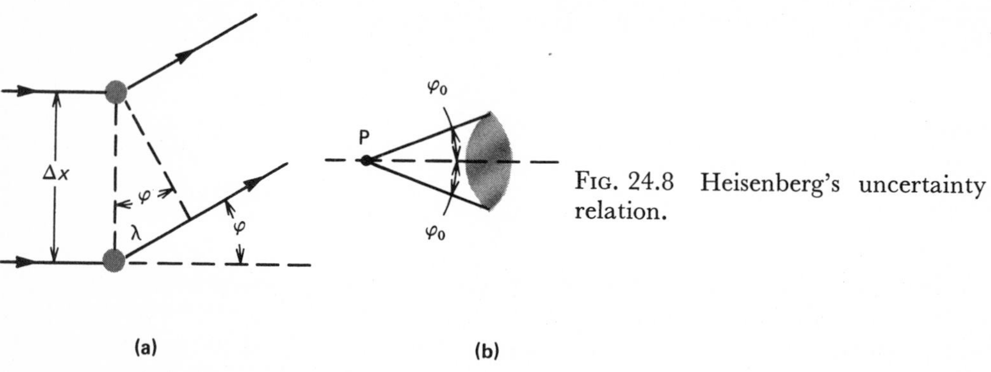

FIG. 24.8 Heisenberg's uncertainty relation.

From Fig. 24.8a we know that the first order maximum for two particles [cf. Eq. (12.14-3)] separated by a distance Δx will occur when

$$(\Delta x) \sin \phi = \lambda.$$

If the lens L of the microscope (Fig. 24.8b) subtends an angle $2\phi_0$ at point P at which we propose to see the particles, then the condition that the first-order diffraction will get into the lens will be

$$\sin \phi \leq \sin \phi_0,$$

i.e.,

$$\lambda/\Delta x \leq \sin \phi_0$$

or

$$\Delta x \geq \lambda/\sin \phi_0. \tag{24.6-1}$$

This inequality gives the condition that we can see as separate two particles which are at a distance Δx apart. For if we saw only the zero order and no first order, we could tell nothing of the separation. We now draw the reasonable conclusion that the Δx given by Eq. (24.6-1) will also give us the uncertainty in locating a single particle at P. This follows from the fact that two particles separated by less than Δx cannot be distinguished; hence we cannot distinguish between two positions of a single particle within this distance.

Under the circumstances of Fig. 24.8b, the light that originally traveled along the axis of the lens will have been scattered within the angular range $\pm\phi_0$.

This means that in the scattering process the light will have communicated momentum to the particle we have been trying to observe (cf. Sec. 24.3). If the total momentum of the photon is $\vec{p}_0$, the momentum at right angles to the original direction will be

$$\Delta p = p_0 \sin \phi_0, \tag{24.6-2}$$

and this must be the *maximum* momentum component communicated to the particle, in the direction of Δx, by the process we have used in observing it. Thus by locating the particle to an accuracy Δx, we may have disturbed its momentum by an amount Δp. It follows that there is an uncertainty Δp in our knowledge of the momentum. Combining Eqs. (24.6-1) and (24.6-2) and using the de Broglie relation

$$p_0 = h/\lambda,$$

we get

$$\Delta x \, \Delta p \geq (h/\lambda) \sin \phi_0 \, \lambda/\sin \phi_0,$$

i.e.,

$$\Delta x \, \Delta p \geq h.$$

In obtaining this result we have considered Δp and Δx to have maximal values. A more meaningful equation would have been obtained had we considered the root-mean-square values of the uncertainties that would be found in many repeated trials. A detailed treatment on this basis shows that the product of the uncertainties is reduced by a factor of 2π, so we shall write

$$\Delta x \, \Delta p \geq h/2\pi = \hbar, \tag{24.6-3}$$

where $\hbar = h/2\pi$. It is called ***aitch bar*** or the ***Dirac h.*** This inequality, which is known as ***Heisenberg's uncertainty relation***, introduces a profound change in our thinking with regard to mechanics. In the discussion of our first ten chapters it was assumed that we could, with sufficient care, measure both the position and the velocity or momentum of a particle to any precision desired. Heisenberg now tells us that if we make Δx small, i.e., if we determine x to a high precision, we shall so disturb the motion of the particle as to make the uncertainty in momentum Δp very large. Similarly, if we determine the momentum very closely, say by using a long wavelength of light for the observation, we introduce a large uncertainty in position. To fix numerical ideas, several examples of the application of this principle are given in Exs. 24.6-1 to 24.6-3.

This change in mechanical ideas led Heisenberg to discuss ***matrix mechanics***, which is one of the formulations of quantum mechanics. A second and somewhat simpler formulation will be discussed in the next few sections.

EXERCISES

24.6-1 A microscope is being used to examine a diffraction grating that has 5000 lines/cm. The grating is illuminated with light of wavelength 6000 Å. What is the smallest angle that the microscope objective lens can subtend at the point being examined if lines of the grating are to be resolved, i.e., are to be seen as distinct from each other?

24.6-2 A microscope with an objective lens that just satisfies the condition of Ex. 24.6-1 is used to examine an object illuminated with light of wavelength 4000 Å. What will be the distance between two points which can just be resolved under these conditions?

24.6-3 It was implied in Sec. 24.6 that either Δx or Δp could be reduced indefinitely by the use of properly chosen photons for the experiment, but that a reduction of one of these quantities would result in an increase of the other. Suppose that a microscope in which $\phi_0 = 30°$ is available and is so arranged that it can focus light, x-rays, or γ-rays (a purely hypothetical instrument). Compute the values of Δx and Δp for each of the following illuminants: (a) visible light of $\lambda = 6000$ Å, (b) ultraviolet light of $\lambda = 2000$ Å, (c) x-rays of $\lambda = 2.00$ Å, (d) γ-rays of $\lambda = 0.0015$ Å.

24.6-4 Suppose that a particle of mass m is known to be traveling in a precisely determined direction, which we shall denote as the x-direction. At time $t = 0$ this particle is known to be at the point $x = 0 \pm \Delta x$ and to be traveling with a speed $v \pm \Delta v$. Within what limits will the x-coordinate of the particle be known at some later time t? Show that, if Δx and Δv are made as small as is consistent with the uncertainty principle, the uncertainty in position at the time t is

$$(\Delta_x)_t = \Delta x + \hbar t / m\,\Delta x.$$

Also show that the product of the uncertainties of the speed and position at the time t is

$$(\Delta x)_t(\Delta v) = (1 + t\,\Delta v/\Delta x)(\hbar/m)$$

and that this quantity is always greater than the value of the product $\Delta v\,\Delta x$ at $t = 0$.

24.7 *Probability in Quantum Mechanics*

Suppose that a particle of mass m is known to be subject to certain forces, which may depend on the position of the particle, on its velocity, or on its acceleration. Then Newton's second law of motion enables us to find its acceleration. If the particle's velocity, or its momentum, is known at any instant, say at $t = 0$, knowledge of its acceleration allows us to calculate its velocity at any later instant; if its position is also known at $t = 0$, the position can also be calculated at any later time. Hence Newtonian mechanics implies strict causality and complete predictability, at least in principle.

It is true that we have encountered cases in which the knowledge of the velocity and momentum of every individual particle in a system at a particular instant did not seem to be attainable. One example was encountered in Chapter 20, where such large numbers of molecules were being dealt with that the calculation of the future of each seemed to be hopeless. We were therefore forced to deal with the behavior of an *average* molecule, rather than with each individual. It was not necessary, however, to abandon faith in, or our use of, Newtonian mechanics. We supposed that the calculation of the behavior of individual molecules would be possible if we had sufficient information about each of them at some instant and if we had computers that would work fast enough to solve the equations before the time for which they were solved had passed!

One phenomenon with which Newtonian mechanics could not cope, even in principle, was found in Sec. 19.7, that the observed laws of radioactive decay could be accounted for only by assuming that it was purely a matter of chance whether or not a particular atom would decay during any short interval of time. If the atoms of a particular isotope are identical in every measurable respect, what determines that atom A will decay within the next microsecond although atom B may not undergo decay for the next million years? Radioactive phenomena seem to be inconsistent with the laws of Newtonian mechanics. If there are variables that determine which atom will decay first, they are "hidden variables" in the sense that none of our measurements have revealed them.

The Heisenberg uncertainty principle seems to indicate that there are no hidden variables, that there are limitations on our ability to predict the future, and that these limitations result from the fact that we live in an atomistic and a quantized universe. If we cannot determine the position and the momentum of a particle simultaneously at some instant, we clearly cannot predict precisely where it will be or what its velocity will be at some later instant (cf. Ex. 24.6-4). If the position at $t = 0$ has an x-component equal to $x_0 \pm \Delta x$ and the x-component of momentum at the same instant is $p_0 \pm \Delta p$, it is probable (but not certain) that the x component of position at time $t = t_1$ will be $x = x_0 + (p_0/m)t_1$. Thus any calculations that involve the uncertainty principle must take into account the notion of probability.

Suppose we wish to discuss the way in which the people of the United States are distributed throughout the country. We might pick a point near the Capitol in Washington, D.C., and with this as center draw a square of area one square mile. We would find a certain number of people located within that square at a certain time of day. If instead of a square we had drawn an equilateral triangle or a circle of the same area about the same center, we should have found approximately the same number of people. A square or circle or triangle of area one-tenth of a square mile would be expected to contain approximately one-tenth of the previous number of people. According to the World Almanac, we would expect to find about 12,500 people in the square mile and about 1,250 in the smaller square. This number, of course, would vary from time to time. It would be smaller at night than in the day, and less on Sunday at noon than on a weekday. We can take an average of all these values and write down a figure P (about 12,500 in this case) which gives the average number of persons per square mile in Washington, D.C. If now we take any area ΔA in the District, the number of people in the area can be expected to be

$$P\,\Delta A.$$

We call this number P the probability (per unit area) of finding people in Washington. If we take a center somewhere in Nevada, the value of P will be about 1 per square mile. Thus the probability of finding people will be a function of position in the country, and if we locate points by a Cartesian system of coordinates we can write

$$P(x, y)\,\Delta A$$

for the number of people we expect to find in an area ΔA centered at x, y. The probability function $P(x, y)$ is then a function that varies with the choice of the point x, y. If x, y is within a city, we shall expect extremely large values for $P(x, y)$; if x, y is in a desert or in the Rockies, we shall expect small values.

There is another way to consider probabilities. In the area centered in Washington, D.C., the chances of finding the President of the United States are quite large. We might examine this area at a number of times chosen at random through the year. Some of these times we shall find zero presidents in the area. Sometimes we shall find one. If we find the president in a square mile in Washington 63 times in 100 tests we say the probability for presidents is 0.63 per square mile. There are locations in the country where the probability for presidents is appreciable for a given president, and there are certain regions in the country where this probability will have an extremely small value.

The reader can invent further examples of these two types of probability. There is, for example, the probable number of moths and other insects to be found in a given volume near a porch lamp in the summer, or the probability distribution for any given college senior as it varies from time to time during the year.

It was by the use of probability concepts essentially similar to these that Erwin Schroedinger (1887–1961) introduced an alternative approach to the problem of the mechanics of small particles. He professed difficulty in understanding the quantum mechanics of Heisenberg and developed a system of ***wave mechanics*** that proved to give identical results with the Heisenberg mechanics, although its form is quite different.

Schroedinger argued that the Heisenberg uncertainty principle demanded that we discuss the probability that a particle be near a certain location (or that it have a momentum close to a certain value), rather than trying to specify its location (or momentum) precisely. Thus, if the momentum of a particle is determined quite precisely, its position will not be well determined, and the probability of finding it within a narrow range of any fixed point at the instant at which the momentum was found will be small. On the other hand, if its momentum is determined only within a wide limit of uncertainty, it may be possible to say that it is highly probable that it will be found near a particular point. On this basis, he discussed probabilities, such as the probability $P(x)$ that an electron will be found in a unit length near x. Thus if one looked in the region of length Δx with the point x as center, one would expect to find an electron in that region in a fraction

$$P(x)\Delta x$$

of all trials. Schroedinger soon realized that it would not be feasible to calculate these probabilities directly, because he remembered that in the case of light waves the intensity of the light was proportional to the square of the amplitude of the wave (cf. Ex. 23.7-6). The intensity of a light wave, of course, is proportional to the number of photons per second falling on a given area.

In the waves discussed by de Broglie, Schroedinger realized that he had available waves which were related to material particles in the same way that light waves were related to photons. He therefore decided to study the properties of de Broglie waves on the assumption that *the square of their amplitude would be proportional to the probability of finding an electron.*

Before studying Schroedinger's idea in more detail, there are several properties of waves that must be developed, so that we must digress from our main theme for several sections.

24.8 The Combination of Waves of Different Wavelengths

Let us consider two waves of wavelengths λ_1 and λ_2 and observe them at a time when the crest of one coincides with the crest of the other at the origin (Fig. 24.9). Two crests will again coincide at a point such as P provided that the distance OP is a whole number of wavelengths of both waves, i.e., if

$$\mathrm{OP} = n_1\lambda_1 = (n_1 - 1)\lambda_2,$$

where n_1 is an integer. It is clear that if λ_1 and λ_2 differ by only a small fraction of either wavelength, then n_1 will have to be large for a second coincidence of two maxima to take place.

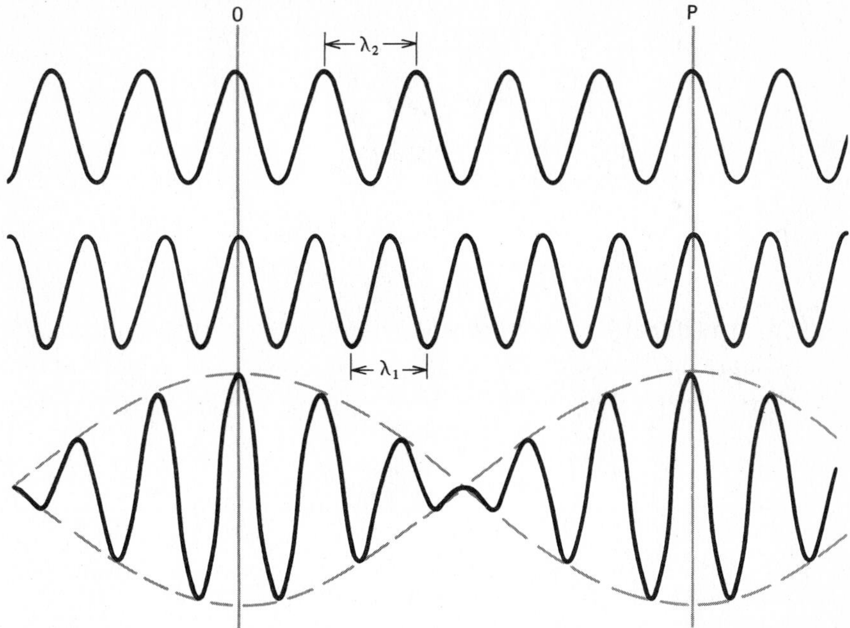

FIG. 24.9 The combination of two waves of different wavelengths.

If the two waves are of the same type, their combined effect may be found by superposition (cf. Sec. 10.10). At points where the crests coincide, the combined wave will have a large effect, as shown at O and P in the bottom curve of Fig. 24.9, while at points halfway between these maxima the resultant wave may vanish or nearly vanish, because of the destructive interference of the two waves.

If, instead of two waves, we add together a great many waves of wavelengths very close to one another, but not identical, we can arrange that all of these waves reinforce one another at the origin. As we go away from the origin, the waves will reinforce one another less and less and the result of their superposition will be a pattern like that shown in Fig. 24.10. Such a pattern is called a ***wave packet***. Within a small region near the origin, all the waves reinforce one another and we have a large amplitude. As we progress further away from the origin the waves get out of step with one another and cancel out. A wave packet is therefore a local disturbance, resulting from the superposition of a large number of waves which interfere destructively everywhere except in the immediate neighborhood of the packet.

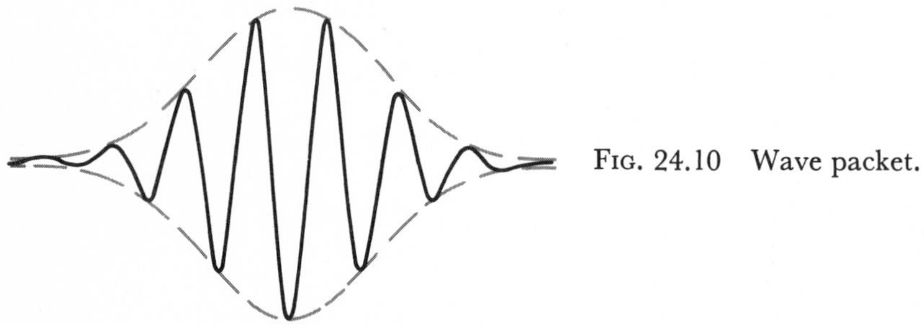

FIG. 24.10 Wave packet.

If all the waves which form the wave packet move with the same speed, then the packet will also move at that speed. We shall now investigate what happens if the waves that combine to form the wave packet move at slightly different speeds.

24.9 Wave Velocity and Group Velocity

Let us now consider the addition of two waves of different wavelengths λ_1 and λ_2 and of respective wave speeds W_1 and W_2. Suppose for the moment that λ_1 is smaller than λ_2, as indicated in Fig. 24.11 and that W_1 is greater than W_2. Initially the two peaks A_1 and A_2 are in coincidence. Peak B_2 will then be ahead of B_1 by a distance $(\lambda_2 - \lambda_1)$. As time goes on, A_1 will get ahead of A_2 while B_1 catches up with B_2. The interference crest will therefore progress to the right along the pattern until points B_1 and B_2 are reinforcing, instead of A_1 and A_2. The time taken by B_1 to catch up with B_2 will be given by

$$T(W_1 - W_2) = (\lambda_2 - \lambda_1).$$

During this time T the crest A_1 will have moved forward a distance $W_1 T$. However, the point at which the two waves reinforce will have moved along the first wave from A_1 to B_1, i.e., a distance λ_1. Thus the total distance traveled by the point of reinforcement will be

$$W_1 T + \lambda_1,$$

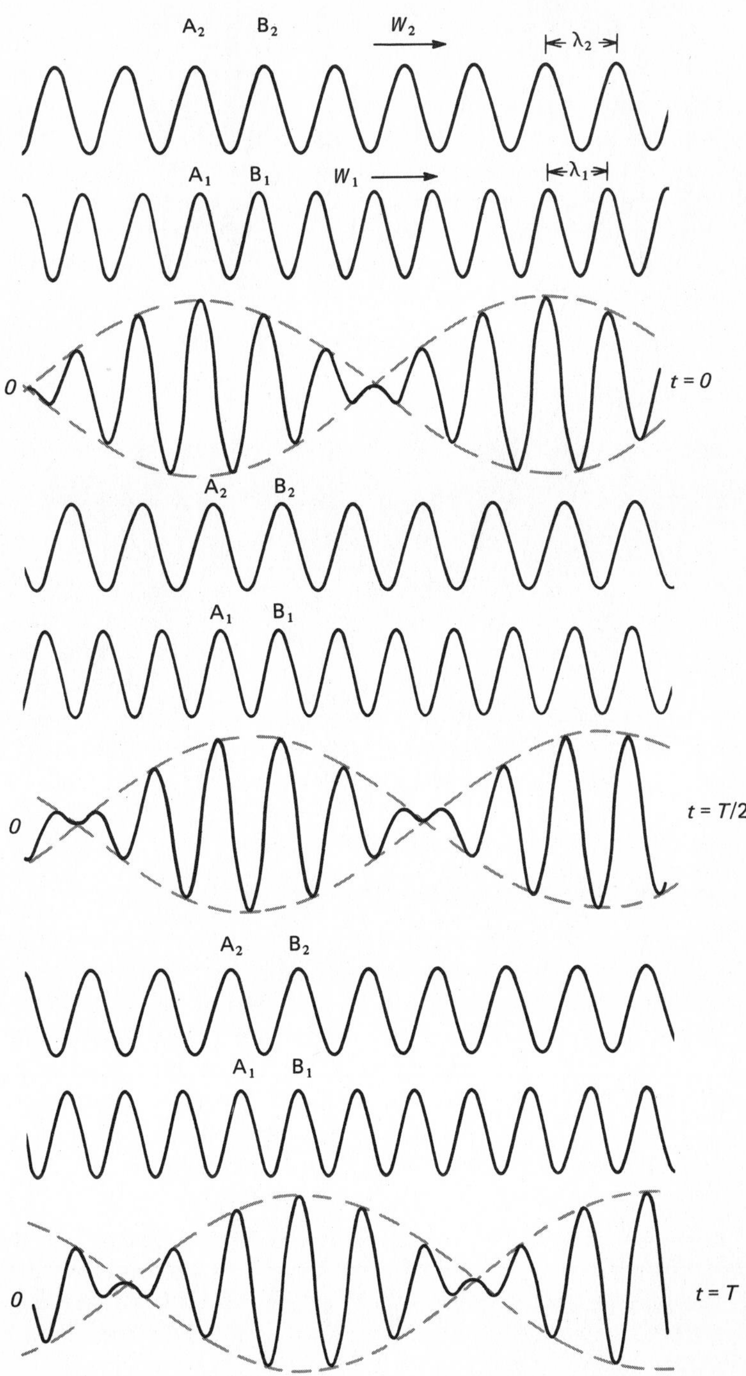

FIG. 24.11 Group velocity.

and the velocity G of this point will be found in the usual way to be

$$G = W_1 + \lambda_1/T = W_1 + \lambda_1(W_1 - W_2)/(\lambda_2 - \lambda_1)$$
$$= (\lambda_2 W_1 - \lambda_1 W_2)/(\lambda_2 - \lambda_1). \quad (24.9\text{-}1)$$

This equation for G can be put into slightly more convenient form if we introduce a new quantity, called the ***wave number,*** defined as the reciprocal of the wavelength. Denoting the wave number by k, we have

$$k_1 = 1/\lambda_1 \qquad \text{and} \qquad k_2 = 1/\lambda_2 .$$

If we divide both the numerator and the denominator of the right-hand side of Eq. (24.9-1) by $\lambda_1\lambda_2$ and then substitute k for $1/\lambda$, we find that

$$G = (k_1 W_1 - k_2 W_2)/(k_1 - k_2).$$

Finally, rewriting Eq. (10.5-3) as

$$W = \nu\lambda = \nu/k$$

and substituting for W_1 and W_2, we obtain

$$G = (\nu_1 - \nu_2)/(k_1 - k_2). \quad (24.9\text{-}2)$$

The speed G defined by Eqs. (24.9-1) and (24.9-2) is called the ***group speed.*** It has been derived by the consideration of the speed of the point at which two waves reinforce. This point need not travel at the same speed as the waves but may travel much faster or much slower. A little consideration will tell us that if we are interested in the point of reinforcement of a large number of waves, all of nearly the same wavelength, as we were in the wave packet of the preceding section, then *the wave packet or wave group will travel at the group speed rather than the wave speed*, and this speed can be either faster or slower than the wave speed of the waves in the group, depending on the way in which the wave speed varies with the frequency.

EXERCISES

24.9-1 A lake contains 25×10^7 cu ft of water and is known to contain 10×10^5 fish, which may be assumed to be distributed uniformly throughout the volume. A bucket of 1.0 cu ft volume is repeatedly dipped into the lake, hauled out, and examined for fish, after which it is emptied back into the lake. What is the probability of finding a fish in the bucket after one dip? What is the probable number of fish that would be found sometimes during 1000 dips of the bucket? Would you be surprised to find one fish during the first 100 dips? No fish? One hundred fish? State reasons for each answer.

24.9-2 As was pointed out in Sec. 12.19, most materials show a dependence of the wave speed of light on the frequency. Suppose that a light signal composed of a combination of two waves, $\lambda = 4861$ Å and $\lambda = 5893$ Å (both measured in vacuo) is sent through water. Using the data of Table 12.1, calculate the wavelength of each wave in the water. Show that the combined effect of the two waves will be a series of pulses. Find the time between these pulses and the speed with which they move through the water.

24.9-3 Reproduce the argument of Sec. 24.9 for a case in which $\lambda_2 > \lambda_1$, but $W_2 > W_1$, and show that the group velocity in this case is also given by Eq. (24.9-2).

24.9-4 An experiment of the Fizeau type (cf. Sec. 3.7) is used to measure the speed of light through water. Does it measure the wave or group speed? Explain your answer.

24.9-5 Light of a known frequency ν is allowed to fall on a diffraction grating, the apparatus being under water. The wavelength λ is thus determined and the product $\nu\lambda$ is computed. Is this the wave or group speed? Explain your answer.

24.10 A Note on Complex Numbers and Wave Amplitudes

Many mathematicians have concerned themselves with ***complex numbers.*** These numbers differ from real numbers in that they contain both a *real* part and an *imaginary* part, the latter being the product of a real number by $i = \sqrt{-1}$. The general complex number may be written as

$$a + ib,$$

where a and b are both real.

There is another form of the complex number that is very useful. It is shown in many mathematics texts that

$$e^{i\theta} = \cos\theta + i\sin\theta, \tag{24.10-1}$$

where e is the base of the ***natural logarithms*** equal to 2.71828. . . . This equality is known as the ***de Moivre theorem.*** The proof of the theorem is outlined in Appendix K.

If we now substitute ωt in Eq. (24.10-1) and multiply $e^{i\theta}$ by a constant A, we get

$$Ae^{i\omega t} = A\cos\omega t + iA\sin\omega t. \tag{24.10-2}$$

This looks very much like the equations used in Sec. 22.1 to describe vibrations. We can, in fact, use it for this purpose if we observe one precaution. We must deal in physics with real quantities wherever we talk about actual measureable things, like displacements, velocities, energies, etc. We shall therefore say that, whenever we use Eq. (24.10-2) to describe a vibration, *we shall take only the real part* of any answer that it gives us before attempting to compare that answer with experiments or observations. As a concrete example, suppose that we employ Eq. (24.10-2) to describe the free and undamped motion of a mass suspended by a spring (Sec. 22.2). We then have

$$x = A\cos\omega_0 t + iA\sin\omega_0 t,$$

where

$$\omega_0 = (k/m)^{1/2}.$$

We want x to be real but it will be complex if A is real. Let us, therefore, make A a complex amplitude, equal to $(a + ib)$. We can then rewrite the equation for x:

$$x = a\cos\omega_0 t + ib\cos\omega_0 t + ia\sin\omega_0 t - b\sin\omega_0 t,$$

where the sign of the last term results from the fact that $i^2 = -1$. Regrouping, we find that

$$x = [a \cos \omega_0 t - b \sin \omega_0 t] + i[a \sin \omega_0 t + b \cos \omega_0 t].$$

The real part of this expression is

$$x_{\text{Real}} = a \cos \omega_0 t - b \sin \omega_0 t,$$

which we can rewrite by using the result of Ex. 22.1-3:

$$x_{\text{Real}} = (a^2 + b^2)^{1/2} \cos (\omega_0 t + \phi),$$

where

$$\tan \phi = -b/a.$$

The amplitude of the vibration is therefore $(a^2 + b^2)^{1/2}$. We now define a new term, the complex conjugate of a complex number. If the number is $(a + ib)$, its ***complex conjugate*** is $a - ib$. The complex conjugate is often denoted by an asterisk, thus if

$$A = a + ib, \qquad A^* = a - ib. \tag{24.10-3}$$

Finally, let us take the quantity

$$AA^* = (a + ib)(a - ib) = a^2 + iab - iab + b^2 = a^2 + b^2 \tag{24.10-4}$$

This is real and positive and is exactly the square of the amplitude of the motion described above. When we use an expression of the form of Eq. (24.10-2) to describe a vibration, we must generally take A as complex and then say that the real amplitude is the square root of the product AA^*.

We may now turn to the description of a wave. For the present we can limit ourselves to the simple case of a one-dimensional wave motion, say a wave moving in the z-direction and with displacement depending on z and t only, i.e., being independent of x and y. We shall also, for simplicity, suppose the wave to be sinusoidal and unattenuated, i.e., with a constant amplitude that does not depend on z. We saw in Chapters 10, and 23 that the displacement at any fixed location varies sinusoidally with time. By choosing the origin of time properly, we can represent the displacement at $z = 0$ as

$$\psi_{z=0} = Ae^{i\omega t},$$

where A is the complex amplitude and ω is the radian frequency. Let us suppose that the wave is moving in the $+z$-direction with a wave speed W. Then a point at $+z$ will have the same displacement at time $t = z/W$, which is just the time taken for the wave to travel from the origin to $+z$. We can therefore get an expression for the displacement at any point by writing

$$\psi = Ae^{i\omega(t - z/W)}.$$

This can be put into a more convenient form by substituting $\nu\lambda = \omega\lambda/2\pi$ for W, ν being the frequency $(=\omega/2\pi)$ and λ being the wavelength. We then have

$$\psi = Ae^{i(\omega t - 2\pi z/\lambda)}. \tag{24.10-5A}$$

It is left as an exercise for the reader to show that a wave traveling in the $-z$-direction can be described by

$$\psi = Ae^{i(\omega t + 2\pi z/\lambda)}. \tag{24.10-5B}$$

At first glance it appears that we have merely complicated our description of vibrations and waves by introducing complex numbers. We shall see later, however, that Eqs. (24.10-5A) and (24.10-5B) are essential for the discussion of some waves.

24.11 Schroedinger Waves

Considerations similar to those of Secs. 24.8 and 24.9 led Schroedinger to the formulation of ***wave mechanics.*** If the velocity v of a particle is known precisely, then that particle can be represented by a plane wave traveling in the direction of motion of the particle, the wave speed being c^2/v, as given by Eq. (24.4-5). This wave will have the precise wavelength $\lambda = h/mv$, given by Eq. (24.4-4). The wave is specified by Eq. (24.10-5A) as

$$\psi = Ae^{i(\omega t - 2\pi z/\lambda)}.$$

When we use the relations $E = h\nu = h\omega/2\pi$ and $\lambda = h/p$, this equation becomes

$$\psi = Ae^{(2\pi i/h)(Et - pz)}, \tag{24.11-1}$$

which is the equation of a sinusoidal wave moving in the $+z$-direction. Correspondingly, a wave with a precisely known speed v that is moving in the $-z$-direction is described by

$$\psi = Ae^{(2\pi i/h)(Et + pz)}. \tag{24.11-2}$$

The Heisenberg uncertainty principle tells us that, since we know the momentum of either of these particles precisely, we can have no knowledge of its position—it can be located anywhere between $z = -\infty$ and $z = +\infty$. This is confirmed if we compute $\psi\psi^*$ from either Eq. (24.11-1) or Eq. (24.11-2). We know that $e^{i\theta}e^{-i\theta} = e^0 = 1$. Therefore,

$$\psi\psi^* = A^2 e^{(2\pi i/h)(Et \pm pz)} e^{-(2\pi i/h)(Et \pm pz)} = A^2,$$

a quantity that is independent of z. The particle is equally likely to be anywhere along the z-axis.

If we wish to specify even approximately where the particle is in this wave, we shall have to construct a wave packet for it. This wave packet will locate the electron to any accuracy we like, but by constructing it we shall be forced to sacrifice knowledge of the momentum of the particle since we shall have to use a range of wavelengths λ, and, by Eq. (24.4-2) this means a range of momentum p. We cannot carry out the calculations here, but it may be shown that the range of momenta Δp necessary to locate a particle within a certain Δx is that given by Eq. (24.6-3).

It is now important to prove that the speed of the Schroedinger wave packet is just that of the particle as required by classical mechanics. If the speed v of the electron (of rest mass m_0) is small compared with the speed of light, we can write its total energy in the form [cf. Eq. (8.11-5)]:

$$E = m_0c^2 + \tfrac{1}{2}m_0v^2 = m_0c^2 + p^2/2m_0,$$

since the momentum $p = mv$. We now consider two electrons having momenta p_1 and p_2 very close to one another. Then

$$\begin{aligned} E_1 - E_2 &= (m_0c^2 + p_1^2/2m_0) - (m_0c^2 + p_2^2/2m_0) \\ &= (p_1^2 - p_2^2)/2m_0 = (p_1 - p_2)(p_1 + p_2)/2m_0. \end{aligned}$$

If we write $p = (p_1 + p_2)/2$ for the average momentum of the two, we have

$$E_1 - E_2 = h(\nu_1 - \nu_2) = p(p_1 - p_2)/m_0,$$

and it follows that

$$\nu_1 - \nu_2 = p(p_1 - p_2)/hm_0. \tag{24.11-3}$$

Using de Broglie's relation, Eq. (24.4-2), we can write for the difference of the wave numbers

$$k_1 - k_2 = (1/\lambda_1) - (1/\lambda_2) = (p_1/h) - (p_2/h) = (p_1 - p_2)/h. \tag{24.11-4}$$

Substituting the values of Eqs. (24.-11.3) and (24.11-4) into the expression of Eq. (24.9-2) for the group speed, we get

$$G = \frac{[p(p_1 - p_2)/hm_0]}{[(p_1 - p_2)/h]} = \frac{p}{m_0} = v. \tag{24.11-5}$$

Thus *the group speed for the Schroedinger waves is exactly the particle speed of classical mechanics. We may therefore consider the wave packet to represent the particle, since it coincides with the particle in position and velocity.*

Thus if we wish to talk of a particle located near a point x at a particular time $t = 0$, and traveling with a momentum approximately p, we must construct a wave packet of Schroedinger waves using wavelengths corresponding to momenta near p. These waves coincide initially near x. The packet thus formed will move with a velocity $p/m = v$. Thus in the Schroedinger wave mechanics, the wave packet moves with the same speed as the particle, although the waves themselves move with the speed c^2/v, which is greater than the speed of light. It may seem that the fact that these waves travel at a speed greater than the speed of light is contradictory to Einstein's relativity theory. This theory, however, states only that mass or energy cannot travel at a speed greater than that of light, and according to the Schroedinger theory, mass travels at the group speed v and not at the wave speed c^2/v.

When a particle is subject to a force, the momentum p will change, and consequently the wavelength will change. In the Schroedinger theory this change of momentum follows the classical law of Eq. (4.9-2) although Schroedinger has developed an entirely new technique for handling such problems, especially adapted to the study of atomic mechanics.

We might ask why it is necessary or desirable to develop a new approach to mechanics, in view of the great success that the mechanics of Newton and Einstein have had in correlating physical phenomena. The fact is that, although the classical approaches have been very successful in dealing with the description of the behavior of large bodies, they have failed in many ways in dealing with small particles, such as the electron, the proton, and the neutron, especially when these particles are interacting with each other or with photons. We now believe that the failure of the old methods in these cases was due to the fact that our description of the particles as particles was incomplete in that it neglected their wave properties. Because of the very short wavelength of the Schroedinger waves associated with large bodies, the incompleteness of description is not important in dealing with them. The newer mechanics of Heisenberg and Schroedinger allow us to deal with either the particle or wave properties and to pass from one description to another with the help of the de Broglie relationships, Eqs. (24.4-1) and (24.4-2), whenever it is convenient to do so. The degree of success that can be achieved by this technique will be illustrated in the next chapter.

24.12 Standing Schroedinger Waves

Suppose that a particle of mass m, e.g., a gas molecule, is enclosed within a box, from which it cannot escape. For the moment we consider only one component of its motion, say along the $+x$- and $-x$-directions, and suppose two walls of the box, separated by a distance L, to be perpendicular to the x-axis at $x=\frac{1}{2}L$ and $x=-\frac{1}{2}L$. We know nothing about the location of the particle at any instant, but we do know that the kinetic energy associated with the x-component of motion has some fixed value E and that the x-component of momentum is $p=\pm\sqrt{2E/m}$. Hence we can write the Schroedinger wave as

$$\psi = Ae^{(2\pi i/h)(Et-px)} + Be^{(2\pi i/h)(Et+px)}, \tag{24.12-1}$$

where the first term on the right represents a wave moving in the $+x$-direction and the second represents one moving in the $-x$-direction [Eqs. (24.11-1) and (24.11-2)].

We may now take account of the fact that the particle cannot get out of the box. The probability of finding it with $x>\frac{1}{2}L$ or $x<-\frac{1}{2}L$ must be zero. We expect that ψ will vary continuously with x, so we will require that it (and the probability) vanish when $x=\pm\frac{1}{2}L$. Substituting $x=\pm\frac{1}{2}L$ into the expression for ψ, we obtain

$$\begin{aligned}\psi &= Ae^{(2\pi i/h)(Et\mp pL/2)} + Be^{(2\pi i/h)(Et\pm pL/2)}\\ &= (Ae^{\mp\pi i pL/h} + Be^{\pm\pi i pL/h})e^{2\pi i Et/h} = 0.\end{aligned} \tag{24.12-2}$$

We may now apply the de Moivre theorem [Eq. (24.10-1)] to show that

$$e^{-\pi i pL/h} = \cos\,(\pi pL/h) - i\sin\,(\pi pL/h)$$

and

$$e^{\pi i pL/h} = \cos\,(\pi pL/h) + i\sin\,(\pi pL/h).$$

Substituting these values into Eq. (24.12-2) and rearranging terms, we find that

$$[(A+B)\cos(\pi pL/h) \pm i(B-A)\sin(\pi pL/h)]\, e^{2\pi iEt/h} = 0.$$

There are two ways to make the expression inside the square brackets vanish:

(1) Let $B=-A$, causing the first term to vanish, and require that $\sin(\pi pL/h)=0$, i.e., that $\pi pL/h = k\pi$, where k is any integer. Solving for p, we have

$$p = kh/L,$$

which is convenient to write as

$$p = 2kh/2L.$$

(2) Let $B=A$, causing the second term to vanish, and requiring that $\cos(\pi pL/h)=0$, i.e., that $\pi pL/h = (2k+1)(\pi/2)$, where k again is any integer. We then have

$$p = (2k+1)h/2L.$$

Method (1) gives p as any even integer times $h/2L$; method (2) gives p as any odd integer times $h/2L$. Hence we can write a general expression for the magnitude of the momentum:

$$p_n = nh/2L, \tag{24.12-3}$$

where n is any positive integer and where the subscript n indicates that there are many possible values of p, one corresponding to every positive integer n.

The requirement that $A=\pm B$, and hence that $AA^* = BB^*$, makes sense—we are equally likely to find the particle moving to the right or to the left. Equation (24.12-3), however, tells us something new. The magnitude of the momentum can take on only certain values, connected to each other by integers. The momenta are limited in much the same way as are the harmonic frequencies of a stretched spring. We have found that Eq. (24.12-1), when subject to the ***boundary conditions*** of Eq. (24.12-2), has solutions only for particular values of p. These values are known as ***eigen values*** (*eigen* from the German and meaning "characteristic" or "proper") the quantity ψ is called an ***eigen function.***

Knowing the eigen values of the momentum, we can find those of the energy to be

$$E_n = p_n^2/2m = n^2h^2/8mL^2. \tag{24.12-4}$$

This is exactly the kind of result that we anticipated in Sec. 24.2, when we concluded that Planck's hypothesis required that only certain values of energy were possible for an oscillator. We speak of a particle having the energy E_n as being in the ***n^{th} state.***

Figure 24.12a indicates schematically the possible energy levels of a particle in a one-dimensional box and Fig. 24.12b the nature of the wave functions ψ for each level (cf. Figs. 10.18–10.21). To see that ψ varies in the manner shown

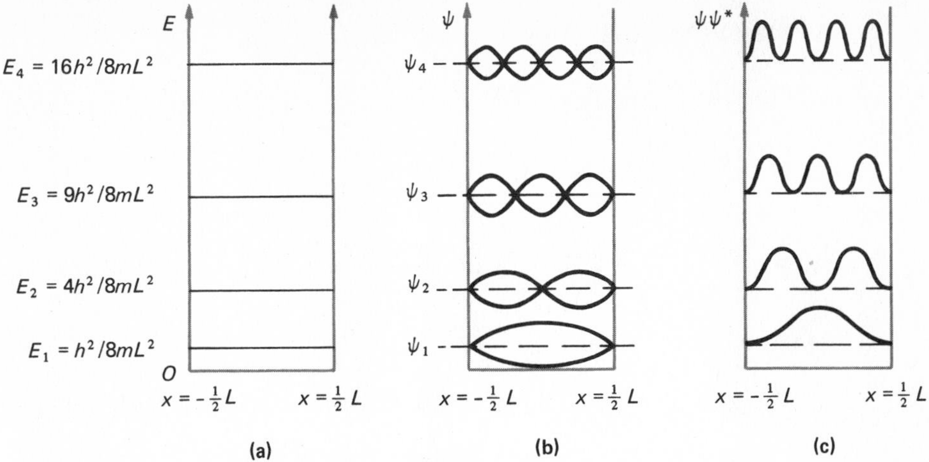

FIG. 24.12 Characteristics of a particle in a box. (a) Energy levels, (b) wave functions, (c) probability amplitude.

in Fig. 24.12b, we substitute the eigen values of p_n and E_n into Eq. (24.12-1), at the same time making $B = \pm A$, depending on whether n is odd or even. For n odd we make $B = A$ and get

$$\begin{aligned} \psi_{\text{odd}} &= Ae^{2\pi iE_nt/h}[e^{-\pi inx/2L} + e^{+\pi inx/2L}] \\ &= Ae^{2\pi iE_nt/h}[\cos(\pi nx/2L) - i\sin(\pi nx/2L) + \cos(\pi nx/2L) \\ &\quad + i\sin(\pi nx/2L)] \\ &= 2A\cos(\pi nx/2L)\, e^{2\pi iE_nt/h}. \end{aligned} \tag{24.12-5}$$

For all odd n, then, ψ varies sinusoidally with time at every point, but its amplitude varies from zero at $x = \pm\frac{1}{2}L$ to a maximum value at the center, with possible minima and maxima in between if $n \geqq 3$. For even n, the same procedure, except that $B = -A$, gives

$$\psi_{\text{even}} = 2iA\sin(\pi nx/2L)\, e^{2\pi iE_n t/h}. \tag{24.12-6}$$

Equations (24.12-5) and (24.12-6) describe the standing wave patterns shown in Fig. 24.12.

Finally, we calculate the probability of finding the particle in any small region of x between $-\frac{1}{2}L$ and $+\frac{1}{2}L$, say between x and $x + dx$. This probability is proportional to $\psi\psi^*$, which for odd n is

$$(\psi\psi^*)_{\text{odd}} = 4A^2\cos^2(\pi nx/2L)$$

and for even n is

$$(\psi\psi^*)_{\text{even}} = 4A^2\sin^2(\pi nx/2L).$$

We can therefore say that dP, the probability of finding the particle between x and $x + dx$ at any instant is

$$dP = \psi\psi^*\, dx. \tag{24.12-7}$$

The probability that the particle is somewhere between $-\frac{1}{2}L$ and $+\frac{1}{2}L$ is unity. Therefore, we know that

$$\int_{-\frac{1}{2}L}^{\frac{1}{2}L} \psi\psi^* \, dx = 1. \tag{24.12-8}$$

The reasoning used in Sec. 22.5 in connection with Fig. 22.3 makes it clear that

$$\int_{-n\pi/2}^{n\pi/2} \cos^2 \theta \, d\theta = \tfrac{1}{2}n\pi.$$

If we substitute θ for $(\pi nx/2L)$ in the expression for $(\psi\psi^*)_{\text{odd}}$ and hence let $dx = (2L/\pi n)\, d\theta$, we find that

$$\int_{-\frac{1}{2}L}^{\frac{1}{2}L} \psi\psi^* \, dx = (4A^2)(2L/\pi n)\int_{-n\pi/2}^{n\pi/2} \cos^2 \theta \, d\theta = (8A^2L/\pi n)(\tfrac{1}{2}n\pi) = 4A^2L.$$

An exactly similar procedure shows that the same result is obtained for even n. Hence we have

$$A^2 = 1/4L,$$

so that

$$(\psi\psi^*)_{\text{odd}} = (1/L) \cos^2 (\pi nx/2L)$$

and

$$(\psi\psi^*)_{\text{even}} = (1/L) \sin^2 (\pi nx/2L).$$

These probabilities per unit distance are plotted in Fig. 24.12c.

We have dealt only with a one-dimensional case, in which the particle shuttles back and forth between parallel walls. It is very easy to extend the results we have obtained to a three-dimensional rectangular box (see Prob. 24.8). It is found that in such a box, with sides of length a, b, and c, the energy levels are given by

$$E_{k,l,n} = (h^2/8m)\left(\frac{k^2}{a^2} + \frac{l^2}{b^2} + \frac{n^2}{c^2}\right), \tag{24.12-9}$$

where k, l, and n are integers.

24.13 *Reflection of Electrons from a Potential Step*

The quantum mechanics have many consequences other than the existence of eigen values of the energy. To examine just one of these, consider the situation indicated in Fig. 24.13. A beam of electrons is coming from the left, each electron having a kinetic energy E. At $x = 0$ the beam encounters a sudden change in electrical potential, $-V_0$, so that any electron crossing the plane $x = 0$ has a kinetic energy $(E - eV_0)$. We wish to inquire what happens at the potential step at $x = 0$.

We can describe the incident beam of electrons by a wave function

$$\psi_{\text{i}} = Ae^{2\pi iEt/h}\, e^{-2\pi ipx/h},$$

which we take over from Eq. (24.11-1). It will be convenient to abbreviate our notation by setting $2\pi p/h$ equal to a constant α. The wave function then takes the form

$$\psi_i = Ae^{2\pi i Et/h}\, e^{-i\alpha x}.$$

Any electrons that pass $x = 0$ form a transmitted beam. The wave function is

$$\psi_t = Be^{2\pi i Et/h}\, e^{-i\beta x}$$

where $\beta = (2\pi/h)[2(E - eV_0)/m]^{1/2}$.

A new rule must now be introduced to be used in dealing with wave functions. In Sec. 24.12 it was required that ψ be continuous, i.e., that it should not undergo abrupt changes between any one point and a closely neighboring

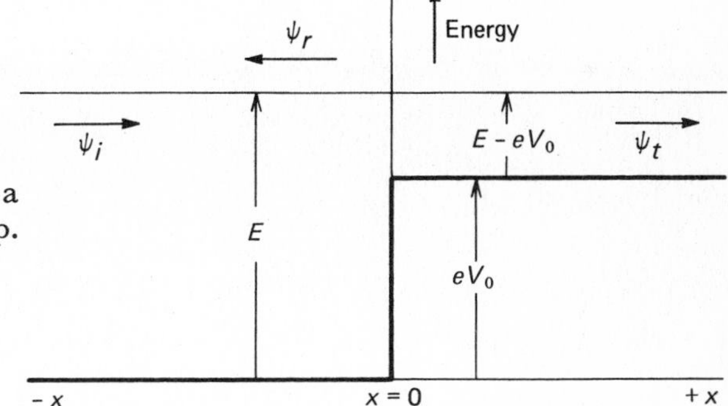

FIG. 24.13 Electron impinging on a potential step.

point. Actually, it has been found necessary to also require that the derivatives of ψ be continuous. Thus in the present case we demand that $d\psi/dx$ be continuous at $x = 0$. We did not satisfy this condition in Sec. 24.12 (notice in Fig. 24.12b that $d\psi/dx$ is zero to the right of $x = \frac{1}{2}L$ but that it is not zero to the left of that point). We were able to violate the requirement only because we were not dealing with a physically realizable situation—no box is so strong that a particle of sufficient energy cannot break through its walls. We must, however, now take it into account.

Let us now try to satisfy both continuity conditions at $x = 0$. Setting $\psi_i = \psi_t$ at this plane gives

$$A = B.$$

Setting $d\psi_i/dx = d\psi_t/dx$ at $x = 0$ [remembering that $(d/dx)\, e^{i\alpha x} = i\alpha e^{i\alpha x}$ and that $e^0 = 1$] gives

$$-i\alpha A = -i\beta B,$$

or

$$A = \beta B/\alpha.$$

We know that $\beta \neq \alpha$ unless we are dealing with the trivial case of $V_0 = 0$. Therefore the two equations relating A and B are inconsistent. Something is seriously wrong! We can escape the difficulty only by supposing that some electrons are reflected from the potential step. This would be absurd in classical mechanics, because every electron has sufficient energy to get past the step and can be expected to do so.

If some electrons are reflected, we may represent them by a wave going to the left, so we have

$$\psi_r = Ce^{2\pi iEt/h}\, e^{i\alpha x},$$

which is like the expression for ψ_i except that the sign of α changes—we replace p by $-p$. We may now rewrite our continuity conditions at $x = 0$:

$$\psi_i + \psi_r = \psi_t,$$

$$\frac{d\psi_i}{dx} + \frac{d\psi_r}{dx} = \frac{d\psi_t}{dx}.$$

The first of these equations gives

$$A + C = B \tag{24.13-1}$$

and the second gives

$$-i\alpha A + i\alpha C = i\beta B. \tag{24.13-2}$$

We may substitute the value of B from Eq. (24.13-1) into Eq. (24.13-2) to find that

$$-\alpha A + \alpha C = -\beta A - \beta C,$$

so that

$$\frac{C}{A} = \frac{\alpha - \beta}{\alpha + \beta} = \frac{E^{1/2} - (E - eV_0)^{1/2}}{E^{1/2} + (E - eV_0)^{1/2}}. \tag{24.13-3}$$

Substitution of the value of C from this equation into Eq. (24.13-1) shows that

$$\frac{B}{A} = \frac{2\alpha}{\alpha + \beta} = \frac{2E^{1/2}}{E^{1/2} + (E - eV_0)^{1/2}}. \tag{24.13-4}$$

The assumption of a reflected wave, a purely quantum mechanical phenomenon, allows us to satisfy the boundary conditions at the potential step.

Remembering that the probability of finding an electron at any point is proportional to $\psi\psi^*$ at that point, we can calculate how many of the electrons are transmitted past the step and how many are reflected from it. We take A, B, and C here as real. The number of electrons per unit length in the incident beam is then proportional to A^2, and the incident current [cf. Eq. (17.2-1)] is proportional to the density of electrons times their velocity, p/m, where $p = (2Em)^{1/2}$. Similarly, the transmitted current is proportional to $B^2[2(E - eV_0)/m]^{1/2}$ and the reflected current to C^2p/m. The ratio of the reflected current to the incident current is

$$\frac{C^2p/m}{A^2p/m} = \frac{(\alpha - \beta)^2}{(\alpha + \beta)^2}. \tag{24.13-5}$$

Similarly, the ratio of the transmitted current to the incident current is

$$\frac{B^2[2(E-eV_0)/m]^{1/2}}{A^2(2E/m)^{1/2}}=\frac{4\alpha\beta}{(\alpha+\beta)^2}. \tag{24.13-6}$$

We may check our results in part by seeing whether the sum of the transmitted and reflected currents is equal to the incident current. We find that

$$\frac{C^2\alpha}{A^2\alpha}+\frac{B^2\beta}{A^2\alpha}=\frac{\alpha^2-2\alpha\beta+\beta^2+4\alpha\beta}{(\alpha+\beta)^2}=1,$$

so that electrons are conserved.

The difference between the quantum mechanical behavior indicated in this reflection from a potential step and the behavior that would be expected classically has many interesting consequences. We shall investigate some of them in Probs. 24.11–24.13.

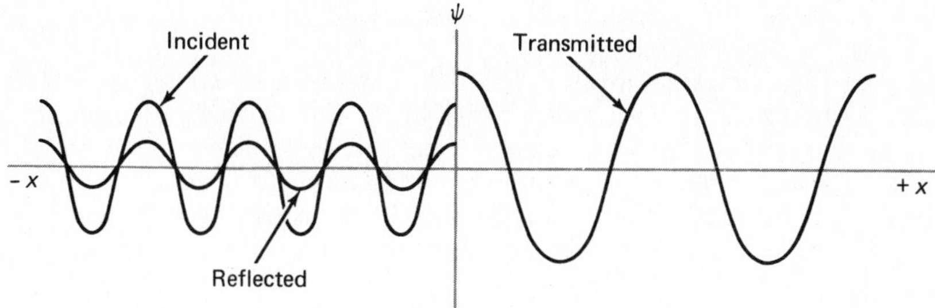

FIG. 24.14 Wave functions at a potential step (real part).

24.14 *Summary*

In the earlier chapters it was established that light can be discussed in terms of either a photon theory or a wave theory. The results of Planck on heat radiation, of Einstein on the photoelectric effect, and of Compton on the scattering of x-rays force attention on the particle aspects of light, while the results on interference and diffraction present equally potent arguments for a wave theory. The work of de Broglie, Heisenberg, and Schroedinger shows that this duality is fundamental. In the theory which they developed, light waves are the probability waves for photons, and photons are wave packets formed of light waves. The Schroedinger waves are probability waves for material particles, and the material particles are wave packets formed of the Schroedinger waves. The concept of wave-particle duality thus has been extended to cover all physical phenomena. By introducing complex numbers, we have been able to arrive at a more flexible equation describing waves, and we have applied this equation to particles that are bound within a box, finding that such particles are allowed only certain discrete energies, rather than a continuous range of energies. It has also been shown that the quantum mechanics of Schroedinger and Heisenberg predict different behavior for an electron encountering a sudden step in potential than do the classical mechanics of Newton.

PROBLEMS

24.1 The rotations of molecules are quantized, i.e., the energy of rotation is equal to $nh\nu$, where ν is the rotational frequency, h is Planck's constant, and n is any positive integer. Consider a molecule composed of two atoms, each of mass m, in rotation about an axis perpendicular to the line joining them and passing through their center of mass. The nuclei of the atoms are separated by a distance r_0.

(a) Show that the possible rotational frequencies are $\nu_n = nh/\pi^2 m r_0^2$. (b) Find the lowest frequency of rotation of the hydrogen molecule, for which r_0 is known to be 1.2 Å. (c) What is the ratio of the lowest energy associated with this rotation to $\frac{1}{2}kT$ (the average energy per degree of freedom according to classical kinetic theory), at 300°K?

24.2 The molar specific heat at constant volume of a diatomic gas at room temperature is $5RT/2$, corresponding to three degrees of translational freedom and two degrees of rotational freedom (Sec. 20.9). We might have expected three degrees of rotational freedom, since there are three mutually independent axes about which the molecule may rotate, two perpendicular to each other and to the line joining the nuclei of the atoms, and one along that line.

(a) Using the information given in Prob. 24.1 and remembering that proton has a radius of about 10^{-15} m, find the order of magnitude of the lowest rotational frequency of the hydrogen molecule about an axis through the two nuclei.

(b) Find the lowest energy of rotation about this axis.

(c) Compute the ratio of this energy to $\frac{1}{2}kT$ at 300°K. Would you expect an appreciable fraction of the molecules to possess enough energy so that rotation about this axis can take place at 300°K?

24.3 (a) Use the data given in Prob. 24.1 to calculate the temperature at which the energy of rotation of a hydrogen molecule about an axis perpendicular to the line joining the nuclei would be equal to $\frac{1}{2}kT$.

(b) If the temperature of hydrogen gas were much lower than that computed in (a), what value would you expect for the molar specific heat at constant volume?

24.4 The Heisenberg uncertainty principle may be considered to be at the very heart of quantum mechanics, and many results can be deduced from it without any recourse to complicated mathematical machinery. Consider the particle in the one-dimensional box of Sec. 24.12.

(a) If $n = 0$ in Eq. (24.12-3), what is the uncertainty in the momentum?

(b) *Estimate* the uncertainty of the position in which we might find the particle if we observed it at any instant.

(c) Show from the results of (a) and (b) that the state with $n = 0$ cannot exist, and so justify the statement made in the text that n must be a positive integer, i.e., greater than zero.

24.5 Using your estimate of the uncertainty in position from part (b) of Prob. 24.4, find the minimal uncertainty Δp in the momentum of the particle. The momentum cannot be much less than its uncertainty. Using this fact, show that the lowest momentum of a particle in a one-dimensional box is of the order of magnitude to that given by Eq. (24.12-3).

24.6 A particle of mass m is subject to a restoring force equal to $-kx$, where x is its displacement from the equilibrium position and k is a constant. Suppose that the particle is undergoing one-dimensional simple harmonic motion under the action of this force.

(a) Show that it is impossible for this system to be in a state of zero energy. (Cf. Prob. 24.4.)

(b) By estimating the uncertainties in position and momentum, both in terms of the amplitude of the motion, show that the lowest energy of the oscillator is of the order of magnitude of $h\omega/4\pi$, where $\omega = (k/m)^{1/2}$. (Cf. Prob. 24.5.)

24.7 The Heisenberg uncertainty principle was stated in Eq. (24.6-3) in terms of the uncertainties in momentum (Δp) and position (Δx). Corresponding relations can be developed for the uncertainties in any two variables whose product has the dimensions of h.

(a) Express Δp and Δx for a moving particle in terms of uncertainties in its energy ΔE and the time at which it is observed (Δt). Hence show that

$$\Delta E \, \Delta t \gtrsim \hbar.$$

(b) Hence show that a quantized oscillator that remains in oscillation for a time Δt must have a frequency that is indeterminate by an amount $\approx 1/\Delta t$.

24.8 Treat the problem of a particle in a three-dimensional rectangular box in a manner similar to that used in starting the development of kinetic theory in Sec. 20.8, i.e., by considering each component of momentum separately. Using the results of Sec. 24.12, find the kinetic energy in terms of the three components of momenta, and hence show that Eq. (24.12-9) is correct.

24.9 Apply the result of Prob. 24.8 to hydrogen molecules in a cubical box of length L on a side.

(a) Show that the energy levels available to the molecule can be expressed as

$$E_N = h^2N^2/8mL^2,$$

where m is the mass of a single molecule and N^2 is the sum of the squares of any three positive integers.

(b) If $L = 10$ cm and a hydrogen molecule is moving at the root-mean-square speed characteristic of hydrogen at 300°K, what is the approximate value of N?

(c) Using the result obtained in (b), comment on the fact that classical kinetic theory gives good predictions for gases under usual conditions.

24.10 Electromagnetic waves, like Schroedinger waves, can produce standing waves if they are confined to some limited region by conducting walls, through which they cannot pass. Suppose that an electromagnetic wave exists in the region of space bounded by two parallel, perfectly conducting walls, located at $x = -\frac{1}{2}L$ and $x = +\frac{1}{2}L$. The only component of the electric field present is parallel to the z-axis.

(a) Using the fact that $\vec{E}$ at the surface of a perfect conductor must be perpendicular to the surface (Sec. 16.22 and Prob. 23.1) show that $E = 0$ at $x = \pm\frac{1}{2}L$.

(b) Combining the notation and reasoning of Sec. 24.12, with the result of (a), show that a standing wave must be set up, and that the frequency has eigen values

$$\nu_n = nc/2L,$$

where n is an integer and c is the speed of light.

(c) What is the direction of $\vec{B}$ in this wave? Is $\vec{B}$ zero at $x = \pm\frac{1}{2}L$?

24.11 Suppose that a beam of electrons approaches the step of Fig. 24.13 from the right with an energy $E - eV_0$. Show that some electrons will be reflected even by an accelerating step in potential and find the fraction of electrons that will be reflected.

24.12 Suppose that the electrons of Sec. 24.13 approach from the left, but have energy $E < eV_0$.

(a) Show that the conditions on ψ and $d\psi/dx$ can be met at $x = 0$ by assuming that the electrons can penetrate into the region in which classical physics says that they would have negative kinetic energies, i.e., to the right of the barrier. To do this, assume a wave function for $x \gtrless 0$:

$$\psi = Be^{2\pi iEt/h}\, e^{-\beta x}$$

where $\beta = (2\pi/h)[2(eV_0 - E)/m]^{1/2}$.

(b) Show that the reflected beam has the same current as the incident beam.

(c) Compute the wave functions at $t = 0$ (use the de Moivre theorem for the incident and reflected waves), taking the amplitude of the incident wave as 1 $m^{-1/2}$ and $E = \frac{1}{2}eV_0$. Plot these and compare your plot with Fig. 24.14.

24.13 Not only can particles penetrate into regions where they would be forbidden by classical mechanics, as shown in Prob. 24.12; they can pass through such a region and appear with positive kinetic energy on the other side. Consider a beam of electrons coming from the left (negative x) with a kinetic energy E. At $x = -a$ the potential changes from zero to eV_0, which is greater than E. At $x = +a$ the potential again drops to zero.

(a) Set up the following wave functions:

$$\psi_1 = Ae^{-i\alpha x} + De^{i\alpha x}, \qquad (x < -a)$$

$$\psi_2 = Be^{-\beta x} + Fe^{\beta x}, \qquad (-a < x < +a)$$

$$\psi_3 = Ce^{-i\alpha x}, \qquad (x > +a)$$

where $\alpha = (2E/m)^{1/2}$ and $\beta = [2(eV_0 - E)/m]^{1/2}$. Then write down the equations applicable at $x = \pm a$.

(b) Without going through the algebra needed to solve these equations, decide whether B, C, D, and F could be found in terms of A, α, and β.

(c) Show that the probability of any electron penetrating the barrier is CC^*/AA^*.

(d) *Sketch* the wave functions for the three regions, taking into account the way in which they match at $x = -a$ and $x = +a$.

24.14 Solve Prob. 24.13 completely and find how the probability of penetration depends on E, V_0, and a. (The algebra can be expected to become involved. It is probably best to solve the four simultaneous equations for C/A by the use of determinants.)

24.15 The assumption of Sec. 24.12, that a particle can be restrained strictly within a "box," is not entirely realistic; any particle can escape from a container if it has sufficient energy. A more physical picture is obtained if we consider a ***well,*** within which the potential energy of the particle is lower by a finite amount than it is outside. Consider a one-dimensional well for which the potential energy of an electron is zero for all x such that $a > x > -a$ and is eV_0 for all other x. An electron in this well has a kinetic energy $E (E < eV_0)$.

(a) *Sketch* wave functions for the two lowest energy states in a plot similar to Fig. 24.14. Show qualitatively that the wavelength for each of these states must be greater than it would be for the corresponding state in a box. Hence show that the magnitudes of the momentum and of the kinetic energy must be lower than in a box.

(b) Take the following expressions for the wave functions:

$$\psi_1 = De^{\beta x}, \qquad (x < -a)$$

$$\psi_2 = Ae^{-i\alpha x} + Be^{i\alpha x}, \qquad (+a \geq x \geq -a)$$

$$\psi_3 = Ce^{-\beta x}, \qquad (x > +a)$$

where A, B, C, and D are constants, $\alpha = (2E/m)^{1/2}$, and $\beta = [2(eV_0 - E)/m]^{1/2}$. By applying the proper boundary conditions, show that

$$B = -Ae^{2i\alpha a}[(\beta + i\alpha)/(\beta - i\alpha)],$$

and hence that ψ_2 is proportional to

$$\beta \sin [\alpha(a + x)] + \alpha \cos [\alpha(a + x)].$$

Note that this quantity goes to zero when

$$\tan[\alpha(a + x)] = \frac{\sin [\alpha(a + x)]}{\cos [\alpha(a + x)]} = -\frac{\alpha}{\beta}.$$

(c) Assume that $\beta \gg \alpha$ (a *very* deep well) and show that ψ_1 and ψ_3 then vanish.

REFERENCES

24A Morris Shamos, editor, *Great Experiments in Physics*, Holt, New York, 1960. Chapter 17 is an extract from Einstein's paper on the photoelectric effect. Appendix 5 presents excerpts from two of Compton's papers on the Compton effect.

24B Arthur H. Compton, "Scattering of X-rays as Particles," *American Journal of Physics*, vol. 29 pp. 817–820, 1961. A personal history of the Compton effect.

24C George P. Thomson, "Early Work in Electron Diffraction," *American Journal of Physics*, vol. 29, pp. 821–825, 1961. A personal account of an important discovery.

24D F. Rief, "Quantized Vortex Rings in Superfluid Helium," *Scientific American*, December 1964, pp. 116–122. Quantum phenomena on a large scale.

24E Fritz Reiche, *The Quantvm Theory*, Dutton, New York, 1922.

24F Ivan Simon, *Infrared Radiation* (Momentum Book No. 12), Van Nostrand, Princeton, 1966.

25 ⇨ *Atomic Theory*

25.1 Review of Evidence Regarding Atoms

The evidence from chemistry and electrochemistry (Chapter 18) forces us to believe that matter is composed of small finite particles, known as atoms. Without the assumption of the existence of such particles, it seems impossible to explain such well established facts as the law of definite proportions or Faraday's laws of electrolysis. As our study has progressed, we have found other and stronger reasons for believing that atoms exist, since we have found that the properties of gases (Chapter 20) and of solids and liquids (Chapter 21) can be correlated with each other on an atomic hypothesis. We have seen further that the mass spectrograph can be used to study the properties of individual atoms and that radioactive processes permit the study of single atomic events (Chapter 19).

While we were discussing atoms and molecules in Chapter 19, we were led to the conclusion that a single normal atom consists of a positively charged nucleus which carries most of its mass, and of a group of from one to about one hundred electrons, which are held in the neighborhood of the nucleus by electrostatic forces. We also saw that the nucleus itself probably consists of a number of protons and neutrons, and that these nuclear particles, or ***nucleons,*** can be affected by bombardment with high-energy particles, or photons. We have not yet discussed in any detail the forces that hold the nucleons together in the nucleus, nor have we investigated the arrangement of the electrons around that nucleus. We have now laid sufficient groundwork to allow us to begin to explore the theory of atomic structure, a theory which has been one of the great triumphs of the present century.

25.2 The Evidence of Spectra

In spite of the interesting observations occasionally made on individual atomic processes, as in radioactive work, most of the experimental data which have contributed to our knowledge of the structure of atoms have come from the observation of bulk matter. Among the most productive of such data are those involved in the ***characteristic spectra*** of the elements. If a discharge tube (Sec. 19.2) is filled with a gas and the light emitted from it is observed through a spectroscope (Sec. 13.15), it is found that the light does not consist of a continuous range of frequencies, but rather of a series of ***spectral lines,*** each of which is composed of light of a single frequency.* The set of such lines characteristic of an element is called the ***spectrum*** of the element. Some gases have very simple spectra, i.e., exhibit only a few visible spectral lines, whereas others have spectra consisting of hundreds of such lines. Regardless of whether the spectrum is simple or complex, only a definite set of lines is ever found in the spectrum of a given elementary gas, and the frequencies of these lines are so characteristic of the element that the spectroscope has become one of the most valuable tools of chemical analysis. It has also become a necessity in astronomical studies, since the spectra of the sun and the stars allow us to identify particular elements as being present in those bodies. The constancy and reproducibility of spectra provide a strong hint that the spectrum of an element is probably directly associated with the structure of the atoms of that element.

Since spectra vary so greatly from element to element, we might expect that the simpler spectra would be characteristic of the simpler atoms. Although this is not uniformly true, it is found that hydrogen, which consists of only a singly charged nucleus plus a single electron (Sec. 19.6) does exhibit a quite simple spectrum. In fact, atomic hydrogen emits strong light at only four wavelengths in the visible region of the spectrum. These spectral lines are so important that they have been given individual names, H-alpha, H-beta, etc. Their wavelengths, as measured in air, are:

H_α	6562.85 Å	H_γ	4340.47 Å
H_β	4861.33 Å	H_δ	4101.74 Å

These four lines, along with a number of other lines in the near ultraviolet (wavelengths between 3646 Å and that of H_δ), are known as the ***Balmer series,*** in honor of Johann Balmer (1825–1898), who made the first step in the theoretical treatment of spectra in 1885.

If the hydrogen spectrum is observed in the ultraviolet, with the help of a grating spectrograph, another series of lines is found. The first three, and the most intense of these, have wavelengths in air of 1215.68 Å, 1025.73 Å, and 973.54 Å. This series of lines is known as the ***Lyman series,*** after Theodore Lyman (1874–1954), who discovered it.

The first important step in the understanding of spectra was made in 1885 by Balmer, who realized that the wavelengths of the Balmer series could be written in the form

$$\lambda = Cm^2/(m^2 - n^2)$$

with $n = 2$ and $m = 3, 4, 5$, etc. Following Balmer's lead, Johannes Robert Rydberg (1854–1919) and Walter Ritz (1878–1909) enunciated the ***combination principle,*** which states that the wave number (cf. Sec. 24.9) $k = 1/\lambda$ of any

* If the gas in the discharge tube is polyatomic, the spectrum usually consists of bands, which may appear to be continuous in an ordinary spectroscope. Examination of the spectra with better instruments, however, shows these bands to be made up of large numbers of spectral lines which have sightly different frequencies.

spectral line can be expressed as the difference of two ***spectral terms.*** In the hydrogen spectrum the ***Rydberg-Ritz principle*** takes the simple form

$$k = 1/\lambda = R(1/n^2 - 1/m^2). \tag{25.2-1}$$

In this formula, $n = 2$ and $m = 3$, 4, 5, etc., for the Balmer series; and $n = 1$, and $m = 2$, 3, 4, etc., for the Lyman series. The ***Rydberg constant*** R has the value

$$R = (10\,967\,776 \pm 5)\ \text{m}^{-1} \tag{25.2-2}$$

for the hydrogen spectrum.

The first and one of the most important tasks of any theory of atomic structure is to explain why these particular spectrum lines are emitted by the hydrogen atom. In the ensuing sections we shall see the extent to which the principles which we have been studying have allowed such an explanation.

EXERCISES

25.2-1 Taking the index of refraction of air as given in Sec. 12.5 and the speed of light as given in Sec. 3.7, find the speed of light in air and then find the frequencies of the first four lines of the Balmer series, and of the first three lines of the Lyman series.

25.2-2 Using the results of Ex. 25.2-1, calculate the energy, in electron volts, of a single photon which is emitted in the H_α line of hydrogen. In each of the first two lines of the Lyman series.

25.2-3 Show that the first four lines of the Balmer series satisfy the Rydberg-Ritz formula. Use the data given for the wavelengths in air and correct to the vacuum value using the refractive index for air given in Sec. 12.5. Hence, compute a value for R and show that it agrees with the value given in Eq. (25.2-2) within the uncertainty of the data.

25.2-4 Repeat the calculation of Ex. 25.2-3 for the first three Lyman lines, and compare the value of R obtained with that of Ex. 25.2-3.

25.3 The Energy States of the Hydrogen Atom

Light of a given frequency consists of photons of fixed energy (Chapter 12). It seems reasonable to suppose that each photon is emitted as a result of some process occurring in a single atom. Since we have every reason to believe that the conservation law for energy holds in atomic processes, the emission of a photon must represent a decrease of the energy of the atom. Finally, because the observable changes of energy which can take place in the hydrogen atom consist only of a few values, each of which is a constant, it is highly probable that the atom itself can exist in only a limited number of ***states,*** each of which is characterized by a fixed energy.

The argument is similar to that which we might use if we were standing near a tall building which we could not see because of a roof over our heads. Through a hole in this roof there occasionally fall balls which are presumably dropped from the building. If we measure the velocity of each ball that drops and find that only a few values of velocity occur, we can conclude that the balls are probably being dropped from fixed points in the building, i.e., that they have been dropped through distances H_n, such that

$$mgH_n = mv_n{}^2/2.$$

We might therefore conclude that the building had a number of distinct floor levels, and we could go further and calculate the heights of the various floors above the ground.

In the case of the atom we have reason to believe, as will be demonstrated later, that the different energy states are due to different arrangements and motions of the electrons which surround the nucleus. As a first approximation, we can imagine the electrons to be traveling in orbits around the nucleus, much as the planets travel around the sun. Since the electrons are pulled toward the nucleus by electrostatic forces, it takes energy to move them from small orbits to larger ones; hence the atoms with large orbits may be said to be in states of higher energy. According to this picture, *the emission of a photon from the atom is the result of the sudden movement of an electron from a state of high energy to one of lower energy.*

The concept of fixed energy states (called ***stationary states***) of an atom was first proposed by the Danish physicist Niels Bohr in 1913, long before the quantum mechanics of Heisenberg and Schroedinger had been developed, and this concept formed the starting point for much of the atomic mechanics which has since been developed. According to Bohr's idea, the excitation of an atom in a gas discharge is accomplished when a moving electron collides with the atom and transfers some of its energy to the atom (cf. Sec. 19.2). This energy "raises" the atom to an ***excited state,*** i.e., gives it energy in excess of the energy which it ordinarily possesses in its ***ground state,*** its state of lowest energy. The atom continues to exist in its excited state for a short time (about 10^{-8} sec for most states) and then gives up some or all of its excess in energy the form of a photon. Thus the atom acts as a temporary storehouse for the energy, which starts as kinetic energy of the colliding electron and is eventually emitted as light.

Bohr realized that if his hypothesis of energy states was correct these states should be calculable from the spectral terms of Rydberg and Ritz. Using Eqs. (24.2-1) and (10.5-3) he could write Eq. (25.2-1) as

$$E_{m\to n} = h\nu = hc/\lambda = Rhc(1/n^2 - 1/m^2), \tag{25.3-1}$$

where $E_{m\to n}$ represents the energy of the photon emitted when the atom goes from the mth state to the nth. He then concluded that the energy of the mth state must be

$$E_m = -Rhc/m^2. \tag{25.3-2}$$

The energies of the ground state and of the first five excited states of the hydrogen atom as computed from Eq. (25.3-2) are shown in Fig. 25.1. The ground state is shown as having the energy

$$E_1 = -Rhc = -13.53 \text{ eV}, \tag{25.3-3}$$

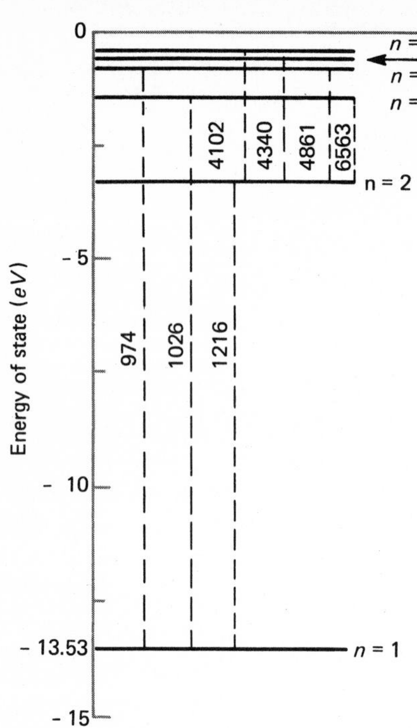

FIG. 25.1 Energy states of the hydrogen atom.

and the solid horizontal lines above it are at heights corresponding to the energies of the successive excited states. Each of the dashed vertical lines represents a transition between two states, and is labeled with the wavelength of the spectral line emitted in this transition. (The wavelengths are given only to the nearest Angstrom unit, to avoid cluttering the figure.)

A glance at Fig. 25.1 immediately suggests one method of checking the validity, or at least the internal consistency, of the scheme of stationary states. Notice that the first and second lines of the Lyman series correspond to transitions from the first and second excited states, respectively, to the ground state. On the other hand, the H_α line results from a transition between these two excited states. If the scheme shown is correct, the energy of an H_α photon should be equal to the difference of the energies of the photons emitted in the first two Lyman lines. Since frequencies and energies are proportional, a similar relation should exist for the frequencies. As the results of Exs. 25.2-1 and 25.2-2 show, these relations are rigorously satisfied.

25.4 The Determination of Planck's Constant from Spectral Excitation Data

A remarkable confirmation of the ideas which we have been studying can be obtained if electrons which have known amounts of energy, as a result of having been accelerated through controlled potential differences, are allowed to impinge on atoms. For example, an electron of less than 10.2 eV energy should never be able to excite a hydrogen atom, this amount of energy being the smallest difference between the ground state and any excited state. If such an experiment is carried out, it is indeed found that none of the lines which we have mentioned are emitted if the energy of the electrons is less than 10.2 eV. As soon as this energy is exceeded, the first line of the Lyman series appears. If the energy of the electrons is raised further, no further lines appear until the value of 12.0 eV is reached, when both the second line of the Lyman series and the first line of the Balmer series show themselves.

As a matter of fact, experiments of the type just outlined form an excellent way of determining Planck's constant, whose value

$$h = 6.624 \times 10^{-34}\ \text{J sec}$$

was determined from the photoelectric effect (Sec. 24.2). The potential difference necessary to accelerate electrons which will just excite a given state of an atom can be determined with considerable precision. If this potential difference is V and the frequency of the light emitted in a transition from the excited state to the ground is ν, the conservation law demands that

$$h\nu = eV. \tag{25.4-1}$$

Since the electronic charge e is known, Eq. (25.4-1) allows us to determine h. One of the best pieces of experimental evidence in support of Bohr's idea of stationary states is the fact that measurements of h, using different atomic types and different states of the same atom, all yield the same value of this constant, a value which agrees with that determined photoelectrically.

Experiments of this type were first carried out James Franck (1882–1964) and Gustav Hertz (1887–) in 1914.

25.5 *The Bohr-Sommerfeld Atom Model*

As we attempt to construct an atom model that will be consistent with the stationary states that are required by the evidence of experimental spectroscopy, we can use two previous results. One is the nuclear atom that grew out of the Rutherford scattering experiments (Sec. 19.6). The other is the set of discrete energy levels that we found for a particle in a box or in a well in Sec. 24.12, and in Probs. 24.8 and 24.15.

Let us assume that a hydrogen atom consists of a heavy nucleus (a proton) carrying a charge $+e$ and an electron with a mass m and a charge $-e$, which is moving about near the nucleus. The electron is held within the atom by the electrostatic attraction of the nucleus. As we saw in Eq. (19.6-1), the potential energy of the electron at a distance r from the nucleus is

$$eV = -e^2/4\pi\varepsilon_0 r. \tag{25.5-1}$$

A plot of this potential energy is shown in Fig. 25.2, where the zero of energy has been taken at $r = \infty$. The energies of several of the stationary states shown in Fig. 25.1 are indicated in the diagram by horizontal lines. If the electron has a total energy of about -13.5 eV, as shown by the level labeled E, classical mechanics would say that it could not get further from the nucleus than is point a, i.e., about one Angstrom unit. It should be clear that the electron can be expected to behave much like a particle in a box or a well. Only certain discrete energies will be allowed.

Equation (24.12-4) showed that the spacing of the energy states was inversely proportional to the width of the box. This, in fact, followed directly from the Heisenberg uncertainty principal. The more closely the electron is confined, the greater must be the uncertainty in its momentum, and hence, the greater its kinetic energy. We might therefore expect that the states with higher energy, i.e., with negative energies of small magnitudes, would be more closely spaced than those with low energies. This is exactly the behavior shown by the experimentally determined states indicated in the figure.

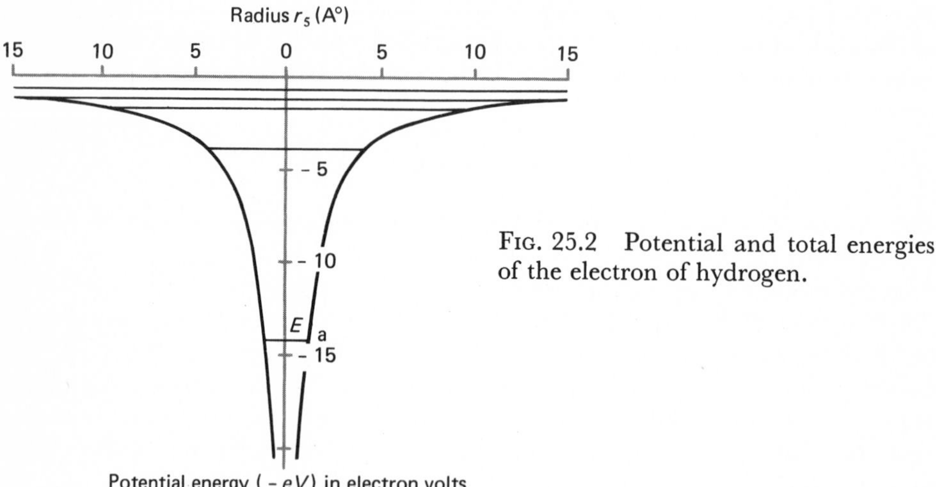

FIG. 25.2 Potential and total energies of the electron of hydrogen.

Were it not for the mathematical complexities involved in computing the eigen functions and the eigen values of the energy for a three-dimensional problem in which the potential energy varies as $1/r$, we should now set up equations for the Schroedinger waves and see whether the atom model that we have been considering yields quantitative agreement with the spectroscopic results. Because these complexities go beyond the scope of our treatment, we shall treat the problem in a less rigorous way. The approach that we shall follow is closely related to one developed by Bohr in 1913 and improved by Arnold Sommerfeld (1868–1951) shortly thereafter. The model that we shall construct is called the ***Bohr-Sommerfeld atom model.***

We start by returning to the particle in a box. We found in Eq. (24.12-3) that the momentum of such a particle is

$$p_n = \pm nh/2L,$$

where h is Planck's constant, L is the width of the box, and n is an integer. Suppose that we take the integral of $p\,ds$ for one full oscillation:

$$\oint p\,ds = \int_{-(1/2)L}^{(1/2)L} (nh/2L)\,dx + \int_{(1/2)L}^{-(1/2)L} (-nh/2L)(dx),$$

where the integral sign with the loop indicates that the integral is taken over a full cycle and where the order of the limits in the second integration indicates that the integration traverses dx in the same direction as the momentum—i.e., in the negative direction. The integrals are elementary, and we find that

$$\oint p\, ds = (nh/2L)(L + L) = nh. \tag{25.5-1A}$$

We shall accept Eq. (25.5-1A) as having general validity without further proof. We have obtained it for a one-dimensional case, but we saw in Prob. 24.8 that each component of momentum behaves in the same way. To generalize Eq. (25.5-1A), let us indicate that we are dealing with a particular component of momentum by attaching a subscript i to the p. Let the infinitesimal displacement along the same coordinate be denoted by dq_i. Then the equation can be rewritten as

$$\oint p_i\, dq_i = nh. \tag{25.5-1B}$$

This statement is known as the ***Bohr-Sommerfeld quantization rule.*** We have not shown it to be valid; we have only indicated that it is plausible. We shall therefore accept it only as an assumption.

It has been found that the quantization rule can be applied to coordinates other than the x, y, and z of a rectangular Cartesian system. Suppose, for example, that we were working in polar coordintaes r and ϕ (Sec. 5.2). Then the angular momentum about the origin (Chapter 7) could be written as p_ϕ. Notice that the dimensions of p_ϕ are $[ml^2/t]$ when ϕ is measured in dimensionless radians. Hence $p_\phi\, d\phi$ has the dimensions of h, so that Eq. (25.5-1B) is at least dimensionally correct. We shall later apply the equation to polar coordinates, accepting the idea that p_i can be any component of momentum, including angular momentum, and that q_i is the corresponding component of displacement. (Note that we have before encountered pairs of quantities whose product has the dimensions of h, in Prob. 24.7.)

Let us now suppose, as did Bohr, that the electron of the hydrogen atom is moving about the nucleus in an orbit, in a manner similar to that of a planet moving about the sun. In both cases the field of force has an inverse square behavior. Hence all the results of Secs. 14.4–14.5 can be applied at once, merely by replacing the product of the masses in Newton's law of gravitation by e^2 and the gravitational constant γ by the permittivity ε_0. We can therefore expect that the orbits will be elliptical, as they are for the planets.

There is one very important difference between the orbits of the Bohr-Sommerfeld model and those of the solar system. Because the atom is so much smaller and the bodies in orbit are so much less massive, we must apply quantum conditions to the orbits in our atom. We shall do so by using the Bohr-Sommerfeld quantization rule.

Let us start with the simplest case of a circular orbit of radius r. Consideration of the centripetal force tells us that

$$-m\omega^2 r = -e^2/4\pi\varepsilon_0 r^2, \tag{25.5-2}$$

where ω is the angular velocity of the electron. Its angular momentum is given by Eq. (7.10-1) as $L = m\omega r^2$. We now use Eq. (25.5-1B) to set

$$\oint L d\phi = kh,$$

where k is any integer. Thus we have

$$\int_0^{2\pi} m\omega r^2 \, d\phi = kh.$$

$$2\pi m\omega r^2 = kh. \tag{25.5-3}$$

If we solve this equation for ω and substitute the value obtained in Eq. (25.5-2), we find that only certain discrete values of r are possible. They are given by

$$r_k = \varepsilon_0 k^2 h^2/\pi m e^2. \tag{25.5-4}$$

We may now substitute this expression for r into Eq. (25.5-3) to find

$$\omega_k = \pi m e^4/2\varepsilon_0{}^2 k^3 h^3. \tag{25.5-5}$$

We are now in a position to find the kinetic energy of the electron.

$$(KE)_k = \tfrac{1}{2} m\omega^2 r^2 = me^4/8\varepsilon_0{}^2 k^2 h^2.$$

Since the potential energy is given by Eq. (19.6-1),

$$(PE)_k = -e^2/4\pi\varepsilon_0 r_k = -me^4/4\varepsilon_0{}^2 k^2 h^2,$$

the total energy has eigen values

$$E_k = (KE)_k + (PE)_k = -me^4/8\varepsilon_0{}^2 k^2 h^2. \tag{25.5-6}$$

We can now compare the prediction of our model with the experimentally determined energy levels given by Eq. (25.3-2). Replacing m in that equation by k, we see that it is in complete agreement with Eq. (25.5-6) if

$$Rhc = me^4/8\varepsilon_0{}^2 h^2$$

or

$$R = me^4/8\varepsilon_0{}^2 h^3 c. \tag{25.5-7}$$

If we put $m = 0.9106 \times 10^{-30}$ kg, $e = 1.602 \times 10^{-19}$ Cb, $\varepsilon_0 = 8.885 \times 10^{-12}$ sec^2 Cb^2/kg m^3, $h = 6.624 \times 10^{-34}$ J/sec, and $c = 2.998 \times 10^8$ m/sec we find that

$$R = 1.090 \times 10^7 \text{ m}^{-1},$$

which agrees with the experimentally determined value of Eq. (25.2-2) to well within the uncertainty resulting from the use of only four significant figures in the values of m, e, ε_0, h, and c. It appears that the Bohr-Sommerfeld model can account very nicely for the hydrogen spectrum.

EXERCISES

25.5-1 Using the wavelengths given in Sec. 25.2, the index of refraction of air as given in Sec. 12.5, and the energy level scheme of Fig. 25.1, calculate the expected wavelength of the fourth line of the Lyman series to five digits.

25.5-2 Check the value of the Rydberg constant as given above.

25.5-3 The atom of ionized helium has only one of the two electrons present in normal helium. By repeating the calculations of this section for a doubly charged nucleus, show that the transition from $n = 4$ to $n = 2$ in the ionized helium spectrum should have the same wavelength as the first Lyman line.

25.6 Elliptical Orbits

Just as the quantization rule restricts the possible radii of circular orbits, so it determines the shapes of the possible elliptical orbits. To see this, remember that the radius in an elliptical orbit varies between $a + c$ and $a - c$, where a is the semimajor axis and c is the distance from the center of the ellipse to either focus. (Fig. 14.3.) Hence there is a radial component of momentum that varies periodically. Denoting this radial component by p_r, we can see from Eq. (25.5-1B) that

$$\oint p_r\, ds_r = 2\int_{a-c}^{a+c} p_r\, dr = n_r h, \tag{25.6-1}$$

where we have taken twice the integral over half of the ellipse to avoid ambiguity in the sign of dr and where n_r is an integer. The integration involved here is not elementary, so we shall use only a qualitative argument to arrive at the effect of the quantization of p_r.

It is clear that the average value of p_r will depend on the $a^2 - b^2$, since the r component of displacement during each half cycle is $2c = 2(a^2 - b^2)^{1/2}$. It must also depend on the period of revolution τ. This quantity is related to the angular momentum by Eq. (14.4-10):

$$L\tau = 2\pi mab,$$

and we have set L equal to $kh/2\pi$ when we quantized the angular momentum. Hence,

$$\tau = 4\pi^2 mab/kh \tag{25.6-2}$$

Therefore, Eq. (25.6-1) must lead to a relation connecting a, b, k, and n_r. When the full mathematical machinery is used, it is found that the relation is a very simple one:

$$b/a = k/(k + n_r) = k/n, \tag{25.6-3}$$

where we have introduced a new integer, $n = k + n_r$, in the final term.

Remembering that b must be greater than zero and less than a, and that k, n_r, and n are integers, we see that Eq. (25.6-3) puts severe limitations on the possible elliptical orbits. As must be true from Eq. (25.6-1), $n_r = 0$ gives $b = a$, and therefore the circular orbits of Sec. 25.5. If $n = 1$, the only possible value of k is also one, so $n_r = 0$; the only orbit with $n = 1$ is circular. If $n = 2$, k can be either 1 or 2 ($n_r = 1$ or 0). Hence, two orbits are possible, one being circular and the other an ellipse with $b = \frac{1}{2}a$. The extension to higher values of n is obvious, with three possible orbits for $n = 3$, etc.

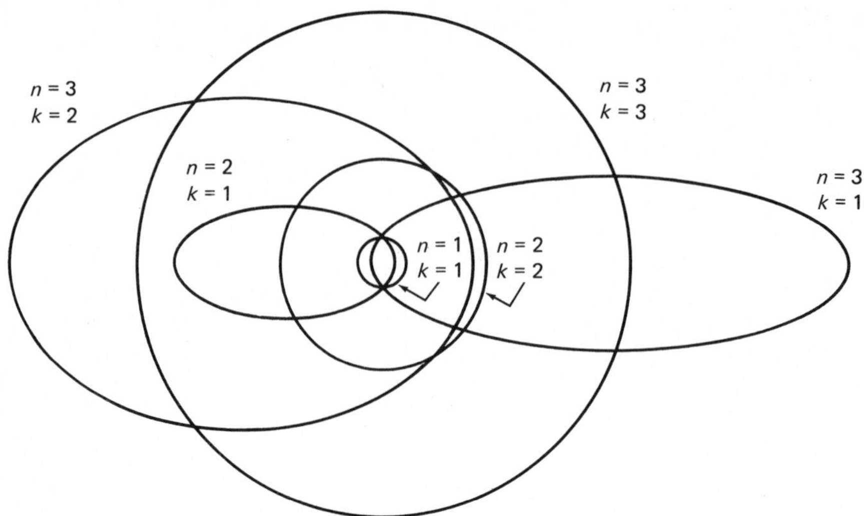

FIG. 25.3 Some low-lying Bohr orbits.

The three integers, k, n_r, and n are called ***quantum numbers***. The first is known as the ***azimuthal quantum number***, the second as the ***radial quantum number***, and the last as the ***principal quantum number***.

We can now proceed in much the same manner that we did in dealing with planetary orbits in Sec. 14.4. We first take advantage of the ease with which the total energy can be calculated when the electron is closest to the nucleus ($r = a - c$) and when it is farthest away ($r = a + c$). Equating these two energies, we have

$$\frac{L^2}{2m(a-c)^2} - \frac{e^2}{4\pi\varepsilon_0(a-c)} = \frac{L^2}{2m(a+c)^2} - \frac{e^2}{4\pi\varepsilon_0(a+c)}.$$

After rearranging the terms and clearing fractions, we find that

$$\frac{2aL^2}{m(a+c)(a-c)} = \frac{e^2}{2\pi\varepsilon_0}.$$

Substitution of $a^2 - c^2 = b^2 = k^2a^2/n^2$ for the product $(a+c)(a-c)$ and of $kh/2\pi$ for L shows that

$$a_n = \frac{n^2h^2\varepsilon_0}{\pi me^2}. \tag{25.6-4}$$

We thus see that the major axis depends on n, not on n_r and k separately. We have placed the subscript n on a to remind us of this dependence. Equation (25.5-4), of course, is a special case of Eq. (25.6-4), valid when $n = k$, i.e., when $n_r = 0$.

Finally, we need to find the energy in the noncircular orbits. To do so, let us return to the expression for the energy when $r = a - c$:

$$E = \frac{k^2h^2}{8\pi^2m(a-c)^2} - \frac{e^2}{4\pi\varepsilon_0(a-c)}.$$

When we substitute the value of a from Eq. (25.6-4), we find that

$$E = -\frac{me^4}{8\varepsilon_0{}^2n^2h^2}\cdot\frac{2(1-c/a)-k^2/n^2}{(1-c/a)^2}.$$

The rather complicated second fraction in this product may be simplified if we remember that

$$k^2/n^2 = b^2/a^2 = (a^2-c^2)/a^2 = 1-c^2/a^2.$$

When this substitution is made, it is found that the fraction reduces to unity, so we have for the energy of an orbit with principal quantum number n,

$$E_n = -me^4/8\varepsilon_0{}^2n^2h^2. \tag{25.6-5}$$

Because the energies of the noncircular orbits are given by an expression identical with Eq. (25.5-6), except that the azimuthal quantum number k is replaced by the principal quantum number n, we have just the same energy levels that we obtained in Sec. 25.5. Table 25.1 shows the energies and the angular momenta of a few of the stationary states, as calculated from Eq. (25.6-5) and from $L = kh/2\pi$.

Table 25.1 *Properties of the Stationary States of the Bohr-Sommerfeld Atom Model*

Quantum Numbers		Energy (eV)	Angular Momentum (units of $\hbar = h/2\pi$)
n	k		
1	1	−13.53	1
2	1	−3.39	1
2	2		2
3	1		1
3	2	−1.51	2
3	3		3
4	1		1
4	2	−0.85	2
4	3		3
4	4		4
5	1		1
5	2		2
5	3	−0.54	3
5	4		4
5	5		5

25.7 *Ionization and Ionization Potential*

The development of the theory of the energy levels in hydrogen enables us to understand more clearly than we could earlier the process of ionization which was discussed in Sec. 19.2. Notice from Eq. (25.6-5) that the energy of the ground state of hydrogen is

$$E_1 = -me^4/8\varepsilon_0{}^2h^2.$$

As n increases, the magnitude of the energy goes down by factors of 4, 9, 16, so that it approaches zero as n increases without limit. Hence we see that the highest terms in the energy level diagram for hydrogen approach closely the energy of the atom with its electron removed to infinite distance from the nucleus, i.e., actually detached from the atom. Since an atom with an electron removed is exactly what has been defined as a singly ionized atom, the ionization of an atom is the same as its excitation to a state of $n = \infty$.

This idea not only allows us to connect the ionization and excitation of atoms, but also allows us to calculate the minimum energy of an electron which, upon collision with a hydrogen atom, can ionize the atom. Since the states of $n = 1$ and $n = \infty$ are separated in energy by 13.56 eV, no particle with less than this amount of kinetic energy can ionize hydrogen. The ***ionization potential*** of an atom is frequently referred to as the potential difference through which an electron must fall in order to have the minimum amount of kinetic energy which can ionize the atom. Hence the ionization potential of hydrogen is 13.56 V.

It will be shown later that ionization potentials can be predicted for other atoms than that of hydrogen, even though the complete theory of these atoms is far more complicated than that of an atom with a single electron.

The process of ionization in the gas discharge is responsible both for the current-carrying ability of the gas and for the emitted light. The gas within a discharge tube always contains a few ions and a few electrons which have been removed from their parent atoms by cosmic rays or radioactive radiations. When a potential is applied across the tube, these electrons are accelerated toward the anode, colliding with atoms or molecules on the way. If the electric field is great enough, some of the electrons will acquire enough energy between collisions to ionize an atom. The resulting positive ions will be accelerated toward the cathode, and the newly formed free electrons will be accelerated toward the anode, forming new ions on their way. The process therefore becomes a cumulative one. It reaches a limit before all the atoms are ionized because some of the positive ions capture electrons from the cloud of electrons around them. During this process of ***recombination,*** the captured electron must lose an amount of potential energy equal to the ionization potential times the electronic charge. This energy is emitted in the form of one or more photons, depending on whether the electron goes to the ground state directly or in several steps.

EXERCISES

25.7-1 Starting from the energy levels deduced in Ex. 25.5-3, find the ionization potential for the second electron in the helium atom (i.e., the ionization potential necessary to convert He^+ to He^{++}).

25.7-2 The beta-particles emitted by $_{83}Bi^{210}$ (cf. Fig. 19.9) have an energy of 1.17 MeV. What is the maximum number of ions that can be formed by such a particle in passing through a Wilson cloud chamber filled with helium, which has an ionization potential of 24.46 eV?

25.8 The Quantum Mechanical Atom

In spite of the remarkable success of the Bohr-Sommerfeld atom model in predicting quantitatively the spectrum of hydrogen, the model cannot be considered a completely satisfactory one. Some of the predictions made from it fail. Among these is that of the angular momentum. According to Eq. (25.5-3) the atom should have an angular momentum of magnitude $kh/2\pi$, with $k = 1, 2, 3, \ldots$. The actual angular momentum of the ground state ($k = n = 1$) can be measured and is found to be zero, rather than $kh/2\pi$.

Not only does the model give some wrong predictions; it also is inconsistent with the quantum mechanical ideas encountered in Chapter 24. For example, consider a circular orbit. In such an orbit the radial component of momentum of the electron is always precisely zero, so that its uncertainty is also zero. But the distance of the electron from the nucleus is also precisely fixed. The uncertainty principle is therefore violated.

Because of these and similar difficulties, we must consider the Bohr-Sommerfeld model to be no more than a rather crude approximation. It must be replaced by a model that is more difficult to visualize but consistent with both quantum mechanics and with the observed properties of atoms. What must be done is clear. Three-dimensional eigen functions that are consistent with the Coulomb potential of Fig. 25.2 must be found. These will give the probability, $\psi\psi^* \, dV$, of finding the electron in any small element of volume, dV, and will allow the energy and momentum of the electron to be computed. The mathematical techniques for doing this are beyond the scope of this book, so we shall merely summarize some of the results of the calculation.

As might be expected, the quantum mechanical hydrogen atom is found to have eigen states, characterized by a principal quantum number (n) and an azimuthal quantum number. The latter is usually denoted by l, and it is found that it is related to the k of the Bohr model, $l = k - 1$. The angular momentum of any state is found to be

$$L = (h/2\pi)[l(l + 1)]^{1/2}, \qquad (25.8\text{-}1)$$

so the value for the ground state is zero, in agreement with experiment.

The energy levels of the quantum mechanical hydrogen atom are the same as those given by Eq. (25.6-5). As in the earlier model, the energy depends only on n, not on $n - l$. The position of the electron is not fixed as sharply as it was in the earlier model, however. Hence the potential energy is not sharply defined. It follows that the kinetic energy is also ill-defined, but the total energy, the sum of these two, is as sharply defined as in the Bohr-Sommerfeld atom.

As we have indicated above, quantum mechanics predicts the probability that the electron will be found in any small volume, rather than an exact orbit.

If the electron is in an eigen state of energy, the boundary conditions clearly require that this probability vanish at very large distances from the nucleus. Figure 25.4 shows a plot of the calculated probability that the electron will be found, at any instant, at a distance r from the nucleus if it is in the state characterized by $l = 0$, $n = 1$. The horizontal scale is given in terms of r/r_0, where r_0 is the radius of the first Bohr orbit, equal to $h^2\varepsilon_0/\pi e^2 m$ by Eq. (25.5-4). Notice that the highest point on this curve occurs at $r = r_0$. The probability of finding the electron within a range dr near a distance r_0 from the nucleus is therefore greater

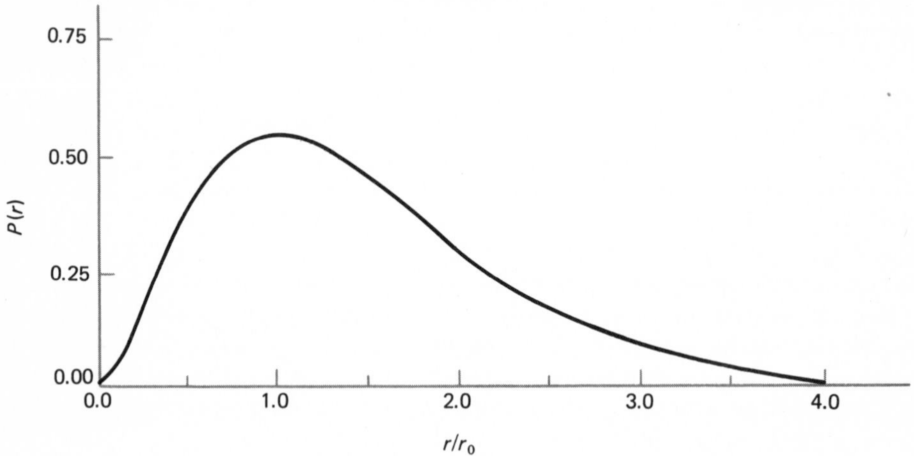

Fig. 25.4 The radial distribution of the electron cloud. $P(r)dr$ is the probability of finding an electron between r and $r + dr$ of the nucleus.

than for finding it within the same range of any other distance. This indicates in part why the Bohr model worked so well in spite of its imperfections—it put the electron in the right position *on the average*. Another way of visualizing the electronic distribution is to suppose that we could make many separate observations of an atom in a given stationary state, each time locating the electron. Were we to make a three-dimensional picture in which we put a point showing the location for each observation, we would obtain a shaded picture, such as is shown in Fig. 25.5. Near the nucleus the dots would be very densely placed; as the distance decreased, they would become less densely packed. We speak of this averaged picture as representing an ***electron cloud*** around the nucleus, very dense at the center and fading off at the edges. Figure 25.5a shows such a cloud for the ground state of hydrogen.

The elliptical orbits of the Bohr-Sommerfeld atom also have an interesting parallel in the quantum mechanical atom. When $l < n - 1$, it is found that the electron cloud is no longer spherically symmetrical. Plots of the clouds for $n = 2$, $k = 0$ are shown in Fig. 25.5b and 25.5c. The first of these has a shape that approximates a doughnut, the other a shape that approximates a dumbbell.

Either of these two represents a given hydrogen atom if an externally magnetic field is present. If we suppose this field to be vertical in the figures, (b) will be characteristic of about two-thirds of the atoms and (c) of about one-third of them. More concerning this ambiguity will be given in Sec. 25.9

FIG. 25.5 Electron clouds for several states of the hydrogen atom.

The quantum mechanical theory of the atom has been remarkably successful. It has not only led to a more complete set of predictions for hydrogen than was previously possible, but it has allowed the stationary states of other and more complex atoms to be studied in considerable detail with the help of approximation methods, to which it is particularly suited. These methods are discussed in reference 25B, at the end of this chapter.

25.9 Orbital Magnetic Moment

Consider an electron moving in a circular Bohr orbit of radius r with an angular velocity ω. The electron passes any point on this orbit $\omega/2\pi$ times per unit time, so that the orbital motion is equivalent to a current in a circular single turn of radius r, the current being equal to the charge passing per unit time, or

$$I = -e\omega/2\pi,$$

where e is the magnitude of the electronic charge. We know from Eq. (16.4-2) that the magnetic moment of such a coil is

$$P_m = \pi r^2 I = -\tfrac{1}{2}e\omega r^2.$$

For the same orbit, the angular momentum is

$$L = m_e \omega r^2,$$

where m_e is the mass of the electron, so that we can compute the ratio:

$$\frac{P_m}{L} = -\frac{e}{2m_e}. \qquad (25.9\text{-}1)$$

It is thus found that every atom has a magnetic moment proportional to the angular momentum of the electron in its orbit. The ratio P_m/L is known as the ***gyromagnetic ratio.***

Equation (25.9-1) was derived on the basis of a circular Bohr orbit, but it applies more broadly than the simple derivation would imply. Thus it can be shown quite easily that the same ratio is obtained for an elliptical orbit (cf. Prob. 25.5). It is also found to hold for the quantum mechanical atom.

It is the existence of the magnetic moment that allows one to measure the angular momenta of atoms. If a beam of atoms (say from a furnace, as in the Zartman apparatus of Fig. 20.11) is projected into a magnetic field, a torque will be exerted on each atom, in such a direction that the magnetic moment of the atom in equilibrium would be parallel to the field. Not all the atoms will come to this equilibrium orientation, for two reasons:

(1) the angular momentum causes the atom to behave much like a spinning top, which does not fall over as long as it is spinning;
(2) collisions with other atoms knock some of the atoms into nonequilibrium positions.

In a famous experiment performed by Otto Stern (1888–) and Walther Gerlach (1889–) in 1921, a beam of neutral sodium atoms was passed through a region of uniform magnetic field, as shown in Fig. 25.6, to align the magnetic

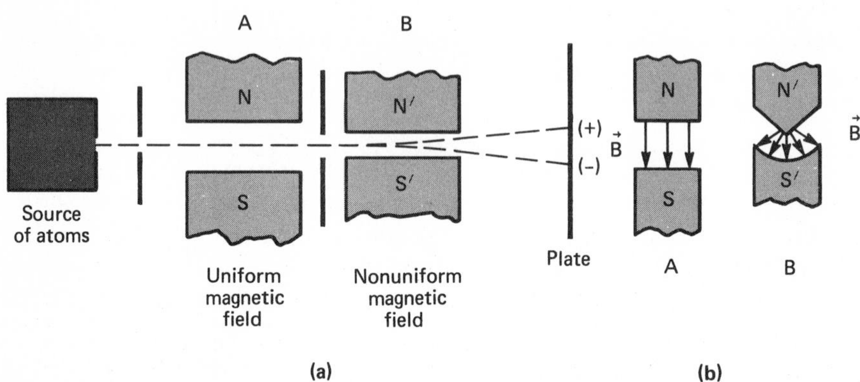

Fig. 25.6 The Stern-Gerlach experiment. (a) Longitudinal section, showing paths of atoms; (b) cross sections of the magnetic pole pieces of the two magnets.

moments and then passed into a region in which there was a nonuniform magnetic field. The magnetic dipoles in the uniform field are subject to a torque but to no net force. On the other hand, a force is exerted on a dipole by the nonuniform field, and the path is no longer a straight line. If the field is stronger near N′ than it is near S′, the magnetic dipoles pointing up will be deflected upward, and dipoles pointing down will be deflected downward. It is found, when the atoms were allowed to condense onto a glass plate, that only two spots [(+) and (−) in the figure] appear. If all the dipoles lined up with the field and all had the same magnetic moment, only a single spot (+) would show. If there were no alignment, the atoms would be smeared out over the whole region between (+) and (−).

The Stern-Gerlach experiment and many related experiments that have been performed with different kinds of atoms all show one common result. Only a few discrete paths are followed by the atoms in the nonuniform field. It follows that only certain orientations of the magnetic dipoles are allowable in the magnetic field. In other words, there are possible only certain discrete values of the component of magnetic moment that is parallel to the magnetic field.

25.10 Quantization of Angular Momentum and Its Components

We have seen from the Stern-Gerlach experiment that an atom in a magnetic field orients itself in such ways that only a few discrete values of the *z*-component of the dipole moment are found. We have also shown that the magnetic moment of an electron in an orbit is proportional to the angular momentum. It follows that only certain discrete values of the component of angular momentum parallel to a magnetic field are possible. This suggests a new quantum condition. Let us guess, by analogy with other quantum phenomena, that the component of angular momentum along the direction of the field (the *z*-axis) is

$$L_z = m\hbar$$

where m is an integer and $\hbar = h/2\pi$. We shall now consider the consequences of this guess and see if they are consistent both with experiments and with the uncertainty principle.

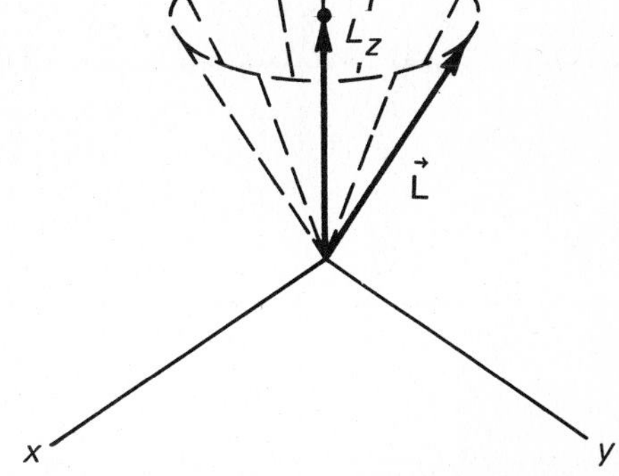

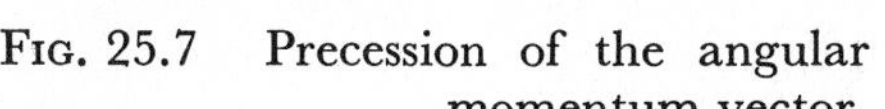
FIG. 25.7 Precession of the angular momentum vector.

Let us take $\vec{L}$ as the total angular momentum of the electron in its orbit. If this value is precisely determined, the uncertainty relation says that there is a large uncertainty in the direction of the angular momentum (cf. Prob. 24.7), and note that L has the same dimensions as $\hbar$, so that the quantity whose uncertainty combines with ΔL is dimensionless. It must be an angle or some trigonometric function of an angle. There are two ways in which the direction of the angular momentum can be uncertain. They are illustrated in Fig. 25.7. (1) There can be an uncertainty in the angle θ that $\vec{L}$ makes with the z-axis. (2) For a given θ, $\vec{L}$ must lie somewhere on the cone with its axis along z. It may, however, be along any line joining the vertex of the cone with the circle shown in the figure, perpendicular to z and passing through the end of L_z, the z-component of angular momentum. If L were equal to L_z, θ would be zero and the uncertainty principle could not be satisfied. Hence we conclude that $\theta > 0$ and that $L > L_z$. It follows that the component of $\vec{L}$ in the z-direction is $L \cos \theta$.

It follows at once that L must be greater than its z-component, $m\hbar$. Also, if L is a fixed quantity, the angle θ must be a constant for each value of the *magnetic quantum number*, m—its cosine is the ratio of two fixed quantities $m\hbar$ and L. It follows that the uncertainty principle can be satisfied only if $\vec{L}$ is precessing around the cone of Fig. 25.7 so that the component of angular momentum perpendicular to z is sometimes directed along x, sometimes along y, and generally along some intermediate direction. Hence the components L_x and L_y are not well defined, although the sum of their squares,

$$L_x^2 + L_y^2 = L^2 - m^2\hbar^2 \tag{25.10-2}$$

is sharply defined. An exception, of course, occurs when $L = 0$; each of its three components must then also be zero. The situation for $L \neq 0$ is somewhat akin to that which arises with the energy. Neither the potential nor the kinetic energy of the electron is sharply defined, but their sum is.

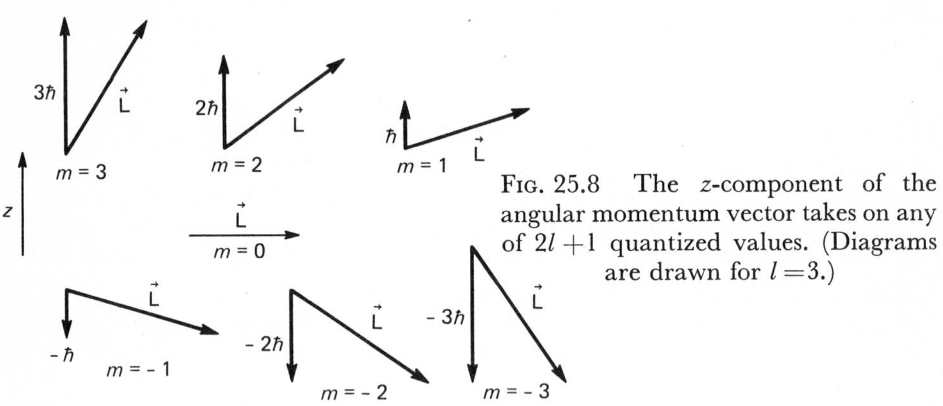

Fig. 25.8 The z-component of the angular momentum vector takes on any of $2l + 1$ quantized values. (Diagrams are drawn for $l = 3$.)

The relation between $\vec{L}$ and L_z is shown in Fig. 25.8 for the specific case of $l = 3$. The angular momentum can make any of three angles with the z-axis, giving magnetic quantum numbers of 1, 2, or 3.

We have not yet found the magnitude of L, except to say that it must be greater than $m\hbar$. A detailed application of the uncertainty principle, which will not be attempted here, shows that m must be equal to or less than l, and that $L^2 = l(l + 1)\hbar^2$, as was given in Eq. (25.8-1).

25.11 Electron Spin

Comparing the conclusions reached with the results of experiments of the Stern-Gerlach type (Sec. 25.9), we find one striking disagreement. According to Eq. (25.9-1) the z-component of the magnetic moment of an atom should be

$$(P_{\mathrm{m}})_z = (-e/2m_{\mathrm{e}})(m\hbar) = -m\mu_{\mathrm{B}}, \tag{25.11-1}$$

where $\mu_{\mathrm{B}} = e\hbar/2m_{\mathrm{e}}$ is a unit of magnetic moment known as the ***Bohr magneton.*** Since m can be any integer, including zero, from $+l$ to $-l$, it can take on any of $(2l+1)$ values. This is an odd number, and we should always expect, therefore, an odd number of discrete electron trajectories to be found in the region of the nonuniform magnetic field. In fact, we sometimes find an odd number and sometimes an even number. For example, two trajectories are found for sodium.

This difficulty with our treatment is closely related to another one, which was found before the Stern-Gerlach experiment was performed. If the spectrum of atomic hydrogen is observed with a high resolution spectrograph, it is found that each of the spectral lines in the Balmer series has a ***fine structure.*** It consists of two or more lines of nearly, but not exactly, the same wavelength. Apparently the predictions of our atom models are not quite as good as was expected.

Both of these difficulties were removed by a new idea, introduced by Samuel Goudsmit (1902–) and George Uhlenbeck (1900–) in 1925. They supposed that every electron is spinning with a fixed angular momentum. The component of this angular momentum along any chosen axis is half of the orbital momentum in the lowest Bohr orbit; that is,

$$(L_{\mathrm{e}})_z = \tfrac{1}{2}\hbar. \tag{25.11-2}$$

If the electron is treated as a little spinning sphere, carrying charge on its surface, it is found that it has the same gyromagnetic ratio as was given in Eq. (25.9-1). It would therefore be expected that the z-component of its magnetic moment would be half of a Bohr magneton [cf. Eq. (25.11-1)]. To achieve agreement with experiment, Goudsmit and Uhlenbeck were forced to assign to the electron a full Bohr magneton. This anomalous result was hard to understand at the time, but it was later shown by Dirac to be a necessary consequence of special relativity theory. We shall accept the result here and take the intrinsic magnetic moment of the spinning electron to be

$$(P_{\mathrm{me}})_z = \mu_{\mathrm{B}} = 2(e/2m_{\mathrm{e}})(\tfrac{1}{2}\hbar). \tag{25.11-3}$$

We have already seen that the angular momentum of atoms can be directed only in such directions as make discrete angles with an external field. In the hydrogen atom, in any state other than one for which $l = 0$, there is always a magnetic field present, due to the orbital motion of the electron. Hence we might expect that the axis about which the electron spins could take only certain directions relative to the orbital angular momentum. Such behavior is indeed consistent with the evidence of both spectra and measurements of magnetic moment. In hydrogen, the spin of the single electron is aligned either parallel or antiparallel (opposite) to the orbital angular momentum. The total angular momentum component along the z-axis is therefore either $(m + \frac{1}{2})\hbar$ or $(m - \frac{1}{2})\hbar$. The corresponding magnetic moments are $(m + 1)\mu_B$ and $(m - 1)\mu_B$.

Because the energy of the atom when the orbital and spin moments are parallel is higher than when they are oppositely directed, each stationary state given by Eq. (25.6-5) will be split into two states of slightly different energies if $l > 0$. The states with $l = 0$ are exceptional because there is no orbital magnetic moment with which the electron spin can interact. The predicted values of the energy agree precisely with the fine structure of the hydrogen spectral lines.

The concept that the electron possesses an intrinsic spin has proved a very productive one. The next section will show that the electron spin plays a very important role in our understanding of atoms other than that of hydrogen. It also directly involved in the explanation of ferromagnetism (cf. Sec. 21.10).

25.12 The Structure and Properties of Complex Atoms

In our study of the hydrogen atom, we were able to deal quite exactly with the potential energy of the electron, since the only force acting upon it was the electrostatic attraction of the nucleus. As soon as we go to the next simplest atom, that of helium, we face a new problem. Since that atom contains two electrons, these will not only be attracted toward the nucleus but will also be repelled from each other. This repulsion must be taken into account in calculating the energy states of helium, and no existing theory other than that of quantum mechanics allows us to take it into account successfully. Fortunately, however, the quantum mechanical treatment does give results corresponding to those found from the spectroscopic data and so merits our confidence. According to the results of this theory, the two electrons of helium possess about equal energies in the ground state and remain at about equal distances from the nucleus in that state. The interaction of these two electrons results in an increased number of allowable energy states and so a spectrum more complicated than that of hydrogen.

In accordance with our treatment of the hydrogen atom, we can ascribe to each of the electrons in a helium atom four quantum numbers, l, n, m, and s, the last being the spin quantum number, which takes on values of $\pm\frac{1}{2}$. Experimental evidence indicates that the helium atom has no magnetic moment in its ground state. When calculations of the energy of the ground state are made, it is found that they agree with the ionization potential of helium only if both electrons have $l = 0$, $m = 0$, and $n = 1$. There is therefore no orbital magnetic moment, and the magnetic moment of the atom can be zero only if the spins of the two electrons are oppositely directed, i.e., if one electron has $s = +\frac{1}{2}$ and the other has $s = -\frac{1}{2}$. This conclusion is found to be a special case of the much more general ***Pauli exclusion principle***, enunciated by Wolfgang Pauli (1900–1958) in 1925. The principle may be stated:

> *No two electrons within an atom can have identical quantum numbers, i.e., identical values of l, n, m, and s.*

The Pauli exclusion principle becomes very important for the understanding of the periodic table of the elements (Table 21.1). Let us consider the ground state of lithium, which has three electrons. Two of these can have quantum numbers $l = 0$, $n = 1$, $s = +\frac{1}{2}$, and $l = 0$, $n = 1$, $s = -\frac{1}{2}$, as in the case of helium. The third electron, however, must have $n = 2$, because no new set of nonidentical quantum numbers with $n = 1$ exists. It has become customary to say that the two electrons with $n = 1$ constitute a ***closed shell*** (cf. Sec. 21.2). The third electron must go into a state of higher energy than either of the first two. It spends most of its time at a greater distance from the nucleus than do the two electrons in the closed shell. In fact, this electron is generally so far away from the nucleus, of charge $+3e$, that a fair degree of accuracy can be obtained if we assume that it stays outside a central core consisting of the nucleus and the two inner electrons. The charge on this core is $+3e - 2e = +e$, identical with that of the nucleus of hydrogen. Hence the behavior of the electron can be expected to be much like that of the electron in hydrogen. This expectation is confirmed by observation, and we say that lithium has a ***hydrogen-like spectrum***.

As we go to atoms with more than three electrons, we can see that eight electrons can have a principal quantum number of two. With $n = 2$, l can be either 0 or 1. The former requires that $m = 0$, but the latter allows $m = -1$, 0, or $+1$. For each combination s can be $\pm\frac{1}{2}$. Hence the eight sets of quantum numbers shown in Table 25.2 are possible without violation of the exclusion

Table 25.2 *Possible Values of l, m, and s for $n = 2$*

l	m	s	l	m	s
0	0	$+\frac{1}{2}$	1	0	$+\frac{1}{2}$
0	0	$-\frac{1}{2}$	1	0	$-\frac{1}{2}$
1	$+1$	$+\frac{1}{2}$	1	$+1$	$+\frac{1}{2}$
1	$+1$	$-\frac{1}{2}$	1	$+1$	$-\frac{1}{2}$

principle. The addition of eight electrons with $n = 2$ to the two with $n = 1$ leads us to atomic number 10, neon. In this element a second closed shell is completed. The next element, sodium, has 11 electrons. One of these must start forming a new shell, with $n = 3$. A tabulation similar to that at Table 25.2 shows that this shell can contain a maximum of 18 electrons, so we might expect the next noble gas, displaying properties similar to helium and neon, to occur at atomic number 28. Actually, we find such a gas at $Z = 18$ (argon). The reason is that the energy of an electron with $n = 4$, $l = 0$ is less than that of one with $n = 3$, $l = 2$. Hence the fourth shell starts to be built before the third shell is completely filled. We can see in a qualitative fashion that this might happen. An electron with $l = 2$ is approximated in the Bohr-Sommerfeld model by a very much elongated elliptical orbit, similar to that shown for $n = 3$, $k = 1$ in Fig. 25.3. This orbit penetates well into the filled shells and comes very close to the nucleus.

Just as helium, with two electrons, has a more complex spectrum than hydrogen, so the elements with more than one electron in an outer unclosed shell exhibit increasingly complex spectra as the number of exterior electrons increases. Because of the interaction of the electrons, the electrostatic forces on them are not inversely proportional to the square of their distances from the nucleus. Further, more than one electron may be excited at the same time, so that the energy of the excited state, relative to the ground state, is the sum of their excitation energies. As a result of such factors, the spectra of most elements cannot be expressed in terms of simple formulas such as those which give the Balmer and Lyman series of hydrogen. It is necessary to construct the energy level diagrams for these atoms from the observed spectral frequencies. These diagrams, however, always bear one marked similarity to that of hydrogen. If one of the exterior electrons is excited to a state of high principal quantum number, it will be, on the average, at a much larger distance from the nucleus than the other electrons. Hence, it will behave as if it were in an electrostatic field caused by a charge of $Ze - (Z - 1)e = e$, located at the nucleus. Z here is the atomic number, so Ze is the nuclear charge and $-(Z - 1)e$ is the charge on all the other electrons. This field is similar to that of a hydrogen atom, so the high energy states of any atom will be hydrogen-like, i.e., they will be successively closer together as n increases, approaching the ionization energy as n approaches infinity. This fact allows us to use spectroscopic data to predict the ionization potential of complex atoms.

The arrangement of the electrons gives us a clue to the chemical behavior of the elements and to the arrangement of the periodic table (Table 21.1). In most chemical reactions, the atoms involved have kinetic energies of less than one electron volt. As two atoms approach each other, their electrons set up an electrostatic repulsion, and this repulsion is sufficient to prevent the closed electron shells from interpenetrating to any great extent, unless the kinetic energies of the atoms are very high (cf. Sec. 21.2, especially Fig. 21.3). In chemical reactions, then, only the outer electrons of the atoms play an appreciable role, and we should expect atoms with similar arrangements of outermost electrons to have similar chemical properties. Helium and neon, for example, both have closed shells of electrons, and so they might be expected to behave similarly. As a matter of fact, both of these elements are among the noble gases (helium, neon, argon, krypton, xenon, radon), which are chemically very inert. Similarly, hydrogen, lithium, and sodium, each of which has one exterior electron, have similar chemical behaviors, as do fluorine and chlorine, each of which has seven electrons exterior to a closed (or partially closed) shell.

25.13 X-ray Spectra

A fixed amount of energy is required to excite an exterior electron from the ground state to a particular state of higher energy, and the electron, in returning to the ground state, gives off the same amount of energy in the form of a photon (Sec. 25.4). If the atom contains more than one electron, the excitation or removal of a second electron will take considerably more energy than did that of the first, since the second is bound to the nucleus by a greater electrostatic force (cf. Exs. 25.5-3 and 25.7-1). In particular, the electrons in the innermost closed shell of an atom of atomic number Z are close to a nucleus of charge $+Ze$, and so are bound to that nucleus by a very great electrostatic attraction. If we wish to excite one of these electrons to a state of higher energy, we have to supply a relatively great amount of energy. Also after the electron has been excited, we should expect to emit a photon of very high energy, i.e., radiation of high frequency and short wavelength.

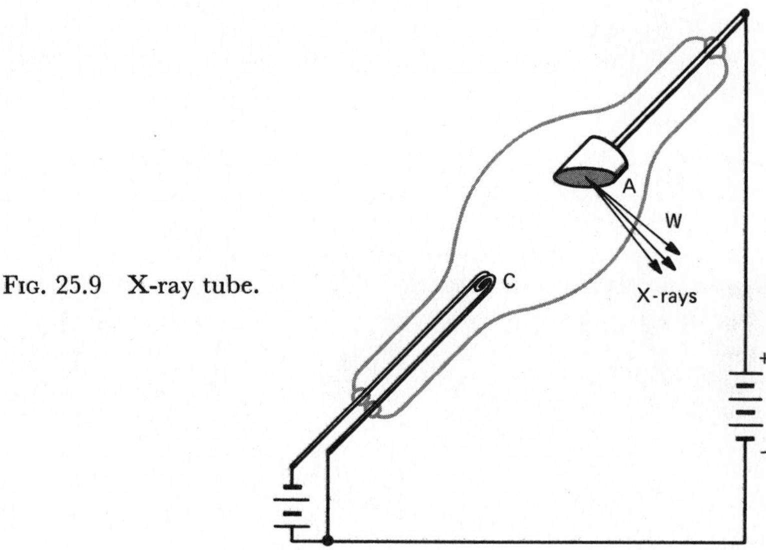

FIG. 25.9 X-ray tube.

The ***x-ray tube,*** shown schematically in Fig. 25.9, gives us a means of exciting and observing the high energy or ***x-ray spectrum*** corresponding to the inner electrons of an atom. This tube consists of a cathode C, which is heated electrically and which emits electrons (cf. Sec. 17.3). These electrons are accelerated toward an anode, or ***anticathode,*** A, which is maintained at a high potential (10^4–10^7 V) positive with respect to the cathode. A good vacuum is maintained in the tube, so that the electrons will pass from the cathode to the anticathode without colliding with atoms or molecules on the way. In this passage between the two electrodes, the electrons acquire high kinetic energies which they give up to the metal atoms of the anticathode when they collide with the latter. If the inner electrons of the atoms are excited by this energy, x-rays are emitted in the process of their return to the ground state. These x-rays are very penetrating, and they can easily pass through the thin window W in the side of the tube, for outside observation.

The x-rays coming from the tube may be studied by diffraction from crystals (Sec. 21.5). It is found, in general, that they include both ***continuous radiation,*** resulting from direct conversion of electron energy to photon energy, and a line spectrum consisting of radiation of discrete wavelengths. The latter lines are always the same for a given anode material and constitute the ***characteristic x-ray spectrum*** of that material. It has been found that the x-ray lines of any element can be arranged in series, similar to those in the hydrogen spectrum.

These series can always be represented by an energy diagram similar to that of hydrogen. Those lines which result from transitions from a higher state to the ground state (called the ***K-state***) are known as ***K-lines,*** those resulting from transitions to the state of the next lowest energy (the ***L-state***) are known as ***L-lines,*** and so on through *M*, *N*, etc. Figure 25.10 shows a typical energy diagram for the deep-lying energy terms of an atom, together with the transitions corresponding to the first few lines of the K- and L-series. These transitions have been labeled according to the usual notation, the longest wavelength line being given the subscript α, the next longest the subscript β, etc.

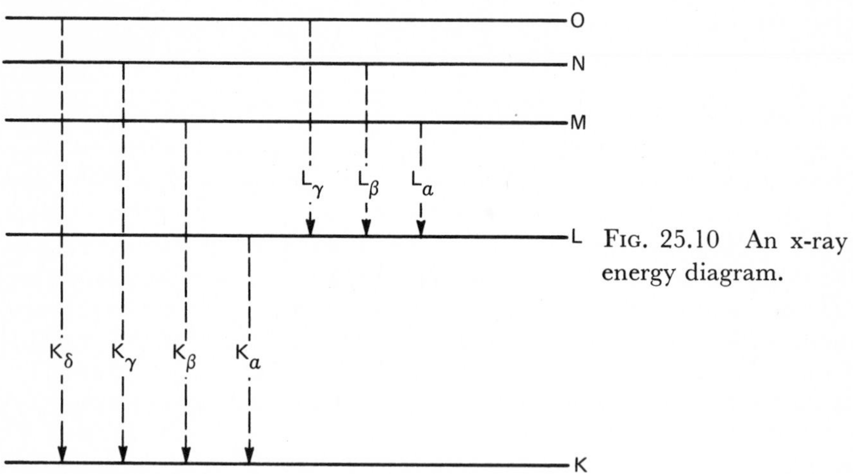

FIG. 25.10 An x-ray energy diagram.

There is one important distinction between x-ray and optical spectra. We saw in Sec. 25.4 that an electron with a kinetic energy equal to or greater than the energy difference between the ground state and a higher state was able to raise an atom to the excited state. A similar phenomenon cannot take place with the deep-lying states that yield x-ray spectra, for the simple reason that the state of higher energy is, in general, already occupied by an electron, and so is not available for occupancy by the electron from the ground state. The minimum potential which can excite the x-ray levels of an atom, therefore, is the energy required to ionize the atom. If the K-lines are to be excited, this ionization must be accomplished by removing an electron that was originally in the ground state, providing an empty K-state into which one of the electrons in an L- or higher state can fall. The L-lines can be excited if an electron initially in the L-state is removed from the atom.

25.14 Moseley's Law and Atomic Numbers

In 1913, H. G. J. Moseley (1884–1915) reported, as the result of a long series of measurements on x-ray spectra, that the wave numbers of the K_α-lines of all elements heavier than sodium could be represented with high accuracy by the expression

$$k = R(Z-1)^2(1-\tfrac{1}{4}) = R(Z-1)^2\left(\frac{1}{1^2}-\frac{1}{2^2}\right), \qquad (25.14\text{-}1)$$

where R is approximately the same Rydberg constant that occurred in Eq. (25.2-1) and Z is the atomic number of the element. Comparison of Eq. (25.14-1) with Eq. (25.2-1) shows that the energy difference between the K- and L-states of any heavy element is greater than the energy difference between the two lowest states of the hydrogen atom by a factor $(Z-1)^2$. Since the nucleus of an atom of atomic number Z carries a charge which is Z times as great as that on the hydrogen nucleus, and since the energy of a hydrogen-like state is proportional to e^4, i.e., to the product of the square of the electronic charge and the square of the nuclear charge [Eq. (25.6-5)], we might have expected the factor Z^2 instead of $(Z-1)^2$. The addition of the unit term indicates that the electron that is excited to give the K_α-line is shielded from the nucleus by the other electron in the lowest energy closed shell. This is not unreasonable, and the beautiful regularity in the x-ray spectra of the elements, as revealed by ***Moseley's law,*** may be taken as a strong confirmation of our ideas of atomic structure.

One interesting application of Moseley's law is that it allows us to check on the atomic number of any element, independently of chemical evidence. For example, nickel and cobalt have very similar chemical and physical properties, and the average atomic mass of nickel is lower than that of cobalt. Yet the fact that the K_α-line of nickel has a shorter wavelength (higher frequency) than that of cobalt convinces us that the atomic numbers as given in Table 21.1 must be correct.

EXERCISES

25.14-1 What is the energy, in electron volts, of a photon emitted in the K_α-line of aluminum? Of silver?

25.14-2 The anticathode of an x-ray tube is composed of a metal of atomic number Z. It is found that a potential difference of at least V_K must be maintained across the tube to excite the K-lines of the anticathode. What is the minimum potential difference which will excite the L-lines?

25.15 Nuclear Energy Levels—Gamma-Ray Emission

In investigating atomic structure we have found that only stationary states of particular energy levels can exist and that transitions between these stationary states account for the emission of optical and x-ray spectra. It is of some interest to inquire whether similar stationary states exist within atomic nuclei. If they do, we might anticipate, by analogy with extranuclear behavior, that transitions between two stationary states would result in the emission of photons whose energy should be a measure of the energy difference between the two states. Such photons, or ***γ-rays,*** are found to be emitted in the course of many radioactive transformations.

For example it is found in the decay of $_{88}Ra^{226}$ (cf. Fig. 19.9) that the emission of the α-particle is sometimes followed immediately by the emission of a γ-ray of 0.19 MeV energy. It is also found that all of the α-particles from $_{88}Ra^{226}$ do not have the same energy, but that some of them have energies 0.19 MeV less than the others. These facts can be explained if we suppose that the ordinary decay,

$$_{88}Ra^{226} \longrightarrow {_{86}Rn^{222}} + {_2He^4},$$

is the usual one, but that sometimes the decay takes place according to the scheme

$$_{88}Ra^{226} \longrightarrow {_{86}Rn^{222*}} + {_2He^4}, \tag{25.15-1}$$

where the asterisk attached to the symbol for radon indicates that the daughter atom is left in an excited state of higher energy than the ground state (in this case 0.19 MeV higher). The excess energy of the excited state of the nucleus is immediately radiated in the form of a γ-ray, a transition indicated by

$$_{86}Rn^{222*} \longrightarrow {_{86}Rn^{222}} + E(\gamma), \tag{25.15-2}$$

where the symbol without an asterisk indicates the radon nucleus in its ground state and $E(\gamma)$ represents the 0.19 MeV energy of the γ-ray. Many excited states similar to that of the radon nucleus have been found, and their energy levels have been obtained from the energies of the γ-rays emitted in radioactive processes.

25.16 Isomers

The recognition of stationary energy levels within the nucleus leads to an interpretation of isomers, such as the two forms of the nucleus $_{91}Pa^{234}$ mentioned in Sec. 19.7. When it was first observed that the decay of $_{90}Th^{234}$ could take place in two different ways, with the products decaying with different half-lives to the common $_{92}U^{234}$, it was thought that the two products of the decay of $_{90}Th^{234}$ were different nuclear species. We can now recognize that these two products differ only in that one of them is $_{91}Pa^{234}$ in an excited state, while the other is the same nucleus in the ground state. To find which is which, we merely need to find the energies of the radiations emitted in the decay of the two varieties. When this is done, it is found that the state which has the 1.1 minute half-life decay is the state of higher energy.

Many ***isomers,*** pairs of nuclei which differ only in their excitation energies, have been found among the naturally and artificially radioactive nuclei.

25.17 The Hydrogen Molecule and Electron-Pair Binding

Just as the electrical interaction between the electrons of an atom and its nucleus, when considered in the light of quantum mechanics, accounts for the observed properties of atoms, so the mutual interactions among the electrons and nuclei of two or more adjacent atoms account for the combination of these atoms into molecules. The ***theory of chemical valence,*** which specifies what combinations of atoms may form molecules, is still incomplete and presents difficulties beyond our present scope. We shall therefore content ourselves with a brief qualitative consideration of the theory of one of the simplest molecules, that of hydrogen.

We have seen that a hydrogen atom has definite energy states and that these states are determined by the electrostatic attraction of the nucleus and the electron. If two such atoms are brought into close proximity, a set of attractions and repulsions replaces the simple attraction that characterized the hydrogen atom. The two positively charged nuclei repel each other; each of the two electrons involved is attracted by both nuclei; the two electrons repel each other. In addition, we must remember that when the two atoms approach one another closely, the region of uncertainty of position of either electron (cf. Secs. 24.6 and 25.8) becomes of the same order of magnitude as the separation of the two nuclei, so that it is impossible for us to say that the electron belongs to one nucleus or the other.

The methods of quantum mechanics permit the calculation of approximate ψ-functions for the hydrogen molecule, and from these we find that there is a very high probability for the two electrons to be found in the region between the two nuclei, and a somewhat lower probability that they be found in the region beyond them. In Fig. 25.11, this condition is indicated by the football-shaped

FIG. 25.11 Electron cloud in the hydrogen molecule.

cloud with the nuclei near its two ends. The presence of the negatively charged cloud between the two nuclei holds them together. The details of the calculation of the ψ-function and of the forces holding the molecule cannot be gone into here. The results of such calculations can, however, be represented in the curve of Fig. 25.12 in which the energy $E(H_2)$ of the hydrogen molecule is plotted as a function of the distance r_{12} between the nuclei. When r_{12} is large, the energy will, of course, be $2E(H)$, where $E(H)$ is the energy of a single hydrogen atom. As r_{12} decreases, the attraction due to the presence of the two electrons will increase, and thus the energy will decrease. However, as the nuclei approach, the repulsion between them will increase, and thus the energy $E(H_2)$ will have a minimum value when the attraction of the electrons for the nuclei is just equal to the repulsive force between the nuclei. This minimum energy E_0 would be expected to occur at a separation r_0, which corresponds to the nuclear separation found in nature. The value of r_0 and the value of the energy $[E_D = 2E(H) - E_0]$ which is required to ***dissociate*** the hydrogen molecule into two hydrogen atoms have been observed experimentally and can be calculated from the quantum mechanical theory. The fact that the agreement lies well within the experimental error gives us great confidence in the theory outlined for the hydrogen molecule. In this way we can explain the ***electron-pair bonding***, or ***covalent bonding***, mentioned in Sec. 21.2. The theory of the hydrogen molecule can thus give us a basis for an understanding of the many molecules of organic and inorganic chemistry that depend on this type of bonding.

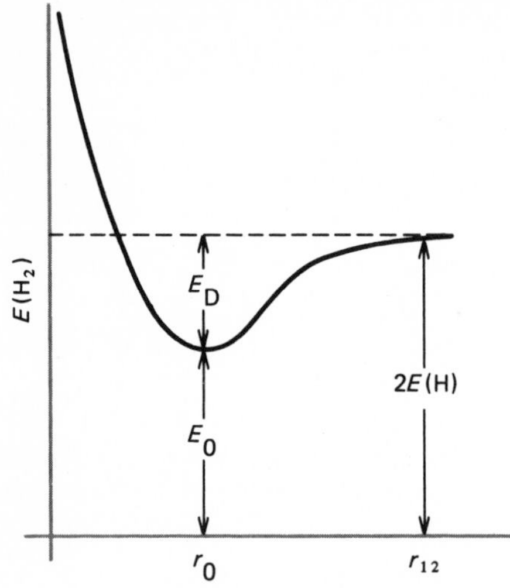

FIG. 25.12 Potential energy diagram for the hydrogen molecule.

25.18 Exchange Forces

The discussion of the hydrogen molecule has introduced into physics the important notion that forces of attraction can result from the ***exchange*** of one or more charged particles between two otherwise uncharged bodies of atomic dimensions. Another example of such ***exchange forces*** is presented by the bonding which occurs between two water molecules in liquid water or in ice. The water molecule (H_2O) when isolated has the appearance of Fig. 25.13. The hydrogen atoms each form a covalent bond by sharing a pair of electrons with the oxygen atom. Calculations agree with experiment in locating the hydrogen nuclei near the boundary of the cloud of 10 electrons $(8+2)$ which surround the oxygen nuclei. The position of the hydrogen is such that the angle HOH is about 109.5°. Thus the upper right-hand and upper left-hand parts of the molecule can be considered to have an excess of positive charge, and the lower front and rear portions have an excess of negative charge. Thus the water molecule has an electric dipole moment (Sec. 15.9), and we can expect that when two water molecules approach one another, the negative region of one will attach itself to the positive region of the other as indicated in Fig. 25.14. In this

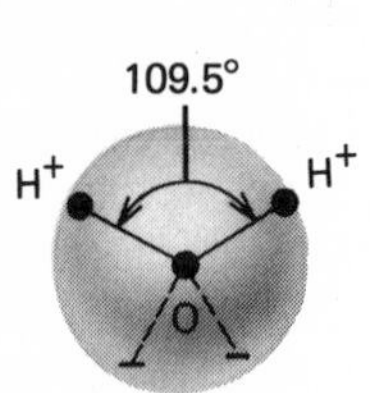

FIG. 25.13. Water molecule.

position the uncertainty principle must be applied to the H-atom in the molecule A which is nearest to the negative region of the molecule B. This H-atom may therefore exchange from A to B, as indicated by the double arrow. At the same time, one of the H-atoms from B must exchange with a neighboring molecule of B, and in addition the molecule A must receive an H-atom from one of its neighbors. Although these exchanges do not occur simultaneously, they must take place within a very short time of one another. Thus, in the picture of water just described, the molecules are continually exchanging hydrogen atoms.

The exchange of hydrogen atoms between two water molecules, and between water molecules and other molecules containing hydrogen, has been demonstrated in two ways, both of which depend on the fact that ***heavy water*** (i.e., water made with deuterons as hydrogen nuclei) can be prepared. First, it can be shown by the mass spectrograph (Sec. 19.2) that substances containing ordinary hydrogen ($_1H^1$) quickly replace hydrogen with deuterium ($_1H^2$) when placed in a heavy water solution. Second, it can be shown that the force holding water molecules together in heavy water are smaller than those holding ordinary water molecules. Since the momentum of the deuterium atom is expected to be larger than that of a hydrogen atom of corresponding energy ($E = p^2/2m$), the uncertainty of position would be smaller and less exchange would be expected for the heavier deuterium atom. This has been confirmed by experiment.

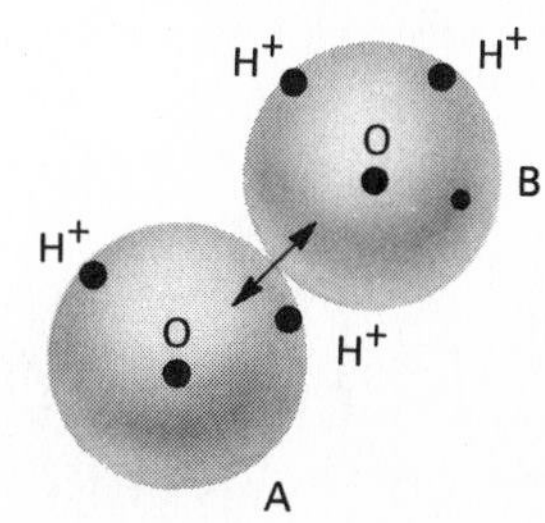

FIG. 25.14 Hydrogen bonding between water molecules.

The exchange of a hydrogen atom between two molecules can be expected to result in an added attractive force between these molecules, since during the transfer, the hydrogen atom (carrying a charge $+e$) is located between two negative regions, one belonging to the atom which it has left and the other to the atom which it is joining. This added force produces a bond between the molecules exchanging a hydrogen nucleus. Such bonds are called ***hydrogen bonds*** and are apparently of great importance in the properties of water-soluble substances.

There are thus two clear examples in which the exchange of particles results in an added attractive force between two atoms. In the one case, electrons are exchanged and the covalent bond results. This type of force will bring two hydrogen atoms together when they are separated by several times their normal separation in the hydrogen molecule. In the second case, the exchange of hydrogen atoms between molecules results in the hydrogen bond. In such cases the attractive force is large when the two molecules are close to one another, but the decrease is rapid when the separation becomes large.

We have earlier encountered exchange forces in our consideration of nuclear structure in Sec. 19.21, where we saw that nuclear binding is the result of the exchange of π-mesons between nucleons.

25.19 Summary

This final chapter has been devoted to an elementary study of some of the problems that have engaged the attention of physicists during the past seventy years. Starting from the observed facts of atomic spectra, we have seen that atoms are characterized by certain definite energy states, and we have seen further that such states necessarily follow from wave-particle duality in the description of physical phenomena. Although atomic theory has not yet progressed to the point where we can predict the spectra of all atomic species, it is in such a state that quite satisfactory models of the simpler atoms (hydrogen and helium) can be developed. These models are sufficiently good to indicate the connections between atomic structure and the chemical behavior of atoms, including the formation of molecules. The same ideas that have been successful in treating these properties of atoms which depend on their electronic structure may be extended to a study of atomic nuclei. We have seen, partially at least, the nature of the forces that hold the neutrons and protons together within the nucleus. The general ideas involved are consistent with the nuclear phenomena discussed in Chapter 19. Much of what is known about nuclear theory at present cannot be put forward in a basic text, and there are many problems in this field which have not yet been solved. In this part of physics, which is changing from week to week, the reader, like the authors, can only watch for and work toward what the future may reveal.

PROBLEMS

25.1 The discussions of Secs. 25.2 and 25.5 might lead one to believe that a hydrogen atom can go from *any* state of higher energy to *any* state of lower energy by emitting a photon. Such is not the case. It has been found that certain ***selection rules*** limit the pairs of states between which transitions can take place. The two states must have the same value of s and must differ by ± 1 in the value of l. What does this rule imply about the angular momentum of a photon?

25.2 ***Absorption spectra*** are obtained by passing light that is continuously distributed in wavelength through a sample of gas. It is found that light of certain discrete wavelengths is absorbed. Every wavelength observed in absorption is also found in the emission spectrum of the gas, but many wavelengths found in emission are absent in absorption. For example, in hydrogen, only those lines for which $n = 1$ in Eq. (25.2-1) occur. Discuss and explain these facts on the bases of Figs. 25.1 and 25.2.

25.3 A magnetic dipole, of magnetic moment $\vec{P}_m$ is so oriented that its dipole axis makes an angle θ with a magnetic field of flux density $\vec{B}$.

(a) Show that there is a torque on the dipole, given by

$$\vec{T} = \vec{P}_m \times \vec{B},$$

so that its magnitude is $P_m B \sin\theta$.

(b) By considering the work needed to rotate the dipole from $\theta = 0$ to any value equal or less than π, show that the potential energy of the dipole is

$$U = -P_m B \cos\theta.$$

25.4 An atom has an orbital angular moment $l\hbar = 0$ and an electron spin $s\hbar = \frac{1}{2}\hbar$. It is in a magnetic field of flux density $\vec{B}$. Use the result of Prob. 25.3(b) in answering the following questions.

(a) What are the possible directions of the spin axis relative to $\vec{B}$?

(b) Which of these directions of spin has the lower energy?

(c) Show that the energy states differ in energy by an amount $\Delta E = \hbar B/em$, where e is the electronic charge and m is the electronic mass. (This splitting of energy levels in a magnetic field is the origin of the ***Zeeman effect.***)

25.5 Show that the gyromagnetic ratio for an elliptic Bohr orbit has the same value as was given for a circular Bohr orbit in Eq. (25.9-1).

25.6 Construct a table similar to Table 25.2 for $n = 3$, and show that there are eighteen possible states with this total quantum number.

25.7 The x-ray spectrum of copper shows a line of wavelength 1.538 Å. (a) Is this consistent with Moseley's law? (b) What is the minimal potential difference across an x-ray tube to excite this line in emission?

25.8 The only molecule for which an exact quantum mechanical solution has been obtained is the ***hydrogen molecular ion.*** This ion is composed of two protons and one electron. A crude approximation to the theory of this ion is possible, using only classical physics and the uncertainty principle.

(a) Consider that the ion is constructed by holding the electron stationary and bringing the two protons in from infinity, all three particles being kept on the same straight line and the two protons always being at equal distances from the electron. Show that the potential energy of the system, when this distance is r, is

$$U = -e^2/4\pi\varepsilon_0 r.$$

Note that this potential energy is negative, which means that the electron between the two protons *may* cause the molecule to be stable.

(b) We have supposed the electron to stay at rest in the exact center of the ion. This would violate the uncertainty principle. Suppose that it moves above in the neighborhood of the two protons, but is at the center on the average. The uncertainty in the position of the electron is then of the order of $2r$. Find the uncertainty in the momentum and show that the kinetic energy of the electron is of the order of magnitude of $\hbar^2/8mr^2$.

(c) Calculate the total energy of the system for values of r in the range 1 Ångstrom unit to 50 Å. Does the shape of the curve indicate that the molecular ion is stable?

(d) Find the equilibrium value of r. Is this a reasonable quantity for a molecule?

(e) From your curve, estimate the energy needed to dissociate a hydrogen molecular ion, i.e., to separate it into two protons and an electron.

(f) Find the difference in energy between that of the molecular ion and that of a proton and a hydrogen atom in its ground state, the two being separated by a large distance.

25.9 The $_8O^{19}$ isotope is radioactive, decaying by β-emission with a half-life of 29.5 sec. It is found that two groups of β-particles are emitted during the decay, having a maximal energy of 2.9 MeV and 4.5 MeV. Gamma-ray photons of 1.6 MeV are also emitted. (a) What is the daughter isotope? (b) Construct an energy level diagram for the nucleus of the daughter isotope that is consistent with data.

25.10 A ***positronium atom*** consists of a single electron and a single positron. (a) Find the radii of the Bohr circular orbits of positronium. (b) Show that the wavelengths of the lines in the positronium spectrum must be twice as great as those in the hydrogen spectrum.

25.11 ***Muonic atoms*** are formed when an atom captures a μ^--meson, which then replaces one of the electrons of the atom. Suppose that an atom of atomic number Z becomes muonic.

(a) Assuming that the Bohr orbit of the μ-meson lies far inside the smallest electron orbit, find the radius of the smallest orbit.

(b) Does the result obtained in (a) justify the assumption used to obtain it, on the basis of Bohr theory? On the basis of quantum mechnics?

(c) What is the energy (in electron volts) necessary to remove the μ-meson from an atom of argon?

25.12 (a) What difference, if any, can be expected between the spectra of hydrogen and deuterium?

(b) The result obtained in Ex. 25.5-3 assumed both the hydrogen nucleus and the helium nucleus to be infinitely massive compared with the electron. What fractional difference in wavelength would be expected between the two lines mentioned in the exercise when the actual masses are taken into account?

REFERENCES

25A Morris Shamos, editor, *Great Experiments in Physics*, Holt, New York, 1960. Appendix 4 contains the gist of Bohr's paper on the hydrogen atom.

25B Walter Heitler, *Elementary Wave Mechanics*, 2nd edition, Oxford, New York, 1956. An excellent introduction to quantum mechanics with a minimum of mathematical apparatus.

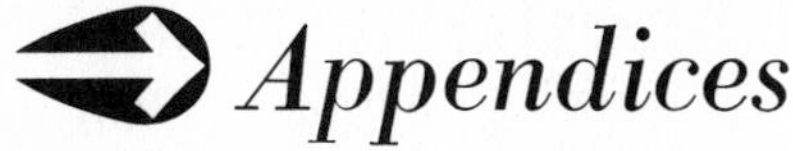

Appendices

Appendix A The Greek Alphabet

A	α	alpha	N	ν	nu
B	β	beta	Ξ	ξ	xi
Γ	γ	gamma	O	o	omicron
Δ	δ	delta	Π	π	pi
E	ε	epsilon	P	ρ	rho
Z	ζ	zeta	Σ	σ	sigma
H	η	eta	T	τ	tau
Θ	θ	theta	Y	υ	upsilon
I	ι	iota	Φ	ϕ	phi
K	κ	kappa	X	χ	chi
Λ	λ	lambda	Ψ	ψ	psi
M	μ	mu	Ω	ω	omega

Appendix B Uncertainties and Significant Figures

B.1 *Sources and Statement of Uncertainties* The result of a physical measurement is never an exactly determined quantity, since uncertainties in the measurement occur from several causes:

1. Every physical instrument has a finite least count (cf. Sec. 2.9.).
2. The quantity being measured may change during the measurement as a result of unrecognized causes (e.g., thermal expansion).
3. Accidental errors may occur due to misuse of the instruments or other causes beyond the control of the experimenter.
4. The instruments themselves may have residual errors due to the uncertainties in their comparison with the primary standards.

Because of the importance attached to the comparison of measured and calculated quantities, it is essential that the statement of the result of every quantitative experiment or observation include not only the magnitude of the quantity measured but also an estimate of the ***uncertainty*** in that magnitude, i.e., of the limits within which it is estimated that the true value may be contained. The full study of uncertainties and of the ways in which they combine to give an error in the result of a calculation involves considerable mathematical and logical complexity, and we shall not concern ourselves with a detailed, exact treatment. On the other hand, the basic principles involved in the estimation of uncertainties are quite straightforward.

Suppose that a series of measurements are made of the same quantity, using the same instruments, and that these give slightly different results, Q_1, Q_2, Q_3, ... The differences are clearly due either to changes in the quantity during measurement or to accidental errors. In the absence of any further information, the best estimate of the quantity is clearly the average value, or ***mean value***, of the observations, i.e., their sum divided by their number. The uncertainty in this mean value may be estimated from the amounts by which the individual measurements depart from it. As a specific example, suppose that the length of a table is measured with a meter stick having a least count of 1 mm and that the values obtained are the first five quantities in the first column of Table B.1. The mean of these observations is 1.050 m,

Table B.1 *Estimate of Uncertainty Due to Accidental Errors*

	Length (m)	Deviation from Mean (m)
	1.051	0.001
	1.056	0.006
	1.041	0.009
	1.049	0.001
	1.053	0.003
Sum	5 | 5.250	5 | 0.020
Mean	1.050	*ad* 0.004

Best estimate of length $= (1.050 \pm 0.004)$ m
$= 1.050$ m $\pm 0.4\%$

which is therefore the best available estimate of the length. The second column shows the ***deviation*** of each individual measurement from the mean, taken without regard to sign. The average of the individual deviations, which is called the ***average deviation*** (usually abbreviated as *ad*), is 0.020 m/5 = 0.004 m. This *ad* is at least a rough measure of the amount by which we expect that the mean may be in error, and we shall not go far astray if we write as the length of the table (1.050 ± 0.004) m, which implies that we believe it to be probable that the length lies somewhere between 1.046 m and 1.054 m.

In the case just considered, in which the *ad* was considerably larger than the least count of the instrument used, the uncertainty could be taken as the *ad*. Had the opposite been true, say if each measurement had yielded the identical result 1.050 m, with an *ad* of zero, we would still have an uncertainty, since we know that no measurement can be better than the least count. Under these circumstances, we should have taken the least count as the uncertainty and have stated the length as (1.050 ± 0.001) m. In general, we may take the uncertainty in the mean of a series of measurements as either the *ad* or the least count, whichever is the larger.

The uncertainties as stated in the preceding paragraph, i.e., in the same type of unit as the quantity being measured, are known as ***absolute uncertainties***.

B.2 *The Uncertainty of a Sum or Difference* Suppose that two similar quantities have been measured and have yielded the respective values $Q_1 \pm q_1$ and $Q_2 \pm q_2$, where q_1

and q_2 are their respective absolute uncertainties. We wish to know how great the uncertainty will be in the sum $Q_s = Q_1 + Q_2$. Direct addition shows that

$$Q_s \pm q_s = Q_1 + Q_2 \pm q_1 \pm q_2,$$

where q_s is the uncertainty in the sum. It follows at once that

$$q_s = q_1 + q_2. \tag{B.1}$$

Since the subtraction of Q_2 from Q_1 would merely have changed the order of the + and − signs before q_2, Eq. (B.1) holds equally well for subtraction. We therefore arrive at the general rule: *When two or more quantities are added or subtracted, the absolute uncertainty in the result is the sum of the absolute uncertainties in the quantities.*

Actually this rule leads to an overestimate of the uncertainty, since it is quite improbable that all of the individual quantities will be in error by their maximum uncertainties in the same direction. In Sec. 3.9, for example, it is asserted that the reading of each displacement from a photograph may be in error by *as much as* 0.5 cm. The first two entries in Column 2 of Table 3.4 would then be (0.027 ± 0.005) m and (0.115 ± 0.005) m. The difference in these two positions might be as much as 0.098 m or as little as 0.078 m. This is consistent, of course, with expressing this difference, in the notation of this section, as

$$\begin{aligned} Q_d \pm q_d &= (Q_2 \pm q_2) - (Q_1 \pm q_1) \\ &= Q_2 - Q_1 \pm q_2 \mp q_1 \\ &= 0.115 - 0.027 \pm 0.005 \mp 0.005 \\ &= 0.088 \pm 0.010, \end{aligned}$$

where all measurements are expressed in meters. This expression is unnecessarily pessimistic on two counts: we do not expect all readings to be in error by as much as 0.005 m, and we do not expect all errors to occur without some compensation. In the data given here, for example, it might be that the readings of both positions are too large by 0.003 m; their difference then would be exactly right, but we cannot know, of course, since we can never measure Q or q but only $Q \pm q$.

A more complete study of the probability of errors reveals that it is more useful to express q_s, the error of the sum or difference of two quantities whose individual errors are q_1 and q_2, as

$$q_s = \pm\sqrt{q_1^2 + q_2^2}. \tag{B.2}$$

Thus, if q_1 and q_2 are each 5×10^{-3} m, as in Sec. 3.9,

$$q = \pm\sqrt{50} \times 10^{-3}\ \text{m} = \pm 0.007\ \text{m}.$$

B.3 *The Uncertainty of a Product or Quotient* Suppose that the two quantities $Q_1 \pm q_1$ and $Q_2 \pm q_2$ are to be multiplied to give the product $Q_p = Q_1 Q_2$. If the uncertainty in Q_p is q_p, we have, by direct multiplication,

$$Q_p \pm q_p = (Q_1 \pm q_1)(Q_2 \pm q_2) = Q_1Q_2 \pm q_1Q_2 \pm q_2Q_1 \pm q_1q_2.$$

This result may be put in a more meaningful form if we divide the left-hand side by Q_p and the right-hand side by the equivalent quantity Q_1Q_2. This gives

$$1 \pm q_p/Q_p = 1 \pm q_1/Q_1 \pm q_2Q_2 \pm (q_1/Q_1)(q_2/Q_2).$$

We now notice that q_1/Q_1 and q_2/Q_2 are the fractional uncertainties of Q_1 and Q_2, and that in most good physical measurements they are very much smaller than one

(100%). Their product will therefore be still smaller and may usually be neglected completely. We therefore make very little error in writing

$$q_p/Q_p = q_1/Q_1 + q_2Q_2. \tag{B.3}$$

Since division is essentially the same process as multiplication, Eq. (B.3) also holds for division (cf. Ex. B.4), and we arrive at the general rule: *When two or more quantities are multiplied or divided, the fractional uncertainty in the result is the sum of the fractional uncertainties in the quantities.* This rule, like that given in Sec. B.2, leads to an overestimate of the uncertainty of the result, but it is good enough for many purposes.

B.4 *Uncertainties and Significant Figures* In Sec. 2.9 we defined a significant figure as a digit which has physical meaning. It is obvious that no meaning can be attached to a digit which indicates a magnitude much less than the uncertainty. On the other hand, every digit that expresses a magnitude equal to or greater than the uncertainty does have meaning. It follows that *every number involved in a physical magnitude should have as many decimal places as are contained in the absolute uncertainty of the quantity, provided that the uncertainty is expressed in the same units as the quantity.* If, as is customary, the uncertainty is expressed to one significant figure, this procedure will lead to the retention of one doubtful digit in the number.

We have seen that the absolute uncertainty of a sum or a difference is the sum of the absolute uncertainties of the quantities entering into it. The largest of these uncertainties will determine the location of the first doubtful figure, and *the number of decimal places in a sum or difference is therefore equal to the number of places in the least accurate piece of data that enters into the sum or difference.* Thus the sum of (20.6 ± 0.2) m and (1.53 ± 0.01) m is (22.1 ± 0.2) m.

The number of significant figures in a quantity is a fairly good measure of the fractional uncertainty in the number. Thus, if one follows the practice of expressing all numbers to ± 1 in the last decimal place, the fractional uncertainty in 10 is $1/10 = 10\%$, while the fractional uncertainty in 99 is $1/99 = 1\%$. Thus all two-digit numbers have uncertainties between 1% and 10%. Similarly, all three-digit numbers have uncertainties between 0.1% and 1%, etc. Since fractional uncertainties add in processes of multiplication or division, the factor with the smallest number of significant figures, i.e., with the greatest fractional uncertainty, will contribute most to the uncertainty in the result. The fractional uncertainty of the result is therefore approximately the fractional uncertainty of the most uncertain factor, and *the number of significant figures in a product or quotient is the same as the smallest number of significant figures in any of the factors.* Thus $(15.2 \pm 0.1)\ \text{m} \times (2.3 \pm 0.1)\ \text{m} = (15.2\ \text{m} \pm 0.7\%) \times (2.3\ \text{m} \pm 4\%) = 35\ \text{m}^2 \pm 5\% = (35 \pm 2)\ \text{m}^2$.

Although the full specification of the uncertainty of a calculated result demands that the rules of Secs. B.2 and B.3 be followed, the rules of this section will give very nearly the same number of significant figures as will the more exact rules, and will do so with a considerable saving of time and effort.

B.5 *Uncertainties in Functions* It is frequently necessary to use trigonometric functions (Appendices E, F, G) or logarithms in the course of calculations. Although rules for finding the uncertainties in such functions can be derived, it is usually simplest to find the uncertainties by looking up the limiting values of the functions in the tables which are being used. Thus, suppose that an angle of $23° \pm 1°$ has been measured, and it is necessary to use the sine of this angle in a calculation. Examination of Table F.1 shows that the sine of 23° is 0.3907, that of 24° is 0.4067, and that of

22° is 0.3746. The difference of the last two values is 0.0321, so that half of this, or 0.0160, will be the uncertainty in the sine. We therefore write

$$\sin(23° \pm 1°) = 0.391 \pm 0.016,$$

where we have retained two doubtful figures, in accordance with our usual practice in calculations.

The same method used in finding the uncertainty of trigonometric functions can be used in finding the uncertainty of any other tabulated function, such as a logarithm. It can be shown, by methods which are beyond the scope of our present treatment, that one introduces no appreciable error into a logarithmic calculation if he uses tables which have one more decimal place than the number of significant figures in the least accurate piece of data involved. Thus in obtaining the product 3.14×2.456, four-place tables are sufficient, but in multiplying 3.14159×2.45678, seven-place tables are needed.

EXERCISES

B.1 A table top has a length of (1.050 ± 0.004) m and a width of (0.752 ± 0.003) m. Find the area of the table top, together with its uncertainty.

B.2 A second table, whose top has the same width as that of Ex. B.1, but whose length is (1.24 ± 0.01) m, is placed end to end with the table of Ex. B.1. What is the length of the surface thus formed and what is the uncertainty in this length? What is the area of the surface and what is its uncertainty?

B.3 Show that the fractional uncertainty in the volume of a sphere is three times the fractional uncertainty in the radius.

B.4 It was stated in Sec. B.3 that the same rule holds for the determination of the uncertainty of a quotient as was there derived for the uncertainty of a product. Show that the fractional uncertainty in the quotient $(Q_1 \pm q_1)/(Q_2 \pm q_2)$ is the sum of the fractional uncertainties in Q_1 and Q_2. (Hint: Expand the quantity $(1 \pm q_2/Q_2)^{-1}$ by the methods of Appendix H, and neglect products of fractional uncertainties.)

B.5 The sine of an angle is known to be 0.41 ± 0.03, and the angle is known to be less than 90°. What is the angle, and what is its uncertainty?

Appendix C Mathematical Symbols

C.1 *Symbols* Since physical reasoning is so often expressed in mathematical form, it is convenient for the reader to be familiar with a number of symbols that serve as abbreviations for frequently used phrases. It is assumed that he is already acquainted with those symbols, such as $=$, $+$, $-$, $(\ \ )$, $\times$, $\div$, and $/$, which are commonly used in elementary algebra. The symbols discussed below are additional ones used in various parts of this book.

C.2 *Inequalities, $>$ and $<$* It is customary to use the symbols $>$ and $<$ to denote the inequality of two quantities. They are read, respectively, "is greater than" and "is less than." Thus the expression

$$x > y \tag{C.1}$$

is read "x is greater than y" and is equivalent to the expression

$$y < x, \tag{C.2}$$

which is read "y is less than x." Equal quantities may be added to or subtracted from both sides of an inequality or both sides may be multiplied or divided by equal positive quantities without disturbing the inequality. Thus, if the above inequalities are true, it is also true that

$$x - 4 > y - 4, \tag{C.3}$$

and that

$$3x > 3y. \tag{C.4}$$

When one quantity is much greater than another, the symbol $\gg$ (read "is much greater than") or the symbol $\ll$ (read "is much less than") is used to express the relation.

C.3 *Approximate Equalities*, $\approx$ It is sometimes sufficient to know that two quantities are almost equal. To express this idea, the symbol $\approx$ is used in the same way that $=$ is used in an equation, and is read "is approximately equal to." Thus, if

$$y \ll 1, \tag{C.5A}$$

the quantity

$$(1 + y)^2 = 1 + 2y + y^2 \approx 1 + 2y, \tag{C.5B}$$

since the two expressions connected by the approximate equality sign differ only by y^2, which is certainly much smaller than y. On the other hand, if

$$x \gg 1, \tag{C.6A}$$

$$(1 + x)^2 = 1 + 2x + x^2 \approx 2x + x^2, \tag{C.6B}$$

since unity is clearly very small compared with x^2 or x. If the difference betweeen the two expressions connected by $\approx$ is less than the uncertainty in one of the expressions, the two are physically indistinguishable and the approximate equality sign may be treated as if it were an exact equality. Whether or not this is legitimate will depend on the uncertainties and therefore upon the particular circumstances in which the equation is being used.

C.4 *Proportionality*, $\propto$ The concept of the proportionality of two quantities is frequently a useful one. Thus, if

$$x = ky, \tag{C.7A}$$

where k is a constant, we know that for every value assigned to y there is a particular value of x which is k times as great. If we denote by $y_1, y_2, \ldots y_n$ a series of particular values of y, and let the corresponding values of x be $x_1, x_2, \ldots x_n$, we can write the equal series of ratios

$$x_1/y_1 = x_2/y_2 = \cdots = x_n/y_n = k.$$

When two variable quantities are related in this way, i.e., when the first is always obtained by multiplying the second by a constant, we say that they are ***proportional*** and use the symbol $\propto$ to connect them. Thus, in the case just cited,

$$x \propto y, \tag{C.7B}$$

which is read "x is proportional to y," or "x is directly proportional to y." On the other hand, if two variable quantities w and z are connected by the relation:

$$w = k/z, \tag{C.8A}$$

where k is a constant, we may say that

$$w \propto 1/z, \tag{C.8B}$$

which is read either "w is proportional to one over z" or "w is inversely proportional to z."

C.5 *Summation,* $\sum$ It is often necessary to express the sum of a large number of similar quantities. The quantities are usually denoted by the same symbol, and their identities are established by attaching a subscript. Thus suppose that we are dealing with a group of n bodies, which are numbered 1, 2, 3, ... n. We may denote the mass of the first body by m_1, that of the second by m_2, and so on to m_n, the mass of the last body. The combined mass of all the bodies is

$$m = m_1 + m_2 + m_3 + \cdots + m_n. \tag{C.9A}$$

Rather than writing out this long sum, it is customary to denote it symbolically. This is done by choosing a previously unused subscript, known as a ***running index***, to denote a general member of the series. Thus, letting j be the running index, which may take any integral value from 1 to n, m_j would denote any one of the masses. The sum shown in Eq. (C.9A) is then written:

$$m = \sum_{j=1}^{j=n} m_j \tag{C.9B}$$

where the Greek capital letter $\sum$ (*sigma*) is used to indicate a summation, and the whole expression is read "m is the sum of all the m_j obtained by assigning to j all the integral values from one to n," or, more simply, "m is the sum of the m_j, taken from one to n."

C.6 *Rate of Change,* Δ, lim, *and Derivatives* The use of the symbol Δ to denote a small change of the quantity that follows it has been discussed at some length in Chapter 3. The useful concept of the limit of the ratio, i.e., the ***derivative***, of two small changes was also introduced in that chapter and has been used freely throughout this book. The present section is intended only to give a few additional illustrations of the use of the limiting process.

Suppose that a square is drawn with each of its sides of length L. The perimeter of the square is then $P = 4L$. If we now suppose L to be a variable quantity, and ask how rapidly the perimeter varies as the length of a side changes, we can write $P + \Delta P$ for the perimeter which corresponds to $L + \Delta L$. It follows that

$$P + \Delta P = 4(L + \Delta L) = 4L + 4\Delta L, \tag{C.10A}$$

or that the change in the perimeter corresponding to a change ΔL in the length of a side is

$$\Delta P = 4\Delta L.$$

Thus the change in the perimeter is always exactly four times the change in the length of a side, so that the ratio

$$\Delta P/\Delta L = 4. \tag{C.10B}$$

If we ask what the value of this ratio is in the limit of $\Delta L \to 0$, we notice that it is the same as for a large value of ΔL, i.e.,

$$dP/dL = \lim_{\Delta L \to 0} \Delta P/\Delta L = 4, \tag{C.10C}$$

since the value of the ratio does not depend on ΔL.

Although the ratio just discussed was a constant, this is not true of all ratios. Let the area of the square be

$$S = L^2. \tag{C.11A}$$

Then the new area, corresponding to a length $L + \Delta L$, is

$$S + \Delta S = (L + \Delta L)^2 = L^2 + 2L\Delta L + (\Delta L)^2. \tag{C.11B}$$

In this case the ratio of the change in area to the change in the length of a side is

$$\Delta S/\Delta L = 2L + \Delta L. \tag{C.11C}$$

This, instead of being a constant, depends on both L and ΔL. If we ask for the rate of change of the area with the length of a side, we find that

$$dS/dL = \lim_{\Delta L \to 0} \Delta S/\Delta L = 2L, \tag{C.11D}$$

since the last term in Eq. (C.11C) vanishes as ΔL approaches zero. We thus conclude that the area of a square changes very slowly with the length of a side if the square is

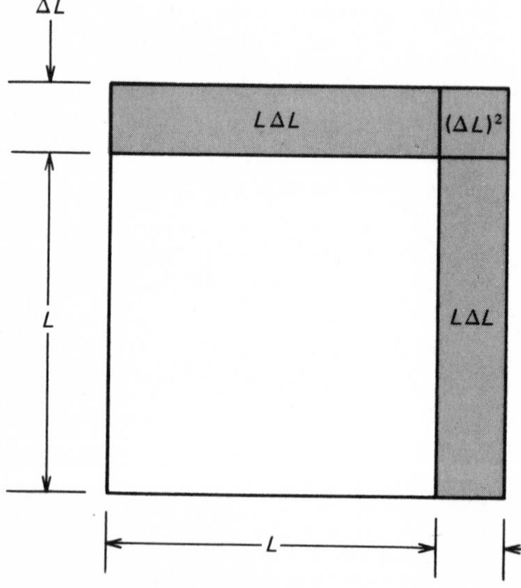

FIG. C.1 Increase in area of a square resulting from an increase in the length of the sides.

small, but very rapidly if the square is large. A study of Fig. C.1, in which the shaded portions show the increase of the area as the length of a side is changed from L to $L + \Delta L$, will confirm this conclusion and show the meaning of the terms on the right-hand side of Eq. (C.11B).

C.7 *The Integral,* $\int$ The *definite integral* of any function, e.g.,

$$\int_{X_1}^{X_2} f(x)\, dx, \tag{C.12}$$

is the limit of the sum

$$\sum_j f_j(x)\,\Delta x \tag{C.13}$$

as Δx approaches zero. Here, $\Delta x = (X_2 - X_1)/N$, where N is an integer and $f_j(x)$ is the value of the function $f(x)$ at $x = X_1 + j\Delta x$.

As we have seen in Chapter 3,

$$\int_{X_1}^{X_2} f(x)\, dx$$

is just the "area under the curve" of $f(x)$ vs. x, i.e., the area bounded by that curve, by the line $f(x) = 0$, and by the lines $x = X_1$ and $x = X_2$. It may be evaluated if this area can be computed or it may be determined by graphical or numerical approximations. (See Secs. 3.16–3.18.)

Many integrals whose computation is not elementary can be found in various tables of integrals.* The integrals shown there are ***indefinite integrals***:

$$\int f(x)\, dx,$$

for which no limits (X_1 and X_2 above) are stated. Such indefinite integrals differ from the definite integrals of Eq. (C.12) by an additive constant. Thus

$$\int_{X_1}^{X_2} f(x)\, dx = \int f(x)\, dx + C, \tag{C.14}$$

where C is independent of x but depends on X_1 and X_2. The constant may be evaluated in either of two ways:

(1) If the value of the definite integral is known at some value of x, this value and the tabulated value of the indefinite integral may be substituted into Eq. (C. 14) and the resulting equation solved for C.

(2) By noting that the definite integral is the value of the indefinite integral when $X = X_2$ (the ***upper limit***) less its value at $X = X_1$ (the ***lower limit***).

Integrals and the derivatives of Appendix C.6 are related by the fact that the derivative of an integral with respect to the upper limit is equal to the ***integrand***, the quantity that multiplies dx in Eq. (C.12). Thus

$$\frac{d\left[\int_{X_1}^{X_2} f(x)\, dx\right]}{dX_2} = f(X_2), \tag{C.15A}$$

* Examples are B. O. Peirce and R. M. Foster, *A Short Table of Integrals*, 4th Ed., Ginn, New York, 1956, and the tables in the *Handbook of Chemistry and Physics*, Chemical Rubber Publishing Co., Cleveland, Ohio.

where $f(X_2)$ denotes the value of the integrand at $x = (X_2)$. Because the indefinite integral is equivalent to a definite integral having x as an upper limit, this is equivalent to saying that

$$\frac{d\left[\int_{X_1}^{X_2} f(x)\,dx\right]}{dX_2} = \frac{d\left[\int f(x)\,dx\right]}{dx}, \tag{C.15B}$$

provided that the quantity on the right be evaluated, after the derivative is taken, by setting $x = X_2$.

Equations (C.15) often allow the value of an integral to be determined even when the calculation of its value is not elementary. It is often possible on physical grounds to *guess* at the form of the integral. One may then take the derivative of this guessed form and compare it with $f(x)$. If the correct expression is thus found, the guess is confirmed. For an example of this process, see Sec. (16.21).

C.8 *Infinity*, ∞ In mathematics and in physics the notion of infinity is of great importance. In mathematics, this notion requires very careful discussion since it is involved quite deeply in the logical treatment of many mathematical processes. When we are concerned with physical quantities, all of which are known only to a limited accuracy, we may consider a quantity to be infinite if it is so large that its reciprocal can be neglected in comparison with other quantities to which it is added. Thus as far as the lens equation (Eq. 13.5-1) is concerned, an object distance x_o may be said to be infinite if $1/x_o$ can be neglected with respect to $1/x_i$ and $1/f$. In general, a quantity is negligible if it is smaller than the uncertainty in the quantity to which it is to be added. It follows that a quantity which is physically infinite in one problem may not be considered infinite in another. The symbol ∞ is used in physical discussions to represent an infinite number.

Appendix D Units and Dimensions

D.1 *Systems of Units* The establishment of a system of units and dimensions, in terms of which physical quantities may be stated, is a process that allows a considerable amount of arbitrary choice. This choice is limited in two ways:

1. The system must insure that each physical quantity involved in a calculation has dimensions that are characteristic of that quantity and only of that quantity.
2. The system must be consistent with physical laws as these are obtained from experimental data.

If these two conditions are met, the choice of the quantities to be considered as fundamental in any system is one which can be made for reasons of convenience. At various stages of history and in various parts of physics, different sets of units have been established. None of the dozens of systems that have been used can be said to have overwhelming advantages for all purposes, but each has a particular suitability for some types of physical problems.

D.2 *Length-Mass-Time Systems* The ***mks system***, which has been used almost exclusively in this book, is one of several systems in which length, mass, and time have been taken as fundamental quantities. The ***cgs*** (cm, g, sec) and the ***fps*** (ft, lb, sec) ***systems*** are other ***length-mass-time*** (*lmt*) ***systems*** which have found wide use.

The conversion from one of these systems to another is simple, since all equations take exactly the same form in all *lmt* systems. The first group of three columns of Table D.1 give the dimensions and units of the more important mechanical quantities in the three principal *lmt* systems.

D.3 *Gravitational Systems* In the various *lmt* systems, including the mks system, the ***unit of force*** is defined as that force which produces unit acceleration when it acts on unit mass. The defining equation for force is therefore Eq. (4.9-4), which may be rewritten as

$$m = F/a. \tag{D.1}$$

Since a change in the unit in which force is measured will not change the proportionality between force and acceleration, Eq. (D.1) could equally well be written in the more general form:

$$m = kF/a, \tag{D.2}$$

where k is a constant of proportionality, to be chosen at our convenience. In the *lmt* systems, k is chosen to be dimensionless and equal to one. In some other systems which are in common use, different, but equally legitimate, choices are made.

In many engineering problems the major forces involved are weights. It is sometimes advantageous, therefore, to consider the weight of a body, rather than its mass, as a fundamental unit. Systems of units which include force, defined in terms of the weight of a standard body, as a fundamental unit are known as ***gravitational systems of units.***

Several ***length-time-force*** (*ltf*) ***systems*** have been established by defining the unit of force as the weight of a standard body, such as the International Prototype Kilogram. When such a definition is used, it is possible to treat mass as a derived quantity and to define the unit of mass from Eq. (D.1). Denoting the units of mass in such systems by the prefix "gee-" we see that

$$1 \text{ geekilogram} = 9.80 \text{ kg}, \tag{D.3A}$$

since we know that 1 kg wt produces an acceleration of 9.80 m/sec^2 in a mass of one kilogram, or an acceleration of 1.00 m/sec^2 in a mass of 9.80 kg. It also follows that

$$1 \text{ geegram} = 980 \text{ g} \tag{D.3B}$$

and that

$$1 \text{ geepound} = 32.2 \text{ lb}. \tag{D.3C}$$

The last named unit of mass is quite widely used, and is usually called a ***slug,*** rather than a geepound. Since the *ltf* systems are like the *lmt* systems in that they are based on the choice of the constant k in Eq. (D.2) as unity and dimensionless, equations retain the same form in these two types of systems. The only difference is in the unit of mass. The most commonly occurring mechanical units in three of the *ltf* systems are given in the second group of three columns of Table D.1.

There are also in common use three ***length-mass-time-force*** (*lmtf*) ***gravitational systems*** which take length, mass, time, and force as fundamental quantities. The unit of mass in such systems is defined as the mass of a standard body, as in the *lmt* systems, and the unit of force is defined as the weight of the same standard body, as in the *ltf* systems. Since such systems define m, F, and a in Eq. (D.2), k cannot be set equal to unity. We can, however, solve Eq. (D.2) for k, to find the value of this constant. In the system based on the meter, kilogram, second, and kilogram weight, for example,

$$k = (1 \text{ kg})(9.80 \text{ m/sec}^2)/1 \text{ kg wt} = 9.80 \text{ kg m sec}^{-2}(\text{kg wt})^{-1}.$$

Table D.1. *Systems of Units for Mechanics*

Type of System		*lmt*			*ltf*			*lmtf*		
Name of System		mks	cgs	fps	m sec kg wt	cs g wt	fs lb wt	m kg sec kg wt	cgs g wt	fps lb wt
Length	Unit	m	cm	ft	m	cm	ft	m	cm	ft
	Dimensions	[l]	[l]	[l]	[l]	[l]	[l]	[l]	[l]	[l]
Time	Unit	sec	sec	sec	sec	sec	sec	sec	sec	sec
	Dimensions	[t]	[t]	[t]	[t]	[t]	[t]	[t]	[t]	[t]
Mass	Unit	kg	g	lb	geekilo	geegram	geepound (slug)	kg	g	lb
	Dimensions	[m]	[m]	[m]	[$l^{-1}t^2f$]	[$l^{-1}t^2f$]	[$l^{-1}t^2f$]	[m]	[m]	[m]
Force	Unit	N	dyne	poundal	kg wt	g wt	lb wt	kg wt	g wt	lb wt
	Dimensions	[mlt^{-2}]	[mlt^{-2}]	[mlt^{-2}]	[f]	[f]	[f]	[f]	[f]	[f]
Work	Unit	J	erg	ft poundal	m kg wt	cm gm wt	ft lb wt	m kg wt	cm gm wt	ft lb wt
	Dimensions	[ml^2t^{-2}]	[ml^2t^{-2}]	[ml^2t^{-2}]	[lf]	[lf]	[lf]	[lf]	[lf]	[lf]
$k = ma/f$	Value	1	1	1	1	1	1	9.80	9.80	32.2
[$mlt^{-2}f^{-1}$]	Unit	—	—	—	—	—	—	kg m/sec^2 kg wt	g cm/sec^2 g wt	ft lb/sec^2 lb wt

Note: The values of k given above are based on the value of g (9.80 m/sec^2) which we have adopted in this book as most suitable for general use in the United States. The "average value" accepted by the International Committee on Weights and Measures is 9.80665 m/sec^2, which is equivalent to 32.174 ft/sec^2. These latter values would be correct to use in this table, but the above values are used to avoid confusion in problems.

Thus k is numerically equal to g, but it is not dimensionally equal to it. In all *lmtf* systems, Eq. (D.2) must be used in place of Eq. (4.9-4), which has been used throughout this book to connect force, mass, and acceleration. There are a number of ways in which the equations appropriate to other mechanical phenomena can be developed, starting from Eq. (D.2). With the introduction given here, the reader should be able to follow any one of these developments that he may meet. The last three columns of Table D.1 give the magnitude and dimensions of the mechanical units in the three most commonly used *lmtf* systems. The reader should verify the values given for k in the last two columns.

Because of the wide use of gravitational systems of units in engineering, many tables of physical constants are given in terms of such units. The only difficulty in comparing such tables with those stated in *lmt* units is that the terms kg, g, and lb are sometimes used interchangeably with kg wt, g wt, and lb wt. The reader who is reasonably familiar with the use of dimensions in physical equations will have little difficulty in judging from the context as to whether mass or force units are implied in any particular case.

A study of the following simple problem, worked in three systems of units, should enable the reader to understand the use of gravitational systems of units.

Illustrative Example

A mass of 2.00 kg rests on a smooth horizontal table and is attached by a taut string to a mass of 3.00 kg, which hangs over the edge of the table. Neglecting all friction, calculate the acceleration of the masses.

Solutions

(a) mks units: Accelerating force = (3.00 kg)(9.80 m/sec^2) = 29.40 N.
Mass to be accelerated = 2.00 kg + 3.00 kg = 5.00 kg.
By Eq. (4.9-4): a = 29.40 N/5.00 kg = 5.88 m/sec^2.

(b) ms kg wt units: Accelerating force = 3.00 kg wt.
Mass to be accelerated (cf. Eq. D.3A)
= 5.00 kg = (5.00 kg)(1 geekilo/9.80 kg)
= 0.5102 geekilo
By Eq. (4.9-4): a = (3.00 kg wt)/0.5102 geekilo)
= 5.88 kg wt/geekilo
= 5.88 m/sec^2.

(c) mkg sec kg wt units: Accelerating force = 3.00 kg wt.
Mass to be accelerated = 5.00 kg.
By Eq. (D.2) and Table D.1:
$a = kF/m$ = (9.80 mkg/sec^2 kg wt)(3.00 kg wt)/(5.00 kg)
= 5.88 m/sec^2.

D.4 *The* cgs *Electrostatic System* In setting up the definition of the coulomb in Chapter 15, we chose the constant of proportionality (k) in Coulomb's law (Eq. 15.5-1)

$$F = kq_1q_2/r^2 \tag{D.4}$$

to be

$$k = 8.986 \times 10^9 \text{ m/F} = 1/(4\pi)(8.855 \times 10^{-12} \text{ F/m}). \tag{D.5}$$

We saw in Secs. 16.7 and 16.8 that there was a good historical reason for this choice. We might otherwise have followed the practice which we used in defining force, and have set $k=1$, a dimensionless quantity. Had we done so, the dimensions of charge would have been determined by Eq. (D.4), and the magnitude of the unit of charge would also have been determined. Thus the dimensions of charge would be given by

$$[q^2]=[Fr^2]=[ml^3t^{-2}]$$

and hence

$$[q]=[m^{1/2}l^{3/2}t^{-1}]; \tag{D.6}$$

and the unit of charge would be defined as the charge which in vacuum repels an identical charge, separated from the first by unit distance, with unit force. Such a definition is not usual in an mks system, but it forms the basis for the ***cgs absolute electrostatic system of units*** (abbreviated ***esu***). This unit of charge is known as the ***es-unit of charge***, or the ***statcoulomb***. All the electrical equations we have obtained may be written in terms of the electrostatic system by repeating the various arguments we have gone through, using the centimeter and gram instead of the meter and kilogram, and using Coulomb's law in the form

$$F=q_1q_2/\kappa_e r^2 \tag{D.7}$$

instead of

$$F=q_1\,q_2/4\pi\kappa\varepsilon_0 r^2$$

[cf. Eqs. (15.5-1), (15.5-3) and (15.6-2)].

For the purposes of the present text, the reader need not concern himself with the electrostatic system. If he meets this system of units in other connections, he may find the conversion factors of Table D.2 to be of value.

D.5 *The* cgs *Electromagnetic System* The choice of the centimeter and gram as units of length and mass and the choice of the permeability of free space as $\mu_0=1$ leads to a system of units that is parallel to the esu system. This system is known as the ***cgs electromagnetic (emu) system,*** and it has a close historical connection with the mks Cb system. The relation between the emu system and the mks Cb system we have used becomes apparent if we set the constant in Eq. (16.6-1) equal to $2\mu_0$ instead of $\mu_0/2\pi$ and simultaneously set μ_0 equal to the dimensionless quantity unity. The magnetic flux density at a distance r from a long, straight wire carrying a current I is then

$$B=H=2I/r. \tag{D.8}$$

(Remember that I is here measured in ***abamperes*** and r in centimeters. The unit of flux density is the ***Maxwell.***)

Charge and current in the emu system will not be measured in coulombs and coulombs per second (amperes), but their dimensions will be determined by the choice made for μ_0. To find the dimensions of the abampere, first notice that Eq. (D.8) connects the dimensions of flux density and current according to the dimensional equation:

$$[B]=[Il^{-1}]. \tag{D.8A}$$

The definition of the magnetic dipole moment of a coil (Eq. 16.4-2) is the same in the emu and the mks Cb systems, so the torque T on a coil of N turns and of area A, which carries a current I and has its normal at an angle θ with a magnetic field of flux density B, is given by Eqs. (16.5-1) and (16.4-2) as

$$T = -BNAI \sin \theta.$$

Substitution of the dimensions of torque and area in this equation leads to another dimensional relation between B and I:

$$[B] = [I^{-1}mt^{-2}]. \tag{D.8B}$$

Elimination of B from Eqs. (D.8) shows that the abampere has the dimensions

$$[I] = [m^{1/2}l^{1/2}t^{-1}]. \tag{D.9}$$

Table D.2 *Equivalent Electrical and Magnetic Quantities*

[The first line in each box gives the magnitude of the mks Cb unit in terms of the corresponding esu or emu unit. The second line gives the dimensions of the quantity in terms of fundamental units. This table is based on $c = 2.998 \times 10^8$ m/sec, $c^2 = 8.986 \times 10^{16}$ (m/sec^2.]

mks Cb System	esu System	emu System
1 coulomb Cb	2.998×10^9 statcoulomb $cm^{3/2}g^{1/2}sec^{-2}$	10^{-1} abcoulomb $cm^{1/2}g^{1/2}$
1 ampere $sec^{-1}Cb$	2.998×10^9 statampere $cm^{3/2}g^{1/2}sec^{-2}$	10^{-1} abampere $cm^{1/2}g^{1/2}sec^{-1}$
1 volt $m^2kg\ sec^{-2}Cb^{-1}$	1/299.8 statvolt $cm^{1/2}g^{1/2}sec^{-1}$	10^8 abvolt $cm^{3/2}g^{1/2}sec^{-2}$
1 ohm $m^2kg\ sec^{-1}Cb^{-2}$	$10^{-11}/8.986$ statohm $cm^{-1}sec$	10^9 abohm $cm\ sec^{-1}$
1 farad $m^{-2}kg^{-1}sec^2Cb^2$	8.986×10^{11} centimeter cm	10^{-9} abfarad $cm^{-1}sec^2$
1 weber $m^2kg\ sec^{-1}Cb^{-1}$	1/299.8 statweber $cm^{1/2}g^{1/2}$	10^8 maxwell $cm^{3/2}g^{1/2}sec^{-1}$
1 amp turn/meter $m^{-1}sec^{-1}Cb$	$4\pi \times 2.998 \times 10^9$ statoersted $cm^{1/2}g^{1/2}\ sec^{-2}$	$4\pi \times 10^{-3}$ oersted $cm^{-1/2}g^{1/2}sec^{-1}$

EXERCISES

D.1 Two masses, one of 2.50 lb and another of 7.50 lb, are hung on the ends of a string that passes over a frictionless pulley. Calculate the acceleration of the masses in each of the three fps systems of Table D.1.

D.2 Two equal masses are each 100 g and are hung on the ends of a string that passes over a frictionless pulley. Calculate the mass which must be added to one of these masses if it is to move downward with an acceleration of 100 cm/sec^2, using one of the two suitable gravitational systems of units.

D.3 Calculate the value of the joule in m kg wt.

D.4 Given that 1 hp = 33,000 ft lb(wt)/min, verify that 1 hp = 745.2 W. This is the ***mechanical horse-power***, which differs slightly from the ***electrical horse-power***, which is defined as 746 W.

D.5 Show that, if the charges and displacement are stated in esu, Gauss' law is stated: The electric displacement flux through any surface is equal to 4π times the sum of all the electric charges enclosed by the surface (cf. Sec. 15.8).

D.6 Following the argument of Sec. 16.22 and using the result of Ex. D.5, show that the capacitance of a plane parallel plate capacitor, in esu, is

$$C = \kappa_e A/4\pi d,$$

where κ_e is the dielectric constant of the material between the plates, which have an area A and are separated by a distance d. Verify that the esu unit of capacitance is the centimeter.

D.7 Using Table D.2 and Eq. (16.10-1), show that the magnetic flux density inside a solenoid of N turns and of length l, which carries a current I, is

$$B = 4\pi NI/l,$$

where both B and I are measured in emu. Show that this reduces to

$$B = 4\pi NI/10l$$

if B is in maxwell per centimeter squared and I is in amperes.

Appendix E Some Properties of Right Triangles

E.1 *Right Triangles* The reader will remember that a number of the properties of right triangles are demonstrated in elementary geometry. Among these, some of the most important are:

1. The sum of the two acute angles of a right triangle is equal to one right angle, i.e., in the triangle MNO, which is right-angled at N (Fig. E.1), $\theta + \phi = 1$ rt angle $= 90°$.

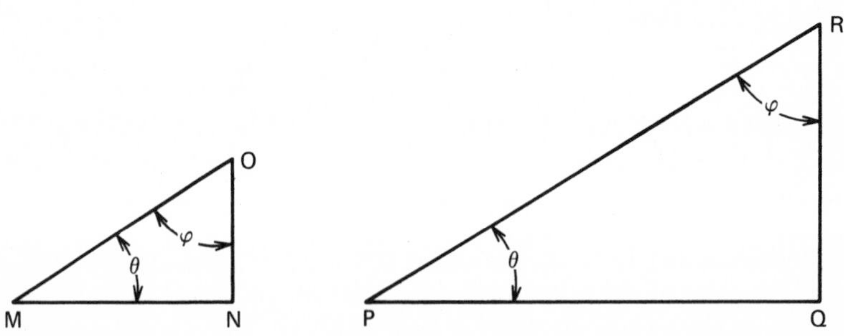

FIG. E.1 Properties of a right triangle.

2. The square of the hypotenuse of a right triangle is equal to the sums of the squares of the other two sides, i.e.,

$$(\text{MO})^2 = (\text{MN})^2 + (\text{NO})^2.$$

3. Two right triangles are similar if an acute angle of one is equal to an acute angle of the other, e.g., triangles MNO and PQR in Fig. E.1 are similar because OMN = RPQ = θ.
4. The corresponding sides of similar triangles are proportional, e.g.,

$$(OM)/(RP) = (MN)/(PQ) = (NO)/(QR).$$

The properties listed above are sufficient for the development of the ***trigonometry*** required in the study of elementary physics. Relation 4 above holds for any pair of right triangles which have the same acute angle θ. If we take from that relation the single equation

$$(OM)/(RP) = (NO)/(QR),$$

we can rewrite it as

$$(QR)/(PR) = (NO)/(MO).$$

This equation tells us that the ratio of the length of the side opposite the acute angle to the length of the hypotenuse is the same for all right triangles having the same angle θ. In other words, this ratio depends only on θ. If we construct carefully a single right triangle with a given value of θ, measure the lengths of the side opposite and the hypotenuse, and take the ratio of the two lengths, we will know the value of this ratio for all other right triangles with the same θ. We might, therefore, draw a series of right triangles, having acute angles of 1°, 2°, 3°, 4°, etc., tabulate the value of the ratio for each triangle, and save ourselves from any future measurements to determine this ratio in other right triangles. In practice, the tables which we shall use are obtained by computing the sides of the triangles, rather than by measurement on a drawing, but the two methods are identical in principle. (See Appendix G.2, for the method of computation.)

E.2 *The Trigonometric Functions* The ratio just considered is the first of the ***trigonometric functions.*** The ratio of the length of the side opposite the angle θ to the length of the hypotenuse of the right triangle is called the ***sine*** of θ (abbreviated sin θ). Values of the sines of all angles from 0° to 90°, by one-degree steps, are given in Appendix F.

By starting with the equation

$$(OM)/(RP) = (MN)/(PQ)$$

from relation 4 we could have shown that the ratio (PQ)/(RP) is the same for all right triangles with the same angle θ. This ratio, of the side adjacent to θ to the hypotenuse, is called the ***cosine*** of θ (abbreviated cos θ). Values of the cosines of angles from 0° to 90° are also tabulated in Appendix F.

A third trigonometric function, called the ***tangent*** of θ (abbreviated tan θ), is defined as the ratio of the side opposite θ to the side adjacent to θ, i.e., (QR)/(PQ). Appendix F includes the values of tan θ for angles from 0° to 90°.

The trigonometric functions and relations 1 and 2 above can be used to find all the sides and angles of any right triangle if we know either the lengths of two sides or the length of one side and the magnitude of one acute angle. In the triangle of Fig. E.2, the possible cases are as follows:

(i) Hypotenuse c and angle A known, then

$$B = 90° - A, \qquad a = c \sin A, \qquad b = c \cos A. \tag{E.1}$$

(ii) Side a and angle A known, then

$$B = 90° - A, \qquad c = a/\sin A, \qquad b = a/\tan A. \tag{E.2}$$

(iii) Side b and angle A known, then

$$B = 90° - A, \qquad a = b \tan A, \qquad c = b/\cos A. \tag{E.3}$$

(iv) Sides a and b known, then

$$\tan A = a/b, \qquad B = 90° - A, \qquad c = \sqrt{a^2 + b^2}. \tag{E.4}$$

(v) Side a and hypotenuse c known, then

$$\sin A = a/c, \qquad B = 90° - A, \qquad b = \sqrt{c^2 - a^2}. \tag{E.5}$$

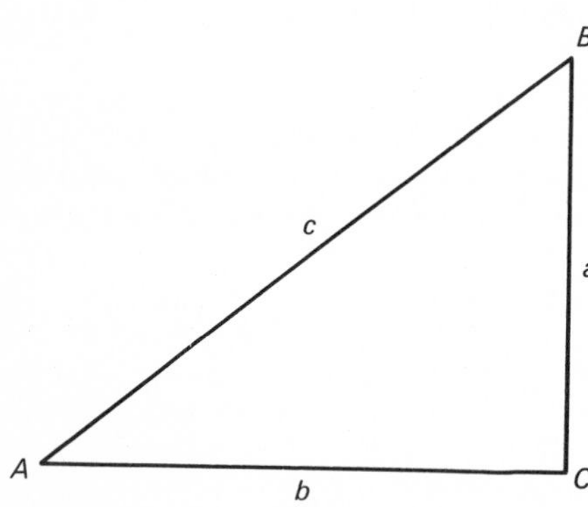

FIG. E.2 Notation for angles and sides of a right triangle.

Illustrative Examples (see Fig. E.2)

1. Given $c = 5.00$ cm, $A = 40.0°$.

$B = 90.0° - 40.0° = 50.0°$.

$a = c \sin A = (5.00 \text{ cm})(\sin 40.0°) = (5.00 \text{ cm})(0.6428) = 3.21$ cm.

$b = c \cos A = (5.00 \text{ cm})(\cos 40.0°) = (5.00 \text{ cm})(0.7660) = 3.83$ cm.

Solution: $B = 50.0°$, $a = 3.21$ cm, $b = 3.83$ cm.

2. Given $a = 4.00$ cm and $b = 5.00$ cm.

$c^2 = a^2 + b^2 = 16.00 \text{ cm}^2 + 25.00 \text{ cm}^2 = 41.00 \text{ cm}^2. \quad \therefore c = 6.40$ cm.

$\tan A = (4.00/5.00) = (0.8000)$.

Reference to the tables gives the following information:

A	$\tan A$	Tab. Diff.
37°	0.7536	
		0.0277
38°	0.7813	
		0.0285
39°	0.8098	
		0.0293
40°	0.8391	

We can see immediately that A lies between 38° and 39°. Since $\tan A - \tan 38° = 0.0187$, while $\tan 39° - \tan 38° = 0.0285$, it is clear that A must lie about 187/285 of the way between 38° and 39°. Since $187/285 = 0.66$,

$$A = 38.7°.$$

This process of finding an angle which lies between two tabulated values is known as ***interpolation.***
Solution: $c = 6.40$ cm, $A = 38.7°$, $B = 51.3°$.

3. Given $b = 4.00$ cm, $c = 5.00$ cm.

$$a^2 = c^2 - b^2 = 25.00 \text{ cm}^2 - 16.00 \text{ cm}^2 = 9.00 \text{ cm}^2, \text{ so } a = 3.00 \text{ cm}.$$

We then have $\cos A = 4.00/5.00 = 0.8000$. Reference to the table shows that A lies between 36° and 37°, and interpolation shows that

$$A = (36 + 90/104)° = 36.9°.$$

Solution: $a = 3.00$ cm, $A = 36.9°$, $B = 53.1°$.

E.3 *Properties of the Functions* There are some interesting relations among the trigonometric functions, which can be demonstrated quite simply. The reader who is meeting trigonometry for the first time can skip the rest of this appendix for the present, but will want to return to it later.

In any right triangle, such as that shown in Fig. E.2,

$$\sin A = a/c \qquad \text{and} \qquad \cos A = b/c.$$

Therefore, for any angle A, we have

$$\sin^2 A + \cos^2 A = a^2/c^2 + b^2/c^2 = (a^2 + b^2)/c^2.*$$

Since $a^2 + b^2 = c^2$ by the Pythagorean theorem, we see that

$$\sin^2 A + \cos^2 A = 1 \tag{E.6}$$

for all values of A.

The second relation of importance involves all three trigonometric functions that we have defined. Taking the ratio $\sin A/\cos A$, we find that

$$\sin A/\cos A = (a/c)/(b/c) = a/b = \tan A. \tag{E.7}$$

Equation (E.7), like Eq. (E.6), is valid for all values of A.

E.4 *Functions of the Sum of Two Angles*

(a) *The Sine of* $\alpha + \beta$. In Fig. E.3, the angle DOA is $\alpha + \beta$. From the definition of the sine of this angle, we get

$$\sin(\alpha + \beta) = \frac{\text{DA}}{\text{OD}} = \frac{\text{DE} + \text{EA}}{\text{OD}} = \frac{\text{DE} + \text{CB}}{\text{OD}}.$$

But CB = OC $\sin \alpha$ as may be seen by writing $\sin \alpha$ for the right triangle COB. Also that DE = DC $\cos \alpha$ follows from applying the definition of $\cos \alpha$ in the right triangle CDE. Thus,

$$\sin(\alpha + \beta) = \frac{\text{DC} \cos \alpha}{\text{OD}} + \frac{\text{OC} \sin \alpha}{\text{OD}}.$$

* It is customary to write the squares of trigonometric functions as $\sin^2 A$, $\cos^2 A$, etc. These are abbreviations for $(\sin A)^2$, $(\cos A^2)$, etc.

From the figure, DC/OD $= \sin\beta$ and OC/OD $= \cos\beta$. Therefore,

$$\sin(\alpha+\beta) = \sin\alpha\cos\beta + \cos\alpha\sin\beta. \tag{E.8}$$

(b) *The Cosine of* $\alpha+\beta$. From Fig. E.3, we write

$$\cos(\alpha+\beta) = \frac{\text{OA}}{\text{OD}} = \frac{\text{OB}-\text{AB}}{\text{OD}} = \frac{\text{OB}-\text{EC}}{\text{OD}}.$$

Also, OB $=$ OC $\cos\alpha$ and EC $=$ CD $\sin\alpha$, whence,

$$\cos(\alpha+\beta) = \frac{\text{OC}\cos\alpha}{\text{OD}} - \frac{\text{CD}\sin\alpha}{\text{OD}}.$$

Then, since OC/OD $= \cos\beta$ and CD/OD $= \sin\beta$, we have

$$\cos(\alpha+\beta) = \cos\alpha\cos\beta - \sin\alpha\sin\beta. \tag{E.9}$$

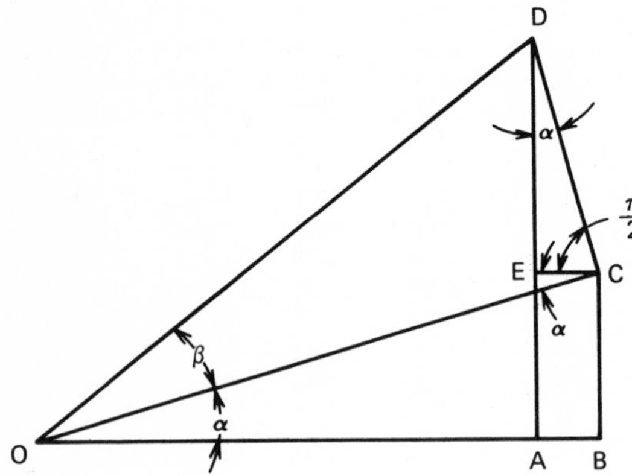

Fig. E.3 Computation of trigonometric functions of $\alpha+\beta$.

Appendix F

Table F.1 *Values of the Trigonometric Functions*

θ (deg)	sin θ	cos θ	tan θ	θ (deg)	sin θ	cos θ	tan θ
0	0.0000	1.0000	0.0000	45	0.7071	0.7071	1.000
1	.0175	0.9998	.0175	46	.7193	.6947	1.036
2	.0349	.9994	.0349	47	.7314	.6820	1.072
3	.0523	.9986	.0524	48	.7431	.6691	1.111
4	.0698	.9976	.0699	49	.7547	.6561	1.150
5	.0872	.9962	.0875	50	.7660	.6428	1.192
6	.1045	..9945	.1051	51	.7771	.6293	1.235
7	.1219	.9925	.1228	52	.7880	.6157	1.280
8	.1392	.9903	.1405	53	.7986	.6018	1.327
9	.1564	.9877	.1584	54	.8090	.5878	1.376
10	.1736	.9848	.1763	55	.8192	.5736	1.428
11	.1908	.9816	.1944	56	.8290	.5592	1.483
12	.2079	.9781	.2126	57	.8387	.5446	1.540
13	.2250	.9744	.2309	58	.8480	.5299	1.600
14	.2419	.9703	.2493	59	.8572	.5150	1.664
15	.2588	.9659	.2679	60	.8660	.5000	1.732
16	.2756	.9613	.2867	61	.8746	.4848	1.804
17	.2924	.9563	.3057	62	.8829	.4695	1.881
18	.3090	.9511	.3249	63	.8910	.4540	1.963
19	.3256	.9455	.3443	64	.8988	.4384	2.050
20	.3420	.9397	.3640	65	.9063	.4226	2.145
21	.3584	.9336	.3839	66	.9135	.4067	2.246
22	.3746	.9272	.4040	67	.9205	.3907	2.356
23	.3907	.9205	.4245	68	.9272	.3746	2.475
24	.4067	.9135	.4452	69	.9336	.3584	2.605
25	.4226	.9063	.4663	70	.9397	.3420	2.747
26	.4384	.8988	.4877	71	.9455	.3256	2.904
27	.4540	.8910	.5095	72	.9511	.3090	3.078
28	.4695	.8829	.5317	73	.9563	.2924	3.271
29	.4848	.8746	.5543	74	.9613	.2756	3.487
30	.5000	.8660	.5774	75	.9659	.2588	3.732
31	.5150	.8572	.6009	76	.9703	.2419	4.011
32	.5299	.8480	.6249	77	.9744	.2250	4.331
33	.5446	.8387	.6494	78	.9781	.2079	4.705
34	.5592	.8290	.6745	79	.9816	.1908	5.145
35	.5736	.8192	.7002	80	.9848	.1736	5.671
36	.5878	.8090	.7265	81	.9877	.1564	6.314
37	.6018	.7986	.7536	82	.9903	.1392	7.115
38	.6157	.7880	.7813	83	.9925	.1219	8.144
39	.6293	.7771	.8098	84	.9945	.1045	9.514
40	.6428	.7660	.8391	85	.9962	.0872	11.43
41	.6561	.7547	.8693	86	.9976	.0698	14.30
42	.6691	.7431	.9004	87	.9986	.0523	19.08
43	.6820	.7314	.9325	88	.9994	.0349	28.64
44	.6947	.7193	.9657	89	.9998	.0175	57.29
45	.7071	.7071	1.0000	90	1.0000	.0000	∞

Appendix G Trigonometric Functions of Large and Small Angles

G.1 *Functions of Angles Greater than* 90° In Appendix E, in the process of studying the properties of right triangles, we learned about the trigonometric functions of the angles which could be parts of such triangles, i.e., of angles less than 90°. The convenience of trigonometric methods is so great that it is well worth while to generalize the definitions of the trigonometric functions, to include angles greater than 90°.

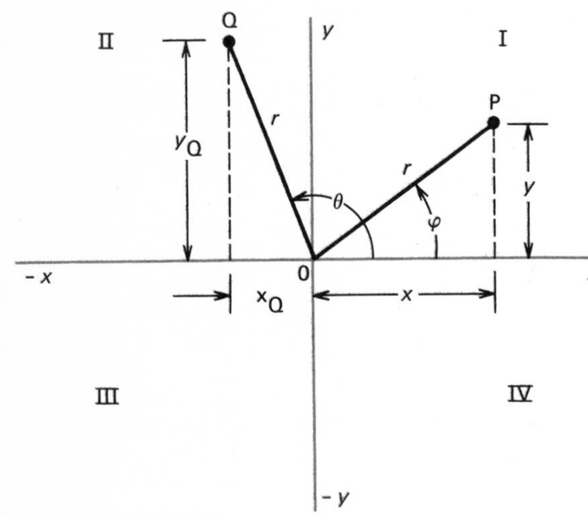

FIG. G.1 Trigonometric functions of angles in the second quadrant.

In the coordinate system shown in Fig. G.1, the position of any point can be defined by specifying its polar coordinates r and ϕ (cf. Sec. 5.2). If ϕ is less than one right angle, we say that the point P lies in the ***first quadrant***. The four quarters of the plane, divided by the rectangular axes x and y, are known as ***quadrants,*** and are customarily numbered in a counterclockwise direction, starting in the upper right-hand corner, as indicated by the Roman numerals in Fig. G.1. If we wish to compute the x- and y- coordinates of the point P, we merely find the sides of the triangle OPA, and get:

$$x = r \cos \phi, \tag{G.1}$$

$$y = r \sin \phi. \tag{G.2}$$

We can use Eqs. (G.1) and (G.2), together with Eq. (E.7), to restate our definitions of the trigonometric functions in terms of the coordinates of Fig. G.1. The definitions then become

$$\sin \phi = y/r, \tag{G.3}$$

$$\cos \phi = x/r, \tag{G.4}$$

$$\tan \phi = y/x. \tag{G.5}$$

Since the x- and y-coordinates of any point can be found, regardless of the quadrant in which the point is located, we may use Eqs. (G.3)–(G.5) as generalized definitions of the trigonometric functions. If this is done, we no longer need to limit ourselves to angles less than 90°. For example, the point Q, which lies in the second quadrant, has the polar coordinates r and θ, and the rectangular coordinates y_Q and x_Q. We can therefore write

$$\sin \theta = y_Q/r,$$

$$\cos \theta = x_Q/r,$$

$$\tan \theta = y_Q/x_Q.$$

The y-coordinate is positive and the x-coordinate is negative for any point, such as Q, in the second quadrant. Further, r is always positive. Hence, for all angles between 90° and 180° the sine is positive, while the cosine and tangent are negative. By considering points in each of the four quadrants, the reader can easily verify that the signs of the trigonometric functions in the various ranges between 0° and 360° are as given in Table G.1.

Table G.1 *Signs of the Trigonometric Functions*

Quadrant	Angle	Sin	Cos	Tan
I	0°–90°	+	+	+
II	90°–180°	+	−	−
III	180°–270°	−	−	+
IV	270°–360°	−	+	−

The trigonometric functions of all angles can be found readily from tables which give the values for the range 0°–90°. Thus, it will be seen in Fig. G.2 that $\sin \theta = y/r$,

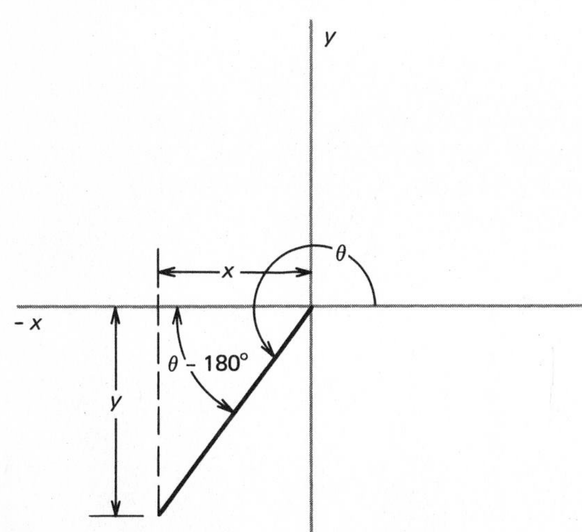

Fig. G.2 Trigonometric functions of angles in the third quadrant.

and that $y = -r \sin (\theta - 180°)$. Substituting this value into the definition of $\sin \theta$, we find at once that

$$\sin \theta = -\sin (\theta - 180°). \tag{G.6}$$

Similarly, $\cos\theta = x/r$ and $x = -r\cos(\theta - 180°)$, so

$$\cos\theta = -\cos(\theta - 180°). \tag{G.7}$$

Finally, $\tan\theta = y/x$ and $\tan(\theta - 180°) = (-y)/(-x) = y/x$, so

$$\tan\theta = \tan(\theta - 180°). \tag{G.8}$$

The three relations just found can be used to find the functions of any angle in the third quadrant if those in the first quadrant are known, or of any angle in the fourth quadrant if those in the second quadrant are known. By considerations similar to those used in the preceding paragraph, and by reference to point Q in Fig. G.1, the reader will be able to verify the relations

$$\sin\theta = \sin(180° - \theta) \tag{G.9}$$

$$\cos\theta = -\cos(180° - \theta) \tag{G.10}$$

$$\tan\theta = -\tan(180° - \theta) \tag{G.11}$$

The three Eqs. (G.9)–(G.11) will allow the values of the functions to be found for all angles between 90° and 180°.

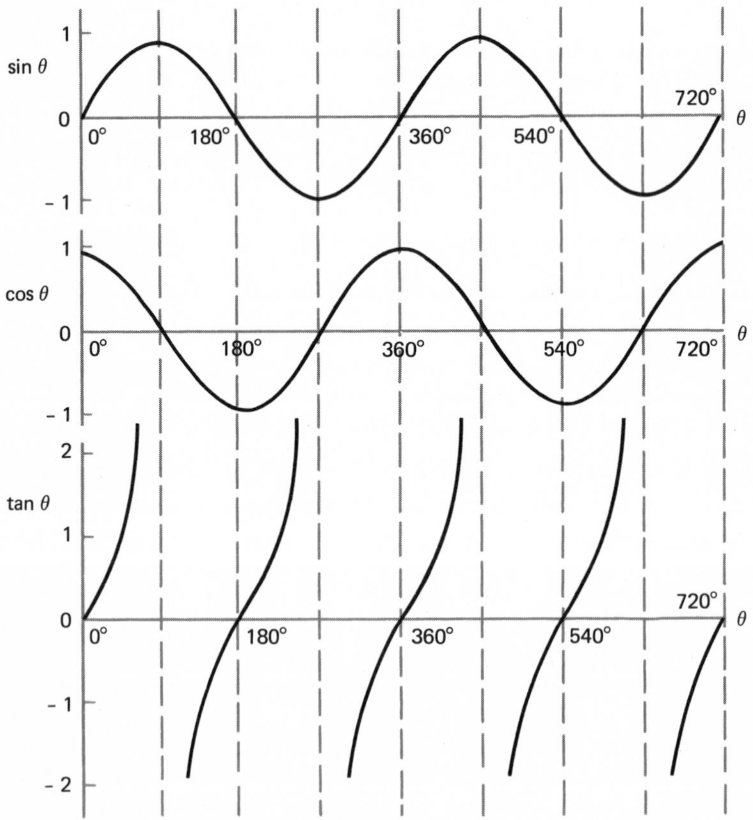

FIG. G.3 Trigonometric functions for all angles.

Not only are these definitions satisfactory for angles between 0° and 360°, but they may also be used for angles greater than one revolution. This is true because the same point is reached by moving through an angle θ or by moving through an angle which is a whole number of revolutions plus θ. The functions of θ will therefore be identical with those of $360° + \theta$, $720° + \theta$, etc.

By using Eqs. (G.6)–(G.11), plus the tables of Appendix F, the trigonometric functions of all angles may be found. As an aid to memory, the values of $\sin\theta$, $\cos\theta$, and $\tan\theta$ are plotted in Fig. G.3, for all values of θ from 0° to 720°.

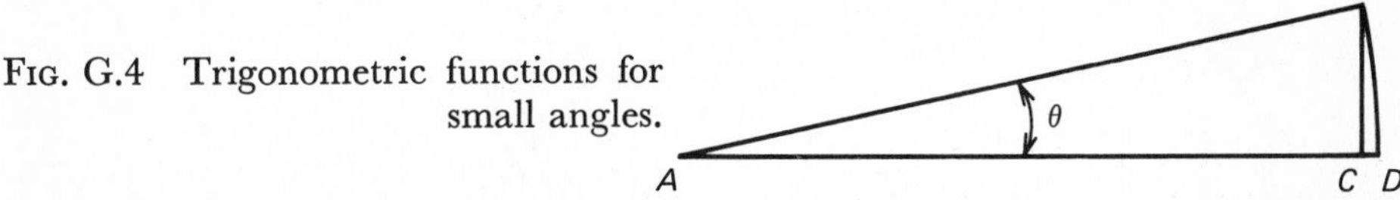

FIG. G.4 Trigonometric functions for small angles.

G.2 *Functions of Small Angles* We are often interested in the trigonometric functions of small angles, i.e., of angles $\theta \ll 1$ radian. The reader will remember that the angle θ (in radians) is the ratio of the arc subtended by a central angle θ to the radius. Hence

$$\theta = (\mathrm{BD})/(\mathrm{AB})$$

in Fig. G.4. As θ approaches zero, the half-chord BC becomes more and more nearly equal to the arc BD. Hence, for small angles,

$$\sin\theta = (\mathrm{BC})/(\mathrm{AB}) \approx (\mathrm{BD})/(\mathrm{AB}) = \theta. \tag{G.12}$$

Similarly, since AD approximates AC very closely when θ is small,

$$\cos\theta = (\mathrm{AC})/(\mathrm{AB}) \approx (\mathrm{AD})/(\mathrm{AB}) = 1. \tag{G.13}$$

Finally,

$$\tan\theta = (\mathrm{BC})/(\mathrm{AC}) \approx (\mathrm{BD})/(\mathrm{AD}) = \theta. \tag{G.14}$$

Equations (G.12)–(G.14) are in error by one percent or less for angles as large as 8° ($\approx$0.15 radian); hence they are sufficiently precise for many physical problems. Algebraic approximations of greater precision are occasionally needed, however. These may be obtained by taking the first few terms of series expressions for the sine and cosine:

$$\sin\theta = \sum_{n=0}^{n=\infty} (-1)^n \frac{\theta^{2n+1}}{(2n+1)!}$$

$$= \theta - \frac{\theta^3}{3!} + \frac{\theta^5}{5!} - \frac{\theta^7}{7!} + \cdots \tag{G.15}$$

and

$$\cos\theta = \sum_{n=0}^{n=\infty} (-1)^n \frac{\theta^{2n}}{(2n)!}$$

$$= 1 - \frac{\theta^2}{2!} + \frac{\theta^4}{4!} - \frac{\theta^6}{6!} + \cdots. \tag{G.16}$$

Factorial zero (0!) for $n = 0$ in Eq. (G.16) is $0! = 1$; 0! is always unity, by mathematical convention. These expressions will be justified in Appendix I.

Appendix H Powers of Binomials

In many physical problems, we are interested in powers of a binomial, say, $(a+b)$. More particularly, we inquire what is the value of $(a+b)^n$ when $b \ll a$. Let us write the successive equations:

$$(a+b)^2 = (a+b)(a+b) = a^2 + 2ab + b^2$$
$$= a^2 + (2/1)ab + b^2;$$

$$(a+b)^3 = (a+b)(a^2+2ab+b^2) = a^3 + 3a^2b + 3ab^2 + b^3$$
$$= a^3 + (3/1)a^2b + (3\cdot 2/2\cdot 1)ab^2 + b^3;$$

$$(a+b)^4 = (a+b)(a+b)^3 = a^4 + 4a^3b + 6a^2b^2 + 4ab^3 + b^4$$
$$= a^4 + (4/1)a^3b + (4\cdot 3/2\cdot 1)a^2b^2 + (4\cdot 3\cdot 2/3\cdot 2\cdot 1)ab^3 + b^4.$$

Any given equation in the list above is simply $(a+b)$ times the result of the preceding equation. In the equation for $(a+b)^3$, note that the coefficient "3" is written once as $(3/1)$ and once as $(3\cdot 2/2\cdot 1)$. Then, by the time we have written the expansion for $(a+b)^4$, a system for the coefficients is suggested. For $(a+b)^n$, we have

$$(a+b)^n = a^n + (n/1)a^{n-1}b + \frac{n(n-1)}{2!}a^{n-2}b^2 + \frac{n(n-1)(n-2)}{3!}a^{n-3}b^3 + \cdots + b^n, \tag{H.1}$$

where we have used the conventional arithmetic notation that $2! = 2\cdot 1$, $3! = 3\cdot 2\cdot 1$, etc. From the expansion of Eq. (H.1) the sixth term of $(a+b)^{10}$ will be

$$\frac{n(n-1)(n-2)(n-3)(n-4)}{5!}a^{n-5}b^5 = \frac{10\cdot 9\cdot 8\cdot 7\cdot 6}{1\cdot 2\cdot 3\cdot 4\cdot 5}a^5b^5 = 252a^5b^5.$$

Equation (H.1) is known as the binomial series, and it can be proven valid for negative and fractional values of n as well as for positive integers.

Let us suppose that we want to know what happens to $(r+\Delta r)^n$ as $\Delta r \to 0$. By Eq. (H.1) we get

$$(r+\Delta r)^n = r^n + nr^{n-1}\,\Delta r + \frac{n(n-1)}{2!}r^{n-2}(\Delta r)^2 + \cdots$$

But as $\Delta r \to 0$, $(\Delta r)^2$ becomes much smaller than Δr. Thus, for Δr sufficiently small we can put

$$(r+\Delta r)^n \approx r^n + nr^{n-1}\,\Delta r. \tag{H.2}$$

Occasionally, in the analysis of physical situations, we are interested in powers of the quantity $(1+x)$, where x is a very small number. We shall assume that x is so small that x^2, x^3, and higher powers of x can be neglected in comparison with 1. Thus, in a physical problem in which $x = 0.01$, $x^2 = 0.0001$ could well be disregarded if the uncertainty were greater than 0.0001.

From Eq. (H.1) we can write

$$(1+x)^n = 1^n + n[1^{(n-1)}]x + \frac{n(n-1)}{2!}[1^{(n-2)}]x^2 + \cdots$$

With x small, this becomes

$$(1+x)^n \approx 1 + nx. \tag{H.3}$$

Without rigorous proof, a few examples using Eq. (H.3) should persuade us of its validity and utility. Thus, if $n = \frac{1}{2}$, we get

$$(1 + x)^{1/2} \approx 1 + \tfrac{1}{2}x. \tag{H.4}$$

Now, if we square both sides, we have

$$1 + x \approx 1 + x + \tfrac{1}{4}x^2,$$

which is correct if x^2 is negligible.

If $n = -\frac{1}{2}$, we write

$$(1 + x)^{-1/2} = \frac{1}{(1 + x)^{1/2}} \approx 1 - \tfrac{1}{2}x. \tag{H.5}$$

If we multiply both sides of Eq. (H.5) by $(1 + x)^{1/2}$ and then square the result, we get

$$\begin{aligned} 1 &\approx (1 - \tfrac{1}{2}x)^2(1 + x) = (1 - x + x^2/4)(1 + x) \\ &\approx (1 - x)(1 + x) = 1 - x^2 \approx 1, \end{aligned}$$

and again the formula is verified when x^2 is negligible.

These results can also be applied to the powers of $(1 - x)$ if we simply replace x by $-x$ in each formula, and remember that all even powers of $-x$ are positive.

Appendix I *Derivatives and Integrals of* sin θ *and* cos θ

It is often necessary to take the derivatives of trigonometric functions. It is easy to show that

$$\frac{d(\sin\theta)}{d\theta} = \cos\theta \tag{I.1}$$

and that

$$\frac{d(\cos\theta)}{d\theta} = -\sin\theta \tag{I.2}$$

To demonstrate that Eq. (I.1) is correct, consider Fig. I.1. There the line segments AB and AE are of equal lengths, so that EB is a circular arc. We have

$$\sin\theta = \frac{(\mathrm{BC})}{(\mathrm{AB})} \quad \text{and} \quad \sin(\theta + \Delta\theta) = \frac{(\mathrm{EF})}{(\mathrm{AE})} = \frac{(\mathrm{EF})}{(\mathrm{AB})}.$$

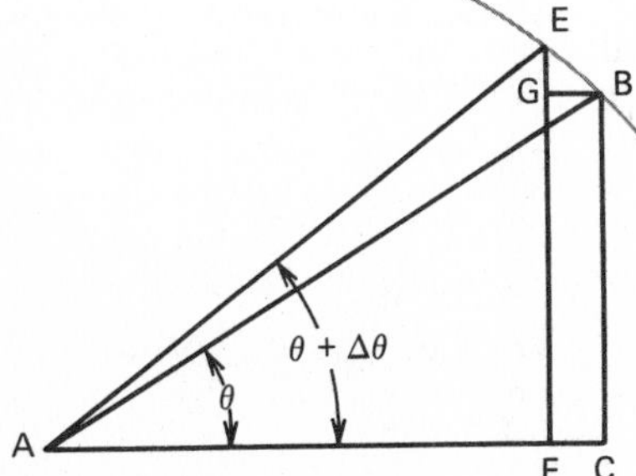

FIG. I.1 Derivation of $d(\sin\theta)/d\theta$ and $d(\cos\theta)/d\theta$.

Subtracting the first of these equations from the second, we can find the change in $\sin\theta$ as the angle increases from θ to $\theta+\Delta\theta$,

$$\Delta(\sin\theta) = \sin(\theta+\Delta\theta) - \sin\theta = \frac{(\text{EF})-(\text{BC})}{(\text{AB})} = \frac{(\text{EG})}{(\text{AB})}.$$

Let us now consider what happens when $\Delta\theta$ becomes very small. The arc BE then approaches a straight line, and we may consider the little figure BGE to approach a triangle, right angled at G and with the angle θ at E. The latter statement follows because EB is perpendicular to AB and EG is perpendicular to AC. Hence, as $\Delta\theta$ becomes small, (EG)/(EB) approaches $\cos\theta$. Since $(\text{EB}) = (\text{AB})\,\Delta\theta$, we have

$$\text{EG} \approx (\text{EB})\cos\theta = (\text{AB})\cos\theta\,\Delta\theta.$$

Substitution of this value into the expression for $\Delta(\sin\theta)$ shows that

$$\Delta(\sin\theta) \approx \cos\theta\,\Delta\theta,$$

an expression that becomes more and more nearly exact as $\Delta\theta$ approaches zero. Hence

$$\frac{d(\sin\theta)}{d\theta} = \lim_{\Delta\theta\to 0}\frac{\Delta(\sin\theta)}{\Delta\theta} = \cos\theta,$$

as stated in Eq. (I.1).

Similar reasoning shows that

$$\Delta(\cos\theta) = \frac{-(\text{BG})}{(\text{AB})} = \frac{-(\text{EB})\sin\theta}{(\text{AB})} = -\sin\theta\,\Delta\theta,$$

so that Eq. (I.2) is proven.

Having found the derivatives of $\sin\theta$ and $\cos\theta$, we may use Eqs. (C.15) to evaluate the integrals:

$$\int \sin\theta\,d\theta = -\cos\theta \tag{I.3}$$

and

$$\int \cos\theta\,d\theta = \sin\theta. \tag{I.4}$$

Taking the derivatives of both sides of Eq. (I.3), we see from Eqs. (C.15) and (I.2) that

$$\sin\theta = \sin\theta,$$

an identity. Taking the derivatives of both sides of Eq. (I.4) also leads to an identity, so it is verified.

We may use the results of this section to arrive at the series expressions for the sine and cosine that were given at the end of Appendix G.2. To do so, we start with the approximation of Eq. (G.12):

$$\sin\theta \approx \theta.$$

We then substitute this approximate value of $\sin\theta$ into the integral:

$$\cos\theta = -\int \sin\theta\,d\theta \approx -\int \theta\,d\theta = -\tfrac{1}{2}\theta^2 + C,$$

where C is a constant. We know that the cosine of zero is one, so $C = 1$, and we have

$$\cos\theta \approx 1 - \tfrac{1}{2}\theta^2, \tag{I.5}$$

as a second approximation to cos θ. This expression is in error by about one percent for angles as large as 40°.

The next approximation for sin θ may be obtained by substituting the value of cos θ from Eq. (I.5) into the integral of Eq. (I.4):

$$\sin\theta = \int \cos\theta\, d\theta \approx \int (1 - \tfrac{1}{2}\theta^2)\, d\theta = \theta - \theta^3/6 + C.$$

Because the sine of zero is zero, $C = 0$ and

$$\sin\theta \approx \theta - \theta^3/6. \qquad \text{(I.6)}$$

EXERCISES

I.1 (a) Using the method employed in deriving Eq. (I.5) and the approximation of Eq. (I.6), show that a better approximation for cos θ than is given by Eq. (I.5) is

$$\cos\theta \approx 1 - \frac{\theta^2}{2} + \frac{\theta^4}{24}. \qquad \text{(I.7)}$$

[Cf. Eq. (G.16).]

(b) Compute the difference between the approximations of Eqs. (I.5) and (I.7) for $\theta = 0.7$ radian, and hence justify the statement following Eq. (I.5).

I.2. Show that the first three terms on the right of Eq. (G.15) result from the use of Eq. (I.7) in a calculation on sin θ.

Appendix J.1 Elements and Atomic Weights, Based on Carbon-12 = 12.00000, Alphabetically by Name

(See also Table 21.1, page 667)

	SYMBOL	ATOMIC NUMBER	ATOMIC WEIGHT
Actinium	Ac	89	
Aluminum	Al	13	26.9815
Americum	Am	95	
Antimony	Sb	51	121.75
Argon	Ar	18	39.948
Arsenic	As	33	74.9216
Astatine	At	85	
Barium	Ba	56	137.34
Berkelium	Bk	97	
Beryllium	Be	4	9.0122
Bismuth	Bi	83	208.980
Boron	B	5	10.811[a]
Bromine	Br	35	79.909[b]
Cadmium	Cd	48	112.40
Calcium	Ca	20	40.08
Californium	Cf	98	
Carbon	C	6	12.01115[a]
Cerium	Ce	58	140.12
Cesium	Cs	55	132.905
Chlorine	Cl	17	35.453[b]
Chromium	Cr	24	51.996[b]
Cobalt	Co	27	58.9332
Copper	Cu	29	63.54
Curium	Cm	96	
Dysprosium	Dy	66	162.50
Einsteinium	Es	99	
Erbium	Er	68	167.26
Europium	Eu	63	151.96
Fermium	Fm	100	
Fluorine	F	9	18.9984
Francium	Fr	87	
Gadolinium	Gd	64	157.25
Gallium	Ga	31	69.72
Germanium	Ge	32	72.59
Gold	Au	79	196.967
Hafnium	Hf	72	178.49
Helium	He	2	4.0026
Holmium	Ho	67	164.930
Hydrogen	H	1	1.00797[a]
Indium	In	49	114.82
Iodine	I	53	126.9044
Iridium	Ir	77	192.2
Iron	Fe	26	55.847[b]
Krypton	Kr	36	83.80
Lanthanum	La	57	138.91
Lawrencium	Lw	103	
Lead	Pb	82	207.19
Lithium	Li	3	6.939
Lutetium	Lu	71	174.97
Magnesium	Mg	12	24.312
Manganese	Mn	25	54.9380
Mendelevium	Md	101	
Mercury	Hg	80	200.59
Molybdenum	Mo	42	95.94
Neodymium	Nd	60	144.24
Neon	Ne	10	20.183
Neptunium	Np	93	
Nickel	Ni	28	58.71
Niobium	Nb	41	92.906
Nitrogen	N	7	14.0067
Nobelium	No	102	
Osmium	Os	76	190.2
Oxygen	O	8	15.9994[a]
Palladium	Pd	46	106.4
Phosphorus	P	15	30.9738
Platinum	Pt	78	195.09
Plutonium	Pu	94	
Polonium	Po	84	
Potassium	K	19	39.102
Praseodymium	Pr	59	140.907
Promethium	Pm	61	
Protactinium	Pa	91	
Radium	Ra	88	
Radon	Rn	86	
Rhenium	Re	75	186.2
Rhodium	Rh	45	102.905
Rubidium	Rb	37	85.47
Ruthenium	Ru	44	101.07
Samarium	Sm	62	150.35
Scandium	Sc	21	44.956
Selenium	Se	34	78.96
Silicon	Si	14	28.086[a]
Silver	Ag	47	107.870[b]
Sodium	Na	11	22.9898
Strontium	Sr	38	87.62
Sulfur	S	16	32.064[a]
Tantalum	Ta	73	180.948
Technetium	Tc	43	
Tellurium	Te	52	127.60
Terbium	Tb	65	158.924
Thallium	Tl	81	204.37
Thorium	Th	90	232.038
Thulium	Tm	69	168.934
Tin	Sn	50	118.69
Titanium[c]	Ti	22	47.90
Tungsten	W	74	183.85
Uranium	U	92	238.03
Vanadium	V	23	50.942
Xenon	Xe	54	131.30
Ytterbium	Yb	70	173.04
Yttrium	Y	39	88.905
Zinc	Zn	30	65.37
Zirconium	Zr	40	91.22

[a] *The atomic weight varies because of natural variations in the isotopic composition of the element. The observed ranges are boron, ±0.003; carbon, ±0.00005; hydrogen, ±0.00001; oxygen, ±0.0001; silicon, ±0.001; sulfur, ±0.003.*

[b] *The atomic weight is believed to have an experimental uncertainty of the following magnitude: bromine, ±0.002; chlorine, ±0.001; chromium, ±0.001; iron, ±0.003; silver, ±0.003. For other elements the last digit given is believed to be reliable to ±0.5.*

[c] *Also known as wolfram.*

Appendix J.2 The Elements, Alphabetically by Symbol

SYMBOL	NAME	ATOMIC NUMBER	SYMBOL	NAME	ATOMIC NUMBER
Ac	Actinium	89	Mn	Manganese	25
Ag	Silver	47	Mo	Molybdenum	42
Al	Aluminum	13	N	Nitrogen	7
Am	Americium	95	Na	Sodium	11
Ar	Argon	18	Nb	Niobium	41
As	Arsenic	33	Nd	Neodymium	60
At	Astatine	85	Ne	Neon	10
Au	Gold	79	Ni	Nickel	28
B	Boron	5	No	Nobelium	102
Ba	Barium	56	Np	Neptunium	93
Be	Beryllium	4	O	Oxygen	8
Bi	Bismuth	83	Os	Osmium	76
Bk	Berkelium	97	P	Phosphorus	15
Br	Bromine	35	Pa	Protactinium	91
C	Carbon	6	Pb	Lead	82
Ca	Calcium	20	Pd	Palladium	46
Cd	Cadmium	48	Po	Polonium	84
Ce	Cerium	58	Pm	Promethium	61
Cf	Californium	98	Pr	Praseodymium	59
Cl	Chlorine	17	Pt	Platinum	78
Cm	Curium	96	Pu	Plutonium	94
Co	Cobalt	27	Ra	Radium	88
Cr	Chromium	24	Rb	Rubidium	37
Cs	Cesium	55	Re	Rhenium	75
Cu	Copper	29	Rh	Rhodium	45
Dy	Dysprosium	66	Rn	Radon	86
Ei	Einsteinium	99	Ru	Ruthenium	44
Er	Erbium	68	S	Sulphur	16
Eu	Europium	63	Sb	Antimony	51
F	Fluorine	9	Sc	Scandium	21
Fe	Iron	26	Se	Selenium	34
Fm	Fermium	100	Si	Silicon	14
Fr	Francium	87	Sm	Samarium	62
Ga	Gallium	31	Sn	Tin	50
Gd	Gadolinium	64	Sr	Strontium	38
Ge	Germanium	32	Ta	Tantalum	73
H	Hydrogen	1	Tb	Terbium	65
He	Helium	2	Tc	Technetium	43
Hf	Hafnium	72	Te	Tellurium	52
Hg	Mercury	80	Th	Thorium	90
Ho	Holmium	67	Ti	Titanium	22
I	Iodine	53	Tl	Thallium	81
In	Indium	49	Tm	Thulium	69
Ir	Iridium	77	U	Uranium	92
K	Potassium	19	V	Vanadium	23
Kr	Krypton	36	W	Tungsten*	74
La	Lanthanum	57	Xe	Xenon	54
Li	Lithium	3	Y	Yttrium	39
Lu	Lutetium	71	Yb	Ytterbium	70
Lw	Lawerencium	103	Zn	Zinc	30
Md	Mendelevium	101	Zr	Zirconium	40
Mg	Magnesium	12			

**Also known as wolfram.*

Appendix K The de Moivre Theorem

It was given in Appendix G.2 that

$$\sin\theta = \theta - \frac{\theta^3}{6} + \frac{\theta^5}{120} - \cdots \pm \frac{\theta^{2n+1}}{(2n+1)!} \mp \cdots$$

and that

$$\cos\theta = 1 - \frac{\theta^2}{6} + \frac{\theta^4}{24} - \cdots \mp \frac{\theta^{2n}}{(2n)!} \pm \cdots$$

It can be shown that the complex exponential, $e^{i\theta}$, where e is the base of natural logarithms and $i = \sqrt{-1}$, is

$$e^{i\theta} \approx 1 + i\theta$$

for small θ. The base of the natural logarithms is so chosen that

$$de^{i\theta}/d\theta = ie^{i\theta}. \tag{K.1}$$

It follows, by the relation between the derivative and the integral [Eqs. (C.15)] that

$$\int e^{i\theta}\, d\theta = -ie^{i\theta}. \tag{K.2}$$

Using these facts and successive integrations, as was done in deriving Eqs. (I.6) and (I.7), it can be shown that

$$e^{i\theta} = 1 + i\theta + \frac{\theta^2}{2} - i\frac{\theta^3}{6} + \cdots \pm i\frac{\theta^{2n+1}}{(2n+1)!} \mp \frac{\theta^{2n}}{(2n)!} \pm \cdots.$$

This series can be rewritten as

$$e^{i\theta} = \left[1 + \frac{\theta^2}{2} - \cdots \mp \frac{\theta^{2n}}{(2n)!} \pm \cdots\right] + i\left[\theta - \frac{\theta^3}{6} + \cdots \pm \frac{\theta^{2n+1}}{(2n+1)!} \mp \cdots\right].$$

Comparison of the two expressions in brackets with the series expressions for $\sin\theta$ and $\cos\theta$ shows the ***de Moivre theorem***,

$$e^{i\theta} = \cos\theta + i\sin\theta, \tag{K.3}$$

to be true.

Computations using complex numbers are often aided by the use of the ***Argand diagram*** of Fig. K.1. This diagram is plotted in the ***complex plane,*** with the real part of the complex number being assigned a horizontal coordinate (x) and the magnitude of the imaginary part a vertical coordinate (y). Thus, for $e^{i\theta}$, the coordinates are, according to Eq. (K.3),

$$x = \cos\theta \text{ and } y = \sin\theta. \tag{K.4}$$

Hence, we may write

$$e^{i\theta} = x + iy, \tag{K.5}$$

where both x and y are real. The interpretation of the diagram may be carried further if we take the magnitude of $e^{i\theta}$ as the square root of the product of $e^{i\theta}$ by its complex conjugate (Sec. 24.10):

$$[(e^{i\theta})(e^{i\theta})^*]^{1/2} = [(x+iy)(x-iy)]^{1/2} = (x^2+y^2)^{1/2}. \tag{K.6}$$

But this quantity is exactly the length of the hypotenuse of the triangle in Fig. K.1. We can therefore use this hypotenuse as a representation of the complex number, its length giving the ***magnitude*** (or ***amplitude***) and its direction indicating the relative magnitudes of the real and imaginary parts. In particular, by comparing Eqs. (K.5)

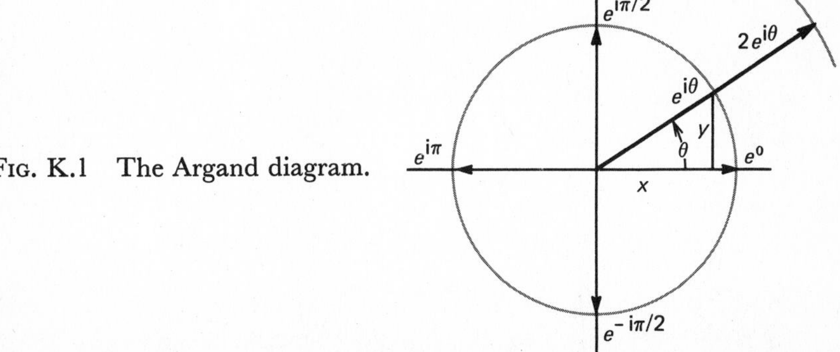

FIG. K.1 The Argand diagram.

and (K.6), we find that the magnitude of $e^{i\theta}$ is $(\cos^2\theta + \sin^2\theta)^{1/2} = 1$. The quantity $e^{i\theta}$ always has unit magnitude. Any other complex number can therefore be represented as

$$\mathbf{z} = Ke^{i\theta}, \tag{K.7}$$

where K is a real constant, equal to the magnitude of the number. Thus $2e^{i\theta}$ is indicated by a vector of twice the length of $e^{i\theta}$.

All complex numbers of unit magnitude may be represented by vectors ending on the circle shown in Fig. K.1. In particular, one may note that

$$e^0 = 1,\ e^{i\pi/2} = i,\ e^{-i\pi/2} = -i,\ e^{i\pi} = -1.$$

Answers to Problems (Odd Numbers)

Chapter 2: **2.1.** 2×10^{-4}. **2.3.** (b) $AP = 225.9 \pm 0.4$ m. **2.5.** 30 rps.

Chapter 3: **3.1.** 14.0 m/sec; 70 m. **3.3.** $a = 1.62$ m/sec^2; $t = 66.6$ sec. **3.5.** $a = (v^2 - v_0{}^2)/2h$. **3.7.** 441 m; 441 m. **3.11.** (a) $s \approx Kt$. (c) $2K/k$; 0.

Chapter 4: **4.1.** (b)

$$\frac{m_A}{m_C} = \frac{v_C(V - u)}{v_A(2u - v)}$$

4.3. (a) 8.3×10^4 N average engine thrust. (b) 4.7×10^7 J. **4.5.** (a) $u = \left(\frac{m}{M} - 1\right)v \Big/ \left(\frac{m}{M} + 1\right)$. (b) $\Delta E = 2mv^2 \frac{m}{M} \Big/ \left(\frac{m}{M} + 1\right)^2$. (d) m/M. **4.7.** (b) $KE' = \frac{1}{2}(m_A + m_B)v'^2 + m_A v'u + \frac{1}{2}m_A u^2 + m_B v'w + \frac{1}{2}m_B w^2$. **4.9.** (a) "5g" $= (5.0007 \pm 0.0001)$g.

Chapter 5: **5.1.**

$$t = \frac{2L\sqrt{v^2 - u_y{}^2}}{v^2 - u^2}.$$

5.3. 8.3 m/sec. **5.5.** $\theta = 88.3°$; $s = 12800$ m. **5.7.** (d) 45 m.

Chapter 6: **6.1.** $T = 108$ N; $P = 76$ N. **6.3.** 50 N + (3.87 m/sec^2)M.

Chapter 7: **7.1.** 25.8 rad/sec, 20.6 m/sec, 1.65 kg m^2/sec. **7.3.** $\theta = 4°$ or 87.8°. **7.5.** (b) 88 ft/sec; 10.3°. (c) 4.39 M ft/sec^2. **7.7.** (b) $0.285\ mL^2 < I < 0.385\ mL^2$. (c) $(\frac{1}{3})mL^2$. **7.9.** 3.4 per cent low.
7.11. (a)

$$x_C = \frac{(m_1 v_1 + m_2 v_2)t + m_2 x_0}{m_1 + m_2}.$$

(d)

$$\frac{1}{2}\frac{m_1 m_2(v_1 - v_2)^2}{m_1 + m_2}.$$

7.13. (a) The weight, the thrust of the plane perpendicular to it, and the friction between the cylinder and the plane, parallel to the plane and directed upslope. (b) $\text{KE} = \frac{1}{2}\left(m + \frac{I}{R^2}\right)V^2$. (d) The cylinder.

Chapter 8: **8.3.** $(2.2 \pm 0.2) \times 10^{-5}$ sec.

Chapter 9: **9.3.** (a) 0.238 m. (b) −0.69 m. **9.5.** (a) $YA\Delta L/L$. (b) $YA(\Delta L)^2/2L$. (d) 1.2 m. **9.7.** (b) $v = \sqrt{2gz}$. **9.9.** (d) $15.8 \times 10^6\ N/m^2$; $\Delta\rho = 7.68$ kg/m^3, so $\rho = 1033$ kg/m^3; less than 10^{-2} percent.

Chapter 10: **10.3.** (b) $z_0 = (\rho Y)^{1/2}$. (c) $m/(l^2 t)$. **10.5.** (a) 17.1 m down to 0.017 m. (b) 1450 m/sec. (c) 72.5 m down to 0.0072 m. **10.7.** (a) $V_i = V_r$. (b) $V_i = -V_r$, $V_t = 0$.

Chapter 11: **11.5.** (a) 3 kcal/hr. (b) 4.5 kcal/hr.

Chapter 12: **12.5.** 28°.

Chapter 13: **13.3.** (a) $x_i' = f(13x_0 + 3f)/9(x_0 - f)$, where x_i' is the distance of the image from the rear lens. (b) $M = -52f/3(13x_0 + 3f)$. **13.5.** (b) $f_C = 4f/3$. (c) No.

13.7. (a) $f_W = \dfrac{\mu_1 r_0}{2\mu - \mu_0 - \mu_1}$.

(b) $f_A = \dfrac{\mu_0 r_0}{2\mu - \mu_1 - \mu_0}$.

(c) No.

Chapter 14: **14.1.** $K = 1.35 \times 10^{-4}$ days²/km³; $\tau = 0.075$ days. **14.3.** If σ is mass/unit area, $G = -\dfrac{\sigma}{2}$ and $g = -\dfrac{\sigma}{2\gamma}$. **14.5.** (b) Infinitely far; no. **14.15.** (b) Accelerating, 1.43 m/sec². (c) 0.50 or $a = 0$.

Chapter 15: **15.1.** $D = \{[8L/(L^2 + 60d^2)^{1/2}] - 1\}d$. **15.3.** (a) For $b > r > a$, $E = \dfrac{Q}{4\pi\varepsilon r^2}$. (b) For $r > b$, $E = 0$. **15.7.** (a) 3.53×10^{-20}; no. **15.11.** $r = \left[\dfrac{Qp}{2\pi\varepsilon_0 mg}\right]^{1/3}$; $a < r < b$ so $2\pi\varepsilon_0 mgb^3 > Qp > 2\pi\varepsilon_0 mga^3$. **15.13.** (b) Away from the origin.

Chapter 16: **16.1.** (a) No. (b) Zero; 4.00×10^{-9} Cb; 3.88×10^{-7} Cb. (c) None without application of other energy. **16.5.** (a) $\mu_0 NI$. (b) One-half. **16.7.** $5k\Omega$. **16.11.** (a) No. (b) $2.000 \times 10^3 \Omega$.

Chapter 18: **18.3.** (b) 3.8×10^{-11} m. **18.7.** (c) If current *inside* a cell goes from (+) to (−), the emf is negative. **18.9.** (a) Silver chloride (AgCl). (b) Insoluble. (c) 16.9 g.

Chapter 19: **19.1.** 4.00247. **19.9.** (a) $B_1 = \sqrt{2m_0 E_0}/Re$. (b) $\nu = \dfrac{1}{\pi R}\sqrt{\dfrac{E_0}{2m_0}}$. **19.13.** (a) 6.9×10^{-13} *J*.

Chapter 20: **20.1.** (a) 100 atmospheres. (b) Yes. **20.7.** Internal energy would decrease. as volume increased. **20.11.** Certainly the right order of magnitude.

Chapter 21: **21.1.** (a) $e^2(\sqrt{2} - 4)/4\pi\varepsilon_0 r = -2.57\ e^2/4\pi\varepsilon_0 r$. (b) $e^2[6\sqrt{2} - 12 - (4/\sqrt{3})]/4\pi\varepsilon_0 r = -5.82\ e^2/4\pi\varepsilon_0 r$. (c) $(-1)e^2/4\pi\varepsilon_0 r$, $(-1.28)e^2/4\pi\varepsilon_0 r$, $(-1.45)e^2/4\pi\varepsilon_0 r$. **21.5.** (a) 8.27×10^{-12} m. (b) 5°. (c) 2.5°.

Chapter 22: **22.1.** (a) $F_x = \frac{4}{3}\pi Gmx$. **22.5.** $I_0 = (\tau_0/\tau_1)^2(\frac{1}{2}mr^2)$.

Chapter 23: **23.3** (a) For $r < a$, $E = 0$; for $a < r < b$, $E = Q/4\pi\varepsilon_0 r^2$; for $r > b$, $E = 0$. **23.5.** (b) In Eq. (23.5-1) set the right side equal to zero; in Eq. (23.5-3) replace $J = \sigma E$.

Chapter 24: **24.1.** (b) 2.79×10^{12} sec⁻¹. (c) 0.9. **24.3.** (a) 268° K. (b) 12.6×10^3 J/kmole degree. **24.9.** (b) 1.12×10^9.

Chapter 25: **25.7.** (a) Yes. (b) 8070 V. **25.9.** ${}_9F^{19}$.

Answers to Exercises (Odd Numbers)

Chapter 2: **2.7-1.** 1.000 m = 39.37 in = 3.281 ft = 1.094 yd. **2.7-3.** 5.00 mi = 8.05 km. **2.7-7.** 100.0 m = 109.4 yds so 100 m dash is 8.6 m or 28 ft longer. **2.10-1.** 1069.3 ft; 1207 ft; −137 ft. **2.16-1.** B and D; the difference between any two readings of B bears a constant ratio to the difference between the corresponding two readings of D. **2.17-1.** 365.2422; three days too many. **2.18-1.** One synodic month is 29.530 mean solar days, which is 29.613 sidereal days. Therefore, with respect to the stars in one synodic month the earth rotates 29.613 revolutions = 93.03 radians = 10660°. **2.19-1.** Zero. **2.21-1.** 90, 45, 30, 15, and 10 flashes/sec, respectively.

Chapter 3: **3.3-1.** 227.4 mi/hr; 333.5 ft/sec; 101.7 m/sec. **3.3-3.** 3.3×10^4 m/sec; 3.3×10^2. **3.6-1.** (a) Positive during intervals $t = 0.00$ to $t = 0.40$ sec and $t = 1.20$ to $t = 2.00$ sec. Negative during interval $t = 0.40$ to $t = 1.20$ sec. (b) Speed is zero at $t = 0.40$ sec, 1.20 sec, and 2.00 sec; displacements of ± 0.10 m. (c) $t = 0.00$ sec, 0.80 sec, and 1.60 sec; speed at $t = 0.20$ sec is less than that at $t = 0.00$ sec but more than that at $t = 0.40$ sec; more nearly equal to that at $t = 0.00$ sec. **3.7-7.** 2.92×10^3 m. **3.9-3.** Between the first two-second interval and the second two-second interval the acceleration was 3.5 ft/sec²; between the second and third two-second intervals it was 3.25 ft/sec²; then 2.5, 1.75, and 1.5 ft/sec². The speed at $t = 0.0$ sec was 36.5 ft/sec. **3.11-3.** 25 m/sec; 125 m. **3.12-1.** 5.0000 m. **3.12-3.** $s' + \Delta s_{(+)} = 5.1005$ m; $s' - \Delta s_{(-)} = 4.9005$ m; $\Delta s_{(+)} = 0.1005$ m. $\Delta s_{(-)} = 0.0995$ m; $\Delta s_{(+)}/\Delta s_{(-)} = 1.01$; yes.

Chapter 4: **4.4-1.** 1 kg. **4.4-3.** 0.153 kg. **4.7-1.** 0.998 m/sec. **4.7-3.** Zero. **4.7-5.** 3.3×10^{-29} m/sec. **4.10-1.** 6.6×10^2 N. **4.10-3.** 1.00×10^3 N. **4.12-1.** −3 m/sec; -2.3×10^4 kg m/sec; -2.3×10^4 N sec; -4.5×10^3 N. **4.12-3.** 19.8 m/sec; 78.4 J; 78.4 J. **4.15-3.** 0.239 m/sec².

Chapter 5: **5.2-1.** $x' = 5.5$ ft, $y' = 22.6$ ft; generally, $x' = 10 - y$ and $y' = 16 + x$. **5.5-1.** 85 mi. **5.5-3.** 5.25 m 30° from the given line; 1.50 m in the opposite direction, or 210° from the reference direction; 9.30 m 210° from reference direction. **5.6-1.** 95 km/hr at 127.7° from original direction. **5.6-3.** 5.45 hr eastward trip and 6.67 hr westward. **5.6-5.** 68° from upstream; 81 sec. **5.7-1.** If headwind equals flying speed in still air, the plane will not move with respect to the ground. The time for the trip is infinite.

Chapter 6: **6.1-1.** 1.7 m/sec at 30° from the original line on the other side of the line. **6.2-1.** 1300 N, 37.7° west of north. **6.2-3.** 10.6 m/sec at 67.8° down from horizontal; 49.1 m/sec at 85.3° down from horizontal. **6.5-1.** $T_1 = 3350$ N, $T_2 = 2880$ N. **6.5-3.** 4410 N; 220 N. **6.6-1.** 9.85×10^4 J. **6.6-3.** Yes; 2400 J. **6.7-5.** 7.2×10^3 J. **6.8-3.** 246 watts.

Chapter 7: **7.3-1.** With respect to the sun 4.16×10^{-3} °/sec or 15 °/hr; with respect to the stars 4.18×10^{-3} °/sec or 15.06 °/hr. **7.3-3.** 1.29 rad/sec². **7.4-1.** Into the face; 12 cm long into the face. **7.6-3.** 5.62×10^4 J; 3.3×10^3 J. **7.7-1.** $\vec{a} = \vec{\omega} \times \vec{v}$; $\vec{a} = \vec{\omega} \times \vec{r}$. **7.8-1.** $T = m\omega^2 r$; $a = \omega^2 r$. **7.8-3.** 710 m. **7.10-1.** 1130 N. **7.10-3.** 0.115 kg m². **7.11.1.** $I_B = 0.013$ kg m²; $I_A = 0.05$ kg m². **7.11-3.** No, KE afterward is only 25 percent of original.

7.13-3. 0.326 J. **7.13-5.** $MR^2\omega_1/\omega_2$. **7.16-1.** 2.20 m. **7.16-5.** $x_C = (m_1x_1 - m_2x_2 - m_3x_3 + m_4x_4)/(m_1 + m_2 + m_3 + m_4)$ with axis chosen at support. **7.17-1.** In all cases through the center of mass; (a) parallel to length, perpendicular to broad faces, perpendicular to sides; (b) one along long axis of football and two mutually perpendicular axes which are perpendicular to the long axis; (c) the earth's axis N-pole to S-pole and two mutually perpendicular axes which are perpendicular to the N-S polar axis (the earth is an oblate spheroid); (d) three mutually perpendicular axes located arbitrarily except for the center of mass restriction.

Chapter 8: **8.9-1.** 10.5×10^{-31} kg; 15.2×10^{-31} kg; 21×10^{-31} kg. **8.9-3.** The particles will have momenta

$$2m_0 v \Big/ \sqrt{1 - \frac{4v^2}{c^2}} \quad \text{and} \quad -2m_0 v \Big/ \sqrt{1 - \frac{v^2}{c^2}}$$

the sum of these is positive. **8.12-1.** 0.77 kg. **8.12-3.** 1.64×10^{-13} J; additional energy would be required for the particles to move apart. **8.12-5.** 0.15; 0.25; 15 percent accuracy.

Chapter 9: **9.2-1.** 16 kg. **9.3-3.** 0.049 m. **9.4-1.** 750 N/m. **9.4-3.** 0.95 J. **9.4-5.** 30 m/sec. **9.6-1.** 7.57 kg/m³. **9.6-3.** 1.15×10^5 N. **9.6-5.** 1560 m. **9.7-1.** 10.35 m. **9.7-3.** 1.27 kg/m³. **9.9-1.**

$$\rho_B = \frac{M_0\rho_L - M_L\rho_0}{M_0 - M_L} \quad \text{or} \quad \rho_B \approx \frac{M_0\rho_L}{M_0 - M_L}$$

9.9-5. 0.97×10^3 m³. **9.9-7.** ρ_C/ρ_L.

Chapter 10: **10.4-3.** $W_{\text{Al}} = 5.1 \times 10^3$ m/sec, $W_{\text{St}} = 4.9 \times 10^3$ m/sec; $W_{\text{Hg}} = 1.41 \times 10^3$ m/sec, $W_{\text{H}_2\text{O}} = 1.45 \times 10^3$ m/sec. **10.9-1.** Rule gives distance 12.5 percent lower than actual distance. **10.9-3.** 0.777 m.

Chapter 11: **11.5-1.** 1.8×10^{-5}/°C. **11.5-3.** (a) 32°F. (b) 212°F. (c) 98.6°F. (d) −40°F. (e) −459.4°F. **11.5-5.** 100.1 cm³, which uses one more significant figure than the data justify. **11.11-1.** 0.785°C. **11.11-3.** 0.07°C. **11.12-1.** 47 kg cold; 28 kg hot. **11.12-3.** 42.7°C. **11.12-5.** 0.35 kcal/kg°C. **11.14-1.** 0.48 kcal/kg°C. **11.14-3.** 0°C. **11.18-1.** 63.8°C. **11.18.3.** It is lower than that of water. **11.19-3.** 837.

Chapter 12: **12.3-3.** The normal to the mirror face must always bisect the angle between the direction to the sun and the axis of the tube; 0.5 rev/day. **12.6-1.** 36.4°. **12.6-3.** 1.414. **12.11-1.** 5.5×10^{-17} m. **12.16-3.** $\alpha = \arcsin(n\lambda/a)$; $n \leqslant (a/\lambda)$. **12.16-5.** $\alpha = 0°, 23.6°, 53.1°$ for maxima; $\alpha = 11.5°, 36.9°, 90°$ for minima. **12.21-1.** (a) 4.07×10^{-19} J, 1.36×10^{-27} kg m/sec. (b) 3.37×10^{-19} J, 1.13×10^{-27} kg m/sec. (c) 3.02×10^{-19} J, 1.01×10^{-27} kg m/sec. **12.22-1.** 324 sec⁻¹. **12.22-3.** 342 sec⁻¹.

Chapter 13: **13.1-1.** 50 cm. **13.6-1.** 0.138 m. **13.6-3.** 0.3 cm toward screen or 29 cm toward box. **13.6-7.** Image to right of lens at distance $2f$. **13.7-1.** (a) 40 cm to right of first lens. (b) 30 cm to right of second lens. (c) −1 and $-\frac{1}{2}, +\frac{1}{2}$. (d) The first image is real and inverted. It is a real object for the second lens. The final image is real and erect. **13.7-3.** $f/3$ on the same side of the lens; $M = +2/3$. **13.8-1.** $x_i = -f$; $M = 2$. **13.11-1.** +0.286 m. **13.11-3.** It will be brought to 0.25 m. **13.13-1.** −239. **13.13-3.** 2.5 m.

Chapter 14: **14.3-1.** $\Lambda = 2c$; $a = c$, $b = 0$, $c = \Lambda/2$ for a degenerate ellipse that is a straight line; $r_p = 0$, $r_a = 2c$. **14.3-3.** An infinite number. **14.3-7.** 253 years. **14.6-1.** 6.67×10^{-11} N. **14.6-3.** 9.78 m/sec². **14.6-5.** 1.98×10^{27} kg. **14.6-7.** 1.52 days. **14.11-1.** 1.61 m/sec².

Chapter 15: **15.6-1.** 0.479 N. **15.8-5.** For $a < r < b$, $E = \left(\frac{1}{K_e}\right)\frac{Q}{4\pi\varepsilon_0 r^2} = \left(\frac{1}{2.10}\right)\frac{Q}{4\pi\varepsilon_0 r^2}$; for $r > b$, $E = \frac{Q}{4\pi\varepsilon_0 r^2}$. **15.9.** $\vec{T} = \vec{p}_e \times \vec{E}$. **15.10-1.** 4.45×10^{-28} Nm.

Chapter 16: **16.2-1.** (a) A: +75 Cb, B: −75 Cb. (b) A: +75 Cb, B: −75 Cb. (c) A: +75 Cb, B: −75 Cb. **16.2-3.** 1.20 A from A to B. **16.8-1.** $m^{1/2}l^{3/2}t^{-1}$. **16.8-3.** $[l/t]$; c, the speed of light. **16.10-1.** The plane of the coil will be parallel to the magnetic equator; clockwise. **16.10-3.** $T = (\mu_0 NnaI^2)/l$. **16.15-1.** $P = g_0 R_E[1 - (R_E/r)]$. **16.17-1.** 0.91 A, 121 Ω. **16.17-3.** 22. **16.17-7.** (a) 3.33 Ω. (b) 0.300 Ω^{-1}. (c) 33.0 A. (d) 11.0 A. **16.18-3.** 0.0165 Ω. **16.18-5.** Copper; 2.83/1.724. **16.20-1.** 0.054 Ω. **16.22-1.** 5.00×10^3 J; -2.00×10^3 J. **16.22-3.** 10^4 V/m. **16.22-5.** 210 V.

Chapter 17: **17.4-1.** If top wire carries current to left flux at bottom wire will be out of paper and $B = (\mu_0 I)/2\pi d$; pushed apart; $F/l = (\mu_0 I^2)/2\pi d$. **17.4-3.** 0.64 cm too short. **17.7-1.** (a) 10^{-4} V. (b) 5×10^{-5} V. (c) From $t = 0$ to $t = 1.00$ sec: $\mathscr{E} = -\dfrac{\Delta\Phi}{\Delta t} = -Blat$ or $-(3 \times 10^{-4})tV$; from $t = 1.00$ to $t = 2.00$ sec: $\mathscr{E} = -(3 \times 10^{-4})(1 - t)V$. **17.7-3.** $\Delta q = 2NAB/R$. **17.9-1.** 0.0148 V. **17.11.** 2.23×10^{-5} V.

Chapter 18: **18.9-3.** C_6H_6. **18.9-5.** 29.2 kg of zinc and 43.9 kg of sulfuric acid. **18.15-1.** 3.05×10^{21}. **18.15-3.** 4.20×10^6 Cb. **18.17-1.** (a) 1.33×10^{-4} A, 1.326 V. (b) 1.20 A, 1.21 V. (c) 6.63 A, 0.663 V. (d) 13.3 A. **18.17-3.** Nine. **18.18-1.** Four in parallel. **18.18-3.** The emf is nV_C while the internal resistance is $(nR_i)/m$.

Chapter 19: **19.9-1.** 8.67×10^4 V/m. **19.9-3.** 0.5 cm too far out. **19.9-5.** 0.95 N_0, 0.902 N_0, 0.814 N_0, 0.661 N_0, 0.437 N_0. **19.9-7.** $\Delta(KE) = (2m_1{}^2 m_2 u^2)/(m_1 + m_2)^2$. **19.9-9.** ${}_3Li^7(\alpha, n){}_5B^{10}$, ${}_4Be^9(\alpha, n){}_6C^{12}$, ${}_9F^{19}(\alpha, n){}_{11}Na^{22}$, ${}_{15}P^{31}(\alpha, n){}_{17}Cl^{34}$. **19.15-1.** 0.9995 c; 53.7×10^{-27} kg. **19.16-1.** 0.999999 c. **19.20-1.** (a) 2.27×10^{-11} J. (b) 17.31×10^{-11} J (total energy). **19.27-1.** 0.86 c. **19.27-3.** 1.15×10^8 kW hr. **19.27-5.** 27 years; 5.5 days.

Chapter 20: **20.1-1.** (a) 17000 m³. (b) 11.4 m³. **20.1-3.** 5.09×10^{-4} m³. **20.4-3.** 1.37×10^5 m³. **20.4-5.** 83.1 Cb. **20.7-1.** 1.08×10^8 J; 0.65×10^8 J. **20.7-3.** For each gas $M_i = 1.013 \times 10^5$ N/m²; the adiabatic bulk moduli are for hydrogen 1.43×10^5 N/m², for oxygen 1.41×10^5 N/m², and for carbon dioxide 1.32×10^5 N/m². **20.7-5.** 0.48 km/sec. **20.10-1.** 1.84 km/sec; the same.

Chapter 21: **21.5-1.** 1.44×10^{-10} m. **21.15-1.** 5.6×10^{-3} N. **21.15-3.** 2.4 mm higher in smaller tube. **21.15-5.** $h = 2\gamma r \cos\theta/\rho g$. **21.17-1.** 4.74 eV.

Chapter 22: **22.2-3.** 0.635 sec. **22.2-5.** 0.144 sec. **22.4-1.** 1.02 m. **22.6-1.** 0.0029 m. **22.6-3.** $X_0 = 0.1119$ cm, $V_0 = 0.375$ cm/sec. **22.6-5.** Dimensionless. **22.7-1.** $F = V_0 Z \cos \omega t$. **22.8-5.** $I = 0.35 \cos(10\pi t - 89^0)$; $I = 0.74 \cos(60\pi t - 88^0)$.

Chapter 23: **23.4-3.** The work done in separating the plates; attractive force; yes. **23.7-3.** 2.66×10^{-15} Wb/m². **23.11-1.** 545 m and 200 m.

Chapter 24: **24.5-1.** 1.93×10^{-33} m; 5.5×10^{-32}. **24.5-5.** 4.51×10^6 m/sec. **24.5-7.** 8.19×10^5 eV; 2.35×10^8 m/sec. **24.5-9.** (a) 1.59×10^{-38} m. (b) 7.4×10^{-11} m. (c) 7.2×10^{-13} m. **24.6-1.** $\phi_0 \geqslant 17.5^0$. **24.6-3.** (a) 1.20×10^{-6} m; 5.52×10^{-28} kg m/sec. (b) 4.00×10^{-7} m; 1.66×10^{-27} kg m/sec. (c) 4.00×10^{-10} m; 1.66×10^{-24} kg m/sec. (d) 3.00×10^{-13} m; 2.21×10^{-21} kg m/sec. **24.9-1.** 4×10^{-3}; 4.0.

Chapter 25: **25.2-1.** 2.997×10^8 m/sec; 4.567×10^{14} sec⁻¹; 6.165×10^{14} sec⁻¹; 6.905×10^{14} sec⁻¹; 7.307×10^{14} sec⁻¹; 2.465×10^{15} sec⁻¹; 2.922×10^{15} sec⁻¹; 3.079×10^{15} sec⁻¹. **25.5-1.** 949.72 Å. **25.7-1.** 55.4 V. **25.14-1.** 1470 eV; 21600 eV.

Index

Pages on which definitions or laws are stated are indicated by **boldface** type, as are pages on which the life dates of particular workers are shown.

ABOUT THE AUTHORS

WALTER C. MICHELS, who is Marion Reilly Professor of Physics, Bryn Mawr College, received his Ph.D. from California Institute of Technology in 1930. He served as editor of the *American Journal of Physics* from 1959 to 1966, and is General Editor of Momentum Books, published by Van Nostrand for the Commission on College Physics. He is the author of *Electrical Measurements and Their Applications*, 1957, published by Van Nostrand. Dr. Michels served as President of the American Association of Physics Teachers in 1956-1957 and was awarded the Oersted Medal by the Association. He is a member of the Commission on College Physics and served as Chairman from 1960 to 1964.

MALCOLM CORRELL is Professor of Physics at the University of Colorado. He received his Ph.D. from the University of Chicago and taught at Oklahoma A. & M., University of Chicago, and De Pauw University before moving to Colorado in 1961. He served as President of the American Association of Physics Teachers in 1961-1962 and has been a member of the Commission on College Physics. In 1964 he was presented a Distinguished Service Citation by the American Association of Physics Teachers.

The late ARTHUR L. PATTERSON received his Ph.D. from McGill University in 1928. He taught at McGill, and was engaged in research at the Rockefeller Institute and the Johnson Foundation for Medical Physics, Philadelphia, before teaching at Bryn Mawr College. At the time of his death in 1966 he was Head of the Department of Molecular Structure, The Institute for Cancer Research, Philadelphia.

A Few Indefinite Integrals That Are Used Frequently in Physics

(In each of the following expressions, x is the variable of integration, while a and b are constants.)

$$\int dx = x$$

$$\int a\,dx = ax$$

$$\int \frac{dx}{x} = \ln x$$

$$\int x^n\,dx = \frac{x^{n+1}}{n+1} \quad (n \neq -1)$$

$$\int \frac{dx}{a^2 + x^2} = \frac{1}{a}\tan^{-1}\left(\frac{x}{a}\right)$$

$$\int (a^2 + x^2)^{1/2}\,dx = \tfrac{1}{2}[x(x^2 + a^2)^{1/2} + a^2 \ln[x + (a^2 + x^2)^{1/2}]$$

$$\int \frac{dx}{(a^2 + x^2)^{1/2}} = \ln[x + (a^2 + x^2)^{1/2}]$$

$$\int \sin(ax)\,dx = -\frac{1}{a}\cos(ax)$$

$$\int \cos(ax)\,dx = \frac{1}{a}\sin(ax)$$

$$\int e^{ax}\,dx = \frac{1}{a}e^{ax}$$

$$\int \ln x\,dx = x \ln x - x$$